W0005990

Bifurcation Theory

GRADUATE STUDIES IN MATHEMATICS 246

Bifurcation Theory

Ale Jan Homburg
Jürgen Knobloch

AMERICAN MATHEMATICAL SOCIETY
Providence, Rhode Island

2020 *Mathematics Subject Classification.* Primary 34-01, 34C23, 37-01, 37Gxx.

For additional information and updates on this book, visit
www.ams.org/bookpages/gsm-246

Library of Congress Cataloging-in-Publication Data

Names: Homburg, Ale Jan, 1966– author.
Title: Bifurcation theory / Ale Jan Homburg, Jürgen Knobloch.
Description: Providence, Rhode Island : American Mathematical Society, [2024] | Series: Graduate studies in mathematics, 1065-7339 ; volume 246 | Includes bibliographical references and index.
Identifiers: LCCN 2024032771 | ISBN 9781470477943 (hardcover) | ISBN 9781470478803 (paperback) | ISBN 9781470478810 (ebook)
Subjects: LCSH: Bifurcation theory. | AMS: Ordinary differential equations – Instructional exposition (textbooks, tutorial papers, etc.). | Ordinary differential equations – Qualitative theory – Bifurcation. | Dynamical systems and ergodic theory – Instructional exposition (textbooks, tutorial papers, etc.). | Dynamical systems and ergodic theory – Local and nonlocal bifurcation theory.
Classification: LCC QA380 .H66 2024 | DDC 515/.392–dc23/eng20241004
LC record available at https://lccn.loc.gov/2024032771

Graduate Studies in Mathematics ISSN: 1065-7339 (print)

DOI: https://doi.org/10.1090/gsm/246

♾ The paper used in this book is acid-free and falls within the guidelines
established to ensure permanence and durability.
Visit the AMS home page at `https://www.ams.org/`

10 9 8 7 6 5 4 3 2 1 29 28 27 26 25 24

Contents

Preface

This is a textbook on the topic of bifurcation theory as a subarea of dynamical systems. It aims for a precise mathematical treatment of the principal ideas and results from bifurcation theory. Bifurcation theory concerns changes in dynamics that occur when parameters in a dynamical system vary. Our primary setting is that of dynamical systems given by flows of ordinary differential equations. Dynamical systems given by iterations of maps naturally arise in this setting as well.

The qualitative study of dynamical systems originates with Henri Poincaré who studied differential equations appearing in problems from celestial mechanics. The study of dynamical systems has been one of the most successful fields of mathematical research with explosive development in the last fifty years. There is a theoretical core of the field that is aimed at the description of typical dynamics. It studies common properties of large classes of dynamical systems. But in particular, with the development of a toolbox for the study of dynamics, the body of research in applied sciences using techniques from dynamical systems has expanded dramatically. Whether in physics, engineering, biology, psychology, or economics, tools from dynamical systems have been highly successful in understanding phenomena where evolution is the focus.

The research area of bifurcation theory has been essential in the development of the theory of dynamical systems, to understand properties of large classes of dynamical systems and to understand how such properties can change. It has however been especially powerful in applications to other sciences. An understanding of bifurcation theory is crucial in finding and appreciating dynamical phenomena in applications. The continual importance of bifurcation theory is reflected in modern terminology such as *tipping point*, *critical transition*, or *regime shift* (examples of their use are in [**331**]). These are tokens of the influence of the ideas of bifurcation theory in applied sciences and society.

The term bifurcation was originally used by Henri Poincaré [**295**] to describe the splitting of equilibria in a family of differential equations. The bibliography in [**412**] describes how Poincaré's work starts a qualitative study of differential equations and bifurcation theory. The first investigations that, when phrased in modern terminology, connect to studies in bifurcation theory appeared much earlier. As examples we mention the work by Apollonius of Perga (who lived from circa 240 BC to circa 190 BC) on minimal distances of points to conic sections, [**192**], and by Jacobi on self-gravitating rotating ellipsoids [**190**]. The original viewpoints focus on changes in the structure of equilibrium solutions with parameters. In modern use, a bifurcation of a dynamical system is a qualitative change in its dynamics produced by varying parameters. A formal approach to the notion of bifurcation and the related notion of structural stability originates with Alexandr Andronov and Lev Pontryagin [**18**].

Our aim was to compose a guide on bifurcation theory assuming a background knowledge covered in bachelor-level courses on topology, analysis, and ordinary differential equations. We wanted it to address techniques, albeit sometimes in simplified settings, in a detailed manner, and further to give a

Figure 0.1. Formal foundations of bifurcation theory were created by Alexandr Andronov. Depicted is a plaque in tribute to him in Nizhny Novgorod.

broad but not encyclopedic overview of results, and demonstrate its usefulness in applications and the modern study of dynamical systems. We also tried to make visible the scientific heritage of the field: the collection of techniques and results that have been guiding its development. If we have to point out one characteristic of the philosophy of the book, it is the detailed treatment of the results that we cover. This includes the advanced bifurcation theory needed for the Bogdanov-Takens bifurcation. This includes also the technical analysis required for various homoclinic bifurcations.

Let us give a brief synopsis of the structure and the contents of the different chapters in the book. After an introduction and a section with preliminaries, the main body of the text with analysis of bifurcations is divided into three parts on local bifurcations, nonlocal bifurcations, and global bifurcations. Local bifurcations are understood as changes in the flow near equilibria and periodic orbits under parameter variation. For nonlocal bifurcations we consider the flow near connecting orbits such as homoclinic orbits and describe the changes in the flow. Under global bifurcation theory we understand global aspects such as descriptions of the flow on the entire state space, but also descriptions of bifurcations occurring in larger parts of the parameter domain. In their titles we name the highlights of the chapters.

Chapter 1. Introductory models. We describe a few instructive models that introduce a first point of view of bifurcation theory. Featuring in three different models are the saddle-node bifurcation, the Hopf bifurcation, and the homoclinic bifurcation.

Chapter 2. Flows and invariant sets. This is a chapter with preliminaries on dynamical systems theory. We discuss notions of invariant sets that appear in the study of long time dynamics. We develop theory to study a flow near a periodic orbit, namely Floquet theory and material on Poincaré return maps. A prototype example of chaotic dynamics is presented in a section on the Smale horseshoe. Our analysis for it has a more analytic flavor than usual in textbooks. We formalize notions of topological equivalence and bifurcation. And we add a brief section in which we indicate connections between bifurcation theory and catastrophe theory.

Chapter 3. Local bifurcations. This chapter contains a careful analysis of bifurcations of equilibria and periodic orbits. We address a limited number of possible bifurcations, including bifurcations that are most relevant to applications. We present in particular the saddle-node, the transcritical, the pitchfork, the cusp, and the Hopf bifurcation of equilibria. We include the Bogdanov-Takens bifurcation. For this bifurcation we give a detailed and complete proof of the bifurcation theorem, avoiding reference to research articles for technical parts.

We then turn to bifurcations of periodic orbits, where we discuss the saddle-node, the period-doubling, and the Neimark-Sacker bifurcation.

Chapter 4. Nonlocal bifurcations. An important theme of this book is the analysis of homoclinic bifurcations. For the bifurcation we discuss involving homoclinic orbits to hyperbolic equilibria, we do this in a detailed manner, discussing separately planar and higher-dimensional cases. We present techniques that are used in nonlocal bifurcation analysis, such as the calculation of Poincaré return maps and the method of cross coordinates used by Leonid Shilnikov. An alternative technique, Lin's method, is presented in Appendix C.

Chapter 5. Global bifurcations. This chapter contains a choice of ideas that have to do with global aspects of bifurcation theory. It contains a discussion of structural stability, and instability, for flows and families of flows on compact manifolds. It discusses bifurcation phenomena such as period-doubling cascades and intermittency. As some of the topics are more advanced, the level of detail is less than in previous chapters. But we have made every effort to properly introduce main ideas and some important results from the development of the theory.

The technical toolbox that has been developed to study dynamical systems and, in particular, bifurcation theory is substantial. We did not want to start the book with the development of technical results and tools, as this would only postpone the discussion of bifurcations. As they are a central part of the research field, we decided to include a treatment in appendices. We offer three appendices, one with tools from analysis, one with tools from dynamical systems, and one with tools from homoclinic bifurcation theory.

Appendix A. Elements of nonlinear analysis. This appendix summarizes some results of calculus on Banach spaces, and it includes the implicit function theorem and the derived Lyapunov-Schmidt reduction method. The implicit function theorem pops up almost always when equations need to be solved and is therefore the prevailing analysis tool in bifurcation theory. We further discuss superposition operators, where a function is applied to sequences of points instead of single points.

Appendix B. Invariant manifolds and normal forms. We refer to results in this appendix throughout the book. One cannot study dynamical systems and bifurcation theory without an understanding of stable and unstable manifolds, and of center manifolds. Consistent with the philosophy of the book we include the results with complete proofs.

In fact we provide novel efficient proofs. These are simplified versions of existing proofs, in the spirit of Perron's proof, but based on the idea of cross coordinates.

This appendix also contains the normal form theorem, which provides a technique to simplify the expression of a vector field near an equilibrium. It includes a number of results on linearization of a flow near an equilibrium. Frequently we apply techniques that are presented here on a case-by-case basis in the main text.

Appendix C. Lin's method. Lin's method gives a functional analytic approach to the study of homoclinic and heteroclinic bifurcations. It provides an alternative approach to the methods in Chapter 4 that are based on the study of Poincaré return maps, and it has been applied to a range of nonlocal bifurcation problems. This appendix contains an exposition and the entire proof of Lin's method, which cannot be readily found elsewhere. In the course of it we also discuss theory of exponential dichotomies needed for the analysis.

During the process of writing this textbook, our appreciation of existing textbooks on bifurcation theory has only grown. Of the many good texts that influenced and inspired us, we want to mention two books in particular. The book *Nonlinear oscillations, dynamical systems, and bifurcations of vector fields* by John Guckenheimer and Philip Holmes [**143**] contains a wealth of ideas and discusses advanced topics in a lively style that we did not manage. And the book *Elements of applied bifurcation theory* by Yuri Kuznetsov [**215**] is exemplary in giving an encyclopedic overview of results and analysis of bifurcations. We wish to refer to it for bifurcations that we do not cover.

Limitations. This book does not aim for an encyclopedic treatment of bifurcation theory. We focus instead on a detailed discussion of main bifurcations that often arise in applications and elaborate the techniques that are used in studying these bifurcations. These techniques will prove valuable in the study of other bifurcations. A number of techniques that are crucial for advanced topics in bifurcation theory are not covered. We do not develop advanced techniques from singularity theory, such as preparation theorems, as we can do without for the bifurcations of low codimension that we do treat. Also methods like blowing up are not systematically developed in this book for the same reason. Our use of global analysis on manifolds is limited, and we do not cover results such as Thom's transversality theorem.

A course on bifurcation theory is not a substitute for a course on dynamical systems theory. Besides, this textbook leaves out many topics that bear a relevance to bifurcation theory, such as topological dynamical systems and smooth chaotic dynamical systems (including nonuniformly hyperbolic systems, singular hyperbolic systems, and partially hyperbolic systems). Advanced or specialized topics, which are interesting from a bifurcation theory point of view, are not considered. This includes complex dynamics, equivariant dynamical systems, reversible dynamical systems, conservative and Hamiltonian systems, dynamics on networks, infinite-dimensional systems (partial differential equations, delay differential equations), singularly perturbed dynamical systems, planar polynomial vector fields and Hilbert's sixteenth problem, nonautonomous dynamical systems, piecewise smooth or impulsive dynamical systems, random dynamical systems (iterated function systems, skew product systems, stochastic differential equations), and ergodic theory.

Also for the general nonconservative differential equations that we consider, we leave out many bifurcations. For instance, we include the saddle-node bifurcation and the cusp bifurcation, but not the swallowtail and butterfly bifurcations and also not the saddle-node-Hopf bifurcation. We treat the Hopf bifurcation, but we do not treat degenerate Hopf bifurcations. The period-doubling bifurcation and the Neimark-Sacker bifurcation are covered, but other bifurcations, such as the Chenciner bifurcation, are not. Similar remarks hold for nonlocal bifurcations. Here we discuss homoclinic bifurcations of codimension 1, but leave out interesting bifurcations of higher codimension, such as inclination-flip and orbit-flip bifurcations. Also bifurcations of double homoclinic orbits and of heteroclinic cycles are not included. The list of bifurcations that we do not cover is endless.

Let us finish by expressing our gratitude to colleagues for the many different ways in which they helped us.

Ale Jan Homburg
Amsterdam, Netherlands

Jürgen Knobloch
Ilmenau, Germany

2024

Chapter 1

Introductory models

In the following we consider examples of the typical appearance of ideas and results from bifurcation theory. We will look at two models from population dynamics involving bifurcations of equilibria, and an artificial model used for numerical exploration of homoclinic bifurcations. The bifurcations occurring in it will all be given a detailed analysis later in the book. Before introducing these models, we look at two explicit examples of bifurcations.

A model saddle-node bifurcation. Consider the following simple model of a family of scalar differential equations,

$$\dot{x} = \lambda - x^2. \tag{1.1}$$

Here $\lambda \in \mathbb{R}$ serves as a parameter. Figure 1.1 displays equilibria and its stability in dependence of λ.

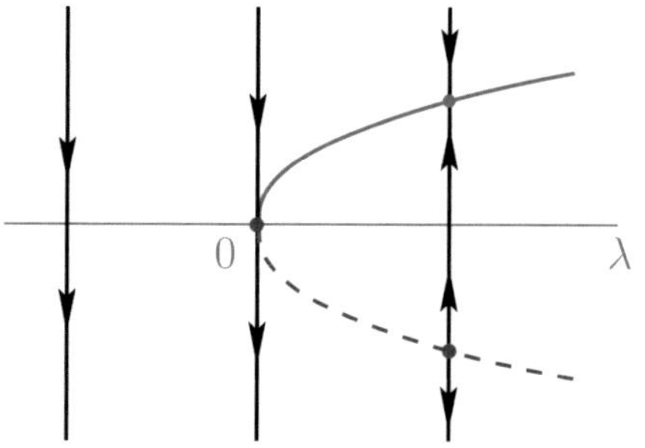

Figure 1.1. The phase portraits of (1.1) for several λ-values. The green solid branch indicates stable equilibria; the red dashed branch, unstable equilibria.

Evidently, there is no equilibrium for $\lambda < 0$ and exactly one for $\lambda = 0$. This changes into two as λ becomes positive. This is the prototypical example of a bifurcation, with a qualitative change in the dynamics as a parameter is changed. This model is in fact the standard model for what is called the saddle-node bifurcation. In a similar scenario in a higher space dimension, typically a saddle and a node collide, which explains the name of the bifurcation. Families other than (1.1) show the same change from zero to two equilibria, when the parameter is moving through a specific parameter value called the bifurcation value. The bifurcation value is determined by a change of the dynamics (here expressed by the change of the number of equilibria). The set of bifurcation values is referred to as the bifurcation set. A diagram like Figure 1.1 displaying typical orbits and the changes in dynamics for varying parameters is a bifurcation diagram.

A model Hopf bifurcation. Consider the one-parameter family in $\mathbb{R}^2$,

$$\begin{pmatrix} \dot{x} \\ \dot{y} \end{pmatrix} = \begin{pmatrix} \lambda & -1 \\ 1 & \lambda \end{pmatrix} \begin{pmatrix} x \\ y \end{pmatrix} - (x^2 + y^2) \begin{pmatrix} x \\ y \end{pmatrix}. \tag{1.2}$$

The matrix $\begin{pmatrix} \lambda & -1 \\ 1 & \lambda \end{pmatrix}$ of the linearization at the (only) equilibrium $(0, 0)$ has eigenvalues $\lambda \pm i$. So, if λ passes zero the equilibrium changes its stability. Note that for each parameter value there is exactly one equilibrium.

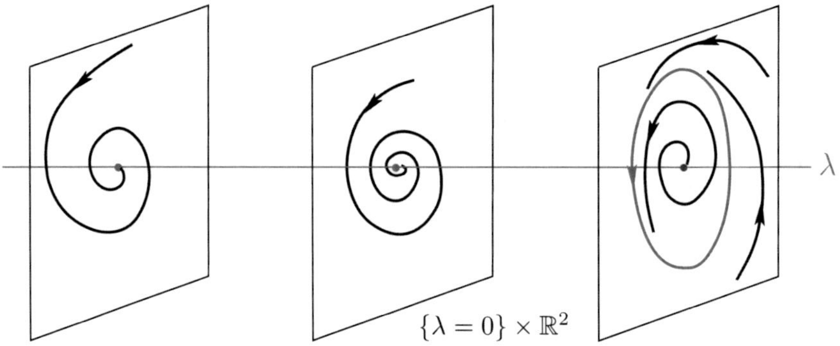

Figure 1.2. The Hopf bifurcation in the system (1.2).

By a change to polar coordinates $x = r \cos \varphi$, $y = r \sin \varphi$, we obtain

$$\dot{r} = r(\lambda - r^2),$$
$$\dot{\varphi} = 1.$$

From this we infer the phase portraits of the family (1.2) which are depicted in Figure 1.2. For $\lambda < 0$ the system has an asymptotically stable hyperbolic equilibrium $(0, 0)$. This is for $\lambda = 0$ still asymptotically stable but no longer hyperbolic. For $\lambda > 0$ the equilibrium $(0, 0)$ becomes unstable. An asymptotically stable periodic orbit with amplitude $\sqrt{\lambda}$ arises. This type of qualitative change of dynamics, or bifurcation, is called Hopf bifurcation, and is named after Eberhard Hopf.

1.1. Saddle-node bifurcation in a budworm growth model

We will illustrate the occurrence of the saddle-node bifurcation in a logistic growth model for a population of budworms. The spruce budworm is an insect living in forests in Eastern United States and Canada. It feeds on the balsam fir tree. Consider a logistic growth model $\dot{N} = r_B N\left(1 - \frac{N}{K_B}\right)$ for the population size N of the spruce budworm, in the absence of predation. Here r_B is the birth rate of the budworm and K_B is the carrying capacity of the forest. Spruce budworms are eaten by birds. The predation rate depends on the budworm population size, and it increases with the population size up to a saturation point. This can be modeled by a rate $p(N) = \frac{BN^2}{A^2+N^2}$ with positive constants A, B. The differential equation governing the budworm population then becomes $\dot{N} = r_B N\left(1 - \frac{N}{K_B}\right) - p(N)$;

$$\dot{N} = r_B N\left(1 - \frac{N}{K_B}\right) - \frac{BN^2}{A^2 + N^2}$$

(see [**232**]). Introducing a coordinate $u = \frac{N}{A}$, parameters $r = \frac{Ar_B}{B}$, $q = \frac{K_B}{A}$, and a time reparametrization $\tau = \frac{B}{A}t$, the differential equation for u as function of τ becomes

$$\frac{du}{d\tau} = f(u, q, r) := ru\left(1 - \frac{u}{q}\right) - \frac{u^2}{1 + u^2}. \tag{1.3}$$

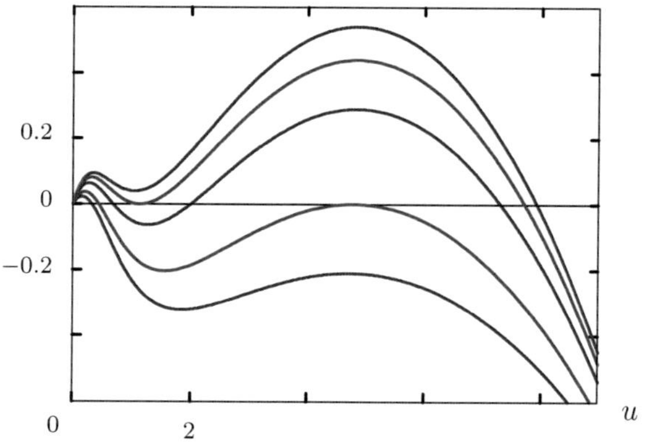

Figure 1.3. Graphs of $u \mapsto f(u, q, r)$ for fixed $q = 10$ and varying r. The graphs are increasing in r, plotted are graphs for $r = 0.3$, 0.384 (red), 0.5, 0.5595 (red), 0.6. The number of positive equilibria of (1.3) (given by zeros of f) varies from one at $r = 0.3$ to three at $r = 0.5$ and back to one at $r = 0.6$. The number of equilibria changes at saddle-node bifurcations, which occur at $r \approx 0.384$ and $r \approx 0.5595$ which are related to the red curves.

Note that this differential equation depends on two parameters q, r. Equilibria of (1.3) are given by $f(u,q,r) = 0$. Figure 1.3 shows graphs of $u \mapsto f(u,q,r)$ for fixed $q = 10$ and varying r. Tangencies of the graph to the u-axis correspond to saddle-node bifurcations, which occur at $r \approx 0.384$ and $r \approx 0.5595$.

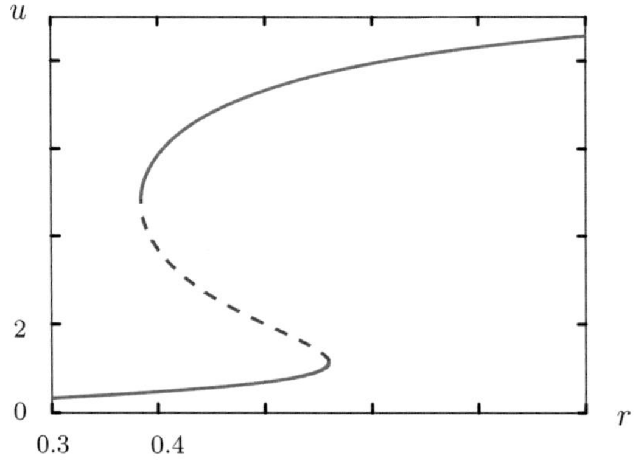

Figure 1.4. Bifurcation diagram of $\dot{u} = f(u,q,r)$ in the parameter r with fixed $q = 10$. Shown is the curve of equilibria where $f(u,10,r) = 0$. The number of equilibria changes by two when varying r at the two saddle-node bifurcations. The green solid curves indicate stable equilibria, the red dashed curve indicates unstable equilibria.

Figure 1.4 shows a bifurcation diagram of f in the parameter r, while having q fixed at 10. Visible are the two saddle-node bifurcations occurring at $r \approx 0.384$ and $r \approx 0.5595$ in which two equilibria are created and annihilated. The curve of equilibria between the two saddle-node bifurcations consists of unstable equilibria. The lower and upper branch of equilibria are asymptotically stable equilibria. Imagine having a parameter value r before the first saddle-node bifurcation value, say $r = 0.3$, and a state of the system close to equilibrium. Increase r in small steps while letting the system converge to an asymptotically stable equilibrium. This will have the system stay close to the stable equilibrium on the lower branch as long as this exists. Having increased r until beyond the second saddle-node bifurcation at $r \approx 0.5595$, the system will settle to the then unique stable equilibrium on the upper branch. If we then let r slowly decrease, the state of the system will remain close to the stable equilibrium on the upper branch, and thus not return to the stable equilibrium on the lower branch, until after r is decreased below the first saddle-node bifurcation at $r \approx 0.384$. This phenomenon of a delay in the response is called hysteresis. Having r periodically slowly increased and decreased until beyond the saddle-node bifurcations gives what is known as a hysteresis loop.

Having looked at the saddle-node bifurcation in (1.3) for a fixed value of $q = 10$, we continue to study bifurcations in (1.3), now as function of both parameters. We will find curves in (q,r)-space of bifurcation values at which saddle-node bifurcations take place. These bifurcation curves are found by distinguishing parameter values at which the equilibria are nonhyperbolic. Nonhyperbolic equilibria occur when both $f(u,q,r) = 0$ and $D_u f(u,q,r) = 0$. Dividing out a factor u for $f(u)$ gives equations

$$
\begin{aligned}
r\left(1-\frac{u}{q}\right) - \frac{u}{1+u^2} &= 0,\\
-\frac{r}{q} - \frac{1-u^2}{(1+u^2)^2} &= 0.
\end{aligned}
\tag{1.4}
$$

The bifurcation equations (1.4) can be solved for q and r as function of u:

$$
\begin{aligned}
q &= \frac{2u^3}{u^2-1},\\
r &= \frac{2u^3}{(u^2+1)^2}.
\end{aligned}
$$

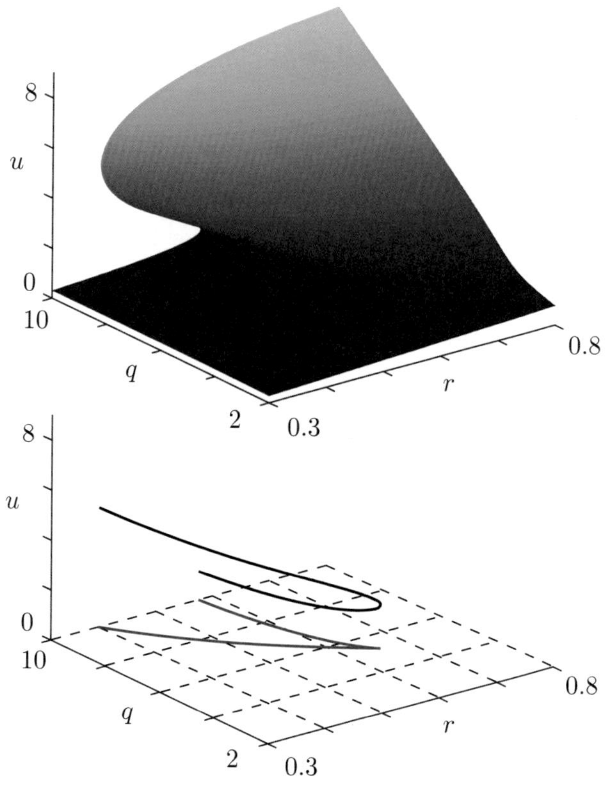

Figure 1.5. Upper panel: the surface $\{f(u,q,r) = 0\}$ in (q,r,u)-space. Lower panel: the curve where both $f(u,q,r) = 0$ and $D_u f(u,q,r) = 0$, with cusp shaped projection on the (q,r)-parameter plane.

In the (q, r)-parameter plane this yields two curves of saddle-node bifurcations that come together in a cusp bifurcation value. Figure 1.5 illustrates the appearance of a cusp bifurcation in the differential equation $\dot{u} = f(u, q, r)$. There are three equilibria for parameters inside the cusp-shaped region, which changes to one equilibrium when crossing the bifurcation curves.

1.2. Hopf bifurcation in the Rosenzweig-MacArthur model

We proceed with discussing Hopf bifurcations in predator-prey models. The derivation of the Rosenzweig-MacArthur model and the discussion of a Hopf bifurcation in it is taken from the syllabus *Modeling Population Dynamics* by André de Roos [**88**], which is available from his website. Alternatively, see [**208**].

The derivation of the model proceeds in steps, starting from a simple Lotka-Volterra model, that leads to increasingly realistic models. The intermediate models do not share the dynamics and bifurcations of the final model. Volterra studied the dynamics of the predator-prey model,

$$\begin{aligned} \dot{F} &= rF - aFC, \\ \dot{C} &= \varepsilon aFC - \mu C. \end{aligned} \tag{1.5}$$

In these equations F and C represent the abundance of prey (food) and predators (consumers), respectively. The parameter r represents the exponential growth rate of prey in the absence of the predator, while μ represents the death or mortality rate of the predators in the absence of prey. Encounters between prey and predators are assumed to be proportional to the product of the abundances F and C. The parameter a represents the attack rate of predators. The parameter ε represents the conversion efficiency, that is, the efficiency with which predators convert consumed prey into offspring. Notice that only positive parameter values are meaningful.

We do not include the derivation of the following facts. The system (1.5) has a trivial steady state $(0, 0)$ and an internal steady state $(\frac{\mu}{\varepsilon a}, \frac{r}{a})$. The function $-\mu \ln(F) + \varepsilon aF - r\ln(C) + aC$ is invariant under the flow and has a minimum at the internal steady state, which explains oscillations in predator and prey abundance around the internal steady state.

A slightly more complicated and realistic version of the Lotka-Volterra predator-prey model (1.5) assumes that prey do not grow indefinitely in the absence of predators, but will ultimately reach a maximum prey abundance. Hence, prey do not grow exponentially, but follow, for example, a logistic growth equation, as in the set of differential equations,

$$\dot{F} = rF\left(1 - \frac{F}{K}\right) - aFC,$$
$$\dot{C} = \varepsilon aFC - \mu C. \tag{1.6}$$

The system has steady states at $(0, 0)$ and $(K, 0)$. Moreover, it turns out that this system has an asymptotically stable internal steady state (that is, with positive abundances of both prey and predator) $\left(\frac{\mu}{\varepsilon a}, \frac{r}{a}\left(1 - \frac{\mu}{\varepsilon a K}\right)\right)$ for $K > K_c = \frac{\mu}{\varepsilon a}$. For $K > K_s = \frac{\mu}{\varepsilon a}\left(\frac{1}{2} + \frac{1}{2}\sqrt{1 + \frac{r}{\mu}}\right)$, the linearization at the internal steady state has complex conjugate eigenvalues with negative real part: the internal steady state is a stable focus.

Both the basic Lotka-Volterra predator-prey model and its variant with logistic prey growth assume that the total predation of prey equals aFC. This assumption implies that the feeding rate of a single predator equals aF, the product of the attack rate and the current prey abundance. Hence, according to this formulation, predators never get satiated as they will eat more and more, the more prey there are: for infinitely large prey abundances the predator feeding rate will also become infinite. The amount of prey eaten by a single predator per unit of time is referred to as the predator's functional response. The basic Lotka-Volterra model assumes that the predator functional is a linear function of the prey abundance. This form is also known as a type I functional response:

$$\varphi_1(F) = aF.$$

For larger values of prey abundance this functional response is not very realistic, as predators get quickly satiated when prey availability is very high. A formulation of the predator's functional response that accounts for the satiation of predators at high food densities is due to Holling. This particular form of the functional response is referred to as Holling's type II functional response or simply a type II functional response. The most mechanistic mathematical formulation of the type II functional response is

$$\varphi_2(F) = \frac{aF}{1 + ahF}$$

in which the parameter a again denotes the rate at which a single predator searches for (attacks) prey whenever it is not currently consuming a prey item and the parameter h is the average time span a predator uses to consume a prey it has caught.

The predator-prey model that accounts for both logistic prey growth and a predator type II (or satiating) functional response can now be represented by the following system of ordinary differential equations,

$$\dot{F} = rF\left(1 - \frac{F}{K}\right) - \frac{aF}{1 + ahF}C,$$

$$\dot{C} = \varepsilon\frac{aF}{1 + ahF}C - \mu C. \tag{1.7}$$

This model is referred to as the Rosenzweig-MacArthur model after two authors that have investigated its dynamics [**311**].

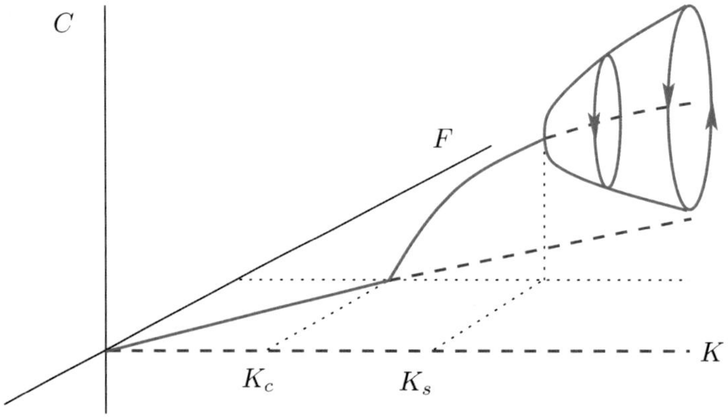

Figure 1.6. Schematic bifurcation diagram for the family (1.7) of differential equations on the first quadrant in the (F, C)-plane, depending on a positive parameter K. The red dashed curves stand for unstable equilibria, green and solid indicates stable equilibria and periodic orbits. There are a transcritical bifurcation at $K = K_c$ and a Hopf bifurcation at $K = K_s$, that creates a stable periodic orbit.

Results of a bifurcation analysis applied to the model are depicted in Figure 1.6 and can be summarized as follows.

(i) The model possesses a trivial steady state

$$(F_1, C_1) = (0, 0),$$

which is always a saddle point.

(ii) The model possesses a prey-only steady state

$$(F_2, C_2) = (K, 0),$$

which is stable as long as $K < K_c = \frac{\mu}{a(\varepsilon - \mu h)}$. For larger values of K the prey-only steady state is a saddle point.

(iii) The model possesses a internal steady state

$$(F_3, C_3) = \left(\frac{\mu}{a(\varepsilon - \mu h)}, \frac{\varepsilon r(aK(\varepsilon - \mu h) - \mu)}{a^2(\varepsilon - \mu h)^2 K}\right),$$

when $K > K_c$. This steady state becomes unstable and limit cycles occur when the carrying capacity K exceeds the value $K_s = \frac{\varepsilon + \mu h}{ah(\varepsilon - \mu h)}$.

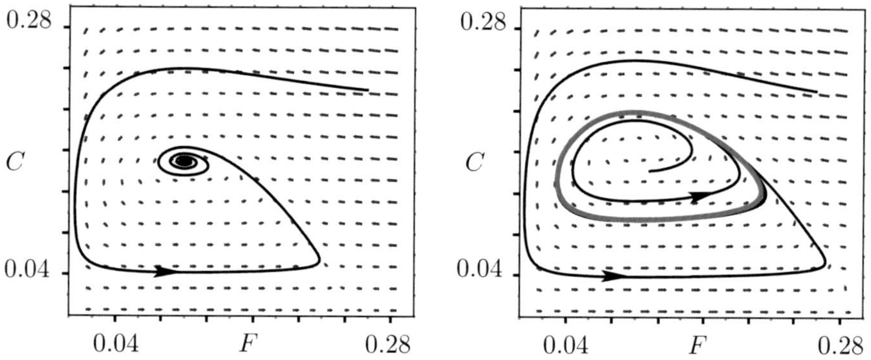

Figure 1.7. Phase portraits of (1.7) for parameter values $\mu = 0.1, a = 5, h = 3, \varepsilon = 0.5, r = 0.5$, and $K = 0.25$ (left picture), $K = 0.3$ (right picture). The equilibrium (F_3, C_3) in the positive first quadrant has lost stability, and a stable limit cycle has appeared in a Hopf bifurcation at $K = K_s = 4/15 \approx 0.267$.

Bifurcations are occurring at $K = K_c$ and $K = K_s$; the one at $K = K_s$ is a Hopf bifurcation; see Figure 1.7.

1.3. Homoclinic orbits and Sandstede's model

An equilibrium p of saddle-type for a differential equation $\dot{x} = f(x)$ in the plane $\mathbb{R}^2$ has two orbits that tend in positive time towards p and two orbits that tend in negative time towards p. Together with $\{p\}$ they form smooth curves

$$W^s(p) = \left\{x_0 \in \mathbb{R}^2 \; ; \; \lim_{t\to\infty} x(t) = p \text{ for the orbit } x(t) \text{ with } x(0) = x_0\right\}$$

and

$$W^u(p) = \left\{x_0 \in \mathbb{R}^2 \; ; \; \lim_{t\to-\infty} x(t) = p \text{ for the orbit } x(t) \text{ with } x(0) = x_0\right\}.$$

Because of the convergence property the curve $W^s(p)$ is called the stable manifold of p and $W^u(p)$ is called the unstable manifold of p. At p, the curve $W^s(p)$ is tangent to the eigenspace corresponding to the negative eigenvalue of $Df(p)$, while the curve $W^u(p)$ is, at p, tangent to the eigenspace corresponding to the positive eigenvalue of $Df(p)$.

The sets $W^s(p)$ and $W^u(p)$ are in the same way defined for an equilibrium of saddle-type of a system in $\mathbb{R}^n$. These form smooth manifolds, called stable and unstable manifolds. Their dimensions are equal to the dimensions of the corresponding stable and unstable spaces of $Df(p)$. For a more detailed discussion of these manifolds, we refer to Appendix B.1.1.

Knowledge of the position and geometry of stable and unstable manifolds of saddles is important to understand the dynamics of a differential equation. Qualitative changes in their properties give rise to bifurcations. The most noticeable example is of a homoclinic bifurcation, featuring in this section. Given two equilibria p_- and p_+ for a differential equation $\dot{x} = f(x)$ in $\mathbb{R}^n$, a nontrivial orbit $h(t)$ with

$$\lim_{t\to-\infty} h(t) = p_- \text{ and } \lim_{t\to\infty} h(t) = p_+$$

is called a *heteroclinic orbit* from p_- to p_+; if $p_- = p_+$, then h is called a *homoclinic orbit* to $p = p_- = p_+$. A planar homoclinic orbit to a hyperbolic saddle equilibrium p lies in both the stable and the unstable manifold of p. Small perturbations of the differential equation are expected to break the homoclinic orbit. In the following example we verify this breakup numerically. We give a detailed analysis of the homoclinic bifurcation in Section 4.1 and in Appendix C.6.

Consider the one-parameter family of differential equations in $\mathbb{R}^2$,

$$\begin{aligned} \dot{x} &= y, \\ \dot{y} &= x + x^2 - xy + \lambda y. \end{aligned} \tag{1.8}$$

These differential equations admit two equilibria for all values of λ, namely a saddle $p = (0,0)$ and a focus $q = (-1,0)$. Figure 1.8 shows the stable and unstable manifolds of the saddle equilibrium at the origin for different parameter values. We make the following observations based on numerical experiments. For a value of λ close to -0.85, the system (1.8) has a homoclinic orbit to p. This homoclinic orbit encloses the equilibrium q. For all points inside the homoclinic orbit, the positive orbit converges to the union of the homoclinic orbit and p, and the negative orbit converges to q. The homoclinic orbit breaks if λ changes. For smaller λ there is a heteroclinic orbit connecting q to p. For larger λ there is a periodic orbit encircling q. For all points P from the region bounded by the periodic orbit, the negative orbit still converges to q. But now the positive orbit set converges to the periodic orbit. There is a heteroclinic orbit connecting p to the periodic orbit. In the bifurcation the periodic orbit disappears in the homoclinic orbit, while its period tends to infinity.

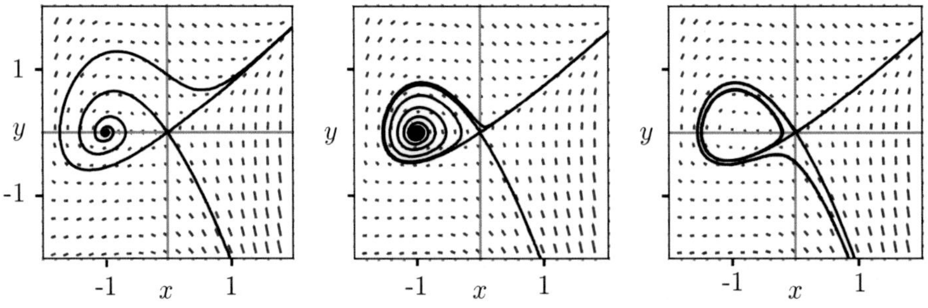

Figure 1.8. The stable and unstable manifolds of the saddle equilibrium p in the phase portraits of (1.8) for $\lambda = -0.7$ (left), $\lambda = -0.85$ (middle), and $\lambda = -0.9$ (right).

In systems of differential equations, or in families thereof, it is not often possible to solve for the existence of a homoclinic orbit. We will describe an explicit construction of families of differential equations in $\mathbb{R}^3$ that admit a homoclinic bifurcation. This has turned out to be helpful for numerical explorations of homoclinic bifurcations. Consider first a planar system $\dot{u} = f(u)$, $u \in \mathbb{R}^2$. For it to have an explicit homoclinic orbit $h(t)$ to an equilibrium at the origin, we first describe an algebraic curve whose shape allows for such a homoclinic. Consider in the plane the Cartesian leaf written as the zero level set of the function

$$\varphi(x, y) = x^2(1 - x) - y^2.$$

We denote the zero level set as

$$\Gamma = \{(x, y) \in \mathbb{R}^2 \; ; \; \varphi(x, y) = 0\},$$

and write $\Gamma^+ = \{(x, y) \in \mathbb{R}^2 \; ; \; \varphi(x, y) = 0, x > 0\}$. The gradient of the Cartesian leaf is given by

$$\nabla\varphi(x) = \begin{pmatrix} x(2 - 3x) \\ -2y \end{pmatrix}.$$

The following lemma describes an explicit system for which Γ is an invariant set, containing no equilibria except at the origin. Therefore, Γ^+ corresponds to a homoclinic orbit $h(t)$.

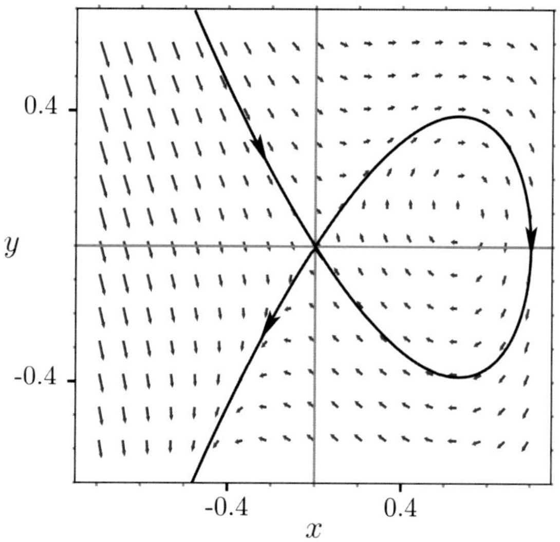

Figure 1.9. Orbits for (1.9), with $a = -1$ and $b = 2$, that converge to the saddle equilibrium at the origin for time to $\pm\infty$, including the homoclinic orbit.

Lemma 1.1. *Consider the system $\dot{u} = f(u)$ on $\mathbb{R}^2$ given by*

$$\begin{pmatrix} \dot{x} \\ \dot{y} \end{pmatrix} = \begin{pmatrix} ax + by - ax^2 \\ bx + ay - \frac{3}{2}bx^2 - \frac{3}{2}axy \end{pmatrix}, \tag{1.9}$$

with $a, b \in \mathbb{R}$, and assume that $a^2 \leq b^2$ and $b \neq 0$. Then the system has a homoclinic solution $h(t)$ to the equilibrium at the origin, which is contained in Γ^+.

Proof. It is clear that $(0,0)$ is an equilibrium of the system. For Γ to be invariant under the flow of the system, we need to have

$$\frac{d}{dt}\varphi(x(t), y(t)) = 0$$

for solutions $(x(t), y(t))$ with $(x(0), y(0)) \in \Gamma$. An application of the chain rule for derivatives gives that it is sufficient to check the condition

$$\langle \nabla\varphi(u), f(u) \rangle = 0$$

for $u \in \Gamma$. Using that $y^2 = x^2(1-x)$ for $u = (x, y) \in \Gamma$, a direct computation indeed gives

$$\begin{aligned} \langle \nabla\varphi(u), f(u) \rangle &= \left\langle \begin{pmatrix} x(2-3x) \\ -2y \end{pmatrix}, \begin{pmatrix} by \\ bx - \frac{3}{2}bx^2 \end{pmatrix} + \begin{pmatrix} ax(1-x) \\ ay - \frac{3}{2}axy \end{pmatrix} \right\rangle \\ &= ay^2(2-3x) - 2ay^2\left(1 - \frac{3}{2}x\right) \\ &= 0 \end{aligned}$$

for $u \in \Gamma$.

It remains to check that Γ^+ does not contain equilibria. On Γ we have $y = \pm x\sqrt{1-x}$. Evaluating the first component of f at $(x, \pm x\sqrt{1-x})$, we get

$$ax \pm bx\sqrt{1-x} - ax^2 = x\sqrt{1-x}(a\sqrt{1-x} \pm b).$$

This expression is zero for $x = 0$, $x = 1$ or $x = 1 - (b/a)^2$. Because of the assumption $a^2 \leq b^2$, the last zero is not contained in Γ^+. The second component of f evaluated at $x = 1$ is $-b/2$, which is not zero under the assumption $b \neq 0$. We conclude that Γ^+ contains no equilibria. □

The eigenvalues of the linearization of f at the origin are given by

$$\lambda_{1,2} = a \pm b.$$

The origin is therefore a hyperbolic saddle if $a^2 \neq b^2$. This system can be extended to three-dimensional systems having an explicit homoclinic orbit.

Theorem 1.2. *For arbitrary functions $G, H : \mathbb{R}^3 \to \mathbb{R}^3$, the three-dimensional system*

$$\begin{pmatrix} \dot{u} \\ \dot{z} \end{pmatrix} = \begin{pmatrix} f(u) \\ 0 \end{pmatrix} + \varphi(u)G(u,z) + zH(u,z)$$

still has the original homoclinic solution $h(t)$ contained in the (x, y)-plane.

Proof. On the set $\Gamma' = \{(x, y, z)|\varphi(x, y) = 0, z = 0\}$, the vector field is given by $(f(x, y), 0)$. So it reduces to the two-dimensional system from before, and therefore the homoclinic orbit $h(t)$ is preserved. □

Björn Sandstede [**325**] managed to apply this theorem to construct explicit examples of systems with various types of homoclinic orbits. Consider for instance the family

$$\begin{pmatrix} \dot{u} \\ \dot{z} \end{pmatrix} = \begin{pmatrix} f(u) \\ 0 \end{pmatrix} + \varphi(u) \begin{pmatrix} 0 \\ \mu \end{pmatrix} + z \begin{pmatrix} -\mu \nabla \varphi(u) \\ c \end{pmatrix}$$

depending on a parameter μ. The origin is an equilibrium with eigenvalues $a \pm b, c$. We note that adding φ here breaks the invariance of the (x, y)-plane, while preserving the original homoclinic. The flow is thus no longer simply a planar flow with a third direction added.

Chapter 2

Flows and invariant sets

This chapter collects prerequisites and some general notions on invariant sets and bifurcations that are needed in the core chapters on bifurcation theory and that may not be part of standard bachelor courses on differential equations. We present general definitions of invariant sets, we include material on Floquet theory and Poincaré return maps needed to study a flow near a periodic orbit, and we discuss the Smale horseshoe map, the prototype model for chaotic dynamics. Among the textbooks that treat differential equations from a dynamical systems point of view, we mention those by James Meiss [**249**], Clark Robinson [**309**] and Gerald Teschl [**379**]. We recommend these for details and further reading. This chapter also provides a section discussing possible formalizations of the notion of bifurcation, and we have a brief section that can be used for a comparison with catastrophe theory.

The context of this book is that of smooth differential equations. Here smooth stands for infinitely often continuously differentiable, or k times continuously differentiable for an unspecified sufficiently high number k. So consider a differential equation

$$\dot{x} = f(x)$$

on an open set $\mathcal{D} \subset \mathbb{R}^n$, where $f : \mathcal{D} \to \mathbb{R}^n$ is a smooth map. The map f is called a vector field. Given $\xi \in \mathcal{D}$, there exists an orbit $t \mapsto \varphi(t, \xi) \in \mathcal{D}$ that solves an initial value problem

$$\begin{aligned} \frac{d}{dt}\varphi(t,\xi) &= f(\varphi(t,\xi)), \\ \varphi(0,\xi) &= \xi. \end{aligned}$$

Here t belongs to an open interval containing 0. Orbits for varying initial conditions give rise to a flow. The following result is the standard existence and uniqueness result for solutions to smooth differential equations. See for instance [**163**] or [**329**]. See also Theorem A.20.

Theorem 2.1. *Suppose f is C^k. For all $\xi \in \mathcal{D}$ there exists a maximal interval $I_\xi \subset \mathbb{R}$ containing 0 and a unique orbit $\varphi(\cdot, x)$ with*

$$\begin{aligned} \frac{d}{dt}\varphi(t,\xi) &= f(\varphi(t,\xi)), \\ \varphi(0,\xi) &= \xi. \end{aligned}$$

The set $W = \bigcup_{\xi \in \mathcal{D}} I_\xi \times \{\xi\}$ is open, and the map $\varphi : W \to \mathcal{D}$ is C^k and defines a local flow, that is,

$$\begin{aligned} \varphi(0,\xi) &= \xi, \\ \varphi(t+s,\xi) &= \varphi(t,\varphi(s,\xi)), \end{aligned}$$

for $\xi \in \mathcal{D}$, $s, t+s \in I_\xi$.

The classical theory gives that such type of result on existence and uniqueness of a flow can be proved under the weaker assumption that f is locally Lipschitz continuous [**147**]. To emphasize the action on the phase variable we also write

$$\varphi(t,\cdot) = \varphi^t(\cdot).$$

These statements apply to families $\dot{x} = f(x,\lambda)$, $f : \mathcal{D} \times \mathbb{R}^m \to \mathbb{R}^n$, of differential equations depending on a parameter λ, by noting that this gives rise to differential equations

$$\begin{aligned} \dot{x} &= f(x,\lambda), \\ \dot{\lambda} &= 0. \end{aligned}$$

The flow of a smooth family of differential equations (meaning that $(x,\lambda) \mapsto f(x,\lambda)$ is smooth) thus is a smooth function of initial conditions and parameters.

Although our focus is on bifurcations in the context of differential equations, there is at several places a need to study iterates of maps. Consider a topological space X, and let $F : X \to X$ be a continuous map. In this setting we call

$$\{F^m(x) \,;\, m \in \mathbb{N}_0\}$$

the positive orbit of x. Here $\mathbb{N}_0 = \mathbb{N} \cup \{0\}$ denotes the set of nonnegative integers. If F is a homeomorphism, we have the orbit

$$\{F^m(x) \,;\, m \in \mathbb{Z}\}$$

of x. The collection of iterates $\{F^m\}_{m\in\mathbb{Z}}$ defines the flow of the discrete time system generated by the homeomorphism F, satisfying $F^0(x) = x$ and $F^{t+s}(x) = F^t(F^s(x))$, $s, t \in \mathbb{Z}$.

2.1. Invariant sets and attractors

Given a flow, we are often interested in its asymptotic behavior as time goes to infinity. A number of definitions capture invariant sets for such long time dynamics. The definitions we present here for differential equations can easily be transferred to a context of iterates of maps. We refer to [**309**] for further information.

Definition 2.2. A set $S \subset \mathcal{D}$ is called *(flow) invariant* if $\varphi^t(x) \in S$ for all $x \in S$ and all $t \in I_x$. If t is restricted to $I_x \cap \mathbb{R}^+$ or $I_x \cap \mathbb{R}^-$ the set S is called *positively or negatively invariant*, respectively.

Note that orbits are invariant sets. Of particular interest are equilibria and periodic orbits.

Definition 2.3. An *equilibrium* p is a point where $f(p) = 0$. A *periodic orbit* is an orbit of a point x where $\varphi(T, x) = x$ with a minimal $T > 0$ called the (minimal) period. A *critical element* is an equilibrium or periodic orbit.

A main part of bifurcation theory, namely local bifurcation theory, is on changes in the set of critical elements and on stability of critical elements.

Definition 2.4. Let φ be a flow and let $\xi \in \mathcal{D}$. A point $x \in \mathcal{D}$ is called *ω-limit point* of ξ if $\mathbb{R}^+ \subset I_\xi$ and there are $t_n \to \infty$, $n \to \infty$, with $\lim_{n\to\infty} \varphi(t_n, \xi) = x$. The set $\omega(\xi)$ of all ω-limit point of ξ is called *ω-limit set* of ξ.

Analogously, a point $x \in \mathcal{D}$ is called *α-limit point* of ξ if $\mathbb{R}^- \subset I_\xi$ and there are $t_n \to -\infty$, $n \to \infty$, with $\lim_{n\to\infty} \varphi(t_n, \xi) = x$. The set $\alpha(\xi)$ of all α-limit point of ξ is called *α-limit set* of ξ.

Let $\xi \in \mathcal{D}$, $\mathbb{R}^+ \subset I_\xi$. Then we have

$$\omega(\xi) = \bigcap_{T\geq 0} \overline{\{\varphi^t(\xi)\ ;\ t \geq T\}}.$$

Similarly, assuming $\mathbb{R}^- \subset I_\xi$, we have

$$\alpha(\xi) = \bigcap_{T\leq 0} \overline{\{\varphi^t(\xi)\ ;\ t \leq T\}}.$$

It follows that limit sets are closed invariant sets.

Definition 2.5. A closed invariant set A is *(Lyapunov) stable* if for each open neighborhood U of A there is a neighborhood $V \subset U$ of A so that $\varphi(t, x) \in U$ for each $t \geq 0, x \in V$. It is otherwise called unstable.

A closed invariant set A is *asymptotically stable* if there is an open neighborhood $\hat{U}$ of A so that for all $x \in \hat{U}$ one has $\omega(x) \subset A$.

Example 2.6. Under these definitions, a closed invariant set A may be asymptotically stable but not stable. An easy example is $\dot{\theta} = 1+\sin(2\pi\theta)$ on the circle $\mathbb{R}/\mathbb{Z}$. This can be embedded in the plane. For another example in the plane, consider the following vector field taken from [**146**]:

$$f(x,y) = \begin{cases} \left(\frac{x^2(y-x)+y^5}{(x^2+y^2)(1+(x^2+y^2)^2)}, \frac{y^2(y-2x)}{(x^2+y^2)(1+(x^2+y^2)^2)}\right), & (x,y) \neq (0,0), \\ (0,0), & (x,y) = (0,0). \end{cases} \tag{2.1}$$

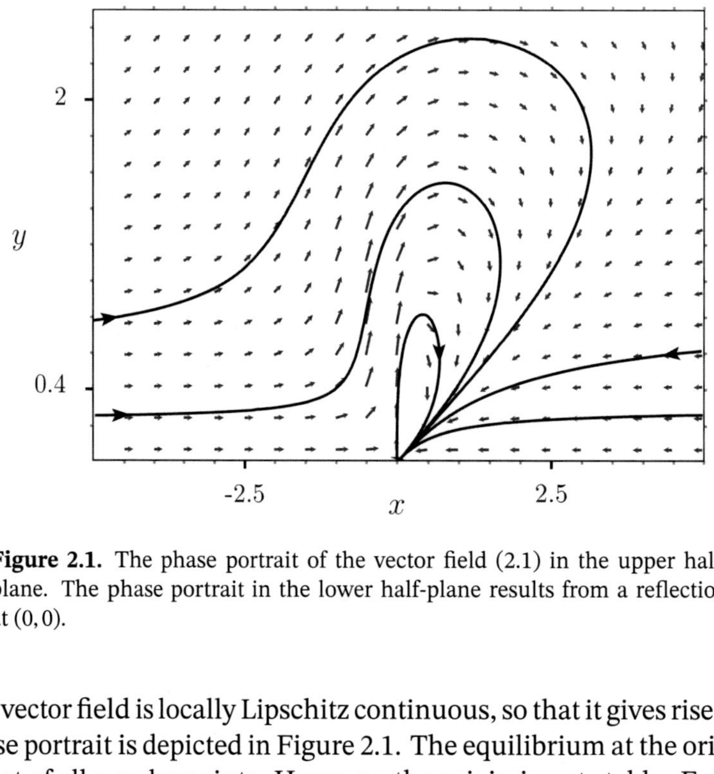

Figure 2.1. The phase portrait of the vector field (2.1) in the upper half-plane. The phase portrait in the lower half-plane results from a reflection at $(0,0)$.

This vector field is locally Lipschitz continuous, so that it gives rise to a flow. The phase portrait is depicted in Figure 2.1. The equilibrium at the origin is the ω-limit set of all nearby points. However, the origin is not stable. Exercise 2.1 asks to prove the statements in this example. ■

Definition 2.7. A point x is a *recurrent point* for a flow φ if $x \in \omega(x)$ (so for any neighborhood U of x, there is $t > 1$ with $\varphi(t,x) \in U$).

Definition 2.8. A point x is called a *nonwandering point* for a flow φ if for any neighborhood U of x, there is $t > 1$ with $\varphi(t,U) \cap U \neq \emptyset$. The *nonwandering set* is the set of nonwandering points.

Although this definition does not make a statement on the positive orbit of x, it means that close to x there are points that return close to x. The nonwandering set forms a closed invariant set. It contains the set of recurrent points.

Definition 2.9. A compact invariant set A of a differential equation $\dot{x} = f(x)$ with flow φ^t is an *attractor* if

(i) A is Lyapunov stable;

(ii) A is asymptotically stable;

(iii) A is indecomposable. There is no strict and nontrivial subset of A satisfying the first two properties.

The *basin of attraction* of an attractor A is the set of all points x with $\omega(x) \subset A$.

A compact invariant set A satisfying the first two conditions, but possibly not the indecomposability condition, is called an attracting set. Given an attractor one may consider whether a point $x \in A$ or x near A exists whose ω-limit set equals A. See Exercise 2.2.

Remark 2.10. Corresponding definitions can be given for continuous maps $F : X \to X$.

(1) A point $p \in X$ is a fixed point of F if $F(p) = p$. A point $q \in X$ is a periodic point of F with (minimal) period $m \in \mathbb{N}$ if $F^m(q) = q$ and $F^k(q) \neq q$ for $0 < k < m$.

(2) A point $x \in X$ is called an ω-limit point of ξ if there are $m_n \to \infty$, $n \to \infty$, with $\lim_{n\to\infty} F^{m_n}(\xi) = x$. The set $\omega(\xi)$ of all ω-limit points of ξ is called an ω-limit set of ξ.

If F is a homeomorphism, one can likewise define an α-limit point and an α-limit set of ξ by letting $m_n \to -\infty$.

(3) A closed set $A \subset X$ is invariant if $A = F(A)$. A closed invariant set A of a map F is (Lyapunov) stable if for each open neighborhood U of A there is a neighborhood $V \subset U$ of A so that $\mathbb{N}_0 \subset I_x$ and $F^m(x) \in U$ for each $m \in \mathbb{N}_0, x \in V$.

A closed invariant set A of a map F is asymptotically stable if there is an open neighborhood $\hat{U}$ of A so that for all $x \in \hat{U}$ one has $\omega(x) \subset A$.

Also recurrent points and nonwandering points have corresponding definitions, for which one replaces the flow $\varphi(t, \cdot)$ by $F^n(\cdot)$, $n \in \mathbb{N}_0$. ■

The above definition leaves out various examples of interest and other definitions have therefore been suggested. Possible different approaches have been suggested by David Ruelle [**317, 318**] and John Milnor [**252**]. John Milnor introduces a notion of attractor as a compact invariant set that has a basin of attraction which may not be open but contains a set of positive Lebesgue measure.

Definition 2.11. A compact invariant set A of a differential equation $\dot{x} = f(x)$ will be called a *Milnor attractor* if it satisfies two conditions:

(i) The *basin of attraction*

$$\rho(A) := \{x \in X \; ; \; \omega(x) \subset A\}$$

has positive Lebesgue measure.

(ii) There is no strictly smaller closed set $A' \subset A$ so that $\rho(A')$ coincides with $\rho(A)$ up to a set of Lebesgue measure zero.

This notion of an attractor was coined by Milnor to have a definition that is less restrictive than topological definitions making use of asymptotic stability. One may add a condition that there is no strictly smaller closed set $A' \subset A$ for which $\rho(A')$ has positive Lebesgue measure.

Example 2.12. We present an artificial example to illustrate the concept of a Milnor attractor in the context of iterates of continuous interval maps. The definition of a Milnor attractor applies in this context as well. Consider the piecewise linear map Π on $[-1,1]$ whose graph contains the points $\pm(1/n, 1/n)$, n odd, and $\pm(1/n, -1/n)$, n even, and connects subsequent points with line pieces. Write $V = \{\pm 1/n \; ; \; n \geq 1\}$. Note that $V \cup \{0\}$ is the set of fixed points plus period-2 points of Π. Let $B(0) = \{x \in [-1,1] \; ; \; \lim_{i\to\infty} \Pi^i(x) = 0\}$ be the basin of attraction of 0. Consider $S = \{x \in [-1,1] \; ; \; \Pi^i(x) \in V\}$, the inverse images of the fixed points and period-2 points in V. Now S is a countable dense subset of $[-1,1]$ and $B(0)$ is its complement. So 0 is a Milnor attractor, with a basin that has full measure but does not contain open sets and in particular does not contain an open neighborhood of 0. See Exercise 2.3. ■

2.2. Periodic orbits

Apart from an equilibrium, the most basic invariant set of a differential equation is a closed curve formed by a periodic orbit. For the study of bifurcations of a periodic orbit, we need techniques for studying the flow near a periodic orbit. This section first develops Floquet theory, the study of solutions of periodic nonautonomous linear differential equations. This is then connected to the notion of Poincaré return map which is the standard technique for studying the flow near a periodic orbit and translates this to the study of dynamics of a diffeomorphism near a fixed point.

2.2.1. Floquet theory. Consider

$$\dot{x} = f(x) \tag{2.2}$$

in $\mathbb{R}^n$. Let γ be a periodic solution of (2.2) of minimal period T; $\gamma(t) = \gamma(t+T)$ with $T > 0$ minimal with this property. Linearizing the differential equation about γ, we obtain the nonautonomous equation

$$\dot{\xi} = Df(\gamma(t))\xi,$$

called the first variation equation or also the variational equation.

This leads us to the study of time periodic linear systems, the topic of Floquet theory. Consider the differential equation

$$\dot{u}(t) = A(t)u(t), \quad A(\cdot) : \mathbb{R} \to \mathbb{R}^{n \times n} \text{ continuous and } T\text{-periodic.} \tag{2.3}$$

We note that solutions are defined for all $t \in \mathbb{R}$.

Theorem 2.13. *The solutions of the system* (2.3) *form an n-dimensional vector space. Moreover, there exists a matrix-valued function* $\Phi(t, t_0) \in \mathbb{R}^{n \times n}$ *such that the solution satisfying the initial condition* $x(t_0) = x_0$ *is given by* $\Phi(t, t_0)x_0$.

Proof. This follows from the existence and uniqueness theorem for differential equations and the linearity of (2.3). □

The principal matrix solution $\Phi(t, t_0)$ is a solution of

$$\begin{aligned} \dot{\Phi}(t, t_0) &= A(t)\Phi(t, t_0), \\ \Phi(t_0, t_0) &= I. \end{aligned} \tag{2.4}$$

Note that the principal matrix solution does exist for every linear differential equation with continuous coefficient matrix $A(\cdot)$ regardless of a possible periodicity. The matrix $\Phi(t, t_0)$ is also called transition matrix.

Lemma 2.14. *Suppose* $A(t)$ *is periodic with period* T. *Then the principal matrix solution satisfies*

$$\Phi(t+T, t_0+T) = \Phi(t, t_0).$$

Proof. By $\frac{d}{dt}\Phi(t+T, t_0+T) = A(t+T)\Phi(t+T, t_0+T) = A(t)\Phi(t+T, t_0+T)$ and $\Phi(t_0+T, t_0+T) = I$, we see that $\Phi(t+T, t_0+T)$ solves (2.4). Hence it is equal to $\Phi(t, t_0)$ by uniqueness. □

We recall Liouville's theorem which is true for every linear differential equation with continuous coefficient matrix $A(\cdot)$ regardless of a possible periodicity.

Lemma 2.15 (Liouville's theorem).

$$\det \Phi(t, t_0) = e^{\int_{t_0}^{t} \operatorname{tr} A(s)\, ds}.$$

Sketch of proof. A direct calculation shows

$$\frac{d}{dt} \det \Phi(t, t_0) = \operatorname{tr}(A(t)) \det \Phi(t, t_0). \tag{2.5}$$

We derive this equation only for the two-dimensional case. Write

$$A(t) = \begin{pmatrix} a(t) & b(t) \\ c(t) & d(t) \end{pmatrix}.$$

Write also

$$\Phi(t, t_0) = \begin{pmatrix} \alpha(t) & \beta(t) \\ \gamma(t) & \delta(t) \end{pmatrix}.$$

Then (suppressing the argument t in the coefficients of $\Phi(t, t_0)$ and $A(t)$),

$$\begin{aligned}
\frac{d}{dt} \det \Phi(t, t_0) &= \frac{d}{dt}(\alpha\delta - \beta\gamma) \\
&= \alpha'\delta + \alpha\delta' - \beta'\gamma - \beta\gamma' \\
&= (a\alpha + b\gamma)\delta + \alpha(c\beta + d\delta) - (a\beta + b\delta)\gamma - \beta(c\alpha + d\gamma) \\
&= (a + d)(\alpha\delta - \beta\gamma) \\
&= \operatorname{tr}(A(t)) \det \Phi(t, t_0).
\end{aligned}$$

The lemma follows by solving (2.5) with initial condition $\det \Phi(t_0, t_0) = 1$. □

Definition 2.16. Consider (2.3). The matrix

$$M(t_0) = \Phi(t_0 + T, t_0)$$

is called the *monodromy matrix.*

So, the monodromy matrix can be seen as the principal matrix solution when moving on by one period. By Lemma 2.14 the monodromy matrix is T-periodic,

$$M(t_0 + T) = M(t_0).$$

By Liouville's theorem

$$\det M(t_0) = e^{\int_{t_0}^{t_0+T} \operatorname{tr} A(s)\, ds} = e^{\int_0^T \operatorname{tr} A(s)\, ds} \tag{2.6}$$

is independent of t_0 and positive.

Recall that the exponential of an $n \times n$ matrix Q is defined by $e^Q = \sum_{n=0}^{\infty} \frac{1}{n!} Q^n$. The inverse operation, taking the logarithm $\ln(P)$ of a matrix, exists for an invertible matrix P.

Lemma 2.17. *If P is an $n \times n$ matrix with* $\det P \neq 0$*, then there is a complex-valued matrix Q with*

$$P = e^Q.$$

If P is real and all real eigenvalues are positive, then Q is real. In particular, if P is real, there is a real logarithm for P^2.

Proof. Using $\ln(V^{-1}PV) = V^{-1} \ln(P)V$, it is no restriction to assume that P is in Jordan normal form and to consider the case of only one Jordan block

$P = \alpha I + N$ (see Theorem B.19 for the Jordan normal form theorem). Taking the formula

$$\ln(1+x) = \sum_{j=1}^{\infty} \frac{(-1)^{j+1}}{j} x^j,$$

put

$$Q = \ln(\alpha) I + \sum_{j=1}^{n-1} \frac{(-1)^{j+1}}{\alpha^j j} N^j.$$

Here $\ln(\alpha)$ is a complex logarithm of $\alpha \neq 0$. This gives $e^Q = P$.

To prove the statements on real logarithms, we only need to consider Jordan blocks with complex eigenvalues. Take the real Jordan normal form and note that from

$$R = \begin{pmatrix} \operatorname{Re}\alpha & \operatorname{Im}\alpha \\ -\operatorname{Im}\alpha & \operatorname{Re}\alpha \end{pmatrix} = r \begin{pmatrix} \cos(\varphi) & \sin(\varphi) \\ -\sin(\varphi) & \cos(\varphi) \end{pmatrix}$$

with $\alpha = re^{i\varphi}$, the logarithm is given by

$$\ln R = \ln(r) I + \begin{pmatrix} 0 & -\varphi \\ \varphi & 0 \end{pmatrix}.$$

For a real Jordan block $RI + N = R(I + R^{-1}N)$, the logarithm is given by

$$\ln(RI + N) = \ln(R) I + \sum_{j=1}^{n} \frac{(-1)^{j+1}}{j} R^{-j} N^j. \qquad \square$$

Floquet's theorem characterizes solutions to the principal matrix equation.

Theorem 2.18 (Floquet's theorem). *The principal matrix solution of* (2.3) *has the form*

$$\Phi(t, t_0) = P(t, t_0) e^{(t-t_0)Q(t_0)},$$

where $P(\cdot, t_0)$ *is T-periodic and* $P(t_0, t_0) = I$.

Proof. According to (2.6) and Lemma 2.17, the logarithm of $M(t_0)$ exists, say $M(t_0) = e^{TQ(t_0)}$ with $Q(t_0 + T) = Q(t_0)$.

Write $\Phi(t, t_0) = P(t, t_0) e^{(t-t_0)Q(t_0)}$. By a straightforward computation one shows that

$$\begin{aligned} P(t+T, t_0) &= \Phi(t+T, t_0) M(t_0)^{-1} e^{-(t-t_0)Q(t_0)} \\ &= \Phi(t+T, t_0+T) e^{-(t-t_0)Q(t_0)} \\ &= \Phi(t, t_0) e^{-(t-t_0)Q(t_0)} \\ &= P(t, t_0). \end{aligned} \qquad \square$$

Definition 2.19. The eigenvalues ρ_j of $M(t_0)$ are known as *Floquet multipliers* (also *characteristic multipliers*) and the eigenvalues γ_j of $Q(t_0)$ are known as *Floquet exponents* (also *characteristic exponents*). They are related via $\rho_j = e^{T\gamma_j}$.

One calls a linear differential equation (asymptotically) stable if $\xi = 0$ is (asymptotically) stable.

Corollary 2.20. *A periodic linear system is asymptotically stable if all Floquet multipliers satisfy $|\rho_j| < 1$ (equivalently, if all Floquet exponents satisfy $\operatorname{Re}\gamma_j < 0$).*

Example 2.21. Hill's equation is a periodic linear second-order system

$$\ddot{x}(t) + q(t)x(t) = 0, \quad q(t+T) = q(t). \tag{2.7}$$

The associated system is

$$\begin{aligned} \dot{x} &= y, \\ \dot{y} &= -qx. \end{aligned}$$

The principal matrix solution is given by

$$\Phi(t, t_0) = \begin{pmatrix} c(t, t_0) & s(t, t_0) \\ \dot{c}(t, t_0) & \dot{s}(t, t_0) \end{pmatrix},$$

where $c(t, t_0)$ is the solution of (2.7) with $c(t_0, t_0) = 1, \dot{c}(_0, t_0) = 0$ and $s(t_0, t_0)$ is the solution of (2.7) with $s(t_0, t_0) = 0, \dot{s}(t_0, t_0) = 1$. Liouville's theorem shows

$$\det \Phi(t, t_0) = 1,$$

and hence the characteristic equation for the monodromy matrix

$$M(t_0) = \begin{pmatrix} c(t_0 + T, t_0) & s(t_0 + T, t_0) \\ \dot{c}(t_0 + T, t_0) & \dot{s}(t_0 + T, t_0) \end{pmatrix}$$

is given by

$$\rho^2 - 2\Delta\rho + 1 = 0,$$

where

$$\Delta = \frac{1}{2}\operatorname{tr}(M(t_0)) = \frac{1}{2}(c(t_0 + T, t_0) + \dot{s}(t_0 + T, t_0)).$$

We obtain that Hill's equation is stable if $|\Delta| < 1$, and it is unstable if $|\Delta| > 1$. ■

If we have an equation of the form

$$\dot{v}(t) = A(t)v + g(t), \tag{2.8}$$

and $\Phi(t, s)$ is the transition matrix of the homogeneous part $\dot{v}(t) = A(t)v(t)$, then a solution to (2.8) is given by an expression

$$v(t) = \Phi(t, 0)v(0) + \int_0^t \Phi(t, s)g(s)\, ds. \tag{2.9}$$

This is the variation of constants formula. Exercise 2.5 asks us to prove this formula. Note that for the case where A is constant, we have $\Phi(t,s) = e^{A(t-s)}$ and

$$v(t) = e^{At}v(0) + \int_0^t e^{A(t-s)}g(s)\,ds. \tag{2.10}$$

2.2.2. Poincaré return maps. We continue studying smooth differential equations $\dot{x} = f(x)$ on $\mathbb{R}^n$, with flow $(t,x) \mapsto \varphi(t,x)$. A set $\Sigma \subset \mathbb{R}^n$ is called a submanifold of codimension 1 (so that its dimension is $n-1$), if it can be written as

$$\Sigma = \{x \in U\,;\; S(x) = 0\}$$

where $U \subset R^n$ is open, $S \in C^k(U,\mathbb{R})$, and $DS(x) \neq 0$ for all $x \in \Sigma$. The submanifold Σ is said to be transverse to the vector field f if $DS(x)f(x) \neq 0$ for $x \in \Sigma$. Such a submanifold is called a cross section.

Theorem 2.22. *Suppose $x \in \mathbb{R}^n$ and let Σ be a cross section with $\varphi(T,x) \in \Sigma$. Then there exists a neighborhood V of x and $\tau \in C^k(V,\mathbb{R})$ such that $\tau(x) = T$ and*

$$\varphi(\tau(y), y) \in \Sigma$$

for all $y \in V$.

Proof. Consider the equation $S(\varphi(t,y)) = 0$ for (t,y) near (T,x). Note that

$$\frac{\partial}{\partial t}S(\varphi(t,y)) = DS(\varphi(t,y))f(\varphi(t,y)) \neq 0$$

for (t,y) in a neighborhood of (T,x) by transversality. So by the implicit function theorem, there exists a neighborhood V of x and function $\tau \in C^k(V,\mathbb{R})$ such that for all $y \in V$ we have $S(\tau(\varphi(y),y)) = 0$, that is, $\varphi(\tau(y),y) \in \Sigma$. □

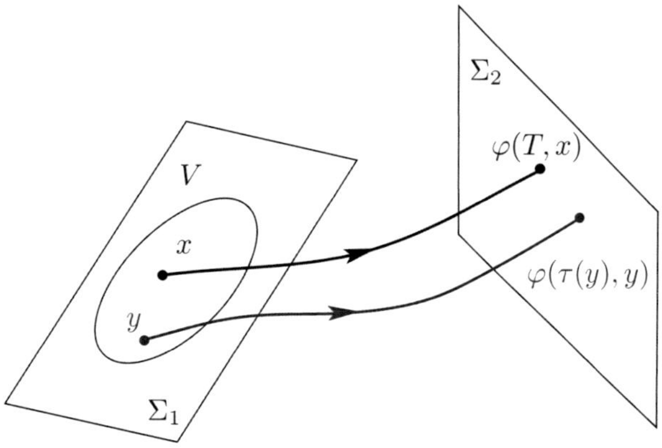

Figure 2.2. The global flow box theorem treats transition maps between cross sections.

The same argument works for the transition map between two different transversals. This immediately yields the following result.

Theorem 2.23 (Global flow box theorem). *Suppose $x \in \mathbb{R}^n$ and let Σ_1, Σ_2 be two cross sections such that $x \in \Sigma_1$, $\varphi(T,x) \in \Sigma_2$. Then there exists a neighborhood V of x and $\tau \in C^k(V,\mathbb{R})$ such that $\tau(x) = T$ and*

$$\varphi(\tau(y), y) \in \Sigma_2$$

for all $y \in V$.

The theorem is depicted in Figure 2.2. This result also applies in the special case of a single cross section $\Sigma_1 = \Sigma_2$. This leads to the following definition of the Poincaré return map. A picture of how this works near a periodic orbit is Figure 2.3.

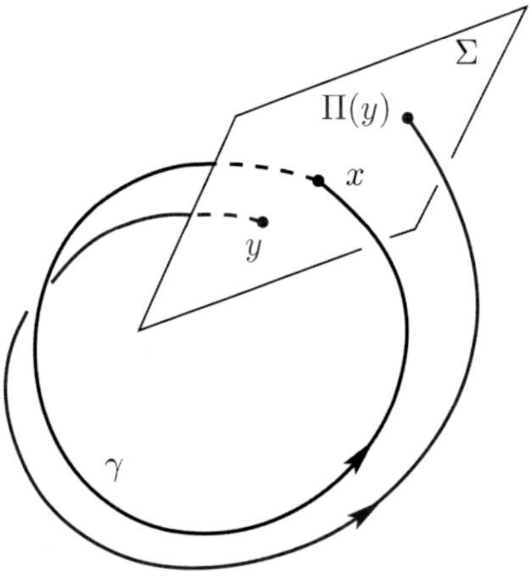

Figure 2.3. In this picture, a Poincaré return map Π on a cross section Σ gives the first return of points to the cross section for points near a point x on a periodic orbit γ.

Definition 2.24. Suppose Σ is a cross section. Let $\tau : \Sigma \to (0,\infty)$ be the function where $\tau(y)$ is defined as the minimal $t > 0$ with $\varphi(t,y) \in \Sigma$, if this exists. If τ is defined on $U \subset \Sigma$, the map $\Pi : U \to \Sigma$ given by

$$\Pi(y) = \varphi(\tau(y), y)$$

is called the *Poincaré return map* on Σ. The cross section Σ is also called the *Poincaré section.*

We will write $\Pi : \Sigma \to \Sigma$ even though Π is defined only on a subset $U \subset \Sigma$. Given a Poincaré return map Π on a cross section Σ, every fixed or periodic point of Π corresponds to a periodic orbit. Assume now that γ is a periodic orbit with period T. Write $x_0 = \gamma(0)$. The following lemma connects the first variation equation $\dot{\xi}(t) = Df(\gamma(t))\xi(t)$ and the principal matrix solution thereof to the derivative of the flow. We take $t_0 = 0$ in the following, and remove reference to t_0 from the notation. So the principal matrix solution is the solution $\Phi(t)$ of $\dot{\Phi}(t) = Df(\gamma(t))\Phi(t)$ with $\Phi(0) = I$.

Lemma 2.25. *The principal matrix solution (for $t_0 = 0$) of the first variation equation is given by*

$$\Phi(t) = D_x\varphi(t, x_0).$$

Moreover, $f(\phi(t, x_0))$ is a solution of the first variation equation,

$$f(\varphi(t, x_0)) = \Phi(t)f(x_0). \tag{2.11}$$

Proof. Abbreviate $J(t, x) = D_x\phi(t, x)$. Then $J(0, x) = I$ and by interchanging t and x derivatives it follows that $\dot{J}(t, x) = Df(\varphi(t, x))J(t, x)$. Hence $J(t, x_0)$ is the principal matrix solution of the first variation equation.

To derive (2.11), we will demonstrate that $f(\varphi(t, x_0))$ is the solution $u(t)$ of

$$\frac{d}{dt}u(t) = Df(\varphi(t, x_0))u(t)$$

with $u(0) = f(x_0)$. This follows from the calculation

$$\frac{d}{dt}f(\varphi(t, x)) = Df(\varphi(t, x))\frac{d}{dt}\varphi(t, x) = Df(\varphi(t, x))f(\varphi(t, x)).$$

Therefore $f(\varphi(t, x_0))$ equals $D_x\varphi(t, x_0)f(x_0)$, which is the solution of this differential equation with the same initial condition. □

From Section 2.2.1 we find that, since the first variation equation along the periodic solution γ is periodic, the principal matrix solution is of the form

$$\Phi(t) = P(t)e^{tQ}$$

for a T-periodic matrix P. The monodromy matrix $M = e^{TQ} = D_x\varphi(T, x_0)$ has eigenvalues independent of the choice of the point x_0 in the orbit. Note that one of the eigenvalues is 1, since $Mf(x_0) = f(x_0)$. Consider a Poincaré return map Π on a cross section Σ that is transverse to f at x_0.

Theorem 2.26. *The eigenvalues of the derivative $D\Pi(x_0)$ of the Poincaré return map Π at x_0 plus the single value 1 coincide with the eigenvalues of the monodromy matrix M. In particular, the eigenvalues are independent of the base point x_0 and the transversal section Σ.*

Proof. By applying a linear transformation, we may assume that $f(x_0) = (0, \ldots, 0, 1)$. Write $x = (y, z) \in \mathbb{R}^{n-1} \times \mathbb{R}$. Then Σ is locally the graph of a function $s : \mathbb{R}^{n-1} \to \mathbb{R}$, and we can take y as local coordinates for the Poincaré return map. Write $M_{j,k}$, $1 \le j, k \le n$, for the coefficients of the matrix M. Since

$$\frac{d}{dx}\varphi(\tau(x), x)\Big|_{x=x_0} = f(x_0)D\tau(x_0) + D_x\varphi(T, x_0),$$

we infer $D\Pi(x_0)_{j,k} = M_{j,k}$ for $1 \le j,k \le n-1$. Moreover, $Mf(x_0) = f(x_0)$ and thus

$$M = \begin{pmatrix} D\Pi(x_0) & 0 \\ m & 1 \end{pmatrix}$$

for some m, from which the result follows. □

Note that $D\Pi(x_0)$ and M have equal determinants. Since the determinant of M does not vanish, Π is a local diffeomorphism at x_0. The periodic orbit γ is an asymptotically stable periodic orbit of f if and only if $x_0 \in \gamma$ is an asymptotically stable fixed point of Π. If the absolute values of all eigenvalues of $D\Pi(x_0)$ are less than one, then x_0 is an asymptotically stable fixed point of Π.

By Liouville's theorem we have

$$\det M = e^{\int_0^T \operatorname{tr}(A(t))\,dt} = e^{\int_0^T \operatorname{div}(f(\varphi(t,x_0)))\,dt}.$$

In two dimensions there is only one eigenvalue which is equal to the determinant, and hence we obtain the following theorem.

Theorem 2.27. *Let f be a planar vector field with a periodic orbit through x_0 of period T. Let Σ be a cross section through x_0 and let Π be the Poincaré return map on Σ. Then*

$$D\Pi(x_0) = e^{\int_0^T \operatorname{div}(f(\varphi(t,x_0)))\,dt}.$$

The periodic orbit through x_0 is asymptotically stable if

$$\int_0^T \operatorname{div}(f(\varphi(t,x_0)))\,dt < 0$$

and unstable if the integral is positive.

Example 2.28. We take up again the differential equation given in (1.2). Consider the differential equation

$$\begin{pmatrix} \dot{x} \\ \dot{y} \end{pmatrix} = \begin{pmatrix} 1 & -1 \\ 1 & 1 \end{pmatrix} \begin{pmatrix} x \\ y \end{pmatrix} - (x^2+y^2) \begin{pmatrix} x \\ y \end{pmatrix}.$$

The transformation $x = r\cos\phi$, $y = r\sin\phi$ leads to the following system in polar coordinates r and ϕ:

$$\begin{aligned} \dot{r} &= r(1-r^2), \\ \dot{\phi} &= 1. \end{aligned} \tag{2.12}$$

We see that $\mathcal{P} = \{x^2 + y^2 = 1\}$ is an invariant set representing the periodic orbit $\gamma_{\mathcal{P}} = (\cos t, \sin t)$ of period $T = 2\pi$. Now choose, in Cartesian coordinates,

$\Sigma = (1,0) + \mathbb{R}\{(1,0)\}$. The solution of the initial value problem (2.12), $r(0) = \hat{r}$, $\phi(0) = 0$, is given by

$$r(t) = \left(1 + (\hat{r}^{-2} - 1)e^{-2t}\right)^{-\frac{1}{2}},$$
$$\phi(t) = t,$$

and leads to an explicit representation of the Poincaré return map Π on Σ,

$$\Pi(x) = \left(1 + (x^{-2} - 1)e^{-4\pi}\right)^{-\frac{1}{2}}.$$

This expression gives

$$D\Pi(1) = e^{-4\pi} < 1,$$

implying that the periodic orbit $\gamma_{\mathcal{P}}$ is asymptotically stable.

We can confirm this by using Theorem 2.27. Write

$$f^1(x,y) = -y + x(1 - x^2 - y^2),$$
$$f^2(x,y) = x + y(1 - x^2 - y^2)$$

for the components of the vector field. Compute

$$\int_0^T \left(f^1_x(\varphi(t,p)) + f^2_y(\varphi(t,p))\right) dt$$
$$= \int_0^{2\pi} \left(2(1 - x^2 - y^2) - 2x^2 - 2y^2\right)|_{(\cos t, \sin t)}\, dt = \int_0^{2\pi} -2\, dt = -4\pi.$$

The argument for Theorem 2.27 yields $D\Pi(1) = e^{-4\pi}$. ■

Further examples are provided in Exercises 2.6 and 2.7. Poincaré return maps arise naturally in periodically forced systems. Consider a nonautonomous differential equation

$$\dot{x} = f(x,t)$$

with $x \in \mathbb{R}^n$, where f is T-periodic:

$$f(x, t+T) = f(x,t).$$

It makes sense to extend the system to a differential equation on $\mathbb{R}^n \times \mathbb{R} \bmod T\mathbb{Z}$ writing

$$\dot{x} = f(x,\theta),$$
$$\dot{\theta} = 1.$$

The Poincaré return map Π on the cross section $\Sigma = \mathbb{R}^n \times \{0\}$ is simply the time T-flow on Σ. As this involves a constant return time, we also refer to Π as a stroboscopic map.

An arbitrary diffeomorphism can be obtained as a Poincaré return map of a suitable differential equation. This goes by a construction called the suspension of a diffeomorphism. Given a diffeomorphism $g : \mathbb{R}^n \to \mathbb{R}^n$, consider the equivalence relation on $\mathbb{R}^n \times \mathbb{R}$ given by

$$(p, s) \sim (q, t) \Longleftrightarrow s - t \in \mathbb{Z} \text{ and } q = g^{t-s}(p).$$

Let $\tilde{M}$ be the quotient space $\mathbb{R}^n \times \mathbb{R}/\sim$ and $\pi : \mathbb{R}^n \times \mathbb{R} \to \tilde{M}$ the natural projection. A flow φ^t on $\tilde{M}$ is given by $\varphi^t(\pi(x, s)) = \pi(x, s + t)$. Then $\varphi^1(\pi(x, 0)) = \pi(g(x), 0)$ is the Poincaré return map on $\pi(\mathbb{R}^n \times \{0\})$ for the flow φ^t. One can view $\tilde{M}$ as a smooth manifold (we briefly review the notion of manifold in Appendix A.3) which makes φ^t a smooth flow coming from a smooth differential equation [**278**, Chapter 3, Proposition 3.7].

2.3. Topological equivalence and bifurcation

The fundamental idea of bifurcation is that small changes of the differential equations can lead to qualitatively different dynamics. For bifurcations of equilibria this is formalized by definitions in this section. We start with flows φ^t of $\dot{x} = f(x)$ on $\mathcal{D}_f \subset \mathbb{R}^n$ and ψ^t of $\dot{x} = g(x)$ on $\mathcal{D}_g \subset \mathbb{R}^n$.

Definition 2.29. The two vector fields f on $\mathcal{D}_f$ and g on $\mathcal{D}_g$ are C^k *equivalent* if there exists a C^k diffeomorphism h from $\mathcal{D}_f$ to $\mathcal{D}_g$ that sends orbits of f to orbits of g preserving the sense of orbits. That is, for $x \in \mathcal{D}_f$ and $t \in I_x$ there is $t' \in \mathbb{R}$ with the same sign as t such that

$$h(\varphi^t(x)) = \psi^{t'}(h(x)).$$

For $k = 0$, h is a homeomorphism and the flows are called *topologically equivalent.*

Linked to topological equivalence is the notion of topological conjugacy, which does not incorporate a time reparametrization.

Definition 2.30. The two vector fields f and g are C^k *conjugate* if there exists a C^k diffeomorphism h from $\mathcal{D}_f$ to $\mathcal{D}_g$ such that for $x \in \mathcal{D}_f$ and $t \in I_x$

$$h(\varphi^t(x)) = \psi^t(h(x)).$$

For $k = 0$, h is a homeomorphism and the flows are called *topologically conjugate.*

A homeomorphism providing conjugacy or equivalence maps orbits to orbits, and thus in particular equilibria to equilibria and periodic orbits to periodic orbits.

Definition 2.31. Two vector fields f at a point $p \in \mathbb{R}^n$ and g at a point $q \in \mathbb{R}^n$ are *locally* C^k *equivalent* if there exist neighborhoods V of p and W of q so that

f on V and g on W are C^k equivalent. For $k = 0$, h is a homeomorphism, and the vector fields are called *locally topologically equivalent.*

Definition 2.32. Two vector fields f at a point $p \in \mathbb{R}^n$ and g at a point $q \in \mathbb{R}^n$ are *locally C^k conjugate* if there exist neighborhoods V of p and W of q so that f on V and g on W are C^k conjugate. For $k = 0$, h is a homeomorphism, and the vector fields are called *locally topologically conjugate.*

The definition of conjugacy can be adapted almost verbatim to the context of maps. Consider for instance continuous maps $F : X \to X$ and $G : Y \to Y$. Then F and G are topologically conjugate if there exists a homeomorphism $h : X \to Y$ such that

$$h \circ F = G \circ h.$$

A formal approach to local bifurcations is provided by the following definition. The definition assumes a given family of vector fields, depending on finitely many parameters. We come back to the notion of bifurcation in Section 5.1 in a context of spaces of vector fields on compact manifolds.

We look at families of vector fields on $\mathbb{R}^n$ depending on a parameter $\lambda \in \mathbb{R}^m$. For an open set $O \subset \mathbb{R}^n \times R^m$, we write $O_\lambda = O \cap (\mathbb{R}^n \times \{\lambda\})$.

Definition 2.33. Let $\{f_\lambda\}$ be a family of vector fields on $\mathbb{R}^n$ depending on a parameter $\lambda \in \mathbb{R}^m$.

Suppose p is an equilibrium of f_{λ_0}. If for any neighborhood O of (p, λ_0) in $\mathbb{R}^n \times \mathbb{R}^m$, there are values of λ arbitrarily close to λ_0 so that f_{λ_0} in O_{λ_0} is not topologically equivalent to f_λ in O_λ, we say that $\{f_\lambda\}$ has a *(local) bifurcation* at $\lambda = \lambda_0$, and λ_0 is a *(local) bifurcation value.*

This definition of bifurcation for an equilibrium can be easily adapted to bifurcations of periodic orbits of flows, or of fixed points of diffeomorphisms. A definition for families of diffeomorphisms makes use of the notion of topological conjugacy. The next three examples may serve to emphasize the ingredients in the definition of local bifurcation.

Example 2.34. Reconsider the family $\dot{x} = \lambda - x^2$ given in (1.1). It is obvious that $\lambda = 0$ is a bifurcation value. Namely, $\dot{x} = f(x, 0)$ has exactly one equilibrium, while for each $\lambda \neq 0$ close to zero, the differential equation has either no or two equilibria. See Exercise 2.8. ■

Example 2.35. Reconsider the family

$$\begin{pmatrix} \dot{x} \\ \dot{y} \end{pmatrix} = \begin{pmatrix} \lambda & -1 \\ 1 & \lambda \end{pmatrix} \begin{pmatrix} x \\ y \end{pmatrix} - (x^2 + y^2) \begin{pmatrix} x \\ y \end{pmatrix}$$

given in (1.2). Here $\lambda = 0$ is a bifurcation value since equilibrium $(0,0)$ changes stability while λ passes through zero. In addition, periodic orbits exist only for $\lambda > 0$. ■

Not having a local bifurcation in a given family of differential equations does not mean that other small perturbations, outside the family, cannot change the dynamics.

Example 2.36. Consider in Cartesian coordinates the planar diffeomorphism $f : \mathbb{R}^2 \to \mathbb{R}^2$, which in polar coordinates is given by $(r,\theta) \mapsto (r, \theta + r^2)$. The origin is a fixed point of f. For real numbers λ write $L_\lambda(x,y) = (1+\lambda)(x,y)$. For λ near 0 consider the family

$$f_\lambda(x,y) = L_\lambda^{-1} \circ f \circ L_\lambda(x,y).$$

For each λ near 0, f_λ and $f_0 = f$ both considered near the origin are locally topologically conjugate using L_λ as conjugacy. That is, for a given ball O_0 around the origin, L_λ conjugates f_λ on $O_\lambda = L_\lambda^{-1} O_0$ with f_0 on O_0. Although there are arbitrarily small perturbations of f that change the stability of the fixed point at the origin, the value $\lambda = 0$ is not a bifurcation value for the family $\{f_\lambda\}$. ■

Remark 2.37. Part of the research on local bifurcation theory has been guided by notions of determinacy and stabilizability. A polynomial vector field f of degree k with $f(0) = 0$ is determining if for all vector fields g with $g(0) = 0$ and with kth order Taylor expansion equal to f we have that g is locally topologically equivalent to f. A polynomial vector field f of degree k can be stabilized if there exists a polynomial vector field g of degree $l \geq k$, whose kth order Taylor expansion equals f, that is determining. A polynomial vector field in dimension 1 or 2 can be stabilized (see [**49**]) but there are examples of polynomial vector fields in dimension 3 and higher that cannot be stabilized [**103, 367, 371**]. ■

A single vector field f is said to admit a local bifurcation if there is a family $\{f_\lambda\}$ with $f_0 = f$ that has a bifurcation in the sense of Definition 2.33. This gives a need for definitions tailored to families of vector fields, with which we continue.

Definition 2.38. Let $\{f_\lambda\}$ and $\{g_\lambda\}$, $\lambda \in \mathbb{R}^m$ be local families of vector fields on $\mathbb{R}^n$ with $f_0(0) = 0$ and $g_0(0) = 0$. The families are *locally (topologically) equivalent families* if there exists a homeomorphism k defined on a open neighborhood V of $0 \in \mathbb{R}^m$ with $k(0) = 0$, and homeomorphisms h_λ defined on a neighborhood W of $0 \in \mathbb{R}^n$ and depending continuously on λ, so that f_λ is locally topologically equivalent to $g_{k(\lambda)}$ by the homeomorphisms h_λ.

One can drop the condition of continuous dependence of h_λ on λ; the resulting property is called locally weakly (topologically) equivalent families. If the transformations are smooth and also depend smoothly on the parameter, we speak of locally smooth equivalence. The paper [**106**] contains a discussion of the role of the boundary of the region W in the definition, for the classes of bifurcations studied therein. A setup without distinguished parameters is considered in [**115**].

The following definition treats the comparison of families with different numbers of parameters, and seeks a minimal number of parameters. For extended treatises and further information we refer to [**21,124**]. An unfolding of a vector field f is any family f_λ of vector fields with $f_0 = f$.

Definition 2.39. A family $\{g_\nu\}$, $\nu \in \mathbb{R}^l$, is called induced by a family $\{f_\lambda\}$, $\lambda \in \mathbb{R}^k$, if there is a smooth mapping $k : \mathbb{R}^l \to \mathbb{R}^k$, so that

$$g_\nu = f_{k(\nu)}.$$

An unfolding $\{f_\lambda\}$, $\lambda \in \mathbb{R}^k$, of f is called a *versal unfolding* if all unfoldings of f are locally equivalent to an unfolding that is induced by $\{f_\lambda\}$.

Suppose f is a vector field with a local bifurcation and $\{f_\lambda\}$ is an unfolding of f. The minimal required number of parameters, in a versal unfolding, is called the *codimension* of the bifurcation.

Example 2.40. Consider a smooth differential equation

$$\dot{x} = f(x, \mu)$$

with $\mu \in \mathbb{R}^k$ and

$$f(0,0) = 0, \quad D_x f(0,0) = 0, \quad D_{xx} f(0,0) \neq 0.$$

We note that this gives a saddle-node bifurcation, which is discussed in Section 3.2.1.1. Here we perform some calculations to illustrate notions of equivalence.

An application of the implicit function theorem (Theorem A.17) gives a smooth curve $\alpha(\mu)$ with $\alpha(0) = 0$ for which $D_x f(\alpha(\mu), \mu) = 0$. By the Morse lemma, Theorem 2.46, one can now write $f(x + \alpha(\mu), \mu) = f(\alpha(\mu), \mu) + a(\mu) h(x, \mu)^2$ for smooth functions a, h with $a(0) \neq 0$ and $h(0, \mu) = 0$, $D_x h(0, \mu) = 1$. In this one-dimensional case such an expression is easily obtained directly. Indeed, if we let $F(x) = f(x + \alpha(\mu), \mu) - f(\alpha(\mu), \mu)$, and write $F(x) = ax^2 + g(x)$ with $g(x) = \mathcal{O}(x^3)$, then $F(x) = a\left(x\sqrt{1 + H(x)}\right)^2$ for $H(x) = g(x)/(ax^2)$.

Now take a coordinate $y = h(x, \mu)$. Then

$$\begin{aligned}\dot{y} &= D_x h(x, \mu) f(x + \alpha(\mu), \mu) \\ &= D_x h(x, \mu)(f(\alpha(\mu), \mu) + a(\mu) y^2).\end{aligned}$$

We get that the original differential equation is smoothly equivalent to the differential equation $\dot{y} = f(\alpha(\mu), \mu) + a(\mu)y^2$. A rescaling of the coordinate makes it possible to get $a = \pm 1$. For this, let $z = ay$ and compute $\dot{z} = a(\mu)f(\alpha(\mu), \mu) + z^2$. So we conclude that the original family of differential equations is smoothly equivalent to a family of differential equations of the form

$$\dot{z} = \lambda(\mu) + z^2 =: p_\mu(z).$$

The one-parameter family p_μ is induced by the family $\lambda + z^2 =: q_\lambda(z)$, namely $p_\mu(x) = q_{\lambda(\mu)}(z)$. The one-parameter family $\dot{z} = \lambda + z^2$ is a versal unfolding. The bifurcation has codimension 1. ■

In practice the notion of codimension is defined more loosely as the number of parameters which must be varied to find, in a persistent way, conditions that determine a bifurcation. In our treatise of bifurcation problems we provide bifurcation diagrams in its meaning of *descriptions of critical elements and their stability in the combined parameter and state space.* Let $\dot{x} = f_\lambda(x)$ be a family of differential equations, with a bifurcation at $\lambda = 0$ of a critical element σ. Let U be a small neighborhood of σ and let V be a small neighborhood of 0 in parameter space. Assume, by way of illustration, the existence of $M > 0$ so that for each $\lambda \in V$, the differential equations has at most M critical elements in U. In such a case one can define the bifurcation diagram for the local bifurcation as the set

$$\Lambda = \{(p, \lambda) \in U \times V\ ;\ p \text{ is a critical element of } \dot{x} = f_\lambda(x)\},$$

combined with a labeling of stability of the critical elements. Such a definition of a bifurcation diagram fails to be a correct definition in cases with more complex dynamics. In such cases we would resort to descriptions of invariant sets (such as nonwandering sets or attractors) occurring for different parameter values. At least in the chapter on local bifurcation theory, where we encounter bifurcations with bounded numbers of critical elements, we adopt this approach to describe the bifurcation diagram of families $\dot{x} = f_\lambda(x)$. This gives a practical point of view of bifurcation theory, in which we typically do not prove that families and small perturbations thereof are locally topologically equivalent families. In Section 5.1 we come back to this discussion.

In Example 2.40 we can distinguish different sorts of conditions. The assumption of an equilibrium $f(0,0) = 0$ with vanishing derivative $D_x f(0,0) = 0$ defines the bifurcation. Thanks to the condition $D_{xx} f(0,0) \neq 0$, the bifurcation is of codimension 1 and not of higher codimension. A condition $D\lambda(0) \neq 0$ would indicate a typical dependence on the parameter. Such a distinction is typical for many bifurcation problems. Here and in other cases we speak of a nondegeneracy condition (a condition like $D_{xx} f(0,0) \neq 0$) and a generic unfolding condition (a condition involving parameters like $D\lambda(0) \neq 0$). We will not formalize these notions, but informally we speak of a nondegenerate bifurcation, and a generically unfolding bifurcation.

In the final part of this section we discuss conditions on equilibria that ensure that local bifurcations do not occur.

Definition 2.41. An equilibrium p of a vector field f is *hyperbolic* if the spectrum of $Df(p)$ is disjoint from the imaginary axis. A fixed point p of a diffeomorphism F is *hyperbolic* if the spectrum of $DF(p)$ is disjoint from the unit circle in the complex plane.

For a hyperbolic equilibrium we call the spectrum to the left of the imaginary axis, its stable spectrum. The complement is called the unstable spectrum. The cardinality of the stable spectrum, counting multiplicity, is the stability index of the equilibrium. This is the dimension of the stable subspace, the sum of the generalized eigenspaces corresponding to the stable spectrum. Corresponding terminology is used for hyperbolic fixed points.

The following result, the Grobman-Hartman theorem, linearizes flows near hyperbolic equilibria and is discussed in Appendix B.2.2. The result is named after Philip Hartman [**152**] and David Grobman [**138, 139**], who proved it independently. We state the version for vector fields, leaving the analogous version for diffeomorphisms to Appendix B.2.2.

Theorem 2.42 (Grobman-Hartman theorem). *The vector field f at a hyperbolic equilibrium $p \in \mathbb{R}^n$ is locally topologically conjugate to the linearized vector field $\dot{v} = Df(p)v$.*

Let $x = 0$ be a hyperbolic equilibrium of the linear vector fields A and B on $\mathbb{R}^n$. It is not hard to see that the flows of these vector fields are topologically conjugate if and only if the numbers of eigenvalues with negative real part coincide [**22**, §22]. Together with the Grobman-Hartman theorem this implies that hyperbolic equilibria do not give rise to local bifurcations. In other words, bifurcations of equilibria can only occur at nonhyperbolic equilibria. We note that if vector fields f at an equilibrium p and g at an equilibrium q are locally smoothly conjugate, then $Df(p)$ and $Dg(q)$ have the same eigenvalues. See Exercise 2.9.

As the following result stipulates, a weaker condition than hyperbolicity suffices for persistence of an equilibrium under perturbations.

Theorem 2.43. *Let $f_\lambda : \mathbb{R}^n \to \mathbb{R}^n$, $\lambda \in \mathbb{R}^m$, be a family of C^1 vector fields such that*

(i) *the map $(x, \lambda) \mapsto f_\lambda(x)$ is C^1,*
(ii) *$f_{\lambda_0}(x_0) = 0$,*
(iii) *0 is not an eigenvalue of $Df_{\lambda_0}(x_0)$.*

Then there are open sets $U \in \mathbb{R}^m, V \in \mathbb{R}^n$ with $\lambda_0 \in U$, $x_0 \in V$, and a C^1 function $\xi : V \to U$ such that for each $\lambda \in U$, $\xi(\lambda)$ is the only equilibrium of $\dot{x} = f_\lambda(x)$ in V.

Proof. The proof is an immediate consequence of the implicit function theorem applied to the map $(x, \lambda) \mapsto f_\lambda(x)$. □

A similar result holds for fixed points of diffeomorphisms, here one assumes that 1 is not an eigenvalue of the linearization. Exercise 2.10 asks for a similar result for periodic orbits in terms of Floquet multipliers. Note that persistence of an equilibrium still allows for a change of stability.

2.4. Singularity theory of smooth functions

Part of bifurcation theory involves the description of the set of equilibria in a family of vector fields. This gives a connection to singularity theory that analyzes the set of singular points of maps and in particular discontinuous changes in its geometry.

A special connection between bifurcation theory and singularity theory arises in the class of gradient vector fields. A gradient vector field on $\mathbb{R}^n$ is obtained as the gradient of a potential function $V : \mathbb{R}^n \to \mathbb{R}$ and is defined by

$$\dot{x} = f(x) = -\nabla V(x). \tag{2.13}$$

A point p is a singular point of V if $DV(p) = 0$. For a gradient flow (2.13), p is an equilibrium if and only if p is a singular point of V. Outside equilibria, the function V is decreasing along orbits as

$$\frac{d}{dt}V(x(t)) = \langle \nabla V(x(t), \dot{x}(t)\rangle = -\langle \nabla V(x(t)), \nabla V(x(t))\rangle < 0.$$

It follows that if p is an isolated minimum of V, then p is an asymptotically stable equilibrium of (2.13). Note also that (2.13) does not have periodic solutions.

Gradient vector fields therefore form a special and simple class of differential equations, where a main interest lies in the description of the set of equilibria. The analysis of singular points of functions and in particular discontinuous changes in their geometry is called catastrophe theory. Catastrophe theory is a creation of René Thom [**380**]. We provide definitions of stability of functions and of families of functions to give the reader the opportunity to compare them with the definitions of topological equivalence and bifurcation in Section 2.3. For a detailed treatment we refer to textbooks on catastrophe theory and singularity theory such as [**242, 255, 298**].

Definition 2.44. Two smooth functions $f, g : \mathbb{R}^n \to \mathbb{R}$ are *right-left equivalent* at 0 if there exist open neighborhoods $U, V \subset \mathbb{R}^n$ of the origin and a smooth diffeomorphism $h : U \to V$ with $h(0) = 0$, a smooth diffeomorphism $j : \mathbb{R} \to \mathbb{R}$,

$$g(x) = j(f(h(x))).$$

If this holds with j a translation, f and g are called *right equivalent*.

Let $C^\infty(\mathbb{R}^n, \mathbb{R})$ denote the space of smooth functions on $\mathbb{R}^n$. In what follows we assume throughout that 0 is a singular point of the considered function.

Definition 2.45. Let $f \in C^\infty(\mathbb{R}^n, \mathbb{R})$ and let the origin be a singular point of f. Then f is of corank q if its Hessian at the origin is of rank $n - q$. If the corank is 0, we call the origin a *nondegenerate singular point.*

The Morse lemma by Marston Morse [**258**] tells that a smooth function f of corank 0 is right equivalent at 0 to $f(0) + \sum_{i=1}^n \epsilon_i x_i^2$ for some coefficients $\epsilon_i = \pm 1$.

Theorem 2.46 (Morse lemma). *Consider $f \in C^\infty(\mathbb{R}^n, \mathbb{R})$ with a nondegenerate singular point $x = 0$. In a neighborhood of $x = 0$ there exists a diffeomorphism $y = h(x)$ with $Dh(0)$ the identity, which transforms $f(x)$ into*

$$y \mapsto f(0) + D^2 f(0) y^2.$$

For functions of a single variable, and assuming $f(0) = 0$, we can write

$$f(x) = ax^2 + g(x).$$

Let $h(x) = g(x)/(ax^2)$ and $y = x\sqrt{(1 + h(x))}$. The functions h and y are smooth (compare Lemma A.4). Then $f(x) = ax^2(1 + h(x))$ and thus $f(y) = ay^2$.

For a function f of n variables, let Q be the $n \times n$ matrix so that $D^2 f(0) y^2 = \langle y, Qy \rangle$. Theorem 2.46 yields a diffeomorphism $y = h(x)$ which transforms $f(x)$ into $y \mapsto f(0) + \langle y, Qy \rangle$. Let k be the number of positive eigenvalues of Q. By an additional linear coordinate change we get the following alternative statement of the Morse lemma: in a neighborhood of $x = 0$ there exists a diffeomorphism $y = j(x)$ which transforms $f(x)$ into

$$y \mapsto f(0) + y_1^2 + y_2^2 + \cdots + y_k^2 - y_{k+1}^2 - \cdots - y_n^2.$$

See also [**198**, Proposition 9.1.1] that proves this statement using induction on the dimension n. For the following proof of Morse's lemma we follow [**179**, Appendix C.6].

Proof of Theorem 2.46. Denote $x = (x_1, \dots, x_n)$. Taylor's theorem gives

$$f(x) = f(0) + \frac{1}{2} D^2 f(x) h^2 + \int_0^1 (1 - s) \left[D^2 f(sh) - D^2 f(0) \right] h^2 \, ds.$$

We may assume $f(0) = 0$. We can thus write

$$f(x) = \frac{1}{2} \sum_{1 \le i,j \le n} b_{ij}(x) x_i x_j$$

with

$$b_{ij}(x) = 2 \int_0^1 (1-s) \frac{\partial^2}{\partial x_i x_j} f(sx)\, ds.$$

So $B(x) = (b_{ij}(x))_{1 \le i,j \le n}$ has values in the vector space of symmetric $n \times n$ matrices. Write $L^2_{\mathrm{sym}}(\mathbb{R}^n, \mathbb{R}^n)$ for the space of symmetric $n \times n$ matrices. Write $y = R(x)x$ for a matrix $R \in L^2_{\mathrm{sym}}(\mathbb{R}^n, \mathbb{R}^n)$ which is to be determined and satisfies $R(0) = \mathrm{id}$ and

$$R(x)QR(x) = B(x). \tag{2.14}$$

Let $F : L^2_{\mathrm{sym}}(\mathbb{R}^n, \mathbb{R}^n) \times \mathbb{R}^n \to L^2_{\mathrm{sym}}(\mathbb{R}^n, \mathbb{R}^n)$ be the map $F(R, x) = RQR - B(x)$. For $x = 0$ we have $B(0) = Q$ and $F(\mathrm{id}) = 0$. For the derivative of F with respect to R we have

$$D_R F(R, 0)H = RQH + HQR.$$

This map is surjective since $RQH + HQR = C$ for a symmetric matrix C is solved uniquely by $H = \frac{1}{2} Q^{-1} R^{-1} C$. By the implicit function theorem we can solve (2.14) for a function $R(x) = F(B(x))$. We conclude that $x \mapsto R(x)$ is a smooth map. The lemma follows with

$$y = F(B(x))x. \qquad \square$$

We add a statement that includes parameter dependence. Consider a function $f \in C^\infty(\mathbb{R}^n \times \mathbb{R}^k, \mathbb{R})$ with a nondegenerate singular point at $x = 0$ for $\lambda = 0$. The implicit function theorem gives a map $x^*(\lambda)$ defined for λ near 0, with $x^*(0) = 0$ and $Df(x^*(\lambda), \lambda) = 0$. A parameter dependent translation thus yields a function f with $Df(0, \lambda) = 0$ for all small λ. The following parameter dependent version of the Morse lemma takes this as a starting point. For the proof, follow the argument for Theorem 2.46 above with parameter λ included.

Theorem 2.47. *If $f \in C^\infty(\mathbb{R}^n \times \mathbb{R}^k, \mathbb{R})$ with $Df(0, \lambda) = 0$ for λ near 0, let $D^2 f(0, \lambda) = Q(\lambda)$. In a neighborhood of $(x, \lambda) = (0, 0)$ there exists a diffeomorphism $y = h(x, \lambda)$ on $\mathbb{R}^n$ with $Dh(0, \lambda)$ the identity, which transforms $f(x)$ into*

$$y \mapsto f(0, \lambda) + \langle y, Q(\lambda) y \rangle.$$

We can endow $C^\infty(\mathbb{R}^n, \mathbb{R})$ with the compact-open topology of convergence of all derivatives on compact sets (see Appendix A.1).

Definition 2.48. A smooth function f with a nondegenerate singularity at the origin is a *stable function*, if any smooth function g that has a singularity at the origin and that is sufficiently close to f, is right-left equivalent at 0 to f.

Table 2.1

name of catastrophe	codimension	corank	model
fold	1	1	$\frac{1}{3}x_1^3 + \sum_{i=2}^n \pm x_i^2$
cusp	2	1	$\frac{1}{4}x_1^4 + \sum_{i=2}^n \pm x_i^2$
swallowtail	3	1	$\frac{1}{5}x_1^5 + \sum_{i=2}^n \pm x_i^2$
butterfly	4	1	$\frac{1}{6}x_1^6 + \sum_{i=2}^n \pm x_i^2$
hyperbolic umbilic	3	2	$x_1^3 + x_2^3 + \sum_{i=3}^n \pm x_i^2$
elliptic umbilic	3	2	$x_1^3 - x_1x_2^2 + \sum_{i=3}^n \pm x_i^2$
parabolic umbilic	4	2	$x_1^2x_2 + x_2^4 + \sum_{i=3}^n \pm x_i^2$

Let $J(f) \subset C^\infty(\mathbb{R}^n, \mathbb{R})$ be the Jacobian ideal

$$J(f) = \left\{ \sum_{i=1}^n \frac{\partial f}{\partial x_i} g_i \; ; \; g_i \in C^\infty(\mathbb{R}^n, \mathbb{R}) \right\}$$

generated by the partial derivatives $\frac{\partial f}{\partial x_i}$. Let

$$\mathcal{M} = \left\{ \sum_{i=1}^n x_i g_i \; ; \; g_i \in C^\infty(\mathbb{R}^n, \mathbb{R}) \right\}$$

be the ideal generated by the coordinate functions $x_1, \dots, x_n$.

Definition 2.49. If $J(f)$ has finite codimension in $C^\infty(\mathbb{R}^n, \mathbb{R})$, then we refer to the dimension of $\mathcal{M}/J(f)$ as the *codimension* of f.

Let the origin be a nondegenerate singularity of f. Then $J(f)$ equals $\mathcal{M}$, that is f has codimension 0. See Exercise 2.12.

Consider functions $(x_1, \dots, x_n) \mapsto f(x_1, \dots, x_n)$ in $C^\infty(\mathbb{R}^n, \mathbb{R})$. The following theorem provides a classification of *catastrophes* up to codimension 4. We refer to [**242**] for the proof.

Theorem 2.50. *A function $f \in C^\infty(\mathbb{R}^n, \mathbb{R})$ of positive codimension $k \leq 4$ is right-left equivalent at* 0 *to a function listed in Table* 2.1.

Let f be a function. A k-parameter family f_t, $t \in \mathbb{R}^k$ with $f_0 = f$ is called an unfolding of f. The next step is to look at unfoldings.

Definition 2.51. Let f_t, g_s be two smooth k-parameter families of functions in $C^\infty(\mathbb{R}^n, \mathbb{R})$. These families are *right-left equivalent families* at $(0,0)$ if there are open neighborhoods U, V of $0 \in \mathbb{R}^n$, W of $0 \in \mathbb{R}^k$, and for $s \in W$, a k-parameter family of smooth diffeomorphisms $h_s : U \to V$ with $h(0) = 0$,

Table 2.2

name of catastrophe	unfolding
fold	$\frac{1}{3}x_1^3 - ax_1 + \sum_{i=2}^{n} \pm x_i^2$
cusp	$\frac{1}{4}x_1^4 - ax_1 - \frac{1}{2}bx_1^2 + \sum_{i=2}^{n} \pm x_i^2$
swallowtail	$\frac{1}{5}x_1^5 - ax_1 - \frac{1}{2}bx_1^2 - \frac{1}{3}cx_1^3 + \sum_{i=2}^{n} \pm x_i^2$
butterfly	$\frac{1}{6}x_1^6 - ax_1 - \frac{1}{2}bx_1^2 - \frac{1}{3}cx_1^3 - \frac{1}{4}dx_1^4 + \sum_{i=2}^{n} \pm x_i^2$
hyperbolic umbilic	$x_1^3 + x_2^3 + ax_1 + bx_2 + cx_1x_2 + \sum_{i=3}^{n} \pm x_i^2$
elliptic umbilic	$x_1^3 - x_1x_2^2 + ax_1 + bx_2 + cx_1^2 + cx_2^2 + \sum_{i=3}^{n} \pm x_i^2$
parabolic umbilic	$x_1^2x_2 + x_2^4 + ax_1 + bx_2 + cx_1^2 + dx_2^2 + \sum_{i=3}^{n} \pm x_i^2$

a k-parameter family of smooth diffeomorphism $j_s : \mathbb{R} \to \mathbb{R}$, and a smooth invertible change of parameters $t = t(s)$, such that

$$g_s(x) = j_s(f_{t(s)}(h_s(x))).$$

Endow the space of smooth families $(x, t) \mapsto f_t(x)$ from $C^\infty(\mathbb{R}^n, \mathbb{R})$ with compact-open topology. Suppose f_0 has a singularity at $0 \in \mathbb{R}^n$. The family f_t is stable if a sufficiently nearby family g_t for which g_0 has a singularity at 0, is right-left equivalent to it. Also for the proof of the next theorem we refer to [**242**].

Theorem 2.52 (The seven elementary catastrophes). *A stable k-parameter family unfolding a singularity of positive codimension $k \leq 4$ is right-left equivalent at 0 to a family listed in Table* 2.2.

We will encounter bifurcation theory equivalents of the fold catastrophe and the cusp catastrophe below, the saddle-node bifurcation in Section 3.2.1 and the cusp bifurcation in Section 3.2.3. The vector fields we consider in these sections are related to the gradients of the catastrophes listed in Table 2.2. In general the relation between unfoldings of catastrophes and versal unfoldings of corresponding gradient vector fields is not straightforward [**141, 409**].

In singularity theory one also studies mappings from $\mathbb{R}^s$ to $\mathbb{R}^t$ using right-left equivalence that incorporates diffeomorphisms in both domain $\mathbb{R}^s$ and range $\mathbb{R}^t$. As the flavor of the approach has connections to bifurcation theory, we present here two results by Hassler Whitney [**417, 418**].

Theorem 2.53. *Let f be a smooth mapping from an open set $U \subset \mathbb{R}^2$ to $\mathbb{R}^2$. Then arbitrarily close to f, in the C^3 topology, there is a smooth map for which every singular point can be brought to one of the two following forms with local smooth coordinate changes in the domain $\mathbb{R}^2$ and the range $\mathbb{R}^2$:*

Fold. $(x, y) \mapsto (x^2, y)$;

Cusp. $(x, y) \mapsto (xy - x^3, y)$.

Moreover, folds occur along smooth curves and cusps are isolated.

Theorem 2.54. *Let f be a smooth mapping from an open set $U \subset \mathbb{R}^2$ to $\mathbb{R}^3$. Then arbitrarily close to f, in the C^2 topology, there is a smooth map for which every singular point is isolated and can be brought to the following form with local smooth coordinate changes in the domain $\mathbb{R}^2$ and the range $\mathbb{R}^3$:*

Whitney umbrella. $(u, v) \mapsto (u, uv, v^2)$; *see Figure* 2.4.

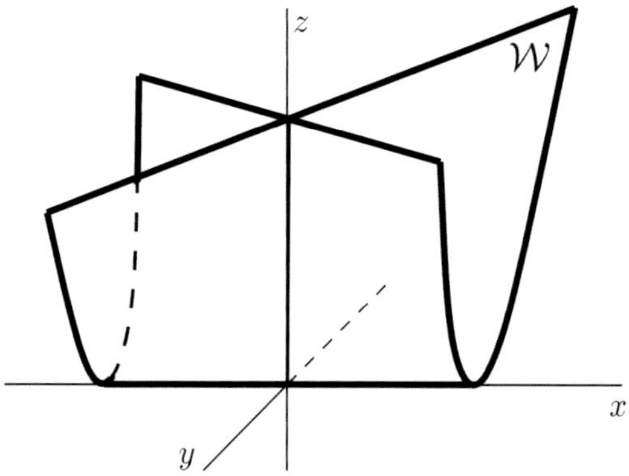

Figure 2.4. The Whitney umbrella $\mathcal{W}$ is parametrized by $(u, v) \mapsto (u, uv, v^2)$.

An example of the appearance of the Whitney umbrella as a bifurcation set is included in Section 4.1.2; see Remark 4.16.

2.5. Smale horseshoe map

The Smale horseshoe map is a geometric model of chaotic dynamics. The construction is due to Stephen Smale [**353**]; see also [**355**]. Smale's motivation was to gain a geometric understanding of dynamics found in driven oscillators considered by Mary Cartwright and John Littlewood [**61**] and further analyzed by Norman Levinson [**227**]. An analysis that connects these works is in [**223**]. The horseshoe map clarifies the chaotic dynamics found in these engineering problems. In general it explains dynamics caused by the existence of homoclinic tangles, studies that started with work by Henri Poincaré [**296**] and George Birkhoff [**38, 39**]. The connection between horseshoe and homoclinic tangles will be discussed in Section 4.2.3.

The Smale horseshoe is discussed in the context of maps, but one may think of the maps arising as return maps to get analogous results for flows. Consider a square $D \subset \mathbb{R}^2$ and a diffeomorphism $f : \mathbb{R}^2 \to \mathbb{R}^2$ that stretches and bends

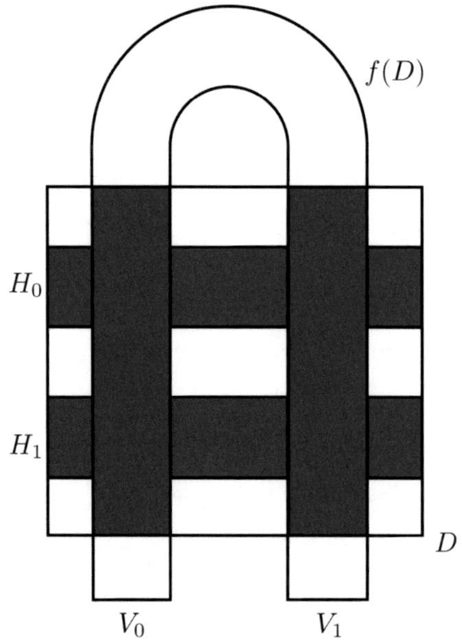

Figure 2.5. The Smale horseshoe map: the square D is mapped in a horseshoe shape over itself by f. The two horizontal strips H_0, H_1 inside the square are mapped onto the vertical strips V_0, V_1 by linear contraction and expansion.

D into a horseshoe shape as shown in Figure 2.5. Assume that f stretches uniformly in the vertical direction by a factor $\mu > 2$ and contracts uniformly in the horizontal direction by $\lambda < 1/2$. Iterate by $f^n(D) = f(D \cap f^{n-1}(D))$. The image $f^n(D) \cap D$ consists of 2^n vertical strips of width λ^n. In the limit $n \to \infty$, $f^n(D) \cap D$ converges a set Λ^+, which is the product of Cantor set (a compact, perfect and totally disconnected set) and a vertical line piece. In the same way, there are 2^n horizontal strips in $f^{-n}(D) \cap D$ that are mapped onto $f^n(D) \cap D$. The horizontal strips have height μ^{-n}. In the limit $n \to \infty$, $f^{-n}(D) \cap D$ converges to the product Λ^- of a Cantor set and a horizontal line piece. The intersection $\Lambda = \Lambda^+ \cap \Lambda^-$ is a Cantor set which is the maximal invariant set

$$\Lambda = \bigcap_{n \in \mathbb{Z}} f^n(D)$$

in D. We refer to this set as a horseshoe.

It can be seen that a connected component in $f^{-n}(D) \cap f^n(D) \cap D$, a rectangle of width λ^n and height μ^{-n}, contains a periodic point. Periodic points are therefore dense in Λ. Indeed, let D_1 be such a rectangle in $f^{-n}(D) \cap f^n(D) \cap D$. Then $f^n(D_1) \cap D_1$ is a vertical strip S_1 in D_1, and we get a decreasing sequence of vertical strips $S_{k+1} = f^n(S_k) \cap S_k$ converging to a vertical line as $k \to \infty$. Likewise we get a decreasing sequence of horizontal strips $T_{k+1} = f^{-n}(T_k) \cap T_k$

with $T_0 = D_1$, converging to a horizontal line. The intersection of the two lines is a periodic point with period at most n inside D_1.

The two-dimensional horseshoe map can easily be generalized to more dimensions. Let D^u be a compact multi-dimensional interval in $\mathbb{R}^k$ and D^s a compact multi-dimensional interval in $\mathbb{R}^l$. For the square $D = D^s \times D^u$ in $\mathbb{R}^n = \mathbb{R}^l \times R^k$, consider a smooth injective map $f_0 : D \to \mathbb{R}^n$ that generalizes the two-dimensional map above. That is, $f_0(D) \cap D$ consists of vertical strips $V_0 = V_0^s \times D^u$ and $V_1 = V_1^s \times D^u$, and there are horizontal strips $H_0 = D^s \times H_0^u$ and $H_1 = D^s \times H_1^u$ inside D that map onto V_0 and V_1 by affine maps. Taking coordinates $(x^s, x^u) \in \mathbb{R}^l \times \mathbb{R}^k$ we thus have $|\left(\frac{\partial f_0}{\partial x_u}\right)^{-1} f_0(x^s, x^u)| < 1$ and $|\frac{\partial f_0}{\partial x_s}(x^s, x^u)| < 1$ if $(x^s, x^u), f_0(x^s, x^u) \in D$. We call the map f_0 a linear horseshoe map.

In order to describe the dynamics of a linear horseshoe map, we introduce shift dynamics. Let $\Sigma^2 = \{0, 1\}^{\mathbb{Z}}$ be the space of infinite sequences of the two symbols $0, 1$. Elements $\omega \in \Sigma^2$ are double infinite sequences $\omega = (\omega_i)_{i \in \mathbb{Z}}$ of symbols $\omega_i \in \{0, 1\}$. The space Σ^2 is equipped with product topology. A basis for product topology is given by cylinders where cylinders are sets of the form

$$C_t(\eta_0 \cdots \eta_k) = \{\omega \in \Sigma^2 \; ; \; \omega_{i+t} = \eta_i, 0 \leq i \leq k\}$$

for $t \in \mathbb{Z}$. The open sets are given by unions and finite intersections of cylinders. A decreasing sequence of neighborhoods of an element $\omega \in \Sigma^2$ is given by cylinders $C_{-N}(\omega_{-N} \cdots \omega_N)$ for increasing N. One can introduce a metric on Σ^2 that metrizes the product topology. A possible choice is

$$d(\omega, \eta) = 2^{-s} \tag{2.15}$$

for $s = \min\{N \in \mathbb{N} \; ; \; \eta \notin C_{-N}(\omega_{-N} \cdots \omega_N)\}$ (with of course $d(\omega, \omega) = 0$).

The dynamical system on Σ^2 that arises in the study of smooth dynamical systems (and in the bifurcation problems in this book) is given by iterates of the left shift operator $\sigma : \Sigma^2 \to \Sigma^2$ determined by

$$(\sigma\omega)_i = \omega_{i+1}.$$

The left shift operator is a homeomorphism on Σ^2.

Here we compile a list of properties of the left shift operator. The proofs will be left as exercises.

Lemma 2.55. *The left shift operator is a homeomorphism on* Σ^2.

See Exercise 2.13. The next lemma says that σ is chaotic in the sense of Devaney [**93**]. In Exercise 2.14 we ask for a proof.

Lemma 2.56. *Consider* Σ^2 *equipped with the metric* (2.15). *The left shift operator* σ *is chaotic in the sense of Devaney, which means that the following properties hold.*

(i) *σ has sensitive dependence on initial conditions: there is an $r > 0$ such that for each $\omega \in \Sigma^2$ and for each $\epsilon > 0$, there is an $\eta \in \Sigma^2$ with $d(\omega, \eta) < \epsilon$ and a $k \in \mathbb{N}$ such that $d(\sigma^k\omega, \sigma^k\eta) \geq r$;*

(ii) *σ is topologically transitive: the forward orbit $\{\sigma^k\omega, k \in \mathbb{N}_0\}$ of some $\omega \in \Sigma^2$ is dense in Σ^2;*

(iii) *The set of periodic points of σ is dense in Σ^2.*

We add the bibliographical remark that the mathematical term *chaos* was coined by Tien-Yien Li and James Yorke [**228**]; see also the definitions in [**27**, **196**] and the precursory work with motivations from fluid dynamics in [**231**]. To get back to the linear horseshoe, the maximal invariant set $\Lambda = \bigcap_{i\in\mathbb{Z}} f_0^i(D)$ of f_0 in D, that is the largest invariant set contained in D, is a Cantor set. One can assign a homeomorphic correspondence between Λ and Σ^2 as follows. Given a point $x \in \Lambda$, each iterate $f_0^i(x)$ is in one of the two vertical strips V_0 or V_1. Define a map $\chi : \Lambda \to \Sigma^2$ by

$$\chi(x)_i = j, \text{ if } f_0^i(x) \in V_j.$$

The symbol sequence $\chi(x)$ is called the itinerary of x or of the orbit of x. We leave the proof of the following lemma as an exercise; see Exercise 2.16.

Lemma 2.57. *The map χ defines a topological conjugacy between f_0 restricted to Λ and the shift map σ on Σ^2:*

$$\chi \circ f|_\Lambda = \sigma \circ \chi.$$

It follows that the horseshoe map $f|_\Lambda$ is chaotic in the sense of Devaney; see Exercise 2.17.

The above description of dynamics on the maximal invariant set of the linear horseshoe map is robust under C^1-small perturbations f of f_0. One needs that iterates $f^n(D) \cap D$ consist of thin strips converging to a collection of curves as $n \to \pm\infty$. A traditional way to investigate is through invariant cone fields introduced by Jürgen Moser [**259**] and is explained for instance in [**198**, Section 6.5] or [**48**, Section 5.4]. We offer an analytic entrance in the following result, which discusses invariant sets for C^1-small perturbations of linear horseshoe maps. Write $d_{C^1}(f, g) = \sup_{x\in D}\{|f(x) - g(x)|, |Df(x) - Dg(x)|\}$ for the C^1-distance between maps defined on D.

Theorem 2.58. *Let f_0 be a linear horseshoe map on D so that on each horizontal strip in $f_0^{-1}(D)$, Df_0 is a constant linear map $\begin{pmatrix} a_0 & 0 \\ 0 & d_0 \end{pmatrix}$. There is $\varepsilon_0 > 0$ so that for f with $d_{C^1}(f, f_0) < \varepsilon \leq \varepsilon_0$, f restricted to the maximal invariant set in D is topologically conjugate to $\sigma|_{\Sigma^2}$.*

Proof. In this proof we will use coordinates (x, y) on D corresponding to the horizontal and vertical directions. Write

$$Df(x) = \begin{pmatrix} a(x,y) & b(x,y) \\ c(x,y) & d(x,y) \end{pmatrix}$$

for a perturbation f of f_0. For a map f that is sufficiently close in the C^1 topology to f_0, we find that $f(D) \cap D$ consists of two connected components that we also denote by V_0 and V_1. Likewise we write $H_0 = f^{-1}(V_0)$ and $H_1 = f^{-1}(V_1)$. The map f consists of two maps $F_0 : H_0 \to V_0, F_1 : H_1 \to V_1$. For a diffeomorphism f that is C^1-close to f_0, the implicit function theorem provides smooth maps $G_i : D \to D$ with

$$G_i(x_0, y_1) = (x_1, y_0)$$

if $(x_1, y_1) = F_i(x_0, y_0)$. Now check that

$$DG_i = \begin{pmatrix} a - bd^{-1}c & bd^{-1} \\ -d^{-1}c & d^{-1} \end{pmatrix}$$

with a, b, c, d calculated in (x_0, y_0). For f_0 we find the matrix $\begin{pmatrix} a_0 & 0 \\ 0 & d_0^{-1} \end{pmatrix}$. For ε_0 small, the matrix DG_i is a small perturbation of this matrix.

Denote by $\mathcal{C}(\mathbb{Z}, D)$ the space of sequences $\xi : \mathbb{Z} \to D$ endowed with the supremum norm $\|\xi\| = \sup_{i\in\mathbb{Z}} |\xi_i|$. For $\omega \in \Sigma^2$, define $\mathcal{H}_\omega : \mathcal{C}(\mathbb{Z}, D) \to \mathcal{C}(\mathbb{Z}, D)$ as follows: if $\gamma_i = (x_i, y_i)$ and $\mathcal{H}_\omega(\gamma) = \eta$ with $\eta_i = (u_i, v_i)$, then

$$(u_{i+1}, v_i) = G_{\omega_{i+1}}(x_i, y_{i+1})$$

for $i \in \mathbb{Z}$. For ε_0 small, the map $\mathcal{H}_\omega$ is a contraction:

$$\|\mathcal{H}_\omega(\gamma) - \mathcal{H}_\omega(\eta)\| \le \lambda \|\gamma - \eta\|$$

for some $0 < \lambda < 1$; see Exercise 2.18. The map $\mathcal{H}_\omega$ therefore possesses a unique fixed point. By uniqueness, the fixed point $\zeta = \zeta(\omega)$ of $\mathcal{H}_\omega$ satisfies $\zeta_{k+1} = f(\zeta_k)$. Thus ζ_k is an orbit of f.

By Lemma A.13, the fixed point depends continuously on $\omega \in \Sigma^2$ in the product topology. We find that $\omega \to \zeta(\omega)$ defines a homeomorphism. The correspondence $\omega \to \zeta(\omega)_0$ defines a topological conjugacy since $\sigma\omega$ is mapped to the shifted sequence $\{\zeta_{k+1}\}, k \in \mathbb{Z}$. □

Remark 2.59. Topological conditions that imply chaotic invariant sets similar to the horseshoe map are investigated in [**201**]. ■

Example 2.60. The Hénon map is given by

$$H(x, y) = (y + 1 - ax^2, bx).$$

The Hénon map is known to possess a horseshoe for small values of b and sufficiently large values of a [**94**]. From the proof of Theorem 2.58 we extract an algorithm to find the horseshoe [**168**]. If (x_n, y_n) denotes an orbit of H, then

$$(x_{n+1}, y_{n+1}) = (y_n + 1 - ax_n^2, bx_n).$$

Rewriting gives $(x_n, y_{n+1}) = I_{\pm 1}(x_{n+1}, y_n)$ with

$$I_{\pm 1}(x_{n+1}, y_n) = \left(\pm\sqrt{\frac{1 + y_n - x_{n+1}}{a}}, \pm b\sqrt{\frac{1 + y_n - x_{n+1}}{a}}\right),$$

where the plus or minus sign is given by the sign of x_n. Fix a sequence of signs $(t_n) \in \{-1, 1\}^{\mathbb{Z}}$. Given a sequence (x_n, y_n), we calculate a new sequence $(u_n, v_n) = \mathcal{H}(\{(x_n, y_n)\})$ by $(u_n, v_{n+1}) = I_{t_n}(x_{n+1}, y_n)$. Repeat the application of $\mathcal{H}$ until convergence to a sequence yielding an orbit of the Hénon map occurs.

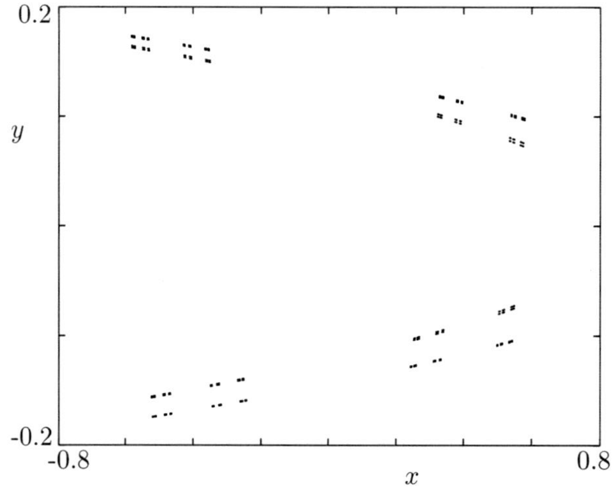

Figure 2.6. A horseshoe for the Hénon map with $a = 5$ and $b = 0.3$, calculated using the numerical scheme described in Example 2.60.

Figure 2.6 illustrates the numerical calculation of a horseshoe, approximated by a periodic orbit of high period, for the Hénon map with $a = 5$ and $b = 0.3$. ■

In Section 5.1.2 we discuss the general notion of hyperbolic set which encompasses hyperbolic equilibria, hyperbolic periodic orbits, and various invariant sets. The maximal invariant set of f is a key example of a hyperbolic set.

2.6. Exercises

Exercise 2.1. Prove the statements in Example 2.6 about the system (2.1) with an equilibrium that is not stable but does attract all nearby orbits.

Exercise 2.2. Given an attractor one may consider whether a point $x \in A$ or x near A exists whose ω-limit set equals A. Give examples where this is or is not the case.

Exercise 2.3. Prove the statements in Example 2.12 on Milnor attractors.

Exercise 2.4. The following example is from [**239**]; see also [**147**]. Consider the periodic linear system $\dot{x} = A(t)x$ with

$$A(t) = \begin{pmatrix} -1 + \frac{3}{2}\cos^2(t) & -1 + \frac{3}{2}\cos(t)\sin(t) \\ 1 + \frac{3}{2}\sin(t)\cos(t) & -1 + \frac{3}{2}\sin^2(t) \end{pmatrix}.$$

(i) Compute the eigenvalues of $A(t)$ to establish that they have negative real parts.

(ii) Verify that $e^{t/2}\begin{pmatrix}\cos(t) \\ \sin(t)\end{pmatrix}$ is a solution of the periodic linear system. Note that this solution is unbounded as $t \to \infty$.

(iii) What are the Floquet multipliers of the system?

Exercise 2.5. Prove formulas (2.9) and (2.10).

Exercise 2.6. Consider the differential equation

$$\begin{aligned} \dot{x} &= -y + x(1 - x^2 - y^2)^2, \\ \dot{y} &= x + y(1 - x^2 - y^2)^2. \end{aligned} \tag{2.16}$$

Show that $\mathcal{P} = \{x_1^2 + x_2^2 = 1\}$ represents a periodic orbit.

Let $\Sigma = (1, 0) + \text{span}\{(1, 0)\}$ and consider the Poincaré return map $\Pi : \Sigma \to \Sigma$. Show that $D\Pi(0) = 1$. Relate this result to the phase portrait of this differential equation shown in Figure 2.7.

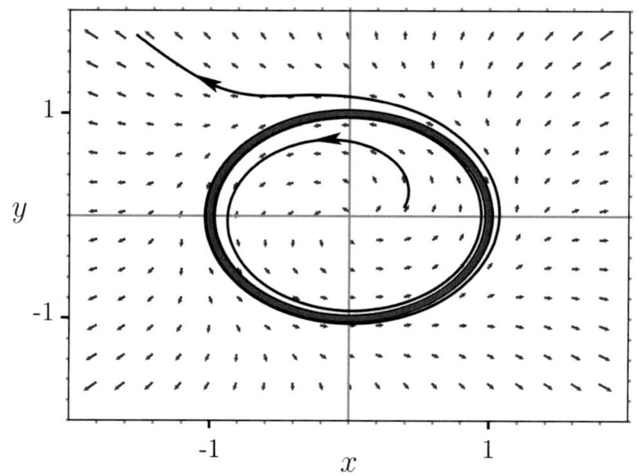

Figure 2.7. Phase portrait of (2.16).

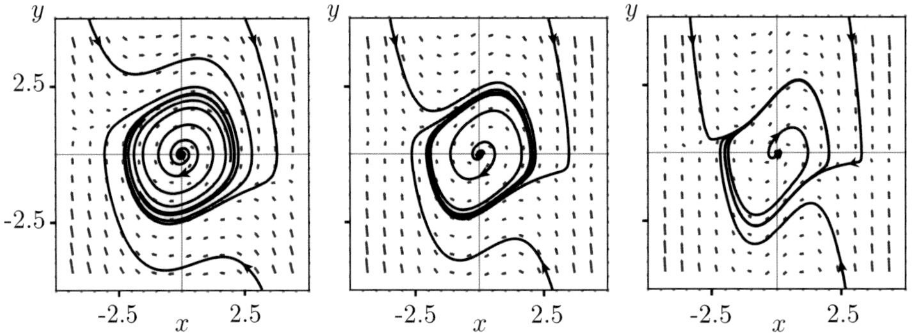

Figure 2.8. Phase portraits of the van der Pol differential equation for $\lambda = 0.27$, $\lambda = 0.51$, and $\lambda = 1$ (from left to right).

Exercise 2.7. Consider the van der Pol differential equation

$$\begin{aligned} \dot{x} &= y, \\ \dot{y} &= \lambda y(1 - x^2) - x. \end{aligned} \tag{2.17}$$

Figure 2.8 displays phase portraits of (2.17) for positive λ. These suggest the existence of a periodic orbit in each case. Show that the periodic orbit is asymptotically stable.

Hint: Use Theorem 2.27. Let $\mathcal{P} = \{(x_{\mathcal{P}}(t), y_{\mathcal{P}}(t))\ ;\ t \in [0, T]\}$ be a representation of the periodic orbit with unknown expressions for $x_{\mathcal{P}}$ and $y_{\mathcal{P}}$. Use $V(x, y) = \frac{1}{2}(x^2 + y^2)$ to show that $\int_0^T \lambda(1 - x_{\mathcal{P}}(t)^2)\, dt < 0$ in the following way. Show that $V(x_{\mathcal{P}}(t), y_{\mathcal{P}}(t)) > \frac{1}{2}$, for $t \in [0, T]$. Use for this that $\mathcal{P}$ is compact and consider the Lie derivative $L_{f_\lambda} V = \frac{d}{dt} V(x(t), y(t))$ of V with respect to the given vector field. An evaluation of $L_{f_\lambda} V$ yields

$$-\int_0^T \frac{L_f V(x_{\mathcal{P}}(t), y_{\mathcal{P}}(t))}{V(x_{\mathcal{P}}(t), y_{\mathcal{P}}(t)) - \frac{1}{2}}\, dt + 2\int_0^T \lambda(1 - x_{\mathcal{P}}(t)^2)\, dt$$

$$= -\lambda \int_0^T \frac{(1 - x_{\mathcal{P}}(t)^2)^2}{V(x_{\mathcal{P}}(t), y_{\mathcal{P}}(t)) - \frac{1}{2}}\, dt.$$

Remark. A rigorous verification of the existence of the periodic orbit is possible by using the Poincaré-Bendixon theorem [**148**], [**309**]. Basically this theorem says that the ω-limit sets of planar vector fields are either equilibria, periodic orbits, or they consist of equilibria and orbits connecting them.

Exercise 2.8. Consider the family given in (1.1). Show that for all $\lambda_0 \neq 0$ there exists a neighborhood $U(\lambda_0)$ such that for all $\lambda \in U(\lambda_0)$ the flow of f_λ is topologically equivalent (on $\mathbb{R}$) to the flow of f_{λ_0}.

Exercise 2.9. Suppose the vector fields f at an equilibrium p and g at an equilibrium q are locally smoothly conjugate through a local diffeomorphism h. Prove that $Df(p)$ and $Dg(q)$ are similar and in particular have the same eigenvalues.

Exercise 2.10. Formulate and prove a result analogous to Theorem 2.43 for periodic orbits.

Exercise 2.11. Let f and g be smooth vector fields on D_f and D_g, respectively. Show that the flows of these vector fields are smoothly conjugate precisely if there is a diffeomorphism $H : D_f \to D_g$ such that

$$DH(x)f(x) = g(H(x)), \quad \forall x \in D_f.$$

Exercise 2.12. Let the origin be a nondegenerate singularity of f. Prove that $J(f)$ equals $\mathcal{M}$, that is f has codimension 0.

Exercise 2.13. Prove Lemma 2.55.

Exercise 2.14. Prove Lemma 2.56.

Exercise 2.15. Show that Σ^2 appearing in Lemma 2.56 is a Cantor set, that is, compact, perfect, and totally disconnected.

Exercise 2.16. Prove Lemma 2.57.

Exercise 2.17. Show that the horseshoe map $f|_\Lambda$ is chaotic in the sense of Devaney.

Hint: Note that the sensitive dependence on initial conditions is not a topological property. That is, in general it will not be transmitted by homeomorphisms—but only in particular situations. Exploit the compactness of Σ^2 (and Λ) and hence that χ^{-1} and χ are uniformly continuous.

Exercise 2.18. Show that the map $\mathcal{H}_\omega$ defined in the proof of Theorem 2.58 is contractive.

Chapter 3

Local bifurcations

In this chapter we treat bifurcations of equilibria and periodic orbits of differential equations. Not all possible bifurcations are covered; we restrict our discussion instead to a collection that frequently arises in applications and that gives a showcase of techniques and results.

Following a preliminary section that introduces methods of analysis for local bifurcations, we offer two sections on bifurcations of equilibria and bifurcations of periodic orbits. The different bifurcations have in common that a critical element changes stability, but we will see different phenomena including the coalescence of critical elements and the creation of new recurrent dynamics. The notation that we adopt in the analysis, for derivatives and Taylor series and so on, is presented in Appendix A.1.

Let us list the bifurcations that we treat in this chapter, starting with bifurcations of equilibria. The context is always a family of differential equations $\dot{x} = f(x, \lambda)$ on some Euclidean space $\mathbb{R}^n$, depending on a parameter λ which is from $\mathbb{R}$ or $\mathbb{R}^2$. A first characteristic that determines the type of bifurcation is given by the spectrum of the linearization $Df(p, \lambda_0)$ of the vector field about the equilibrium p at a parameter value λ_0; bifurcations occur when this spectrum intersects the imaginary axis. We will provide detailed treatments of the following bifurcations:

(i) A single eigenvalue zero for the linearization gives the saddle-node bifurcation as a codimension-1 bifurcation, which is the first bifurcation we discuss. We also treat the transcritical bifurcation and the pitchfork bifurcation which arise when additional conditions force the persistence of the equilibrium under parameter variation. And we treat the codimension-2 cusp bifurcation, arising when a second derivative vanishes. We do not treat bifurcations of still higher codimension, such as the swallowtail bifurcation. For these we refer to [**255**].

(ii) We discuss the codimension-1 Hopf bifurcation, occurring for a pair of complex conjugate eigenvalues for the linearization. We do not treat higher codimension bifurcations, such as the Bautin bifurcation (see [**369**] or [**215**]).

(iii) We analyze the bifurcation of codimension 2 arising for a double zero eigenvalue for the linearization, the Bogdanov-Takens bifurcation. We do not consider higher codimension variants [**105, 106**].

Various other bifurcations, for instance where the spectrum on the imaginary axis consists of a union of a single eigenvalue zero and a pair of complex conjugate eigenvalues (giving the saddle-node Hopf bifurcation) are not discussed. We refer to [**143, 215**].

Local bifurcations of periodic orbits are triggered by the set of Floquet multipliers intersecting the unit circle. We treat the following often-occurring bifurcations:

(i) A single Floquet multiplier 1 gives the saddle-node bifurcation of a periodic orbit. We confine our discussion to the bifurcation of codimension 1.

(ii) A single Floquet multiplier -1 gives the period-doubling bifurcation of a periodic orbit. We only consider the codimension-1 bifurcation.

(iii) A complex conjugate pair of Floquet multipliers gives the Neimark-Sacker bifurcation, which can be viewed as a Hopf bifurcation of a periodic orbit. We look at one-parameter families, and do not consider higher codimension cases, such as strong resonance bifurcations [**21**] and the Chenciner bifurcation ([**65–67**]; see also [**25, 215**]).

The general reference to look at for other bifurcations is [**215**].

3.1. Methods of local bifurcation theory

There are a number of techniques available for the study of local bifurcations. Here we comment on the more relevant techniques that are used below. The full theory is developed in Appendices A and B. The following reduction methods and techniques are fundamental in bifurcation analysis.

(i) Implicit function theorem and Lyapunov-Schmidt reduction,

(ii) Center manifold reduction,

(iii) Normal forms and singular rescalings.

The first two deal with reductions of the number of static equations and variables that has to be considered (Lyapunov-Schmidt reduction) or the reduction of the differential equation to lower-dimensional invariant manifolds (center manifold reduction). The final techniques involve bringing the expression of the differential equation to simpler form. Here we provide a first glance at these methods.

3.1.1. Lyapunov-Schmidt reduction.

Solving for variables as functions of remaining variables is standard practice in bifurcation theory. Appendix A.2 develops the techniques. To illustrate the ideas we look at an elementary example.

Example 3.1. Consider a family of differential equations $(\dot{x}, \dot{y}) = f(x, y, \lambda)$ of the form

$$\begin{aligned} \dot{x} &= \lambda - x^2 + xy^2, \\ \dot{y} &= -y + xy + \lambda x. \end{aligned} \tag{3.1}$$

Suppose we want to know number and position of the equilibria as function of the parameter λ. We must therefore solve the static equation $f(x, y, \lambda) = 0$. For $\lambda = 0$ there is an equilibrium $(x, y) = (0, 0)$, which is nonhyperbolic. To study nearby equilibria, we consider

$$\begin{aligned} f_1(x, y, \lambda) &= \lambda - x^2 + xy^2 = 0, \\ f_2(x, y, \lambda) &= -y + xy + \lambda x = 0 \end{aligned}$$

in a neighborhood of $(x, y, \lambda) = (0, 0, 0)$.

Since $D_y f_2(0, 0, 0) \neq 0$, the second equation can be solved for $y = y^*(x, \lambda)$ by the implicit function theorem. This way the original equation $f(x, y, \lambda) = 0$ reduces to the single equation

$$g(x, \lambda) = \lambda - x^2 + xy^*(x)^2 = 0.$$

This is the principal idea of the Lyapunov-Schmidt reduction: decompose a given (static) equation into a system of two equations of which one can be solved by the implicit function theorem, and then study the remaining equation.

In the example we find $y^*(x) = \lambda x + \mathcal{O}(x^2)$ and hence

$$g(x, \lambda) = \lambda - x^2 + \mathcal{O}(|(x, \lambda)|^3). \tag{3.2}$$

We conclude that (3.1) has no equilibria (locally around $(x, y) = (0, 0)$) for $\lambda < 0$, there is one equilibrium at $\lambda = 0$, and there are two equilibria for $\lambda > 0$. ■

3.1.2. Center manifold reduction. The geometric reduction method we introduce here is the center manifold reduction: a reduction to an invariant manifold that contains the recurrent points. The center manifold theorem and its proof are in Appendix B.1.2, but here we present the result in order to be able to use it in the bifurcation studies. We discuss this reduction method for both vector fields and maps.

3.1.2.1. *Center manifold reduction for vector fields.* Start with a family

$$\dot{x} = f(x, \lambda), \quad x \in \mathbb{R}^n, \lambda \in \mathbb{R}^k,$$

and assume that $x = 0$ is a nonhyperbolic equilibrium at $\lambda = 0$. So $f(0,0) = 0$ and the spectrum $\sigma(D_x f(0,0))$ of $D_x f(0,0)$ intersects the imaginary axis. The study of bifurcations of the equilibrium in the family $\dot{x} = f(x, \lambda)$ can be reduced to a system $\dot{y} = g(y, \lambda)$, $y \in \mathbb{R}^m$, via a center manifold reduction. Here m is determined by the center spectrum $\sigma^c(D_x f(0,0)) = \sigma(D_x f(0,0)) \cap i\,\mathbb{R}$. The goal of this section is to describe this reduction of the family to its *nonhyperbolic part.* It is helpful to consider the extended system

$$\begin{aligned} \dot{x} &= f(x, \lambda), \\ \dot{\lambda} &= 0. \end{aligned} \tag{3.3}$$

Decompose $\mathbb{R}^n = E^c \oplus E^h$ into invariant subspaces E^c and E^h, so that the spectrum $\operatorname{spec} Df(0,0)|_{E^c}$ lies on the imaginary axis in the complex plane and $\operatorname{spec} Df(0,0)|_{E^h}$ lies off the imaginary axis. That is, E^c and E^h are the generalized center and hyperbolic eigenspaces of $D_x f(0,0)$. Introduce new coordinates from the center and hyperbolic directions

$$x = (y, z), \quad y \in E^c, z \in E^h.$$

Let $P_c : \mathbb{R}^n \to \mathbb{R}^n$ be the projection on E^c along E^h, that is $\operatorname{im} P_c = E^c$ and $\ker P_c = E^h$. We may write (3.3) as

$$\begin{aligned} \dot{y} &= P_c f(y, z, \lambda), \\ \dot{z} &= (\mathrm{id} - P_c) f(y, z, \lambda), \\ \dot{\lambda} &= 0. \end{aligned} \tag{3.4}$$

The extended system (3.4) has an $(m+k)$-dimensional invariant manifold containing $(0,0,0)$, the local center manifold W^c_{loc}. This manifold is tangential to $E^c \times \mathbb{R}^k$ and can therefore be expressed as the graph of a function

$$W : E^c \times \mathbb{R}^k \to E^h \tag{3.5}$$

with $W(0,0) = 0$, $DW(0,0) = 0$. All equilibria near the origin are located in the center manifold.

The flow on the center manifold is determined by

$$\begin{aligned} \dot{y} &= P_c f(y, W(y,\lambda), \lambda), \\ \dot{\lambda} &= 0. \end{aligned} \tag{3.6}$$

The equation for the y-variable gives a reduced system

$$\dot{y} = g(y, \lambda).$$

In fact, the systems $\dot{x} = f(x, \lambda)$ and

$$\begin{aligned} \dot{y} &= g(y, \lambda), \\ \dot{z} &= (D_x f(0,0)|_{E^h})\, z \end{aligned}$$

are (for λ with $|\lambda|$ sufficiently small) locally topologically equivalent, by a result due to Aleksandr Shoshitaishvili [**345, 346**].

Example 3.2. We take up again the differential equation (3.1) from Example 3.1. Consider the extended system

$$\begin{aligned} \dot{x} &= \lambda - x^2 + xy^2, \\ \dot{y} &= -y + xy + \lambda x, \\ \dot{\lambda} &= 0. \end{aligned}$$

The center subspace E^c and hyperbolic subspace E^h of the differential equation (3.1) coincide with the x-axis and y-axis, respectively. So, in accordance with (3.6), the flow on the center manifold will be determined by an equation

$$\begin{aligned} \dot{x} &= \lambda - x^2 + xW(x,\lambda)^2, \\ \dot{\lambda} &= 0. \end{aligned}$$

or just by the family $\dot{x} = \lambda - x^2 + xW(x,\lambda)^2$. We find that this family has the form

$$\dot{x} = \lambda - x^2 + \mathcal{O}(|(x,\lambda)|^3),$$

similar to (3.2). ■

In some cases it is necessary to get a grip on higher order terms in a Taylor expansion of W. The Taylor expansion of W can be obtained by considering both $z = W(y, \lambda)$ and the differential equation in the z-direction,

$$\big(W(y,\lambda)\big)^{\cdot} = \dot{z} = (\mathrm{id} - P_c) f(y, W(y,\lambda), \lambda). \tag{3.7}$$

When inserting $W(y,\lambda) = a_0(\lambda) + a_1(\lambda)y + a_2(\lambda)y^2 + \cdots$ in this equation, a comparison of coefficients provides expressions for the a_i. Note that (3.5) implies $a_0(0) = 0$, $Da_0(0) = 0$, and $a_1(0) = 0$.

Example 3.3. We continue Example 3.2 and show how to determine the second order terms of the Taylor expansion $W(x,\lambda) = a\lambda^2 + b\lambda x + cx^2 + \mathcal{O}(|(x,\lambda)|^3)$. Starting from the corresponding counterpart of (3.7) we find

$$D_x W(x,\lambda)\dot{x} + D_\lambda W(x,\lambda)\dot{\lambda} = \dot{y} = (-1+x)\,W(x,\lambda) + \lambda x,$$

and thus

$$\begin{aligned}\big(b\lambda + 2cx + \mathcal{O}(|(x,\lambda)|^2)\big)\big(\lambda - x^2 + \mathcal{O}(|(x,\lambda)|^3)\big)&\\ = (-1+x)\big(a\lambda^2 + b\lambda x + cx^2 + \mathcal{O}(|(x,\lambda)|^3)\big) + \lambda x.&\end{aligned}$$

This gives

$$b\lambda^2 + 2c\lambda x + \mathcal{O}(|(x,\lambda)|^3) = -a\lambda^2 + (1-b)\lambda x - cx^2 + \mathcal{O}(|(x,\lambda)|^3).$$

Comparing coefficients provides $c = 0$, $b = 1$, and $a = -1$, and therefore

$$W(x,\lambda) = -\lambda^2 + \lambda x + \mathcal{O}(|(x,\lambda)|^3).$$

■

3.1.2.2. *Center manifold reduction for maps.* In our study of local bifurcations of periodic orbits, diffeomorphisms arise as return maps on cross sections. The periodic orbit becomes a fixed point for the return map. A theory of center manifolds for diffeomorphisms near a nonhyperbolic fixed point is developed in complete analogy with center manifolds for nonhyperbolic equilibria of differential equations.

Start with a family

$$x \mapsto \Pi(x,\lambda), \quad x \in \mathbb{R}^n,\ \lambda \in \mathbb{R}^k,$$

of diffeomorphisms and assume that $x = 0$ is a nonhyperbolic fixed point at $\lambda = 0$. So $\Pi(0,0) = 0$ and the spectrum $\sigma(D_x\Pi(0,0))$ of $D_x\Pi(0,0)$ intersects the unit circle in the complex plane. The study of bifurcations of the fixed point in the family $\Pi(x,\lambda)$ can be reduced to a system $y \mapsto g(y,\lambda)$, $y \in \mathbb{R}^m$, via a center manifold reduction. Here m is determined by the center spectrum $\sigma^c(D_x f(0,0)) = \sigma(D_x f(0,0)) \cap \mathbb{T}$. As earlier, we consider an extended system

$$(x,\lambda) \mapsto \hat{\Pi}(x,\lambda) = (\Pi(x,\lambda),\lambda). \tag{3.8}$$

Decompose $\mathbb{R}^n = E^c \oplus E^h$, so that the spectrum $\operatorname{spec} D\Pi(0)|_{E^c}$ lies on the unit circle in the complex plane and $\operatorname{spec} D\Pi(0)|_{E^h}$ lies off the unit circle. That is, E^c and E^h are the generalized center and hyperbolic eigenspaces of $D_x\Pi(0,0)$. Introduce new coordinates according to its center and hyperbolic directions

$$x = (y,z),$$

where $y \in E^c$, $z \in E^h$. Let $P_c : \mathbb{R}^n \to \mathbb{R}^n$ be again the projection on E^c along E^h. Using these coordinates, (3.8) reads

$$\hat{\Pi}(y,z,\lambda) = (P_c\Pi(y,z,\lambda), (\mathrm{id} - P_c)\Pi(y,z,\lambda), \lambda). \tag{3.9}$$

Now by the center manifold theorem (Theorem B.7), system (3.9) has an $(m+k)$-dimensional local center manifold

$$W^c_{loc} = \{(y, W(y,\lambda), \lambda)\ ;\ (y,\lambda) \in U(0)\},$$

where $U(0)$ is an open neighborhood of zero in the (y,λ)-space, and W is a smooth function defined on $U(0)$ with $W(0,0) = 0$ and $DW(0,0) = 0$. The locally invariant manifold W^c_{loc} in particular contains all fixed points of (3.9) which are close to $(0,0)$. The dynamics on the center manifold is determined by

$$y_{n+1} = \tilde{\Pi}(y_n, \lambda) = P_c\Pi(y_n, W(y_n,\lambda), \lambda).$$

In particular we have obtained a reduced family

$$y_{n+1} = \tilde{\Pi}(y_n, \lambda).$$

Example 3.4. Consider the family of maps

$$\Pi(x,y,\lambda) = (\Pi_1(x,y,\lambda), \Pi_2(x,y,\lambda)) = \left(x + \lambda - x^2 + xy, \frac{1}{2}y + xy + \lambda x\right).$$

Denote the extended system by

$$\hat{\Pi}(x,y,\lambda) = \left(x + \lambda - x^2 + xy, \frac{1}{2}y + xy + \lambda x, \lambda\right).$$

Note that $\Pi(0,0,0) = (0,0)$ and $D_{(x,y)}\Pi(0,0,0)$ is the diagonal matrix with diagonal entries 1 and $\frac{1}{2}$. The (x,λ)-plane spans the center subspace, and the y-axis is the hyperbolic direction. There exists a center manifold $y = W(x,\lambda)$ with $W(0,0) = 0$ and $DW(0,0) = 0$ defined for values of (x,λ) near $(0,0)$. The dynamics on the center manifold is determined by

$$x_{n+1} = \tilde{\Pi}(x_n, \lambda) = x_n + \lambda - x_n^2 + \mathcal{O}\left(|(x_n,\lambda)|^3\right).$$

The fixed points of $\tilde{\Pi}$ are determined by $\lambda - x^2 + \mathcal{O}\left(|(x_n,\lambda)|^3\right) = 0$.

As in Example 3.3 we can determine a Taylor expansion of W. We do this here up to second order terms. The counterpart of (3.7) in the present context is given by

$$\begin{aligned} y_{n+1} &= W(\Pi^1(x_n, y_n, \lambda), \lambda), \\ y_{n+1} &= \Pi^2(x_n, y_n, \lambda). \end{aligned}$$

With $y_n = W(x_n, \lambda)$ we see

$$W(\Pi^1(x, W(x,\lambda), \lambda)) = \Pi^2(x, W(x,\lambda), \lambda).$$

Writing $W(x,\lambda) = a\lambda^2 + b\lambda x + cx^2$ yields

$$\begin{aligned} &(a+b+c)\lambda^2 + (b+2c)\lambda x + cx^2 + \mathcal{O}\left(|(x_n,\lambda)|^3\right) \\ &\qquad = \frac{1}{2}a\lambda^2 + \left(\frac{1}{2}b + 1\right)\lambda x + \frac{1}{2}cx^2 + \mathcal{O}\left(|(x_n,\lambda)|^3\right). \end{aligned}$$

This gives us $W(x,\lambda) = -4\lambda^2 + 2\lambda x + \mathcal{O}\left(|(x_n,\lambda)|^3\right)$. ■

3.1.3. Normal forms. Coordinate changes can bring expressions of differential equations near an equilibrium (or periodic orbit) to simpler expressions, called normal forms. The idea is to perform transformations to get the vector field into a form that is most suitable for further analysis. Most of the techniques will be developed as we need them. Appendix B.2.1 contains some general ideas of normal form theory.

To give an elementary example of the effect of coordinate changes, consider the family of differential equations

$$\dot{x} = \lambda + \lambda x + 4x^2. \tag{3.10}$$

The λ-dependent transformation of the state variable x given by $x = y + a\lambda$, transforms this differential equation into $\dot{y} = \lambda + (a + 4a^2)\lambda^2 + (1 + 8a)\lambda y + 4y^2$. For $a = -\frac{1}{8}$ this transformation removes the λy-term, and we obtain

$$\dot{y} = \lambda - \frac{1}{16}\lambda^2 + 4y^2.$$

After a second transformation $z = 4y$ and a reparametrization $\mu = \lambda - \frac{1}{16}\lambda^2$, we end up with

$$\dot{z} = \mu + z^2.$$

Example 2.40 discussed a normal form for a more general family of vector fields that in addition makes use of a time reparametrization.

Example 3.5. In Example 3.1 we took the system of differential equations (3.1) and discussed the use of the Lyapunov-Schmidt method to find its equilibria. The same equations were studied in Examples 3.2 and 3.3 from the point of view of a reduction to a center manifold. For completeness we discuss the equations again from the perspective of normal form theory. The reasoning relies upon the theory on strong stable foliations from Appendix B.1.3 and is not used in the bifurcation analysis further in this chapter.

Recall that the differential equations are given by

$$\begin{aligned}\dot{x} &= \lambda - x^2 + xy^2,\\ \dot{y} &= -y + xy + \lambda x.\end{aligned}$$

The system admits a local strong stable manifold tangent to the y-axis at the origin; see Appendix B.1.3. There is moreover a smooth strong stable foliation near the origin that contains the local strong stable manifold as one of its leaves. This can be seen by methods discussed in Appendix B.1.3, where we note that Theorem B.14 can be extended to the current situation with a nonhyperbolic equilibrium (see also [**54**]). The existence of a smooth strong stable foliation means that one can take new coordinates $(u, v) = h(x, y)$ with h a smooth local diffeomorphism and $Dh(0, 0) = \mathrm{id}$, in which the strong stable foliation is affine and consists of leaves $\{(u, v)\ ;\ u = \text{constant}\}$. In these coordinates, the differential equation is such that $\dot{u}$ is a function of u alone (and of course the parameter λ). We may take the coordinates so that the u-axis is a local center manifold. Using Example 2.40 we can further simplify the equation for the u variable; see also transformations performed on equation (3.10). Consequently, with an additional parameter change, the above system of differential equations is locally smoothly equivalent to a system of the form

$$\begin{aligned} \dot{u} &= \lambda - u^2, \\ \dot{v} &= -a(u)v, \end{aligned} \tag{3.11}$$

where a is a smooth function with $a(0) = -1$. A detailed treatment of normal forms for such and similar systems can be found in [**184**].

As was mentioned earlier, by a result of Shoshitaishvili, when allowing for a parameter change, the system is locally topologically equivalent to

$$\begin{aligned} \dot{u} &= \lambda - u^2, \\ \dot{v} &= -v. \end{aligned} \tag{3.12}$$

This normal form cannot be achieved by smooth equivalence; see Exercise 3.5. ∎

Blowing-up is a useful technique that allows a study of the flow near degenerate equilibria. We refer to [**104**, Chapter 3] for an introduction. For the bifurcation problems of low codimension that we study, we do not need to develop the theory. We occasionally use a related technique of singular rescalings, where one should think of parameter dependent rescalings that become undefined when the parameter vanishes. It plays a central role in the analysis of the Bogdanov-Takens bifurcation (see section 3.2.5) and will be discussed there.

3.2. Bifurcations of equilibria

As we have seen in Chapter 2, an equilibrium can only undergo a bifurcation if it is nonhyperbolic, so the linearization about it has eigenvalues on the imaginary axis. The bifurcations we consider are of codimension 1 and codimension 2, which means that the bifurcation conditions hold in typical one-parameter and two-parameter families of differential equations. The codimension is determined by the number of nonhyperbolic eigenvalues and their multiplicities, and in addition by conditions on higher derivatives.

We consider families

$$\dot{x} = f(x, \lambda), \quad x \in \mathbb{R}^n, \lambda \in \mathbb{R}^k,$$

where $k = 1$ or $k = 2$ depending on the codimension of the bifurcation problem. Throughout we assume that $x = 0$ is a nonhyperbolic equilibrium at $\lambda = 0$:

$$f(0,0) = 0, \quad \sigma\big(D_x f(0,0)\big) \cap i\,\mathbb{R} \neq \emptyset.$$

In other words we assume that $D_x f(0,0)$ has nonhyperbolic eigenvalues 0 or $\pm i\,\omega$ for some real ω. In the simplest cases we assume that these eigenvalues are simple; see for instance the saddle-node bifurcation and the Hopf bifurcation. If 0 is a simple eigenvalue the corresponding bifurcation scenario can already be observed in one-dimensional equations, that is, $n = 1$.

The following three sections concern local bifurcations of an equilibrium with a simple eigenvalue 0. The general case, the codimension-1 bifurcation, is the saddle-node bifurcation. After that we treat cases with extra conditions that make the unfolding special (the transcritical and the pitchfork bifurcation). The third section is devoted to the codimension-2 bifurcation, which is the cusp bifurcation. Following these three sections we study the Hopf bifurcation of an equilibrium with complex conjugate purely imaginary eigenvalues. We finish with the more laborious analysis of the Bogdanov-Takens bifurcation, which is the codimension-2 bifurcation characterized by a double zero eigenvalue.

3.2.1. Saddle-node bifurcation. Consider the following simple model in $\mathbb{R}^2$:

$$\dot{x} = \lambda + x^2, \quad \dot{y} = -y. \tag{3.13}$$

As depicted in Figure 3.1 a saddle equilibrium and a node (stable equilibrium) collide and disappear as the parameter λ crosses zero. From this scenario the notion of the saddle-node bifurcation was derived. However, in dimensions different from 2, two hyperbolic equilibria whose stability indices differ by one collide and disappear in the course of a saddle-node bifurcation; see Theorem 3.8 below. So none of the involved equilibria has to be a node. The saddle-node bifurcation is sometimes called a fold bifurcation.

The *essential changes* in the dynamics of (3.13) take place in the x-direction, making the bifurcation in essence one dimensional. In what follows we first study the saddle-node bifurcation in equations with a one-dimensional state space. Afterwards we consider saddle-node bifurcations in higher dimensions.

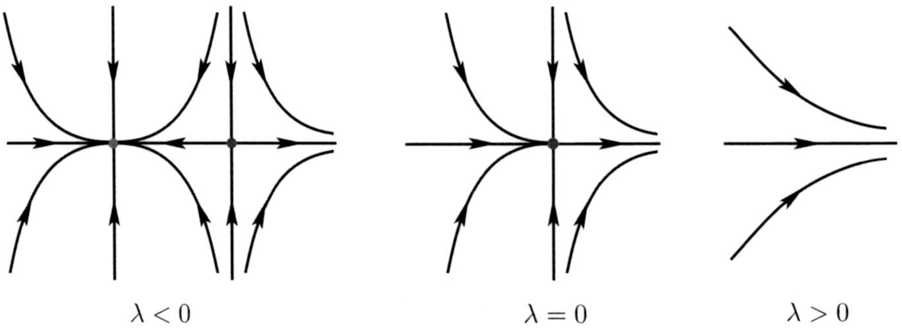

Figure 3.1. The saddle-node bifurcation in the system (3.13).

There we show how the problem can be reduced to a one-dimensional equation. We distinguish two approaches of reduction. In one approach we determine the equilibria of a vector field $f(x, \lambda)$ by solving the steady-state equation $f(x, \lambda) = 0$. This employs a Lyapunov-Schmidt reduction, for which the theory is worked out in Appendix A.2.3. The alternative approach uses a center manifold reduction as presented in Appendix B.1.2 and takes dynamics into account.

3.2.1.1. *One-dimensional saddle-node bifurcation.* Suppose the system

$$\dot{x} = f(x, \lambda),$$

with $x \in \mathbb{R}$ and $\lambda \in \mathbb{R}$, has a nonhyperbolic equilibrium $x = 0$ at $\lambda = 0$, thus $f(0, 0) = 0$ and $D_x f(0, 0) = 0$. This equation can be considered as an equation obtained by a reduction to a center manifold, but can also be considered in its own right.

Expanding $f(x, \lambda)$ in a Taylor series with respect to x at $x = 0$, we can write

$$f(x, \lambda) = f_0(\lambda) + f_1(\lambda)x + f_2(\lambda)x^2 + \mathcal{O}(|x|^3)$$

with $f_0(0) = 0$ and $f_1(0) = 0$. The $\mathcal{O}$-term is uniformly in λ as $|x| \to 0$. Introduce a coordinate $\xi = x + \delta$ where $\delta = \delta(\lambda)$. A computation shows

$$\begin{aligned}\dot{\xi} = &\big(f_0(\lambda) - f_1(\lambda)\delta + f_2(\lambda)\delta^2 + \mathcal{O}(|\delta|^3)\big) + \big(f_1(\lambda) - 2f_2(\lambda)\delta + \mathcal{O}(|\delta|^2)\big)\,\xi \\ &+ (f_2(\lambda) + \mathcal{O}(|\delta|))\,\xi^2 + \mathcal{O}(|\xi|^3).\end{aligned}$$

Assume that

$$f_2(0) = \frac{1}{2} D_x^2 f(0, 0) \neq 0.$$

Then it follows from the implicit function theorem that there is a smooth function $\delta(\lambda)$ that annihilates the linear term in the differential equation for ξ for all sufficiently small λ. It also follows that

$$\delta(\lambda) = \frac{f_1'(0)}{2f_2(0)}\lambda + \mathcal{O}(\lambda^2).$$

The equation for ξ is now without linear terms:

$$\dot{\xi} = f_0'(0)\lambda + \mathcal{O}(\lambda^2) + (f_2(0) + \mathcal{O}(|\lambda|))\xi^2 + \mathcal{O}(|\xi|^3). \tag{3.14}$$

Consider as a new parameter $\mu = \mu(\lambda)$ the constant term above,

$$\mu(\lambda) = f_0'(0)\lambda + \phi(\lambda)\lambda^2,$$

where ϕ is a smooth function. Note that $\mu(0) = 0$ and $\mu'(0) = f_0'(0) = D_\lambda f(0, 0)$. If we assume that

$$D_\lambda f(0, 0) \neq 0,$$

then the implicit function theorem implies the existence of an inverse function $\lambda(\mu)$ of $\mu(\lambda)$ with $\lambda(0) = 0$. The differential equation (3.14) becomes

$$\dot{\xi} = \mu + \tilde{\lambda}(\mu)\xi^2 + \mathcal{O}(|\xi|^3),$$

where $\tilde{\lambda}(\mu)$ is a smooth function with $\tilde{\lambda}(0) = f_2(0) \neq 0$. Let a rescaling be given by $\eta = |\tilde{\lambda}(\mu)|\xi$ and $\beta = |\tilde{\lambda}(\mu)|\mu$. Then we get

$$\dot{\eta} = \beta + s\eta^2 + \mathcal{O}(|\eta|^3)$$

with $s = \text{sign } f_2(0)$.

We have proved the following theorem.

Theorem 3.6. *Suppose that a one-dimensional system*

$$\dot{x} = f(x, \lambda),$$

$x \in \mathbb{R}$, $\lambda \in \mathbb{R}$, *has at* $\lambda = 0$ *an equilibrium at* $x = 0$, *with* $D_x f(0,0) = 0$. *Assume that the following conditions are satisfied:*

(i) $D_x^2 f(0,0) \neq 0$,

(ii) $D_\lambda f(0,0) \neq 0$.

Then there is a smooth coordinate change $\eta = h(x, \lambda)$ *and a smooth parameter change* $\beta = g(\lambda)$, *transforming the system into*

$$\dot{\eta} = \beta \pm \eta^2 + \mathcal{O}(|\eta|^3), \quad \textit{as } \eta \to 0. \tag{3.15}$$

The vector field in (3.15) can be seen as a normal form for the saddle-node bifurcation in $\mathbb{R}$; compare also Example 2.40. In what follows we consider the equation (3.15) where we rename the variables $x = \eta$ and $\lambda = \beta$,

$$\dot{x} = f(x, \lambda) = \lambda + \alpha x^2 + \mathcal{O}(|x|^3), \tag{3.16}$$

$x \in \mathbb{R}$, $\lambda \in \mathbb{R}$, $\alpha \in \{-1, 1\}$. Note that the term $\mathcal{O}(|x|^3)$ may depend on λ. In order to detect the equilibria of (3.16), we solve

$$f(x, \lambda) = 0. \tag{3.17}$$

Note that $f(0,0) = 0$ and $D_\lambda f(0,0) = 1 \neq 0$. Hence (3.17) can be solved, locally around $(0,0)$, by means of the implicit function theorem for $\lambda = \lambda^*(x)$. Analyzing $f(x, \lambda^*(x)) = 0$ we find (see also Exercise 3.6)

$$\lambda^*(x) = -\alpha x^2 + \mathcal{O}(|x|^3).$$

By considering the sign of the vector field (for fixed λ), we get the complete phase portrait including stability statements. For $\alpha = -1$ this is depicted in Figure 3.2. To establish hyperbolicity of the bifurcating equilibria and calculate their stability, we compute the sign of $D_x f(x, \lambda^*(x))$. From (3.16) we infer $D_x f(x, \lambda^*(x)) = 2\alpha x + \mathcal{O}(x^2)$. Hence

$$\text{sign}\, D_x f(x, \lambda^*(x)) = \text{sign}\, \alpha x.$$

Clearly, $x \neq 0$ yields $\text{sign}\, \alpha x \neq 0$. Hence the bifurcating equilibria are hyperbolic. One equilibrium is asymptotically stable, while the other one is unstable.

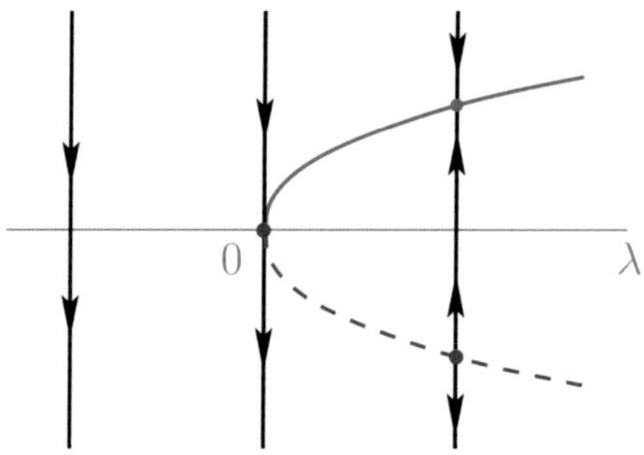

Figure 3.2. The saddle-node bifurcation in the system (3.16) for $\alpha = -1$.

Remark 3.7. Let f be given as in Theorem 3.6. Then the implicit function theorem can be used to solve $f(x,\lambda) = 0$ for $\lambda = \lambda^*(x)$ (as done for (3.16)). In other words, the analysis performed for the normal form (3.16) can already be performed for f without further ado. ■

3.2.1.2. *Higher-dimensional saddle-node bifurcation.* As motivation, consider the differential equation

$$\begin{aligned}\dot{y} &= By + \beta\lambda + \hat{g}(y,z,\lambda),\\ \dot{z} &= Cz + \hat{h}(y,z,\lambda),\\ \dot{\lambda} &= 0,\end{aligned}$$

for $x = (y,z)$ with $y \in \mathbb{R}$, $z \in \mathbb{R}^{n-1}$. Here

$$\begin{aligned}g(0,0,0) &= 0, D_{(y,z,\lambda)}g(0,0,0) = 0,\\ h(0,0,0) &= 0, D_{(y,z,\lambda)}h(0,0,0) = 0.\end{aligned}$$

An extended system is given by

$$\begin{aligned}\dot{y} &= \beta\lambda + g(y,z,\lambda),\\ \dot{z} &= Cz + h(y,z,\lambda),\\ \dot{\lambda} &= 0,\end{aligned} \tag{3.18}$$

The spectrum of C lies off the imaginary axis. The center manifold theorem yields a locally invariant center manifold $z = W(y,\lambda)$ for (3.18) with $W(0,0) = 0$ and where also the derivatives $W_y(0,0)$ and $W_\lambda(0,0)$ vanish. Restricted to the center manifold, we find an equation

$$\dot{y} = \beta\lambda + g(y,0,\lambda) + \mathcal{O}(\|(y,\lambda)\|^3)$$

for the y-variable, where further $g(y,0,\lambda)$ can be replaced by its second order Taylor expansion. This can be studied as a one-dimensional bifurcation problem. Assuming $\beta \neq 0$ and $D_y^2 g(0,0,0) \neq 0$ the system undergoes a saddle-node bifurcation.

We provide a formulation of the higher-dimensional saddle-node bifurcation that does not assume (an initial coordinate change to) an expression in the center and hyperbolic coordinates. Let

$$\dot{x} = f(x, \lambda) \tag{3.19}$$

be an ordinary differential equation in $\mathbb{R}^n$ depending on a parameter $\lambda \in \mathbb{R}$. See [**356**] by Jorge Sotomayor or, for instance, [**143**, Thm. 3.4.1] for the following formulation of the higher-dimensional saddle-node bifurcation.

Theorem 3.8 (Saddle-node bifurcation). *Assume that* (3.19) *for* $\lambda = 0$ *has an equilibrium* $p = 0$ *for which the following assumptions hold:*

(i) $D_x f(0,0)$ *has a simple eigenvalue* 0 *with right eigenvector* v *and left eigenvector* w. *Further,* $D_x f(0,0)$ *has* k *eigenvalues with negative real part and* $n - k - 1$ *eigenvalues with positive real part.*

(ii) $\langle w, D_\lambda f(0,0)\rangle \neq 0$.

(iii) $\langle w, D_x^2 f(0,0)v^2\rangle \neq 0$.

Then there is a smooth curve of equilibria in $\mathbb{R}^n \times \mathbb{R}$, *passing through* $(0,0)$ *and tangent to* $(v,0)$ *at* $(0,0)$.

Depending on the signs of the expressions in (ii) *and* (iii) *there are no equilibria for* $\lambda < 0$ *(or* $\lambda > 0$*), and there are two equilibria for* $\lambda > 0$ *(or* $\lambda < 0$*). The two equilibria are hyperbolic and have a stability index (dimension of the stable manifold) of* k *and* $k+1$, *respectively.*

Remark 3.9. From $\langle w, D_x f(0,0)u\rangle = \langle (D_x f(0,0))^T w, u\rangle = 0$, for all u, we see that w is perpendicular to the image im $D_x f(0,0)$. Note that the left eigenvector is a (right) eigenvector of the transposed matrix. Conditions (ii) and (iii) stipulate that $D_\lambda f(p,\lambda_0)$ and $D_x f(p,\lambda_0)v^2$ are not contained in the range of $D_x f(p,\lambda_0)$. ■

We provide two proofs of Theorem 3.8, one applying a Lyapunov-Schmidt reduction and another using a center manifold reduction. The first proof we give is based on the Lyapunov-Schmidt reduction explained in Appendix A.2.3. To this end we write the equation for the equilibria $f(x,\lambda) = 0$ as a system

$$\begin{aligned} (\mathrm{id} - P)f(uv + z, \lambda) &= 0, \\ Pf(uv + z, \lambda) &= 0, \end{aligned}$$

where P is an appropriate projection and $z \in \operatorname{im} D_x f(0,0)$. The projection P is chosen such that the second equation can be solved for $z = z^*(u,\lambda)$. Then we show that the remaining one-dimensional equation $(\mathrm{id} - P)f(uv + z^*(u,\lambda),\lambda) = 0$ satisfies the assumptions of Theorem 3.6.

Proof of Theorem 3.8 using the Lyapunov-Schmidt method. First we prove the existence of a smooth curve of equilibria in $\mathbb{R}^n \times \mathbb{R}$. Define $N(x,\lambda) = D_x f(0,0)x - f(x,\lambda)$ and write the equation $f(x,\lambda) = 0$ as

$$D_x f(0,0)x - N(x,\lambda) = 0. \tag{3.20}$$

From its definition we infer that $D_x N(0,0) = 0$, $D_x^2 N(0,0) = -D_x^2 f(0,0)$ and $D_\lambda N(0,0) = -D_\lambda f(0,0)$.

We will apply the Lyapunov-Schmidt reduction to (3.20). In the notation from Appendix A.2.3, write

$$A = D_x f(0,0)$$

and let Q be the projection onto $\ker A$ with $Q(\operatorname{im} A) = 0$. Then $\mathrm{id} - Q$ is the projection onto $\operatorname{im} A$ with $(\mathrm{id} - Q)(\ker A) = 0$. Further, let P be the orthogonal projection onto $\operatorname{im} A$, so $\ker P = \mathbb{R}w$. Here orthogonality refers to an inner product $\langle \cdot, \cdot \rangle$ in $\mathbb{R}^n$. Without loss of generality, we may assume that $\langle w, w \rangle = 1$. Then the projection $\mathrm{id} - P$ has the representation $(\mathrm{id} - P)\cdot = \langle w, \cdot \rangle w$.

The Lyapunov-Schmidt reduction (see Lemma A.23) applied to (3.20) yields a reduced bifurcation equation

$$(\mathrm{id} - P)N(uv + z^*(u,\lambda), \lambda) = 0, \tag{3.21}$$

where z^* solves

$$z - KPN(uv + z, \lambda) = 0. \tag{3.22}$$

Here $x = uv + z$ with $u \in \mathbb{R}$ and $z \in \operatorname{im} A$ and $K = \left(A|_{\operatorname{im} A}\right)^{-1}$.

Clearly, $z^*(0,0) = 0$, and from (3.22) we obtain

$$D_u z^*(0,0) - KPD_x N(0,0)(\mathrm{id} + D_u z^*(0,0)) = 0.$$

Since $D_x N(0,0) = 0$ we get $D_u z^*(0,0) = 0$. In order to find the curve of equilibria from the formulation of the theorem, we discuss the remaining equation (3.21). To this end we rewrite (3.21) as

$$\hat{f}(\eta, \lambda) = (\mathrm{id} - P)N(\eta v + z^*(\eta v, \lambda), \lambda) = 0, \quad \eta \in \mathbb{R}.$$

In particular we show that $\hat{f}$ has the same properties as the function f considered in Theorem 3.6. Note first that by construction $\hat{f}(0,0) = 0$. Further

$$\begin{aligned} D_\lambda \hat{f}(0,0) &= (\mathrm{id} - P)(D_x N(0,0) D_\lambda z^*(0,0) + D_\lambda N(0,0)) \\ &= (\mathrm{id} - P) D_\lambda N(0,0) \\ &= \langle w, D_\lambda N(0,0) \rangle w \\ &= -\langle w, D_\lambda f(0,0) \rangle w, \end{aligned}$$

which is nonzero by Theorem 3.8(ii). Further

$$D_\eta \hat{f}(\eta, \lambda) = (\mathrm{id} - P) D_x N(\eta v + z^*(\eta v, \lambda), \lambda)(v + D_u z^*(\eta v, \lambda) v),$$

so that $D_\eta \hat{f}(0,0) = 0$, using $D_x N(0,0) = 0$, $D_u z^*(0,0) = 0$. Differentiating $D_\eta \hat{f}(\eta,\lambda)$ again we find

$$\begin{aligned} D^2_\eta \hat{f}(0,0) &= (\mathrm{id} - P) D^2_x N(0,0) v^2 \\ &= \langle w, D^2_x N(0,0) v^2 \rangle w \\ &= -\langle w, D^2_x f(0,0) v^2 \rangle w, \end{aligned}$$

which is nonzero by Theorem3.8(iii). Now, the stated curve of equilibria follows from Theorem 3.6. More precisely, locally around $(0,0)$ the function $\hat{f}(\eta,\lambda)$ can be solved for $\lambda = \lambda^*(\eta)$, where $\lambda^*(0) = D\lambda^*(0) = 0$ and $D^2\lambda^*(0) \neq 0$. hence the curve of equilibria reads

$$\left\{(x,\lambda) = \left(\eta v + z^*(\eta v, \lambda^*(\eta)), \lambda^*(\eta)\right),\ \eta \in U(0)\right\},$$

where $U(0)$ is an open interval containing 0. From this we find that the tangent of this curve at $(0,0)$ is spanned by $(v,0)$.

It remains to prove the statement on stability. Define

$$A(\eta) = D_\eta f(\eta v + z^*(\eta v, \lambda^*(\eta)), \lambda^*(\eta)).$$

Note that $A(0) = A$. We show that for $\eta \neq 0$, the spectrum of $A(\eta)$ has no nonhyperbolic eigenvalues: $\sigma\big(A(\eta)\big) \cap i\,\mathbb{R} = \emptyset$. Since this spectrum cannot contain any purely imaginary eigenvalues it remains to show that $0 \notin \sigma\big(A(\eta)\big)$. For that purpose we consider an appropriate matrix representation of $A(\eta)$: let $\{w_2,\dots,w_n\}$ be a basis of $\operatorname{im} A$, and let $\mathcal{A}(\eta) = \big(a_{ij}(\eta)\big)_{i,j=1,\dots,n}$ be the matrix representation of $A(\eta)$ with respect to $(\mathbb{R}^n,\{v,w_2,\dots,w_n\}) \to (\mathbb{R}^n,\{w,w_2,\dots,w_n\})$. Since $v \in \ker A$ and $A(\operatorname{im} A) = \operatorname{im} A$, the matrix $\mathcal{A}(0)$ has the form

$$\mathcal{A}(0) = \begin{pmatrix} 0 & 0 \\ 0 & \mathcal{A}_r(0) \end{pmatrix}, \tag{3.23}$$

where $\mathcal{A}_r(0)$ is the related matrix representation of $A|_{\operatorname{im} A}$. Note that the determinant $\det \mathcal{A}_r(0)$ is not zero.

Now $\det \mathcal{A}(\eta)$ is a function of η, and our statement on stability is proved if the derivative $D(\det \mathcal{A}(0)) \neq 0$. Because of (3.23) it is enough to show that $Da_{11}(0) \neq 0$. Note for this that a determinant is a multilinear mapping of the columns of the matrix. By the construction of $\mathcal{A}(\eta)$ we have $a_{11}(\eta) = \langle w, \mathcal{A}(\eta) v\rangle$. Hence, taking into consideration that $D\lambda^*(0) = 0$ and $D_u z^*(0,0) = 0$, we find

$$Da_{11}(0) = \langle w, D\mathcal{A}(0) v\rangle = \langle w, D^2_\eta f(0,0) v^2\rangle,$$

which is different from zero by Theorem 3.8(iii). Thus $\det \mathcal{A}(\eta) \neq 0$ and therefore $0 \notin \sigma\big(A(\eta)\big)$ for $\eta \neq 0$ in each case. Moreover $\det \mathcal{A}(\eta)$ changes its sign while η crosses 0. So exactly one eigenvalue of $A(\eta)$ changes its sign while η crosses 0. □

Example 3.10. Consider the system $(\dot{x}, \dot{y}) = f(x, y, \lambda)$ given by

$$\begin{aligned}\dot{x} &= 2x - 4y + x^2 - 2xy,\\ \dot{y} &= \lambda + 2x - (4+\lambda)y + y^2 + x^2.\end{aligned}$$

For $\lambda = 0$, the origin is an equilibrium and because

$$A = D_{(x,y)}f(0,0,0) = \begin{pmatrix} 2 & -4 \\ 2 & -4 \end{pmatrix}$$

has zero determinant, it is nonhyperbolic with a single zero eigenvalue. Let $v = (2,1)$ be a right eigenvector for the eigenvalue 0 of $D_{(x,y)}f(0,0,0)$. Let $w = (1,-1)$ be a left eigenvector. Note that $\langle v, w\rangle = 1$. Now compute

$$\langle w, D_\lambda f(0,0,0)\rangle = \left\langle \begin{pmatrix} 1 \\ -1 \end{pmatrix}, \begin{pmatrix} 0 \\ 1 \end{pmatrix} \right\rangle = -1$$

and

$$\left\langle w, D^2_{(x,y)} f(0,0,0)v^2 \right\rangle = \left\langle \begin{pmatrix} 1 \\ -1 \end{pmatrix}, \begin{pmatrix} 0 \\ 10 \end{pmatrix} \right\rangle = -10.$$

As both numbers $\langle w, D_\lambda f(0,0,0)\rangle$ and $\langle w, D^2_{(x,y)} f(0,0,0)v^2\rangle$ are nonzero, Theorem 3.8 gives a generically unfolding saddle-node bifurcation.

In what follows we trace the above proof of Theorem 3.8 for the current example. For equation (3.20) we have

$$N(x,y,\lambda) = \begin{pmatrix} 2xy - x^2 \\ -\lambda + \lambda y - x^2 - y^2 \end{pmatrix} = \begin{pmatrix} N^1 \\ N^2 \end{pmatrix}.$$

The projections P with $\operatorname{im} P = \operatorname{im} A$ and $\ker P = \operatorname{span}\{w\}$ and Q with $\operatorname{im} Q = \ker A$ and $\ker Q = \operatorname{im} A$ read

$$P(\cdot) = \frac{1}{2}\left\langle \cdot, \begin{pmatrix} 1 \\ 1 \end{pmatrix} \right\rangle \begin{pmatrix} 1 \\ 1 \end{pmatrix} \quad \text{and} \quad Q(\cdot) = \left\langle \cdot, \begin{pmatrix} 1 \\ -1 \end{pmatrix} \right\rangle \begin{pmatrix} 2 \\ 1 \end{pmatrix}.$$

Further, $A|_{\operatorname{im} A}$ acts as -2 id on $\operatorname{im} A$. So,

$$K = \left(A|_{\operatorname{im} A}\right)^{-1} = -\frac{1}{2}\,\mathrm{id}\,.$$

Writing $z = t(1,1)^T$, we find

$$\begin{pmatrix} x \\ y \end{pmatrix} = uv + z = uv + t\begin{pmatrix} 1 \\ 1 \end{pmatrix} = u\begin{pmatrix} 2 \\ 1 \end{pmatrix} + t\begin{pmatrix} 1 \\ 1 \end{pmatrix} = \begin{pmatrix} 2u + t \\ u + t \end{pmatrix}.$$

Now (3.22) reads

$$z - KPN(uv + t, \lambda) = \left(t + \frac{1}{4}\left(N^1(uv + t, \lambda) + N^2(uv + t, \lambda)\right)\right)\begin{pmatrix} 1 \\ 1 \end{pmatrix} = 0.$$

This is equivalent to

$$\begin{aligned} t &= -\frac{1}{4}\left(N^1(uv+t,\lambda)+N^2(uv+t,\lambda)\right)\\ &= -\frac{1}{4}\left(2(2u+t)(u+t)-2(2u+t)^2-\lambda+\lambda(u+t)-(u+t)^2\right)\\ &= \frac{1}{4}\lambda-\frac{5}{4}u^2+ut-\frac{1}{4}\lambda u+\mathcal{O}(t^2)+\mathcal{O}(\lambda t). \end{aligned}$$

This equation can be solved for $t = t^*(u,\lambda)$. It turns out that

$$t^*(u,\lambda) = \frac{1}{4}\lambda + \mathcal{O}(|(u,\lambda)|^2).$$

Plugging this into the equivalent of (3.21) yields

$$(\mathrm{id}-P)N(uv + t^*(u,\lambda)(1,1)^T,\lambda) = 0,$$

which is equivalent to

$$0 = N^1(uv + t^*(u,\lambda)(1,1)^T,\lambda) - N^2(uv + t^*(u,\lambda)(1,1)^T,\lambda),$$

and written out reads

$$\begin{aligned} 0 &= 2(2u+t^*(u,\lambda))(u+t^*(u,\lambda))+\lambda-\lambda(u+t^*(u,\lambda))+(u+t^*(u,\lambda))^2\\ &= \lambda+5u^2+\mathcal{O}(\lambda u)+\mathcal{O}(\lambda^2)+\mathcal{O}(|(u,\lambda)|^3). \end{aligned}$$

From this bifurcation equation we can determine equilibria as a function of λ. ■

We provide a second proof that uses a reduction to a center manifold.

Proof of Theorem 3.8 using a center manifold reduction. Write E^c for the center subspace spanned by the right eigenvector v. Let $E^h = \operatorname{im} D_x f(0,0)$ be the hyperbolic subspace. Note that w is perpendicular to E^h. If w is scaled such that $\langle w, v\rangle = 1$, then $P_c : \mathbb{R}^n \to E^c$ given by

$$P_c x = \langle w, x\rangle v$$

is the projection onto E^c along E^h. Further, $P_h : \mathbb{R}^n \to E^h$ given by

$$P_h x = x - P_c x = x - \langle w, x\rangle v$$

is the projection onto E^h along E^c. Decompose $x = yv + z$ with $yv = P_c x$ and $z = x - P_c x = P_h x \in E^h$.

Following Section 3.1.2, consider a two-dimensional local center manifold W^c_{loc} of the extended system

$$\begin{aligned} \dot{x} &= f(x,\lambda),\\ \dot{\lambda} &= 0. \end{aligned} \tag{3.24}$$

We can write W^c_{loc} as the graph of a map $W : E^c \times \mathbb{R} \to E^h$. We have $W(0,0) = 0$ and $DW(0,0) = 0$. The reduction to the center manifold reads

$$\dot{y} = \langle w, f(yv + W(yv, \lambda), \lambda)\rangle. \tag{3.25}$$

Write down a Taylor expansion of f at $(0,0)$,

$$\begin{aligned} f(x,\lambda) = f(0,0) + D_x f(0,0)x + D_\lambda f(0,0)\lambda + \frac{1}{2}D^2_\lambda f(0,0)\lambda^2 \\ + D_\lambda D_x f(0,0)\lambda x + \frac{1}{2}D^2_x f(0,0)x^2 + \mathcal{O}(|(y,\lambda)|^3). \end{aligned}$$

Plugging this into (3.25) and incorporating the assumptions of the theorem and $W(0,0) = 0$, $D_x W(0,0) = 0$, we find
(3.26)

$$\dot{y} = \langle w, D_\lambda f(0,0)\rangle\lambda + \langle w, \frac{1}{2}D^2_x f(0,0)v^2\rangle y^2 + \mathcal{O}(|\lambda y|) + \mathcal{O}(\lambda^2) + \mathcal{O}(|(y,\lambda)|^3).$$

Applying Theorem 3.6 shows that (3.26) undergoes a saddle-node bifurcation and hence (3.24) undergoes a saddle-node bifurcation within the center manifold W^c_{loc}. □

3.2.2. Transcritical bifurcation and pitchfork bifurcation. In models from population dynamics, one often has an equilibrium at the origin, meaning without population, that exists for all parameter values. More generally, such models often have invariant subspaces corresponding to the absence of a species, and an equilibrium that lies in such a subspace can be nonhyperbolic but hyperbolic restricted to the subspace. It is therefore persistent inside the subspace. Bifurcations that result in the existence of additional equilibria can arise when the equilibrium changes stability as an eigenvalue of the linearization moves through zero. The bifurcation scenario differs from the saddle-node bifurcation, because the equilibrium persists. Associated bifurcation scenarios are the transcritical bifurcation and the pitchfork bifurcation.

We start with bifurcations in the context of scalar vector fields.

3.2.2.1. *One-dimensional transcritical bifurcation.*

Example 3.11. Consider an equation $\dot{x} = \lambda x - x^2$ on $\mathbb{R}$. This equation has the property that $x = 0$ is an equilibrium for all values of λ. At $\lambda = 0$, the origin is a nonhyperbolic equilibrium. There is a second curve of equilibria along $x = \lambda$. As indicated in Figure 3.3, the equilibria exchange stability at the bifurcation. This is a prototypical example of the transcritical bifurcation. ■

The transcritical bifurcation is a generalization of Example 3.11. We first formulate an easier version with a persistent equilibrium at the origin.

Theorem 3.12. *Consider $\dot{x} = f(x,\lambda)$, $x \in \mathbb{R}$, depending on a parameter $\lambda \in \mathbb{R}$. Assume $f(0,\lambda) = 0$ for all λ,*

$$D_x f(0,0) = 0$$

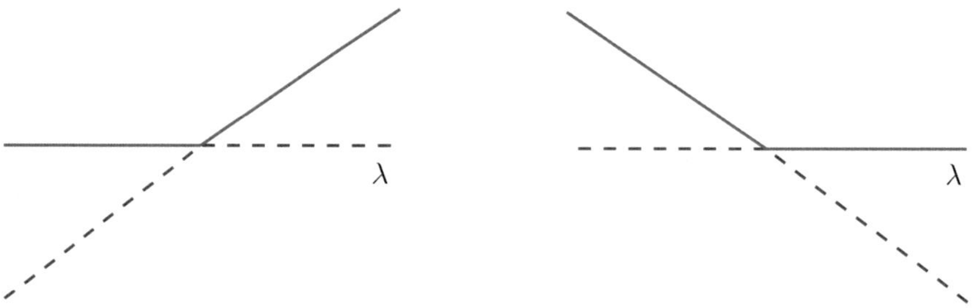

Figure 3.3. Bifurcation diagrams for the transcritical bifurcation $\dot{x} = \lambda x - x^2$ (left) and $\dot{x} = -\lambda x - x^2$ (right). Shown are curves of equilibria in the λ, x plane: green solid curves indicate stable equilibria and red dashed curves indicate unstable equilibria.

and

$$D_x^2 f(0,0) \neq 0, \quad D_\lambda D_x f(0,0) \neq 0.$$

There are two curves $x = \kappa_1(\lambda)$ and $x = \kappa_2(\lambda)$ of equilibria that intersect transversely in $(0,0)$. The stability of an equilibrium along a curve changes at $\lambda = 0$. The equilibria for $\lambda \neq 0$ on the two curves have different stability.

The transcritical bifurcation is usually presented for systems for which $x = 0$ is an equilibrium for all parameter values, as in the above formulation. There is however a general result without assuming a persistent equilibrium at 0, presented below. The above theorem is then a special case.

Theorem 3.13 (One-dimensional transcritical bifurcation). *Consider $\dot{x} = f(x, \lambda)$, $x \in \mathbb{R}$, depending on a parameter $\lambda \in \mathbb{R}$. Assume $f(0,0) = 0$,*

$$D_x f(0,0) = 0, \quad D_\lambda f(0,0) = 0, \quad D_\lambda^2 f(0,0) = 0$$

and

$$D_x^2 f(0,0) \neq 0, \quad D_\lambda D_x f(0,0) \neq 0.$$

There are two curves $(x, \lambda) = (\kappa_1(\lambda), \lambda)$ and $(x, \lambda) = (\kappa_2(\lambda), \lambda)$ of equilibria that intersect transversely in $(0,0)$. The stability of an equilibrium along a curve changes at $\lambda = 0$. The equilibria for $\lambda \neq 0$ on the two curves have different stability.

Remark 3.14. If one assumes that $f(0, \lambda) = 0$ for all λ near zero, then the assumptions $D_\lambda f(0,0) = 0$ and $D_\lambda^2 f(0,0) = 0$ are automatically fulfilled, and we are back in the setting of Theorem 3.12. See also Remark 3.19, following the one-dimensional pitchfork bifurcation theorem. ■

Proof of Theorem 3.13. The assumptions on f imply that one can write

$$f(x, \lambda) = a\lambda x + h(x, \lambda),$$

for some $a \neq 0$, where $h(0,0) = 0$, $Dh(0,0) = 0$, $D^2 h(0,0) = 0$, and $D_x^2 h(0,0) = D_x^2 f(0,0) \neq 0$.

We wish to solve $f(x,\lambda) = 0$. Consider a new variable y given by an expression $x = y + \lambda j(\lambda)$. Writing $g(y,\lambda) = f(x,\lambda)$, we find $g(y,\lambda) = a\lambda y + a\lambda^2 j(\lambda) + h(y + \lambda j(\lambda), \lambda)$. We will find the function j so that $g(0,\lambda) = 0$. For this, j must satisfy

$$a\lambda^2 j + h(\lambda j, \lambda) = 0.$$

This equation can be divided by λ^2 since h and Dh vanishes in $(0,0)$. We then get the equation

$$aj + h(\lambda j, \lambda)/\lambda^2 = 0.$$

Since $D_\lambda^2 h(0,0) = 0$, this can be solved by the implicit function theorem to give a function $j(\lambda)$ with $j(0) = 0$.

The above procedure yields the curve κ_1 of equilibria determined by $\kappa_1(\lambda) = \lambda j(\lambda)$. The second curve κ_2 is found by dividing out $y = 0$. This yields an equation

$$a\lambda + \frac{1}{y}\left(h(y + \lambda j, \lambda) - h(\lambda j, \lambda)\right) = 0.$$

Expanding h in the state variable gives

$$a\lambda + D_y h(0,\lambda) + \frac{1}{2} D_y^2 h(0,\lambda) y + \mathcal{O}(y^2) = 0.$$

This equation can be solved near $(y,\lambda) = (0,0)$ for $y = y_2(\lambda)$. So, in terms of the original differential equation, the curve κ_2 is determined by

$$\kappa_2(\lambda) = y_2(\lambda) + \lambda j(\lambda).$$

For the transversality of κ_1 and κ_2 it is enough to show that $D\kappa_1(0) \neq D\kappa_2(0)$. Write $b = D_x^2 h(0,0)$. Because of $j(0) = 0$ we have $D\kappa_1(0) = 0$ and $D\kappa_2(0) = Dy_2(0) = -\frac{2a}{b} \neq 0$.

It remains to prove the stability statement. It suffices to show that

$$\frac{d}{d\lambda} D_x f(\kappa_i(\lambda), \lambda)|_{\lambda=0}, \qquad i = 1,2,$$

are different from zero and that the signs of these two derivatives are different. Calculate

$$\begin{aligned} \frac{d}{d\lambda} D_x f(\kappa_i(\lambda), \lambda)|_{\lambda=0} &= D_x^2 f(0,0) D\kappa_i(0) + D_\lambda D_x f(0,0) \\ &= b D\kappa_i(0) + a. \end{aligned}$$

Therefore

$$\frac{d}{d\lambda} D_x f(\kappa_1(\lambda), \lambda)|_{\lambda=0} = a,$$

while

$$\begin{aligned} \frac{d}{d\lambda} D_x f(\kappa_2(\lambda), \lambda)|_{\lambda=0} &= -\frac{2a}{b} \cdot b + a \\ &= -a. \end{aligned}$$

□

Remark 3.15. There are other ways to prove Theorem 3.13. One is to use the Morse lemma to verify the existence of transversely intersecting curves $\varkappa_1$ and $\varkappa_2$; see Exercise 3.10.

We provide a third proof which follows [**230**]. This proof constructs a differential equation with a hyperbolic equilibrium whose stable and unstable manifolds coincide with the curves $\varkappa_1$ and $\varkappa_2$. Let $f = f(x, y)$ be a function as assumed in Theorem 3.13 (with λ formally replaced by y). Take the differential equations

$$\begin{aligned} \dot{x} &= D_y f(x, y), \\ \dot{y} &= -D_x f(x, y). \end{aligned} \tag{3.27}$$

One easily checks that f is a first integral of (3.27) (and thus is constant along orbits). The origin is a hyperbolic saddle equilibrium point for (3.27). It thus possesses a local stable and a local unstable manifold; see Appendix B.1.1. These manifolds are curves and lie within the level set $\{f = 0\}$ (since $f(0, 0) = 0$). Moreover, since ∇f is nonzero outside the origin, f is nonzero along orbits of (3.27) that are outside but close to the local stable and unstable manifolds. It follows that f vanishes precisely along the local stable and unstable manifolds.

The curves that represent the local stable and unstable manifolds of (3.27) are tangent to the eigenspaces of the Jacobian of the right hand side $(D_y f(x, y), -D_x f(x, y))$ at $(x, y) = (0, 0)$. These eigenspaces are

$$\operatorname{span}\{(0, 1)\} \quad \text{and} \quad \operatorname{span}\left\{\left(-\frac{2a}{b}, 1\right)\right\}.$$

Arguing along the lines of the proof of Theorem 3.13 will now complete the proof. ∎

3.2.2.2. *One-dimensional pitchfork bifurcation.*

Example 3.16. Replacing the quadratic term x^2 in the differential equation from Example 3.11 by a cubic term x^3, we get $\dot{x} = \lambda x - x^3$. Note that the function $\lambda x - x^3$ is odd and the differential equation is therefore symmetric with respect to reflection in 0 (if $x(t)$ is a solution, then also $-x(t)$ is a solution). Equilibria occur along $x = 0$ and $\lambda - x^2 = 0$. This is the prototypical example of a pitchfork bifurcation, where the number of equilibria goes from 1 for $\lambda < 0$ to 3 for $\lambda > 0$. When the equilibrium at zero becomes unstable, two new stable equilibria appear. This case is called a supercritical pitchfork bifurcation.

A variant with different stability properties is seen in $\dot{x} = \lambda x + x^3$. Here the number of equilibria goes from 3 for $\lambda < 0$ to 1 for $\lambda > 0$ and the nonzero equilibria are unstable. This is called a subcritical pitchfork bifurcation; see Figure 3.4. ∎

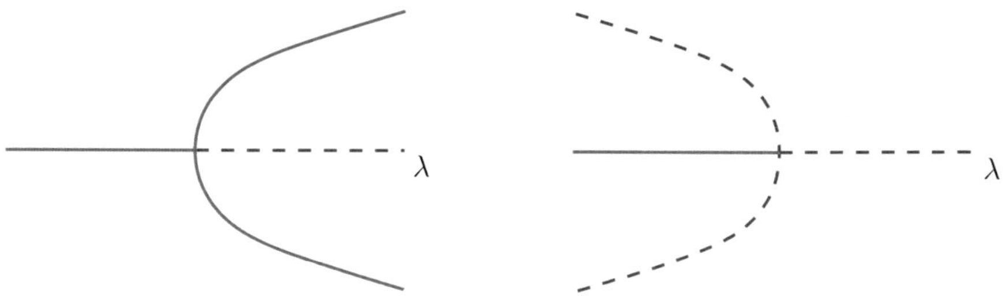

Figure 3.4. Bifurcation diagrams for the supercritical pitchfork bifurcation $\dot{x} = \lambda x - x^3$ (left) and the subcritical pitchfork bifurcation $\dot{x} = \lambda x + x^3$ (right). Shown are curves of equilibria in the λ, x plane: green solid curves indicate stable equilibria and red dashed curves indicate unstable equilibria.

The pitchfork bifurcation is a generalization of Example 3.16. It is often presented for symmetric systems, as in Example 3.16, for which $x = 0$ is forced to be an equilibrium for all parameter values. The following version does not assume symmetry, but does assume a persistent equilibrium at the origin.

Theorem 3.17. *Consider* $\dot{x} = f(x, \lambda)$, $x \in \mathbb{R}$, $\lambda \in \mathbb{R}$. *Assume* $f(0, \lambda) = 0$ *for all* λ,

$$D_x f(0,0) = 0, \quad D_x^2 f(0,0) = 0$$

and

$$D_\lambda D_x f(0,0) \neq 0, \quad D_x^3 f(0,0) \neq 0.$$

Then the following holds.

(1) *There are two curves of equilibria,* $(x, \lambda) = (\kappa_1(\lambda), \lambda)$ *with* $\kappa_1 \equiv 0$, *and* $(x, \lambda) = (x, \kappa_2(x))$ *with* $\kappa_2'(0) = 0$, $\kappa_2''(0) \neq 0$, *that intersect transversely in* $(0, 0)$.

(2) *The equilibria along the curve* κ_1 *change stability at* $\lambda = 0$. *The equilibria along the curve* κ_2 *do not change stability. For fixed* λ *the equilibria along the curve* κ_1 *and those along the curve* κ_2 *have opposite stability.*

We present and prove a general result that comprises Theorem 3.17 without assuming either symmetry or a persistent equilibrium at 0.

Theorem 3.18 (One-dimensional pitchfork bifurcation). *Consider* $\dot{x} = f(x, \lambda)$, $x \in \mathbb{R}$, $\lambda \in \mathbb{R}$. *Assume* $f(0, 0) = 0$,

$$D_x f(0,0) = 0, \quad D_\lambda f(0,0) = 0, \quad D_\lambda^2 f(0,0) = 0, \quad D_x^2 f(0,0) = 0,$$

and

$$D_\lambda D_x f(0,0) \neq 0, \quad D_x^3 f(0,0) \neq 0.$$

Then the following holds.

(1) *There are two curves of equilibria, $(x,\lambda) = (\kappa_1(\lambda),\lambda)$ with $\kappa_1'(0) = 0$, and $(x,\lambda) = (x,\kappa_2(x))$ with $\kappa_2'(0) = 0$, $\kappa_2''(0) \neq 0$, that intersect transversely in $(0,0)$.*

(2) *The equilibria along the curve κ_1 change stability at $\lambda = 0$. The equilibria along the curve κ_2 do not change stability. For fixed λ the equilibria along the curve κ_1 and those along the curve κ_2 have opposite stability.*

Remark 3.19. If one assumes the symmetry condition $f(x,\lambda) = -f(-x,\lambda)$, than $f(0,\lambda) = 0$ for all λ and the assumptions $D_\lambda f(0,0) = 0$ and $D_\lambda^2 f(0,0) = 0$ are automatically fulfilled, and we are back in the setting of Theorem 3.17. Exercise 3.11 adapts an exercise in [**124**, Chapter I, § 1] to provide a possible proof of Theorem 3.17; the original exercise in [**124**] leads to a proof of Theorem 3.18 different from the one we give below.

Further discussion of the transcritical and pitchfork bifurcation can be found in [**397**] and [**261**, Chapter 6]. The discussion in these references and in [**124**] works without the assumption that the second derivative with respect to λ vanishes at $(0,0)$. For the pitchfork bifurcation then also $\kappa_1'(0)$ may be different from 0. There is in this case a simple parameter dependent coordinate change that turns the system into one with vanishing second derivativef with respect to λ; see Exercise 3.12. ■

Proof of Theorem 3.18. The proof follows the reasoning to prove Theorem 3.13 on the transcritical bifurcation. The assumptions on f imply that one can write

$$f(x,\lambda) = a\lambda x + h(x,\lambda),$$

for some $a \neq 0$, where $h(0,0) = 0$, $Dh(0,0) = 0$, $D^2h(0,0) = 0$.

We wish to solve $f(x,\lambda) = 0$. Consider a new variable y given by an expression $x = y + \lambda j(\lambda)$. Writing $g(y,\lambda) = f(x,\lambda)$, we find $g(y,\lambda) = a\lambda y + a\lambda^2 j(\lambda) + h(y+\lambda j(\lambda),\lambda)$. As in the proof of Theorem 3.13 one finds a function j with $j(0) = 0$ so that $g(0,\lambda) = 0$. This gives the curve of equilibria $y = 0$, or $x = \lambda j(\lambda)$. Hence

$$\kappa_1(\lambda) = \lambda j(\lambda).$$

A second curve is found by dividing out $y = 0$. This yields an equation

$$a\lambda + \frac{1}{y}(h(y+\lambda j,\lambda) - h(\lambda j,\lambda)) = 0.$$

Expanding h in the state variable gives

$$a\lambda + D_y h(0,\lambda) + \frac{1}{2}D_y^2 h(0,\lambda)y + \frac{1}{6}D_y^3 h(0,\lambda)y^2 + \mathcal{O}(y^3) = 0.$$

This equation can be solved near $(y, \lambda) = (0, 0)$ for $\lambda = \lambda^*(y)$, with

$$\lambda^*(y) = -\frac{1}{6a} D_y^3 h(0,0) y^2 + \mathcal{O}(y^3).$$

Further, $x = y + \lambda^*(y) j(\lambda^*(y))$ can be solved for $y = y^*(x)$. Taking into consideration that $D_y^3 h(0,0) = D_x^3 f(0,0)$, κ_2 emerges as

$$\kappa_2(x) = \lambda^*(y^*(x)) = -\frac{1}{6a} D_x^3 f(0,0) x^2 + \mathcal{O}(x^3).$$

It remains to verify the stability statements. As in the proof of Theorem 3.13 we find

$$\frac{d}{d\lambda} D_x f(\kappa_1(\lambda), \lambda)|_{\lambda=0} = a.$$

The stability of the equilibria along the curve κ_1 follows in the same way. Writing $b = \frac{1}{6} D_x^3 f(0,0)$, we get

$$D_x f(x, \kappa_2(x)) = 2bx^2 + \mathcal{O}(x^3).$$

This expression allows us to get the stability of the equilibria along κ_2. □

Assume for definiteness that $D_\lambda D_x f(0,0) > 0$. This can be arranged by reversing the parameter. If $D_x^3 f(0,0) < 0$, then there is one equilibrium for $\lambda < 0$ and there are three equilibria for $\lambda > 0$. The number of equilibria changes from 1 to 3. The equilibrium for $\lambda < 0$ is asymptotically stable. For $\lambda > 0$, there are two asymptotically stable equilibria. This is the supercritical pitchfork bifurcation. In the other case $D_x^3 f(0,0) > 0$, the number of equilibria changes from 3 to 1. For $\lambda < 0$, there are two unstable equilibria. This is the subcritical pitchfork bifurcation. Both scenarios are depicted in Figure 3.4.

3.2.2.3. *Higher-dimensional transcritical and pitchfork bifurcation.* We consider transcritical bifurcations on $\mathbb{R}^n$ in Theorem 3.21. Pitchfork bifurcations on $\mathbb{R}^n$ are subject of Theorem 3.26. Michael Crandall and Paul Rabinowitz in [**79**] consider higher-dimensional transcritical and pitchfork bifurcations, in fact on Banach spaces, starting with a given curve of equilibria. In such a setting they formulate a result on the branching of a secondary curve of equilibria, encompassing transcritical and pitchfork bifurcations, which is also referred to as the Crandall-Rabinowitz theorem [**202**]. In [**230**] the authors consider the bifurcation study that does not start from an assumption of a curve of equilibria. An analysis of the pitchfork bifurcation that replaces some conditions by topological assumptions can be found in [**299**].

Example 3.20. Consider the following systems of differential equations,

$$\begin{aligned} \dot{x} &= \lambda x - x^2 + xy, \\ \dot{y} &= -y + 2x^2. \end{aligned}$$

The origin is an equilibrium for all values of λ. To study bifurcations of equilibria we consider the extended system

$$\begin{aligned}\dot{x} &= \lambda x - x^2 + xy,\\ \dot{y} &= -y + 2x^2,\\ \dot{\lambda} &= 0.\end{aligned}$$

This system has a two-dimensional local center manifold W^c_{loc} at $(0,0,0)$. This manifold can be written as graph of a function $y = W(x,\lambda)$ with an expansion

$$W(x,\lambda) = a_0(\lambda) + a_1(\lambda)x + a_2(\lambda)x^2 + \mathcal{O}(x^3),$$

where $a_0(0) = Da_0(0) = 0$ and $a_1(0) = 0$. Restricted to the center manifold, we have both

$$\begin{aligned}\dot{y} &= -y + 2x^2\\ &= -(a_0(\lambda) + a_1(\lambda)x + a_2(\lambda)x^2 + \mathcal{O}(x^3)) + 2x^2\\ &= -a_0(\lambda) - a_1(\lambda)x + (2 - a_2(\lambda))x^2 + \mathcal{O}(x^3))\end{aligned}$$

and

$$\begin{aligned}\dot{y} &= \big(W(x,\lambda)\big)^{\cdot}\\ &= D_x W(x,\lambda)\dot{x} + D_\lambda W(x,\lambda)\dot{\lambda}\\ &= \big(a_1(\lambda) + 2a_2(\lambda)x + \mathcal{O}(x^2))\big)\big(\lambda x - x^2 + xy\big)\\ &= \big(a_1(\lambda) + 2a_2(\lambda)x + \mathcal{O}(x^2))\big)\\ &\qquad \big(\lambda x - x^2 + x(a_0(\lambda) + a_1(\lambda)x + a_2(\lambda)x^2 + \mathcal{O}(x^3))\big)\\ &= a_1(\lambda)(\lambda + a_0(\lambda))x + 2\lambda a_2(\lambda)x^2 + \mathcal{O}(x^3)).\end{aligned}$$

Comparing coefficients yields

$$W(x,\lambda) = \frac{2}{1+2\lambda}x^2 + \mathcal{O}(x^3).$$

On the center manifold we find, by plugging this expression into the differential equation for x,

$$\dot{x} = \lambda x - x^2 + \mathcal{O}(x^3). \tag{3.28}$$

Note that the explicit knowledge of the second order terms in the expression of $W(x,\lambda)$ does not enter in the derivation of (3.28), it suffices to know that $W(x,\lambda) = \mathcal{O}(x^2)$. Equilibria of (3.28) are easily found to be given by $\{x = 0\} \cup \{\lambda = x + \mathcal{O}(x^2)\}$. ■

The following result gives conditions for a transcritical bifurcation in higher-dimensional space, with a similar flavor as Theorem 3.8 for the saddle-node bifurcation in higher-dimensional space.

Theorem 3.21 (Transcritical bifurcation). *Consider $\dot{x} = f(x,\lambda)$, $x \in \mathbb{R}^n$, depending on a parameter $\lambda \in \mathbb{R}$. Assume that $f(0,0) = 0$ and assume further that the following assumptions hold:*

(i) *$D_x f(0,0)$ has a simple eigenvalue 0 with right eigenvector v and left eigenvector w. Further, $D_x f(0,0)$ has k eigenvalues with negative real part and $n-k-1$ eigenvalues with positive real part;*

(ii) *$D_\lambda f(0,0) = 0$;*

(iii) *$\langle w, D_\lambda^2 f(0,0)\rangle = 0$;*

(iv) *$\langle w, D_\lambda D_x f(0,0)v\rangle \neq 0$;*

(v) *$\langle w, D_x^2 f(0,0)v^2\rangle \neq 0$.*

There are two curves $x = \kappa_1(\lambda)$ and $x = \kappa_2(\lambda)$ of equilibria that intersect transversely in $(0,0)$ within a two-dimensional local center manifold of the extended system $\dot{x} = f(x,\lambda)$, $\dot{\lambda} = 0$. The stability index of an equilibrium along a curve changes at $\lambda = 0$ between $k+1$ and k. The equilibria for $\lambda \neq 0$ on the two curves have different stability index.

Remark 3.22. Assumptions (ii) and (iii) hold if one assumes $f(0,\lambda) = 0$ for all small λ. ■

Proof of Theorem 3.21. Write E^c for the center subspace spanned by the right eigenvector v. Let $E^h = \operatorname{im} D_x f(0,0)$ be the hyperbolic subspace. Note that w is perpendicular to E^h. If w is scaled such that $\langle w, v\rangle = 1$, then $P_c : \mathbb{R}^n \to E^c$ given by

$$P_c x = \langle w, x\rangle v$$

is the projection onto E^c along E^h. Further, $P_h : \mathbb{R}^n \to E^h$ given by

$$P_h x = x - P_c x = x - \langle w, x\rangle v$$

is the projection onto E^h along E^c. Decompose $x = yv + z$ with $yv = P_c x$ and $z = x - P_c x = P_h x \in E^h$.

Following Section 3.1.2, consider a two-dimensional local center manifold W^c_{loc} of the extended system

$$\begin{aligned} \dot{x} &= f(x,\lambda), \\ \dot{\lambda} &= 0. \end{aligned} \tag{3.29}$$

We can write W^c_{loc} as the graph of a map $W : E^c \times \mathbb{R} \to E^h$. We have $W(0,0) = 0$ and $DW(0,0) = 0$. The reduction to the center manifold reads

$$\dot{y} = \langle w, f(yv + W(yv,\lambda),\lambda)\rangle. \tag{3.30}$$

Write down a Taylor expansion of f at $(0,0)$,

$$f(x,\lambda) = f(0,0) + D_x f(0,0)x + D_\lambda f(0,0)\lambda + \frac{1}{2}D_\lambda^2 f(0,0)\lambda^2$$
$$+ D_\lambda D_x f(0,0)\lambda x + \frac{1}{2}D_x^2 f(0,0)x^2 + \mathcal{O}(|(y,\lambda)|^3).$$

Plugging this into (3.30) and incorporating the assumptions of the theorem and the properties $W(0,0) = 0$, $DW(0,0) = 0$, we find

$$\dot{y} = \langle w, D_\lambda D_x f(0,0)v\rangle \lambda y + \langle w, \frac{1}{2}D_x^2 f(0,0)v^2\rangle y^2 + \mathcal{O}(|(y,\lambda)|^3). \tag{3.31}$$

Applying Theorem 3.13 shows that (3.31) undergoes a transcritical bifurcation and hence (3.29) undergoes a transcritical bifurcation within the center manifold W^c_{loc}. □

We provide an example of a transcritical bifurcation in a mathematical model from epidemiology. We follow [**241**], which explains the model in more detail.

Example 3.23. We discuss a basic SIR epidemic model for the development of an infectious disease in a population with a size that is not constant. We have a population that is composed of susceptible individuals, infected individuals, and recovered individuals. The number of them is denoted by S, I and R. The total number of the population, $N = S+I+R$, varies according to the differential equation $\dot{N} = \Lambda - \mu N$. Here Λ is the total birth rate and μ is the per capita death rate. The population size converges to Λ/μ as time goes to infinity. The epidemic model is given by

$$\begin{aligned}\dot{S} &= \Lambda - \beta I S - \mu S,\\ \dot{I} &= \beta I S - \alpha I - \mu I,\\ \dot{R} &= \alpha I - \mu R.\end{aligned} \tag{3.32}$$

Here β is called the transmission rate constant for the disease and α is the recovery rate. Consider the differential equations for S and I that do not involve R. Introduce coordinates $x = \frac{\mu}{\Lambda}S$ and $y = \frac{\mu}{\Lambda}I$ and a reparametrization of time $\tau = (\alpha + \mu)t$. This results in differential equations

$$\begin{aligned}x' &= \rho(1-x) - R_0 xy,\\ y' &= (R_0 x - 1)y\end{aligned} \tag{3.33}$$

for x and y as functions of τ, with positive parameters

$$\rho = \frac{\mu}{\alpha+\mu},$$
$$R_0 = \frac{\Lambda\beta}{\mu(\alpha+\mu)}.$$

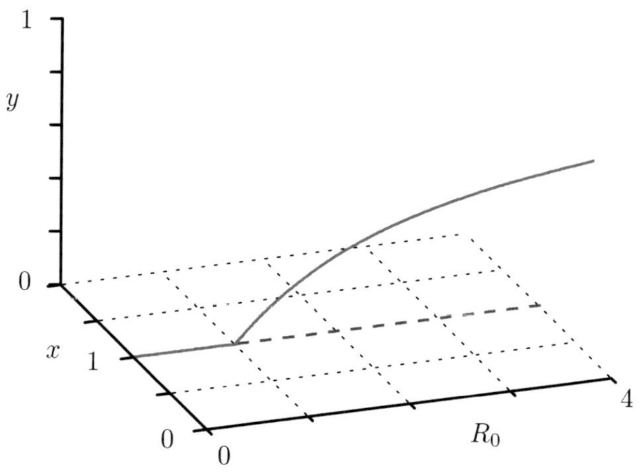

Figure 3.5. Bifurcation diagram of (3.33). A transcritical bifurcation of the equilibrium $(1, 0)$ occurs at the parameter value $R_0 = 1$. Green solid graphs stand for asymptotically stable equilibria and red dashed graphs for unstable equilibria. Note that the variables x and y are restricted to nonnegative values.

The number R_0 is the reproduction number. Its interpretation is that of the number of secondary infections that one infectious individual will produce in a population of susceptible individuals. The differential equation is defined for $\{x \geq 0, y \geq 0\}$, as negative values have no meaning.

It is easily computed that (3.33) admits two equilibria, the disease-free equilibrium at $(1, 0)$ that exists for all values of ρ, R_0, and a second equilibrium

$$E = \left(\frac{1}{R_0}, \rho\left(1 - \frac{1}{R_0}\right)\right)$$

that exists if $R_0 > 1$. For any value of $\rho > 0$, a transcritical bifurcation of the equilibrium at the origin occurs at $R_0 = 1$; see Figure 3.5 and see Exercise 3.15. ■

We add a second example of population dynamics following [**88**], to which we refer for more details on the model.

Example 3.24. We consider a model for the dynamics of a cannibalistic population, in which adult individuals forage on juvenile conspecifics, next to feeding on an alternative resource. Let J denote the number of juvenile individuals, and let A be the number of adults. The dynamics of the population can then be described by the system of differential equations,

$$\begin{aligned} \dot{J} &= \alpha A - \delta J - \beta JA, \\ \dot{A} &= \delta J - \frac{\mu}{\rho + \beta J} A. \end{aligned}$$

In these equations α denotes the per capita reproduction rate of the adult individuals. The coefficient δ represents the developmental rate of the juvenile individuals. The term βJA represents the cannibalism of adult individuals on the juveniles. Adult individuals are assumed to forage also for an external, non-cannibalistic food source, the density of which is represented by ρ. The death rate of adult individuals is assumed to be inversely proportional to their total food intake rate, which equals $\rho + \beta J$. The proportionality constant is denoted by μ.

By a reparametrization of time, a rescaling of coordinates and of parameters (we do not change notation), we can write the system as

$$\begin{aligned} \dot{x} &= \alpha y - x - xy, \\ \dot{y} &= x - \frac{\mu}{\rho + x} y. \end{aligned} \tag{3.34}$$

Define $R_0 = \frac{\alpha\rho}{\mu}$. This reproduction number can be interpreted as the expected number of offspring produced by a single individual during its entire life under conditions of very low population numbers. Taking R_0 as bifurcation parameter, one can analyze that a transcritical bifurcation of the equilibrium at the origin occurs at $R_0 = 1$. It has different consequences for the model interpretation in case $\alpha < \rho$ or $\alpha > \rho$; see Figure 3.6. In studies from population dynamics or mathematical epidemiology, the transcritical bifurcations depicted are sometimes referred to as forward bifurcation and backward bifurcation. In case $\alpha > \rho$ one finds two stable equilibria for values of R_0 slightly smaller than 1. Notice also the saddle-node bifurcation that is visible in Figure 3.6. Exercise 3.16 asks us to provide detailed analysis of this model. ■

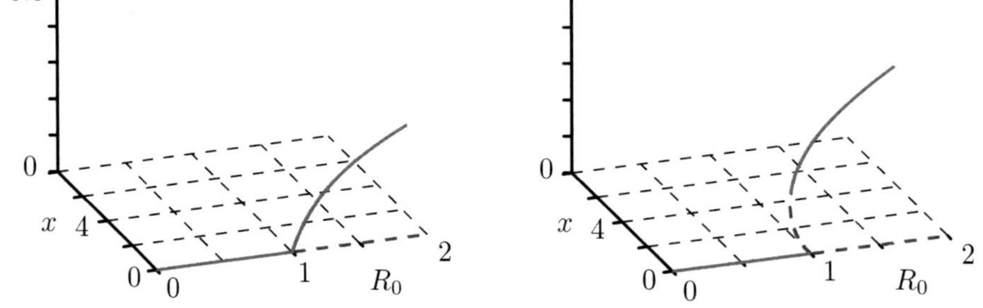

Figure 3.6. Bifurcation diagram of (3.34). A transcritical bifurcation of the equilibrium (0, 0) occurs at the parameter value $R_0 = 1$. Green solid graphs stand for asymptotically stable equilibria and red dashed graphs for unstable equilibria. Note that the variables x and y are restricted to nonnegative values. In the left image parameters α, ρ are fixed and satisfy $\alpha < \rho$. For the right image we have $\alpha > \rho$.

We continue with the pitchfork bifurcations in higher dimensions, starting with a variant of Example 3.20.

Example 3.25. Consider the following system of differential equations $(\dot{x}, \dot{y}) = f(x, y, \lambda)$ of the form

$$\begin{aligned}\dot{x} &= \lambda x - x^3 + xy,\\ \dot{y} &= -y + 2x^2.\end{aligned}$$

As in Example 3.20 we find a center manifold $y = W(x, \lambda)$ given by

$$W(x, \lambda) = \frac{2}{1 + 2\lambda} x^2 + \mathcal{O}(x^3).$$

On the center manifold we have

$$\begin{aligned}\dot{x} &= \lambda x - x^3 + xW(x, \lambda)\\ &= \lambda x + x^3 + \mathcal{O}(\lambda x^3) + \mathcal{O}(x^4).\end{aligned}$$

Equilibria are easily found to be given by $\{x = 0\} \cup \{\lambda = -x^2 + \mathcal{O}(x^3)\}$. The point of this elementary example is that for this pitchfork bifurcation, in contrast to a transcritical bifurcation of Example 3.20, the second order term $\frac{2}{1+2\lambda} x^2$ of the expansion of the center manifold matters in determining the relevant third order term x^3 in the differential equation restricted to the center manifold. ■

This example makes clear that a higher-dimensional bifurcation theorem for the pitchfork bifurcation with a formulation following Theorem 3.21, must involve an approximation of the center manifold up to quadratic terms. The starting point is (3.19) with for $\lambda = 0$ an equilibrium at the origin 0 for which $D_x f(0, 0)$ has a simple eigenvalue 0. As before, denote a right eigenvector corresponding to the eigenvalue 0 by v and a left eigenvector by w.

Theorem 3.26 (Pitchfork bifurcation). *Consider $\dot{x} = f(x, \lambda)$, $x \in \mathbb{R}^n$, depending on a parameter $\lambda \in \mathbb{R}$. Assume that $f(0, 0) = 0$ and assume further that the following assumptions hold:*

(i) *$D_x f(0, 0)$ has a simple eigenvalue 0 with right eigenvector v and left eigenvector w. Further, $D_x f(0, 0)$ has k eigenvalues with negative real part and $n - k - 1$ eigenvalues with positive real part;*

(ii) $D_\lambda f(0, 0) = 0$;

(iii) $\langle w, D_\lambda^2 f(0, 0)\rangle = 0$;

(iv) $\left\langle w, D_x^2 f(0, 0) v^2 \right\rangle = 0$;

(v) $\langle w, D_\lambda D_x f(0, 0) v\rangle \neq 0$;

(vi) $\left\langle w, D_x^3 f(0, 0) v^3 \right\rangle - 3 \left\langle w, D_x^2 f(0, 0)\, (v, v^*(v)) \right\rangle \neq 0$, *where*

$$v^*(v) = \left(D_x f(0, 0)|_{\{w\}^\perp}\right)^{-1} D_x^2 f(0, 0) v^2.$$

Then there is a two-dimensional center manifold W^c_{loc} of the extended system $\dot{x} = f(x,\lambda)$, $\dot{\lambda} = 0$ on which a pitchfork bifurcation takes place.

Remark 3.27. Assumptions (ii) and (iii) hold if one assumes $f(0,\lambda) = 0$ for all small λ. For instance this is the case if there exists an involution R (a linear map with $R^2 = \mathrm{id}$) with $Rv = -v$ and $Rf(x,\lambda) = f(Rx,\lambda)$. ■

Proof of Theorem 3.26. The proof follows the reasoning in the proof of Theorem 3.21, and we take notation from that proof. In particular we assume $\langle w, v\rangle = 1$. As in the proof of Theorem 3.21 we reduce the system to a two-dimensional local center manifold. We derive differential equations on the local center manifold and apply Theorem 3.18 to it. Again let the center manifold be written as the graph of a function $W = W(yv,\lambda)$. The reduction to the center manifold reads

$$\dot{y} = \langle w, f(yv + W(yv,\lambda),\lambda)\rangle.$$

We insert a Taylor expansion of f at $(0,0)$ up to third order,

$$\begin{aligned} f(yv + W(yv,\lambda),\lambda) &= f(0,0) + Df(0,0)(yv + W(yv,\lambda),\lambda) \\ &\quad + \frac{1}{2}D^2 f(0,0)(yv + W(yv,\lambda),\lambda)^2 \\ &\quad + \frac{1}{6}D^3 f(0,0)(yv + W(yv,\lambda),\lambda)^3 + \mathcal{O}(|(y,\lambda)|^4). \end{aligned}$$

Using the assumptions of the theorem and taking into account $W(0,0) = 0$ and $DW(0,0) = 0$, the flow on the center manifold is given by

$$\begin{aligned} \dot{y} &= \Big\langle w, D_\lambda D_x f(0,0)(v,1)\lambda y + \frac{1}{2}D_x^2 f(0,0)(yv + W(yv,\lambda))^2 \\ &\quad + \frac{1}{6}D_x^3 f(0,0)(yv + W(yv,\lambda))^3\Big\rangle \\ &\quad + \mathcal{O}(\lambda y^2) + \mathcal{O}(\lambda^2 y) + \mathcal{O}(\lambda^3) + \mathcal{O}(|(y,\lambda)|^4) \\ &= \Big\langle w, D_\lambda D_x f(0,0)(v,1)\lambda y + \frac{1}{2}D_x^2 f(0,0)(yv + \frac{1}{2}D_y^2 W(0,0)(yv)^2)^2 \\ &\quad + \frac{1}{6}D_x^3 f(0,0)(yv)^3\Big\rangle \\ &\quad + \mathcal{O}(\lambda y^2) + \mathcal{O}(\lambda^2 y) + \mathcal{O}(\lambda^3) + \mathcal{O}(|(y,\lambda)|^4) \\ &= \Big\langle w, D_\lambda D_x f(0,0)(v,1)\lambda y + \frac{1}{2}D_x^2 f(0,0)(yv, D_y^2 W(0,0)(yv)^2) \\ &\quad + \frac{1}{6}D_x^3 f(0,0)(yv)^3\Big\rangle \\ &\quad + \mathcal{O}(\lambda y^2) + \mathcal{O}(\lambda^2 y) + \mathcal{O}(\lambda^3) + \mathcal{O}(|(y,\lambda)|^4). \end{aligned} \tag{3.35}$$

In comparison with the conditions from Theorem 3.18, we find from this expression that the condition for an unfolding is

$$\langle w, D_\lambda D_x f(0,0)v\rangle \neq 0.$$

The nondegeneracy condition on the third derivative in Theorem 3.18 is given by

$$\langle w, D_x^3 f(0,0)v^3 + 3D_x^2 f(0,0)(v, D_y^2 W(0,0)v^2)\rangle \neq 0.$$

This translates to

$$v^*(v) = -D_y^2 W(0,0)v^2$$

for the term $v^*(v)$ in Theorem 3.26(vi). We will express $D_y^2 W(0,0)v^2$ in terms of the original vector field f. To do this we derive an expression for the local center manifold up to second order terms. Write

$$\begin{aligned} z &= W(yv, \lambda) \\ &= a_0(\lambda) + a_1(\lambda)yv + a_2(\lambda)(yv)^2 + \mathcal{O}(y^3). \end{aligned}$$

Of course $a_0(0) = Da_0(0) = 0$ and $a_1(0) = 0$, and $D_y^2 W(0,0) = 2a_2(0)$. The expression of W follows from

$$\big(W(yv,\lambda)\big)^{\cdot} = \dot{z} = P_h f(yv + W(yv,\lambda), \lambda).$$

Because $\dot{\lambda} = 0$ and using Theorem 3.26(ii) this yields

$$\begin{aligned} D_y W(yv, 0)\dot{y}v &= P_h D_x f(0,0)(yv + W(yv,0)) \\ &\quad + \frac{1}{2} P_h D_x^2 f(0,0)(yv + W(yv,0))^2 + \mathcal{O}(y^3). \end{aligned}$$

From (3.35) we see that for the left-hand side we have $D_y W(yv,0)\dot{y}v = \mathcal{O}(y^3)$. The second order term of right-hand side must therefore be absent. Recalling that $v \in \ker D_x f(0,0)$ and $\operatorname{im} P_h = \operatorname{im} D_x f(0,0)$, we get

$$0 = D_x f(0,0) a_2(0)v^2 + \frac{1}{2} P_h D_x^2 f(0,0)v^2.$$

Since $a_2(0)v^2 \in \operatorname{im} D_x f(0,0) = \{w\}^\perp$ and $D_x f(0,0)$ restricted to its image is invertible, we infer

$$a_2(0)v^2 = -\left(D_x f(0,0)|_{\{w\}^\perp}\right)^{-1} \left(\frac{1}{2} P_h D_x^2 f(0,0)v^2\right).$$

As $D_y^2 W(0,0)v^2 = 2a_2(0)v^2$ this yields

$$v^*(v) = \left(D_x f(0,0)|_{\{w\}^\perp}\right)^{-1} \left(D_x^2 f(0,0)v^2 - \langle w, D_x^2 f(0,0)v^2\rangle v\right).$$

With Theorem 3.26(iv) we get

$$v^*(v) = \left(D_x f(0,0)|_{\{w\}^\perp}\right)^{-1} D_x^2 f(0,0)v^2.$$

The theorem now follows from Theorem 3.18. □

Example 3.28. We take up Example 3.25 and verify a pitchfork bifurcation by demonstrating that the assumptions of Theorem 3.26 are satisfied. The vector field f reads

$$f(x,y,\lambda) = \begin{pmatrix} \lambda x - x^3 + xy \\ -y + 2x^2 \end{pmatrix}.$$

For $\lambda = 0$ the origin is an equilibrium. The linearization at the origin reads

$$D_{(x,y)}f(0,0,0) = \begin{pmatrix} 0 & 0 \\ 0 & -1 \end{pmatrix},$$

with corresponding right eigenvector $v = (1,0)^T$ and left eigenvector $w = (1,0)^T$. It is easily shown that Theorem 3.26(ii) and (iii) are satisfied.

Next compute

$$D_{(x,y)}f(x,y,\lambda) = \begin{pmatrix} \lambda - 3x^2 + y & x \\ 4x & -1 \end{pmatrix} \tag{3.36}$$

and

$$\begin{aligned} &D^2_{(x,y)}f(0,0,0)\big((h,k)^T,(H,K)^T\big) \\ &\quad = D_{(x,y)}\big(D_{(x,y)}f(x,y,0)(h,k)^T\big)|_{(x,y)=(0,0)}(H,K)^T = \begin{pmatrix} kH + hK \\ 4hH \end{pmatrix}. \end{aligned} \tag{3.37}$$

We find that Theorem 3.26(iv) is satisfied as

$$\langle w, D^2_{(x,y)}f(0,0,0)v^2\rangle = \langle (1,0)^T,(0,4)^T\rangle = 0.$$

Using (3.36) it follows that Theorem 3.26(v) is satisfied, as we have

$$\langle w, D_\lambda D_{(x,y)}f(0,0,0)v\rangle = \left\langle \begin{pmatrix} 1 \\ 0 \end{pmatrix}, \begin{pmatrix} 1 & 0 \\ 0 & 0 \end{pmatrix}\begin{pmatrix} 1 \\ 0 \end{pmatrix} \right\rangle = 1 \neq 0.$$

It remains to show that Theorem 3.26(vi) is satisfied. From the Taylor expansion of f we see that

$$D^3_{(x,y)}f(0,0,0)\begin{pmatrix} x \\ y \end{pmatrix}^2 = \begin{pmatrix} -6x^3 \\ 0 \end{pmatrix}.$$

Hence

$$D^3_{(x,y)}f(0,0,0)v^3 = \begin{pmatrix} -6 \\ 0 \end{pmatrix}.$$

Note that $\big(D_{(x,y)}f(0,0,0)|_{\{w\}^\perp}\big)^{-1}$ acts as $-\,\mathrm{id}$. So

$$v^*(v) = \big(D_{(x,y)}f(0,0,0)|_{\{w\}^\perp}\big)^{-1} D^2_{(x,y)}f(0,0,0)v^2 = \begin{pmatrix} 0 \\ -4 \end{pmatrix}.$$

From (3.37) we infer

$$D^2_{(x,y)}f(0,0,0)\,(v, v^*(v)) = D^2_{(x,y)}f(0,0,0)\left(\begin{pmatrix} 1 \\ 0 \end{pmatrix}, \begin{pmatrix} 0 \\ -4 \end{pmatrix}\right) = \begin{pmatrix} -4 \\ 0 \end{pmatrix}.$$

Putting everything together we find

$$\left\langle w, D^3_{(x,y)}f(0,0,0)v^3\right\rangle - 3\left\langle w, D^2_{(x,y)}f(0,0,0)\,(v,v^*(v))\right\rangle = -6 + 12 = 6 \neq 0.$$

This proves that also Theorem 3.26(vi) is satisfied. ■

3.2.3. Cusp bifurcation. Section 3.2.1 treated a local bifurcation of codimension 1: the saddle-node bifurcation of an equilibrium involved an eigenvalue 0. Local bifurcations of higher codimension arise if nondegeneracy conditions are violated. We consider the bifurcation where the second derivative that appears in the conditions for the saddle-node bifurcation vanishes. The resulting codimension-2 bifurcation is the cusp bifurcation.

3.2.3.1. *One-dimensional cusp bifurcation.*

Example 3.29. Consider the polynomial differential equation $\dot{x} = f(x, \lambda)$ given by

$$\dot{x} = -x^3 - \lambda_1 x - \lambda_2, \tag{3.38}$$

where $\lambda = (\lambda_1, \lambda_2)$. For (3.38) it is easy to determine the bifurcation curves of equilibria in (λ_1, λ_2)-space. These curves are exactly the curves across which the number of solutions of

$$f(x, \lambda) = 0 \tag{3.39}$$

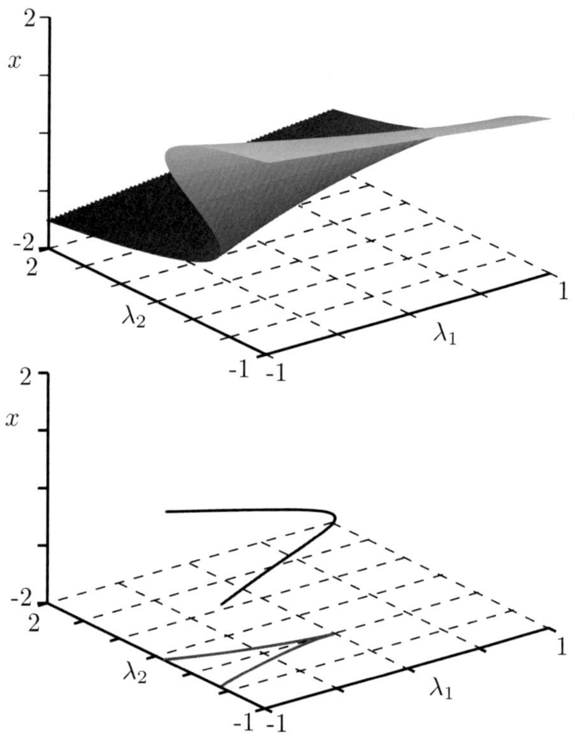

Figure 3.7. Top image: the surface $\{-x^3 - \lambda_1 x - \lambda_2 = 0\}$ in $(\lambda_1, \lambda_2, x)$-space. Bottom image: the curve where both $-x^3 - \lambda_1 x - \lambda_2 = 0$ and $-3x^2 - \lambda_1 = 0$, with cusp shaped projection on the (λ_1, λ_2)-parameter plane.

changes. This occurs when both (3.39) holds as well as

$$D_x f(x,\lambda) = -3x^2 - \lambda_1 = 0. \tag{3.40}$$

Equations (3.39) and (3.40) uniquely define λ_1, λ_2 as functions of x, namely,

$$\begin{aligned} \lambda_1 &= -3x^2, \\ \lambda_2 &= 2x^3. \end{aligned}$$

This is a parametric representation of the cusp $4\lambda_1^3 + 27\lambda_2^2 = 0$ depicted in Figure 3.7. ■

With the techniques used to prove Theorem 3.6, one obtains the following result. We leave the proof as an exercise; see Exercise 3.17 (or see [**215**, Section 8.2]).

Theorem 3.30 (One-dimensional cusp bifurcation). *Suppose that a one-dimensional system*

$$\dot{x} = f(x,\lambda),$$

$x \in \mathbb{R}$, $\lambda = (\lambda_1, \lambda_2) \in \mathbb{R}^2$, *has at* $\lambda = 0$ *an equilibrium at* $x = 0$, *with* $D_x f(0,0) = 0$ *and* $D_x^2 f(0,0) = 0$. *Assume that the following conditions are satisfied:*

(i) $\det D_\lambda\left(f(x,\lambda), D_x f(x,\lambda)\right) \neq 0$ *in* $(x,\lambda) = (0,0)$,

(ii) $D_x^3 f(0,0) \neq 0$.

Then there is a smooth coordinate change $\eta = h(x,\lambda)$ *and a smooth parameter change* $\beta = (\beta_1, \beta_2) = g(\lambda)$, *transforming the system into*

$$\dot{\eta} = -\beta_2 - \beta_1 \eta \pm \eta^3 + \mathcal{O}(|\eta|^4), \quad \text{as } \eta \to 0. \tag{3.41}$$

Remark 3.31. Working out Theorem 3.30(i), this assumption can be written as

$$D_{\lambda_1} f(0,0) D^2_{\lambda_2 x} f(0,0) - D_{\lambda_2} f(0,0) D^2_{\lambda_1 x} f(0,0) \neq 0.$$

■

The vector field in (3.41) is a normal form for the cusp bifurcation in $\mathbb{R}$. We consider the equation (3.41) in renamed variables $x = \eta$ and $\lambda = \beta$, for definiteness restricting to the case of a positive coefficient for the x^3 term.

$$\dot{x} = -\lambda_2 - \lambda_1 x + x^3 + \mathcal{O}(|x|^4). \tag{3.42}$$

Write $f(x,\lambda)$ with $\lambda = (\lambda_1, \lambda_2)$ for the right-hand side of (3.42). The higher-order terms may depend on λ. Equilibria are given as zeros of $f(x,\lambda)$. The number of equilibria can change if moreover $D_x f(x,\lambda)$ vanishes. This gives equations

$$\begin{aligned} x^3 - \lambda_1 x - \lambda_2 + \mathcal{O}(|x|^4) &= 0, \\ 3x^2 - \lambda_1 + \mathcal{O}(|x|^3) &= 0. \end{aligned}$$

By the implicit function theorem one can solve $\lambda = \lambda^*(x)$. In fact $\lambda_1^*(x) = 3x^2 + \mathcal{O}(|x|^3)$ and $\lambda_2^*(x) = -2x^3 + \mathcal{O}(|x|^4)$. Projecting to the λ-parameter plane this gives two curves branching from the cusp point at the origin. One curve is contained in $\{\lambda_1 > 0, \lambda_2 > 0\}$, this curve is parametrized by $x < 0$. And the other curve is contained in $\{\lambda_1 > 0, \lambda_2 < 0\}$; this curve is parametrized by $x > 0$. The second derivative $D_x^2 f(x, \lambda^*(x))$ equals $6x + \mathcal{O}(|x|^2)$ and is thus nonzero for $x \neq 0$. As also $D_{\lambda_1} f(x, \lambda^*(x)) \neq 0$ (or $D_{\lambda_2} f(x, \lambda^*(x)) \neq 0$) for small x, the saddle-node bifurcations are generically unfolding, and by the results of Section 3.2.1.1, the number of equilibria changes by two when crossing a curve of saddle-node bifurcations. One checks that inside the cusp-shaped region bounded by the saddle-node bifurcation curves in the parameter plane, the system has three hyperbolic equilibria, while outside the system has one hyperbolic equilibrium.

We encountered the cusp bifurcation in Section 1.1 when treating a model for dynamics of populations of spruce budworms. We give another example of cusp bifurcations due to Sir Christopher Zeeman.

Example 3.32. Zeeman's catastrophe machine, depicted in Figure 3.8, is a simple mechanical device that represents the cusp catastrophe [**424**]. The setup consists of a wheel that is free to rotate about its axis, with one end of two rubber bands connected at a point on its rim. The other end of the first rubber band is fixed on the horizontal axis, while the other end of the second rubber band is freely movable. The state of the system is the angle, θ, between the point of

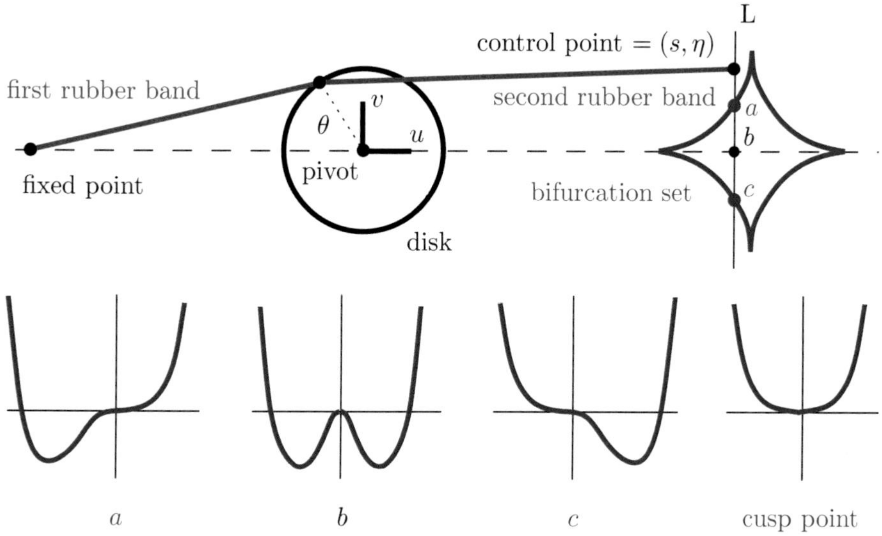

Figure 3.8. Zeeman's catastrophe machine (upper row) and potential function V (lower row) for different positions of the control point on the vertical line L.

attachment of the two rubber bands and the horizontal, while the control parameters (u, v) are the coordinates of the free end of the second rubber band. The dynamics can be modeled by a differential equation

$$\dot{\theta} = -V'(\theta),$$

for some potential function $V : \mathbb{T} \to \mathbb{R}$ on the circle $\mathbb{T}$, that depends on the parameters (u, v). The lower row in Figure 3.8 contains sketches of the graphs of the potential function for different values of the control parameters.

A singular point of V corresponds to an equilibrium of the system, stable for a minimum and unstable for a maximum. The potential function has a number of singular points that varies between 1 and 3 depending on the control parameters. The bifurcation set is indicated in the plane of control parameters. It contains four cusp points, near each of which the graph of V is qualitatively like depicted in Figure 3.7.

For a partial analysis we take control parameters (u, v) close to line of symmetry $\{(u, 0)\}$. First we restrict the control parameters to the line of symmetry. The system seeks a configuration, in particular an angle θ, that minimizes the energy in the rubber bands. The potential energy is

$$V(\theta) = \frac{1}{2}\mu((r_1 - 1)^2 + (r_2 - 1)^2),$$

where r_1 and r_2 are the lengths of the first and second rubber band. Here we suppose that the rubber bands have length 1 when not stretched, and the distance between the fixed point and the pivot (see Figure 3.8) is 2. The radius of the wheel is 1/2. The factor μ is a modulus of elasticity. Consider a control $(s, 0)$; here s is the distance between the pivot and the control point. By the law of cosines we have

$$\begin{aligned} r_1^2 &= 4 + \frac{1}{4} - 2\cos(\theta), \\ r_2^2 &= s^2 + \frac{1}{4} + s\cos(\theta). \end{aligned}$$

By symmetry, $V(\theta)$ has singular points at $\theta = 0$ and $\theta = \pi$, for all control parameters $(u, 0)$. We consider only θ near 0. Developing in a Taylor series around $\theta = 0$, we get

$$\begin{aligned} r_1 &= \frac{3}{2} + \frac{1}{3}\theta^2 - \frac{7}{108}\theta^4 + \mathcal{O}(\theta^5), \\ r_2 &= \left(s + \frac{1}{2}\right)\left(1 - \frac{s}{4(s+\frac{1}{2})^2}\theta^2 + \frac{1}{16}\left(\frac{s}{3(s+\frac{1}{2})^2} - \frac{s^2}{2(s+\frac{1}{2})^4}\right)\theta^4\right) \\ &\quad + \mathcal{O}(\theta^5), \end{aligned}$$

so that

$$V(\theta) = \frac{1}{2}\mu\left(\left(s - \frac{1}{2}\right)^2 + \frac{1}{4} + \left(\frac{1}{3} - \frac{s(2s-1)}{2(2+1)}\right)\theta^2\right.$$
$$\left. + \left(\frac{s}{24} - \frac{s}{12(2s+1)} + \frac{s^2}{2(2s+1)^3} + \frac{5}{108}\right)\theta^4\right) + \mathcal{O}(\theta^5).$$

By symmetry there is no linear term in $V(\theta)$. As already noted, this gives $V'(0) = 0$ and thus an equilibrium $\theta = 0$ for each $(u, 0)$. The second derivative $V''(0)$ changes sign at $s = \frac{7+\sqrt{97}}{12}$.

Now take the origin of the control parameters at $(u, 0)$ for which $s = \frac{7+\sqrt{97}}{12}$. Writing (ξ, η) for the translated control parameters, we repeat the analysis with

$$r_1^2 = 4 + \frac{1}{4} - 2\cos(\theta),$$
$$r_2^2 = \left(s + \frac{1}{2}\cos(\theta)\right)^2 + \left(\frac{1}{2}\sin(\theta) - \eta\right)^2.$$

Developing $V(\theta)$ in a Taylor series, retaining only lowest-order terms in (ξ, η), yields an expression

$$V(\theta) = b_0 + b_1\eta\theta + b_2\xi\theta^2 + b_3\eta\theta^3 + b_4\theta^4 + \mathcal{O}(\theta^5) + \mathcal{O}(\eta^2\theta) + O(\xi^2\theta^2) + \mathcal{O}(\eta\theta^2)$$

(we do not provide formulas for $b_1, \dots, b_4$; these constants turn out to be nonzero). The cubic term can be eliminated by a substitution $x = \theta + \frac{1}{4}b_3\eta$. That is, writing V as a function of x gives a function without the cubic term. This leaves the other low-order terms unaltered. We have obtained an expression for which $V'(x)$ is like the cusp example treated above. ■

3.2.3.2. *Higher-dimensional cusp bifurcation.* Let

$$\dot{x} = f(x, \lambda) \tag{3.43}$$

be an ordinary differential equation in $\mathbb{R}^n$ depending on a parameter $\lambda \in \mathbb{R}^2$. A cusp bifurcation occurs when a reduction to a local center manifold gives a family of differential equations fulfilling the conditions of Theorem 3.30. For the saddle-node, transcritical and pitchfork bifurcation we derived higher-dimensional bifurcation theorems using conditions in terms of the system of differential equations, without the need to first calculate a local center manifold. This just means that the reduction to the center manifold is computed systematically, after which the one-dimensional bifurcation theorem is invoked. One may choose to perform the explicit calculations for a concrete example, but the general approach can also be done for the cusp bifurcation. For completeness we include the result.

Theorem 3.33 (Cusp bifurcation). *Assume that* (3.43) *for* $\lambda = 0$ *has an equilibrium at the origin* 0 *for which the following assumptions hold:*

(i) $D_x f(0,0)$ *has a simple eigenvalue* 0 *with right eigenvector* v *and left eigenvector* w*. Further,* $D_x f(0,0)$ *has* k *eigenvalues with negative real part and* $n-k-1$ *eigenvalues with positive real part;*

(ii) $\langle w, D_x^2 f(0,0)v^2\rangle = 0$*;*

(iii) $\det D_\lambda \left(\langle w, f(0,\lambda)\rangle, \langle w, D_x f(0,\lambda)v + \frac{1}{2}D_x^2 f(0,0)(v,\alpha\lambda)\rangle\right) \neq 0$ *in* $\lambda = 0$*, where*

$$\alpha = -(D_x f(0,0)|_{\{w\}^\perp})^{-1}\,(D_\lambda f(0,0) - \langle w, D_\lambda f(0,0)\rangle v)\,;$$

(iv) $\langle w, D_x^3 f(0,0)v^3\rangle - 3\left\langle w, D_x^2 f(0,0)\,(v, v^*(v))\right\rangle \neq 0$*, where*

$$v^*(v) = \left(D_x f(0,0)|_{\{w\}^\perp}\right)^{-1} D_x^2 f(0,0)v^2.$$

Then the system restricted to a local center manifold undergoes a cusp bifurcation.

Proof. We use the same notation as before in, for instance, the proof of Theorem 3.21, and we assume that $\langle w, v\rangle = 1$. So we write $P_c x = \langle w, x\rangle v$ for the projection of x to the line spanned by v, with kernel equal to the image of $D_x f(0,0)$. And we write $P_h = \mathrm{id} - P_c$, thus $P_h x = x - \langle w, x\rangle v$, for the projection onto $\mathrm{im}\, D_x f(0,0)$ with kernel $\mathrm{span}\{v\}$. Decompose $x = yv + z$ with $yv = P_c x \in \mathrm{span}\{v\}$ and $z = P_h x \in \mathrm{im}\, D_x f(0,0)$.

The derivation of the nondegeneracy condition (iv) proceeds as for the pitchfork bifurcation in Theorem 3.26. For the unfolding in λ, write a local center manifold $z = W(y,\lambda)$ as $z = \alpha\lambda + \mathcal{O}(|(\lambda, x)|^2)$. Plug this into the equation

$$\begin{aligned}\dot y = \langle w, D_\lambda f(0,0)\lambda + D_\lambda D_x f(0,0)\lambda(yv + z) + \frac{1}{2}D_x^2 f(0,0)(yv+z)^2\rangle \\ + \mathcal{O}(\lambda|x|^2) + \mathcal{O}(\lambda^2).\end{aligned}$$

This yields

$$\begin{aligned}\dot y = \langle w, D_\lambda f(0,0)\lambda\rangle + \langle w, D_\lambda D_x f(0,0)\lambda v + D_x^2 f(0,0)(v,\alpha\lambda)\rangle y \\ + \mathcal{O}(y^2) + \mathcal{O}(\lambda^2).\end{aligned}$$

The unfolding condition copied from the one-dimensional cusp bifurcation gives the condition

$$\det D_\lambda\left(\langle w, D_\lambda f(0,0)\lambda\rangle, \langle w, D_\lambda D_x f(0,0)\lambda v + D_x^2 f(0,0)(v,\alpha\lambda)\rangle\right) \neq 0.$$

As in Section 3.1.2, α can be calculated as

$$\alpha = -(D_x f(0,0)|_{\{w\}^\perp})^{-1} P_h D_\lambda f(0,0).$$

This equals the condition in the statement of the theorem. □

3.2.4. Hopf bifurcation. The Hopf bifurcation is named after Eberhard Hopf, who wrote a fundamental paper on it [**177**], after earlier work by Henri Poincaré and by Aleksandr Andronov, who treated the bifurcation in the plane. The Hopf bifurcation explains the birth of oscillatory dynamics as an equilibrium changes stability. This phenomenon is widespread and entire books are devoted to it [**153, 240**].

3.2.4.1. *Planar Hopf bifurcation.* We start with a study of the Hopf bifurcation in the plane. Consider a family of differential equations $\dot{u} = f(u, \lambda)$, $u \in \mathbb{R}^2$, $\lambda \in \mathbb{R}$. Assume that at $\lambda = \lambda_0$ there is an equilibrium u_0 for which $D_u f(u_0, \lambda_0)$ has complex conjugate eigenvalues $\pm\beta i$. By the implicit function theorem, there exists a curve $u^*(\lambda)$ of equilibria for λ near λ_0, $u^*(\lambda_0) = u_0$. Denote the eigenvalues of $D_u f$ at $u^*(\lambda)$ by $\alpha(\lambda) \pm \beta(\lambda)i$. A parameter dependent coordinate change $v = u - u^*(\lambda)$ and a parameter change $\mu = \lambda - \lambda_0$ transforms the family of differential equations to one for which the origin is the equilibrium for parameter values near 0. We rename the new variables u and λ, respectively.

By a linear coordinate transformation, the linearization $D_u f(0, \lambda)$ is put into normal form

$$D_u f(0, 0) = \begin{pmatrix} \alpha(\lambda) & -\beta(\lambda) \\ \beta(\lambda) & \alpha(\lambda) \end{pmatrix}$$

for λ near 0, where α, β are smooth functions of λ with

$$\alpha(0) = 0, \quad \beta(0) \neq 0. \tag{3.44}$$

Note that $D_u f(0, \lambda)$ has eigenvalues $\alpha \pm \beta i$, which are on the imaginary axis for $\lambda = 0$. Using the coordinates $u = (x, y)$, we may write the family as

$$\begin{pmatrix} \dot{x} \\ \dot{y} \end{pmatrix} = \begin{pmatrix} \alpha(\lambda) & -\beta(\lambda) \\ \beta(\lambda) & \alpha(\lambda) \end{pmatrix} \begin{pmatrix} x \\ y \end{pmatrix} + \begin{pmatrix} g(x, y, \lambda) \\ h(x, y, \lambda) \end{pmatrix}, \tag{3.45}$$

where $g(0, 0, \lambda) = h(0, 0, \lambda) = 0$ and $D_{(x,y)} g(0, 0, \lambda) = D_{(x,y)} h(0, 0, \lambda) = 0$.

Theorem 3.34 (Planar Hopf bifurcation). *Consider the family of differential equations* (3.45) *which satisfies* (3.44) *and further*

(i) $\alpha'(0) > 0$;

(ii) *the number (the first Lyapunov coefficient)*

$$a = \frac{1}{16\beta}\Big((g_{xxx} + g_{xyy} + h_{xxy} + h_{yyy})\beta + g_{xy}(g_{xx} + g_{yy}) - h_{xy}(h_{xx} + h_{yy}) - g_{xx}h_{xx} + g_{yy}h_{yy}\Big)$$

computed at $(x, y, \lambda) = (0, 0, 0)$ *is nonzero.*

Then the bifurcation is as follows, depending on the sign of a:

(1) *A supercritical Hopf bifurcation occurs for $a < 0$: for $\lambda \leq 0$ the origin is stable and attracts all nearby orbits, while for $\lambda > 0$ the origin is unstable and there is a stable periodic orbit that attracts all nearby orbits except for the origin.*

(2) *A subcritical Hopf bifurcation occurs for $a > 0$: for $\lambda < 0$ there is an unstable periodic orbit; the stable equilibrium at the origin attracts only points inside the periodic orbit; for $\lambda \geq 0$ the origin is unstable and no other orbits stay close to the origin.*

Figure 3.9 depicts the dynamics described in the theorem. Assumption (i) says that the curves of eigenvalues $\{\alpha(\lambda) \pm i\,\beta(\lambda)\}$ intersect the imaginary axis transversely while λ crosses zero.

Example 3.35. Consider a smooth family of planar differential equations

$$\begin{aligned}\dot{x} &= \alpha(\lambda)x - \beta(\lambda)y - x(x^2 + y^2),\\ \dot{y} &= \beta(\lambda)x + \alpha(\lambda)y - y(x^2 + y^2),\end{aligned}$$

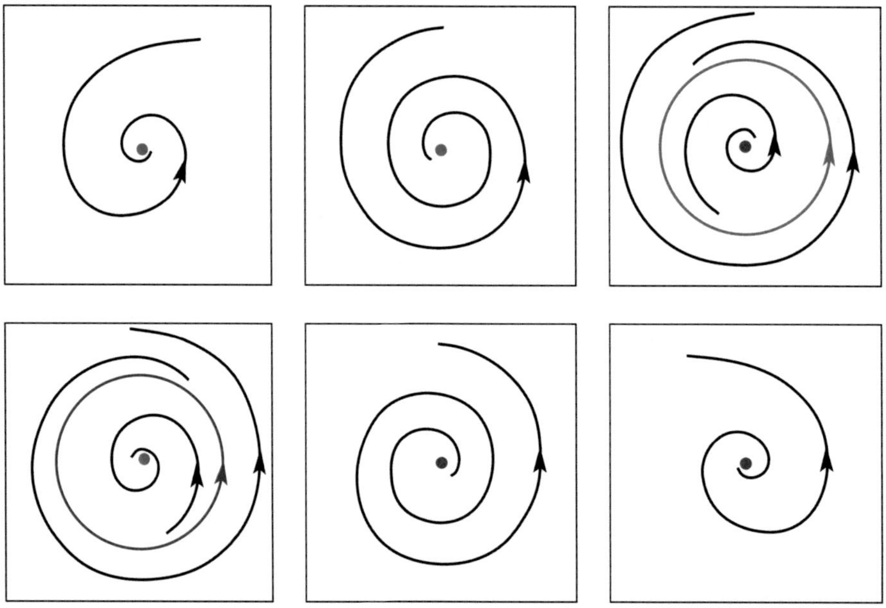

Figure 3.9. The upper panels show the phase diagrams for the supercritical Hopf bifurcation: as the parameter increases, the equilibrium becomes unstable and a stable limit cycle appears. The lower panels show the phase diagrams for the subcritical Hopf bifurcation: as the parameter increases, the equilibrium becomes unstable and unstable periodic orbit disappears.

depending on a real parameter λ. The origin is an equilibrium, and the eigenvalues of the linearized system at the origin equal $\alpha(\lambda) \pm i\,\beta(\lambda)$. In polar coordinates the system becomes

$$\dot r = \alpha(\lambda) r - r^3,$$
$$\dot\varphi = \beta(\lambda).$$

A straightforward analysis shows that under assumptions $\alpha(0) = 0, \alpha'(0) > 0$ and $\beta(0) \neq 0$ a supercritical Hopf bifurcation occurs at $\lambda = 0$. ■

In the proof of Theorem 3.34 we use a normal form similar to the equations in the above example to facilitate the analysis.

Lemma 3.36. *A smooth parameter dependent coordinate change brings* (3.45) *into the normal form, which in polar coordinates has an expression*

$$\dot r = \alpha r + \operatorname{Re}(c_1) r^3 + \mathcal{O}(r^4),$$
$$\dot\varphi = \beta + \operatorname{Im}(c_1) r^2 + \mathcal{O}(r^3). \tag{3.46}$$

Here $c_1 : \mathbb{R} \to \mathbb{C}$ *is a smooth function of the parameter* λ.

We give the proof of this lemma below, but first we use it to finish the proof of Theorem 3.34.

Proof of Theorem 3.34. We start from (3.46) and first make some additional transformations. A time reparametrization $t = t(s)$ with $t'(s) = 1/\dot\varphi(s)$ brings this to (after renaming back to the original variables)

$$\dot r = (\alpha/\beta) r + a r^3 + \mathcal{O}(r^4),$$
$$\dot\varphi = 1,$$

with

$$a = (1/\beta)\operatorname{Re}(c_1) - (\alpha/\beta^2)\operatorname{Im}(c_1).$$

Note that $a = a(\lambda)$ is a smooth function of the parameter λ. This time reparametrization can be used as long as

$$\dot\varphi(s) = \beta + \operatorname{Im}(c_1)(r(s))^2 + \mathcal{O}(r(s)^3) \neq 0.$$

So it can be used as long as $|r(s)|$ is sufficiently small. By (3.44) we have $a(0) = (1/\beta(0))\operatorname{Re}(c_1(0))$. We further note that $\beta < 0$ causes a time reversal for the time reparametrization. This means that the direction of the orbits changes and hence stability properties of equilibria and periodic orbits change. The quantity a is the first Lyapunov coefficient from Theorem 3.34(ii). The expression of a given in assumption (ii) follows from the proof of Lemma 3.36; see also Remark 3.37 below. We assume $a \neq 0$. Note that the higher-order terms in the equation for $\dot r$ are functions of r, φ and the parameter λ.

To find periodic orbits, we rescale r by $r = \big(1/\sqrt{|a|}\big)\rho$. This yields

$$\dot\rho = (\alpha/\beta)\rho + (\operatorname{sign} a)\rho^3 + \mathcal{O}(|\rho|^4),$$
$$\dot\varphi = 1.$$

Renaming ρ to r again and considering the case where $a < 0$, we obtain

$$\dot r = (\alpha/\beta)r - r^3 + \mathcal{O}(|r|^4),$$
$$\dot\varphi = 1. \tag{3.47}$$

System (3.47) transformed into Cartesian coordinates reads

$$\begin{pmatrix}\dot x\\ \dot y\end{pmatrix} = \begin{pmatrix}\alpha/\beta & -1\\ 1 & \alpha/\beta\end{pmatrix}\begin{pmatrix}x\\ y\end{pmatrix} - (x^2+y^2)\begin{pmatrix}x\\ y\end{pmatrix} + \mathcal{O}(|(x,y)|^4). \tag{3.48}$$

This family is the result of the normal form transformations applied to (3.45).

We use (3.47) to construct a return map Π of (3.48) on a cross section

$$\Sigma = (-\hat x, \hat x) \times \{y = 0\},$$

where $\hat x$ is sufficiently small. In what follows we omit $y = 0$ in the notation and consider $\Pi(\cdot,\lambda)$ as a map

$$\Pi(\cdot,\lambda) : (-\hat x, \hat x) \to \mathbb{R}.$$

From (3.47) we obtain r as function of φ, where r solves the phase differential equation

$$r' = (\alpha/\beta)r - r^3 + \mathcal{O}(|r|^4). \tag{3.49}$$

Let $r(\cdot,\rho,\lambda)$ be the solution of the initial value problem (3.49), $r(0) = \rho$. Note that for sufficiently small initial values $r(0) = x$, solutions of (3.49) exist on the interval $[0, 2\pi]$. We consider a return map given by

$$\Pi(x,\lambda) = r(2\pi, x, \lambda);$$

see Figure 3.10. It suffices to consider $\Pi(\cdot,\lambda)$ only for nonnegative x; the extension of the domain of definition to $(-\hat x, \hat x)$ merely eases the discussion of the differentiability at $x = 0$.

Write $r(\cdot,\rho,\lambda)$ in a Taylor series

$$r(\varphi,\rho,\lambda) = R_1(\varphi)\rho + R_2(\varphi)\rho^2 + R_3(\varphi)\rho^3 + \mathcal{O}(|\rho|^4).$$

Then (3.49) yields

$$\begin{aligned}&R_1'\rho + R_2'\rho^2 + R_3'\rho^3 + \mathcal{O}(|\rho|^4)\\ &\qquad = (\alpha/\beta)R_1\rho + (\alpha/\beta)R_2\rho^2 + ((\alpha/\beta)R_3 - R_1^3)\rho^3 + \mathcal{O}(|\rho|)^4,\end{aligned}$$

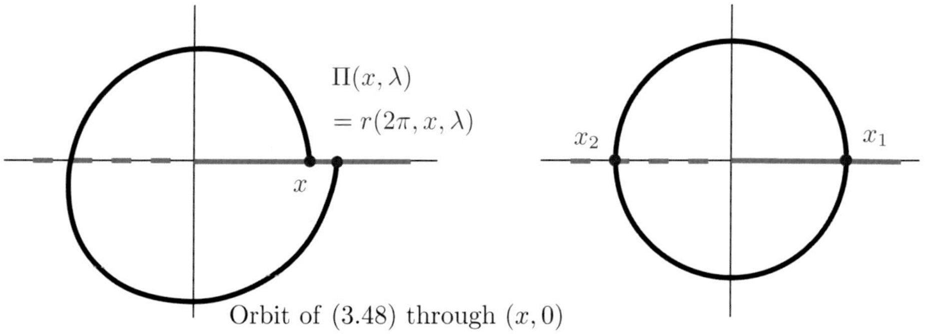

Figure 3.10. The return map Π defined on $(-\hat{x}, \hat{x})$. The picture on the right shows that a periodic orbit generates two fixed points of Π.

so that

$$R_1' = (\alpha/\beta)R_1,$$
$$R_2' = (\alpha/\beta)R_2,$$
$$R_3' = (\alpha/\beta)R_3 - R_1^3.$$

Solving with $R_1(0) = 1$, $R_2(0) = 0$, $R_3(0) = 0$, we get

$$R_1(\varphi) = e^{(\alpha/\beta)\varphi},$$
$$R_2(\varphi) = 0,$$
$$R_3(\varphi) = e^{(\alpha/\beta)\varphi}\frac{1 - e^{2(\alpha/\beta)\varphi}}{2(\alpha/\beta)}.$$

So $\Pi(\cdot, \lambda)$ is defined by

$$\Pi(x, \lambda) = e^{2\pi\alpha/\beta}x - e^{2\pi\alpha/\beta}(2\pi + \mathcal{O}(\alpha))x^3 + \mathcal{O}(|x|^4). \tag{3.50}$$

Periodic solutions of (3.46) are related to the nonzero solutions of $\Pi(x, \lambda) = x$, or equivalently

$$\Pi(x, \lambda) - x = \big((e^{2\pi\alpha/\beta} - 1) - e^{2\pi\alpha/\beta}(2\pi + \mathcal{O}(\alpha))x^2 + \mathcal{O}(|x|^3)\big)x = 0.$$

To find solutions $x \neq 0$, we thus need to solve

$$(e^{2\pi\alpha/\beta} - 1) - e^{2\pi\alpha/\beta}(2\pi + \mathcal{O}(\alpha))x^2 + \mathcal{O}(|x|^3) = 0. \tag{3.51}$$

The expression on the left-hand side has the same properties as the (one-dimensional) vector field in Theorem 3.6. As in Section 3.2.1 we see that the solutions of (3.51) form a curve $\{(x, \lambda^*(x))\}$ through $(0, 0)$. Note that a fixed λ-value is related to either no, exactly one, or exactly two fixed points of $\Pi(\cdot, \lambda)$, respectively. In the latter case the two fixed points determine the same periodic orbit; see Figure 3.10.

To prove the stability statement, compute the derivative $D_x\Pi(x, \lambda^*(x))$ of Π with respect to the first variable along the curve of the nontrivial fixed points of Π. Differentiating $\Pi(x, \lambda^*(x)) \equiv x$ with respect to x, we find

$$D_x\Pi(x, \lambda^*(x)) = 1 - D_\lambda\Pi(x, \lambda^*(x))D\lambda^*(x).$$

Since $D\lambda^*(0) = 0$ we find $D_x\Pi(0,0) = 1$. Let $P(x) = D_x\Pi(x, \lambda^*(x))$. Then $P(0) = 1$. In what follows we show that $P(\cdot)$ has an extremum in $x = 0$. Calculate

$$\begin{aligned} DP(x) = -\Big[&D_xD_\lambda\Pi(x, \lambda^*(x))D\lambda^*(x) + D_\lambda^2\Pi(x, \lambda^*(x))(D\lambda^*(x))^2 \\ &+ D_\lambda\Pi(x, \lambda^*(x))D^2\lambda^*(x)\Big]. \end{aligned} \tag{3.52}$$

As $\Pi(0, \lambda) \equiv 0$ and therefore $D_\lambda\Pi(0,0) = 0$, we find $DP(0) = 0$. Differentiating (3.52) again yields

$$D^2P(0) = -2D_xD_\lambda\Pi(0,0)D^2\lambda^*(0). \tag{3.53}$$

From (3.50) we learn that

$$D_\lambda D_x\Pi(0,0) = 2\pi\big(\alpha'(0)/\beta(0)\big). \tag{3.54}$$

For further discussions we specify

$$\alpha'(0) > 0, \quad \beta(0) > 0. \tag{3.55}$$

Assuming (3.55), equation (3.51) is only solvable for $\lambda \geq 0$. For the solution λ^* we have $D^2\lambda^*(0) > 0$; compare Section 3.2.1. Together with (3.53), (3.54) it follows that $P(\cdot)$ has a maximum in $x = 0$. This means that $D_x\Pi(x, \lambda^*(x)) < 1$ for $x \neq 0$, so that the corresponding periodic orbits are asymptotically stable. We find dynamics as described in the supercritical bifurcation case of the theorem. The statement for a subcritical bifurcation follows in the same manner. □

It remains to prove the normal form statement Lemma 3.36.

Proof of Lemma 3.36. Take the differential equation (3.45) with the linear part in real Jordan normal form. Consider a complex coordinate $z = x + iy$. Observe that

$$\dot{z} = (\alpha + i\beta)z + r(z, \bar{z}, \lambda) \tag{3.56}$$

with $r(z, \bar{z}, \lambda) = \mathcal{O}(|z|^2)$ as $z \to 0$.

We start with a coordinate transformation that removes quadratic terms. Expand (3.56) as

$$\dot{z} = \nu z + \frac{g_{20}}{2}z^2 + g_{11}z\bar{z} + \frac{g_{02}}{2}\bar{z}^2 + \mathcal{O}(|z|^3), \tag{3.57}$$

with $\nu = \alpha + i\beta$. Consider a coordinate w given by

$$z = w + \frac{h_{20}}{2}w^2 + h_{11}w\bar{w} + \frac{h_{02}}{2}\bar{w}^2.$$

The inverse change of variable is given by

$$w = z - \frac{h_{20}}{2}z^2 - h_{11}z\bar{z} - \frac{h_{02}}{2}\bar{z}^2 + \mathcal{O}(|z|^3).$$

Therefore

$$\begin{aligned}
\dot{w} &= \dot{z} - h_{20}z\dot{z} - h_{11}(\dot{z}\bar{z} + z\dot{\bar{z}}) - h_{02}\bar{z}\dot{\bar{z}} + \cdots \\
&= \nu z + \left(\frac{g_{20}}{2} - \nu h_{20}\right)z^2 + (g_{11} - \nu h_{11} - \bar{\nu}h_{11})z\bar{z} + \left(\frac{g_{02}}{2} - \bar{\nu}h_{02}\right)\bar{z}^2 + \cdots \\
&= \nu w + \frac{1}{2}(g_{20} - \nu h_{20})w^2 + (g_{11} - \bar{\nu}h_{11})w\bar{w} + \frac{1}{2}(g_{02} - (2\bar{\nu} - \nu)h_{02})\bar{w}^2 \\
&\quad + \mathcal{O}(|w|^3).
\end{aligned}$$

Putting

$$h_{20} = \frac{g_{20}}{\nu}, \quad h_{11} = \frac{g_{11}}{\bar{\nu}}, \quad h_{02} = \frac{g_{02}}{2\bar{\nu} - \nu}$$

kills the quadratic terms in (3.57) (close to the bifurcation value $\lambda = 0$).

The next step is removing as many third-order terms as possible, by the same technique. That is, start with an expansion

$$\dot{z} = \nu z + \frac{g_{30}}{6}z^3 + \frac{g_{21}}{2}z^2\bar{z} + \frac{g_{12}}{2}z\bar{z}^2 + \frac{g_{03}}{6}\bar{z}^3 + \mathcal{O}(|z|^4).$$

We claim that the introduction of a coordinate

$$z = w + \frac{h_{30}}{6}w^3 + \frac{h_{21}}{2}w^2\bar{w} + \frac{h_{12}}{2}w\bar{w}^2 + \frac{h_{03}}{6}\bar{w}^3 \tag{3.58}$$

transforms the equation into a form

$$\dot{w} = \nu w - c_1 w^2\bar{w} + \mathcal{O}(|w|^4).$$

The inverse transformation of (3.58) is

$$w = z - \frac{h_{30}}{6}z^3 - \frac{h_{21}}{2}z^2\bar{z} - \frac{h_{12}}{2}z\bar{z}^2 - \frac{h_{03}}{6}\bar{z}^3 + \mathcal{O}(|z|^4).$$

Therefore

$$\begin{aligned}
\dot{w} &= \dot{z} - \frac{h_{30}}{2}z^2\dot{z} - \frac{h_{21}}{2}(2z\bar{z}\dot{z} + z^2\dot{\bar{z}}) - \frac{h_{12}}{2}(\dot{z}\bar{z}^2 + 2z\bar{z}\dot{\bar{z}}) - \frac{h_{03}}{2}\bar{z}^2\dot{\bar{z}} + \cdots \\
&= \nu z + \left(\frac{g_{30}}{6} - \nu\frac{h_{30}}{2}\right)z^3 + \left(\frac{g_{21}}{2} - \nu h_{21} - \bar{\nu}\frac{h_{21}}{2}\right)z^2\bar{z} \\
&\qquad + \left(\frac{g_{12}}{2} - \nu\frac{h_{12}}{2} - \bar{\nu}h_{12}\right)z\bar{z}^2 + \left(\frac{g_{03}}{6} - \bar{\nu}\frac{h_{03}}{2}\right)\bar{z}^3 + \cdots \\
&= \nu w + \frac{1}{6}(g_{30} - 2\nu h_{30})w^3 + \frac{1}{2}(g_{21} - (\nu + \bar{\nu})h_{21})w^2\bar{w} \\
&\qquad + \frac{1}{2}(g_{12} - 2\bar{\nu}h_{12})w\bar{w}^2 + \frac{1}{6}(g_{03} + (\nu - 3\bar{\nu})h_{03})\bar{w}^3 + \mathcal{O}(|w|^4).
\end{aligned}$$

Putting

$$h_{30} = \frac{g_{30}}{2\nu}, \quad h_{12} = \frac{g_{12}}{2\bar{\nu}}, \quad h_{03} = \frac{g_{03}}{3\bar{\nu} - \nu}$$

annihilates all cubic terms except the $w^2\bar{w}$ term. Here, putting $h_{21} = g_{21}/(\nu+\bar{\nu})$ does not work, since the denominator vanishes for $\lambda = 0$. We put $h_{21} = 0$ and define

$$c_1 = (1/2)g_{21}.$$

The above transformations bring the differential equation into the form

$$\dot{z} = (\alpha + i\beta)z + c_1 z^2\bar{z} + \mathcal{O}(|z|^4),$$

as $z \to 0$. In polar coordinates this gives the desired expression

$$\begin{aligned}\dot{r} &= \alpha r + \operatorname{Re}(c_1)r^3 + \mathcal{O}(r^4),\\ \dot{\varphi} &= \beta + \operatorname{Im}(c_1)r^2 + \mathcal{O}(r^3).\end{aligned}$$ □

Remark 3.37. Starting with expression (3.57), following the calculations shows that

$$c_1 = \frac{g_{20}g_{11}(\nu+\bar{\nu})}{2|\nu|^2} + \frac{|g_{11}|^2}{\nu} + \frac{|g_{02}|^2}{2(2\nu-\bar{\nu})} + \frac{g_{21}}{2}.$$

Then $a(0) = \frac{1}{\beta(0)}\operatorname{Re} c_1(0)$. The actual verification of the expression of the first Lyapunov coefficient given in Theorem 3.34(ii) we leave to the reader; see Exercise 3.22.

The book [**215**, Section 5.4] provides a formula for the first Lyapunov coefficient without first bringing the linear part into normal form. Let $Av = i\beta(0)v$ and $A^T w = -i\beta(0)w$ be left and right eigenvectors. Then

$$\begin{aligned}a(0) = \frac{1}{2\beta(0)}\operatorname{Re}\Big[&\big\langle w, D_x^3 f(0,0)(v,v,\bar{v})\big\rangle\\ &- 2\big\langle w, D_x^2 f(0,0)(v, A^{-1}D_x^2 f(0,0)(v,\bar{v}))\big\rangle\\ &+ \big\langle w, D_x^2 f(0,0)(\bar{v}, (2i\beta(0)\operatorname{id} - A)^{-1}D_x^2 f(0,0)(v,v))\big\rangle\Big],\end{aligned}$$

where $A = D_x f(0,0)$. ■

Remark 3.38. The proof of Theorem 3.34 shows a way to compute the period of the bifurcating periodic orbits. Let $x \neq 0$ be a fixed point of $\Pi(\cdot,\lambda)$. For (3.47) the periodic orbit has period 2π. Note that this is the period with respect to the reparametrized time. The period T with respect to the original time is given by

$$T = \int_0^{2\pi} \frac{1}{\dot{\varphi}(s)}\,ds = \int_0^{2\pi} \frac{1}{\beta + \operatorname{Im}(c_1)r^2 + \mathcal{O}(r^3)}\,ds,$$

where $r = \big(1/\sqrt{|a|}\big)\rho(s,x)$. ■

In Exercise 3.19 the proof of Theorem 3.34 is reproduced using the normal form derived in Example B.23. This normal form is based on the more general normal form Theorem B.20 avoiding the excursion to complex systems in the proof of Lemma 3.36. In both approaches the transformation of the differential equation into polar coordinates ends up with an equation of the form (3.46).

In the following example we show the occurrence of a Hopf bifurcation for the van der Pol oscillator.

Example 3.39. Van der Pol's oscillator is given by the second-order differential equation

$$\ddot{x} - (2\lambda - x^2)\dot{x} + x = 0$$

with a real parameter λ. The van der Pol oscillator was originally proposed by the electrical engineer Balthasar van der Pol. It models an oscillator with nonlinear damping, of different signs for small and large $|y|$. It provides non-sinusoidal oscillations that are also called relaxation oscillations [**399**]. The second-order differential equation is equivalent to the planar system

$$\begin{pmatrix} \dot{x}_1 \\ \dot{x}_2 \end{pmatrix} = \begin{pmatrix} 0 & 1 \\ -1 & 2\lambda \end{pmatrix}\begin{pmatrix} x_1 \\ x_2 \end{pmatrix} + \begin{pmatrix} 0 \\ -x_1^2 x_2 \end{pmatrix} = A(\lambda)\begin{pmatrix} x_1 \\ x_2 \end{pmatrix} + f(x_1, x_2). \tag{3.59}$$

First we show that (3.59) satisfies the assumptions of Theorem 3.34. The eigenvalues of the linearization $A(\lambda)$ about the equilibrium at the origin are $\lambda \pm i\sqrt{1-\lambda^2}$. The curve of eigenvalues intersects the imaginary axis transversely, or in other words, when λ crosses zero, the origin changes stability. To verify the remaining assumption on the first Lyapunov coefficient, let $x = (x_1, x_2)^T$, $y = (y_1, y_2)^T$ and $y = T(\lambda)x$. With

$$T(\lambda) = \begin{pmatrix} (\lambda/\sqrt{1-\lambda^2}) & -(1/\sqrt{1-\lambda^2}) \\ 1 & 0 \end{pmatrix},$$

(3.59) is transformed in

$$\begin{aligned} \begin{pmatrix} \dot{y}_1 \\ \dot{y}_2 \end{pmatrix} &= T(\lambda)A(\lambda)T(\lambda)^{-1}y + T(\lambda)f(T(\lambda)^{-1}y) \\ &= \begin{pmatrix} \lambda & \sqrt{1-\lambda^2} \\ -\sqrt{1-\lambda^2} & \lambda \end{pmatrix}\begin{pmatrix} y_1 \\ y_2 \end{pmatrix} + \begin{pmatrix} -y_1 y_2^2 + \sqrt{1-\lambda^2}y_2^3 \\ 0 \end{pmatrix}. \end{aligned}$$

Therefore, the first Lyapunov coefficient is given by

$$a = (1/16)D_{y_1}D_{y_2}^2(-y_1 y_2^2) = 1/8.$$

As this is different from zero, Theorem 3.34 applies.

We now convert (3.59) into polar coordinates and analyze the bifurcation directly. We restart from (3.59). Setting $x = r\cos\varphi$ and $y = r\sin\varphi$, we arrive at the counterpart of (3.47),

$$\begin{aligned} \dot{r} &= 2\lambda r \sin^2\varphi - r^3\cos^2\varphi\sin^2\varphi, \\ \dot{\varphi} &= -1 + 2\lambda\sin\varphi\cos\varphi - r^2\cos^3\varphi\sin\varphi. \end{aligned} \tag{3.60}$$

The orbits of the differential equation (3.60) will be determined by the phase differential equation

$$(3.61)\qquad r' = R(\varphi, r, \lambda) = \frac{2\lambda \sin^2\varphi - r^2\cos^2\varphi\sin^2\varphi}{-1 + 2\lambda\sin\varphi\cos\varphi - r^2\cos^3\varphi\sin\varphi}r;$$

compare (3.49). Let $r(\cdot, \rho, \lambda)$ be the solution of the initial value problem (3.61), $r(0) = \rho$. Periodic orbits of (3.59) are determined by

$$(3.62)\qquad \Pi(\rho, \lambda) = r(2\pi, \rho, \lambda) = \rho;$$

compare (3.50). A Taylor expansion of $R(\varphi, \cdot, \lambda)$ around $r = 0$ yields

$$R(\varphi, r, \lambda) = \big(\lambda(\cos(2\varphi) - 1) + \mathcal{O}(\lambda^2)\big)r + \frac{1}{8}(1 - \cos(4\varphi) + \mathcal{O}(\lambda))r^3 + \mathcal{O}(r^4).$$

With the transformation $\eta = re^{-(\lambda/2)\sin(2\varphi)}$, the equation $r' = R(\varphi, r, \lambda)$ becomes

$$\eta' = (-\lambda + \mathcal{O}(\lambda^2))\eta + \frac{1}{8}(1 - \cos(4\varphi) + \mathcal{O}(\lambda))\eta^3 + \mathcal{O}(\eta^4).$$

To alter the cubic terms, let $\varrho = \eta + a(\varphi)\eta^3$ with $\frac{da}{d\varphi} = \frac{1}{8}\cos(4\varphi)$. This gives

$$(3.63)\qquad \varrho' = \big(-\lambda + \mathcal{O}(\lambda^2)\big)\varrho + \left(\frac{1}{8} + \mathcal{O}(\lambda)\right)\varrho^3 + \mathcal{O}(\varrho^4).$$

Write $\varrho(\cdot, \rho, \lambda)$ for the solution of the initial value problem (3.63) with $\varrho(0) = \rho$. Then, in this new coordinate, the return map reads

$$\tilde{\Pi}(\rho, \lambda) = \varrho(2\pi, \rho, \lambda).$$

Proceeding in the same way as with (3.49) we find

$$\tilde{\Pi}(\rho, \lambda) = \big(1 - 2\pi\lambda + \mathcal{O}(\lambda^2)\big)\rho + \left(\frac{2\pi}{8} + \mathcal{O}(\lambda)\right)\rho^3 + \mathcal{O}(\rho^4).$$

The fixed points of $\tilde{\Pi}(\cdot, \lambda)$ are discussed in the same way as for the return map from (3.50). ∎

The proof of Theorem 3.34 relies on the construction of a normal form of a Poincaré return map, which is based on a normal form of the underlying differential equation. With somewhat less effort, and under fewer assumptions, the existence of a curve $\{(x, \lambda^*(x))\}$ (using notation from the proof of Theorem 3.34; see in particular in the paragraph following (3.51)), which defines the bifurcating branch of periodic orbits, can be proved.

Consider again a smooth differential equation

$$(3.64)\qquad \dot{x} = A(\lambda)x + f(x, \lambda)$$

for $x \in \mathbb{R}^2$ and $\lambda \in \mathbb{R}$, with

$$A(\lambda) = \begin{pmatrix} \alpha(\lambda) & -\beta(\lambda) \\ \beta(\lambda) & \alpha(\lambda) \end{pmatrix}$$

and $f(0,0) = 0$, $D_x f(0,0) = 0$. The eigenvalues of $A(\lambda)$ are $\alpha(\lambda) \pm i\beta(\lambda)$, for which we assume $\alpha(0) = 0$, $\alpha'(0) \neq 0$ and $\beta(0) > 0$.

Theorem 3.40. *For λ and a parameter ρ near 0, there are smooth functions $\lambda^*(\rho)$ with $\lambda^*(0) = 0$, $\omega^*(\rho)$ with $\omega^*(0) = 2\pi/\beta$, and $x^*(\rho)$, so that $x^*(\rho)(t)$ is $\omega^*(\rho)$-periodic and a solution to (3.64). For $x^* = (x_1^*, x_2^*)^T$ one has an expansion*

$$x_1^*(\rho)(t) = a\cos(\omega(\rho)t) + o(|\rho|),$$
$$x_2^*(\rho)(t) = -a\sin(\omega(\rho)t) + o(|\rho|),$$

as $\rho \to 0$. Any small periodic solution of (3.64) is of the form $x^*(\rho)$ for some small ρ.

Remark 3.41. To clarify the contents of the theorem, we point out a similarity with the saddle-node bifurcation. Consider $\dot{x} = f(x,\lambda)$ on $\mathbb{R}$ depending on a parameter $\lambda \in \mathbb{R}$. Suppose that $f(0,0) = 0$ and $D_x f(0,0) = 0$. If $D_\lambda f(0,0) \neq 0$, then the implicit function theorem allows us to solve $f(x,\lambda) = 0$ for λ as function of x: there exists a function λ^* defined near 0 with $\lambda^*(0) = 0$ solving $f(x,\lambda^*(x)) = 0$. The curve $x \mapsto (x,\lambda^*(x))$ is tangent to the x-axis as $(\lambda^*)'(0) = 0$, but for further specifics, conditions on higher derivatives are needed. The condition $D_x^2 f(0,0) \neq 0$ implies that the curve $x \mapsto (x,\lambda^*(x))$ has a quadratic tangency with the x-axis and allows conclusions on the number of equilibria for positive and negative values of λ. The above theorem should be understood similarly; see Exercise 3.23. ∎

Proof of Theorem 3.40. Using polar coordinates $x_1 = r\cos\varphi$ and $x_2 = r\sin\varphi$, (3.45) becomes

$$\dot{r} = \alpha(\lambda)r + R(\varphi,r,\lambda),$$
$$\dot{\varphi} = \beta(\lambda) + \Phi(\varphi,r,\lambda), \tag{3.65}$$

with $\Phi(\varphi,0,\lambda) = 0$, $R(\varphi,0,\lambda) = 0$, $D_r R(\varphi,0,\lambda) = 0$ and where these functions are 2π-periodic in φ. Eliminating t (as before in (3.49) or (3.61)) one obtains

$$r' = \frac{dr}{d\varphi} = \frac{\alpha(\lambda)}{\beta(\lambda)}r + R^*(\varphi,r,\lambda) \tag{3.66}$$

with $R^*(\varphi,0,\lambda) = 0$, $D_r R^*(\varphi,0,\lambda) = 0$ and R^* being 2π-periodic in φ. The 2π-periodic solutions of (3.66) near $r = 0$ yield periodic solutions of (3.64) near $x = 0$ and conversely.

Let $r(\cdot,\rho,\lambda)$ be the solution of the initial value problem (3.66), $r(0) = \rho$. Periodic orbits of (3.64) correspond to solutions of

$$r(2\pi,\rho,\lambda) = \rho.$$

Apply the variation of constants formula to (3.66). Then $r(2\pi) = r(0) = \rho$ yields an equation of the form

$$(1 - e^{-2\pi\alpha(\lambda)/\beta(\lambda)})\rho = h(\rho,\lambda) \tag{3.67}$$

for a function h with $h(0,\lambda) = 0$. Hence h may be written as $h(\rho,\lambda) = \rho g(\rho,\lambda)$. Dividing by ρ gives

$$G(\rho,\lambda) := 1 - e^{-2\pi\alpha(\lambda)/\beta(\lambda)} - g(\rho,\lambda) = 0 \tag{3.68}$$

for a function g with $g(0,\lambda) = 0$. Apply the implicit function theorem to determine $\lambda = \lambda^*(\rho)$ satisfying (3.68) and $\lambda^*(0) = 0$. To do so, note that $G(0,0) = 0$ and $D_\lambda G(0,0) = -2\pi\alpha'(0)/\beta(0)) \neq 0$. One obtains $\omega^*(\rho)$ from the equation for φ in (3.65). □

Example 3.42. We revisit Example 3.39 on the van der Pol oscillator. We start with equation (3.62) determining periodic orbits. Clearly $r(2\pi, 0, \lambda) = 0$ and hence we can write $\Pi(\rho,\lambda) = \rho\tilde{\Pi}(\rho,\lambda)$. Periodic orbits of (3.59) are now determined by

$$F(\rho,\lambda) := \tilde{\Pi}(\rho,\lambda) - 1 = 0. \tag{3.69}$$

We apply the implicit function theorem to solve (3.69) for $\lambda = \lambda^*(\rho)$ locally around $(\rho,\lambda) = (0,0)$. To this end we show that $F(0,0) = 0$ and $D_\lambda F(0,0) \neq 0$, or equivalently that $\tilde{\Pi}(0,0) = 1$ and $D_\lambda\tilde{\Pi}(0,0) \neq 0$.

From the definition of $\tilde{\Pi}$ we find

$$\tilde{\Pi}(0,\lambda) = D_\rho\Pi(0,\lambda) = D_\rho r(2\pi, 0, \lambda).$$

Recall that $D_\varphi r(\varphi,\rho,\lambda) = R(\varphi, r(\varphi,\rho,\lambda),\lambda)$. Therefore

$$D_\varphi D_\rho r(\varphi,\rho,\lambda) = D_\rho D_\varphi r(\varphi,\rho,\lambda) = D_\rho R(\varphi, r(\varphi,\rho,\lambda),\lambda) D_\rho r(\varphi,\rho,\lambda).$$

So $D_\rho r(\cdot, 0, \lambda)$ solves the initial value problem $u' = D_\rho R(\varphi, 0, \lambda)\, u$, $u(0) = 1$. As $r(\varphi, 0, \lambda) \equiv 0$ and $r(0,\rho,\lambda) \equiv \rho$, we have $D_\rho r(0,0,\lambda) = 1$. From the definition of R in (3.61), we find $D_\rho r(\varphi, 0, \lambda) = \frac{2\lambda\sin^2\varphi}{-1+2\lambda\sin\varphi\cos\varphi}$. This yields that $D_\rho r(\cdot, 0, \lambda)$ solves the initial value problem

$$u' = \frac{2\lambda\sin^2\varphi}{-1 + 2\lambda\sin\varphi\cos\varphi} u, \quad u(0) = 1. \tag{3.70}$$

At $\lambda = 0$ this reduces to $u' = 0$, $u(0) = 1$. This implies $D_2 r(2\pi, 0, 0) = 1$ and hence $\tilde{\Pi}(0,0) = 1$. To evaluate $D_\lambda\tilde{\Pi}(0,0)$, we write (3.70) as

$$u' = \big(- 2\lambda\sin^2\varphi + \mathcal{O}(\lambda^2)\big)\, u = \big(\lambda(\cos 2\varphi - 1) + \mathcal{O}(\lambda^2)\big)\, u, \quad u(0) = 1.$$

Its solution is $u(\varphi,\lambda) = D_\rho r(\varphi, 0, \lambda) = e^{-\lambda\varphi + (\lambda/2)\sin 2\varphi + \mathcal{O}(\lambda^2)\varphi}$. Hence

$$D_\lambda\tilde{\Pi}(0,0) = D_\lambda(D_\rho r(2\pi, 0, 0)) = e^0(-2\pi) \neq 0.$$

We can conclude that there exists a function $\lambda = \lambda^*(\rho)$ which solves (3.69), locally around $(\rho,\lambda) = (0,0)$.

The period $\omega^*(\lambda)$ of the bifurcating periodic orbit is calculated as (recall Remark 3.38)

$$\omega^*(\lambda) = \int_0^{2\pi} \frac{1}{|-1+2\lambda\sin\varphi\cos\varphi - \big(r(\varphi,\rho,\lambda)\big)^2\cos^3\varphi\sin\varphi|}\,d\varphi$$
$$= 2\pi + \mathcal{O}(\lambda).$$

■

3.2.4.2. *Higher-dimensional Hopf bifurcation.* Higher-dimensional versions of the Hopf bifurcation theorem are obtained from center manifold reductions. To verify the conditions, one has to derive asymptotic expansions of the differential equation on the center manifold. Start with a differential equation

$$\begin{aligned}\dot{x} &= \alpha x - \beta y + g(x,y,z,\lambda),\\ \dot{y} &= \beta x + \alpha y + h(x,y,z,\lambda),\\ \dot{z} &= Bz + j(x,y,z,\lambda),\end{aligned}$$

for $(x,y,z) \in \mathbb{R}\times\mathbb{R}\times\mathbb{R}^p$, B a hyperbolic $p\times p$ matrix depending on λ, α and β depending on λ with $\alpha(0) = 0$, and g, h, i as higher-order terms. Then there is a local center manifold $z = V(x,y,\lambda)$, tangent to $\{x,y\} = 0$ at the origin. Computing for $\lambda = 0$, local invariance means

$$\begin{aligned}BV(x,y,0) &+ j(x,y,V(x,y,0),0)\\ &= D_xV(x,y,0)(-\beta y + g(x,y,V(x,y,0),0))\\ &\qquad + D_yV(x,y,0)(\beta x + h(x,y,V(x,y,0),0)).\end{aligned}$$

This formula allows us to compute the Taylor expansion up to second order for V, plugging this into the equations for $\dot{x}$ and $\dot{y}$ allows us to calculate the first Lyapunov coefficient and thus to check the conditions of the Hopf bifurcation theorem. See [**215**] for an explicit formula for the first Lyapunov coefficient in terms of the original differential equation.

We will not pursue this here, but we do present an n-dimensional equivalent of Theorem 3.40, where we used the implicit function theorem to discuss the Hopf bifurcation in $\mathbb{R}^n$ for $n = 2$. The same ideas yield a similar theorem for arbitrary n. For a connection with the Lyapunov center theorem [**233**] that gives a sheet of periodic orbits in Hamiltonian systems, we refer to [**11**, **240**] and Exercise 3.23. Suppose

$$\dot{x} = f(x,\lambda) = Df(0)(\lambda)x + h(x,\lambda) \tag{3.71}$$

is a smooth differential equation for $x \in \mathbb{R}^n$, $\lambda \in \mathbb{R}$, satisfying $h(0,\lambda) = 0$, $D_xh(0,\lambda) = 0$, and

$$Df(0)(\lambda) = \begin{pmatrix} A(\lambda) & 0 \\ 0 & B(\lambda), \end{pmatrix}, \qquad A(\lambda) = \begin{pmatrix} \lambda & \beta(\lambda) \\ -\beta(\lambda) & \lambda \end{pmatrix},$$

where $\beta(0) = 1$ and $(e^{2\pi B(0)} - I)^{-1}$ exists.

Theorem 3.43. *Assume the above hypotheses. For λ and a parameter ρ near 0, there are smooth functions $\lambda^*(\rho)$ with $\lambda^*(0) = 0$, $\omega^*(\rho)$ with $\omega^*(0) = 2\pi$, and $x^*(\rho)$, so that $x^*(\rho)(t)$ is $\omega^*(\rho)$-periodic and a solution to (3.71). One has*

$$x^*(\rho)(t) = \begin{pmatrix} \rho\cos(\omega(\rho)t) \\ -\rho\sin(\omega(\rho)t) \\ 0 \\ \vdots \\ 0 \end{pmatrix} + o(|\rho|),$$

as $\rho \to 0$. Any small periodic solution of (3.64) is of the form $x^*(\rho)$ for some small ρ.

Proof. Consider polar coordinates $x = (r\cos\varphi, -r\sin\varphi, y)$ in (3.71). The differential equation gets an expression

$$\begin{aligned} \dot r &= \lambda r + R(\varphi, r, y, \lambda), \\ \dot\varphi &= \beta(\lambda) + \Phi(\varphi, r, y, \lambda), \\ \dot y &= C(\lambda)y + Y(\varphi, r, y, \lambda). \end{aligned}$$

Eliminate t to obtain

$$\begin{aligned} r' &= \frac{dr}{d\varphi} = \frac{\lambda}{\beta(\lambda)}r + R^*(\varphi, r, y, \lambda), \\ y' &= \frac{dy}{d\varphi} = \frac{1}{\beta(\lambda)}C(\lambda)y + Y^*(\varphi, r, y, \lambda), \end{aligned} \tag{3.72}$$

where the functions R^*, Y^* are 2π-periodic in φ, vanishing at $r = 0$ and where also $D_{(r,y)}R^*$, $D_{(r,y)}Y^*$ vanishes at $r = 0$. The reasoning in the proof of Theorem 3.40 can be repeated to obtain the desired conclusion. Let $r(\cdot, \rho, \eta, \lambda)$, $y(\cdot, \rho, \eta, \lambda)$ be the solution of the initial value problem (3.72) with $r(0) = \rho$ and $y(0) = \eta$. Periodic orbits of (3.71) are determined by the fixed point equation

$$\begin{aligned} r(2\pi, \rho, \eta, \lambda) &= \rho, \\ y(2\pi, \rho, \eta, \lambda) &= \eta. \end{aligned}$$

Analogous to (3.67) we find

$$\begin{aligned} (1 - e^{-2\pi\alpha(\lambda)/\beta(\lambda)})\rho &= h(\rho, \eta, \lambda), \\ (I - e^{-2\pi C(\lambda)/\beta(\lambda)})\eta &= k(\rho, \eta, \lambda). \end{aligned} \tag{3.73}$$

The second equation in (3.73) can be solved for $\eta = \eta^*(\rho, \lambda)$. Plugging the solution into the first equation and dividing by ρ, we arrive at

$$G(\rho, \eta, \lambda) := 1 - e^{-2\pi\alpha(\lambda)/\beta(\lambda)} - g(\rho, \eta, \lambda) = 0.$$

This equation can be treated just as (3.68). □

The first Lyapunov coefficient for the higher-dimensional Hopf bifurcation is given by the formula in Example 3.37. See [**215**, Section 5.4].

Example 3.44. Alan Turing in [**395**] described models of biological cells that are inert in themselves but pulse when in interaction via diffusion. Turing's work led to the study of pattern formation in reaction-diffusion equations such as

$$\frac{\partial}{\partial t}u = d_u \triangle u + f(u, v),$$
$$\frac{\partial}{\partial t}v = d_v \triangle v + g(u, v),$$

for functions $(x, y, t) \mapsto u(x, y, t), v(x, y, t)$. These are model density functions for chemicals that diffuse and interact. Different constants d_u, d_v give rise to different diffusion speeds of the chemicals. Assume an equilibrium at (u_0, v_0): $f(u_0, v_0) = g(u_0, v_0) = 0$. Turing instability is the effect that, without diffusion, the equilibrium is a stable equilibrium for ordinary differential equations, but diffusion causes instability: increasing d_u and d_v from zero can cause a change of stability, that is, a bifurcation. We will not analyze this Turing bifurcation here, but we refer to the textbooks [**180**] and [**262, 263**] for explanations of the mechanism.

We will glance at an analogue for ordinary differential equations. Motivated by Turing's study, Stephen Smale studied simple models of differential equations exhibiting a comparable phenomenon. In his study, included in [**240**], a single cell is modeled by a vector field

$$\dot{x} = f(x)$$

on a domain in $\mathbb{R}^4$ (for simplicity we assume it is given on all of $\mathbb{R}^4$), with the following property. The differential equation $\dot{x} = f(x)$ is globally asymptotically stable and possesses a unique equilibrium $\bar{x}$ that attracts every solution in $\mathbb{R}^4$. Two interacting cells are modeled by the differential equations

$$\begin{aligned} \dot{x}_1 &= f(x_1) + D(x_2 - x_1), \\ \dot{x}_2 &= f(x_2) + D(x_1 - x_2) \end{aligned} \tag{3.74}$$

on $\mathbb{R}^4 \times \mathbb{R}^4$, where

$$D = \begin{pmatrix} d_1 & 0 & 0 & 0 \\ 0 & d_2 & 0 & 0 \\ 0 & 0 & d_3 & 0 \\ 0 & 0 & 0 & d_4 \end{pmatrix}$$

with $d_1, \ldots, d_4 \geq 0$. For the choice of f in Smale's work there exists D, so that (3.74) is a global oscillator. That is, it has a nontrivial periodic solution that attracts all solutions in $\mathbb{R}^4 \times \mathbb{R}^4$ except for points on the stable manifold of the equilibrium $(\bar{x}, \bar{x})$. The example is related to the Hopf bifurcation as one can let D move from zero to the values in Smale's result to create the oscillator.

The paper [**30**] constructs a map f in $\mathbb{R}^2$ with an asymptotically stable equilibrium, so that

$$\begin{aligned} \dot{x}_1 &= f(x_1) + D(x_2 - x_1), \\ \dot{x}_2 &= f(x_2) + D(x_1 - x_2) \end{aligned} \tag{3.75}$$

for a properly chosen

$$D = \begin{pmatrix} d_1 & 0 \\ 0 & d_2 \end{pmatrix}$$

has bounded positive orbits but no stable equilibria. Other examples of systems of the form (3.75) are described in [**313**] and [**10**] and further papers in this direction are [**270, 294, 385, 386**]. We comment on an instability analysis of a symmetric equilibrium $(\bar{x}, \bar{x})$. Linearizing (3.75) at $(\bar{x}, \bar{x})$ gives the following system, with $A = Df(\bar{x})$:

$$\begin{pmatrix} \dot{u}_1 \\ \dot{u}_2 \end{pmatrix} = \begin{pmatrix} A - D & D \\ D & A - D \end{pmatrix} \begin{pmatrix} u_1 \\ u_2 \end{pmatrix} =: M \begin{pmatrix} u_1 \\ u_2 \end{pmatrix}.$$

Using the linear transformation

$$S = \begin{pmatrix} \mathrm{id} & \mathrm{id} \\ -\mathrm{id} & \mathrm{id} \end{pmatrix},$$

and consequently

$$S^{-1} = \frac{1}{2} \begin{pmatrix} \mathrm{id} & -\mathrm{id} \\ \mathrm{id} & \mathrm{id} \end{pmatrix},$$

one gets that

$$SMS^{-1} = \begin{pmatrix} A & 0 \\ 0 & A - 2D \end{pmatrix}.$$

So we conclude that the spectrum of M is the union of the spectrum of A and the spectrum of $A - 2D$. The key observation now is that, even though A and $-2D$ have only eigenvalues with negative (or nonpositive) real part, their sum can have a positive eigenvalue. To provide an explicit and simple example on the level of the linear algebra, consider

$$A = \begin{pmatrix} 1/4 & -1 \\ 1 & -1/2 \end{pmatrix}, \qquad D = \begin{pmatrix} 0 & 0 \\ 0 & \lambda \end{pmatrix}.$$

Then A has two eigenvalues in the left half-plane, but

$$A - 2D = \begin{pmatrix} 1/4 & -1 \\ 1 & -1/2 - 2\lambda \end{pmatrix}$$

has a positive eigenvalue for $\lambda > 7/4$. In this case, when increasing λ from zero, a single eigenvalue of M crosses zero at $\lambda = 7/4$. For the original nonlinear system one would expect a transcritical bifurcation or a pitchfork bifurcation. ■

3.2.5. Bogdanov-Takens bifurcation. Bifurcations studied in previous sections involved equilibria with a single zero eigenvalue or a pair of complex conjugate eigenvalues on the imaginary axis. A more involved bifurcation arises for equilibria with two zero eigenvalues. We will consider the unfolding of a differential equation $(\dot{x}, \dot{y}) = f(x, y, \lambda)$ in the plane with an equilibrium at the origin that admits a nilpotent but not semisimple derivative. This means we have $D_{(x,y)} f(0,0,0) = \begin{pmatrix} a & ab \\ -a/b & -a \end{pmatrix}$ for some $a, b \neq 0$, but by a linear coordinate change we may assume

$$D_{(x,y)} f(0,0,0) = \begin{pmatrix} 0 & 1 \\ 0 & 0 \end{pmatrix}.$$

An equilibrium with a nilpotent linearization can occur robustly in two-parameter families of planar vector fields, so we will consider families of vector fields depending on two parameters $\lambda = (\lambda_1, \lambda_2)$. This bifurcation is called the Bogdanov-Takens bifurcation after the mathematicians Rifkat Bogdanov [**41, 42**] and Floris Takens [**370**] (see [**376**] for a reprint) who studied it independently.

We will see that in the unfolding, different bifurcations of codimension 1 appear: saddle-node and Hopf bifurcations. There is also a third bifurcation of codimension 1 that arises in the unfolding, namely the homoclinic bifurcation. The (planar) homoclinic bifurcation will be treated in Section 4.1.1 in the chapter on nonlocal bifurcations. The treatment of the Bogdanov-Takens bifurcation uses terminology and results from Section 4.1.1.

Example 3.45. Consider the two-parameter family of differential equations in $\mathbb{R}^2$:

$$\left.\begin{aligned} \dot{x} &= y, \\ \dot{y} &= x^2 + \lambda_1 + \lambda_2 y + xy \end{aligned}\right\} =: f(x, y, \lambda), \quad \lambda = (\lambda_1, \lambda_2). \tag{3.76}$$

Note that

$$D_{(x,y)} f(0,0,0) = \begin{pmatrix} 0 & 1 \\ 0 & 0 \end{pmatrix},$$

so that this family is an unfolding of an equilibrium with nilpotent derivative. We investigate bifurcations of equilibria.

Equilibria are located on the x-axis and satisfy $\lambda_1 + x^2 = 0$. We find

$$\begin{aligned} \lambda_1 < 0 &: \quad \text{there are two different equilibria } E^{\pm} = (\pm\sqrt{-\lambda_1}, 0), \\ \lambda_1 = 0 &: \quad \text{there is exactly one equilibrium } (0,0), \\ \lambda_1 > 0 &: \quad \text{there is no equilibrium.} \end{aligned}$$

A saddle-node bifurcation occurs along the curve $\mathrm{SN} = \{\lambda_1 = 0\}$. More precisely, restricting λ to a curve intersecting SN transversely, (3.76) can be considered as a one-parameter family, and a saddle-node bifurcation occurs within

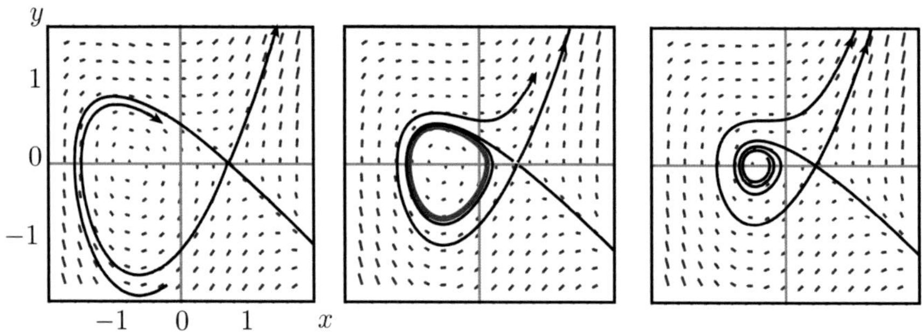

Figure 3.11. Phase portraits of the model system (3.76) at $\lambda_2 = 0.5$ and $\lambda_1 = -0.55$, $\lambda_1 = -0.33$ and $\lambda_1 = -0.2$ from left to right. In the middle image the unstable periodic orbit (red) generated in the Hopf bifurcation is depicted.

this one-parameter family. Let $\lambda_1 < 0$. The eigenvalues of the equilibria $E^{\pm} = E^{\pm}(\lambda)$ are the eigenvalues $\mu_i^{\pm} = \mu_i^{\pm}(\lambda)$, $i = 1, 2$, of

$$D_{(x,y)}f(E^{\pm},\lambda) = \begin{pmatrix} 0 & 1 \\ \Lambda_{21}^{\pm} & \Lambda_{22}^{\pm} \end{pmatrix}.$$

Here $\Lambda_{21}^{\pm} = \pm 2\sqrt{-\lambda_1}$ and $\Lambda_{22}^{\pm} = \lambda_2 \pm \sqrt{-\lambda_1}$. We find that $\mu_i^{\pm}$ are the solutions of

$$\mu^2 - \Lambda_{22}^{\pm}\mu - \Lambda_{21}^{\pm} = 0. \tag{3.77}$$

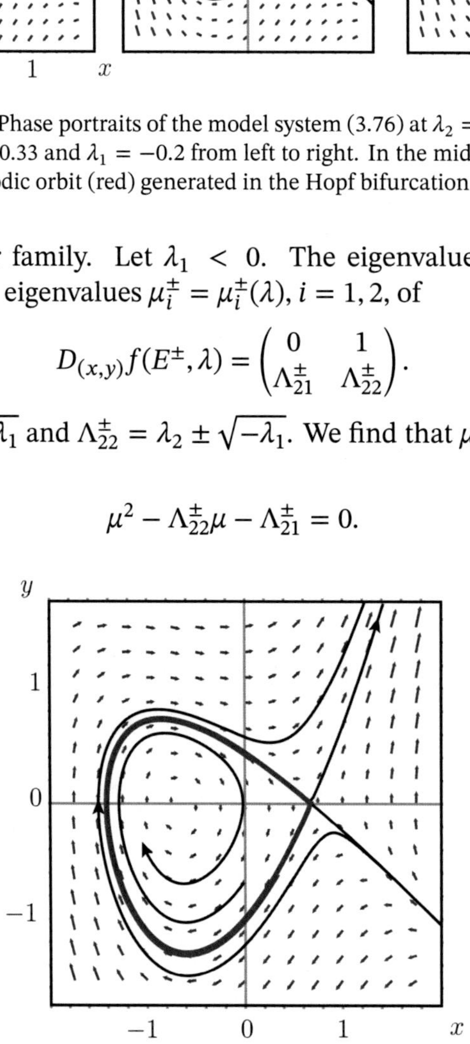

Figure 3.12. Phase portrait of the model system (3.76) at $\lambda_2 = 0.5$ and $\lambda_1 = -0.475$. The homoclinic orbit to E^+ is shown in blue. The orbit inside the homoclinic orbit indicates that the equilibrium E^- is stable.

First consider the equilibrium E^+. Then Λ_{21}^{+} is positive. By Vieta's formula $\mu_1^+\mu_2^+ = -\Lambda_{21}^{+} < 0$. This implies that $\mu_1^+, \mu_2^+ \in \mathbb{R} \setminus \{0\}$ and $\operatorname{sign} \mu_1^+ \neq \mu_2^+$. That means that throughout E^+ is a saddle.

For the other equilibrium E^-, $\Lambda_{21}^- < 0$. Hence $\mu_1^-\mu_2^- > 0$. This implies that either

$$\begin{aligned} &\text{(i)} \quad \mu_1^-, \mu_2^- \notin \mathbb{R} \quad \text{and} \quad \mu_1^- = \overline{\mu_2^-}, \quad \text{or} \\ &\text{(ii)} \quad \mu_1^-, \mu_2^- \in \mathbb{R} \quad \text{and} \quad \operatorname{sign}\mu_1^- = \operatorname{sign}\mu_2^-. \end{aligned}$$

That means that E^- is either asymptotically stable or unstable. Because of $\mu_1^- + \mu_2^- = \Lambda_{22}^-$, we find that E^- changes its stability if $\Lambda_{22}^- = \lambda_2 - \sqrt{-\lambda_1}$ changes sign. It follows from Theorem 3.49 that this is a curve of Hopf bifurcations. Exercise 3.24 asks us to analyze Hopf bifurcations for the present example.

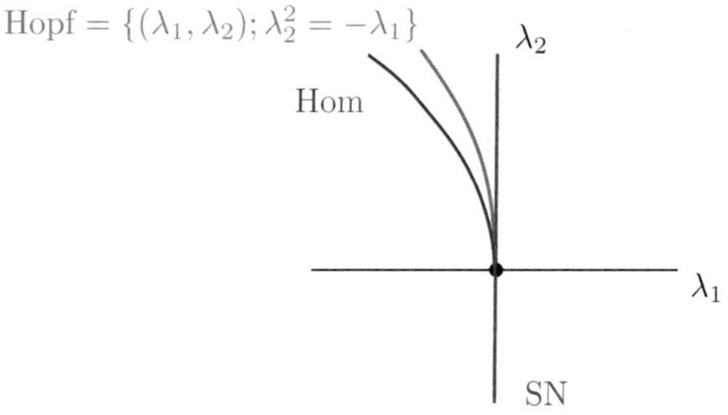

Figure 3.13. Tentative bifurcation set related to (3.76). Here SN stands for saddle-node, Hom stands for homoclinic.

In Figure 3.11 we see that (for fixed $\lambda_2 = 0.5$) the stable and unstable manifolds of E^+ change their relative position as λ_1 moves from -0.33 to -0.55. At the λ_1-value at which these manifolds coalesce, they form a homoclinic orbit to E^+; see Figure 3.12. When varying λ_2 we find a curve $\lambda_1^*(\lambda_2)$, the Hom curve, along which homoclinic orbits exist. Both the Hopf and the Hom curve are depicted in Figure 3.13. Their actual existence and shape will be verified in the proof of Theorem 3.49.

Studying the discriminant of (3.77) we find that there is a curve, located between SN and the Hopf curve at which $\mu_{1,2}^-$ changes from (i) to (ii). Note that this is not a bifurcation curve. The eigenvalues are real if λ is close to SN. So, at SN a node and a saddle coalesce and disappear. The node is stable if $\lambda_2 < 0$ and unstable if $\lambda_2 > 0$. ■

The following example indicates the occurrence of Bogdanov-Takens bifurcations in a simple model for neural oscillators.

Example 3.46. The following description is taken from [**178**], to which we refer for more information. The Wilson-Cowan model is a system of differential equations modeling a network of inhibitory and excitatory neurons. For a single inhibitory and excitatory neuron the model becomes a system $(\dot{x}, \dot{y}) =$

$f(x,y)$ of the form

$$\begin{aligned} \dot{x} &= -x + S(\rho + ax - by), \\ \dot{y} &= -y + S(\nu + cx - dy), \end{aligned} \tag{3.78}$$

for parameters ρ, ν and given constants a, b, c, d. For the activation function S we take the S-shaped function

$$S(x) = \frac{1}{1 + e^{-x}}.$$

Note that $S^{-1}(x) = \ln(x/(1-x))$.

Equilibria occur if

$$\begin{aligned} x &= S(\rho + ax - by), \\ y &= S(\nu + cx - dy), \end{aligned} \tag{3.79}$$

or, solving for ρ and ν, if

$$\begin{aligned} \rho &= S^{-1}(x) - ax + by, \\ \nu &= S^{-1}(y) - cx + dy, \end{aligned}$$

for $x, y \in (0,1)$. At an equilibrium (x,y), we find a Jacobian matrix

$$Df(x,y) = \begin{pmatrix} -1 + aS'(\rho + ax - by) & -bS'(\rho + ax - by) \\ cS'(\nu + cx - dy) & -1 - dS'(\nu + cx - dy) \end{pmatrix}.$$

As $S' = S(1-S)$ and using (3.79), we find

$$Df(x,y) = \begin{pmatrix} -1 + ax(1-x) & -bx(1-x) \\ cy(1-y) & -1 - dy(1-y) \end{pmatrix}.$$

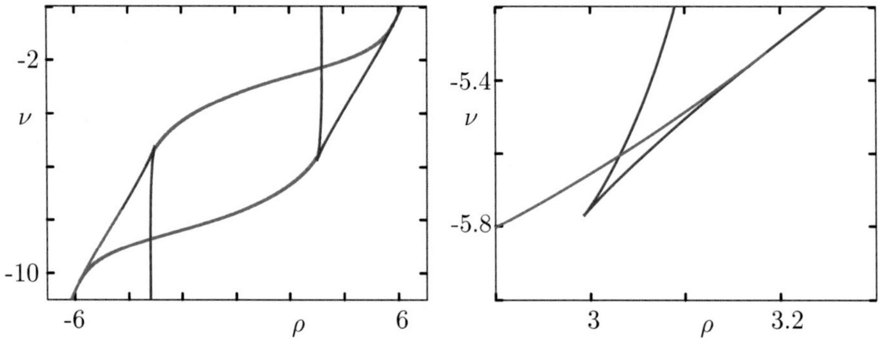

Figure 3.14. Curves of saddle-node bifurcations (red) and Hopf bifurcations (green) of (3.78) in the (ρ, ν)-parameter plane, for $a = b = c = 10$, $d = -1$. Visible are two cusp bifurcation values, and four Bogdanov-Takens bifurcation values where the saddle-node curves and Hopf curves touch tangentially. On the right is an enlargement of the bifurcation set near one of the cusp and Bogdanov-Takens bifurcation values.

A Hopf bifurcation occurs if the trace of $Df(x,y)$ vanishes, while the determinant is positive. A saddle-node bifurcation occurs if the determinant vanishes. Further conditions must be fulfilled for these bifurcations to be nondegenerate. An equilibrium with a double zero eigenvalue occurs if both determinant and trace of $Df(x,y)$ vanish. Writing $X = x(1-x)$ and $Y = y(1-y)$, this means

$$\begin{aligned} aX - dY &= 2, \\ (-ad+bc)XY &= 1, \end{aligned}$$

with $X, Y \in (0, 1/4]$. For fixed values of a, b, c, d one can solve these equations, find equilibria and parameter values ρ, ν with double zero eigenvalues for the Jacobian, and check bifurcation conditions from Theorem 3.49 for a nondegenerate and generically unfolding Bogdanov-Takens bifurcation. Figure 3.14 shows numerically calculated bifurcation curves, restricted to bifurcations of equilibria, for (3.78) with $a = b = c = 10$ and $d = -1$; see Exercise 3.27. ■

3.2.5.1. *Derivation of a normal form.* We look at a general family of differential equations

$$(\dot{x}, \dot{y}) = f(x, y, \lambda) \tag{3.80}$$

on the plane with $f(0,0,0) = (0,0)$ and $D_{(x,y)}f(0,0,0) = \begin{pmatrix} 0 & 1 \\ 0 & 0 \end{pmatrix}$. The parameter λ is two dimensional from $\mathbb{R}^2$. Before starting the actual bifurcation analysis, we put the differential equations into normal form. This is done in the next two lemmas.

Lemma 3.47. *The differential equations* (3.80) *are smoothly equivalent to*

$$\begin{aligned} \dot{x} &= y, \\ \dot{y} &= G_0(x,\lambda) + yG_1(x,\lambda) + y^2 G_2(x,y,\lambda), \end{aligned}$$

where G_0, G_1, G_2 are smooth functions in their arguments.

Proof. In Example B.24, the normal form theorem, Theorem B.20, is applied to provide the following normal form for $\lambda = 0$ (Exercise 3.28 asks for details): the vector field (3.80) is smoothly equivalent to

$$\begin{aligned} \dot{x} &= y + Q_1(x,y), \\ \dot{y} &= G(x) + yH(x) + Q_2(x,y), \end{aligned} \tag{3.81}$$

where $G(x)$ is a quadratic term ax^2, $H(x)$ is a linear term bx, and

$$Q_1, Q_2 = \mathcal{O}\left(\|(x,y)\|^3\right).$$

We may thus write

$$\begin{aligned} \dot{x} &= y + Q_1(x,y,\lambda), \\ \dot{y} &= G(x,\lambda) + yH(x,\lambda) + Q_2(x,y,\lambda), \end{aligned}$$

where G, H, Q_1, Q_2 are smooth functions that equal the functions in (3.81) if $\lambda = 0$.

Write $(u, v) = (x, y + Q_1(x, y, \lambda))$. This defines (u, v) as new coordinates near $(0, 0)$. In these new coordinates we get $\dot{u} = v$. Recycling notation and writing the obtained differential equations again in terms of x, y, we thus find an equation of the desired form

$$\begin{aligned} \dot{x} &= y, \\ \dot{y} &= G_0(x, \lambda) + yG_1(x, \lambda) + y^2 G_2(x, y, \lambda). \end{aligned}$$ □

The following lemma gives simplified expressions for G_0, G_1 that can be obtained under open conditions on derivatives. We keep writing G_0, G_1, G_2 for the functions appearing in the formulas. Two possible normal forms arise. They differ in the sign of a coefficient.

Lemma 3.48. *Assuming conditions (3.83) and (3.84) on derivatives of G_0 and G_1 stated in the proof below, the differential equations (3.80) are smoothly equivalent to differential equations*

$$\begin{aligned} \dot{x} &= y, \\ \dot{y} &= G_0(x, \lambda) + yG_1(x, \lambda) + y^2 G_2(x, y, \lambda), \end{aligned} \tag{3.82}$$

with

$$\begin{aligned} G_0(x, \lambda) &= \mu(\lambda) + x^2, \\ G_1(x, \lambda) &= \nu(\lambda) \pm x + x^2 G_3(x, \lambda). \end{aligned}$$

Here $\mu, \nu, G_0, G_1, G_2, G_3$ are smooth functions in their arguments.

Proof. We can start with differential equations of the form (3.82) with smooth functions G_0, G_1, G_2. First we simplify the expression for $G_0(x, \lambda)$. Multiply the differential equations by the smooth positive function $1 + \alpha x$:

$$\begin{aligned} \dot{x} &= (1 + \alpha x)y, \\ \dot{y} &= (1 + \alpha x)G_0(x, \lambda) + y(1 + \alpha x)G_1(x, \lambda) + y^2(1 + \alpha x)G_2(x, y, \lambda). \end{aligned}$$

Consider a corresponding coordinate change (in a sufficiently small neighborhood of $(x, y) = (0, 0)$)

$$\begin{aligned} u &= x, \\ v &= y(1 + \alpha x). \end{aligned}$$

In the new coordinates,

$$\begin{aligned}\dot{u} &= v,\\ \dot{v} &= (1+\alpha u)^2 G_0(u,\lambda) + v(1+\alpha u)G_1(u,\lambda) + v^2 G_2\left(u, \frac{v}{1+\alpha u}, \lambda\right)\\ &\quad + \alpha\frac{v^2}{1+\alpha u}.\end{aligned}$$

Writing $G_0(x,\lambda) = a + bx + cx^2 + \mathcal{O}(x^3)$ with coefficients a, b, c that depend on the parameter λ, we get

$$\begin{aligned}\dot{u} &= v,\\ \dot{v} &= a + (b + 2\alpha a)u + (c + 2\alpha b + \alpha^2 a)u^2 + \mathcal{O}(u^3)\\ &\quad + v(1+\alpha u)G_1(u,\lambda) + v^2 G_2\left(u, \frac{v}{1+\alpha u}, \lambda\right) + \frac{\alpha v^2}{1+\alpha u}.\end{aligned}$$

Choose $\alpha = -b/(2a)$ so that the coefficient $b + 2\alpha a$ of the u term in the expression for $\dot{v}$ becomes zero. Going back to notation with x and y coordinates, we have equations of the form

$$\begin{aligned}\dot{x} &= y,\\ \dot{y} &= G_0(x,\lambda) + yG_1(x,\lambda) + y^2 G_2(x,y,\lambda),\end{aligned}$$

with $G_0(x,\lambda) = a + \tilde{c}x^2 + \mathcal{O}(x^3)$. We have thus removed $\mathcal{O}(x)$ terms from G_0. Note that G_0, G_1, G_2 are different from before.

Now assume the condition

$$\tilde{c} \neq 0. \tag{3.83}$$

A similar technique provides a smooth equivalence to an equation in which $\tilde{c} = 1$. Consider the case where $\tilde{c} > 0$. Multiply the differential equations by a positive parameter dependent factor γ and change coordinates $u = x$, $v = \gamma y$. Choosing γ such that $\gamma^2\tilde{c} = 1$, we arrive at differential equations (again taking notation x and y for the variables)

$$\begin{aligned}\dot{x} &= y,\\ \dot{y} &= G_0(x,\lambda) + yG_1(x,\lambda) + y^2 G_2(x,y,\lambda),\end{aligned}$$

with $G_0(x,\lambda) = \mu(\lambda) + x^2 + \mathcal{O}(x^3)$ for a smooth function μ. Note that G_1 and G_2 have also changed. If $\tilde{c} < 0$, we multiply by $-\gamma$, with $\gamma > 0$ satisfying $-\gamma^2\tilde{c} = 1$, and take new coordinates $u = -x$, $v = \gamma y$.

By the Morse lemma, Theorem 2.46, one can write $G_0(x,\lambda) = \mu(\lambda) + h(x,\lambda)^2$ for a smooth function $h(x,\lambda)$ with $D_x h(0,0) = 1$. See also Exercise 3.29 and computations in Example 2.40 (note that we include the parameter λ here). Take a coordinate $z = h(x,\lambda)$ and calculate $\dot{z} = D_x h(x,\lambda)\dot{x} = y(1 + R(x,\lambda))$

with $R(x,\lambda) = \mathcal{O}(x)$ and $\dot{y} = \mu(\lambda) + z^2 + \mathcal{O}(y)$. Performing a time reparametrization by multiplying with the factor $1/(1+R(x,\lambda))$, we arrive at differential equations (again taking notation x and y for the variables)

$$\begin{aligned}\dot{x} &= y,\\ \dot{y} &= G_0(x,\lambda) + yG_1(x,\lambda) + y^2G_2(x,y,\lambda),\end{aligned}$$

with $G_0(x,\lambda) = (\mu(\lambda) + x^2)/(1 + R(x,\lambda))$. Note that G_1 and G_2 have also changed.

We continue the reasoning from here to remove the term $1 + R(x,\lambda)$. For convenience we write $S(x,\lambda) = 1/(1 + R(x,\lambda))$. So we have a system of differential equations

$$\begin{aligned}\dot{x} &= y,\\ \dot{y} &= (\mu + x^2)S(x,\lambda) + yG_1(x,\lambda) + y^2G_2(x,y,\lambda),\end{aligned}$$

where $S(x,\lambda) = 1 + \mathcal{O}(x)$. Multiply with a positive function $T(x,\lambda)$:

$$\begin{aligned}\dot{x} &= yT(x,\lambda),\\ \dot{y} &= (\mu + x^2)S(x,\lambda)T(x,\lambda) + yT(x,\lambda)G_1(x,\lambda) + y^2T(x,\lambda)G_2(x,y,\lambda).\end{aligned}$$

Take new coordinates

$$\begin{aligned}u &= x,\\ v &= yT(x,\lambda).\end{aligned}$$

Then

$$\begin{aligned}\dot{u} &= v,\\ \dot{v} &= (\mu + u^2)S(u,\lambda)T(u,\lambda)^2 + vT(u,\lambda)G_1(u,\lambda) + v^2G_2(u, v/T(u,\lambda),\lambda)\\ &\quad + v^2\frac{D_xT(u,\lambda)}{T(u,\lambda)}.\end{aligned}$$

Since S is close to 1, we can choose T such that $S(u,\lambda)T(u,\lambda)^2 = 1$. Recycling notation and writing x and y for the variables, we have obtained equations of the form

$$\begin{aligned}\dot{x} &= y,\\ \dot{y} &= \mu + x^2 + yG_1(x,\lambda) + y^2G_2(x,y,\lambda).\end{aligned}$$

Note again that G_1 and G_2 have changed.

Finally we simplify the expression for $G_1(x,\lambda)$. Write $G_1(x,\lambda) = \nu + ex + \mathcal{O}(x^2)$, with ν and e smooth functions of λ. Assume

$$e \neq 0. \tag{3.84}$$

We can get $e = \pm 1$. This can be achieved by a time transformation $t = |e|s$ by which effectively the vector field will be multiplied by $|e|$, and afterwards taking coordinates $(u, v) = (e^2 x, e^2|e|y)$. Note that in this process μ and ν will be changed. The lemma is thus proved assuming the conditions (3.83) and (3.84). □

3.2.5.2. *Bifurcation theorem.* We start from the normal form in Lemma 3.48. Assume that $(\mu(0), \nu(0)) = (0, 0)$ and that the derivative of $\lambda \to (\mu(\lambda), \nu(\lambda))$ at $\lambda = (0, 0)$ has maximal rank. Then we may take μ and ν as parameters. With this the normal form derived in Lemma 3.48 is given by

$$\begin{aligned} \dot{x} &= y, \\ \dot{y} &= x^2 + \mu + \nu y \pm xy + \mu + x^2 + yx^2 G_3(x, \mu, \nu) + y^2 G_2(x, y, \mu, \nu). \end{aligned} \tag{3.85}$$

Here functions of the form $g(\ldots, \lambda(\mu, \nu))$ have been renamed $g(\ldots, \mu, \nu)$. In the same spirit we denote the vector field related to (3.85) by $f = f(x, y, \mu, \nu)$.

The following bifurcation theorem describes the unfolding for the normal form (3.85).

Theorem 3.49 (Planar Bogdanov-Takens bifurcation). *Consider* (3.85) *in the case where the coefficient of the xy term in the equation for $\dot{y}$ is $+1$. In the (μ, ν) parameter plane, the bifurcation set consists of the following bifurcation curves.*

(1) *Saddle-node bifurcations occur along $\mu = 0$. Two equilibria arise for $\mu < 0$.*
(2) *There is a curve*

$$\text{Hopf} = \{(\mu, \nu)\ ;\ \nu > 0,\ \nu^2 = -\mu + o(\mu)\}$$

of subcritical Hopf bifurcations; repelling periodic orbits are created when crossing the curve along lines with constant μ with ν decreasing.
(3) *There is a curve*

$$\text{Hom} = \{(\mu, \nu)\ ;\ \nu > 0,\ \nu^2 = -\frac{25}{49}\mu + o(\mu)\}$$

of homoclinic bifurcations; repelling periodic orbits are created when crossing the curve along lines with constant μ with ν increasing.

For each parameter value in between the Hopf bifurcation and the homoclinic bifurcation curve, the system has a unique repelling periodic orbit.

The bifurcation diagram of the Bogdanov-Takens bifurcation is displayed in Figure 3.15.

Remark 3.50. The case where the coefficient of the xy term in the equation for $\dot{y}$ equals -1 is reduced to the case where it equals $+1$ by changing the direction of time and signs of y and ν; see Exercise 3.30. ■

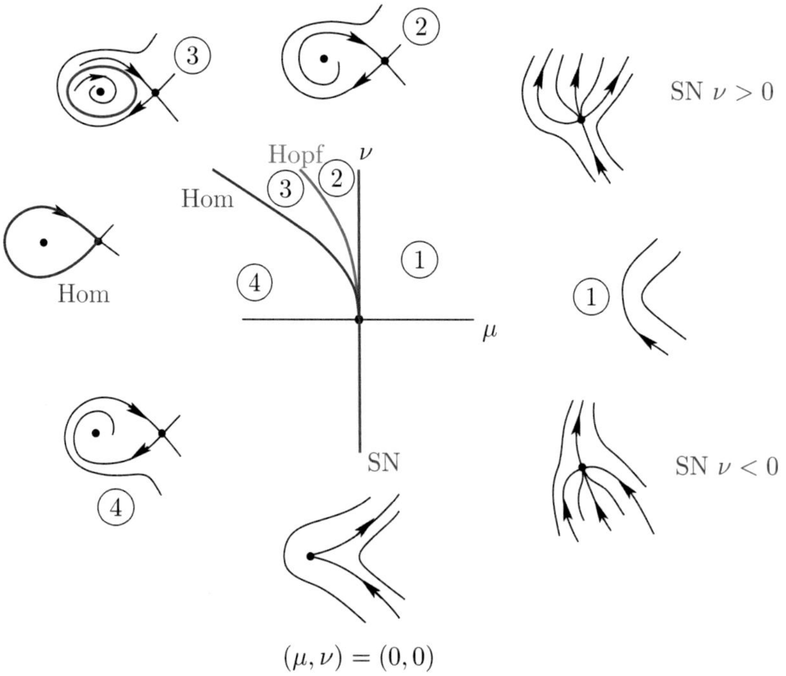

Figure 3.15. The bifurcation diagram from Theorem 3.49.

3.2.5.3. *Proof of Theorem* 3.49. In the following we start analyzing the system to derive the bifurcation diagram. With adaptations to make the presentation self-contained, we follow arguments from [**316**].

We start with an analysis of the equilibria and their stability. Equilibria occur if

$$\begin{aligned} y &= 0, \\ x^2 + \mu &= 0. \end{aligned}$$

Consider the differential equation along curves $(\hat{\mu}(s), \hat{\nu}(s))$ with $\hat{\mu}(0) = 0$ and $\hat{\mu}'(0) > 0$ in parameter space. Then the above shows that for $s < 0$ there are two equilibria $E^+ = (x^+, 0)$ and $E^- = (x^-, 0)$, with $x^+ > 0$ and $x^- < 0$, which merge to $(x, y) = (0, 0)$ and disappear if s passes zero. Analyzing $D_{(x,y)} f(E^\pm, \mu^*(E^\pm, \nu), \nu)$ yields (compare also the corresponding calculations in Example 3.45) that E^+ is a saddle and E^- is a node (for $|s|$ sufficiently small). Moreover, E^- is unstable for $\nu > 0$ and stable for $\nu < 0$.

This shows that along each curve $(\hat{\mu}(s), \hat{\nu}(s))$ with $\hat{\mu}(0) = 0$ and $\hat{\mu}'(0) > 0$, that is along each curve which intersects the ν-axis transversely, a saddle-node bifurcation of the equilibrium $(0, 0)$ occurs at $s = 0$.

Singular rescaling to a perturbed Hamiltonian system. The further investigation, including an analysis of the Hopf bifurcation, will use a singular rescaling. This will effectively blow up a small parameter dependent region to unit size. It also rescales parameters. The formulas of the singular rescaling, depending on a small parameter $\varepsilon > 0$, are

$$\begin{aligned} x &= \varepsilon^2 u, \qquad & y &= \varepsilon^3 v, \\ \mu &= \varepsilon^4 \bar{\mu}, \qquad & \nu &= \varepsilon^2 \bar{\nu}. \end{aligned} \tag{3.86}$$

The rescaling is defined on a compact domain: variables (u, v) are taken from a (large enough) compact set. Also $\bar{\nu}$ is taken from a compact sufficiently large interval $[-\bar{\nu}_0, \bar{\nu}_0]$ and ε from some compact interval $[0, K]$; see Figure 3.16.

In what follows we use variables u, v and parameters ε and $\bar{\nu}$, while having $\bar{\mu}$ fixed as -1. Then a curve $\mu = a\nu^2$, $a < 0$, $\nu > 0$ in the (μ, ν)-plane will be transformed into straight line $\bar{\nu}^2 = -1/a$.

In the new coordinates u, v the differential equation (3.85) becomes

$$\begin{aligned} \varepsilon^2 \dot{u} &= \varepsilon^3 v, \\ \varepsilon^3 \dot{v} &= -\varepsilon^4 + \varepsilon^4 u^2 + \varepsilon^3 v \left(\varepsilon^2 \bar{\nu} + \varepsilon^2 u + \varepsilon^4 u^2 G_3(\varepsilon^2 u, \varepsilon, \bar{\nu})\right) \\ &\quad + \varepsilon^6 v^2 G_2(\varepsilon^2 u, \varepsilon^3 v, \varepsilon, \bar{\nu}) \\ &= -\varepsilon^4 + \varepsilon^4 u^2 + \varepsilon^5 v(\bar{\nu} + u) + \mathcal{O}(\varepsilon^6). \end{aligned} \tag{3.87}$$

Hence

$$\begin{aligned} \frac{1}{\varepsilon}\dot{u} &= v, \\ \frac{1}{\varepsilon}\dot{v} &= -1 + u^2 + \varepsilon v(\bar{\nu} + u) + \mathcal{O}(\varepsilon^2). \end{aligned}$$

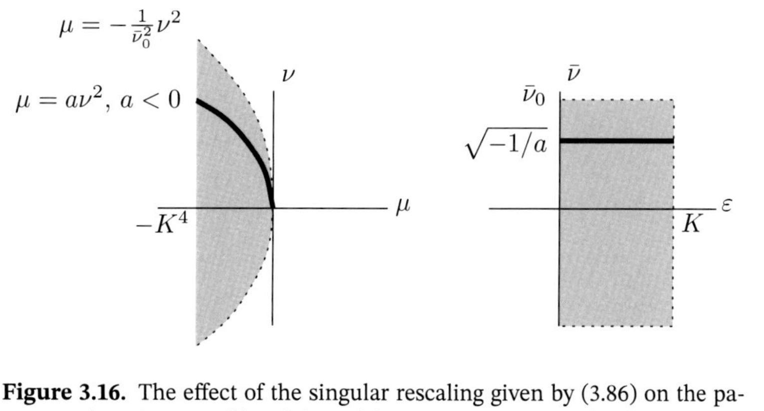

Figure 3.16. The effect of the singular rescaling given by (3.86) on the parameter domain: a small bowl shaped domain in the original (μ, ν)-parameter plane maps to a square in the new parameters $(\varepsilon, \bar{\nu})$.

Removing the factor $\frac{1}{\varepsilon}$ which amounts to a time rescaling, we arrive at a system of differential equations

$$\begin{aligned} \dot{u} &= v, \\ \dot{v} &= -1 + u^2 + \varepsilon v(\bar{v} + u) + \mathcal{O}(\varepsilon^2). \end{aligned} \tag{3.88}$$

The thing to observe here is that (3.88) is a perturbation of the Hamiltonian vector field

$$\begin{aligned} \dot{u} &= v, \\ \dot{v} &= -1 + u^2 \end{aligned} \tag{3.89}$$

with Hamiltonian

$$H(u, v) = \frac{1}{2}v^2 + u - \frac{1}{3}u^3.$$

The Hamiltonian vector field (3.89) has two equilibria, a hyperbolic saddle $S = (1, 0)$ and a focus $E = (-1, 0)$. The stable manifold of S is the union of the equilibrium S and two separate orbits, each called a stable separatrix, that converge to S in positive time. The unstable manifold likewise contains two unstable separatrices. Visible in Figure 3.17 is that one of the unstable separatrices of S equals one of its stable separatrices, thus forming a homoclinic orbit.

From (3.87) we find that equilibria of the perturbed vector field (3.88) are, for all values of $\varepsilon, \bar{v}$, at

$$\begin{aligned} E &= (-1, 0), \\ S &= (1, 0). \end{aligned}$$

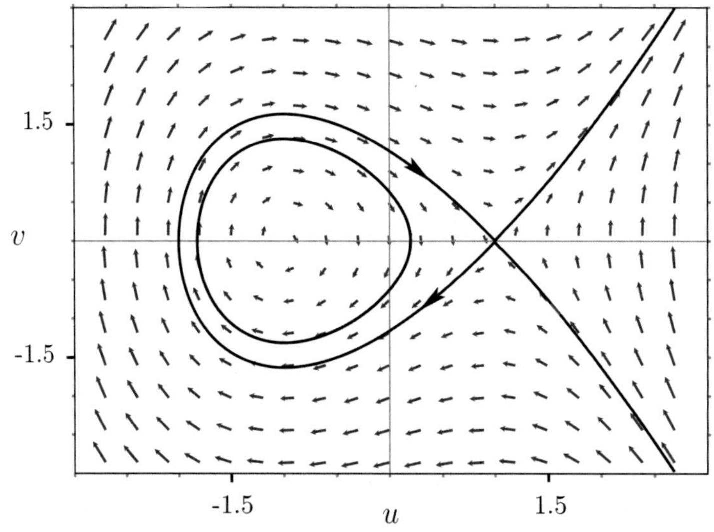

Figure 3.17. Phase portrait of the Hamiltonian vector field (3.89).

First return maps and the Bogdanov function. We will spend considerable space to study dynamics and bifurcations of the perturbed Hamiltonian system (3.88). Use the value of the Hamiltonian as coordinate on the line segment $L = \{v = 0, u \leq -1\}$ to the left of E. That is, we introduce a coordinate

$$h = H(u, 0). \tag{3.90}$$

Note that $H(\cdot, 0)$ is strictly monotonically decreasing on $(-\infty, -1]$.

The Hamiltonian at the equilibrium E has a value $H(E) = -\frac{2}{3}$. For $h \in L$ take the positive orbit piece until its first intersection with L and write $\Pi = \Pi_{\varepsilon,\bar{\nu}}$ for the resulting first return map; see Figure 3.18. Note that Π is defined on the interval in L between the first intersection W of a stable separatrix of S with L, and E. Denoting by $\hat{\Pi}$ the first return map in a u-coordinate, we find

$$H(\hat{\Pi}(u), 0) = \Pi(H(u, 0)) = \Pi(h). \tag{3.91}$$

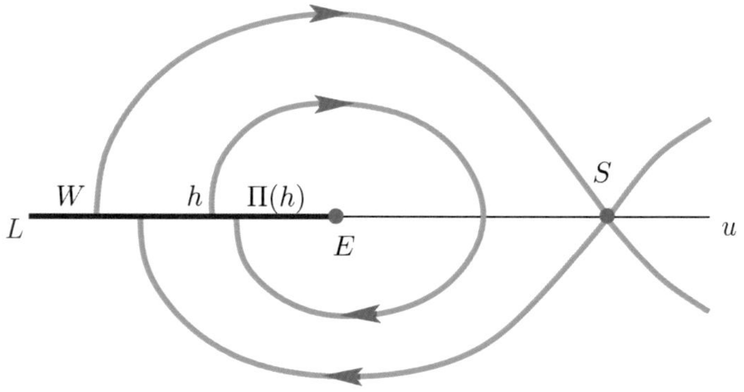

Figure 3.18. The first return map Π is defined on the line piece in $\{v = 0\}$ connecting W to E. The splitting function Δ is given as the difference $\Pi(h) - h$.

A periodic orbit occurs if $\Pi(h) = h$, and so we are interested in solving the fixed point equation $\Pi(h) = h$. Write

$$\Delta(h) = \Pi(h) - h \tag{3.92}$$

for the splitting function. Note that Δ, as also Π, depends also on ε and $\bar{\nu}$. In case we want to stress this dependence, we write $\Delta_{\varepsilon,\bar{\nu}}(h)$. Let $H(u_h, 0) = h$. Then (see also (3.91) and (3.90))

$$\Delta(h) = H(\hat{\Pi}(u_h), 0) - H(u_h, 0). \tag{3.93}$$

The following lemma gives an expansion for Δ. Let

$$\omega = \omega_1\, du + \omega_2\, dv = (1 - u^2)\, du + v\, dv - \varepsilon v(\bar{\nu} + u)\, du + o(\varepsilon)$$

be the one-form dual to the vector field (if $X = (X_1, X_2)$ is the vector field that gives the differential equations (3.88), then $\omega(X) = \omega_1 X_1 + \omega_2 X_2 = 0$). With

$H = \frac{1}{2}v^2 + u - \frac{1}{3}u^3$ we have $dH = (1-u^2)\,du + v\,dv$. The one-form ω is a perturbation of the Hamiltonian form dH. Denote

$$\omega_D = v(\bar{\nu} + u)\,du.$$

So

$$\omega = dH - \varepsilon\omega_D + o(\varepsilon).$$

Lemma 3.51. *Given $h \in L$, write γ_h for the closed orbit of the Hamiltonian system* (3.89) *that contains the point h. Then*

$$\Delta(h) = \varepsilon \int_{\gamma_h} \omega_D + o(\varepsilon).$$

Proof. Let Γ_1 be the orbit piece of (3.88) through h from h to $\Pi(h)$, and let Γ_2 be the line piece connecting h and $\Pi(h)$ inside the u-axis. Write $\Gamma = \Gamma_1 \cup \Gamma_2$ for the resulting closed curve by combining both pieces. As Γ_1 is an orbit piece and $\omega(X) = 0$, we get $\int_{\Gamma_1} \omega = 0$. Compute

$$\begin{aligned}
\int_\Gamma \omega &= \int_{\Gamma_1} \omega + \int_{\Gamma_2} \omega \\
&= \int_{\Gamma_2} \omega \\
&= \int_{\Gamma_2} dH + \varepsilon \int_{\Gamma_2} -\omega_D + o(\varepsilon) \\
&= -\Delta(h) + o(\varepsilon)
\end{aligned} \tag{3.94}$$

as $\int_{\Gamma_2} dH = -\Delta(h)$ (see (3.93)) and the length of Γ_2 shrinks to 0 as $\varepsilon \to 0$. The one-chain $\Gamma - \gamma_h$ bounds a two-chain σ. From Stokes's theorem it follows that

$$\begin{aligned}
\int_{\Gamma - \gamma_h} \omega &= \int_\sigma d\omega \\
&= \int_\sigma ddH - \varepsilon d\omega_D + o(\varepsilon) \\
&= -\varepsilon \int_\sigma d\omega_D + o(\varepsilon) \\
&= o(\varepsilon)
\end{aligned} \tag{3.95}$$

since the area of σ shrinks to 0 as $\varepsilon \to 0$. Combining (3.94) and (3.95) and using $\int_{\gamma_h} dH = 0$ (recall that γ_h is an orbit of the related Hamiltonian system (3.89)) proves

$$\begin{aligned}\Delta(h) &= -\int_{\Gamma} \omega + o(\varepsilon) \\ &= -\int_{\gamma_h} \omega + o(\varepsilon) \\ &= \varepsilon \int_{\gamma_h} \omega_D + o(\varepsilon).\end{aligned}$$ □

To get further we must study the Melnikov function $\frac{d}{d\epsilon}\Delta(h)|_{\epsilon=0}$,

$$I(h, \bar{\nu}) = \int_{\gamma_h} \omega_D. \tag{3.96}$$

Decompose

$$I(h, \bar{\nu}) = \bar{\nu} I_0(h) + I_1(h)$$

with

$$I_0(h) = \int_{\gamma_h} v\, du \quad \text{and} \quad I_1(h) = \int_{\gamma_h} vu\, du.$$

Due to the structure of ω_D both I_0 and I_1 depend only on h.

Proposition 3.52. *The function I_0 is a continuous function that is positive for all $h \in (-\frac{2}{3}, \frac{2}{3}]$. The Bogdanov function*

$$B(h) = -I_1(h)/I_0(h)$$

is well defined and continuous on $[-\frac{2}{3}, \frac{2}{3}]$ with $B(-\frac{2}{3}) = 1$, $B(\frac{2}{3}) = \frac{5}{7}$. It is continuously differentiable on $[-\frac{2}{3}, \frac{2}{3})$ with $B'(h) < 0$ on $[-\frac{2}{3}, \frac{2}{3})$ and $B'(h) \to -\infty$ as $h \to \frac{2}{3}$.

Proof. Write σ_h for the domain bounded by γ_h. Using Stokes's theorem,

$$\begin{aligned}I_0(h) &= -\int_{\gamma_h} v\, du \\ &= -\int_{\sigma_h} dv du \\ &= \int_{\sigma_h} du dv\end{aligned}$$

equals the area of σ_h and is therefore positive for $h \in (-\frac{2}{3}, \frac{2}{3}]$. From the similarly derived formula

$$I_1(h) = \int_{\sigma_h} u\, du dv$$

we find that $m(h) \le I_i(h) \le M(h)$ for

$$m(h) = \min\{u\ ;\ (u,v) \in \gamma_h\},$$
$$M(h) = \max\{u\ ;\ (u,v) \in \gamma_h\}$$

and $h \in (-\frac{2}{3}, \frac{2}{3}]$. Note that $\lim_{h\to -\frac{2}{3}} m(h) = \lim_{h\to -\frac{2}{3}} M(h) = -1$. We conclude that $\lim_{h\to -\frac{2}{3}} B(h) = 1$ and that B is well defined and continuous on $[-\frac{2}{3}, \frac{2}{3}]$.

Calculations show that B satisfies a Ricatti differential equation

$$(9h^2 - 4)B' - 7h^2 - 3hB + 5 = 0.$$

We postpone the calculations to Lemma 3.53 below. From it we infer that the graph of $B(h)$ is an orbit of

$$\dot{h} = -(9h^2 - 4),$$
$$\dot{b} = -(7b^2 + 3hb - 5). \tag{3.97}$$

Since $B(-\frac{2}{3}) = 1$ and $\dot{b} = 5$ along $b = 0$, the upper half-plane $\{b > 0\}$ is forward invariant. The graph of B is contained in the upper half-plane. In the upper half-plane, this differential equation has equilibria at $(-\frac{2}{3}, 1)$ and $(\frac{2}{3}, \frac{5}{7})$. One checks that $(-\frac{2}{3}, 1)$ is a hyperbolic saddle, while $(\frac{2}{3}, \frac{5}{7})$ is a hyperbolic sink. The region

$$K = \left\{(h,b)\ ;\ -\frac{2}{3} \le h \le \frac{2}{3}, 0 \le b \le C\right\}$$

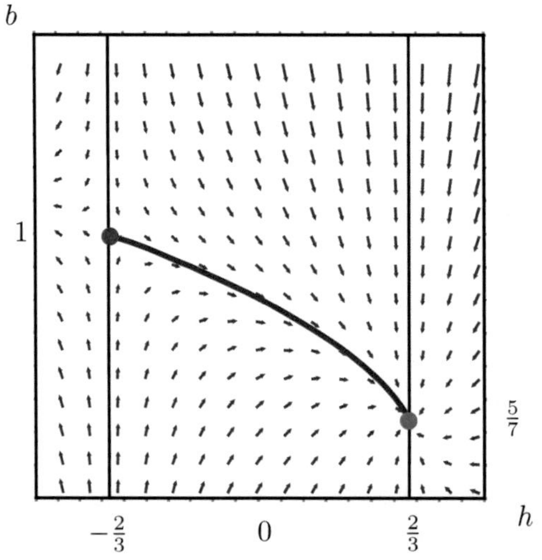

Figure 3.19. The flow of (3.97) including the orbit connecting the saddle $(-\frac{2}{3}, 1)$ to the sink $(\frac{2}{3}, \frac{5}{7})$ that defines the graph of the Bogdanov function B.

for large enough $C > 0$ is forward invariant. In the interior of K, orbits move to larger values of h and hence converge to $(\frac{2}{3}, \frac{5}{7})$. It follows that the graph of B is given as the unstable separatrix of $(-\frac{2}{3}, 1)$ inside K; see Figure 3.19.

Look at the linearization of the vector field (3.97) around $(\frac{2}{3}, \frac{5}{7})$:

$$\begin{pmatrix} -12 & 0 \\ -\frac{15}{7} & -12 \end{pmatrix}.$$

The linear vector field given by this linearization has solution

$$\begin{aligned} x(t) &= e^{-12t} x_0, \\ y(t) &= -\frac{15}{7} x_0 t e^{-12t} + y_0 e^{-12t}. \end{aligned}$$

We find that y is given as function of x with formula

$$y(x) = \frac{5}{28} x \ln(x/x_0) + (y_0/x_0)x.$$

By Remark B.29 there are smooth coordinates linearizing the flow near $(\frac{2}{3}, \frac{5}{7})$. We conclude

$$B(h) = \frac{5}{7} + \frac{5}{28}\left(h - \frac{2}{3}\right)\ln\left(\left|h - \frac{2}{3}\right|\right) + \psi(h), \tag{3.98}$$

for a continuously differentiable ψ with $\psi(\frac{2}{3}) = 0$. Therefore $B'(h) \to -\infty$ as $h \to \frac{2}{3}$. □

In the proof of Proposition 3.52 we made use of a Ricatti equation for B. This Ricatti equation is obtained in the following lemma.

Lemma 3.53. *The Bogdanov function B satisfies a Ricatti differential equation*

$$(9h^2 - 4)B' - 7h^2 - 3hB + 5 = 0.$$

Proof. The equation for γ_h is $H(u, v) = \frac{1}{2}v^2 + u - \frac{1}{3}u^3 = h$. Write $v^+(u, h) = \sqrt{2\left(\frac{1}{3}u^3 - u + h\right)}$ for the function whose graph gives the part of γ_h in $\{v \geq 0\}$. By symmetry,

$$\begin{aligned} I_0(h) &= 2\int_{m(h)}^{M(h)} v^+(u, h)\, du, \\ I_1(h) &= 2\int_{m(h)}^{M(h)} u v^+(u, h)\, du. \end{aligned}$$

Differentiating with respect to h yields

$$\begin{aligned} I_0'(h) &= 2\int_{m(h)}^{M(h)} \frac{1}{v^+(u,h)}\,du + 2v^+(M(h),h)M'(h) - 2v^+(m(h),h)m'(h) \\ &= 2\int_{m(h)}^{M(h)} \frac{1}{v^+(u,h)}\,du \end{aligned}$$

and

$$\begin{aligned} I_1'(h) &= 2\int_{m(h)}^{M(h)} \frac{1}{v^+(u,h)}\,du \\ &\quad + 2M(h)v^+(M(h),h)M'(h) - 2m(h)v^+(m(h),h)m'(h) \\ &= 2\int_{m(h)}^{M(h)} \frac{1}{v^+(u,h)}\,du. \end{aligned}$$

We introduce notation $I_j(h) = 2\int_{m(h)}^{M(h)} u^j v^+(u,h)\,du$. Rewriting $I_0(h)$ and $I_1(h)$ gives

$$\begin{aligned} I_0(h) &= 2\int_{m(h)}^{M(h)} \frac{1}{v^+(u,h)}(v^+(u,h))^2\,du \\ &= 2\int_{m(h)}^{M(h)} \frac{1}{v^+(u,h)}\left(2h - 2u + \frac{2}{3}u^3\right)du \\ &= 2hI_0'(h) - 2I_1'(h) + \frac{2}{3}I_3'(h) \end{aligned} \tag{3.99}$$

and likewise

$$I_1(h) = 2hI_1'(h) - 2I_2'(h) + \frac{2}{3}I_4'(h). \tag{3.100}$$

Partial integration gives further relations

$$\begin{aligned} I_0(h) &= uv^+(u,h)\big|_{m(h)}^{M(h)} + \int_{m(h)}^{M(h)} \frac{1}{v^+(u,h)}u(1-u^2)\,du \\ &= I_1'(h) - I_3'(h) \end{aligned} \tag{3.101}$$

and

$$I_0(h) = I_2'(h) - I_4'(h). \tag{3.102}$$

Eliminating $I_3'(h)$ from (3.99) and (3.101), and likewise eliminating $I_4'(h)$ from (3.100) and (3.102), gives

$$\begin{aligned} 5I_0(h) &= -4I_1'(h) + 6hI_0'(h), \\ 7I_1(h) &= -4I_2'(h) + 6hI_1'(h). \end{aligned} \tag{3.103}$$

It turns out that $I_0 = I_2$. To see this, observe

$$\begin{aligned} v\,du - vu^2\,du &= v(1-u^2)\,du + v^2\,dv - v^2\,dv \\ &= v\,dH - d(\frac{1}{3}v^3), \end{aligned}$$

so that $\int_{\gamma_h} v\,du - vu^2\,du = \int_{\gamma_h} v\,dH - d(\frac{1}{3}v^3) = 0$ since γ_h is a closed level curve of H. So indeed $I_0 = I_2$. Plugging $I_2 = I_0$ into equations (3.103) we get

$$\begin{aligned} 5I_0(h) &= -4I_1'(h) + 6hI_0'(h), \\ 7I_1(h) &= -4I_0'(h) + 6hI_1'(h). \end{aligned}$$

Solve this linear system for $I_0'(h)$ and $I_1'(h)$ as functions of $I_0(h), I_1(h)$ to get

$$\begin{aligned} I_0'(h) &= \frac{1}{9h^2-4}\left(\frac{15}{2}hI_0(h) + 7I_1(h)\right), \\ I_1'(h) &= \frac{1}{9h^2-4}\left(5I_0(h) + \frac{21}{2}hI_1(h)\right). \end{aligned}$$

Putting this in $B'(h) = \frac{I_0'(h)I_1(h) - I_1'(h)I_0(h)}{I_0^2(h)}$ yields $(9h^2-4)B'(h) = 7B^2(h) + 3hB(h) - 5$. □

The previous analysis gives most of the information we need on asymptotics of the first return map Π, with which we can analyze bifurcations of periodic orbits. In the following we use analysis to discuss the Hopf bifurcation and the homoclinic bifurcation, and more generally the existence of periodic orbits, for the perturbed Hamiltonian system (3.88).

The Hopf bifurcation curve. Here we discuss the existence of the Hopf bifurcation curve in Theorem 3.49 and periodic orbits close to it. Periodic orbits are given by fixed points $\Pi(h) = h$ and thus, compare (3.92), by zeros $\Delta(h) = 0$. Let

$$G_{\varepsilon,\bar{\nu}}(h) = \frac{1}{\varepsilon}\Delta_{\varepsilon,\bar{\nu}}(h) = I(h,\bar{\nu}) + o(1)$$

as $\varepsilon \to 0$. The latter equality follows from Lemma 3.51 and the definition of the Melnikov function in (3.96). To find periodic orbits we must find zeros of $\Delta_{\varepsilon,\bar{\nu}}$ which, for $\varepsilon \neq 0$, is equivalent to finding zeros of $G_{\varepsilon,\bar{\nu}}$. As $I_0(h)$ appearing in $I(\bar{\nu},h) = \bar{\nu}I_0(h) + I_1(h)$ is bounded away from zero by Proposition 3.52, this is equivalent to finding zeros of

$$F(h,\varepsilon,\bar{\nu}) = \frac{G_{\varepsilon,\bar{\nu}}(h)}{I_0(h)}.$$

Here

$$F(h,\varepsilon,\bar{\nu}) = \bar{\nu} - B(h) + o(1) \tag{3.104}$$

with the Bogdanov function $B = -I_1/I_0$ from Proposition 3.52. Using this notation, $\Delta(h)$ is given by

$$\Delta(h) = \varepsilon I_0(h)F(h, \varepsilon, \bar{\nu}). \tag{3.105}$$

At $h = \frac{2}{3}$ the Bogdanov function B is not differentiable. To avoid this complication we first consider values of h away from $\frac{2}{3}$. So take β with $-\frac{2}{3} < \beta < \frac{2}{3}$ and consider values of h from a compact interval $[-\frac{2}{3}, \beta]$ on which B is differentiable. Write

$$F(h, \varepsilon, \bar{\nu}) = \bar{\nu} - B(h) + \Xi(h, \varepsilon, \bar{\nu}),$$

where we know that $\Xi(h, \varepsilon, \bar{\nu}) \to 0$, together with derivatives, uniformly as $\varepsilon \to 0$.

Lemma 3.54. *Given $\beta < \frac{2}{3}$, there is $T_{\text{Hopf}} > 0$ and a function $L = L(h, \varepsilon)$ defined for all $\varepsilon \in [0, T_{\text{Hopf}}]$, $h \in [-\frac{2}{3}, \beta]$, such that $F(h, \varepsilon, L(h, \varepsilon)) = 0$. For fixed h*

$$\bar{\nu} = L(h, \varepsilon)$$

describes a curve of periodic orbits. The periodic orbits related to h are repelling. The curve $\bar{\nu} = L(-\frac{2}{3}, \varepsilon)$ is the Hopf curve.

Proof. First we prove the existence of periodic orbits for fixed h and ε. The reasoning is based on the intermediate value theorem. Recall that we consider $(\varepsilon, \bar{\nu})$ from a compact set $[0, K] \times [-\bar{\nu}_0, \bar{\nu}_0]$. We assume $\bar{\nu}_0 > 1$ so that $\bar{\nu}_0 - B(h)$ is positive (see Proposition 3.52). Note $\frac{\partial}{\partial \bar{\nu}} F(h, 0, \bar{\nu}) = 1$. There is $T \leq K$ depending on $\bar{\nu}_0$ and β so that

$$\frac{\partial F}{\partial \bar{\nu}}(h, \varepsilon, \bar{\nu}) > 0$$

for all $\varepsilon \in [0, T]$, $h \in [-\frac{2}{3}, \beta]$, $\bar{\nu} \in [-\bar{\nu}_0, \bar{\nu}_0]$. Letting $\bar{\nu}$ decrease from $\bar{\nu}_0$, we find a value $\bar{\nu} = L(h, \varepsilon)$ which solves $F(h, \varepsilon, \bar{\nu}) = 0$.

By the implicit function theorem, $(h, \varepsilon) \mapsto L(h, \varepsilon)$ is a continuously differentiable function which describes for fixed h a curve in $(\varepsilon, \bar{\nu})$-space; see also Figure 3.21.

From $F(h, \varepsilon, L(h, \varepsilon)) = 0$ we get by differentiating with respect to h that $\frac{\partial F}{\partial h} + \frac{\partial F}{\partial \bar{\nu}} \frac{\partial L}{\partial h} = 0$ and thus $\frac{\partial L}{\partial h} = -\frac{\partial F}{\partial h} / \frac{\partial F}{\partial \bar{\nu}}$. We see that for suitable $T_{\text{Hopf}} \leq T$,

$$\frac{\partial L}{\partial h}(h, \varepsilon) < 0.$$

So if $F(h, \varepsilon, \bar{\nu}) = 0$ for $\bar{\nu} = L(h, \varepsilon)$, then the periodic orbit through h is the unique periodic orbit at the parameter values $(\varepsilon, \bar{\nu})$.

Recall that $h = -\frac{2}{3}$ is related to the equilibrium E; see Figure 3.18. So, plugging in $h = -\frac{2}{3}$, the curve $\bar{\nu} = L(-\frac{2}{3}, \varepsilon)$ yields the Hopf bifurcation curve; see the green curve in Figure 3.21. From (3.104) we infer that the Hopf bifurcation curve is determined by

$$\bar{\nu}(\varepsilon) = L(-\tfrac{2}{3}, \varepsilon) = 1 + o(1) \tag{3.106}$$

using $B(-\frac{2}{3}) = 1$. The Hopf bifurcation is subcritical in the sense that periodic orbits occur when decreasing $\bar{\nu}$.

Finally we consider the stability of the periodic orbits. Finding zeros of $G_{\varepsilon,\bar{\nu}}$ is equivalent to finding fixed points of Π. Now, according to (3.92) and (3.105),

$$\Pi(h) = h + \Delta = h + \varepsilon I_0(h) F(h, \varepsilon, \bar{\nu}).$$

Fixing h and taking $\bar{\nu} = L(h, \varepsilon)$, so that $F(h, \varepsilon, L(h, \varepsilon)) = 0$, we find

$$\Pi'(h) = 1 + \varepsilon I_0(h) \frac{\partial F}{\partial h}(h, \varepsilon, L(h, \varepsilon)).$$

That this is larger than 1 for $\varepsilon > 0$ follows from $I_0(h) > 0$ (see Proposition 3.52) and $\frac{\partial F}{\partial h}(h, \varepsilon, L(h, \varepsilon)) > 0$ (see (3.104)). The periodic orbits are therefore repelling. □

The homoclinic bifurcation curve. Having discussed the Hopf bifurcation curve, we now look at the homoclinic bifurcation curve in Theorem 3.49 and periodic orbits near it. As noted the Bogdanov function B is not differentiable at $h = \frac{2}{3}$, so also F is not differentiable here, and we cannot apply the implicit function theorem as above to find periodic orbits. To proceed we need better understanding of the asymptotics of F near $h = \frac{2}{3}$. To figure out how $F(h, \varepsilon, \bar{\nu})$ depends on the variables for h close to $\frac{2}{3}$, we look at local transition maps near S. The differential equation

$$\begin{aligned} \dot{u} &= v, \\ \dot{v} &= -1 + u^2 + \varepsilon v(\bar{\nu} + u), \end{aligned}$$

which is (3.88) up to order ε terms, has derivative in $S = (1, 0)$ equal to $\begin{pmatrix} 0 & 1 \\ 2 & \varepsilon(\bar{\nu}+1) \end{pmatrix}$ with eigenvalues $\mu_\pm = \frac{1}{2}\varepsilon(\bar{\nu}+1) \pm \frac{1}{2}\sqrt{\varepsilon^2(\bar{\nu}+1)^2 + 8}$. The quotient $-\mu_-/\mu_+$ equals

$$-\mu_-/\mu_+ = \frac{8}{(\varepsilon(\bar{\nu}+1) + \sqrt{\varepsilon^2(\bar{\nu}+1)^2 + 8})^2}. \tag{3.107}$$

Define $\rho(\varepsilon, \bar{\nu})$ by

$$1 + \rho(\varepsilon, \bar{\nu}) = -\mu_-/\mu_+.$$

From (3.107) it is clear that $\rho(0, \bar{\nu}) = 0$ and $\rho(\varepsilon, \bar{\nu}) < 0$ for $\varepsilon > 0$. In fact, ρ has negative derivative $\frac{\partial \rho}{\partial \varepsilon} = -\frac{1}{2}\sqrt{2}(\bar{\nu}+1)$ at $\varepsilon = 0$ (assuming $\bar{\nu} > 0$).

The following analysis uses results from Section 4.1.1 on planar homoclinic orbits. We refer also to Remark 3.56. Take local cross sections Σ_{in} and Σ_{out} near S transverse to the local stable and local unstable separatrix of the homoclinic

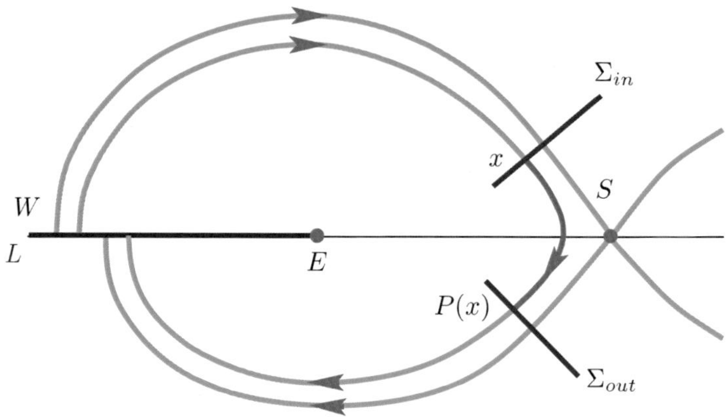

Figure 3.20. A local transition map $P : \Sigma_{in} \to \Sigma_{out}$ is given near the saddle equilibrium S.

orbit. As in Section 4.1.1 we consider a local transition map $P : \Sigma_{in} \to \Sigma_{out}$ (in fact defined on a subinterval of Σ_{in}); see Figure 3.20. In suitable smooth local coordinates near S, given by Lemma 4.6, Lemma 4.11 provides an expansion

$$P(x) = x^{1+\rho} + \varepsilon R(x, \varepsilon, \bar{\nu}).$$

The factor ε in front of the R appears because there is also a factor ε in front of the $v(\bar{\nu} + u)$ term. Here $R(x, \varepsilon, \bar{\nu}) \le C|x|^{1+c}$ and $\frac{\partial}{\partial x} R(x, \varepsilon, \bar{\nu}) \le C|x|^{c}$, for some $c > 0$.

Observe that $\frac{x^\rho - 1}{\rho}$ converges to $\ln(x)$ uniformly in x as $\varepsilon \to 0$. Therefore

$$\lim_{\varepsilon \to 0} \frac{P(x) - x}{\rho} = x \ln(x).$$

The transition maps $L \to \Sigma_{in}$ and $\Sigma_{out} \to L$ are smooth local diffeomorphisms by the global flow box theorem; see Theorem 2.23. We can combine the transition maps to obtain expansions for the first return map on L. First take the transition map from L to Σ^{in}. Perform the smooth coordinate change to go to the coordinate given by Lemma 4.6 and compose the obtained map with the local transition map P. Perform a smooth coordinate change to go to the original coordinates and compose the obtained map with the transition map from Σ^{out} to L. We conclude the following expansion for F. Recall that W is the first intersection of a stable separatrix of S with L; see Figure 3.20. By the stable manifold theorem, W is a smooth function of ε and $\bar{\nu}$ which is equal to $-\frac{2}{3}$ if $\varepsilon = 0$. In terms of $z = h - W$, by abuse of notation (we keep writing F) and introducing

$$w(z) = \frac{z^{1+\rho} - 1}{\rho},$$

we can write

$$F(z,\varepsilon,\bar{\nu}) = a(\varepsilon,\bar{\nu}) + b(\varepsilon,\bar{\nu})zw(z) + \varphi(z,\varepsilon,\bar{\nu}).$$

Knowledge on the value of the coefficients comes from Proposition 3.52. In particular, recalling $F(z,0,\bar{\nu}) = \bar{\nu} - B(W-z)$ from (3.104) and asymptotics for B given in (3.98),

$$a(0,\bar{\nu}) = \bar{\nu} - \frac{5}{7},$$
$$b(0,\bar{\nu}) = \frac{5}{28}.$$

Further, φ is continuously differentiable with $|\varphi(z,\varepsilon,\bar{\nu})| \leq C|z|^{1+c}$ and $\frac{\partial\varphi}{\partial z}(z,\varepsilon,\bar{\nu})| \leq C|z|^c$ for some $C>0$.

Since $\frac{\partial a}{\partial\bar{\nu}}(0,\bar{\nu}) \neq 0$, there is a smooth function $\bar{\nu}_C$ so that $a(\varepsilon,\bar{\nu}_C(\varepsilon)) = 0$. This yields the curve of homoclinic orbits. The following lemma gives periodic orbits at parameter values close to the homoclinic bifurcation curve.

Lemma 3.55. *Given β_1 near $\frac{2}{3}$, there is $T_{\mathrm{Hom}} > 0$ so that for all $\varepsilon \in [0, T_{\mathrm{Hom}}]$, $h \in [\beta_1, \frac{2}{3}]$, there is a curve*

$$\bar{\nu} = L(h,\varepsilon)$$

solving $F(h,\varepsilon,\bar{\nu}) = 0$. The corresponding periodic orbit through $h \in L$ is repelling.

Proof. We proceed as in the proof of Lemma 3.54. By compactness of $[-\bar{\nu}_0, \bar{\nu}_0]$ and differentiability of a, b, φ, there exist constants $T \leq K, \beta_1$ so that

$$\begin{aligned}\frac{\partial F}{\partial\bar{\nu}}(z_0,\varepsilon,\bar{\nu}) &= \frac{\partial a}{\partial\bar{\nu}} + \frac{\partial a}{\partial\bar{\nu}}z_0 w(z_0) + \frac{\partial\varphi}{\partial\bar{\nu}}\\ &> 0\end{aligned} \tag{3.108}$$

for $\varepsilon \in [0,T]$ and $z_0 \in [0,\beta_1]$. This is true since $\frac{\partial a}{\partial\bar{\nu}}$ is near 1 and the other terms are small by choosing T, β_1 appropriately. Thus for $z_0 = \beta_1$ there is a differentiable function $\bar{\nu}_{\beta_1}(\varepsilon)$ with $F(\beta_1,\varepsilon,\bar{\nu}_{\beta_1}(\varepsilon)) = 0$. Note

$$\frac{\partial F}{\partial z}(z,\varepsilon,\bar{\nu}) > 0 \tag{3.109}$$

for appropriate $T_{\mathrm{Hom}} \leq T$ and β_1 since then $w(z)$ is close to $\ln(z)$ and φ is C^1-small. Fix $z \in [0,\beta_1]$ and $\varepsilon \in [0,T]$. By (3.109) we have $F(z,\varepsilon,\bar{\nu}_C(\varepsilon)) > F(0,\varepsilon,\bar{\nu}_C(\varepsilon)) = 0$. By (3.109) we have $F(z,\varepsilon,\bar{\nu}_{\beta_1}(\varepsilon)) < F(\beta_1,\varepsilon,\bar{\nu}_{\beta_1}(\varepsilon)) = 0$. There thus exists $\bar{\nu} = L(z,\varepsilon)$ with $\bar{\nu}_C < \bar{\nu} < \bar{\nu}_{\beta_1}$ and $F(z,\varepsilon,L(z,\varepsilon)) = 0$. By (3.108) $L(z,\varepsilon)$ is unique. With $0 \leq z_1 < z_2 \leq \beta_1$ we have $F(z_2,\varepsilon,L(z_2,\varepsilon)) = 0 = F(z_1,\varepsilon,L(z_1,\varepsilon)) < F(z_2,\varepsilon,L(z_1,\varepsilon))$ and by (3.108) we get $L(z_1,\varepsilon) < L(z_2,\varepsilon)$.

In the same way as we derived the representation (3.106) for the Hopf curve, we find a corresponding representation for the Hom curve. In this case we exploit that $h = \frac{2}{3}$ is related to the equilibrium S; see Figure 3.20. So, plugging in $h = \frac{2}{3}$, the curve $\bar{\nu} = L(\frac{2}{3}, \varepsilon)$ yields the Hom bifurcation curve; see the blue curve in Figure 3.21. From (3.104) we infer that the Hopf bifurcation curve is determined by

$$\bar{\nu}(\varepsilon) = L(\tfrac{2}{3}, \varepsilon) = \tfrac{5}{7} + o(1), \tag{3.110}$$

using $B(\frac{2}{3}) = \frac{5}{7}$.

The statement that the periodic orbits are repelling follows from (3.109) as in the previous part on the Hopf bifurcation curve. □

When choosing $\beta = \beta_1$ the statements of the two Lemmas 3.54 and 3.55, which are then both true for an ε-range $[0, \min\{T_{\text{Hopf}}, T_{\text{Hom}}\}]$, can be combined. Hence there is a unique repelling periodic orbit for parameter values from the region in between the Hopf curve and the Hom curve. This result is visualized in Figure 3.21.

We conclude with a remark that connects the above analysis for $h = H(S) = \frac{2}{3}$, to the bifurcation analysis of planar homoclinic orbits in Section 4.1.1.

Remark 3.56. The homoclinic orbit of (3.89) is contained in the level set $\{H(x,y) = \frac{2}{3}\}$ of the Hamiltonian $H(x,y) = \frac{1}{2}y^2 + x - \frac{1}{3}x^3$. This is given

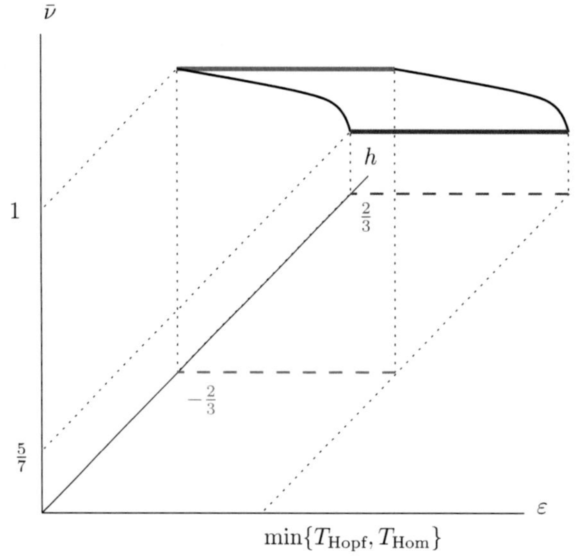

Figure 3.21. In $\varepsilon, \bar{\nu}, h$ space there is a surface, the graph $L(\cdot,\cdot)$, of periodic orbits through $h \in \overline{ES}$. The green curve, the graph of $L(-\frac{2}{3}, \cdot)$, is related to the Hopf curve and the blue curve, the graph of $L(\frac{2}{3}, \cdot)$, is related to the Hom curve.

by $\{y^2 = \frac{2}{3}x^3 - 2x + \frac{4}{3}\}$. The homoclinic orbit $(x(t), y(t))$ thus satisfies $\dot{x} = \pm\sqrt{\frac{2}{3}x^3 - 2x + \frac{4}{3}}$ and $y = \dot{x}$. Solving the differential equation shows that the homoclinic orbit is given by an expression

$$(x(t), y(t)) = \left(1 - 3\,\mathrm{sech}^2\left(\frac{1}{2}\sqrt{2}t\right), 3\sqrt{2}\,\mathrm{sech}^2\left(\frac{1}{2}\sqrt{2}t\right)\tanh\left(\frac{1}{2}\sqrt{2}t\right)\right).$$

Recall that $\mathrm{sech}(\cdot)$ is the hyperbolic secant defined by $\mathrm{sech}(x) = 1/\cosh(x)$. We get the following identities for the Melnikov function for the homoclinic loop $\gamma_{2/3}$:

$$\begin{aligned}\int_{\gamma_{2/3}} \omega_D &= \int_{\gamma_{2/3}} v(\bar{\nu} + u)\,du \\ &= \int_{-\infty}^{\infty} y(t)\,(\bar{\nu}y(t) + x(t)y(t))\,dt \\ &= \bar{\nu}9\sqrt{2}\int_{-\infty}^{\infty} \mathrm{sech}^4(s)\tanh^2(s)\,ds \\ &\quad + 9\sqrt{2}\int_{-\infty}^{\infty} (1 - 3\,\mathrm{sech}^2(s))\,\mathrm{sech}^4(s)\tanh^2(s)\,ds \\ &= \bar{\nu}\frac{36}{15}\sqrt{2} - \frac{36}{21}\sqrt{2}.\end{aligned}$$

These formulas, in particular the integral $\int_{-\infty}^{\infty} y(t)\,(\bar{\nu}y(t) + x(t)y(t))\,dt$, also appear in Section 4.1.1, Remark 4.8, and Remark 4.9. We find that $\int_{\gamma_{2/3}} \omega_D = 0$ for $\bar{\nu} = \frac{5}{7}$. By Lemma 3.51, the homoclinic bifurcation curve in the $(\varepsilon, \bar{\nu})$ parameter plane occurs along $\bar{\nu} = \frac{5}{7} + o(1)$. We also note that calculating the saddle quantity and establishing that it is nonzero, allows us to apply Theorem 4.3. Exercise 3.31 asks us to work out the calculations. ■

Returning to original coordinates. It is straightforward to write down formulas for the Hopf and Hom curve in original parameters. Starting from (3.106) while taking into account the singular rescaling (3.86) yields for the Hopf curve in the original parameters, the formula

$$\nu^2 = -\mu + o(\mu),\ \nu > 0.$$

The same way results in the representation of the Hom curve. Starting from (3.110) gives

$$\nu^2 = -\tfrac{25}{49}\mu + o(\mu),\ \nu > 0.$$

The above proof for the existence and bifurcations of periodic orbits is for the system written in (u, v)-coordinates from the rescaling (3.86), and for corresponding parameters ε and $\bar{\nu}$. The (u, v)-domain $\mathcal{D}$ to which the analysis applies is transformed into a domain D_ε in the original coordinates. However, the domain D_ε shrinks to zero as $\varepsilon \to 0$. Also, the considered parameters (μ, ν) are from a bowl shaped region as depicted in Figure 3.16. We must consider parameters outside the bowl shaped region and also dynamics outside D_ε.

We first look at parameters μ, ν outside the bowl shaped region, and more in particular for $\mu \leq 0$ between the ν-axis and the bowl shaped region. For $\mu > 0$ there no equilibria and therefore no periodic orbits. In Exercise 3.32 we consider a different rescaling that allows us to study the vector field near the saddle-node bifurcation. It shows that in a region $\{(\mu, \nu)\ ;\ |\nu| \leq T, |\mu| \leq \nu^4 M\}$ for positive constants T, M, there are no periodic orbits in a small neighborhood of $(0,0)$. This region and the bowl shaped region do not overlap.

For $\mu = 0$ there is exactly one equilibrium $(x, y) = (0,0)$. This has a one-dimensional center manifold of the form $y = w(x) = -\frac{1}{\nu}x^2 + o(x^2)$. Restricted to this manifold, the flow is topologically conjugate to the flow of $\dot{x} = -\frac{1}{\nu}x^2 + o(x^2)$. So there cannot exist a periodic orbit encircling $(0,0)$.

Now, let $\mu < 0$. Recall that there are two equilibria $E^+ = (\sqrt{-\mu}, 0)$, which is a saddle, and $E^- = (-\sqrt{-\mu}, 0)$. Consider the curve κ given by $\{\mu = -\frac{1}{\bar{\nu}_0^2}\nu^2, \nu \geq 0\}$, where $\bar{\nu}_0 > 1$ is the value appearing in the proof of Lemma 3.54; see Figure 3.16. The curve κ lies above the curve of Hopf bifurcations. From the proofs of Lemmas 3.54 and 3.55 we get that for (μ, ν) below the curve κ there is a periodic orbit only for those (μ, ν) lying within the wedge delimited by the Hopf and Hom curve. we must therefore make clear that there are no periodic orbits for parameters within the wedge delimited by κ and the ν-axis. Recall that we have the normal form (3.85) given by

$$\begin{aligned}
\dot{x} &= y, \\
\dot{y} &= x^2 + \mu + \nu y + xy + yx^2 G_3(x, \mu, \nu) + y^2 G_2(x, y, \mu, \nu).
\end{aligned}$$

Note that orbits, which cross the x-axis in a perpendicular way, move to the right in the upper half-plane and to the left in the lower half-plane.

The technique below is that of rotated vector fields (originating from [**101**]; see [**287, 288**] and [**289**]). Consider vector fields $f(\cdot, \cdot, \mu, \nu)$ and $f(\cdot, \cdot, \mu, \tilde{\nu})$ as in (3.85). Note that only the ν-values differ. Take the difference

$$f(x, y, \mu, \nu) - f(x, y, \mu, \tilde{\nu}) =: \begin{pmatrix} \Delta f^1 \\ \Delta f^2 \end{pmatrix}.$$

From the expressions for $f(x, y, \mu, \nu)$ it follows immediately that $\Delta f^1 = 0$ and

$$\begin{aligned}
\Delta f^2 = y(\nu - \tilde{\nu}) &+ yx^2 (G_3(x, \mu, \nu) - G_3(x, \mu, \tilde{\nu})) \\
&+ y^2 \left(G_2(x, y, \mu, \nu) - G_2(x, y, \mu, \tilde{\nu}) \right).
\end{aligned}$$

We can write the above difference as

$$f(x,y,\mu,\nu) - f(x,y,\mu,\tilde{\nu}) = \begin{pmatrix} 0 \\ (\nu-\tilde{\nu})\,y(1+\zeta(x,y,\mu,\nu,\tilde{\nu})) \end{pmatrix} \tag{3.111}$$

for a smooth function ζ, vanishing at $(x,y) = (0,0)$. Restricting to a small neighborhood of $(0,0)$ we may assume $|\zeta| < \frac{1}{2}$, so that $1+\zeta$ is strictly positive. If $\theta(x,y,\mu,\nu)$ denotes the angle of $f(\cdot,\cdot,\mu,\nu)$, then this means that $D_\nu\theta > 0$ for $y \neq 0$. This is the background for the expression *rotated vector field* [**288**].

Consider, for $\mu < 0$ fixed, a value ν greater than the Hopf bifurcation value. Write $\upsilon(\nu)$ for the y-coordinate of the intersection of the unstable manifold of the saddle E^+ with the y-axis. By (3.111) with $1+\zeta$ strictly positive, υ is strictly increasing if the value of ν increases. Figure 3.22 provides a visualization. The existence of the α-limit set of the stable separatrix of E^+ is therefore ensured for all values of ν above the Hopf curve. By contradiction we show that this α-limit set cannot be a periodic orbit. Assume that for some ν the α-limit of the stable separatrix of E^+ is a periodic orbit $\mathcal{P}$. Take $\tilde{\nu} < \nu$ so that $(\mu,\tilde{\nu})$ belongs to the wedge in between the Hopf curve and κ. We know that the stable separatrix of E^+ for the vector field $f(\cdot,\cdot,\mu,\tilde{\nu})$ connects the unstable node E^- to E^+. So there must be an intersection point of this stable separatrix with $\mathcal{P}$, such as the red point indicated in Figure 3.23. The orbit of such an intersection point for $f(\cdot,\cdot,\mu,\nu)$, because of the expression for $f(x,y,\mu,\nu) - f(x,y,\mu,\tilde{\nu})$, escapes to x-values to the right of E^+. The original assumption that for those ν the α-limit of the stable separatrix of E^+ is a periodic orbit $\mathcal{P}$ must be dropped. Hence there are no periodic orbits for parameter values above the Hopf curve.

We will now show that recurrent dynamics appears only in D_ε. Consider an appropriate domain $\hat{D}$ in the original coordinates containing D_ε. We will

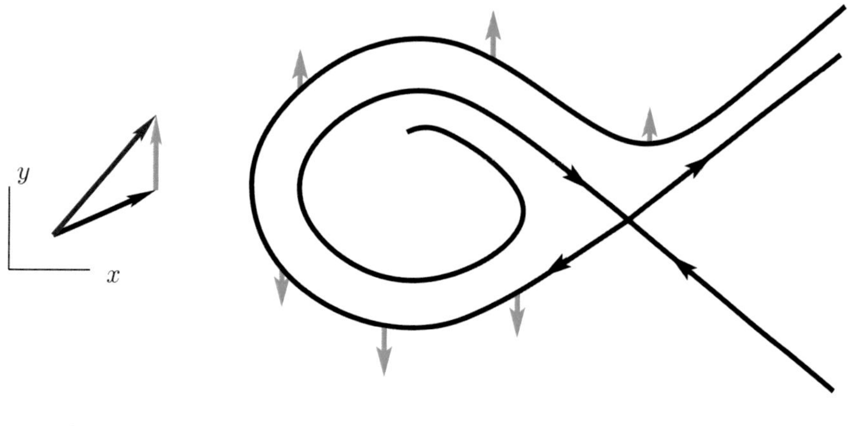

Figure 3.22. The difference between two vector fields $f(\cdot,\cdot,\mu,\nu)$ and $f(\cdot,\cdot,\mu,\tilde{\nu})$ that differ only in the value for ν as in (3.111), is in the direction of the y-coordinate.

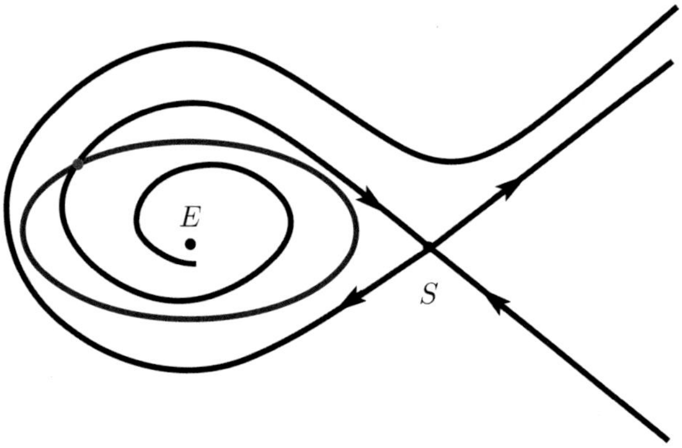

Figure 3.23. The closed blue curve represents the periodic orbit $\mathcal{P}$ which is related to ν. The phase portrait of the vector field $f(\cdot, \cdot, \mu, \tilde{\nu})$, $\tilde{\nu} < \nu$, is displayed in black.

show that there is no recurrent dynamics within $\hat{D} \setminus D_\varepsilon$. This is a consequence of the Poincaré-Bendixon theorem in the following way. For a ball $B((0,0),\delta)$ centered at $(0,0)$ with radius δ, there are no equilibria inside $B((0,0),\delta) \setminus D_\varepsilon$. At all points $(x,0) \in B((0,0),\delta) \setminus D_\varepsilon$, the vector field points into the upper half-plane. This implies that there is no periodic orbit in $(x,0) \in B((0,0),\delta) \setminus D_\varepsilon$. Namely: a periodic orbit encircles an equilibrium, and since there is none inside $B((0,0),\delta) \setminus D_\varepsilon$, the periodic orbit would have to encircle an equilibrium located in D_ε. The periodic orbits within D_ε are discussed above. So a potential periodic orbit in $B((0,0),\delta)$ which is not entirely in D_ε, would either encircle D_ε, and this is prevented by the direction of the vector field on the x-axis, or intersect D_ε. However, an orbit which leaves D_ε will also leave $B((0,0),\delta)$. Figure 3.24 provides a visualization.

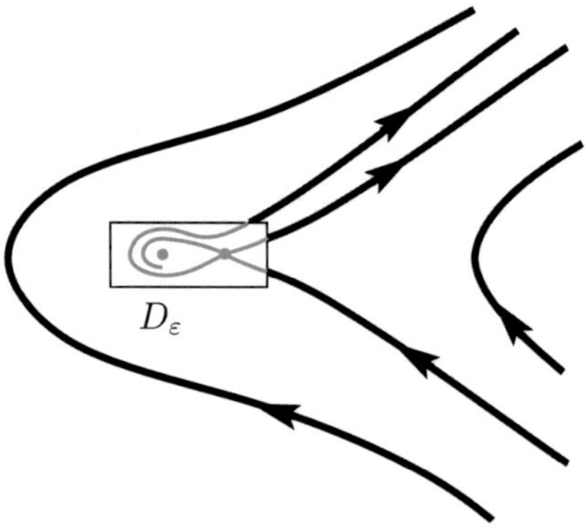

Figure 3.24. The singular rescaling means that the dynamics is studied on a set D_ε that shrinks to $(0,0)$ as $\varepsilon \to 0$. This procedure is justified as the recurrent set is shown to be inside D_ε.

3.3. Bifurcations of periodic orbits

Differential equations can admit periodic solutions, and such periodic orbits can change stability under variation of parameters in the equations. This is expressed by Floquet exponents that lie on the imaginary axis or move through the imaginary axis. As for equilibria there are different bifurcation scenarios showing for instance coalescence of periodic orbits or the creation of new recurrent dynamics near a periodic orbit.

We will look at a family of differential equations

$$\dot{x} = f(x, \lambda), \quad x \in \mathbb{R}^n, \lambda \in \mathbb{R}^k. \tag{3.112}$$

The bifurcations that we will treat are restricted to one-parameter families with $k = 1$. We assume that (3.112), for $\lambda = 0$, has a periodic solution γ with minimal period T; $\gamma(t) = \gamma(t + T)$ with $T > 0$ minimal with this property:

$$\dot{\gamma}(t) = f(\gamma(t), 0), \quad \gamma(t) = \gamma(t + T), \quad \gamma(t) \neq \gamma(t + \tau) \quad \text{for } \tau \in (0, T). \tag{3.113}$$

Let $x_0 \in \gamma$ and let Σ be a hyperplane of $\mathbb{R}^n$ containing x_0 such that $\Sigma = x_0 + H$ with a hyperplane H and $\mathbb{R}^n = H \oplus \mathbb{R} f(x_0, 0)$. The Poincaré return map on Σ will be denoted by $\Pi(\cdot, \lambda)$.

Bifurcations of the periodic orbit γ can be studied through bifurcations of the fixed point x_0 of Π. Bifurcations occur if γ is nonhyperbolic, or equivalently if the related fixed point of Π is nonhyperbolic. This happens if the linearization $D\Pi(x_0)$ has an eigenvalue on the unit circle.

3.3.1. Saddle-node bifurcation of periodic orbits.

First we assume a Floquet multiplier 1 for a periodic orbit γ as in (3.113) of the family of differential equations (3.112). The related Poincaré return map has a fixed point with eigenvalue 1. We will find a bifurcation scenario that is very similar to the saddle-node bifurcation of equilibria, featuring the coalescence of two periodic orbits.

3.3.1.1. *One-dimensional saddle-node bifurcation of fixed points.* We state the bifurcation results in the case $n = 2$. The cross section Σ is one dimensional and the Poincaré return map $\Pi : \Sigma \to \Sigma$ becomes a one-dimensional map.

Example 3.57. Consider the model in $\mathbb{R}$ given by the map

$$\Pi(h, \lambda) = h + \lambda - h^2.$$

The fixed points of Π are determined by

$$\lambda - h^2 = 0.$$

The bifurcation diagram is the same as presented in Figure 3.2. ∎

Theorem 3.58 (Saddle-node bifurcation for one-dimensional maps). *Let $I \subset H$ and $J \subset \mathbb{R}$ be open intervals, and let the Poincaré return map $\Pi : I \times J \to \mathbb{R}$ be* *a C^2 map such that for $\Pi = \Pi(h, \lambda)$:*

(i) $\Pi(0, 0) = 0$ *and* $D_h\Pi(0, 0) = 1$,

(ii) $D_h^2\Pi(0, 0) \neq 0$,

(iii) $D_\lambda\Pi(0, 0) \neq 0$.

Then there are $\varepsilon, \delta > 0$ and a C^2 function $\lambda^* : (-\varepsilon, \varepsilon) \to (-\delta, \delta)$ with $\lambda^*(0) = 0$, $D\lambda^*(0) = 0$, $D^2\lambda^*(0) \neq 0$ such that

(1) *Each $h \in (-\varepsilon, \varepsilon)$ is a fixed point of $\Pi(\cdot, \lambda^*(\cdot))$, thus $\Pi(h, \lambda^*(h)) = h$. Moreover, these are all fixed points of $\Pi(\cdot, \lambda)$ in $(-\varepsilon, \varepsilon)$ for $\lambda \in (-\delta, \delta)$,*

(2) *For each $\lambda \in (0, \delta)$ or $\lambda \in (-\delta, 0)$, depending on the signs of the quantities in* (ii) *and* (iii)*, there are exactly two fixed points $h_1(\lambda), h_2(\lambda) \in (\lambda^*)^{-1}(\lambda)$ of $\Pi(\cdot, \lambda)$ in $(-\varepsilon, \varepsilon)$; one is stable and the other one is unstable. $\Pi(\cdot, \lambda)$ does not have fixed points in $(-\varepsilon, \varepsilon)$ for each $\lambda \in (-\delta, 0)$ or $\lambda \in (0, \delta)$, respectively.*

We translate the result into the context of periodic orbits of differential equations.

Corollary 3.59. *Consider* (3.112) *under the assumption* (3.113)*, write $\mathbb{R}^2 = H \times$* span$\{f(x_0, 0)\}$. *Assume further that the corresponding Poincaré return map $h \mapsto \Pi(h, \lambda)$ satisfies the assumptions of Theorem* 3.58. *Then there are $\varepsilon, \delta > 0$ and a C^2 function $\lambda^* : (-\varepsilon, \varepsilon) \to (-\delta, \delta)$ with $\lambda^*(0) = 0$, $D\lambda^*(0) = 0$, $D^2\lambda^*(0) \neq 0$ such that the following hold.*

(1) *For each $h \in (-\varepsilon, \varepsilon)$ there is a periodic orbit γ_h of $f(\cdot, \lambda^*(h))$ with $(h, 0) \in \gamma_h$. Moreover, these are all periodic orbits of $\dot{x} = f(x, \lambda)$ intersecting $(-\varepsilon, \varepsilon) \times \{0\}$ for $\lambda \in (-\delta, \delta)$.*

(2) *For each $\lambda \in (0, \delta)$ or $\lambda \in (-\delta, 0)$, depending on the signs of the quantities in* (ii) *and* (iii)*, there are exactly two periodic orbits $\gamma_{h_1(\lambda)}, \gamma_{h_2(\lambda)}$ of* (3.112) *with $h_1(\lambda), h_2(\lambda) \in (\lambda^*)^{-1}(\lambda)$. The dimensions of the unstable manifolds of $\gamma_{h_1(\lambda)}$ and $\gamma_{h_2(\lambda)}$ differ by two. Equation* (3.112) *does not have any periodic orbits intersecting $(-\varepsilon, \varepsilon) \times \{0\}$ for each $\lambda \in (-\delta, 0)$ or $\lambda \in (0, \delta)$, respectively.*

Proof of Theorem 3.58. Consider the function

$$p(h, \lambda) := \Pi(h, \lambda) - h.$$

The zeros of $p(\cdot, \lambda)$ coincide with the fixed points of $\Pi(\cdot, \lambda)$. Moreover, p satisfies the assumptions of Theorem 3.6. So the statement of the present theorem follows directly from Theorem 3.6 and the discussion following it. □

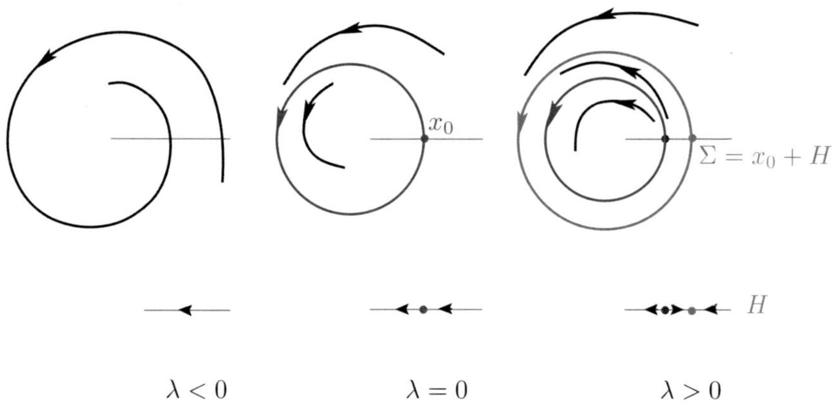

Figure 3.25. Upper part: the saddle-node bifurcation of periodic orbits of (3.112), assuming (3.114). Lower part: the corresponding dynamics of $\Pi(\cdot, \lambda)$.

Let Π be a map as considered in Theorem 3.58. Assume more in particular that

$$D_h^2\Pi(0,0) < 0 \quad \text{and} \quad D_\lambda \Pi(0,0) > 0. \tag{3.114}$$

Computations along the lines of the proof of Theorem 3.58 yield

$$D^2\lambda^*(0) = -D_h^2\Pi(0,0) \cdot D_\lambda\Pi(0,0) > 0$$

and, with $h_1(\lambda), h_2(\lambda) \in (\lambda^*)^{-1}(\lambda)$, $h_1(\lambda) < h_2(\lambda)$,

$$D_h\Pi(h_1(\lambda), \lambda) > 1, \; 0 < D_h\Pi(h_2(\lambda), \lambda) < 1,$$

In Figure 3.25 we present the corresponding bifurcation diagram for periodic orbits of (3.112).

Example 3.60. Consider

$$\dot{x} = \lambda(1 + \cos(2\pi t)) + x^2 - \cos(2\pi t)^2 - 2\pi\sin(2\pi t), \tag{3.115}$$

where $x \in \mathbb{R}$ and λ is a real parameter. The equation is constructed to have a solution $x(t) = \cos(2\pi t)$ for $\lambda = 0$. This nonautonomous differential equation is periodic in time with period 1. We rewrite it into an autonomous system on $\mathbb{T} \times \mathbb{R}$:

$$\begin{aligned} \dot{\theta} &= 1, \\ \dot{x} &= \lambda\big(1 + \cos(2\pi\theta)\big) + x^2 - \cos(2\pi\theta)^2 - 2\pi\sin(2\pi\theta). \end{aligned} \tag{3.116}$$

When $\lambda = 0$, this differential equation has a periodic orbit $(\theta(t), x(t)) = (t, \cos(2\pi t))$. We will analyze the system for varying λ near 0 and show that the periodic orbit undergoes a saddle-node bifurcation, with two periodic orbits for a small negative λ that coalesce and disappear when λ increases through 0.

Note that $\Sigma = \{0\} \times \mathbb{R} \subset \mathbb{T} \times \mathbb{R}$ is a global Poincaré section for this periodic orbit. The periodic orbit γ intersects Σ in $(0, 1)$. The corresponding Poincaré return map Π is the time 1 map of (3.116), or more precisely

$$\Pi(\cdot, \lambda) : \Sigma \to \Sigma, \quad (0, u) \mapsto (0, x^*(1, u, \lambda)),$$

where $x^*(\cdot, u, \lambda)$ solves the initial value problem (3.115), $x(0) = u$. It is enough to study Π near $1 \in \Sigma \cong \mathbb{R}$ and for small λ.

With the new variable $h(t) = x(t) - \cos(2\pi t)$, equation (3.115) is transformed into

$$\dot{h} = \lambda(1 + \cos(2\pi t)) + 2\cos(2\pi t)h + h^2, \tag{3.117}$$

and then Π will be transformed into (where we do not change the notation Π)

$$\Pi(\cdot, \lambda) : \mathbb{R} \to \mathbb{R}, \quad u \mapsto h^*(1, u, \lambda),$$

where $h^*(\cdot, u, \lambda)$ solves the initial value problem (3.117), $h(0) = u$. We have $h^*(t, 0, 0) \equiv 0$. It is enough to discuss Π near $0 \in \mathbb{R}$ and for small λ.

In what follows we perform a number of further transformations which bring the vector field in (3.117) in an appropriate form, which allows us to analyze Π. First we remove the linear term from the vector field. To this end let $u(t) = e^{-\sin(2\pi t)/\pi}h(t)$. Then

$$\dot{u} = \lambda(1 + \cos(2\pi t))e^{-\sin(2\pi t)/\pi} + e^{\sin(2\pi t)/\pi}u^2.$$

Next we change the coefficient of the quadratic term to a constant, by a transformation of the form $u(t) = w(t) + \beta(t)w(t)^2$ for β a smooth function of period 1. Plugging this expression for $u(t)$ into the differential equation, we see that we can take $\dot{\beta} = e^{\sin(2\pi t)/\pi} - c_0$ for $c_0 = \int_0^1 e^{\sin(2\pi t)/\pi}\, dt > 0$. Then

$$\dot{w} = \lambda q(t) - 2\lambda q(t)\beta(t)w + (c_0 + \mathcal{O}(\lambda))w^2 + \mathcal{O}(w^3) =: f(w, t, \lambda), \tag{3.118}$$

where $q(t) = (1 + \cos(2\pi t))e^{-\sin(2\pi t)/\pi}$. For $\lambda = 0$ we find $\dot{w} = c_0 w^2 + \mathcal{O}(w^3)$.

After these transformations Π is defined by (again we keep writing Π)

$$\Pi(\cdot, \lambda) : \mathbb{R} \to \mathbb{R}, \quad u \mapsto w^*(1, u, \lambda),$$

where $w^*(\cdot, u, \lambda)$ solves the initial value problem (3.118), $w(0) = u$. As is true for h^*, also

$$w^*(t, 0, 0) \equiv 0, \tag{3.119}$$

which implies $w^*(1, 0, 0) = 0$. Hence $\Pi(0, 0) = 0$. In what follows we show that $(u, \lambda) \mapsto \Pi(u, \lambda)$ satisfies the assumptions of Theorem 3.58. In particular we will establish that

(i) $D_u\Pi(0, 0) = 1$,
(ii) $D_u^2\Pi(0, 0) > 0$,
(iii) $D_\lambda\Pi(0, 0) > 0$.

This implies the bifurcation scenario of a stable and an unstable periodic orbit for (3.115) for negative λ that vanishes in a saddle-node bifurcation at $\lambda = 0$, so that no periodic orbits remain for $\lambda > 0$; see Figure 3.26.

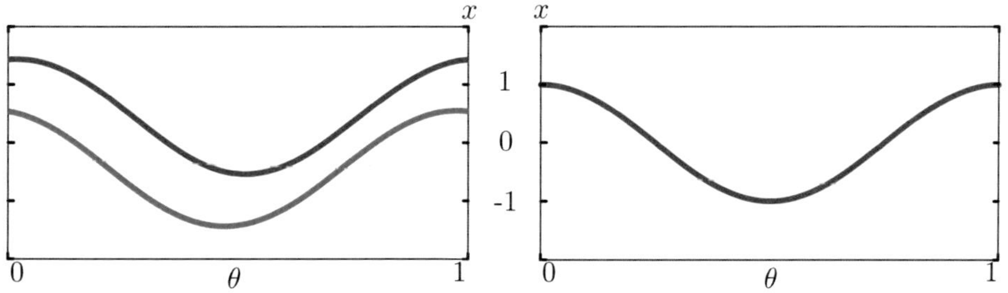

Figure 3.26. Periodic orbits for (3.116). The right picture shows the periodic orbit $(\theta(t), x(t)) = (t, \cos(2\pi t))$ for $\lambda = 0$. The left picture shows numerically calculated periodic orbits for $\lambda = -0.2$. The upper periodic orbit is repelling, the lower is attracting.

First we consider $D_u\Pi(0,0) = D_u w^*(1,0,0)$. We start with recapitulating from (3.118) and the definition of w^*, that

$$D_t w^*(t,u,\lambda) = f(w^*(t,u,\lambda), t, \lambda), \tag{3.120}$$

$$w^*(0,u,\lambda) = u. \tag{3.121}$$

Considering equation (3.120) at $\lambda = 0$ and differentiating with respect to u yields

$$D_u D_t w^*(t,u,0) = D_u f(w^*(t,u,0), t, 0) D_u w^*(t,u,0). \tag{3.122}$$

From that we infer for $u = 0$ that

$$D_u D_t w^*(t,0,0) = D_u f(w^*(t,0,0), t, 0) D_u w^*(t,0,0).$$

Because of $D_u D_t w^* = D_t D_u w^*$, (3.119) and the observation that f has no linear term in w if $\lambda = 0$, this means that $D_u w^*(\cdot,0,0)$ solves an equation $\dot{v} = 0$. Hence $D_u w^*(t,0,0)$ is constant, which implies that $D_u w^*(1,0,0) = D_u w^*(0,0,0)$. Further, (3.121) gives $D_u w^*(0,u,0) \equiv 1$. Together this yields

$$D_u\Pi(0,0) = 1.$$

Next we consider $D_u^2\Pi(0,0) = D_u^2 w^*(1,0,0)$. Proceeding from (3.122) we find

$$D_u^2 D_t w^*(t,0,0) = D_u^2 f(w^*(t,0,0), t, 0)\,(D_u w^*(t,0,0))^2 + D_u f(w^*(t,0,0), t, 0) D_u^2 w^*(t,0,0).$$

Similar reasoning as above shows that $D_u^2 w^*(\cdot,0,0)$ solves the initial value problem $\dot{v} = 2c_0$, $v(0) = 0$. Hence

$$D_u^2\Pi(0,0) = 2c_0 > 0.$$

It remains to consider $D_\lambda \Pi(0,0) = D_\lambda w^*(1,0,0)$. Proceeding from (3.120) yields

$$D_\lambda D_t w^*(t,0,0) = D_u f(w^*(t,0,0),t,0) D_\lambda w^*(t,0,0) + D_\lambda f(w^*(t,0,0),t,0).$$

Hence $D_\lambda w^*(\cdot,0,0)$ solves the initial value problem $\dot{v} = q(t)$, $v(0) = 0$. This finally means that

$$D_\lambda \Pi(0,0) = \int_0^1 q(t)\,dt > 0.$$

We have now shown that Π satisfies the assumptions of Theorem 3.58. ∎

3.3.1.2. *Higher-dimensional saddle-node bifurcation of fixed points.* We include an explicit bifurcation statement in higher dimensions, akin to Theorem 3.8 for the saddle-node bifurcation of an equilibrium. The proof is essentially the same (Exercise 3.33). Let $\Pi : \mathbb{R}^n \times \mathbb{R} \to \mathbb{R}^n$ be a smooth diffeomorphism.

Theorem 3.61 (Saddle-node bifurcation for maps). *Assume that $\Pi(\cdot,\lambda)$ for $\lambda = 0$ has a fixed point at the origin for which*

(i) *$D_x\Pi(0,0)$ has a simple eigenvalue 1 with right eigenvector v and left eigenvector w. Further, $D_x\Pi(0,0)$ has k eigenvalues with modulus smaller than one and $n-k-1$ eigenvalues with modulus larger than one.*

(ii) $\langle w, D_\lambda \Pi(0,0)\rangle \neq 0$.

(iii) $\langle w, D_x^2 \Pi(0,0) v^2\rangle \neq 0$.

Then there is a smooth curve of fixed points in $\mathbb{R}^n \times \mathbb{R}$, passing through $(0,0)$ and tangent to $(v,0)$ at $(0,0)$.

Depending on the signs of the expressions in (ii) *and* (iii) *there are no fixed points for $\lambda < 0$ (or $\lambda > 0$), and there are two fixed points for $\lambda > 0$ (or $\lambda < 0$). The two fixed points are hyperbolic and have a stability index k and $k+1$, respectively.*

3.3.2. Period-doubling bifurcation. A periodic solution of a family of differential equations can loose stability when a Floquet multiplier moves through -1 and becomes larger than 1 in modulus, while the moduli of the other Floquet multipliers remain inside the unit disc. Note that periodic orbits with negative Floquet multiplier can occur in $\mathbb{R}^n$ for $n \geq 3$, and not for $n = 2$. As we shall see, periodic orbits of roughly double the period can occur in an unfolding. A possible scenario is that a stable periodic orbit looses stability and becomes of saddle type, while the stability is inherited by a periodic orbit of a doubled period.

As before we consider a differential equation $\dot{x} = f(x,\lambda)$ on $\mathbb{R}^n$ depending on a parameter $\lambda \in \mathbb{R}$, with a periodic orbit γ of period T (see (3.112) and (3.113)). We state the main bifurcation results in terms of a Poincaré return map Π. We consider the Poincaré return map Π restricted to a center manifold W^c_{loc}. This defines an extended map $(h, \lambda) \mapsto (\Pi(h; \lambda), \lambda)$, where h belongs to the center subspace of the nonhyperbolic fixed point.

3.3.2.1. *One-dimensional period-doubling bifurcation of fixed points.*

Example 3.62. Let $\Pi : \mathbb{R} \times \mathbb{R} \to \mathbb{R}$ be defined as

$$\Pi(h, \lambda) = -(1 + \lambda)h + h^3. \tag{3.123}$$

Observe that $\Pi(0, \lambda) = 0$ and $D_h\Pi(0, \lambda) = -(1 + \lambda)$. The fixed point at the origin is therefore hyperbolic for $\lambda \neq 0$, and in particular it is stable if $\lambda < 0$ and unstable if $\lambda > 0$. Period-two points of $\Pi(\cdot, \lambda)$ are fixed points of $\Pi^2(\cdot, \lambda)$. To find these, calculate

$$\begin{aligned}\Pi^2(h, \lambda) &= \Pi(\Pi(h, \lambda), \lambda) \\ &= (1 + \lambda)^2 h - (1 + \lambda)\big(1 + (1 + \lambda)^2\big)h^3 + \mathcal{O}(h^4).\end{aligned} \tag{3.124}$$

As the origin is a fixed point, the points with period two are determined by $\Pi^2(h, \lambda)/h = 0$. This yields the equation

$$2\lambda + \lambda^2 - (1 + \lambda)\big(1 + (1 + \lambda)^2\big)h^2 + \mathcal{O}(h^3) = 0.$$

Near $(h, \lambda) = (0, 0)$ this equation can be solved for $\lambda = \lambda^*(h)$ by means of the implicit function theorem,

$$\lambda^*(h) = \frac{1}{2}h^2 + \mathcal{O}(h^3). \tag{3.125}$$

So, period-two points exist for $\lambda > 0$. To determine their stability, we consider $D_h\Pi^2(h, \lambda^*(h))$. From (3.124) and (3.125) we calculate

$$\begin{aligned}D_h\Pi^2(h, \lambda^*(h)) &= (1 + \lambda^*(h))^2 - 3(1 + \lambda^*(h))\big(1 + (1 + \lambda^*(h))^2\big)h^2 + \mathcal{O}(h^3) \\ &= 1 - 2h^2 + \mathcal{O}(h^3),\end{aligned}$$

which is in $(0, 1)$ for small values of h. This means that the bifurcating period-two points are hyperbolic and in fact locally asymptotically stable. The bifurcation diagram for the fixed points of Π^2 is depicted in Figure 3.27. This case

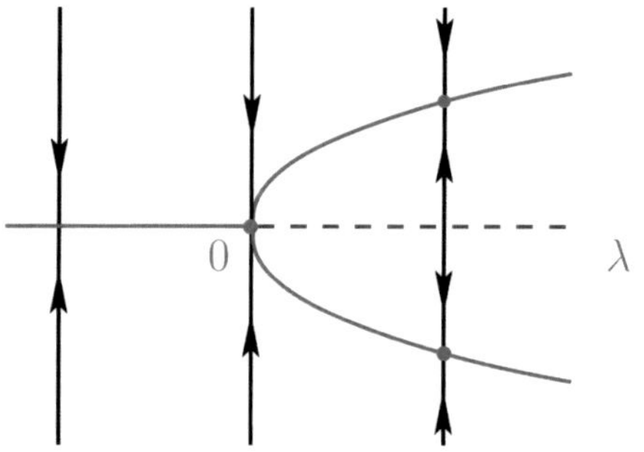

Figure 3.27. The bifurcation diagram of fixed points of Π^2 with Π from (3.123).

is called a supercritical period-doubling bifurcation. A subcritical bifurcation, in which the period-two periodic orbit exists for $\lambda < 0$ and is unstable, occurs for $\Pi(h,\lambda) = -(1+\lambda)h - h^3$. ■

The following theorem generalizes the above example.

Theorem 3.63 (Period-doubling bifurcation for one-dimensional maps). *Let $I \subset W^c_{\mathrm{loc}}$ and $J \subset \mathbb{R}$ be open intervals containing 0, and let $\Pi : I \times J \to \mathbb{R}$ be a smooth map $(h,\lambda) \mapsto \Pi(h,\lambda)$. Assume that $\Pi(\cdot,\lambda)$ for $\lambda = 0$ has a fixed point 0 for which $D_h\Pi(0,0)$ has a simple eigenvalue -1. Then there are $\varepsilon, \delta > 0$ and a smooth function $\xi : (-\delta,\delta) \to \mathbb{R}^n$ with $\xi(0) = 0$ and such that the following hold.*

$$\Pi(\xi(\lambda),\lambda) = \xi(\lambda)$$

and $\xi(\lambda)$ is the only fixed point in $(-\varepsilon,\varepsilon)$ for $\lambda \in (-\delta,\delta)$. Assume that

(i) $\frac{d}{d\lambda}\left(D_h\Pi(\xi(\lambda),\lambda)\right)|_{\lambda=0} \neq 0$,

(ii) $D_h^3\Pi^2(0,0) \neq 0$.

Then the fixed point $\xi(\lambda)$ changes stability while λ is passing through zero. There are $\varepsilon, \delta > 0$ and a smooth function $\lambda^* : (-\varepsilon,\varepsilon) \to \mathbb{R}$ with $\lambda^*(0) = 0$, $D\lambda^*(0) = 0$ and $D^2\lambda^*(0) \neq 0$, such that the following holds. For each $\lambda \in (0,\delta)$ or $\lambda \in (-\delta,0)$, depending on the signs of the quantities in (i) *and* (ii)*, the map $\Pi(\cdot,\lambda)$ has, in addition to the fixed point $\xi(\lambda)$, exactly two period-two points $h_1(\lambda), h_2(\lambda)$ in the interval $(-\varepsilon,\varepsilon)$. Moreover, $\lambda^*(h_i(\lambda)) = \lambda$ and $h_i(\lambda) \to 0$ as $\lambda \to 0$ for $i = 1,2$. For $\lambda \in (-\delta,0]$ or $\lambda \in [0,\delta)$, respectively, there are no period-two points in $(-\varepsilon,\varepsilon)$. The period-two points are hyperbolic and their stability differs from that of the fixed point $\xi(\lambda)$.*

The period-doubling bifurcation is sometimes called a flip bifurcation.

Remark 3.64. It follows from the calculations in the proof that the conditions for a nondegenerate bifurcation and a generic unfolding can be cast in the following form:

(i) $\frac{1}{2}D_\lambda\Pi(0,0) \cdot D_h^2\Pi(0,0) + D_\lambda D_h\Pi(0,0) \neq 0$,

(ii) $2D_h^3\Pi(0,0) + 3\left(D_h^2\Pi(0,0)\right)^2 \neq 0$.

This form does not involve an explicit mention of the fixed point ξ and uses only the map Π and not the second iterate Π^2. ■

Proof of Theorem 3.63. As $D_h\Pi(0,0) = -1$ we have in particular that $D_h\Pi(0,0) \neq 0$ and so we can apply the implicit function theorem to solve $\Pi(h,\lambda) = h$ near $(0,0)$ for $h = \xi(\lambda)$. As for the change in stability of the fixed point, since $D_h\Pi(0,0) = -1$, this follows immediately from the assumption

$$\frac{d}{d\lambda}\left(D_h\Pi(\xi(\lambda),\lambda)\right)|_{\lambda=0} \neq 0. \tag{3.126}$$

We will work out this formula into an expression without explicit occurrence of ξ. Compute

$$\frac{d}{d\lambda}\left(D_h\Pi(\xi(\lambda),\lambda)\right)|_{\lambda=0} = D_h^2\Pi(0,0)\xi'(0) + D_\lambda D_h\Pi(0,0).$$

In order to compute $\xi'(0)$, we differentiate $\Pi(\xi(\lambda),\lambda) = \xi(\lambda)$ with respect to λ. This gives

$$\frac{d}{d\lambda}\Pi(\xi(\lambda),\lambda) = D_h\Pi(\xi(\lambda),\lambda)\xi'(\lambda) + D_\lambda\Pi(\xi(\lambda),\lambda) = \xi'(\lambda)$$

and hence

$$\xi'(\lambda) = \frac{D_\lambda\Pi(\xi(\lambda),\lambda)}{1 - D_h\Pi(\xi(\lambda),\lambda)}.$$

Using $D_h\Pi(0,0) = -1$, we find $\xi'(0) = \frac{1}{2}D_\lambda\Pi(0,0)$. Therefore

$$\frac{d}{d\lambda}\left(D_h\Pi(\xi(\lambda),\lambda)\right)|_{\lambda=0} = \frac{1}{2}D_h^2\Pi(0,0)D_\lambda\Pi(0,0) + D_\lambda D_h\Pi(0,0). \tag{3.127}$$

Write

$$\eta = \frac{d}{d\lambda}\left(D_h\Pi(\xi(\lambda),\lambda)\right)\big|_{\lambda=0} \tag{3.128}$$

appearing in (3.127). For the stability of the fixed point we find

$$\begin{aligned} D_h\Pi(\xi(\lambda),\lambda) &\\ = D_h\Pi(0,0) + \frac{d}{d\lambda}\left(D_h\Pi(\xi(\lambda),\lambda)\right)\big|_{\lambda=0}\lambda + o(\lambda) &= -1 + \eta\lambda + o(\lambda). \end{aligned} \tag{3.129}$$

For the statements on the period-two points, consider the fixed points of $\Pi^2(\cdot,\lambda)$. These are solutions to

$$\Pi^2(h,\lambda) = \Pi(\Pi(h,\lambda),\lambda) = h.$$

The change of variables $y = h - \xi(\lambda)$ transforms this equation into

$$p(y,\lambda) := \Pi^2(y + \xi(\lambda),\lambda) - \xi(\lambda) = y.$$

Direct computations show that

$$p(0,\lambda) = 0, \quad D_y p(0,0) = 1, \quad \text{and} \quad D_y^2 p(0,0) = 0,$$

so that the graph of the second iterate of $\Pi(\cdot,0)$ is tangent to the diagonal at $(0,0)$ with vanishing second derivative. A direct calculation also shows that

$$D_y^3 p(0,0) = D_h^3\Pi^2(0,0) = -\left(2D_h^3\Pi(0,0) + 3\left(D_h^2\Pi(0,0)\right)^2\right).$$

Define

$$\zeta = D_h^3\Pi^2(0,0). \tag{3.130}$$

By Theorem 3.63(ii) we have

$$\zeta \neq 0.$$

We can write

$$p(y,0) = y + \frac{1}{6}\zeta y^3 + o(y^3) \tag{3.131}$$

for $y \to 0$. And, since $\xi(\lambda)$ is a fixed point of $\Pi(\cdot,\lambda)$, we have

$$p(0,\lambda) = 0$$

in an interval around 0. Therefore there is a differentiable function $\tilde{p}$ such that $p(y,\lambda) = y\tilde{p}(y,\lambda)$. To find the period-two points of $\Pi(\cdot,\lambda)$ different from $\xi(\lambda)$ means to find fixed points of $p(\cdot,\lambda)$ different from $y = 0$, and that means we must solve

$$\bar{p}(y,\lambda) := \tilde{p}(y,\lambda) - 1 = 0.$$

From (3.131) we obtain, as $y \to 0$,

$$\bar{p}(y,0) = \frac{1}{6}\zeta y^2 + o(y^2).$$

So

$$\bar{p}(0,0) = 0,\ D_y\bar{p}(0,0) = 0,\ D_y^2\bar{p}(0,0) = \frac{1}{3}\zeta \neq 0. \tag{3.132}$$

As for the derivative with respect to λ we find, since $D_\lambda p(0,0) = 0$ and using (3.127),

$$\begin{aligned}
D_\lambda\bar{p}(0,0) &= \lim_{y\to 0}\frac{1}{y}D_\lambda p(y,0)\\
&= \lim_{y\to 0}\frac{1}{y}\big(D_\lambda p(y,0) - D_\lambda p(0,0)\big)\\
&= D_y D_\lambda p(0,0)\\
&= D_\lambda D_y p(0,0)\\
&= \frac{d}{d\lambda}\left(D_h\Pi^2(\xi(\lambda),\lambda)\right)\big|_{\lambda=0}\\
&= \frac{d}{d\lambda}\left(D_h\Pi(\xi(\lambda),\lambda)\right)^2\big|_{\lambda=0}\\
&= -2\left(\frac{1}{2}D_\lambda\Pi(0,0)\cdot D_h^2\Pi(0,0) + D_\lambda D_h\Pi(0,0)\right)\\
&= -2\eta. \qquad (3.133)
\end{aligned}$$

Because of Theorem 3.63(i), $D_\lambda\bar{p}(0,0) \neq 0$. The existence of the function λ^* providing the period-two points now follows with Theorem 3.6 and the discussion following it.

It remains to prove the statement on the stability of the period-two points. For this we have to consider $D_h\Pi^2$ along the branch of the period-two points. In terms of the new coordinate y this translates into $D_y p(y,\lambda^*(y))$. Recall that

$$p(y,\lambda) = y\tilde{p}(y,\lambda) = y(\bar{p}(y,\lambda) + 1).$$

We find

$$\begin{aligned} D_y p(y,\lambda^*(y)) &= 1 + \bar{p}(y,\lambda^*(y)) + yD_y\bar{p}(y,\lambda^*(y)) \\ &= 1 + yD_y\bar{p}(y,\lambda^*(y)). \end{aligned} \tag{3.134}$$

Since y changes its sign when passing 0 and also $D_y\bar{p}(y,\lambda^*(y))$ changes its sign when y passes through 0 (compare Theorem 3.6), we find that $D_y p(y,\lambda^*(y))$ is for all $y \neq 0$ either greater than one or smaller than one. Hence all the period-two points are hyperbolic. The precise stability is determined by the sign of ζ. By (3.132) and $D\lambda^*(0) = 0$ we find

$$\begin{aligned} D_y p(y,\lambda^*(y)) &= 1 + y(\frac{1}{3}\zeta y + o(y)) \\ &= 1 + \frac{1}{3}\zeta y^2 + o(y^2). \end{aligned} \tag{3.135}$$

Further, from (3.132) and (3.133) we find

$$\lambda^*(y) = \frac{\zeta}{12\eta}y^2 + o(y^2). \tag{3.136}$$

Combining (3.129) and (3.134), (3.135), (3.136), yields the statements on the period-two points. □

Let $\eta < 0$ and $\zeta < 0$ with η and ζ given in (3.128) and (3.130). From (3.129) we see that the fixed points $\xi(\lambda)$ change from stable to unstable as λ passes through zero (from negative to positive). According to (3.136) period-two points exist only for positive λ. From (3.134) and (3.135) it follows that period-two points are stable. This case of a supercritical period-doubling bifurcation is as shown in Figure 3.27.

3.3.2.2. *Higher-dimensional period-doubling bifurcation of fixed points.* We add a discussion of the period-doubling bifurcation in more dimensions, with a formulation that does not involve explicit reductions to local center manifolds.

Example 3.65. Consider the following family of local diffeomorphisms near the origin in $\mathbb{R}^2$,

$$\Pi(x,y) = \left(-x + \alpha x^2 + \gamma x^3 + xy, -\frac{1}{2}y + \delta x^2\right).$$

The origin is a nonhyperbolic fixed point with a linearization that has an eigenvalue -1 and a hyperbolic eigenvalue $-\frac{1}{2}$. A local center manifold is given by $y = W(x) = cx^2 + \mathcal{O}(x^3)$ with $c = \frac{2}{3}\delta$; see Exercise 3.34. Compute

$$\begin{aligned} \Pi^2(x,y) = \Big(&x + (-2\alpha^2 - 2\gamma)x^3 - \frac{1}{2}xy + \mathcal{O}(x^4) + \mathcal{O}(x^2y) + \mathcal{O}(xy^2), \\ &\frac{1}{4}y + \frac{1}{2}\delta x^2 + \mathcal{O}(x^3) + \mathcal{O}(xy)\Big). \end{aligned}$$

So the second iterate of Π restricted to the local center manifold is given by

$$x \mapsto x - \Big(2\alpha^2 + 2\gamma + \frac{4}{3}\delta\Big)x^3 + \mathcal{O}(x^4).$$

The condition for a nondegenerate period-doubling bifurcation derived from this equation on the local center manifold (namely $\alpha^2 + \gamma + \frac{2}{3}\delta \neq 0$) thus depends on δ. ■

Theorem 3.66 (Period-doubling bifurcation for maps). *Assume that $\Pi(\cdot, \lambda)$ for $\lambda = 0$ has a fixed point 0 for which $D_x\Pi(0,0)$ has a simple eigenvalue -1. Further, $D_x\Pi(0,0)$ has k eigenvalues with modulus smaller than one and $n-k-1$ eigenvalues with modulus larger than one. Then there are $\varepsilon, \delta > 0$ and a smooth function $\xi : (-\delta, \delta) \to \mathbb{R}^n$ with $\xi(0) = 0$ and such that*

$$\Pi(\xi(\lambda), \lambda) = \xi(\lambda)$$

and $\xi(\lambda)$ is the only fixed point in $(-\varepsilon, \varepsilon)$ for $\lambda \in (-\delta, \delta)$. Write $s(\lambda)$ for the smooth function that is the eigenvalue of $D_h\Pi(\xi(\lambda), \lambda)$ with $s(0) = -1$. Take a right eigenvector v and a left eigenvector w corresponding to the eigenvalue -1 of $D_x\Pi(0,0)$, so that $\langle w, v\rangle = 1$. Assume that

(i) $s'(0) \neq 0$;

(ii) $\big\langle w, D_x^3\Pi^2(0,0)v^3\big\rangle + 6\big\langle w, D_x^2\Pi^2(0,0)(v, y_2)\big\rangle \neq 0$, *where*

$$y_2 = -\frac{1}{2}(D_x\Pi(0,0) - \mathrm{id})^{-1}\left(D_x^2\Pi(0,0)v^2 - \langle w, D_x^2\Pi(0,0)v^2\rangle v\right).$$

Then the fixed point $\xi(\lambda)$ changes stability index, between $k+1$ and k, while λ is passing through zero. There are $\varepsilon, \delta > 0$ and a smooth function $\lambda^* : (-\varepsilon, \varepsilon) \to \mathbb{R}$ with $\lambda^*(0) = 0$, $D\lambda^*(0) = 0$ and $D^2\lambda^*(0) \neq 0$, such that the following holds. For each $\lambda \in (0, \delta)$ or $\lambda \in (-\delta, 0)$, depending on the signs of the quantities in (i) *and* (ii)*, the map $\Pi(\cdot, \lambda)$ has, in addition to the fixed point $\xi(\lambda)$, exactly two period-two points $h_1(\lambda), h_2(\lambda)$ in the interval $(-\varepsilon, \varepsilon)$. Moreover, $\lambda^*(h_i(\lambda)) = \lambda$ and $h_i(\lambda) \to 0$ as $\lambda \to 0$ for $i = 1, 2$. For $\lambda \in (-\delta, 0]$ or $\lambda \in [0, \delta)$, respectively, there are no period-two points in $(-\varepsilon, \varepsilon)$. The period-two points are hyperbolic and their stability indices differ from that of the fixed point $\xi(\lambda)$.*

This theorem translates immediately into a corresponding bifurcation result for periodic orbits, as depicted in Figure 3.28.

Proof of Theorem 3.66. Just as in the proof of Theorem 3.26 (the pitchfork bifurcation), we reduce the map to a one-dimensional center manifold. We will show that the reduced map satisfies the assumptions of Theorem 3.63. It is obvious that the existence of $\xi(\cdot)$ follows with the implicit function theorem. Due to the assumption $s'(0) \neq 0$, the reduced map complies Theorem 3.63(i). So we may focus on condition (ii) for a nondegenerate bifurcation. Since this

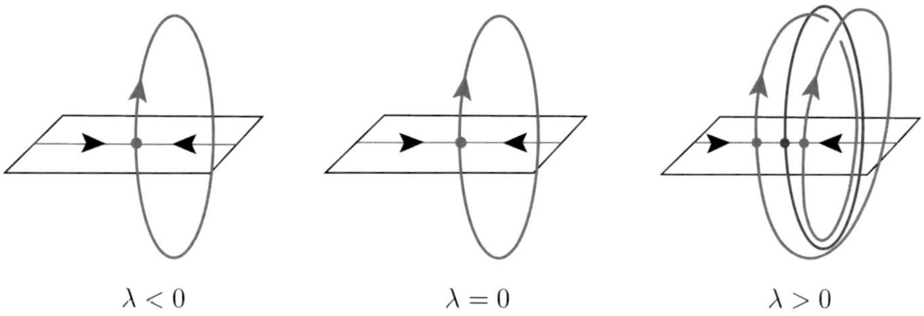

Figure 3.28. The period-doubling bifurcation of periodic orbits of (3.112), assuming a supercritical bifurcation.

condition does not contain derivatives with respect to λ, we may restrict our attention to the center manifold intersected with $\{\lambda = 0\}$.

Fix $\lambda = 0$ and write the map as $x \mapsto \Pi(x)$. A Taylor series for Π up to second order is then

$$\Pi(x) = D\Pi(0)x + \frac{1}{2}D^2\Pi(0)x^2 + \mathcal{O}(|x|^3).$$

Introduce

$$A = D\Pi(0) + \mathrm{id}.$$

Note that $\mathrm{span}\{v\} = \ker A$ and $\{w\}^\perp = \mathrm{im}\, A$. Since -1 is a simple eigenvalue of $D\Pi(0)$, we have $\ker A \cap \mathrm{im}\, A = \{0\}$. Let $\langle \cdot, \cdot \rangle$ be the related scalar product. Using $\langle w, v \rangle = 1$, we have that P_c given by $P_c x = \langle w, x \rangle v$, is the projection to the line spanned by v, with kernel equal to the image of A. Write $P_h = \mathrm{id} - P_c$, thus $P_h x = x - \langle w, x \rangle v$, for the projection onto im A with kernel $\ker A$. Since the projections leave both the kernel and the image of A invariant they commute with A. Hence they also commute with $D\Pi(0)$,

$$P_{c/h} D\Pi(0) = D\Pi(0) P_{c/h}. \tag{3.137}$$

We decompose x according to these projections and write $x = uv + y$ with $uv = P_c x \in \ker A$ and $y = P_h x \in \mathrm{im}\ A$.

Now we consider a local center manifold $W^c = \{uv + W(uv)\}$, $W(uv) \in \mathrm{im}\ A$,

$$W(uv) = y_2 u^2 + y_3 u^3 + \mathcal{O}(u^4), \tag{3.138}$$

with $y_2, y_3 \in \mathrm{im}\ A$. The restriction of Π to the center manifold is determined by the one-dimensional map

$$\hat{\Pi} : u \mapsto \langle w, \Pi(uv + W(uv)) \rangle;$$

see also Figure 3.29. Recall that $P_c \Pi(uv + W(uv)) = \langle w, \Pi(uv + W(uv)) \rangle v$. By

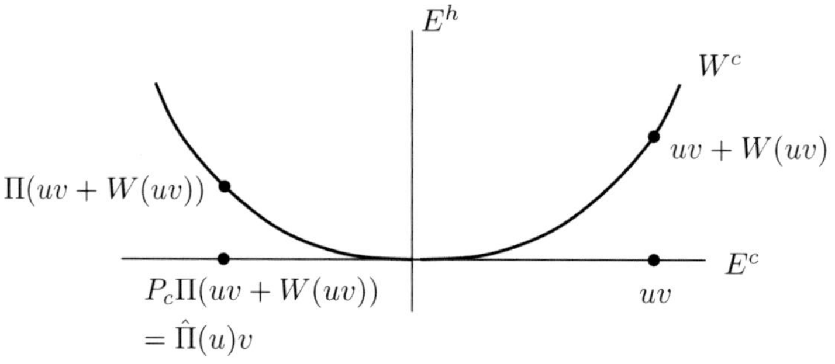

Figure 3.29. Restriction of Π to the center manifold W^c.

construction, $\hat{\Pi}^n(u) = \langle w, \Pi^n(uv + W(uv))\rangle$, and hence in particular $\hat{\Pi}^2(u) = \langle w, \Pi^2(uv + W(uv))\rangle$. Inserting a Taylor expansion of Π^2 yields

$$\hat{\Pi}^2(u) = \Big\langle w, D\Pi^2(0)(uv + W(uv)) + \frac{1}{2}D^2\Pi^2(0)(uv + W(uv))^2 + \frac{1}{6}D^3\Pi^2(0)(uv + W(uv))^3 + \mathcal{O}(u^4)\Big\rangle.$$

Incorporating (3.138), we find for the condition Theorem 3.63(ii) applied to $\hat{\Pi}^2$,

$$D^3\hat{\Pi}^2(0) = \langle w, 6D\Pi^2(0)y_3 + 6D^2\Pi^2(0)(v, y_2) + D^3\Pi^2(0)v^3\rangle \neq 0.$$

Since $x = 0$ is a fixed point of Π, one has $D\Pi^2(0) = (D\Pi(0))^2$. Further, using $y_3 \in \operatorname{im} A = \{w\}^\perp$, we find

$$\begin{aligned}\langle w, D\Pi^2(0)y_3\rangle &= \langle w, (D\Pi^2(0) - \mathrm{id})y_3\rangle = \langle w, (D\Pi(0) + \mathrm{id})(D\Pi(0) - \mathrm{id})y_3\rangle \\ &= 0,\end{aligned}$$

since $\langle w, (D\Pi(0) + \mathrm{id})y\rangle = 0$ for any vector y. This results in

$$D^3\hat{\Pi}^2(0) = \langle w, 6D^2\Pi^2(0)(v, y_2) + D^3\Pi^2(0)v^3\rangle \neq 0.$$

To verify Theorem 3.63(ii) it remains to determine y_2. This quantity can be obtained by exploiting the local invariance of W^c, meaning $x \in W^c \Rightarrow \Pi(x) \in W^c$, or in other words,

$$P_h\Pi(uv + W(uv)) = W(P_c\Pi(uv + W(uv))). \tag{3.139}$$

Consider, using (3.137) and (3.138),

$$\begin{aligned}P_h\Pi(uv + W(uv)) &= P_h\Pi(uv + y_2u^2 + \mathcal{O}(u^3)) \\ &= P_h\Big(D\Pi(0)(uv + y_2u^2) + \frac{1}{2}D^2\Pi(0)(uv)^2 + \mathcal{O}(u^3)\Big) \\ &= P_h\big((D\Pi(0)y_2 + \frac{1}{2}D^2\Pi(0)v^2)u^2\big) + \mathcal{O}(u^3) \\ &= \big(D\Pi(0)y_2 + \frac{1}{2}P_hD^2\Pi(0)v^2\big)u^2 + \mathcal{O}(u^3), \qquad (3.140)\end{aligned}$$

and

$$
\begin{aligned}
W\Big(P_c\Pi(uv + W(uv))\Big) &= W\Big(P_c\Pi(uv + y_2u^2 + \mathcal{O}(u^3))\Big) \\
&= W\Big(P_c(D\Pi(0)(uv + y_2u^2) + \frac{1}{2}D^2\Pi(0)(uv)^2 + \mathcal{O}(u^3))\Big) \\
&= W\Big(\big(-u + \mathcal{O}(u^2)\big)v\Big) \\
&= y_2u^2 + \mathcal{O}(u^3). \qquad (3.141)
\end{aligned}
$$

The local invariance (3.139) together with (3.140) and (3.141) implies

$$D\Pi(0)y_2 + \frac{1}{2}P_hD^2\Pi(0)v^2 = y_2.$$

With the definition of P_h this yields

$$y_2 = -\frac{1}{2}(D\Pi(0) - \mathrm{id})^{-1}\big(D^2\Pi(0)v^2 - \langle w, D^2\Pi(0)v^2\rangle v\big).$$

Note that indeed $y_2 \in \operatorname{im} A = \operatorname{im} P_h$. These expressions translate into Theorem 3.63(ii). □

Remark 3.67. As in Remark 3.64 the condition for a nondegenerate bifurcation, Theorem 3.63(ii), can be cast in a form without a second iterate of Π. To do so we apply the condition stated in Remark 3.64(ii) to $\hat{\Pi}$, the restriction of Π to the center manifold at $\lambda = 0$. With similar computations as performed in the proof, thus writing $W(uv) = y_2u^2 + y_3u^3 + \mathcal{O}(u^4)$ for the map yielding the center manifold and expanding

$$
\begin{aligned}
\hat{\Pi}(u) &= \langle w, \Pi(uv + W(uv))\rangle \\
&= \Big\langle w, D\Pi(0)(uv + W(uv)) + \frac{1}{2}D^2\Pi(0)(uv + W(uv))^2 \\
&\qquad + \frac{1}{6}D^3\Pi(0)(uv + W(uv))^3 + \mathcal{O}(u^4)\Big\rangle,
\end{aligned}
$$

we find

$$
\begin{aligned}
D^3\hat{\Pi}(0) &= \langle w, D\Pi(0)y_3 + 6D^2\Pi(0)(v, y_2) + D^3\Pi(0)v^3\rangle \\
&= \langle w, 6D^2\Pi(0)(v, y_2) + D^3\Pi(0)v^3\rangle.
\end{aligned}
$$

The latter equality follows from $y_3 \in \operatorname{im} A = \{w\}^\perp$ and

$$\langle w, D\Pi(0)y_3\rangle = \langle w, (D\Pi(0) + \mathrm{id})y_3\rangle = 0.$$

Likewise,

$$D^2\hat{\Pi}(0) = \langle w, D^2\Pi(0)v^2\rangle.$$

So the counterpart of Remark 3.64(ii), $2D^3\hat{\Pi}(0) + 3(D^2\hat{\Pi}(0))^2 \neq 0$, becomes

$$\langle w, 12D^2\Pi(0)(v, y_2)\rangle + \langle w, 2D^3\Pi(0)v^3\rangle + 3\big(\langle w, D^2\Pi(0)v^2\rangle\big)^2 \neq 0;$$

see also [**215**, Section 5.4].

A little more effort is required to formulate the generic unfolding condition Remark 3.64(i) for the present higher-dimensional context. Because of the derivatives with respect to λ, the entire center manifold must be considered. Write the center manifold as $\{uv + \tilde{W}(uv, \lambda)\}$ with

$$\tilde{W}(uv, \lambda) = y_2 u^2 + y_{11} u\lambda + y_{02}\lambda^2 + \mathcal{O}\left(|(u, \lambda)|^3\right),$$

where y_2 is given above and $y_{11}, y_{02} \in \operatorname{im} A$. We denote by $\tilde{\Pi}$ the restriction of Π to the center manifold which we consider as a function of u and λ:

$$\tilde{\Pi}(u, \lambda) = \langle w, \Pi(uv + \tilde{W}(uv, \lambda), \lambda)\rangle.$$

Now apply the condition stated in Remark 3.64(i) to $\tilde{\Pi}$. First we compute the single terms appearing there:

$$D_u^2\tilde{\Pi}(0, 0) = D^2\hat{\Pi}(0) = \langle w, D^2\Pi(0)v^2\rangle$$

and

$$\begin{aligned} D_\lambda\tilde{\Pi}(0, 0) &= \langle w, D_x\Pi(0, 0)D_\lambda\tilde{W}(0, 0) + D_\lambda\Pi(0, 0)\rangle \\ &= \langle w, D_\lambda\Pi(0, 0)\rangle \end{aligned}$$

and

$$\begin{aligned} &D_\lambda D_u\tilde{\Pi}(0, 0) = D_\lambda\big(D_u\tilde{\Pi}(0, \lambda)\big)|_{\lambda=0} \\ &= D_\lambda\big(\langle w, D_x\Pi(\tilde{W}(0, \lambda), \lambda)(v + D_{(uv)}\tilde{W}(0, \lambda)v)\rangle\big)|_{\lambda=0} \\ &= D_\lambda\big(\langle w, D_x\Pi(\tilde{W}(0, \lambda), \lambda)(v + y_{11}\lambda + \mathcal{O}(\lambda^2))\rangle\big)|_{\lambda=0} \\ &= \langle w, D_x^2\Pi(0, 0)(D_\lambda\tilde{W}(0, 0), v) + D_\lambda D_x\Pi(0, 0)(1, v) + D_x\Pi(0, 0)y_{11}\rangle \\ &= \langle w, D_\lambda D_x\Pi(0, 0)(1, v)\rangle. \end{aligned}$$

Note that $\langle w, D_x\Pi(0, 0)y_{11}\rangle = 0$ follows just as $\langle w, D_x\Pi(0, 0)y_3\rangle = 0$, shown above. We insert these terms in Remark 3.64(i) applied to $\tilde{\Pi}$, so

$$\frac{1}{2}D_\lambda\tilde{\Pi}(0, 0) \cdot D_h^2\tilde{\Pi}(0, 0) + D_\lambda D_h\tilde{\Pi}(0, 0) \neq 0$$

gives a form of Theorem 3.66(i) without an explicit mention of ξ:

$$\frac{1}{2}\langle w, D_\lambda\Pi(0, 0)\rangle \cdot \langle w, D^2\Pi(0)v^2\rangle + \langle w, D_\lambda D_x\Pi(0, 0)(1, v)\rangle \neq 0.$$

■

Example 3.68. The following equations provide an artificial example that models an interaction of hysteresis and a Hopf bifurcation [**220**]:

$$\begin{aligned} \dot{x} &= (z - \beta)x - \omega y, \\ \dot{y} &= \omega x + (z - \beta)y, \\ \dot{z} &= 0.6 + z - \frac{1}{3}z^3 - (x^2 + y^2)(1 + \rho z) + \varepsilon z x^3. \end{aligned} \tag{3.142}$$

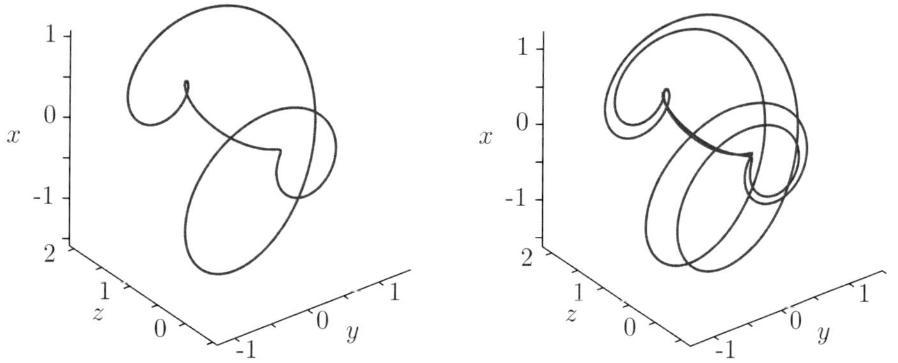

Figure 3.30. Periodic attractors in system (3.142). The values of β, ω, ρ are fixed at $0.7, 3.5, 0.25$. The left picture is with $\varepsilon = 0.05$; the right picture with $\varepsilon = 0.06$.

Fix $\beta = 0.7$ and $\omega = 3.5$. This gives a two-parameter family of differential equations with (ρ, ε) as parameters. Numerical evidence shows that a period-doubling bifurcation of a periodic orbit occurs for $\rho = 0.25$ and increasing ε from 0 to positive values. Figure 3.30 shows periodic attractors just before and after the period-doubling bifurcation.

The system will return in Example 3.77. ■

Period-doubling bifurcations return in Chapter 5 on global bifurcations. In Section 5.2.5 the occurrence of cascades of period-doubling bifurcations is discussed. Example 5.65 will discuss period-doubling bifurcations in the Rössler system.

3.3.3. Neimark-Sacker bifurcation. The discrete time analogue of the Hopf bifurcation, the unfolding of a diffeomorphism with a fixed point and a linearization with complex conjugate eigenvalues on the unit circle, is called the Neimark-Sacker bifurcation after independent work on it by Juri Neimark [**264**] and Robert Sacker [**320, 321**]. In its unfolding, an invariant circle appears, where we use the word "circle" to indicate a simple smooth closed curve. For a diffeomorphism arising as a Poincaré return map of a differential equation, this scenario translates to an invariant torus appearing in a bifurcation where complex conjugate Floquet multipliers of a periodic orbit move through the unit circle. The dynamics on the invariant torus depends on details of the vector field; one may find periodic orbits or dense orbits on the torus, and further bifurcations of the flow on the torus.

As before we start with differential equations (3.112) with a periodic orbit as in (3.113). The bifurcation results will be stated in terms of a Poincaré return map. The corresponding bifurcation scenario is also known as Hopf bifurcation for diffeomorphisms (from [**319**]). We restrict our inquiry to differential equations in three-dimensional space so that a center manifold reduction is not needed. From the textbooks discussing the bifurcation, we mention [**186**, **187**], [**215**], [**240**], and [**339**, **340**].

3.3.3.1. *Planar Neimark-Sacker bifurcation.* We start by exploring a model system.

Example 3.69. Let, for some fixed θ, $\Pi : \mathbb{R}^2 \times \mathbb{R} \to \mathbb{R}^2$ be given as

$$\Pi(h,\lambda) = (1+\lambda)\begin{pmatrix}\cos\theta & -\sin\theta\\ \sin\theta & \cos\theta\end{pmatrix}\left[\begin{pmatrix}h_1\\ h_2\end{pmatrix} + (h_1^2+h_2^2)\begin{pmatrix}a & -b\\ b & a\end{pmatrix}\begin{pmatrix}h_1\\ h_2\end{pmatrix}\right], \tag{3.143}$$

with $h = (h_1, h_2)$ and where $a = a(\lambda)$ and $b = b(\lambda)$ are smooth functions with $a(0) \neq 0$. Rewrite $\Pi(\cdot, \lambda)$ in polar coordinates. With

$$h_1 = h_1(r,\varphi) = r\cos\varphi, \quad h_2 = h_2(r,\varphi) = r\sin\varphi,$$

we find

$$\Pi(h,\lambda) = \big(1+\lambda\big)r\begin{pmatrix}\cos(\varphi+\theta)\\ \sin(\varphi+\theta)\end{pmatrix} + ar^3\begin{pmatrix}\cos(\varphi+\theta)\\ \sin(\varphi+\theta)\end{pmatrix} + br^3\begin{pmatrix}-\sin(\varphi+\theta)\\ \cos(\varphi+\theta)\end{pmatrix}.$$

For the radial and angular coordinates we get

$$|\Pi(h(r,\varphi),\lambda)| = |1+\lambda+ar^2+\mathcal{O}(r^4)|r,$$
$$\arg\big(\Pi(h(r,\varphi),\lambda)\big) = \varphi+\theta+\mathcal{O}(r^2).$$

So the map written in polar coordinates, denoted

$$\hat{\Pi}(r,\varphi,\lambda) = \big(\hat{\Pi}^{(1)}(r,\varphi,\lambda), \hat{\Pi}^{(2)}(r,\varphi,\lambda)\big),$$

reads

$$\hat{\Pi}(r,\varphi,\lambda)(r,\varphi) = \big(|1+\lambda+ar^2+\mathcal{O}(r^4)|\, r, \varphi+\theta+\mathcal{O}(r^2)\big).$$

The fixed points of $\hat{\Pi}^{(1)}(\cdot,\varphi,\lambda)$, with r near 0, are determined by

$$r = 0 \quad \text{or} \quad \lambda + ar^2 + \mathcal{O}(r^4) = 0.$$

The latter equation can be solved for $\lambda = \lambda^*(r) = -a(0)r^2 + \mathcal{O}(r^3)$ (recall that we assumed that $a(0) \neq 0$). For (at least sufficiently small) nonnegative r the function λ^* is invertible. Its inverse determines the radius of an invariant circle. It has the form

$$r^*(\lambda) = \sqrt{-\lambda/a(0)} + \mathcal{O}(\lambda). \tag{3.144}$$

So, for λ with $\operatorname{sign}\lambda = -\operatorname{sign} a(0)$ there exists a $\Pi(\cdot,\lambda)$-invariant circle

$$C_\lambda = \{(h_1,h_2)\ ;\ h_1^2+h_2^2 = r^*(\lambda)^2\}.$$

Its radius shrinks to zero if $\lambda \to 0$. For $a(0) < 0$ we find the bifurcation diagram depicted in Figure 3.31.

Consider $\Pi(\cdot,\lambda)$ as a mapping in the complex plane and calculate

$$\Pi^{\mathbb{C}}(\cdot,\lambda) : \mathbb{C} \to \mathbb{C}, \quad z \mapsto e^{i\theta}z\big(1+\lambda+(a+ib)|z|^2\big); \tag{3.145}$$

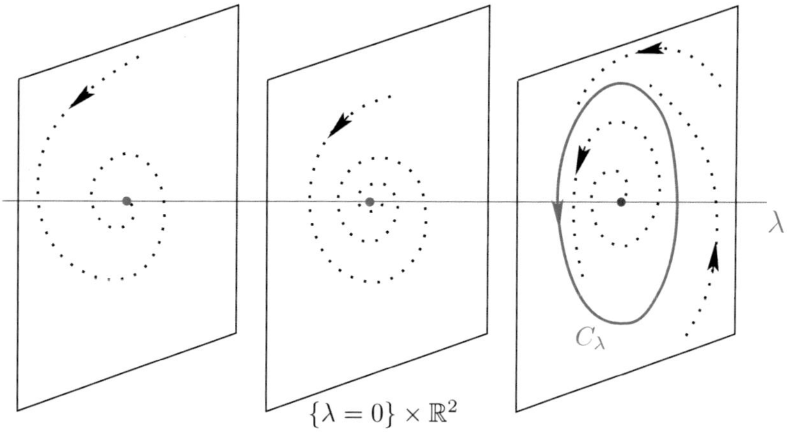

Figure 3.31. The Neimark-Sacker bifurcation of the mapping Π given in (3.143) with positive θ.

see Exercise 3.35. From this expression we see that the motion on C_λ is a rigid rotation about an angle $\theta_\lambda = \theta + \mathcal{O}\left((r^*(\lambda))^2\right)$. So, if $2\pi/\theta_\lambda \in \mathbb{Q}$, the invariant circle C_λ is filled with periodic $\Pi(\cdot,\lambda)$-orbits. If $2\pi/\theta_\lambda \notin \mathbb{Q}$, then C_λ is filled with $\Pi(\cdot,\lambda)$-orbits which are dense in C_λ. See Example 5.44 in Section 5.2.3 on the dynamics of circle diffeomorphisms. ■

Now we consider the general case. Take a smooth map

$$\Pi : \mathbb{R}^2 \times \mathbb{R} \to \mathbb{R}^2, \quad (x,\mu) \mapsto \Pi(x,\mu) = (\Pi^1(x,\mu), \Pi^2(x,\mu)). \tag{3.146}$$

We denote $x = (x_1, x_2)$. Assume that $x = 0$ is a fixed point of $\Pi(\cdot, 0)$: $\Pi(0,0) = 0$. Assume further that $D_x\Pi(0,0)$ has eigenvalues $e^{\pm i\theta}$ for some $\theta \in (0,\pi)$. Then, near $(x,\mu) = (0,0)$, the fixed point equation $\Pi(x,\mu) = x$ can be solved for $x = x^*(\mu)$ by the implicit function theorem. An appropriate coordinate transformation brings $x^*(\mu) \equiv 0$. We may therefore assume

$$\Pi(0,\mu) \equiv 0, \quad \sigma D_x\Pi(0,\mu) = \{\varsigma(\mu)e^{\pm i\,\vartheta(\mu)}\}. \tag{3.147}$$

Of course $\varsigma(0) = 1$ and $\vartheta(0) = \theta$. For the formulation of the bifurcation theorem it is convenient to have Π written in complex coordinates $z = x_1 + i x_2$ and $\bar{z} = x_1 - i x_2$. Note that

$$\begin{pmatrix} z \\ \bar{z} \end{pmatrix} = \begin{pmatrix} 1 & i \\ 1 & -i \end{pmatrix} \begin{pmatrix} x_1 \\ x_2 \end{pmatrix}$$

and

$$\begin{pmatrix} x_1 \\ x_2 \end{pmatrix} = \begin{pmatrix} \frac{1}{2} & \frac{1}{2} \\ -\frac{1}{2}i & \frac{1}{2}i \end{pmatrix} \begin{pmatrix} z \\ \bar{z} \end{pmatrix}.$$

Using these identities, define $\Pi^{\mathbb{C}} : \mathbb{C} \times \mathbb{R} \to \mathbb{C}$ as

$$\Pi^{\mathbb{C}}(z,\lambda) = \Pi^1(x_1, x_2, \mu(\lambda)) + i\,\Pi^2(x_1, x_2, \mu(\lambda)).$$

Theorem 3.70 (Planar Neimark-Sacker bifurcation). *Consider a smooth map* (3.146) *that satisfies* (3.147) *and assume further*

(i) $\varsigma'(0) > 0$,

(ii) *The value of*

$$a(\lambda) = -\mathrm{Re}\left[\frac{(1-2e^{i\theta})e^{-i2\theta}}{2(1-e^{i\theta})}\Pi^{\mathbb{C}}_{zz}(0,\lambda)\Pi^{\mathbb{C}}_{z\bar{z}}(0,\lambda)\right] - \frac{1}{2}|\Pi^{\mathbb{C}}_{z\bar{z}}(0,\lambda)|^2 - \frac{1}{4}|\Pi^{\mathbb{C}}_{\bar{z}\bar{z}}(0,\lambda)|^2 + \mathrm{Re}\left[\frac{e^{-i\theta}}{2}\Pi^{\mathbb{C}}_{zz\bar{z}}(0,\lambda)\right]$$

computed at $\lambda = 0$, *is nonzero,*

(iii) *Strong nonresonance conditions:* $e^{ik\theta} \neq 1$ *for* $k = 1, 2, 3, 4$.

Then the bifurcation is as follows, depending on the sign of a:

(1) *If* $a < 0$, *there is a supercritical bifurcation: for* $\lambda \leq 0$ *the origin is stable and attracts all nearby orbits, while for* $\lambda > 0$ *the origin is unstable and there is a stable invariant circle* C_λ *that attracts all nearby orbits except for the origin.*

(2) *If* $a > 0$, *there is a subcritical bifurcation: for* $\lambda < 0$ *there is an unstable invariant circle* C_λ; *the stable equilibrium at the origin attracts only points inside* C_λ, *for* $\lambda \geq 0$ *the origin is unstable and no other orbits stay close to the origin.*

For each positive integer k there is $0 < \lambda_0$ *so that the invariant circle* C_λ *is* C^k *for* $|\lambda| < \lambda_0$.

One can consider θ as a second parameter. Changing θ may change the dynamics on the invariant circle. Basic aspects of the relevant theory on dynamics of circle diffeomorphisms are discussed in Section 5.2.3. The bifurcation theorem will be proved below.

In the following example we perform the calculations to check for a Neimark-Sacker bifurcation in an explicit family of planar diffeomorphisms. Other examples can be found in the literature. For instance [**215**, Example 4.2] treats a Neimark-Sacker bifurcation in delayed logistic maps $x_{n+1} = \mu x_n(1 - x_{n-1})$ (which are equivalent to planar maps $(x_{n+1}, y_{n+1}) = (\mu x_n(1 - y_n), x_n)$). And [**132**] contains a bifurcation study of generalized Hénon maps $(x, y) \mapsto (a - x^2 + Sx^3 + Rxy - by, x)$ that includes a study of Neimark-Sacker bifurcations.

Example 3.71. Consider planar maps of the form

$$\Pi(x, y, b) = (g(x) + xy - by, x), \tag{3.148}$$

for a smooth function $g(x) = x + a_2x^2$, and depending on a positive parameter b. Note that

$$D\Pi(x, y, b) = \begin{pmatrix} g'(x) + y & x - b \\ 1 & 0 \end{pmatrix}.$$

We find $\Pi(0, 0, b) = (0, 0)$ and

$$D\Pi(0, 0, b) = \begin{pmatrix} 1 & -b \\ 1 & 0 \end{pmatrix},$$

so that Π is a local diffeomorphism near the origin. The determinant of $D\Pi(0, 0, b)$ equals b.

We will investigate the local bifurcation occurring if $b = 1$. The eigenvalues of $D\Pi(0, 0, b)$ are $\frac{1\pm\sqrt{1-4b}}{2}$ and have modulus $\sqrt{b}$ for b near 1. The modulus of the eigenvalues moves through 1 with nonzero speed in b, at $b = 1$. The eigenvalues of $D\Pi(0, 0, 1)$ are $\lambda = \frac{1}{2} + \frac{1}{2}\sqrt{3}\,i$ and $\bar{\lambda}$. We can write $\lambda = e^{i\theta}$ with $\theta = \pi/3$.

The eigenvector corresponding to λ is $(\lambda, 1)$, the eigenvector corresponding to $\bar{\lambda}$ is $(\bar{\lambda}, 1)$. Let

$$U = \begin{pmatrix} \lambda & \bar{\lambda} \\ 1 & 1 \end{pmatrix}.$$

Then

$$U^{-1} = -\frac{i}{\sqrt{3}}\begin{pmatrix} 1 & -\bar{\lambda} \\ -1 & \lambda \end{pmatrix}.$$

Take complex coordinates

$$(z, \bar{z}) = U^{-1}(x, y).$$

Write $h(x) = g(x) - x = a_2x^2$ and compute

$$\begin{aligned} z_{n+1} &= \lambda z_n - \frac{i}{\sqrt{3}}\left[h(\lambda z_n + \bar{\lambda}\bar{z}_n) + (\lambda z_n + \bar{\lambda}\bar{z}_n)(z_n + \bar{z}_n)\right] \\ &= \lambda z_n + \left(\frac{1}{2} + \frac{1}{2}a_2 + \left(-\frac{1}{6}\sqrt{3} + \frac{1}{6}\sqrt{3}a_2\right)i\right)z_n^2 \\ &\quad + \left(-\frac{1}{3}\sqrt{3} - \frac{2}{3}\sqrt{3}a_2\right)iz_n\bar{z}_n + \left(\frac{1}{2} + \frac{1}{2}a_2 + \left(-\frac{1}{6}\sqrt{3} - \frac{1}{6}\sqrt{3}a_2\right)i\right)\bar{z}_n^2. \end{aligned}$$

Denoting the right-hand side as $\lambda z_n + R(z_n, \bar{z}_n)$, we calculate the number a from the assumptions in Theorem 3.70 as

$$\begin{aligned} a &= -\mathrm{Re}\left[\left(-\frac{3}{4} - \frac{1}{4}\sqrt{3}\,i\right) D^2_{zz}R(0,0) D^2_{z\bar{z}}R(0,0)\right] \\ &\quad - \frac{1}{4}|D^2_{\bar{z}\bar{z}}R(0,0)|^2 - \frac{1}{2}|D^2_{z\bar{z}}R(0,0)|^2 \\ &= -\mathrm{Re}\left[\left(-\frac{3}{4} - \frac{1}{4}\sqrt{3}\,i\right)\left(-\frac{1}{3}\sqrt{3} + \frac{1}{3}\sqrt{3}a_2\right)\left(\frac{1}{3}\sqrt{3} + \frac{2}{3}\sqrt{3}a_2\right)\right] \\ &\quad - \mathrm{Re}\left[\left(-\frac{3}{4} - \frac{1}{4}\sqrt{3}\,i\right)\left((1+a_2)\left(-\frac{1}{3}\sqrt{3} - \frac{2}{3}\sqrt{3}a_2\right) i\right)\right] \\ &\quad - \frac{1}{4}\left|1 + a_2 + \left(-\frac{1}{3}\sqrt{3} - \frac{1}{3}\sqrt{3}a_2\right) i\right|^2 - \frac{1}{2}\left(\frac{1}{3}\sqrt{3} + \frac{2}{3}\sqrt{3}a_2\right)^2 \\ &= \frac{1}{2}a_2(1+2a_2) - \frac{1}{3}(1+a_2)^2 - \frac{1}{6}(1+2a_2)^2 \\ &= -\frac{1}{6}\,(5a_2 + 3)\,, \end{aligned}$$

which is nonzero for all values of a_2 apart from the root $-3/5$ of $5a_2 + 3$. The conditions in the bifurcation theorem for the Neimark-Sacker bifurcation, Theorem 3.70, are then applicable. The bifurcation is supercritical for $a_2 > -3/5$; compare Figure 3.32.

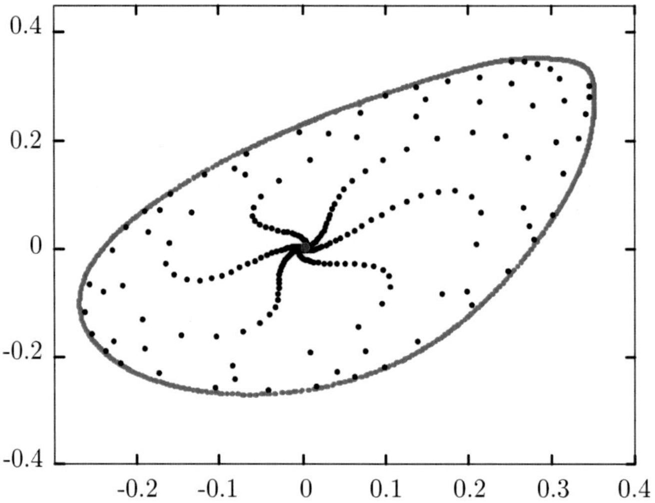

Figure 3.32. A numerically computed attracting invariant circle for (3.148) with $b = 1.05$ and $a_2 = 1$.

One may consider somewhat more general maps

$$(x, y) \mapsto (g(x) + rxy - by, x) \tag{3.149}$$

with $g(x) = x + a_2x^2 + a_3x^3 + \mathcal{O}(x^4)$ and $r > 0$. A rescaling of the variables makes $r = 1$. Without the xy term though, one would have $a(0) = 0$ as the maps then have constant Jacobian b. Exercise 3.36 asks us to investigate these more general maps. ■

3.3.3.2. *Proof of Theorem* 3.70. In different steps we prove Theorem 3.70: we provide a normal form for the map Π, analyze the existence of an invariant circle for the normal form, and analyze basins of attraction. We start with a reparametrization. Under the assumption

$$\varsigma'(0) \neq 0,$$

we may write $\varsigma(\mu) = 1 + \lambda(\mu)$ with $\lambda'(0) \neq 0$, and we can introduce $\lambda = \lambda(\mu)$ as new parameter. We denote the inverse of $\lambda(\cdot)$ by $\mu(\cdot)$, and we replace $\Pi(x, \mu)$ by $\Pi(x, \mu(\lambda))$. Recycling notation, we write $\Pi(x, \lambda)$ for the map with the new parameter λ. If we further write $\theta(\lambda) = \vartheta(\mu(\lambda))$, we find for the spectrum of $D_x\Pi(0, \lambda)$,

$$\sigma D_x\Pi(0, \lambda) = \{(1 + \lambda)e^{\pm i\,\theta(\lambda)}\}, \quad \theta(0) = \theta. \tag{3.150}$$

Normal form. The following normal form provides the expression of Example 3.69 with additional higher-order terms added. We will then prove the bifurcation theorem for the map in normal form. Note that we keep writing Π for the map in the new coordinates.

Lemma 3.72. *Consider a smooth map* $\Pi : \mathbb{R}^2 \times \mathbb{R} \to \mathbb{R}^2$ *with* $\Pi(0, \lambda) = 0$ *that satisfies* (3.150) *and the strong nonresonance conditions in Theorem* 3.70. *Then there exists a smooth transformation* $x = T(h)$ *such that* Π *in the new coordinates has the form*

$$\begin{aligned}\Pi(h, \lambda) &\\ = (1 + \lambda)&\begin{pmatrix}\cos\theta(\lambda) & -\sin\theta(\lambda)\\ \sin\theta(\lambda) & \cos\theta(\lambda)\end{pmatrix}\left[\begin{pmatrix}h_1\\ h_2\end{pmatrix} + (h_1^2 + h_2^2)\begin{pmatrix}a(\lambda) & -b(\lambda)\\ b(\lambda) & a(\lambda)\end{pmatrix}\begin{pmatrix}h_1\\ h_2\end{pmatrix}\right]\\ &\qquad + \mathcal{O}(|h|^4),\end{aligned}$$

where $\theta(\cdot)$, $a(\cdot)$, *and* $b(\cdot)$ *are smooth functions with* $\theta(0) = \theta$.

Proof. Write $\Lambda = (1 + \lambda)e^{i\,\theta(\lambda)}$. Expand

$$\Pi^{\mathbb{C}}(z, \lambda) = \Lambda z + \sum_{k+l=2} \frac{1}{k!\,l!} p_{kl} z^k \bar{z}^l + \mathcal{O}(|z|^3). \tag{3.151}$$

We will remove the quadratic terms, and after that part of the third-order terms, by coordinate transformations.

REMOVING SECOND-ORDER TERMS. In a first step we remove the quadratic terms from the expression (3.151) by a transformation $T^{(1)} : \mathbb{C} \to \mathbb{C}$ defined by

$$z = T^{(1)}(w) = w + \sum_{k+l=2} \frac{1}{k!\,l!} t_{kl}^{(1)} w^k \bar{w}^l$$

with coefficients $t_{kl}^{(1)}$ such that

$$\left(\left(T^{(1)}\right)^{-1} \circ \hat{\Pi}^{\mathbb{C}}(\cdot,\lambda) \circ T^{(1)}\right)(w) = \Lambda w + \mathcal{O}(|w|^3).$$

Using

$$\left(T^{(1)}\right)^{-1}(z) = z - \sum_{k+l=2} \frac{1}{k!\,l!} t_{kl}^{(1)} z^k \bar{z}^l + \mathcal{O}(|z|^3),$$

we find

$$\begin{aligned}
&\left(T^{(1)}\right)^{-1} \circ \hat{\Pi}^{\mathbb{C}}(\cdot,\lambda) \circ T^{(1)}(w) \\
&\quad = \Lambda w + \frac{1}{2}\left(p_{20} + (\Lambda - \Lambda^2) t_{20}^{(1)}\right) w^2 + \left(p_{11} + (\Lambda - |\Lambda|^2) t_{11}^{(1)}\right) w\bar{w} \\
&\qquad\qquad + \frac{1}{2}\left(p_{02} + (\Lambda - \bar{\Lambda}^2) t_{02}^{(1)}\right) \bar{w}^2 + \mathcal{O}(|w|^3).
\end{aligned}$$

The quadratic terms disappear if

$$t_{20}^{(1)} = -\frac{p_{20}}{\Lambda - \Lambda^2}, \quad t_{11}^{(1)} = -\frac{p_{11}}{\Lambda - |\Lambda|^2}, \quad t_{02}^{(1)} = -\frac{p_{02}}{\Lambda - \bar{\Lambda}^2}.$$

Because of the strong nonresonance conditions these terms are defined for small $|\lambda|$:

$$\begin{aligned}
\Lambda(0) - \Lambda^2(0) = (1 - e^{i\theta})e^{i\theta} \neq 0 \quad &\Leftrightarrow \quad e^{i\theta} \neq 1, \\
\Lambda(0) - |\Lambda(0)|^2 = e^{i\theta} - 1 \neq 0 \quad &\Leftrightarrow \quad e^{i\theta} \neq 1, \\
\Lambda(0) - \bar{\Lambda}^2(0) = (1 - e^{-i3\theta})e^{i\theta} \neq 0 \quad &\Leftrightarrow \quad e^{i3\theta} \neq 1.
\end{aligned}$$

So, by means of the transformation $T^{(1)}$ we obtain an expression for Π of the form

$$\Pi(z,\lambda) = \Lambda z + \sum_{k+l=3} \frac{1}{k!\,l!} p_{kl} z^k \bar{z}^l + \mathcal{O}(|z|^4).$$

REMOVING NONRESONANT THIRD-ORDER TERMS. We apply a further transformation $T^{(2)} : \mathbb{C} \to \mathbb{C}$ of the form

$$z = T^{(2)}(w) = w + \sum_{k+l=3} \frac{1}{k!\,l!} t_{kl}^{(2)} w^k \bar{w}^l,$$

with coefficients $t_{kl}^{(2)}$. Note that

$$\left(T^{(2)}\right)^{-1}(z) = z - \sum_{k+l=3} \frac{1}{k!\,l!} t_{kl}^{(2)} z^k \bar{z}^l + \mathcal{O}(|z|^4).$$

We find

$$\left(T^{(2)}\right)^{-1} \circ \hat{\Pi}^{\mathbb{C}}(\cdot,\lambda) \circ T^{(2)}(w)$$
$$= \Lambda w + \frac{1}{6}\left(p_{30} + (\Lambda - \Lambda^3)\, t_{30}^{(1)}\right) w^3 + \frac{1}{2}\left(p_{21} + (\Lambda - \Lambda|\Lambda|^2)\, t_{21}^{(2)}\right) w^2\bar{w}$$
$$+ \frac{1}{2}\left(p_{12} + (\Lambda - \bar{\Lambda}|\Lambda|^2)\, t_{12}^{(2)}\right) w\bar{w}^2 + \frac{1}{6}\left(p_{03} + (\Lambda - \bar{\Lambda}^3)\, t_{03}^{(2)}\right) \bar{w}^3 + \mathcal{O}(|w|^4).$$

Choose

$$t_{30}^{(2)} = -\frac{p_{30}}{\Lambda - \Lambda^3}, \quad t_{12}^{(2)} = -\frac{p_{12}}{\Lambda - \bar{\Lambda}|\Lambda|^2}, \quad t_{03}^{(2)} = -\frac{p_{02}}{\Lambda - \bar{\Lambda}^3}.$$

Because of the strong nonresonance conditions, the denominators of these terms are different from zero for small $|\lambda|$:

$$\Lambda(0) - \Lambda^3(0) = (1 - e^{i2\theta})e^{i\theta} \neq 0 \quad \Leftrightarrow \quad e^{i2\theta} \neq 1,$$
$$\Lambda(0) - \bar{\Lambda}(0)|\Lambda(0)|^2 = \left(1 - e^{-i2\theta}\right)e^{i\theta} \neq 0 \quad \Leftrightarrow \quad e^{i2\theta} \neq 1,$$
$$\Lambda(0) - \bar{\Lambda}^3(0) = \left(1 - e^{-i4\theta}\right)e^{i\theta} \neq 0 \quad \Leftrightarrow \quad e^{i4\theta} \neq 1.$$

These terms are therefore well defined for small $|\lambda|$. This choice removes coefficients of the $w^3, w\bar{w}^2, \bar{w}^3$ terms. This does not work for the $w^2\bar{w}$ term, but taking $t_{21}^{(2)} = 0$ will keep the coefficient of the $w^2\bar{w}$ term unaltered. Going back to Cartesian coordinates gives the expression of Π in the statement of the lemma. □

The formula for $a(0)$ as stated in the bifucation theorem, Theorem 3.70(ii), can be derived by making the calculations for the normal form explicit. We refer to [**215**, Section 4.7], [**186**, Chapter 3] and [**414**].

The invariant circle. We continue, as announced, with the bifurcation result for the normal form. The lemma below provides the existence of the invariant circle. Afterward a lemma will handle the stability statements. These two lemmas are formulated for the supercritical case, but the subcritical case is treated similarly.

Again we consider Π as a mapping in the complex plane, $\Pi^{\mathbb{C}}(\cdot,\lambda) : \mathbb{C} \to \mathbb{C}$ given as

(3.152) $$\Pi^{\mathbb{C}}(z,\lambda) = e^{i\theta} z\left(1 + \lambda + (a + i\,b)|z|^2\right) + \mathcal{O}\left(|z|^4\right),$$

where $a = a(\lambda)$ and $b = b(\lambda)$ are smooth functions of λ. We restrict our inquiry to the case $a(0) < 0$, the other case being similar. The map (3.152) without the higher-order terms was considered in Example 3.69, where we found an invariant circle with radius $\sqrt{-\lambda/a}$. Anticipating the existence of an invariant circle for $\Pi^{\mathbb{C}}$ close to it, we introduce a singular rescaling for $\lambda > 0$ and take coordinates (ρ, φ) by

(3.153) $$z(\rho,\varphi,\lambda) = \sqrt{-\lambda/a}\left(1 + \sqrt{\lambda}\,\rho\right)e^{i\varphi}.$$

Exercise 3.37 asks us to analyze a different rescaling. Note that $\rho = 0$ corresponds to $|z| = \sqrt{-\lambda/a}$. If we write $z = re^{i\varphi}$, we find (for $\lambda > 0$),

$$r = r(\rho,\lambda) = \sqrt{-\lambda/a}\left(1+\sqrt{\lambda}\,\rho\right),$$
$$\rho = \rho(r,\lambda) = (1/\sqrt{\lambda})\left(\sqrt{-a/\lambda}\,r - 1\right).$$

Now rewrite $\Pi^{\mathbb{C}}$ in terms of the new coordinates (ρ,φ). Plugging (3.153) into the expression for $\Pi^{\mathbb{C}}$, we get

$$\begin{aligned}
&\Pi^{\mathbb{C}}(z(\rho,\varphi,\lambda),\lambda)\\
&= \sqrt{\frac{-\lambda}{a}}\left(1+\sqrt{\lambda}\,\rho\right)e^{i(\varphi+\theta)}\left(1+\lambda-\lambda\left(1+\sqrt{\lambda}\,\rho\right)^2 - i\left(\frac{b}{a}\right)\lambda\left(1+\sqrt{\lambda}\,\rho\right)^2\right)\\
&\quad + (\lambda^2/a^2)(1+\sqrt{\lambda}\rho)^2 p^{(1)}(\rho,\varphi,\lambda)\\
&= \sqrt{\frac{-\lambda}{a}}\left(1+\sqrt{\lambda}\,\rho\right)e^{i(\varphi+\theta)}\left(1-2\lambda\sqrt{\lambda}\,\rho-\lambda^2\rho^2 - i\left(\frac{b}{a}\right)\lambda\left(1+\sqrt{\lambda}\,\rho\right)^2\right)\\
&\quad + (\lambda^2/a^2)(1+\sqrt{\lambda}\rho)^2 p^{(1)}(\rho,\varphi,\lambda),
\end{aligned}$$

for a smooth function $p^{(1)}$ which is 2π-periodic in φ. Let $(\rho,\varphi)\mapsto\hat{\Pi}(\rho,\varphi,\lambda)$ be the mapping which represents $\Pi^{\mathbb{C}}$ in (ρ,φ)-coordinates. With $\hat{\Pi} = (\hat{\Pi}^{(1)},\hat{\Pi}^{(2)})$ in coordinates,

$$\hat{\Pi}^{(1)}(\rho,\varphi,\lambda) = (1/\sqrt{\lambda})\left(\sqrt{-a/\lambda}\,|\Pi^{(1)}(\rho,\varphi,\lambda)| - 1\right)$$

has an expression

$$\hat{\Pi}^{(1)}(\rho,\varphi,\lambda) = (1-2\lambda)\rho + \lambda\hat{p}_0^{(1)}(\varphi,\lambda) + \lambda^{3/2}\hat{p}_1^{(1)}(\rho,\varphi,\lambda),$$

for smooth functions $\hat{p}_0^{(1)}$ and $\hat{p}_1^{(1)}$ which are 2π-periodic in φ. And the second coordinate $\hat{\Pi}^{(2)}(\rho,\varphi,\lambda)$ satisfies

$$\hat{\Pi}^{(2)}(\rho,\varphi,\lambda) = \varphi + \theta - \lambda(b/a) + \lambda^{3/2}\hat{p}_1^{(2)}(\rho,\varphi,\lambda), \tag{3.154}$$

with $\hat{p}_1^{(2)}$ smooth and 2π-periodic in φ.

The following lemma yields, for positive values of λ, a 2π-periodic map $\rho_\lambda^* : \mathbb{R}\to\mathbb{R}$ so that its graph, graph $\rho_\lambda^* = \{(\rho_\lambda^*(\varphi),\varphi)\ ;\ \varphi\in\mathbb{R}\}$, is invariant for $\hat{\Pi}$:

$$\hat{\Pi}\left(\operatorname{graph}\rho_\lambda^*,\lambda\right) = \operatorname{graph}\rho_\lambda^*.$$

For the normal form Π, the graph of ρ_λ^* corresponds to an invariant circle C_λ which shrinks to $\{h = 0\}$ as λ tends to zero. In the proof we adapt argumentation in [**327**], that discusses local center manifolds using the graph transform, to the present context.

Lemma 3.73. *Consider $\hat{\Pi}$ with $a(0) < 0$. Then for $\lambda > 0$ there exists a 2π-periodic map $\rho_\lambda^* : \mathbb{R} \to \mathbb{R}$ so that its graph is invariant for $\hat{\Pi}$. For any positive integer k, there is λ_0 so that for $0 < \lambda < \lambda_0$, ρ_λ^* is k times continuously differentiable.*

Proof. Let $C_{2\pi}$ be the Banach space of continuous 2π-periodic functions,

$$C_{2\pi} = \{f : \mathbb{R} \to \mathbb{R} \; ; \; f \text{ is continuous and } f(x + 2\pi) = f(x)\},$$

equipped with the supremum norm $\|f\| = \sup_{x\in\mathbb{R}} |f(x)|$. Let $C^{k,1}(\mathbb{R}, \mathbb{R})$ denote the space of C^k functions $f : \mathbb{R} \to \mathbb{R}$ with $D^k f$ being uniformly Lipschitz continuous. Given positive constants $M_0, \dots, M_{k+1}$, let

$$\begin{aligned} &B(M_0, \dots, M_{k+1}) \\ &\quad = \Big\{f \in C_{2\pi} \cap C^{k,1}(\mathbb{R}, \mathbb{R}) \; ; \; \|f\| \le M_0, \|D^i f\| \le M_i, \\ &\qquad\qquad |D^k f(x_1) - D^k f(x_2)| \le M_{k+1}|x_1 - x_2|, 1 \le i \le k, x_1, x_2 \in \mathbb{R}\Big\}. \end{aligned}$$

Note that $B(M_0, M_1)$ consists of bounded Lipschitz continuous maps, that are bounded by M_0 in absolute value and have Lipschitz constant bounded by M_1. We consider these spaces as subspaces of the space $C_{2\pi}$ of 2π-periodic continuous functions on the real line equipped with the supremum norm. By Lemma A.3, $B(M_0, \dots, M_{k+1})$ is closed in $C_{2\pi}$.

Let $\lambda > 0$ be fixed. We will frequently suppress dependence on λ from notation. For some $M_0, M_1 > 0$, take $\rho \in B(M_0, M_1)$. Consider the graph $\{(\rho(\varphi), \varphi) \; ; \; \varphi \in \mathbb{R}\}$. The $\hat{\Pi}$-image of it is, as we will show, a graph of a 2π-periodic function which can thus be written as $\{(\hat{\rho}(\varphi), \varphi) \; ; \; \varphi \in \mathbb{R}\}$. So

$$\hat{\Pi}\,(\text{graph}\,\rho) = \text{graph}\,\hat{\rho},$$

and we can define a graph transform $\Gamma : B(M_0, M_1) \to C_{2\pi}$ by $\Gamma(\rho) = \hat{\rho}$, or

$$\Gamma(\rho) = \hat{\Pi}^{(1)} \circ (\rho, \text{id}) \circ \left(\hat{\Pi}^{(2)}(\rho, \text{id})\right)^{-1}.$$

In a sequence of steps we will establish that, for a given positive integer k, there is $\lambda_0 > 0$, so that for $0 < \lambda < \lambda_0$ there are suitable $M_0, \dots, M_{k+1}$, for which Γ is a contraction on $B(M_0, \dots, M_{k+1})$:

$$\Gamma(B(M_0, \dots, M_{k+1})) \subset B(M_0, \dots, M_{k+1})$$

and

$$\|\Gamma(\rho_1) - \Gamma(\rho_2)\| \le L,$$

for some positive constant $L < 1$. By the contraction mapping theorem, the map Γ has a unique fixed point ρ^*. As $\rho^* \in B(M_0, \dots, M_{k+1})$, it is, in particular, k times continuously differentiable. By construction, the graph $\{(\rho^*(\varphi), \varphi) \; ; \; \varphi \in \mathbb{R}\}$ is $\hat{\Pi}$-invariant.

THE GRAPH TRANSFORM IS WELL DEFINED. Consider Γ on $B(M_0, M_1)$, $M_0, M_1 > 0$. Let

$$(\bar{\rho}(\varphi), \bar{\varphi}(\varphi)) = \hat{\Pi}(\rho(\varphi), \varphi).$$

First we show that $\bar{\varphi}$ has an inverse function. From (3.154) we have

$$\bar{\varphi}(\varphi) = \varphi + \theta - \lambda(b/a) + \lambda^{3/2}\hat{p}_1^{(2)}(\rho(\varphi), \varphi). \tag{3.155}$$

So

$$\bar{\varphi}(\varphi_1) - \bar{\varphi}(\varphi_2) = \varphi_1 - \varphi_2 + \lambda^{3/2}\left[\hat{p}_1^{(2)}(\rho(\varphi_1), \varphi_1) - \hat{p}_1^{(2)}(\rho(\varphi_2), \varphi_2)\right].$$

As $\hat{p}_1^{(2)}$ is smooth and $\rho \in B(M_0, M_1)$, we find that

$$\left|\hat{p}_1^{(2)}(\rho(\varphi_1), \varphi_1) - \hat{p}_1^{(2)}(\rho(\varphi_2), \varphi_2)\right| \le C|\varphi_1 - \varphi_2|$$

for some $C > 0$. Hence, for sufficiently small λ, the function $\bar{\varphi}$ is strictly increasing. So, $\bar{\varphi}$ has an inverse function φ. Moreover, by construction we have that for $\varphi \in [0, 2\pi)$, also $\bar{\varphi}(\varphi)$ covers an interval of a length which is a multiple of 2π. For small λ we infer from (3.155) that this length is equal to 2π. We thus have that the inverse function $\varphi(\bar{\varphi})$ and the graph transform of ρ is given as the 2π-periodic function

$$\hat{\rho}(\bar{\varphi}) = \bar{\rho}(\varphi(\bar{\varphi})) = \hat{\Pi}^{(1)}(\rho(\varphi(\bar{\varphi})), \varphi(\bar{\varphi})).$$

THE GRAPH TRANSFORM CONTRACTS IN THE SUPREMUM NORM. We consider Γ acting on $B(M_0, M_1)$, and we will establish that there is a (positive) constant $L < 1$ such that

$$||\Gamma(\rho_1) - \Gamma(\rho_2)|| \le L||\rho_1 - \rho_2||.$$

Write $\Gamma(\rho_i) = \hat{\rho}_i$ for $i = 1, 2$, and estimate

$$\begin{aligned}
||\hat{\rho}_1 - \hat{\rho}_2|| &= \sup_{\bar{\varphi}\in\mathbb{R}} |\hat{\rho}_1(\bar{\varphi}) - \hat{\rho}_2(\bar{\varphi})| \\
&= \sup_{\bar{\varphi}\in\mathbb{R}} |\bar{\rho}_1(\varphi(\bar{\varphi})) - \bar{\rho}_2(\varphi(\bar{\varphi}))| \\
&= \sup_{\bar{\varphi}\in\mathbb{R}} \Big|(1-2\lambda)(\rho_1(\varphi(\bar{\varphi})) - \rho_2(\varphi(\bar{\varphi}))) + \hat{p}_0^{(1)}(\varphi(\bar{\varphi})) - \hat{p}_0^{(1)}(\varphi(\bar{\varphi})) \\
&\qquad + \hat{p}_1^{(1)}(\rho_1(\varphi(\bar{\varphi})), \varphi(\bar{\varphi})) - \hat{p}_1^{(1)}(\rho_2(\varphi(\bar{\varphi})), \varphi(\bar{\varphi}))\Big| \\
&\le \sup_{\bar{\varphi}\in\mathbb{R}}(1-2\lambda)\,|\rho_1(\varphi(\bar{\varphi})) - \rho_2(\varphi(\bar{\varphi}))| \\
&\qquad + \sup_{\bar{\varphi}\in\mathbb{R}} \lambda^{3/2}\left|\hat{p}_1^{(1)}(\rho_1(\varphi(\bar{\varphi})), \varphi(\bar{\varphi})) - \hat{p}_1^{(1)}(\rho_2(\varphi(\bar{\varphi})), \varphi(\bar{\varphi}))\right| \\
&\le (1-2\lambda)||\rho_1 - \rho_2|| + \lambda^{3/2} \sup_{\varphi,\psi\in\mathbb{R}} \left|\hat{p}_1^{(1)}(\rho_1(\varphi), \psi) - \hat{p}_1^{(1)}(\rho_2(\varphi), \psi)\right| \\
&\le (1-2\lambda)||\rho_1 - \rho_2|| + \lambda^{3/2} \sup_{|r|\le M_0, \psi\in\mathbb{R}} \left|D_\rho \hat{p}_1^{(1)}(r, \psi)\right| \, ||\rho_1 - \rho_2||.
\end{aligned}$$

This shows that for sufficiently small λ, Γ contracts in the supremum norm, because

$$1 - 2\lambda + \lambda^{3/2} \sup_{|r| \leq M_0, \psi \in \mathbb{R}} \left| D_\rho \hat{p}_1^{(1)}(r, \psi) \right| < 1,$$

for sufficiently small λ (using that $\hat{p}_1^{(1)}(\rho, \cdot)$ is 2π-periodic). See Figure 3.33 for an illustration of the action of Γ.

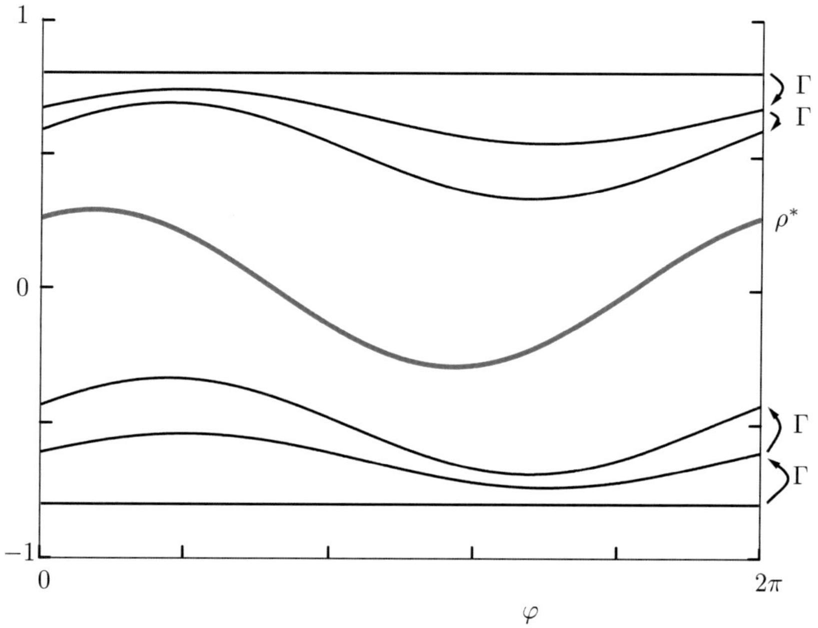

Figure 3.33. This figure illustrates the action of a graph transform on 2π-periodic functions. The graph transform Γ is obtained by applying $\hat{\Pi}$ to the graph of the function. The plot is numerically calculated using, for Γ, an expression as in (3.156): $\Gamma(\rho)(\varphi) = (1 - 2\lambda)\rho(\varphi + \pi/10) + \lambda \sin(\varphi + \pi/10)$ with $\lambda = 1/10$.

THE GRAPH TRANSFORM MAPS $B(M_0, \ldots, M_{k+1})$ INTO ITSELF. We will show that for given k, one can find positive constants $M_0, \ldots, M_{k+1}$ so that Γ maps $B(M_0, \ldots, M_{k+1})$ into itself, for sufficiently small λ. Consider $\hat{\Pi}$ up to first-order terms in λ and ignoring terms of order λ^2. This yields a map $\hat{\Pi}_0 = (\hat{\Pi}_0^{(1)}, \hat{\Pi}_0^{(2)})$ with expressions

$$\hat{\Pi}_0^{(1)}(\rho, \varphi) = (1 - 2\lambda)\rho + \lambda \hat{p}_0^{(1)}(\varphi),$$
$$\hat{\Pi}_0^{(2)}(\rho, \varphi) = \varphi + \theta - \lambda(b/a).$$

Note that $\Pi_0^{(1)}$ is affine in ρ and is contracting with a factor $1 - 2\lambda < 1$. The graph transform Γ_0 corresponding to $\hat{\Pi}_0$ has a simple expression,

$$\begin{aligned}\Gamma_0(\rho)(\varphi) &= \Pi_0^{(1)} \circ (\rho, \mathrm{id}) \circ \left(\Pi_0^{(2)}(\rho, \mathrm{id})\right)^{-1} (\varphi) \\ &= \Pi_0^{(1)} \circ (\rho, \mathrm{id})(\varphi - \theta + \lambda(b/a)) \\ &= (1 - 2\lambda)\rho(\varphi - \theta + \lambda(b/a)) + \lambda \hat{p}_0^{(1)}(\varphi - \theta + \lambda(b/a)).\end{aligned} \tag{3.156}$$

Given this explicit expression, it is not difficult to check that Γ_0 maps a space $B(M_0, \dots, M_{k+1})$ into itself. We will calculate formulas for derivatives of $\Gamma(\rho)$ and use proximity of these formulas to corresponding ones for $\Gamma_0(\rho)$ to prove such a statement for Γ.

Recall that the relation $\bar{\varphi} = \Pi^{(2)}(\rho, \varphi)$ defines φ as a function of $\bar{\varphi}$: $\varphi(\bar{\varphi})$. Write $\rho_g = (\rho, \mathrm{id})$. We calculate derivatives of $\Gamma(\rho)(\bar{\varphi}) = \Pi^{(1)} \circ \rho_g \circ \varphi(\bar{\varphi})$. To reduce notation we will regularly not write down arguments of functions, but they follow from the context. This gives

$$\begin{aligned}\frac{d}{d\bar{\varphi}}\Gamma(\rho)(\bar{\varphi}) &= D(\Pi^{(1)} \circ \rho_g)D\varphi, \\ \frac{d^2}{d\bar{\varphi}^2}\Gamma(\rho)(\bar{\varphi}) &= D^2(\Pi^{(1)} \circ \rho_g)(D\varphi)^2 + D(\Pi^{(1)} \circ \rho_g)D^2\varphi\end{aligned}$$

and, for higher derivatives,

$$\frac{d^k}{d\bar{\varphi}^k}\Gamma(\rho)(\bar{\varphi}) = D^k(\Pi^{(1)} \circ \rho_g)(D\varphi)^k + D(\Pi^{(1)} \circ \rho_g)D^k\varphi + R, \tag{3.157}$$

where R is an expression with derivatives (of $\Pi^{(1)} \circ \rho_g$ and φ) of order at most $k-1$. Also below we will write R to mean some expression involving derivatives of lower order. Differentiating $\bar{\varphi} = \Pi^{(2)}(\rho, \varphi(\bar{\varphi}))$ with respect to $\bar{\varphi}$ gives formulas for derivatives of φ with respect to $\bar{\varphi}$:

$$\begin{aligned}1 &= \frac{d}{d\bar{\varphi}}\Pi^{(2)}(\rho, \varphi(\bar{\varphi})) = D(\Pi^{(2)} \circ \rho_g)D\varphi, \\ 0 &= \frac{d^2}{d\bar{\varphi}^2}\Pi^{(2)}(\rho, \varphi(\bar{\varphi})) = D^2(\Pi^{(2)} \circ \rho_g)(D\varphi)^2 + D(\Pi^{(2)} \circ \rho_g)D^2\varphi\end{aligned}$$

and, for higher derivatives,

$$0 = \frac{d^k}{d\bar{\varphi}^k}\Pi^{(2)}(\rho, \varphi(\bar{\varphi})) = D^k(\Pi^{(2)} \circ \rho_g)(D\varphi)^k + D(\Pi^{(2)} \circ \rho_g)D^k\varphi + R,$$

where again R stands for an expression with derivatives (of $\Pi^{(2)} \circ \rho_g$ and φ) of order at most $k-1$. Solving for $D^k\varphi$ and combining with (3.157), we get

$$\frac{d^k}{d\bar{\varphi}^k}\Gamma(\rho)(\bar{\varphi}) = D^k(\Pi^{(1)} \circ \rho_g)(D\varphi)^k - \frac{1}{D(\Pi^{(2)} \circ \rho_g)} D(\Pi^{(1)} \circ \rho_g) D^k(\Pi^{(2)} \circ \rho_g)(D\varphi)^k + R,$$

with again R meaning terms with derivatives of $\Pi^{(1)} \circ \rho_g$, $\Pi^{(2)} \circ \rho_g$ and φ of lower order. Using the chain rule to write $D^k(\Pi^{(1)} \circ \rho_g) = D\Pi^{(1)} D^k \rho_g + R$, and similar for $D^k(\Pi^{(2)} \circ \rho_g)$, we find

$$\frac{d^k}{d\bar{\varphi}^k}\Gamma(\rho)(\bar{\varphi}) = \left[\frac{D\Pi^{(1)}}{(D(\Pi^{(2)} \circ \rho_g))^k} - \frac{D(\Pi^{(1)} \circ \rho_g) D\Pi^{(2)}}{(D(\Pi^{(2)} \circ \rho_g))^{k+1}} \right] D^k \rho_g + R.$$

Here R stands for an expression with derivatives of ρ_g up to order $k-1$. For the simplified graph transform we have a formula,

$$\frac{d^k}{d\bar{\varphi}^k}\Gamma_0(\rho)(\bar{\varphi}) = (1-2\lambda) D^k \rho_g + \lambda S,$$

where we made visible that the remaining terms, $R = \lambda S$, are of order λ. As all expressions are smooth in $\bar{\varphi}$ and $\sqrt{\lambda}$, we find

$$\left| \frac{d^k}{d\bar{\varphi}^k}\Gamma(\rho)(\bar{\varphi}) - \frac{d^k}{d\bar{\varphi}^k}\Gamma_0(\rho)(\bar{\varphi}) \right| \le C_k \lambda \sqrt{\lambda}, \tag{3.158}$$

for some positive constant C_k.

An induction argument proves that Γ maps $B(M_0, \dots, M_{k+1})$ into itself, for suitable values of $M_0, \dots, M_{k+1}$. Consider $k = 0$. The space $C^1(\mathbb{R}, \mathbb{R}) \cap B(M_0, M_1)$ is dense in $B(M_0, M_1)$; see Lemma 3.74. By continuity of Γ, if $\rho_n \in C^1(\mathbb{R}, \mathbb{R}) \cap B(M_0, M_1)$ converges to $\rho \in B(M_0, M_1)$ as $n \to \infty$, then $\Gamma(\rho_n)$ converges to $\Gamma(\rho)$. So, if we prove that Γ maps $\rho \in C^1(\mathbb{R}, \mathbb{R}) \cap C_{2\pi}$ with $\sup_{\varphi \in \mathbb{R}} |\rho(\varphi)| \le M_0$, $\sup_{\varphi \in \mathbb{R}} |D\rho(\varphi)| \le M_1$ to a map $\Gamma(\rho)$ with the same bounds, then Γ maps $B(M_0, M_1)$ into itself. First consider Γ_0. Note that Γ_0 maps $\rho \in B(M_0, M_1)$ to a map $\Gamma_0(\rho)$ with

$$\|\Gamma_0(\rho)\| \le (1-2\lambda) M_0 + \lambda \max_{\varphi \in \mathbb{R}} \hat{\rho}_0^{(1)}.$$

We find $\|\Gamma_0(\rho)\| < M_0$ for

$$M_0 > \max_{\varphi \in \mathbb{R}} |\hat{\rho}_0^{(1)}(\varphi)|/2.$$

By (3.158) we will also have $\|\Gamma(\rho)\| < M_0$ for λ sufficiently small. A similar calculation proves the existence of $M_1 > 0$ so that $\sup_{\varphi \in \mathbb{R}} |D(\Gamma_0(\rho))(\varphi)| \le M_1$

if $\sup_{\varphi\in\mathbb{R}} |D\rho(\varphi)| \leq M_1$. In fact,

$$M_1 > \max_{\varphi\in\mathbb{R}} |D\hat{p}_0^{(1)}(\varphi)|/2.$$

The same estimate holds for Γ if λ is sufficiently small. This implies that Γ maps $B(M_0, M_1)$ into itself. Further estimates along these lines provide constants $M_2, M_3, \ldots$. We find an estimate $\sup_{\varphi\in\mathbb{R}} |D^k(\Gamma_0(\rho))(\varphi)| \leq M_k$ if $\sup_{\varphi\in\mathbb{R}} |D^k\rho(\varphi)| \leq M_k$, for

$$M_k > \max_{\varphi\in\mathbb{R}} |D^k\hat{p}_0^{(1)}(\varphi)|/2.$$

For each k we have $\lambda_0 > 0$ so that also Γ maps $B(M_0, \ldots, M_k)$ into itself for $0 < \lambda < \lambda_0$. □

One cannot expect the circle to be C^∞; see Exercise 3.38. The following lemma, whose proof uses standard arguments, was applied in the above proof of Lemma 3.73.

Lemma 3.74. *$B(M_0, \ldots, M_{k+1}) \cap C^{k+1}(\mathbb{R}, \mathbb{R})$ is dense in $B(M_0, \ldots, M_{k+1})$.*

Proof. For $\varepsilon > 0$ consider a smooth nonnegative bump function $\psi : \mathbb{R} \to \mathbb{R}$ with compact support and integral one. Let $\psi_\varepsilon(x) = \frac{1}{\varepsilon}\psi(x/\varepsilon)$. For $f \in B(M_0, \ldots, M_{k+1})$, take $f_\varepsilon = f * \psi_\varepsilon$, that is,

$$f_\varepsilon(x) = \int_{-\infty}^{\infty} f(s)\psi_\varepsilon(x-s)\,ds = \int_{-\infty}^{\infty} f(x-s)\psi_\varepsilon(s)\,ds.$$

It follows from these expressions that f_ε is a 2π-periodic smooth function and converges to f uniformly as $\varepsilon \to 0$. For $0 \leq i \leq k$ we have

$$D^i f_\varepsilon(x) = \int_{-\infty}^{\infty} D^i f(s)\psi_\varepsilon(x-s)\,ds.$$

This gives $|D^i f_\varepsilon(x)| \leq M_i$. Compute

$$\begin{aligned}
|D^k f_\varepsilon(x) - D^k f_\varepsilon(y)| &= \left|\int_{-\infty}^{\infty} \left(D^k f(x-s) - D^k f(y-s)\right)\psi_\varepsilon(s)\,ds\right| \\
&\leq \int_{-\infty}^{\infty} \left|D^k f(x-s) - D^k f(y-s)\right|\psi_\varepsilon(s)\,ds \\
&\leq M_{k+1}\int_{-\infty}^{\infty} |x-y|\psi_\varepsilon(s)\,ds \\
&= M_{k+1}|x-y|.
\end{aligned}$$

This shows that $f_\varepsilon \in B(M_0, \ldots, M_{k+1})$ and in fact $|D^{k+1} f_\varepsilon| \leq M_{k+1}$. □

Stability statements. It remains to prove that the circle C_λ from Lemma 3.74 is attracting and to consider its basin of attraction.

Lemma 3.75. *Consider the normal form* Π *stated in Lemma* 3.72, *with* $a(0) < 0$. *There is a small neighborhood* U *of the origin in* $\mathbb{R}^2$ *so that the following holds.*

(1) *For* $\lambda > 0$, *the basin of attraction of the* $\Pi(\cdot,\lambda)$*-invariant circle* C_λ *for* $\lambda > 0$, *equals* $U \setminus \{(0,0)\}$.

(2) *For* $\lambda < 0$, *the basin of attraction of the origin contains* U.

Proof. Consider $\lambda > 0$. Go back to the (ρ,φ)-coordinates from the proof of Lemma 3.73, and take the annulus $\mathcal{A}_\lambda$ given by $\{|\rho| \le M_0\}$. In (r,φ)-coordinates the annulus $\mathcal{A}_\lambda$ is given by

$$\sqrt{-\lambda/a(\lambda)}\left(1-\sqrt{\lambda}M_0\right) \le |z| \le \sqrt{-\lambda/a(\lambda)}\left(1+\sqrt{\lambda}M_0\right).$$

It thus has width $\mathcal{O}(\lambda)$ around the invariant circle of the truncated map (3.143). The radius $r^* = r^*(\lambda)$ of this circle is of order $\mathcal{O}\left(\sqrt{\lambda}\right)$; compare (3.144).

For each $h \in \mathcal{A}_\lambda$ the ω-limit set $\omega(h)$ of h is a subset of C_λ. To verify this consider the following: Let $C(h)$ be the circle around 0 of radius $|h|$ and thus contains h. Clearly, $C(h) \subset \mathcal{A}_\lambda$. The proof of Lemma 3.73 implies that $\Pi^n(C(h),\lambda) \to C_\lambda$ with respect to the Hausdorff metric. (Recall that two compact sets are within distance ε in the Hausdorff metric, if each set is included in a ε neighborhood of the other set. The Hausdorff distance between the compact sets is the minimum of such ε.) We find that for $\hat{h} \in C(h)$, the limit set $\omega(\hat{h})$ is a subset of C_λ, and therefore that $\mathcal{A}_\lambda$ is in the basin of attraction of C_λ.

Equation (3.152) gives

$$\begin{aligned}|\Pi^{\mathbb{C}}(z,\lambda)| &= |z|\,|1+\lambda+(a+i\,b)|z|^2| + \mathcal{O}(|z|^4) \\ &= |z|\left(1+\lambda+a|z|^2\right) + \mathcal{O}(|z|^4).\end{aligned}$$

Take a point z in the disk bounded by $\mathcal{A}_\lambda$. Using a bound

$$|z| < \sqrt{-\lambda/a(\lambda)}\left(1-\sqrt{\lambda}M_0\right).$$

we find that $|\Pi^{\mathbb{C}}(z,\lambda)| > |z|$ and λ small; see Exercise 3.39. Some iterate of z will therefore lie in $\mathcal{A}_\lambda$ and the ω-limit set of z is contained in C_λ. A similar argument can be applied to points outside the disk bounded by C_λ, as well as to points for $\lambda \le 0$; see Exercise 3.39. □

3.3.3.3. *Torus bifurcation.* We translate the results from the previous section into the language of families of vector fields and obtain a description of a bifurcation of a periodic orbit that leads to the creation of an invariant torus.

Theorem 3.76 (Torus bifurcation). *Consider a family of differential equations*

$$\dot{x} = f(x,\lambda)$$

with, for $\lambda = 0$, a periodic orbit γ. Assume that the Floquet multipliers of γ are $e^{\pm i\theta}$.

Then for λ near 0, there is a smooth family of periodic orbits γ_λ with Floquet multipliers $\varsigma(\lambda)e^{\pm i\theta(\lambda)}$ for smooth functions ς, θ. Assume further that

(i) $\varsigma'(0) > 0$,

(ii) *The number a from Theorem 3.70 (computed for a first return map on a center manifold) is nonzero,*

(iii) $e^{ik\theta} \neq 1$ *for* $k = 1, 2, 3, 4$.

Then the bifurcation is as follows, depending on the sign of a.

(1) *If $a < 0$, there is a supercritical bifurcation: for $\lambda \leq 0$ the periodic orbit γ_λ is stable and attracts all nearby orbits, while for $\lambda > 0$ the periodic orbit γ_λ is unstable and there is a stable invariant torus C_λ around γ_λ that attracts all nearby orbits except for γ_λ.*

(2) *If $a > 0$, there is a subcritical bifurcation: for $\lambda < 0$ there is an unstable invariant torus C_λ around γ_λ; the stable periodic orbit γ_λ attracts only points inside C_λ, for $\lambda \geq 0$ the periodic orbit γ_λ is unstable and no other orbits stay close to the origin.*

Example 3.77. For an example of a torus bifurcation we return to the system (3.142) in Example 3.68, which was given by

$$\dot{x} = (z - 0.7)x - 3.5y,$$
$$\dot{y} = 3.5x + (z - 0.7)y,$$
$$\dot{z} = 0.6 + z - \frac{1}{3}z^3 - (x^2 + y^2)(1 + \rho z) + \varepsilon z x^3. \qquad (3.159)$$

We fix $\varepsilon = 0$ and vary ρ. In [**243**] it is verified numerically that a torus bifurcation occurs in (3.159) for ρ near 0.61544465. Figure 3.34 shows numerically

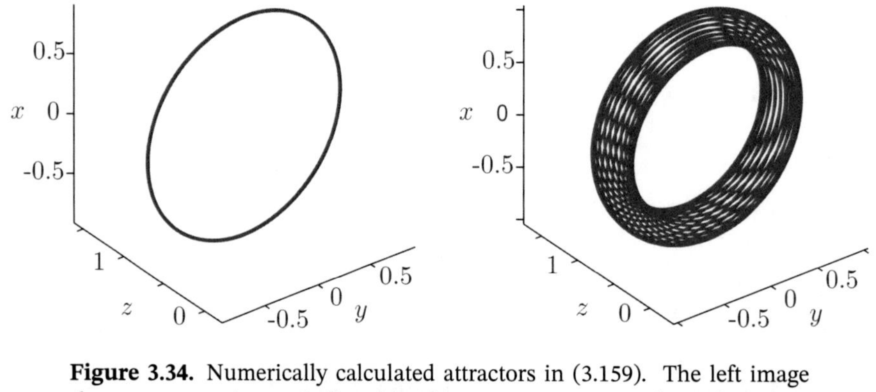

Figure 3.34. Numerically calculated attractors in (3.159). The left image shows an attracting periodic orbit with $\varepsilon = 0$, $\rho = 0.63$; the right image, an attracting torus with $\varepsilon = 0$, $\rho = 0.6$.

computed images of the attracting periodic orbit and the bifurcating attracting torus that occur on opposite sides of the bifurcation value. ■

We refer to [**113**] for a treatment of the asymptotic phase of orbits converging to the invariant torus, which stands for identifying orbits on the torus to which such orbits converge.

3.4. Exercises

Exercise 3.1. Consider the two-dimensional system

$$\begin{aligned} \dot{x} &= x^2, \\ \dot{y} &= -y. \end{aligned}$$

Show that the local center manifold of the equilibrium $(0, 0)$ is not uniquely determined.

Exercise 3.2. Consider the two-dimensional system

$$\begin{aligned} \dot{x} &= xy + y^2, \\ \dot{y} &= -y - x^2 + xy. \end{aligned}$$

Show by means of a center manifold reduction that $(0, 0)$ is an asymptotically stable equilibrium.

Exercise 3.3. Consider the local diffeomorphism Π near the origin on the plane with expression

$$\Pi(x, y) = (x - xy - y^2, \frac{1}{2}y + x^2).$$

Show by means of a center manifold reduction that $(0, 0)$ is an asymptotically stable fixed point of Π.

Exercise 3.4. Consider the three-dimensional system

$$\begin{aligned} \dot{x} &= -y + xz - x^4, \\ \dot{y} &= x + yz + xyz, \\ \dot{z} &= -z - x^2 - y^2 + z^2 + \sin(x^3). \end{aligned}$$

Determine the stability of the equilibrium $(0, 0, 0)$.

Hint: Determine the flow on the center manifold and use polar coordinates.

Exercise 3.5. In Example 3.5 a normal form (3.11) is derived up to smooth equivalence and a reparametrization of the parameter. The normal form (3.12) for the same system is obtained by using topological equivalence. Prove that the normal form (3.12) cannot be achieved by smooth equivalence (and reparametrization of the parameter).

Hint: Consider parameter values for which there are two equilibria and consider eigenvalues at these equilibria.

Exercise 3.6. Consider the function $f(x,\lambda) = \lambda + \alpha x^2 + g(x,\lambda)$, where $g(0,0) = 0$, $D_x g(0,0) = 0$, $D_x^2 g(0,0) = 0$ and $D_\lambda g(0,0) = 0$. Show that locally around $(0,0)$, the equation $f(x,\lambda) = 0$ can be solved for $\lambda = \lambda^*(x)$. Compute the leading order term in the Taylor expansion of λ^*.

Exercise 3.7. Suppose that $f : \mathbb{R}^3 \to \mathbb{R}^2$ is given by

$$f(x,y,\lambda) = (\lambda - x^2 + xy, -2y + x^2 + y^2)$$

and $u = (x,y)$. Show that the differential equation generated by f satisfies the conditions of Theorem 3.8 and hence has a saddle-node bifurcation. Draw the phase portrait near $(u,\lambda) = (0,0)$ for $\lambda < 0$, $\lambda = 0$, $\lambda > 0$.

Exercise 3.8. Formulate and prove a theorem based on the implicit function theorem which can be used to show that a small perturbation of a family of differential equations with a saddle-node bifurcation has a nearby saddle-node bifurcation. A possible formulation can have the following flavor: suppose $\dot{x} = f(x,\mu)$ with $\mu \in \mathbb{R}$ unfolds a saddle-node bifurcation. Consider a family $\dot{x} = f(x,\mu,\nu)$ with $f(x,\mu,0) = f(x,\mu)$. Prove that $\dot{x} = f(x,\mu,\nu)$ unfolds a saddle-node bifurcation for each small value of ν.

Exercise 3.9. Consider the differential equation given in Example 3.10. Determine the differential equation on a center manifold, and verify a saddle-node bifurcation for the reduced equation.

Exercise 3.10. Prove Theorem 3.13 by means of the Morse lemma, Theorem 2.46.

Exercise 3.11. This exercise follows a more general exercise in [**124**, Chapter I, § 1] and provides a proof of Theorem 3.17. Let $f(x,\lambda)$ be a smooth function such that

$$f(0,\lambda) = 0 \text{ for all } \lambda$$

and further

$$D_x f(0,0) = D_x^2 f(0,0) = 0, \qquad D_x^3 f(0,0) D_\lambda D_x f(0,0) < 0.$$

Show that there exist smooth functions $M(x,\lambda)$ and $\phi(x)$ defined on neighborhoods of the origin such that

$$f(x,\lambda) = \left(\lambda - \phi(x)x^2\right) x M(x,\lambda), \tag{3.160}$$

where

$$\phi(0) > 0, \ M(0,0) \neq 0.$$

Prove (3.160) by the following steps.

(i) Let $s(x) = f(x,\mu x)$ for fixed μ. Show that $s(0) = s'(0) = 0$. Using Taylor's theorem, conclude that we can write

$$f(x,\mu x) = x^2 K(x,\mu).$$

(ii) Show that $K(0,0) = 0$, $D_xK(0,0) = D_x^3 f(0,0)/6$, and $D_\mu K(0,0) = D_\lambda D_x f(0,0)$. Then use the implicit function theorem to find a smooth function $\mu(x)$ satisfying

$$K(x, \mu(x)) \equiv 0,$$

with $\mu(0) = 0$ and $\mu'(0) > 0$.

(iii) Conclude that $\mu(x) = x\phi(x)$ where $\phi(0) > 0$. Hence

$$f(x, x^2\phi(x)) \equiv 0.$$

Use Taylor's theorem again to show that

$$f(x,\lambda) = \left(\lambda - x^2\phi(x)\right) L(x,\lambda).$$

(iv) Show that $L(0,\lambda) \equiv 0$ and $D_xL(0,0) \neq 0$, and use this to obtain (3.160).

Determine from (3.160) the number n_f of equilibria of f in a neighborhood of the origin for $\lambda < 0$, $\lambda = 0$ and $\lambda > 0$. Discuss stability of the equilibria.

Exercise 3.12. This exercise refers to Remark 3.19. Consider the function $g(x,\lambda) = \lambda x - x^3 + \lambda^2$. Find a smooth coordinate change $y = h_\lambda(x)$ that removes the λ^2 term, so that the transformed function

$$f(y,\lambda) = Dh(h_\lambda^{-1}(y))g(h_\lambda^{-1}(y), \lambda)$$

satisfies $D_\lambda^2 f(0,0) = 0$.

Exercise 3.13. Consider the equation $f(x,\lambda) := x^3 - 3\lambda x + \lambda^3 = 0$. Two solution curves near $(0,0)$ are given by

$$x = \frac{1}{3}\lambda^2 + \frac{1}{81}\lambda^5 + o(\lambda^5),$$
$$x = \pm\sqrt{3}\sqrt{\lambda} - \frac{1}{6}\lambda^2 + o(\lambda^2),$$

as $\lambda \to 0$. Prove these formulas. See [**396**, Example 5.1].

Exercise 3.14. Compute the bifurcation diagram of equilibria in

$$\dot{x} = y,$$
$$\dot{y} = \mu x - x^3 - y.$$

Find a symmetry of the phase diagram and relate the bifurcation diagram to the symmetry.

Exercise 3.15. Prove that a transcritical bifurcation occurs in the epidemic model (3.32) in Example 3.23.

Exercise 3.16. Example 3.24 discusses bifurcations in a model for cannibalism in a population.

(i) Derive system (3.34).

(ii) Assume $\alpha \neq \rho$. Show that a transcritical bifurcation occurs when $R_0 = 1$.

(iii) Discuss the bifurcation when $\alpha = \rho$.

Exercise 3.17. Prove Theorem 3.30.

Exercise 3.18. Work out the details of the proof of Theorem 3.33.

Exercise 3.19. In this exercise the proof of Theorem 3.34 will be reproduced using the normal form derived in Example B.23. Consider a family of differential equations of the form; compare (1.2) or more generally Example B.23,

(3.161)

$$\begin{pmatrix} \dot{x} \\ \dot{y} \end{pmatrix} = \begin{pmatrix} \alpha_0(\lambda) & -\beta_0(\lambda) \\ \beta_0(\lambda) & \alpha_0(\lambda) \end{pmatrix} \begin{pmatrix} x \\ y \end{pmatrix} + \begin{pmatrix} \alpha_1(\lambda) & -\beta_1(\lambda) \\ \beta_1(\lambda) & \alpha_1(\lambda) \end{pmatrix} \begin{pmatrix} x \\ y \end{pmatrix} (x^2 + y^2) + R(x, y, \lambda),$$

where

(i) $\alpha_0(0) = 0, \beta_0(0) = 1$,

(ii) $R(x, y, \lambda) = \mathcal{O}(\|(x, y)\|^4)$, uniformly in λ as $(x, y) \to 0$,

(iii) $D\alpha_0(0) \neq 0$,

(iv) $\alpha_1(0) \neq 0$.

Work through the following tasks. Compare also with explanations in the proof of Theorem 3.34.

(1) Show that after a transformation to polar coordinates $x = r\cos\varphi$, $y = r\sin\varphi$, the differential equation has the form

$$\dot{r} = \alpha_0(\lambda) r + \alpha_1(\lambda) r^3 + \hat{R}^1(r, \varphi, \lambda) =: h_r(r, \varphi, \lambda),$$
$$\dot{\varphi} = \beta_0(\lambda) + \beta_1(\lambda) r^2 + \hat{R}^2(r, \varphi, \lambda) =: h_\varphi(r, \varphi, \lambda),$$

where both $R^1(r, \varphi, \lambda)$ and $R^2(r, \varphi, \lambda)$ are of order $\mathcal{O}(r^4)$, uniformly in φ and λ as $r \to 0$.

(2) Show that the periodic orbits of (3.161) correspond to fixed points of

$$\Pi(\rho, \lambda) := r(2\pi, \rho, \lambda),$$

where $r(\cdot, \rho, \lambda)$ solves the initial value problem $r' = \frac{h_r(r,\varphi,\lambda)}{h_\varphi(r,\varphi,\lambda)}$, $r(0) = \rho$. Interpret $\Pi(\cdot, \lambda)$ as a Poincaré return map for (3.161).

(3) Because of $\Pi(0, \lambda) \equiv 0$, the map Π can be written as $\Pi(\rho, \lambda) = \rho\tilde{\Pi}(\rho, \lambda)$. Show that $\tilde{\Pi}(\rho, \lambda) = \rho$ can (locally around $(0, 0)$) be solved for $\lambda = \lambda^*(\rho)$, with $\lambda^*(0) = 0$, $D\lambda^*(0) = 0$ and $D^2\lambda^*(0) = -2\frac{\alpha_1(0)}{D\alpha_0(0)}$.

(4) Discuss the stability of the appearing periodic orbits by means of $D_\rho \Pi(\rho, \lambda^*(\rho))$.

(5) Compute the first Lyapunov coefficient and compare the stability of the periodic orbits with the corresponding statement in Theorem 3.34.

Detailed explanations can be found in [**404**].

Exercise 3.20. Consider the predator-prey model

$$\dot{x} = x\left(b - x - \frac{y}{1+x}\right),$$
$$\dot{y} = y\left(\frac{x}{1+x} - ay\right),$$

where $x, y \geq 0$ represent the populations and $a, b > 0$ are parameters.

(i) Show that a positive fixed point (x^*, y^*), $x^* > 0$, $y^* > 0$, exists for all $a, b > 0$.

(ii) Show that a Hopf bifurcation occurs at the positive fixed point if

$$a = \frac{4(b-2)}{b^2(b+2)}$$

and $b > 2$.

Exercise 3.21. Show that the equation

$$\dot{x} = \lambda x - y + xy^2,$$
$$\dot{y} = x + \lambda y + y^3$$

has a subcritical Hopf bifurcation.

Hint: Change to polar coordinates and compute, explicitly, the Poincaré return map defined on the positive x-axis. Recall that Bernoulli's equation $\dot{z} = a(t)z + b(t)z^{n+1}$ is transformed to a linear equation by the change of variables $w = z^{-n}$.

Exercise 3.22. Verify the precise expression of the first Lyapunov coefficient given Theorem 3.34(ii). To this end see also Remark 3.37.

Exercise 3.23. Consider the planar Hamiltonian system

$$\dot{q} = \frac{\partial}{\partial p} H(q, p),$$
$$\dot{p} = -\frac{\partial}{\partial q} H(q, p),$$

where $H : \mathbb{R}^2 \to \mathbb{R}$ is a smooth function. Assume H has a nondegenerate singular point at $(q, p) = (0, 0)$, and that the linearized vector field about $(0, 0)$ has a complex imaginary pair of eigenvalues on the imaginary axis. Now consider the family of vector fields depending on a real parameter λ,

$$\dot{q} = \frac{\partial}{\partial p}H(q,p) + \lambda\frac{\partial}{\partial q}H(q,p),$$
$$\dot{p} = -\frac{\partial}{\partial q}H(q,p) + \lambda\frac{\partial}{\partial p}H(q,p).$$

(i) Find the sheet of periodic orbits near $(0,0,0)$ in (λ, q, p) space by applying Theorem 3.40.

(ii) Formulate and prove a corresponding theorem for a sheet of periodic orbits in Hamiltonian systems in $\mathbb{R}^n$ by applying Theorem 3.43.

Exercise 3.24. Examine the Hopf bifurcation in Example 3.45. For this, prove subcriticality by translating the equilibrium to the origin, putting the linear part into normal form, and computing the first Lyapunov coefficient. Details can be found in [**143**].

Exercise 3.25. Section 1.2 explains the Rosenzweig-MacArthur predator-prey model (1.7). Its derivation proceeds through intermediate models, namely a Lotka-Volterra system (1.5) and a predator-prey system with logistic growth (1.6). Perform a bifurcation analysis of the three models, and compare the different models.

Exercise 3.26. The Brusselator is a differential equation in the plane that models autocatalytic reaction. It is given by

$$\dot{x} = 1 - (b+1)x + ax^2y,$$
$$\dot{y} = bx - ax^2y,$$

with parameters $a, b > 0$. The variables x, y represent concentrates of two reactants. Do a local bifurcation analysis of equilibria.

Exercise 3.27. This exercise asks us to study some aspects of the Wilson-Cowan model (3.78) from Example 3.46.

(i) Take $a = b = c = 10$ and $d = -1$. Analyze Bogdanov-Takens bifurcations; compare the bifurcation analysis in [**178**, Section 2.2].

(ii) Under varying a, b, c, d, the number of equilibria with nilpotent linearization can change, leading to higher-codimension bifurcations (nilpotent singularities of codimension three are studied in [**105, 106**]). Investigate the number of equilibria with nilpotent linearization for $a = b = c$ and $d = -a$.

Exercise 3.28. Provide details for the normal form calculations needed for the Bogdanov-Takens bifurcation, as sketched in Example B.24.

Exercise 3.29. Consider a smooth function $G(x,\mu) = \mu + x^2 + \mathcal{O}(x^3)$, where the $\mathcal{O}$-term is uniform in μ. Prove that one can write $G(x,\mu) = \mu + h(x,\mu)^2$

for a smooth function $h(x,\mu)$ with $D_x h(0,0) = 1$. To do so, consider the proof of the Morse lemma for parameter-dependent functions for the particular case $n = 1$. See also the computations in Example 2.40.

Exercise 3.30. Treat the Bogdanov-Takens bifurcation from Theorem 3.49 for the case where the coefficient of the xy term in the equation for $\dot{y}$ is -1, by bringing it to the case of a coefficient $+1$; see Remark 3.50.

Exercise 3.31. Provide details for Remark 3.56.

Exercise 3.32. In the Bogdanov-Takens bifurcation in the family of differential equations (3.82), a saddle-node bifurcation occurs at $\mu = 0$. Two equilibria exist for $\mu < 0$. Consider the singular rescaling,

$$x = \varepsilon^2 u, \qquad y = \varepsilon^3 v,$$
$$\mu = \varepsilon^4 \bar{\mu}, \qquad \nu = \varepsilon \bar{\nu}.$$

Show that in the new coordinates u, v, and after a time rescaling, the vector field becomes

$$\dot{u} = v,$$
$$\dot{v} = \bar{\mu} + u^2 + v\bar{\nu} + \mathcal{O}(\varepsilon).$$

Derive from this that the saddle-node bifurcation is nondegenerate and generically unfolding.

Exercise 3.33. Prove Theorem 3.61.

Exercise 3.34. Consider the diffeomorphism given in Example 3.65 near the origin in $\mathbb{R}^2$,

$$f(x,y) = (-x + \alpha x^2 + \gamma x^3 + xy, -\frac{1}{2}y + \delta x^2).$$

Show that

(i) $E^c = \operatorname{span}\{(0,1)\}$ and $E^h = \operatorname{span}\{(1,0)\}$.

(ii) There is local center manifold which is the graph of a function $W : E^c \to E^h$, $W(x) = \frac{2}{3}\delta x^2 + \mathcal{O}(x^3)$.

Exercise 3.35. Do the exercises mentioned in Example 3.69 on a model for the Neimark-Sacker bifurcation:

(i) Prove formula (3.145).

(ii) Make the calculations in Example 3.69 explicit for $\begin{pmatrix} a & -b \\ b & a \end{pmatrix}$ the identity matrix.

Exercise 3.36. Check whether a nondegenerate and generically unfolding Neimark-Sacker bifurcation occurs in (3.149) for various values of a_2, a_3, r.

Exercise 3.37. In the analysis of the Neimark-Sacker bifurcation, to find the invariant circle, a singular rescaling (3.153) was applied. This exercise starts from (3.153), but considers an alternative rescaling. For $\lambda > 0$, take coordinates (ρ, φ) by

$$z(\rho, \varphi, \lambda) = \sqrt{-\lambda/a}\,(1+\rho)\,e^{i\varphi}.$$

Following the recipe after (3.153), rewrite $\Pi^{\mathbb{C}}$ in terms of the new coordinates (ρ, φ). Let $(\rho, \varphi) \mapsto \hat{\Pi}(\rho, \varphi, \lambda)$ be the mapping which represents Π in (ρ, φ)-coordinates. With $\hat{\Pi} = (\hat{\Pi}^{(1)}, \hat{\Pi}^{(2)})$ in coordinates, derive expressions

$$\hat{\Pi}^{(1)}(\rho, \varphi, \lambda) = (1-2\lambda)\rho - 3\lambda\rho^2 - \lambda\rho^3 + \lambda^2 \hat{p}^{(1)}(\rho, \varphi, \lambda),$$

$$\hat{\Pi}^{(2)}(\rho, \varphi, \lambda) = \varphi + \theta - \lambda(b/a)(1+\rho)^2 + \lambda^2 \hat{p}^{(2)}(\rho, \varphi, \lambda)$$

for functions $\hat{p}^{(1)}$ and $\hat{p}^{(2)}$ that are smooth and 2π-periodic in φ.

Exercise 3.38. Let Π_λ be a generic unfolding of a nondegenerate Neimark-Sacker bifurcation. Write C_λ for the invariant circle arising in the unfolding. For definiteness assume invariant circles arise for $\lambda > 0$. Prove that one can find arbitrarily small perturbations of the family Π_λ so that for any $\lambda_0 > 0$ there is a positive integer k, so that for some $0 < \lambda < \lambda_0$, the invariant circle is C^k but not C^{k+1}. Use the material in Section 5.2.3 and compare Example B.10.

Exercise 3.39. Prove the remaining steps to finish the proof of Lemma 3.75.

Exercise 3.40. This exercise, extracted from [**219**], provides an example to illustrate some intricacies of nonautonomous bifurcation theory. We refer to [**14**] for more on nonautonomous bifurcation theory. Consider the equation

$$\dot{x} = \mu x - \nu(t)x^3$$

on $\mathbb{R}$, depending on a real parameter μ and with $\nu(t) > 0$. If ν is constant, this gives a pitchfork bifurcation with for $\mu < 0$ a stable equilibrium at 0, while for $\mu > 0$ this becomes unstable and two stable equilibria $\pm\sqrt{\mu/\nu}$ appear.

Show that

$$x(t) = \operatorname{sign}(\bar{x})\sqrt{\frac{e^{2\mu t}}{\frac{e^{\mu s}}{\bar{x}^2} + \int_s^t e^{2\mu r}\nu(r)\,dr}}$$

is a solution to the equation with $x(s) = \bar{x}$. Show that for $\mu < 0$, solutions $x(t)$ starting at $x(s) = \bar{x}$ converge to 0 as $t \to \infty$. Assume that $\nu(t) \to 0$ as $t \to \infty$. Show that for $\mu > 0$, solutions $x(t)$ starting at $x(s) = \bar{x}$ satisfy $\lim_{t\to\infty} |x(t)| = \infty$. Conclude that orbits do not stay bounded.

Chapter 4

Nonlocal bifurcations

The previous chapter focused on bifurcations of critical elements (equilibria and periodic orbits). This chapter continues with bifurcations of connecting orbits between equilibria and periodic orbits. Connecting orbits are orbits that converge to a critical element for positive times as well as for negative times; they connect the two critical elements. These are called heteroclinic orbits if the critical elements are different, and homoclinic orbits if the critical elements are identical. We point out that we speak of homoclinic and heteroclinic orbits connecting critical elements, so for instance an orbit with an equilibrium as an α-limit set and a periodic orbit as an ω-limit set is referred to as a heteroclinic orbit.

The possibilities to have bifurcations are large. We focus on homoclinic orbits which are connecting orbits from an equilibrium to itself. Homoclinic orbits from a periodic orbit to itself are also considered. Of these we treat some selected bifurcation problems, of codimension 1 and codimension 2, in detail. The technical machinery, which is also used in other bifurcation problems, is explained. For extended expositions of nonlocal bifurcation theory we refer the reader to the textbooks [**339, 340**] and to the review article [**172**].

Example 4.1. A partial differential equation of the form

$$\frac{\partial u}{\partial t}(x,t) = \frac{\partial^2 u}{\partial t^2}(x,t) + f(u(x,t)) \tag{4.1}$$

with $x \in \mathbb{R}$, $u(x,t) \in \mathbb{R}$ is a reaction diffusion equation. Solutions can be thought of as profiles $x \mapsto u(x,t)$ that vary with time t.

Traveling waves are particular solutions given by a profile that moves in time, with which we mean a solution of the form $u(x,t) = \xi(x - ct)$ for some constant c. It is a standing wave if $c = 0$. A traveling pulse is a traveling wave for which $\lim_{s\to-\infty} \xi(s) = \lim_{s\to\infty} \xi(s)$ equals some constant value.

A traveling wave is a solution to an ordinary differential equation. Writing $\xi(s)$ for the traveling wave solution, we get

$$-c\frac{d}{ds}\xi(s) = \frac{d^2}{ds^2}\xi(s) + f(\xi(s)).$$

Rewriting this as a first-order ordinary differential equation, we find the planar system

$$\begin{aligned}\dot{\xi} &= \zeta,\\ \dot{\zeta} &= -c\zeta - f(\xi).\end{aligned} \tag{4.2}$$

A solution $(\xi(s), \zeta(s))$ that converges to an equilibrium point P as $t \to \pm\infty$ yields a traveling pulse solution. Such a solution is a homoclinic orbit.

The Nagumo equation is given by (4.1) with $f(u) = u(1-u)(u-p)$ with $p \in (0,1)$. It was proposed by Nagumo for the study of shape and speed of pulses in the nerve of a squid. The traveling wave differential equation (4.2) for the Nagumo equation is given by

$$\begin{aligned}\dot{\xi} &= \zeta,\\ \dot{\zeta} &= -c\zeta - \xi(1-\xi)(\xi - p).\end{aligned}$$

The equilibrium solutions for the differential equation are $(0,0)$, $(p,0)$, and $(1,0)$. Consider this equation for the standing wave case $c = 0$ and take $p = \frac{1}{4}$. The above traveling wave differential equation is then Hamiltonian

$$\begin{aligned}\dot{\xi} &= -\frac{\partial H}{\partial \zeta},\\ \dot{\zeta} &= \frac{\partial H}{\partial \xi},\end{aligned}$$

for the Hamiltonian function

$$H(\xi,\zeta) = -\frac{1}{2}\zeta^2 + \frac{1}{8}\xi^2 - \frac{5}{12}\xi^3 + \frac{1}{4}\xi^4 :$$

$$\begin{aligned}\dot{\xi} &= -\zeta,\\ \dot{\zeta} &= -\xi(1-\xi)(\xi - \frac{1}{4}).\end{aligned} \tag{4.3}$$

This equation admits a homoclinic orbit to the equilibrium at the origin, lying inside the Hamiltonian level set $\{(\xi,\zeta)\ ;\ H(\xi,\zeta) = 0\}$. The homoclinic orbit is shown in Figure 4.1. ■

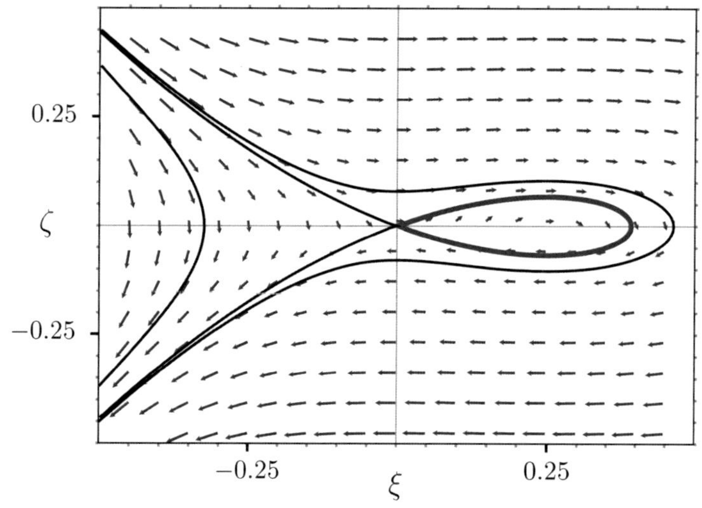

Figure 4.1. The flow of (4.3) including the homoclinic orbit (blue) that makes up the standing pulse.

4.1. Homoclinic orbits to equilibria

Definition 4.2. Given an equilibrium p for a differential equation $\dot{x} = f(x)$ in $\mathbb{R}^n$, a nontrivial orbit $h(t)$ with

$$\lim_{t\to\infty} h(t) = \lim_{t\to-\infty} h(t) = p$$

is called a *homoclinic orbit* to the equilibrium p.

The goal of homoclinic bifurcation theory is to investigate the maximal invariant set in a small neighborhood of the homoclinic orbit $h(t)$ and to investigate its bifurcations under perturbations of the vector field. In other words, we are interested in finding all orbits that stay in a fixed tubular neighborhood of a given homoclinic orbit for all times, for the vector field and small perturbations thereof.

A natural way to approach homoclinic bifurcation problems is by using Poincaré return maps. Denote by S a local cross section placed at $h(0)$. Starting with an initial condition x_0 in S, we then follow the positive orbit $x(t)$, $x(0) = x_0$, until it hits S again. Given a tubular neighborhood $\mathcal{U}$ of the closure of the homoclinic orbit, only orbits that stay in $\mathcal{U}$ are considered. Define the Poincaré return map $P : S \to S$ as $P(x_0) = x(T)$ with $x(t) \in \mathcal{U}$ for $0 \leq t \leq T$ and $T = \min\{t > 0 \; ; \; x(t) \in S\}$. The main technical difficulty is that solutions spend a very long time near the equilibrium, thus spoiling most finite-time error estimates for P from the standard variation of constants formulas.

In the following sections we will treat a number of homoclinic bifurcation problems using Poincaré return maps. We will show how to treat the technicalities that come with handling the flow near equilibria, and discuss a number of bifurcation results. Appendix C develops the more functional analytic approach of what is commonly called Lin's method to these bifurcation problems. Lin's method is a reduction technique that leads to bifurcation equations for orbits. The insight in the geometrical properties of the flow becomes less clear in Lin's method, but it has been more straightforward to generalize to settings such as partial differential equations.

4.1.1. Planar homoclinic orbits. The monograph [**17**] contains a careful treatment of both structurally stable differential equations on the plane and of bifurcations of planar differential equations. The presented bifurcations include nonlocal bifurcations such as bifurcations from a planar homoclinic orbit to a saddle equilibrium. This is the bifurcation discussed in this section. The treatment of the planar case avoids additional complications that arise in higher dimensions. These bifurcation results are originally due to Aleksandr Andronov and Evgeniya Leontovich [**15**].

The stable manifold of a hyperbolic saddle-type equilibrium p in the plane is a smooth curve that is the union of two orbits and p; each such orbit is called a *stable separatrix* of p. The unstable manifold is likewise the union of two orbits and p; each such orbit is called an *unstable separatrix* of p. In a planar homoclinic orbit, a stable separatrix of a saddle equilibrium equals an unstable separatrix. Under suitable small perturbations of the differential equation these separatrices will disconnect causing the homoclinic orbit to break. We state the bifurcation theorem for the codimension-1 bifurcation of a planar homoclinic loop.

Theorem 4.3. *Let*

$$\dot{x} = f_\lambda(x) = f(x, \lambda) \tag{4.4}$$

be a smooth family of vector fields on the plane $\mathbb{R}^2$*, depending on a real parameter* $\lambda \in \mathbb{R}$*. Assume that for* $\lambda = 0$ *there is hyperbolic saddle equilibrium* p *so that* $Df_0(p)$ *has real eigenvalues* μ^s, μ^u *with* $\mu^s < 0 < \mu^u$*. Assume that* f_0 *admits a homoclinic orbit* $h(t)$ *with*

$$\lim_{t\to\infty} h(t) = \lim_{t\to-\infty} h(t) = p.$$

Assume the following.

(i) (*Negative saddle quantity*)

$$\mu^s + \mu^u < 0.$$

(ii) (*Generic unfolding*)

$$M = \int_{-\infty}^{\infty} \langle \eta(t), D_\lambda f(h(t), 0)\rangle \, dt \neq 0,$$

where η is a bounded solution of the adjoint variational equation $\dot{x} = -Df_0(h(t))^T x$ along h.

If $\eta(0)$ is chosen as in Figure 4.5 below and $M < 0$, then there exists $\delta > 0, \varepsilon > 0$ so that for $\lambda \in (-\delta, 0)$, there is a stable limit cycle $\zeta_\lambda(t)$ of (4.4) of period $T(\lambda)$ such that $T(\lambda)$ goes to infinity as $\lambda \to 0$ and ζ_λ approaches h as $\lambda \to 0$. Furthermore, if $\mathcal{U}$ denotes the ε-neighborhood of h, then ζ_λ is the unique limit cycle in $\mathcal{U}$ for $\lambda \in (-\delta, 0)$. There is no limit cycle in $\mathcal{U}$ for $\lambda \in [0, \delta)$.

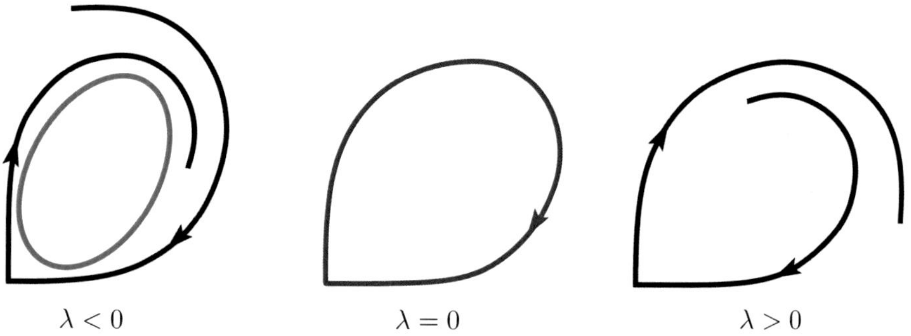

Figure 4.2. Bifurcation diagram related to the statement of Theorem 4.3.

Remark 4.4. The number $\mu^s + \mu^u$ is called the saddle quantity. The case $\mu^s + \mu^u > 0$ of a positive saddle quantity follows by time reversal. This reverses the stability of the periodic orbit. The case $\mu^s + \mu^u = 0$ of a neutral saddle is excluded and yields a bifurcation of higher codimension. This bifurcation is treated in Section 4.1.4.

The integral M is called a Melnikov integral after Viktor Melnikov. The case $M > 0$ follows by reversing the parameter λ, replacing it by $-\lambda$. ■

The proof of this theorem is given after preliminary discussions involving, first, a normal form for the differential equations near the equilibrium, and, second, a splitting function that measures the distance between the stable and unstable separatrices that correspond to the homoclinic orbit. Here we describe the general setup of the proof. Let Σ_{in} and Σ_{out} be cross sections transverse to, respectively, the local stable and local unstable separatrix corresponding to the homoclinic orbit. We define a Poincaré return map on Σ_{in} by composing a local transition map $P_{loc} : \Sigma_{in} \to \Sigma_{out}$ and a global transition map $P_{glob} : \Sigma_{out} \to \Sigma_{in}$ as depicted in Figure 4.3. Both parts P_{loc} and P_{glob} are defined by means of the flow of (4.4). The main effort lies in deriving an asymptotic expression for the local transition map. This is done in Lemma 4.11. In deriving it, we use a local normal form of the vector field which is provided in Lemma 4.6. The actual proof of the theorem reduces to the discussion of the fixed points of the composition $\Pi = P_{glob} \circ P_{loc}$.

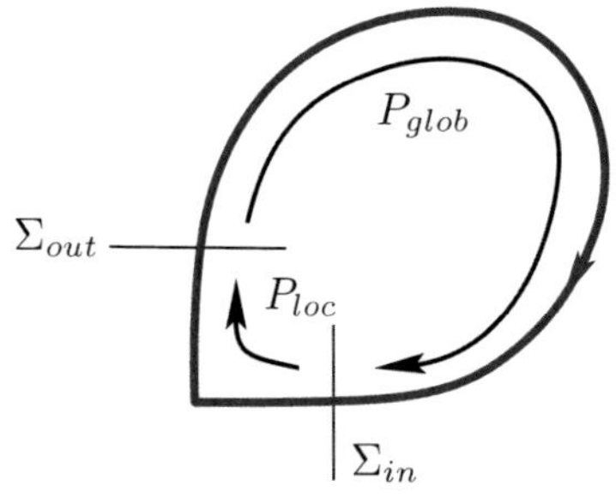

Figure 4.3. The transition maps.

Example 4.5. Suppose we have a family of differential equations $\dot{x} = f_\lambda(x)$ in $\mathbb{R}^2$ with a homoclinic orbit to a hyperbolic saddle at the origin, such that the differential equations are linear on a neighborhood U of the origin. So on U the differential equations can be written

$$\dot{x} = \mu^s x,$$
$$\dot{y} = \mu^u y,$$

where $\mu^s < 0 < \mu^u$ are smooth functions of λ. Take the cross sections Σ_{in} and Σ_{out} as depicted in Figure 4.3 to lie inside U. By a rescaling we may assume $\Sigma_{in} \subset \{x = 1\}$ and $\Sigma_{out} \subset \{y = 1\}$. On U the linear flow is given by $\varphi^t(x_0, y_0) = (e^{\mu^s t} x_0, e^{\mu^u t} y_0)$. Solving for the transition time τ from $\varphi^\tau(1, y_0) = (e^{\mu^s \tau}, 1)$ we get $\tau = -\frac{1}{\mu^u} \ln(y_0)$. Plugging this value of τ into $\varphi^\tau(1, y_0)$ we find

$$P_{loc}(1, y_0) = (y_0^{-\mu^s/\mu^u}, 1).$$

The transition map P_{glob} is a local diffeomorphism by the global flow box theorem, Theorem 2.23. Write $\beta = -\mu^s/\mu^u$. Using y as a coordinate on Σ_{in}, we find that $\Pi(y) = P_{glob}(y^\beta)$ can be expanded as

$$\Pi(y) = d_0 + d_1 y^\beta + \mathcal{O}(y^{2\beta}),$$

as $y \to 0$. The coefficients d_0, d_1, as well as β, depend on the parameter λ. By the assumption of a negative saddle quantity, we have $\beta(0) > 1$ and hence $\beta > 1$ for small values of λ. Assuming $d_0'(0) \neq 0$, which as we will see is equivalent to the generic unfolding condition, the bifurcation result from Theorem 4.3 is readily obtained in the case of locally linear vector fields. ■

4.1.1.1. *Local normal form.* Denote by $p(\lambda) = p_\lambda$ the continuation of the equilibrium p for λ near 0. The eigenvalues of $Df_\lambda(p(\lambda))$ vary smoothly with the parameter λ. So we have eigenvalues $\mu^s(\lambda)$ and $\mu^u(\lambda)$ as function of λ.

We prepare for the proof by a normal form lemma. The goal is to bring the vector field near p close to linear in order to control expressions for orbits near p. In the notation we frequently suppress dependence on the parameter λ. A different approach would be to use linearizing coordinates as provided by Theorem B.30. Linearizing coordinates in general are only C^1 and do not lend themselves to other bifurcation problems that involve for instance saddle-node bifurcations of periodic orbits. Also, C^1 linearizing coordinates may not exist in higher dimensions.

Lemma 4.6. *In smooth local coordinates (x, y) near p and after a multiplication by a smooth positive function, the vector field f_λ considered in Theorem 4.3 is given by the set of differential equations*

$$\begin{aligned} \dot{x} &= \mu^s x + f_\lambda^s(x, y), \\ \dot{y} &= \mu^u y, \end{aligned}$$

where $f_\lambda^s(x, y)$ satisfies

$$f_\lambda^s(x, y) = \mathcal{O}(x^2 y),$$

as $|(x, y)| \to 0$.

Proof. In what follows we drop λ from the notation. The linearization $Df(p)$ admits an invariant splitting $\mathbb{R}^2 = E^s \oplus E^u$ in stable and unstable subspaces, the eigenspaces related to μ^s and μ^u. We take coordinates (x, y) lying in the direction of these eigenspaces. The coordinates are smooth and vary smoothly with the parameter λ. In such coordinates we have

$$\begin{aligned} \dot{x} &= \mu^s x + f^s(x, y), \\ \dot{y} &= \mu^u y + f^u(x, y), \end{aligned}$$

for smooth functions f^s, f^u with $f^s(x, y) = \mathcal{O}(|(x, y)|^2)$ and $f^u(x, y) = \mathcal{O}(|(x, y)|^2)$. The functions f^s, f^u also depend smoothly on λ. We may further take the coordinates (x, y) near p, so that the local stable and unstable manifolds are contained in coordinate axes:

$$\begin{aligned} W^s_{loc}(p) &= \{y = 0\}, \\ W^u_{loc}(p) &= \{x = 0\}. \end{aligned}$$

In these coordinates we have $f^s(0, y) = 0$ and hence $f^s(x, y) = \mathcal{O}(|x||(x, y)|)$ and $f^u(x, 0) = 0$ which implies $f^u(x, y) = \mathcal{O}(|y||(x, y)|)$.

Dividing the vector field by the positive function $1 + f^u(x, y)/(\mu^u y)$ gives an expression

$$\dot{x} = \mu^s x + f^s(x, y),$$
$$\dot{y} = \mu^u y,$$

which means $f^u = 0$ and still $f^s(x, y) = \mathcal{O}(|x||(x, y)|)$. Note that we keep the same notation for expressions of the vector field in new coordinates.

By Theorem B.27 we may locally linearize the vector field on the stable manifold. More precisely, let H be the diffeomorphism on the stable manifold ($\{y = 0\}$) that conjugates the flow of $f_\lambda(\cdot, 0)$ to that of $Df_\lambda(0, 0)|_{\{y=0\}}$. Then the diffeomorphism $\mathcal{H} : \mathbb{R}^2 \to \mathbb{R}^2$, $\mathcal{H}(x, y) := (H(x), y)$ conjugates the flow of $f_\lambda(\cdot, \cdot)$ to that of some vector field g_λ whose flow leaves both $\{x = 0\}$ and $\{y = 0\}$ invariant. Moreover, the flow of g_λ restricted to $\{y = 0\}$ is conjugate to that of $Df_\lambda(0, 0)|_{\{y=0\}}$ by H. This ensures $\dot{x} = \mu^s x$ along $\{y = 0\}$. This implies that an expansion of f^s contains only a quadratic term of the form kxy, or in other words $f^s(x, y) = \mathcal{O}(|x||y|)$.

We will next remove terms of the form $xp(y)$ from the equation for x, starting with quadratic terms. Write $f^s(x, y) = kxy + g^s(x, y)$ with $\frac{\partial^2}{\partial x \partial y} g^s(x, y) = 0$ in $(x, y) = (0, 0)$. A direct computation shows that a polynomial coordinate change removes the term kxy from the differential equation for x. To do the computation, let $u = x + axy$ and $v = y$. Then $\dot{v} = \mu^u v$ and $x = \frac{u}{1+av}$ and hence $x = u\big(1 - av + \mathcal{O}(v^2)\big)$. With that we get

$$\begin{aligned}
\dot{u} &= \dot{x} + a(\dot{x}y + x\dot{y}) \\
&= \mu^s x + f^s(x, y) + a\big((\mu^s x + f^s(x, y))y + x\mu^u y\big) \\
&= \mu^s x + (k + a\mu^s + a\mu^u)xy + h.o.t. \\
&= \mu^s u + (k + a\mu^u)uv + h.o.t.
\end{aligned}$$

where h.o.t. stands for terms of order three and higher. As $\mu^u \neq 0$, we can choose a such that $k + a\mu^u = 0$.

We have obtained $f^s(x, y) = \mathcal{O}(|x||y||(x, y)|)$, again not changing notation for the vector field. Consider a coordinate change $u = x + q(y)x$ for a function $y \mapsto q(y)$ that vanishes at $y = 0$, and $v = y$. Similar to the above we get

$$\begin{aligned}
\dot{u} &= \dot{x} + q'(y)\dot{y}x + q(y)\dot{x} \\
&= \mu^s x + f^s(x, y) + q'(y)\mu^u yx + q(y)(\mu^s x + f^s(x, y)) \\
&= \mu^s u + Q(u, v)u,
\end{aligned}$$

So, the differential equations in the new coordinates reads

$$\dot{u} = \mu^s u + Q(u, v)u,$$
$$\dot{v} = \mu^u v,$$

where Q satisfies

$$Q(0, v) = q'(v)\mu^u v + \hat{Q}(q(v), v),$$
$$\hat{Q}(q(v), v) = \mathcal{O}(|(q(v), v)|^2),$$

and from the above $Q(u, 0) = 0$.

Now, if $Q(0, v) \equiv 0$, then the differential equation for u can be written as $\dot{u} = \mu^s u + \tilde{Q}(u, v)u^2$, for some $\tilde{Q}$, which proves the lemma. So it remains to show that there is a q that results in $Q(0, v) \equiv 0$. To this end consider the differential equation

$$\dot{v} = \mu^u v,$$
$$\dot{h} = -\hat{Q}(h, v).$$

The nonhyperbolic equilibrium $(v, h) = (0, 0)$ has a one-dimensional strong unstable manifold $\hat{W}^u$ which can be represented as graph of a function $\hat{q}$, graph $\hat{q} = \{(v, \hat{q}(v))\}$. For the existence of the one-dimensional strong unstable manifold we resort to Appendix B.1.3; we cannot use Theorem B.4 as the equilibrium is not hyperbolic. Clearly $\hat{q}(0) = 0$. Then, along the unstable manifold $\hat{W}^u$, that means along the curve $\{(v(t), h(t) = \hat{q}(v(t)))\}$, we have

$$\dot{v} = \mu^u v,$$
$$-\hat{Q}(\hat{q}(v(t)), v(t)) = \big(q(v(t))\big)^{\cdot} = \hat{q}'(v(t))\dot{v}(t).$$

Therefore

$$\hat{q}'(v(t))\mu^u v(t) + \hat{Q}(\hat{q}(v(t)), v(t)) \equiv 0.$$

Hence, for $q = \hat{q}$ we have $Q(0, v) \equiv 0$. □

4.1.1.2. *Splitting function.* Now we comment on the generic unfolding condition (ii) of Theorem 4.3. We show that under this condition the extended stable and unstable manifolds

$$\mathcal{W}^s = \bigcup_\lambda (W^s(p(\lambda)) \times \{\lambda\}),$$
$$\mathcal{W}^u = \bigcup_\lambda (W^u(p(\lambda)) \times \{\lambda\})$$

intersect transversely, as indicated in Figure 4.4.

Take a line piece Σ through $h(0)$, perpendicular to the homoclinic orbit. Let $\eta_0 \perp f_0(h(0))$, $|\eta_0| = 1$. So $\Sigma \subset h(0) + \mathbb{R}\eta_0$. Consider the adjoint of the linearization along the homoclinic orbit

$$\dot{x} = -(Df_0(h(t)))^T x. \tag{4.5}$$

Observe that for solutions ξ of the first variation equation

$$\dot{x}(t) = Df_0(h(t))x(t),$$

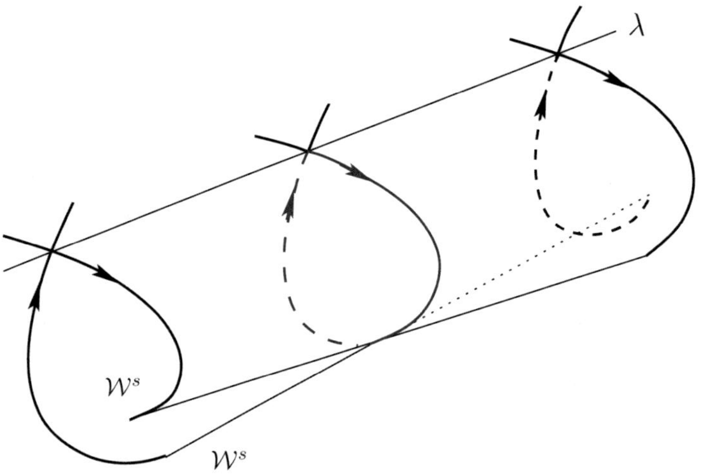

Figure 4.4. Transversal intersection of W^s and W^u.

and η of (4.5),

$$\frac{d}{dt}\langle \xi(t), \eta(t)\rangle = 0.$$

In particular, if $\langle \xi(0), \eta(0)\rangle = 0$, so that $\xi(0)$ and $\eta(0)$ are perpendicular, then $\xi(t)$ and $\eta(t)$ are perpendicular for all t.

We note that the solution η of the initial value problem (4.5), $x(0) = \eta_0$ is bounded on $\mathbb{R}$, and what is more $\eta(t)$ tends to zero as $t \to \pm\infty$. The general theory that gives this is that of exponential dichotomies, presented in Appendix C.2.1, but the statements are straightforward in the normal form coordinates from Lemma 4.6. The normal form coordinates imply that for large positive t, $\eta(t) = (0, \eta^u(t))$ and $\dot{\eta^u} = \lambda^u(t)\eta^u(t)$ for a function λ^u with $\lambda^u(t) \to \mu^u$ as $t \to \infty$. So $\eta(t)$ converges to 0 exponentially fast as $t \to \infty$. Likewise, for large negative t, $\eta(t) = (\eta^s(t), 0)$ and $\dot{\eta^s} = \lambda^s(t)\eta^s(t)$ for a function λ^s with $\lambda^s(t) \to \mu^s$ as $t \to -\infty$. So $\eta(t)$ also converges to 0 exponentially fast as $t \to -\infty$. The set of bounded solutions of (4.5) is spanned by η.

Consider the solutions $h^s_\lambda(t)$ in $W^s(p_\lambda)$ with $h^s_\lambda(0) \in \Sigma$ and $h^u_\lambda(t)$ in $W^u(p_\lambda)$ with $h^u_\lambda(0) \in \Sigma$. Then

$$d(\lambda) = h^u_\lambda(0) - h^s_\lambda(0) \tag{4.6}$$

measures the signed distance between stable and unstable manifolds of p_λ inside Σ.

Lemma 4.7. *Let η be the solution of the initial value problem* (4.5)*, $x(0) = \eta_0$. Then*

$$\langle \eta(0), d(\lambda)\rangle = \lambda \int_{-\infty}^{\infty} \langle \eta(t), D_\lambda f(h(t), 0)\rangle\, dt + \mathcal{O}(\lambda^2).$$

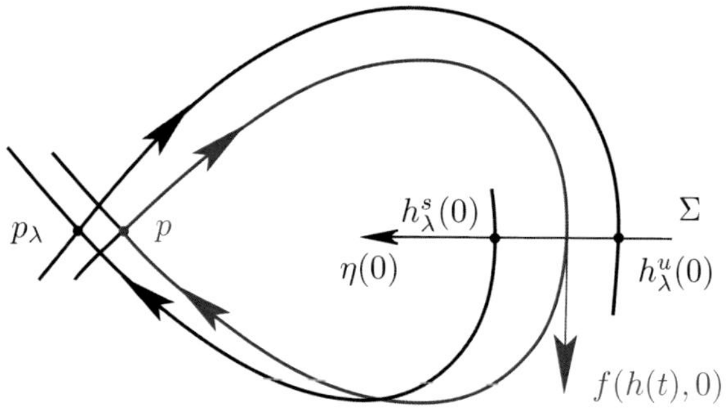

Figure 4.5. Measuring the distance of W^s and W^u. In the situation depicted the vectors $h^u_\lambda(0) - h^s_\lambda(0)$ and $\eta(0)$ point in opposite directions.

Proof. Since the stable and unstable manifolds are smooth and depend smoothly on λ, we may develop

$$h^s_\lambda(t) = h(t) + \lambda v^s(t) + \mathcal{O}(\lambda^2), \quad t \geq 0,$$
$$h^u_\lambda(t) = h(t) + \lambda v^u(t) + \mathcal{O}(\lambda^2), \quad t \leq 0.$$

Since h^s_λ and h^u_λ satisfy (4.4) the functions v^s and v^u satisfy

$$\dot{x} = D_x f(h(t),0)x + D_\lambda f(h(t),0),$$

for $t \geq 0$ or $t \leq 0$, respectively.

Note that

$$\langle \eta(0), d(\lambda)\rangle = \lambda\langle \eta(0), v^u(0) - v^s(0)\rangle + \mathcal{O}(\lambda^2). \tag{4.7}$$

Define

$$\Delta^u(t) = \langle \eta(t), v^u(t)\rangle \quad \text{and} \quad \Delta^s(t) = \langle \eta(t), v^s(t)\rangle,$$

and let

$$\Delta(t) = \Delta^u(t) - \Delta^s(t).$$

Compute

$$\begin{aligned}
\dot{\Delta^s}(t) &= \langle \dot{\eta}(t), v^s(t)\rangle + \langle \eta(t), \dot{v^s}(t)\rangle \\
&= \langle -D_x f(h(t),0)^T \eta(t), v^s(t)\rangle + \langle \eta(t), D_x f(h(t),0)v^s(t) \\
&\qquad + D_\lambda f(h(t),0)\rangle \\
&= \langle \eta(t), -D_x f(h(t),0)v^s(t) + D_x f(h(t),0)v^s(t) + D_\lambda f(h(t),0)\rangle \\
&= \langle \eta(t), D_\lambda f(h(t),0)\rangle.
\end{aligned}$$

Hence

$$\lim_{t\to\infty} \Delta^s(t) - \Delta^s(0) = \int_0^\infty \langle \eta(t), D_\lambda f(h(t),0)\rangle\, dt.$$

Because $\eta(t)$ tends to zero and $v^s(t)$ remains bounded as $t \to \infty$, we find

$$-\Delta^s(0) = \int_0^\infty \langle \eta(t), D_\lambda f(h(t), 0)\rangle \, dt.$$

Similarly we find

$$\Delta^u(0) = \int_{-\infty}^0 \langle \eta(t), D_\lambda f(h(t), 0)\rangle \, dt.$$

Inserting in (4.7) gives the lemma. □

Remark 4.8. Let $f_\lambda = (f_\lambda^1, f_\lambda^2)$. Then

$$e^{-\int_0^t \operatorname{div} f_0(h(s))\, ds}(f_0^2(h(t)), -f_0^1(h(t)))$$

is a bounded solution of (4.5); see Exercise 4.8. So for M in condition (ii) in Theorem 4.3 we may also use

$$M = \frac{1}{|f_0(h(0))|} \int_{-\infty}^\infty e^{-\int_0^t \operatorname{div} f_0(h(s))\, ds} f_0(h(t)) \wedge \frac{\partial}{\partial \lambda} f_\lambda(h(t))|_{\lambda=0} \, dt.$$

Here the wedge product $a \wedge b$ of vectors $a = (a_1, a_2)$ and $b = (b_1, b_2)$ is defined by $a \wedge b = a_1 b_2 - a_2 b_1$.

We include a brief independent derivation of the formula for M. Let h_λ^s, h_λ^u, v^s, v^u and $d = h_\lambda^u(0) - h_\lambda^s(0)$ be as in the above proof, and write

$$\Theta^s(t) = f_0(h(t)) \wedge v^s(t),$$
$$\Theta^u(t) = f_0(h(t)) \wedge v^u(t).$$

So for instance $\Theta^s(t)$ stands for the signed area of the parallelogram spanned by $f_0(h(t))$ and $v^s(t)$. Then, with $\Theta(t) = \Theta^u(t) - \Theta^s(t)$, we have

$$d = \lambda \frac{1}{|f_0(h(0))|} \Theta(0) + \mathcal{O}(\lambda^2).$$

Compute

$$\begin{aligned}
\dot{\Theta}^s(t) &= Df_0(h(t))\dot{h}(t) \wedge v^s(t) + f_0(h(t)) \wedge \dot{v}^s(t) \\
&= Df_0(h(t)) f_0(h(t)) \wedge v^s(t) \\
&\quad + f_0(h(t)) \wedge \left(Df_0(h(t)) v^s(t) + \frac{\partial f_\lambda}{\partial \lambda}(h(t))|_{\lambda=0} \right) \\
&= \operatorname{div} f_0(h(t)) \Theta^s(t) + f_0(h(t)) \wedge \frac{\partial f_\lambda}{\partial \lambda}(h(t))|_{\lambda=0}.
\end{aligned}$$

The variation of constants formula gives

$$\Theta^s(\infty) - \Theta^s(0) = \int_0^\infty e^{-\int_0^t \operatorname{div} f_0(h(s))\, ds} f_0(h(t)) \wedge \frac{\partial f_\lambda}{\partial \lambda}(h(t))|_{\lambda=0} \, dt.$$

Combined with an analogous formula for $\Theta^u(0) - \Theta^u(\infty)$, this proves the formula. ■

Remark 4.9. In a continuation of the previous remark, consider the case of perturbations from a Hamiltonian vector field. Let $\dot{x} = f(x) + \lambda g(x)$ with $\operatorname{div} f \equiv 0$. Suppose $\dot{x} = f(x)$ admits a homoclinic orbit h. In this case the value of M from Remark 4.8 reads

$$M = \frac{1}{|f(h(0))|} \int_{-\infty}^{\infty} f(h(t)) \wedge g(h(t))\, dt.$$

This sort of context appeared in the study of the Bogdanov-Takens bifurcation studied in Scction 3.2.5. ■

Remark 4.10. Lemma 4.7 assumes a single real parameter, but the reasoning shows that a similar formula holds with higher-dimensional parameters. Assume a context with $\lambda = (\lambda_1, \ldots, \lambda_k) \in \mathbb{R}^k$. Then the expression in Lemma 4.7 becomes

$$\langle \eta(0), d(\lambda) \rangle = \sum_{i=1}^{k} \lambda_i \int_{-\infty}^{\infty} \langle \eta(t), D_{\lambda_i} f(h(t), 0) \rangle\, dt + \mathcal{O}(|\lambda|^2).$$

■

4.1.1.3. *Analysis of the return map.* Take local coordinates x, y near the equilibrium as given by Lemma 4.6. Considering a Taylor expansion of f^s with second-order residual term yields that for a compact set (containing $(0,0)$ in its interior) there is constant $C > 0$ such that

$$f^s(x, y) \le C x^2 |y|.$$

Further, for $\sigma > 0$ small, let $\Sigma_{in} = \{x = \sigma, |y| < \sigma\}$ and $\Sigma_{out} = \{|x| < \sigma, y = \sigma\}$ be local cross sections, transverse to the flow φ^t as depicted in Figure 4.3. We may assume that h intersects Σ_{in} and Σ_{out}. By a rescaling $\sigma\hat{x} = x$, $\sigma\hat{y} = y$ and renaming $(\hat{x}, \hat{y})$ (x, y), we get $\Sigma_{in} = \{x = 1, |y| < 1\}$ and $\Sigma_{out} = \{|x| < 1, y = 1\}$. This changes the bound $f^s(x, y) \le C x^2 |y|$ to

$$f^s(x, y) \le C\sigma^3 x^2 |y|. \tag{4.8}$$

Define the local transition map $P_{loc} : \Sigma_{in} \to \Sigma_{out}$ by letting $P_{loc}(y)$ be the first point $\varphi^t(1, y) \in \Sigma_{out}$; P_{loc} is defined on an open domain in Σ_{in}.

We will derive asymptotics for the local transition map. Write $\beta = |\mu^s / \mu^u|$. If the vector field is linear, $P_{loc}(y) = y^\beta$. The crux of the following lemma is that in normal form coordinates P_{loc} have the same expression up to higher-order terms. Informally the lemma gives $P_{loc}(y) = y^\beta + \mathcal{O}(y^{\beta+\omega})$ for some $\omega > 0$, plus induced estimates for derivatives.

Lemma 4.11. *The map P_{loc} satisfies*

$$\left| \frac{d^k}{dy^k} \left(P_{loc}(y) - y^\beta \right) \right| \le C_k |y|^{\beta+\omega-k}, \tag{4.9}$$

for positive constants C_k.

Proof. Consider the orbit $(x(t), y(t))$ starting at a point $(1, y) \in \Sigma_{in}$. Observe that this orbit reaches Σ_{out} at time $t(y) = -\frac{1}{\mu^u}\ln y$. Thus $y(t) = e^{\mu^u t}y = e^{\mu^u(t-t(y))}$ and, using the variation of constants formula,

$$x(t) = e^{\mu^s t} + \int_0^t e^{\mu^s(t-s)} f^s(x(s), e^{\mu^u(s-t(y))})ds. \tag{4.10}$$

Below we show that (4.10) has, for given y, a unique solution $x(t)$. That means, for each $(1, y) \in \Sigma_{in}$ there is a unique solution $(x(t), y(t))$ with $(x(0), y(0)) = (1, y)$ which terminates in Σ_{out} after time $t(y)$. Hence, for $P_{loc}(y)$, which is defined by means of the solution $x(t)$ of (4.10), we find

$$\begin{aligned} P_{loc}(y) &= x(t(y)) \\ &= e^{\mu^s t(y)} + \int_0^{t(y)} e^{\mu^s(t(y)-s)} f^s(x(s), e^{\mu^u(s-t(y))})ds \\ &= y^\beta + \int_0^{t(y)} e^{\mu^s(t(y)-s)} f^s(x(s), e^{\mu^u(s-t(y))})ds. \end{aligned} \tag{4.11}$$

We will mimic Picard iteration (see for instance [**163**] or [**329**]) on a weighted Banach space to construct the solution $x(t)$ and at the same time obtain asymptotics for it. Let

$$\mathfrak{B}_\tau = \{x : [0, \tau] \to E^s \mid \sup_{t\in[0,\tau]} |x(t)|e^{-\mu^s t} < \infty\}.$$

Equipped with the norm

$$|x|_\tau = \sup_{t\in[0,\tau]} |x(t)|e^{-\mu^s t},$$

$\mathfrak{B}_\tau$ is a Banach space. Write $\Gamma : \mathfrak{B}_{t(y)} \to \mathfrak{B}_{t(y)}$ for the map given by the right-hand side of (4.10). We show by means of the Banach fixed point theorem that Γ has a unique fixed point. First we claim that there is a closed ball $B(R) \subset \mathfrak{B}$ so that $\Gamma(B(R)) \subset B(R)$. Compute for $\tau = t(y)$

$$\begin{aligned} |\Gamma x|_\tau &= \sup_{t\in[0,\tau]} e^{-\mu^s t}\left| e^{\mu^s t} + \int_0^t e^{\mu^s(t-s)} f^s(x(s), y(s))\, ds \right| \\ &= \sup_{t\in[0,\tau]} \left| 1 + \int_0^t e^{-\mu^s s} f^s(x(s), y(s))\, ds \right| \\ &\le 1 + C\sigma \int_0^\tau e^{-\mu^s s}|x(s)|^2\, ds, \end{aligned}$$

for some $C > 0$, using Lemma 4.6, the estimate (4.8), and that $|y(s)| \le 1$. Hence

$$|\Gamma x|_\tau \le 1 + C\sigma|x|_\tau^2 \int_0^\tau e^{\mu^s s}\, ds.$$

It follows that, for σ small enough, there exists $R > 0$ so that for $|x|_\tau \leq R$, also $|\Gamma x|_\tau \leq R$. Note that R can be chosen from a neighborhood of 1.

Next we show that Γ is a contraction. Consider

$$\begin{aligned}
&|\Gamma x_1 - \Gamma x_2|_\tau \\
&\quad = \sup_{t\in[0,\tau]} e^{-\mu^s t} \left| \int_0^t e^{\mu^s(t-s)} \left(f^s(x_1(s), y(s)) - f^s(x_1(s), y(s))\right) ds \right| \\
&\quad = \sup_{t\in[0,\tau]} \left| \int_0^t e^{-\mu^s s} D_1 f^s(\hat{x}(s), y(s)) \left(x_1(s) - x_2(s)\right) ds \right| \\
&\quad \leq \int_0^\tau |D_1 f^s(\hat{x}(s), y(s))| \, ds |x_1 - x_2|_\tau \\
&\quad \leq C\sigma \int_0^\tau |\hat{x}(s)| \, ds |x_1 - x_2|_\tau \\
&\quad \leq CR\sigma \int_0^\tau e^{\mu^s s} \, ds |x_1 - x_2|_\tau.
\end{aligned}$$

In the course of these estimates we applied the mean value theorem (from which the $\hat{x}$ arises), and furthermore the estimate (4.8) (exploiting that $\sigma < 1$ and that $|y(s)| \leq 1$) and that $x_i \in B(R) \subset \mathcal{B}_\tau$, $i = 1, 2$, which implies $|\hat{x}(s)| \leq Re^{\mu^s s}$.

Finally, σ can be chosen small enough that $CR\sigma \int_0^\tau e^{\mu^s s} \, ds < 1$. This proves the existence of the orbit connecting $(1, y) \in \Sigma_{in}$ to Σ_{out}. Moreover, $|x|_\tau \leq R$ implies that x satisfies a bound

$$|x(t)| \leq Re^{\mu^s t}. \tag{4.12}$$

Now (4.9) for P_{loc} follows from (4.11) together with Lemma 4.6 and (4.12):

$$\begin{aligned}
|P_{loc}(y) - y^\beta| &= \left| \int_0^{t(y)} e^{\mu^s(t(y)-s)} f^s(x(s), e^{\mu^u(s-t(y))}) \, ds \right| \\
&\leq \int_0^{t(y)} e^{\mu^s(t(y)-s)} C\sigma e^{2\mu^s s} e^{\mu^u(s-t(y))} \, ds \\
&= C\sigma \int_0^{t(y)} e^{(\mu^s-\mu^u)(t(y)-s)} e^{2\mu^s s} \, ds \\
&= C\sigma e^{(\mu^s-\mu^u)t(y)} \int_0^{t(y)} e^{(\mu^u+\mu^s)s} \, ds \\
&\leq C_k y^{\beta+1}.
\end{aligned}$$

Bounds for derivatives are obtained similarly by differentiating the variation of constants formula and estimating as before. □

Proof of Theorem 4.3. Expansions for the local transition map $P_{loc} : \Sigma_{in} \to \Sigma_{out}$ are in Lemma 4.11. The global transition map $P_{glob} : \Sigma_{out} \to \Sigma_{in}$ is a local diffeomorphism by the global flow box theorem. We can write $P_{glob}(x, \lambda) = d_0 + d_1 x + \mathcal{O}(x^2)$ as $x \to 0$, where d_0, d_1 are smooth functions of the parameter λ. The composition $\Pi = P_{glob} \circ P_{loc}$ thus has an expansion

$$\Pi(y, \lambda) = d_0(\lambda) + d_1(\lambda) y^{\beta} + \mathcal{O}(y^{\beta+\omega})$$

with $\beta > 1$ and some $\omega > 0$, where one can differentiate this formula to obtain estimates for derivatives. Note that $d_0 = d_0(\lambda)$ measures the distance of the unstable and stable manifold in Σ_{in}; see Figure 4.6.

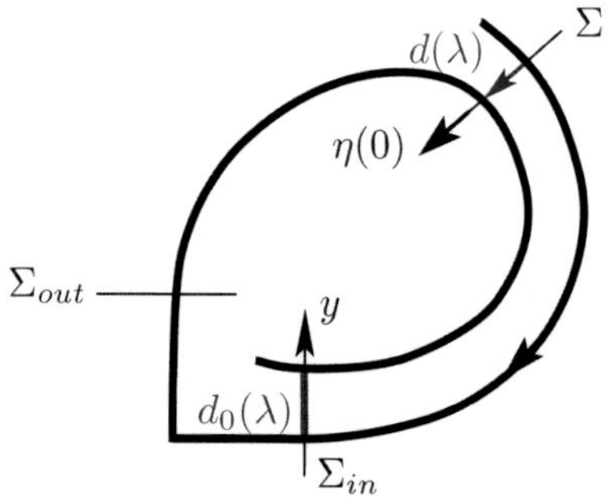

Figure 4.6. The term $d_0(\lambda)$. Note that the situation depicted is related to $\lambda < 0$; compare also Figure 4.2. Meaning that $\lambda < 0$ implies $d_0(\lambda) > 0$. The term $d(\lambda)$ is defined in (4.6). Compare also with Figure 4.5.

Lemma 4.7 implies $\frac{d}{d\lambda} d_0 > 0$. The theorem now follows easily from a graphical analysis as executed in Figure 4.7. From $D_y \Pi(0, \lambda) = 0$ we infer that at the fixed point, $|D_y \Pi(\cdot, \lambda)| < 1$. This shows the stability statement. □

We give an example of homoclinic bifurcations in planar differential equations. We recall definitions and notation of hyperbolic functions that arise in

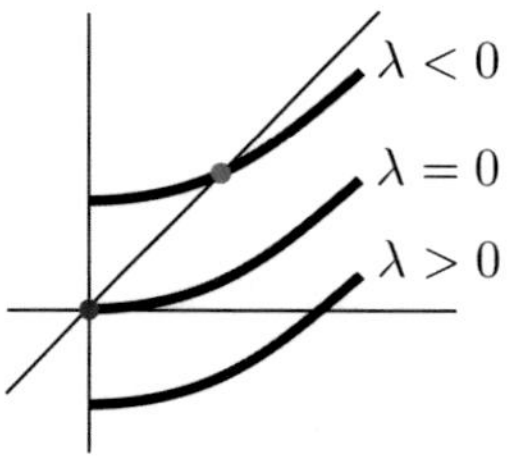

Figure 4.7. Drawn are the graphs of $\Pi(\cdot, \lambda)$ and its fixed points. Recall that $d_0(\lambda < 0) > 0$, $d_0(0) = 0$ and $d_0(\lambda > 0) < 0$. The green point corresponds to a periodic orbit while the blue one corresponds to the original homoclinic orbit; compare Figure 4.2.

it. The hyperbolic sine and cosine functions are given by

$$\sinh(x) = \frac{1}{2}(e^x - e^{-x}),$$
$$\cosh(x) = \frac{1}{2}(e^x + e^{-x}).$$

The hyperbolic tangent is $\tanh(x) = \sinh(x)/\cosh(x)$, its inverse is given by $\operatorname{arctanh}(x) = \frac{1}{2}\ln(1+x) - \frac{1}{2}\ln(1-x)$, and the hyperbolic secant is $\operatorname{sech}(x) = 1/\cosh(x)$.

Example 4.12. A Josephson junction consists of two closely spaced superconductors separated by a weak connection. Brian Josephson suggested that it should be possible for a current to pass between the two superconductors, by a quantum mechanical tunneling effect. A simplified model is

$$\ddot{\phi} + \alpha\dot{\phi} + \sin(\phi) = I$$

on the circle $\mathbb{R}/2\pi\mathbb{Z}$, with real parameters $\alpha > 0, I$. As a system,

$$\begin{aligned} \dot{\phi} &= y, \\ \dot{y} &= -\sin(\phi) + I - \alpha y \end{aligned} \tag{4.13}$$

on the cylinder $(\mathbb{R}/2\pi\mathbb{Z}) \times \mathbb{R}$. Exercise 4.9 provides a strategy to prove the existence of a unique attracting periodic orbit for $I > 1$, $\alpha > 0$. For small values of α, when decreasing I, at some value the periodic orbit vanishes in a homoclinic bifurcation [**224**]; see also the explanation in [**365**]. For small values of α, I one can detect homoclinic orbits by using Melnikov functions. We give a brief account, leaving details to the exercises. An analysis can also be found in [**143**, pp. 201–202].

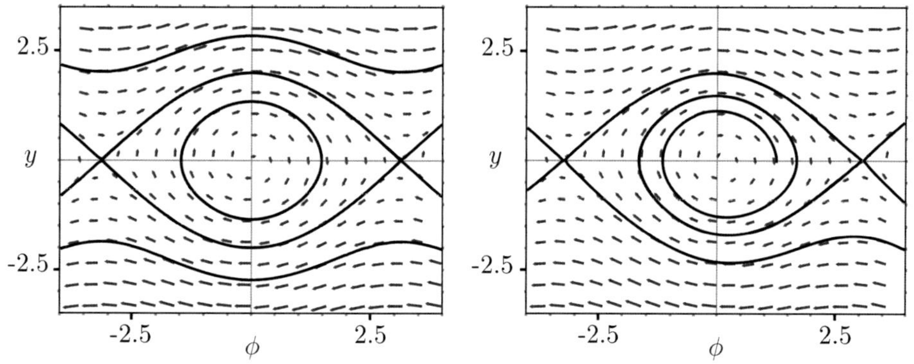

Figure 4.8. The left picture gives the phase portrait of the Hamiltonian vector field (4.14) with two homoclinic orbits to $(-\pi, 0)$. (Note that the horizontal ϕ-coordinate is taken modulo 2π: the two saddle equilibria are identified.) The right picture shows a homoclinic orbit for the differential equations given by (4.13) for some small value of I, α.

For $I = \alpha = 0$ we find the equation

$$\begin{aligned} \dot{\phi} &= y, \\ \dot{y} &= -\sin(\phi), \end{aligned} \tag{4.14}$$

which is Hamiltonian with a Hamilton function $H(\phi, y) = \frac{1}{2}y^2 - \cos(\phi)$; see Figure 4.8. This system admits a homoclinic orbit

$$\gamma(t) = (2\arctan(\sinh(t)), 2\,\mathrm{sech}(t))$$

connecting $(-\pi, 0)$ and $(\pi, 0)$, which are considered identified. Lemma 4.7 allows us to derive an equation for a curve in an (I, α)-parameter space along which a homoclinic orbit exists:

$$I = \frac{4}{\pi}\alpha + o(\alpha), \tag{4.15}$$

as $\alpha \to 0$. Exercise 4.10 asks us to derive this formula (note Remark 4.10).

In the treatment of the Bogdanov-Takens bifurcation in Section 3.2.5 we encountered a similar situation of perturbations from a Hamiltonian vector field. There we defined a splitting function Δ whose vanishing indicated the occurrence of a periodic or a homoclinic loop; see Lemma 3.51. This lemma is a general statement and can also be used in the present context for perturbations from (4.14). For comparison reasons we work out this approach for the homoclinic orbit in the Josephson junction model (4.13). The saddle equilibrium of (4.13) occurs at $y = 0$ and $\sin(\phi) = I$ with ϕ near $-\pi$ if I is small. Write $(\ell, 0)$ for this saddle equilibrium, with ℓ a function of I. Note that $\ell = -\pi - I + \mathcal{O}(I^2)$ if I is small. It is convenient to move the equilibrium to $(-\pi, 0)$ for all small values of I, α by a rescaling. For that, let $\theta = -\frac{\pi}{\ell}\phi$ and calculate

$$\begin{aligned} \dot{\theta} &= -\frac{\pi}{\ell}y, \\ \dot{y} &= -\sin\left(-\frac{\ell}{\pi}\theta\right) + I - \alpha y. \end{aligned}$$

Rescale time to get

$$\begin{aligned} \dot{\theta} &= y, \\ \dot{y} &= \frac{\ell}{\pi}\sin\left(-\frac{\ell}{\pi}\theta\right) - \frac{\ell}{\pi}(I - \alpha y). \end{aligned}$$

As $-\ell/\pi = 1 + I/\pi + \mathcal{O}(I^2)$, for small values of I, α this equals

$$\begin{aligned} \dot{\theta} &= y, \\ \dot{y} &= -\sin(\theta) - \frac{I}{\pi}(\sin(\theta) + \cos(\theta)\theta) + I - \alpha y + \mathcal{O}(|(I, \alpha)|^2). \end{aligned} \tag{4.16}$$

Take a line piece $L = \{(\theta, y)\ ;\ \theta = -\pi, y \geq 0\}$ parametrized by the value h of the Hamiltonian function. Consider the Poincaré return map Π for the flow of (4.16) on L, and define $\Delta(h) = \Pi(h) - h$ as in (3.92) in Section 3.2.5.3. Note that $H(-\pi, 0) = 1$. The value $\Delta(1)$ is defined by continuity. We are interested in the equation $\Delta(1) = 0$ which corresponds to a homoclinic orbit to the saddle equilibrium $(-\pi, 0)$. The corresponding formula, similar to Lemma 3.51, is

$$\Delta(1) = \int_\gamma -\frac{I}{\pi}\,(\sin(\theta) + \cos(\theta)\theta) + I - \alpha y\, d\theta + o(|(I, \alpha)|).$$

Noting that $\theta \mapsto \sin(\theta)$ and $\theta \mapsto \cos(\theta)\theta$ are odd functions in θ and using $\dot{\theta} = y$, we find

$$\begin{aligned}
\int_\gamma -\frac{I}{\pi}(\sin(\theta) + \cos(\theta)\theta) + I - \alpha y\, d\theta &= \int_\gamma I - \alpha y\, d\theta \\
&= \int_{-\pi}^{\pi} I\, d\theta - \int_{-\infty}^{\infty} \dot{\theta}(t)\alpha y(t)\, dt \\
&= 2\pi I - \int_{-\infty}^{\infty} \alpha (y(t))^2\, dt \\
&= 2\pi I - \int_{-\infty}^{\infty} \alpha (\operatorname{sech}(t))^2\, dt \\
&= 2\pi I - 8\alpha.
\end{aligned}$$

We recover the formula $I = \frac{4}{\pi}\alpha + o(\alpha)$ for the curve along which a homoclinic orbit exists. ■

4.1.2. Higher-dimensional homoclinic orbits. We will treat a higher-dimensional analogue of Theorem 4.3 due to Leonid Shilnikov [**337**]. This involves geometric conditions absent in the planar case. Given a hyperbolic equilibrium p of a vector field f in $\mathbb{R}^n$, the eigenvalues closest to the imaginary axis, either in the left complex half-plane or in the right complex half-plane, are called leading eigenvalues. The eigenvalues in the left complex half-plane that are closest to the imaginary axis are leading stable eigenvalues. Those in the right half-plane are leading unstable eigenvalues. The remaining eigenvalues are strong stable and strong unstable eigenvalues. The invariant directions corresponding to leading eigenvalues are called leading directions. Those corresponding to strong stable eigenvalues are called strong stable directions, and likewise for all strong unstable directions.

We will look at homoclinic orbits to hyperbolic equilibria with simple real leading eigenvalues. Assume that $\dot{x} = f(x)$ possesses a hyperbolic saddle equilibrium p and $Df(p)$ has simple real leading eigenvalues μ^s, μ^u with

$$\mu^s < 0 < \mu^u$$

and a homoclinic orbit $h(t)$ with

$$\lim_{t\to\infty} h(t) = \lim_{t\to-\infty} h(t) = p.$$

The linearization $Df(p)$ admits an invariant splitting

(4.17) $$\mathbb{R}^n = E^{ss} \oplus E^s \oplus E^u \oplus E^{uu}$$

in strong stable, leading stable, leading unstable, and strong unstable directions.

The equilibrium p has a stable manifold $W^{ss,s}(p)$, tangent to $E^{ss} \oplus E^s$ at p, and an unstable manifold $W^{u,uu}(p)$, tangent to $E^u \oplus E^{uu}$ at p. Inside $W^{ss,s}(p)$ there is a codimension-1 strong stable manifold $W^{ss}(p)$ consisting of orbits $u(t)$ that converge at a faster rate to p:

$$\lim_{t\to\infty} |u(t) - p|/e^{\mu^s t} = 0.$$

Moreover, the stable manifold is foliated by a strong stable foliation $\mathcal{F}^{ss}$ (see Appendix B.1.3) with $W^{ss}(p)$ as one of its leaves. Inside $W^{u,uu}(p)$ there is a codimension-1 strong unstable manifold $W^{uu}(p)$ which is a leaf of the strong unstable foliation $\mathcal{F}^{uu}$.

As a corollary to Theorem B.15 and Proposition B.17 in Appendix B.1.4 (rather, the equivalent versions of these results for vector fields), we have the following statement on the existence and properties of center stable and center unstable manifolds.

Proposition 4.13. *Let f be a vector field on $\mathbb{R}^n$ with a hyperbolic equilibrium p, such that the linearization $Df(p)$ admits an invariant splitting*

$$\mathbb{R}^n = E^{ss} \oplus E^s \oplus E^u \oplus E^{uu}$$

in strong stable, leading stable, leading unstable, and strong unstable directions.

There is a center unstable manifold $W^{s,u,uu}(p)$ with tangent space $E^s \oplus E^u \oplus E^{uu}$ at p, and a center stable manifold $W^{ss,s,u}(p)$ with tangent space $E^{ss} \oplus E^s \oplus E^u$ at p. The center stable and center unstable manifolds are not unique, but the tangent bundles

$$T_{W^{ss,s}(p)} W^{ss,s,u}(p) = \{T_x W^{ss,s,u}(p)\ ;\ x \in W^{ss,s}(p)\}$$

along $W^{ss,s}(p)$ and

$$T_{W^{u,uu}(p)} W^{s,u,uu}(p) = \{T_x W^{s,u,uu}(p)\ ;\ x \in W^{u,uu}(p)\}$$

along $W^{u,uu}(p)$ are unique and smooth bundles.

For a family of differential equations $\dot{x} = f_\lambda(x)$ unfolding $\dot{x} = f(x)$, we denote invariant manifolds using a subscript λ, such as $W^{ss,s}_\lambda(p)$. Also $p = p(\lambda)$ depends on λ, which is often suppressed from the notation.

Theorem 4.14. *Let*

(4.18) $$\dot{x} = f_\lambda(x) = f(x, \lambda)$$

be a smooth family of vector fields on $\mathbb{R}^n$, depending on a real parameter $\lambda \in \mathbb{R}$. Assume that for $\lambda = 0$ there is a hyperbolic saddle equilibrium p and $Df_0(p)$ has simple real leading eigenvalues μ^s, μ^u with $\mu^s < 0 < \mu^u$ and a homoclinic orbit $h(t)$ with

$$\lim_{t\to\infty} h(t) = \lim_{t\to-\infty} h(t) = p.$$

Assume the following:

(i) (*Negative saddle quantity*)

$$\mu^s + \mu^u < 0.$$

(ii) (*Nondegenerate homoclinic orbit*)

$$T_{h(0)}W^{ss,s}(p) \cap T_{h(0)}W^{u,uu}(p) = T_{h(0)}\{f(h(0))\}.$$

(iii) (*No-inclination-flip*)

$$W^{ss,s,u}(p) \pitchfork_h W^{u,uu}(p),$$
$$W^{s,u,uu}(p) \pitchfork_h W^{ss,s}(p).$$

(iv) (*No-orbit-flip*) *h approaches p along the leading directions*

$$\lim_{t\to\infty} \dot{h}(t)/|\dot{h}(t)| \in E^s,$$
$$\lim_{t\to-\infty} \dot{h}(t)/|\dot{h}(t)| \in E^u.$$

(v) (*Generic unfolding*)

$$M = \int_{-\infty}^{\infty} \langle \eta(t), D_\lambda f(h(t), 0)\rangle\, dt \neq 0,$$

where η is a bounded solution of the adjoint variational equation $\dot{x} = -Df_0(h(t))^T x$ along h.

Depending on the sign of M, there exists $\delta > 0, \varepsilon > 0$ so that for $\lambda \in (-\delta, 0)$ (or $\lambda \in (0, \delta)$) there is a hyperbolic periodic orbit $\zeta_\lambda(t)$ of (4.18) of period $T(\lambda)$ such that $T(\lambda)$ goes to infinity as $\lambda \to 0$ and ζ_λ approaches h as $\lambda \to 0$. Furthermore, if $\mathcal{U}$ denotes the ε neighborhood of h, then ζ_λ is the unique periodic orbit in $\mathcal{U}$ for $\lambda \in (-\delta, 0)$ (respectively, $\lambda \in (0, \delta)$). There is no periodic orbit in $\mathcal{U}$ for $\lambda \in [0, \delta)$ (respectively, $\lambda \in (-\delta, 0]$).

As in the planar case we construct a return map to prove the statement. We summarize the strategy. Let Σ_{in} and Σ_{out} be cross sections of the local stable and unstable manifold, respectively. Define a Poincaré return map on Σ_{in} by composing a local transition map $P_{loc} : \Sigma_{in} \to \Sigma_{out}$ and a global transition map $P_{glob} : \Sigma_{out} \to \Sigma_{in}$; see Figure 4.9.

As will be substantiated below, we work with suitable local coordinates $x = (x_{ss}, x_s, x_u, x_{uu})$ near p corresponding to strong stable, leading stable,

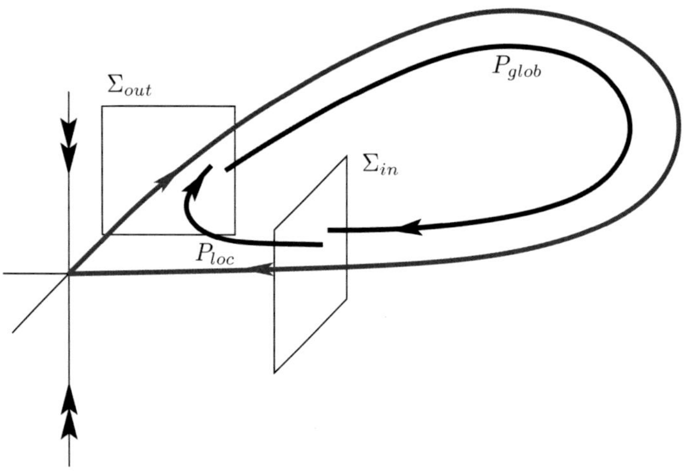

Figure 4.9. A homoclinic orbit in $\mathbb{R}^3$ indicating two cross sections Σ_{in} and Σ_{out} and the definition of the transition maps $P_{loc} : \Sigma_{in} \to \Sigma_{out}$ and $P_{glob} : \Sigma_{out} \to \Sigma_{in}$.

leading unstable, and strong unstable directions. The section Σ_{in} is given by fixed small x_s coordinate, and the section Σ_{out} is given by fixed small x_u coordinate. A point on Σ_{in}, written in coordinates as $(x_{ss}^{in}, x_u^{in}, x_{uu}^{in})$, will be mapped to a point on Σ_{out}, written as $(x_{ss}^{in}, x_u^{in}, x_{uu}^{in})$, by the local transition map. The main work lies in deriving an asymptotic expression for this local transition map $P_{loc}(x_{ss}^{in}, x_u^{in}, x_{uu}^{in}) = (x_{ss}^{in}, x_u^{in}, x_{uu}^{in})$. In contrast to the planar case, this is done in cross coordinates (sometimes called Shilnikov-coordinates) in which we solve $(x_{ss}^{out}, x_s^{out}, x_{uu}^{in})$ as function of $(x_{ss}^{in}, x_u^{in}, x_{uu}^{out})$. This gives a function $(x_{ss}^{out}, x_s^{out}, x_{uu}^{in}) = T(x_{ss}^{in}, x_u^{in}, x_{uu}^{out})$, and we provide asymptotic expansions for T. This is done in Lemma 4.22. In deriving it we use a local normal form of the vector field given in Lemma 4.17. The point of the local normal form is that we get formulas equal to those for locally linear differential equations, plus added small perturbations. The actual proof of the theorem reduces to writing down and solving equations for fixed points of a Poincaré return map, making use of cross coordinates. As in the homoclinic bifurcation in the plane, the unfolding condition involves a Melnikov integral M.

Before starting with the preparations for the proof, we comment the two geometric assumptions, the no-inclination-flip condition and the no-orbit-flip condition, in the following remark.

Remark 4.15. If the homoclinic orbit approaches p along a strong stable direction, small perturbations would create homoclinic orbits that approach p along the leading stable direction from either side. Small perturbations would thus flip the approaching direction. This is called an orbit-flip, which is excluded in the above theorem and gives a homoclinic bifurcation of higher codimension.

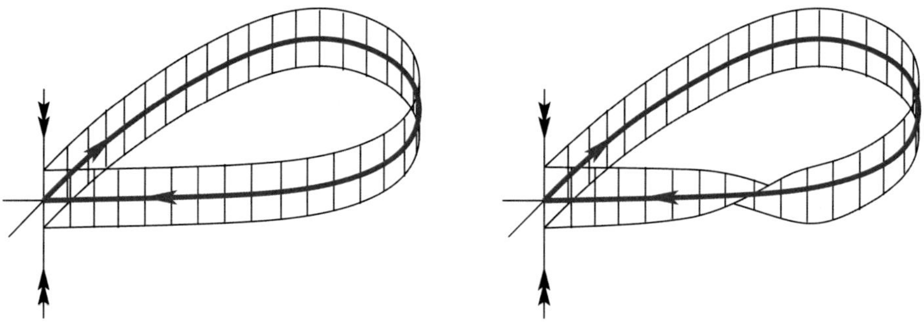

Figure 4.10. Homoclinic orbits in $\mathbb{R}^3$ where the two-dimensional stable manifold of the equilibrium forms a surface near the homoclinic orbit, homeomorphic to an orientable cylinder or a nonorientable Möbius band. The stable manifold is foliated by one-dimensional leaves of the strong stable foliation.

Something similar occurs if $W^{ss,s,u}(p)$ and $W^{u,uu}(p)$ or $W^{s,u,uu}(p)$, and $W^{ss,s}(p)$ have a common tangent direction (in addition to the vector field direction). Then small perturbations cause a transverse intersection of the manifolds. Figure 4.10 shows how in three dimensions a two-dimensional stable manifold, under the no-inclination-flip condition, forms a surface near the homoclinic orbit (we come back to this in Lemma 4.24 below). The surface can be orientable or nonorientable. With an inclination-flip configuration, both geometries arise after suitable small perturbations. ∎

Remark 4.16. Multiple homoclinic orbits can bifurcate from a degenerate homoclinic orbit. This is a bifurcation with codimension 3 or higher. To understand this, consider by example a differential equation $\dot{x} = f(x)$ in $\mathbb{R}^4$ with a saddle equilibrium p that has two-dimensional stable and two-dimensional unstable manifold, and assume the existence of a degenerate homoclinic orbit h. In a cross section Σ transverse to the homoclinic orbit at $h(0)$, the stable and unstable manifolds intersect as curves. The fact that the homoclinic orbit is degenerate means that these two curves are tangent at $h(0)$, and have in fact identical tangent line at $h(0)$; see Figure 4.11.

Take an unfolding $\dot{x} = f_\lambda(x)$ with $f_0 = f$, depending on a parameter $\lambda \in \mathbb{R}^3$. We may take coordinates (x, y, z) on Σ so that

$$W^s(p) \cap \Sigma = \{y = 0, z = 0\},$$
$$W^u(p) \cap \Sigma = \{y = W_1(x,\lambda), z = W_2(x,\lambda)\}.$$

The curves being tangent for $\lambda = 0$ means $W_i(0,0) = 0$ and $D_x W_i(0,0) = 0$ for $i = 1, 2$. Homoclinic orbits occur when W_1 and W_2 are both zero for some value of (x, λ). The resulting bifurcation set is the set of values of λ for which $W_1(x,\lambda) = W_2(x,\lambda) = 0$ for some value of x. If we write $\lambda = (\lambda_1, \lambda_2, \lambda_3)$, and we can solve, say, λ_1 and λ_2 as functions of x and λ_3 from these equations,

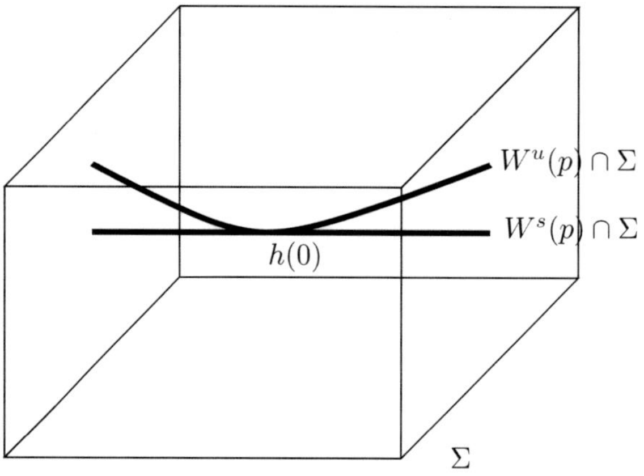

Figure 4.11. Tangent stable and unstable manifolds in a cross section.

we are left with a mapping that assigns $(\lambda_1, \lambda_2, \lambda_3)$ as function of x and λ_3. As a singularity of this mapping, one expects a Whitney umbrella; see Theorem 2.54.

We can make this explicit. A detailed analysis that includes degenerate homoclinic orbits in dimensions higher than four is in [**405**]. Write $\lambda = (\lambda_1, \lambda_2, \lambda_3)$ and assume that

$$\det D_{x,\lambda}(W_1, W_2, D_x W_1, D_x W_2)(0,0) \neq 0, \tag{4.19}$$

$$\det D_{x,\lambda_3}(W_1, W_2)(0,0) \neq 0. \tag{4.20}$$

For (4.19) to hold we need at least a three-dimensional parameter space. Condition (4.20) allows us to solve λ_1 and λ_2 as function of x and λ_3:

$$(W_1, W_2)(x, \tilde{\lambda}_1(x, \lambda_3), \tilde{\lambda}_2(x, \lambda_3), \lambda_3) = (0,0)$$

for x and λ_3 near 0 and with $(\tilde{\lambda}_1(0,0), \tilde{\lambda}_2(0,0)) = (0,0)$. Also,

$$(D_x\tilde{\lambda}_1(0,0), D_x\tilde{\lambda}_2(0,0)) = (0,0).$$

The bifurcation surface is obtained as the image of

$$(x, \lambda_3) \mapsto (\tilde{\lambda}_1(x, \lambda_3), \tilde{\lambda}_2(x, \lambda_3), \lambda_3).$$

By (4.19), $D_{xx}W_1(0,0)$ and $D_{xx}W_2(0,0)$ cannot both be zero. Assume that $D_{xx}W_2(0,0) \neq 0$. Solve $D_x\tilde{\lambda}_2(x, \lambda_3) = 0$ by the implicit function theorem for x as a function of λ_3: $D_x\tilde{\lambda}_2(\tilde{x}(\lambda_3), \lambda_3) = 0$ with $\tilde{x}(0) = 0$ and λ_3 near 0. Change to a new variable $\eta = x - \tilde{x}(\lambda_3)$. Again writing x for the variable, we find $D_x\tilde{\lambda}_2(0, \lambda_3) = 0$ for all small values of λ_3. By the Morse lemma we can simplify the expression for $\tilde{\lambda}_2$. Explicitly, we can write $\tilde{\lambda}_2(x, \lambda_3) = \tilde{\lambda}_2(0, \lambda_3) + \alpha(x, \lambda_3)x^2$ for a smooth function α with $\alpha(0,0) \neq 0$. For definiteness, assume $\alpha(0,0) > 0$. A negative value of α is treated similarly. Change to a new variable $\eta = x\sqrt{\alpha(x, \lambda_3)}$. Again writing x for the variable, we have obtained $\tilde{\lambda}_2(x, \lambda_3) = \tilde{\lambda}_2(0, \lambda_3) + x^2$. Now apply a local diffeomorphism in parameter space. Let

$$\phi_1(\lambda_1, \lambda_2, \lambda_3) = (\lambda_1, \lambda_2 - \tilde{\lambda}_2(0, \lambda_3), \lambda_3).$$

Then

$$\phi_1(\tilde{\lambda}_1(x, \lambda_3), \tilde{\lambda}_2(x, \lambda_3), \lambda_3) = (\tilde{\lambda}_1(x, \lambda_3), x^2, \lambda_3).$$

Write $\tilde{\lambda}_1(x, \lambda_3) = \beta(\lambda_3)x + \gamma(x, \lambda_3)x^2$. Note that $\beta(0) = 0$. One can deduce from (4.19) that

$$\beta'(0) \neq 0. \tag{4.21}$$

(Exercise 4.15 asks us to do this.) Decompose the function $x \mapsto \gamma(x, \lambda_3)$ in its even part $\frac{1}{2}(\gamma(x, \lambda_3) + \gamma(-x, \lambda_3))$ and odd part $\frac{1}{2}(\gamma(x, \lambda_3) - \gamma(-x, \lambda_3))$, and write

$$\gamma(x, \lambda_3) = \gamma_1(x^2, \lambda_3) + \gamma_2(x^2, \lambda_3)x.$$

Here $x \mapsto \gamma_1(x^2, \lambda_3)$ is even in x and $x \mapsto x\gamma_2(x^2, \lambda_3)$ is odd in x [**416**] (see also [**242, 255**]). Apply the local diffeomorphism ϕ_2 in the parameter space given by

$$\phi_2(\lambda_1, \lambda_2, \lambda_3) = (\lambda_1 - \lambda_2\gamma_1(\lambda_2, \lambda_3), \lambda_2, \beta(\lambda_3) + \lambda_2\gamma_2(\lambda_2, \lambda_3)).$$

This results in

$$\begin{aligned} &\phi_2 \circ \phi_1(\tilde{\lambda}_1(x, \lambda_3), \tilde{\lambda}_2(x, \lambda_3), \lambda_3) \\ &\quad = (\tilde{\lambda}_1(x, \lambda_3) - \gamma_1(x^2, \lambda_3)x^2, x^2, \beta(\lambda_3) + \gamma_2(x^2, \lambda_3)x^2) \\ &\quad = (\beta(\lambda_3)x + \gamma_2(x^2, \lambda_3)x^3, x^2, \beta(\lambda_3) + \gamma_2(x^2, \lambda_3)x^2). \end{aligned}$$

The image of $(x, \lambda_3) \mapsto \phi_2 \circ \phi_1(\tilde{\lambda}_1(x, \lambda_3), \tilde{\lambda}_2(x, \lambda_3), \lambda_3)$ is the Whitney umbrella. A corresponding investigation for bifurcating periodic orbits is in [**205**]. ■

4.1.2.1. *Local normal form.* As in the planar homoclinic bifurcation the proof makes use of a normal form, so that expressions for orbits near p resemble those of linear vector fields. Improving the normal form makes later estimates easier to carry out. We refer also to [**339**]. In the proof of the following lemma we use the following notation: for manifolds N_1, N_2 and $M \subset N_1 \cap N_2$, we write $N_1 \bar{\cap}_M N_2$ if $T_x N_1 = T_x N_2$ for $x \in M$.

Lemma 4.17. *Near p there exists a smooth local coordinate system $x = (x_{ss}, x_s, x_u, x_{uu})$ in which the vector field f_λ is given by a set of differential equations*

$$\begin{aligned} \dot{x}_{ss} &= A^{ss}x_{ss} + f^{ss}(x), \\ \dot{x}_s &= \mu^s x_s + f^s(x), \\ \dot{x}_u &= \mu^u x_u + f^u(x), \\ \dot{x}_{uu} &= A^{uu}x_{uu} + f^{uu}(x), \end{aligned}$$

where $A^{ss}, \mu^s, \mu^u, A^{uu}$ depend smoothly on λ and where $f^{ss}(x), \dots, f^{uu}(x)$ depend smoothly on (x, λ). Further, satisfy

$$\begin{aligned} f^{ss}(x) &= \mathcal{O}(|x_{ss}||x|) + \mathcal{O}(|x_s|^2), \\ f^s(x) &= \mathcal{O}(|x_s|^2|x_{u,uu}|) + \mathcal{O}(|x_{ss}|\,|x_{u,uu}|), \\ f^u(x) &= \mathcal{O}(|x_u|^2|x_{ss,s}|) + \mathcal{O}(|x_{s,ss}|\,|x_{uu}|), \\ f^{uu}(x) &= \mathcal{O}(|x_{uu}||x|) + \mathcal{O}(|x_u|^2), \end{aligned}$$

with $x_{ss,s} = (x_{ss}, x_s)$ and $x_{u,uu} = (x_u, x_{uu})$. Here x_s and x_u are one-dimensional coordinates, and x_{ss} and x_{uu} have the dimensions of E^{ss} and E^{uu}, respectively.

Proof. Take smooth coordinates $x = (x_{ss}, x_s, x_u, x_{uu})$ where the single coordinates are lying in directions in accordance with the splitting (4.17). In these coordinates we have

$$\begin{aligned} \dot{x}_{ss} &= A^{ss}x_{ss} + f^{ss}(x), \\ \dot{x}_s &= \mu^s x_s + f^s(x), \\ \dot{x}_u &= \mu^u x_u + f^u(x), \\ \dot{x}_{uu} &= A^{uu}x_{uu} + f^{uu}(x), \end{aligned}$$

where smooth the functions $f^{ss}(x), \dots, f^{uu}(x)$ are of order $\mathcal{O}(|x|^2)$. We may further take the coordinates $(x_{ss}, x_s, x_u, x_{uu})$ so that near p,

$$W^{ss,s}(p) = \{x_{u,uu} = 0\}, \tag{4.22}$$

$$W^{u,uu}(p) = \{x_{ss,s} = 0\}, \tag{4.23}$$

$$W^{ss,s,u}(p) \overline{\cap}_{W^{ss,s}(p)} \{x_{uu} = 0\}, \tag{4.24}$$

$$W^{s,u,uu}(p) \overline{\cap}_{W^{u,uu}(p)} \{x_{ss} = 0\}. \tag{4.25}$$

In particular, for $q \in W^{ss,s}(p)$ we have $T_q W^{ss,s,u}(p) = \{x_{uu} = 0\}$, and for $q \in W^{u,uu}(p)$ we have $T_q W^{s,u,uu}(p) = \{x_{ss} = 0\}$. As in the $\mathbb{R}^2$-case, the identities (4.23) and (4.22) imply $f^{ss}(0,0,x_u,x_{uu}) = 0$, $f^s(0,0,x_u,x_{uu}) = 0$ and $f^u(x_{ss},x_s,0,0) = 0$, $f^{uu}(x_{ss},x_s,0,0) = 0$. It follows that f^{ss}, f^s are $\mathcal{O}(|x_{ss,s}||x|)$ and that f^u, f^{uu} are $\mathcal{O}(|x_{u,uu}||x|)$.

In the following we discuss the consequences of (4.25) and (4.24), as example for (4.25). Consider for fixed $\hat{x}_{u,uu}$ the intersection

$$W^{s,u,uu}(p) \cap \{x_{u,uu} = \hat{x}_{u,uu}\} =: \hat{W}^{s,u,uu}(p).$$

There is a function $\hat{g}^{ss}$ such that

$$\hat{W}^{s,u,uu}(p) = \{(\hat{g}^{ss}(x_s), x^s)\}, \quad \hat{g}^{ss}(x_s) = \mathcal{O}(x_s^2).$$

Now consider f^{ss} along $\hat{W}^{s,u,uu}(p)$: $f^{ss}(\hat{g}^{ss}(x_s), x_s, \hat{x}_{u,uu})$. Now there is a function $\tilde{g}$ such that

$$\frac{d}{dx_s} f^{ss}(\hat{g}^{ss}(x_s), x_s, \hat{x}_{u,uu}) = \tilde{g}(\hat{x}_{u,uu}) + \mathcal{O}(x_s).$$

Hence

$$\frac{d}{dx_s} f^{ss}(\hat{g}^{ss}(x_s), x_s, \hat{x}_{u,uu})|_{x_s=0} = \tilde{g}(\hat{x}_{u,uu}). \tag{4.26}$$

On the other hand

$$\begin{aligned}\left(f^{ss}(\hat{g}^{ss}(x_s), x_s, \hat{x}_{u,uu}), f^{s}(\hat{g}^{ss}(x_s), x_s, \hat{x}_{u,uu})\right)& \\ \in T_{(\hat{g}^{ss}(x_s),x_s)}\hat{W}^{s,u,uu}(p) &= \mathbb{R}((g^{ss})'(x_s), 1).\end{aligned} \tag{4.27}$$

Note that $(g^{ss})'(x_s) = \mathcal{O}(x_s)$. Since $f^s = \mathcal{O}(|x_{ss,s}||x|)$ we have

$$f^s(\hat{g}^{ss}(x_s), x_s, \hat{x}_{u,uu}) = \mathcal{O}(x_s).$$

Together with (4.27) this implies $f^{ss}(\hat{g}^{ss}(x_s), x_s, \hat{x}_{u,uu}) = \mathcal{O}(|x_s|^2)$. With (4.26) we get $\tilde{g}(\hat{x}_{u,uu}) = 0$. This finally yields $f^{ss} = \mathcal{O}(|x_{ss}||x|) + \mathcal{O}(|x_s|^2)$. Applying the same type of argument on (4.24) yields $f^{uu} = \mathcal{O}(|x_{uu}||x|) + \mathcal{O}(|x_u|^2)$. Of course still $f^s = \mathcal{O}(|x_{ss,s}||x|)$ and $f^u = \mathcal{O}(|x_{u,uu}||x|)$. To summarize, after these initial coordinate changes, we have obtained

$$f^{ss}(x) = \mathcal{O}(|x_{ss}||x|) + \mathcal{O}(|x_s|^2), \tag{4.28}$$

$$f^{s}(x) = \mathcal{O}(|x_{ss,s}||x|), \tag{4.29}$$

$$f^{u}(x) = \mathcal{O}(|x_{u,uu}||x|), \tag{4.30}$$

$$f^{uu}(x) = \mathcal{O}(|x_{uu}||x|) + \mathcal{O}(|x_u|^2). \tag{4.31}$$

The remaining coordinate changes to improve expressions for $\dot{x}_s$ and $\dot{x}_u$ follow the reasoning in the proof of the planar case. First we accomplish corresponding coordinate changes for x_s leaving the other coordinates, in particular x_u, unaltered. Then similar coordinate changes can be performed on x_u. To start with, we perform a polynomial coordinate change

$$u_s = x_s + (a_u x_u + a_{uu} x_{uu}) x_s \quad \text{and} \quad u_{ss} = x_{ss},\ u_u = x_u,\ u_{uu} = x_{uu},$$

which removes quadratic terms $x_s x_{u,uu}$ from the differential equations for x_s. Note that $a_{uu} x_{uu}$ represents a scalar product of (possibly) vector-valued quantities. The argumentation is similar to the $\mathbb{R}^2$-case. Regarding the $x_s x_u$-term, we again exploit that $\mu^u \neq 0$, while for the term $x_s x_{uu}$ we exploit that A^{uu} is invertible.

After renaming u to x the function f^s can be written in the form

$$f^s(x) = \mathcal{O}(|x_{ss}|\,|x_{u,uu}|) + \mathcal{O}(|x_{ss,s}|^2) + \mathcal{O}(|x|^3).$$

Next we consider a change of coordinates of the form

$$u_s = x_s + q(x_{u,uu}) x_s \quad \text{and} \quad u_{ss} = x_{ss},\ u_u = x_u,\ u_{uu} = x_{uu}, \tag{4.32}$$

where $q(x_{u,uu}) = \mathcal{O}(|x_{u,uu}|^2)$, with the goal to remove terms of the form $p(x_{u,uu})x_s$ from the representation of f^s.

From (4.32) we conclude

$$x_s = u_s\left(\frac{1}{1+q_s(u_{u,uu})}\right) = u_s\left(1 - q_s(u_{u,uu}) + \mathcal{O}\big(q_s(u_{u,uu})^2\big)\right)$$

and further

$$\begin{aligned}\dot{u}_s &= \dot{x}_s + \big(D_{x_u}q(x_{u,uu})\dot{x}_u + D_{x_{uu}}q(x_{u,uu})\dot{x}_{uu}\big)x_s + q(x_{u,uu})\dot{x}_s\\ &= \mu^s x_s + f^s(x) + \big(D_{x_u}q(x_{u,uu})\dot{x}_u + D_{x_{uu}}q(x_{u,uu})\dot{x}_{uu}\big)x_s\\ &\quad + q(x_{u,uu})(\mu^s x_s + f^s(x))\\ &= \mu^s x_s + \mathcal{O}(|x_{ss}|\,|x_{u,uu}|) + \mathcal{O}(|x_{ss,s}|^2) + \mathcal{O}(|x|^3)\\ &\quad + \big(D_{x_u}q(x_{u,uu})\dot{x}_u + D_{x_{uu}}q(x_{u,uu})\dot{x}_{uu}\big)x_s\\ &\quad + q(x_{u,uu})\big(\mu^s x_s + \mathcal{O}(|x_{ss}|\,|x_{u,uu}|) + \mathcal{O}(|x_{ss,s}|^2) + \mathcal{O}(|x|^3)\big).\end{aligned}$$

This allows a representation

$$\dot{u}_s = \mu^s u_s + Q_s(u_{ss,s}, u_{u,uu})u_s + Q_{ss}(u_{ss}, u_{u,uu})u_{ss},$$

where

$$Q_s(u_{ss,s}, u_{u,uu}) = \big(D_{u_u}q(u_{u,uu})\dot{u}_u + D_{u_{uu}}q(u_{u,uu})\dot{u}_{uu}\big)\,u_s + \mathcal{O}(u_s) + \mathcal{O}(q_s)$$

and

$$Q_{ss}(u_{ss}, u_{u,uu}) = \mathcal{O}(|(u_{ss}, u_{u,uu})|).$$

Together this yields the set of differential equations

$$\begin{aligned}\dot{u}_{ss} &= A^{ss}u_{ss} + f^{ss}(u),\\ \dot{u}_s &= \mu^s u_s + Q_s(u_{ss,s}, u_{u,uu})u_s + Q_{ss}(u_{ss}, u_{u,uu})u_{ss}\\ &= \mu^s u_s + f^s(u),\\ \dot{u}_u &= \mu^u u_u + f^u(u),\\ \dot{u}_{uu} &= A^{uu}u_{uu} + f^{uu}(u).\end{aligned}$$

Note that here f^{ss}, f^s, f^u, and f^{uu} denote the transformed vector field. However, the properties stated in (4.28), (4.30), and (4.31) are transferred to the current f^{ss}, f^u, and f^{uu}.

So, if $Q_s(0, u_{u,uu}) = 0$, then f^s has a representation

$$f^s(u) = \mathcal{O}(|u_s|^2) + \mathcal{O}(|u_s|^2|u_{u,uu}|) + \mathcal{O}(|(u_{ss}, u_{u,uu})|\,|u_{ss}|). \tag{4.33}$$

Note that the term $\mathcal{O}(|(u_{ss}, u_{u,uu})|\,|u_{ss}|)$ does not depend on u_s at all.

From the above we find that $Q_s(0, u_{u,uu})$ allows a representation

$$Q_s(0, u_{u,uu}) = D_{u_u}q_s(u)\dot{u}_u + D_{u_{uu}}q_s(u)\dot{u}_{uu} + \hat{Q}_s(q_s(u_{u,uu}), u_{u,uu}),$$

where $\hat{Q}_s(q_s(u_{u,uu}), u_{u,uu})$ is of order $\mathcal{O}(|(q_s(u_{u,uu}), u_{u,uu})|^2)$.

Now, similar to the $\mathbb{R}^2$-case, consider the differential equation

$$\begin{aligned}\dot{w}_s &= -\hat{Q}_s(w_s, u_{u,uu}),\\ \dot{u}_u &= \mu^u u_u + f^u(0, u_{u,uu}),\\ \dot{u}_{uu} &= A^{uu} u_{uu} + f^{uu}(0, u_{u,uu}).\end{aligned}$$

The two-dimensional unstable manifold $\hat{W}^{u,uu}$ of equilibrium $(0,0)$ can be written by means of a function $\hat{q}_s$ as

$$\hat{W}^{u,uu} = \{(\hat{q}_s(u_{u,uu}), u_{u,uu})\}.$$

Then along an orbit within the unstable manifold, which means along a curve

$$\{(w_s(t) = \hat{q}_s(u_{u,uu}(t)), u_{u,uu}(t))\},$$

we have

$$-\hat{Q}_s(\hat{q}_s(u_{u,uu}(t)), u_{u,uu}(t)) = \left(\hat{q}_s(u_{u,uu}(t))\right)^{\cdot} = \hat{q}_s'(u_{u,uu}(t))\dot{u}_{u,uu}(t).$$

Hence

$$-\hat{Q}_s(\hat{q}_s(u_{u,uu}(t)), u_{u,uu}(t)) = D_{u_u}\hat{q}_s(u_{u,uu})\dot{u}_u + D_{u_{uu}}\hat{q}_s(u_{u,uu})\dot{u}_{uu}.$$

So, for $q = \hat{q}$ we have $Q_s(0, u_{u,uu}) = 0$, and therefore f^s allows a representation (4.33).

Finally we remove the $\mathcal{O}(|u_s|^2)$-term in the representation (4.33) of f^s. We rename the u variables to x variables. We show that we may take the coordinates so that the equation for x_s inside the stable manifold is linear. This amounts to linearizing the strong stable foliation inside the stable manifold and then linearizing the resulting differential equation for x_s. More precisely, let $\mathcal{F}^{ss}(x_s)$ be the strong stable leaf within $W^{ss,s}(p)$ allocated to x_s. There is a transformation, so that for the transformed leaves (which we again denote by $\mathcal{F}^{ss}(x_s)$) the following holds true:

$$\mathcal{F}^{ss}(x_s) = x_s + E^{ss},$$

which means that all leaves are parallel to the strong stable subspace. Now, let $\{\varphi^t_{ss,s}\}$ be the corresponding (transformed) flow on the stable manifold. Write $\varphi^t_{ss,s} = (\varphi^t_{ss}, \varphi^t_s)$. Then $\varphi^t_{ss,s}(x_s + E^{ss}) = x_s(t) + E^{ss}$, where $x_s(0) = x_s$, or in other words,

$$\frac{\partial}{\partial x_{ss}}\varphi^t_{ss}(x_{ss}, x_s) \equiv 0,$$

for all x_{ss}, x_s, t. Hence

$$\frac{\partial}{\partial x_{ss}}\frac{\partial}{\partial t}\varphi^t_{ss}(x_{ss}, x_s)|_{t=0} = \frac{\partial}{\partial t}\frac{\partial}{\partial x_{ss}}\varphi^t_{ss}(x_{ss}, x_s)|_{t=0} = 0.$$

Because of

$$\frac{\partial}{\partial t}\varphi^t_{ss}(x_{ss}, x_s)|_{t=0} = \mu^s x_s + f^s(x_{ss}, x_s, 0),$$

we find that $f^s(x_{ss}, x_s, 0)$ does not depend on x_{ss}. So, because of (4.33), we find that

$$f^s(x) = \mathcal{O}(|x_s|^2) + \mathcal{O}(|x_s|^2|x_{u,uu}|) + \mathcal{O}(|x_{ss}||x_{u,uu}|).$$

Write $f^s(x_{ss}, x_s, 0) = \hat{f}^s(x_s)$. Hence inside the stable manifold the x_s-differential equation reads

$$\dot{x}_s = \mu^s x_s + \hat{f}^s(x_s).$$

By Theorem B.27 we may locally linearize this differential equation; compare also the corresponding discussion within the proof of Lemma 4.6. It follows that $\hat{f}^s(x_s) = f^s(x_{ss}, x_s, 0) = 0$, which proves the statement regarding f^s.

As all the performed coordinate changes left x_u unaltered, similar coordinate changes for f^u can be carried out. □

4.1.2.2. *Splitting function.* We comment upon the generic unfolding condition. In the planar case we introduced orbits h^s_λ and h^u_λ in the stable and unstable manifolds of p and looked at the difference $h^u_\lambda(0) - h^s_\lambda(0)$. In the higher-dimensional case, where stable and unstable manifolds may also be of higher dimension, one picks specific solutions to the measure distance between stable and unstable manifolds of p. The definition of orbit pieces h^s_λ and h^u_λ is adjusted as follows. Let Σ be a codimension-1 cross section through $h(0)$ and perpendicular to $f_0(h(0))$ at $h(0)$:

$$\Sigma = h(0) + \{f(h(0), 0)\}^\perp. \tag{4.34}$$

Define also

$$Z = \left(T_{h(0)}W^{ss,s}(p) + T_{h(0)}W^{u,uu}(p)\right)^\perp,$$

which is a one-dimensional subspace of Σ (using assumption (ii) of Theorem 4.14, stating that the homoclinic orbit is nondegenerate).

Lemma 4.18. *For each λ close to 0 there are unique pairs $(h^s_\lambda(\cdot), h^u_\lambda(\cdot))$ of orbits of (4.18) such that*

(i) *$h^{s/u}_\lambda(0)$ depend smoothly on λ and $h^{s/u}_0(0) = h(0)$,*
(ii) *$h^s_\lambda(0) \in \Sigma \cap W^{ss,s}(p, \lambda)$, $\quad h^u_\lambda(0) \in \Sigma \cap W^{u,uu}(p, \lambda)$,*
(iii) *$|h^s_\lambda(t) - h(t)|$ small $\forall t \in \mathbb{R}^+$ and $|h^u_\lambda(t) - h(t)|$ small $\forall t \in \mathbb{R}^-$,*
(iv) *$h^s_\lambda(0) - h^u_\lambda(0) \in Z$.*

Proof. As a consequence of assumption (ii) of Theorem 4.14, stating that the homoclinic orbit is nondegenerate, the sets $W^{u,uu}(p, \lambda) \cap \Sigma$ and

$$\bigcup_{x \in W^s(p,\lambda)} (x + Z) \cap \Sigma$$

intersect, for sufficiently small $|\lambda|$, transversely inside Σ. Observe that the intersection consists of a single point. This point defines $h^u_\lambda(0)$. The point $h^s_\lambda(0)$

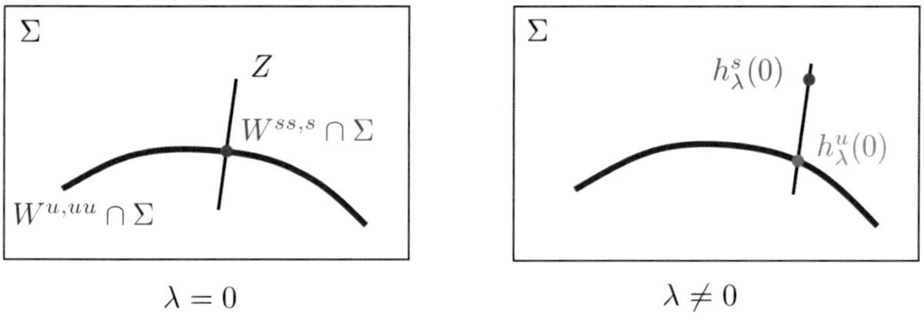

Figure 4.12. The starting points of the orbits h^s_λ and h^u_λ. The difference $h^s_\lambda(0) - h^u_\lambda(0)$ is parallel to Z.

is given as $\left(h^u_\lambda(0) + Z\right) \cap W^{ss,s}(p,\lambda)$; see Figure 4.12 for visualization in $\mathbb{R}^3$ or $\dim \Sigma = 2$. □

As in the planar homoclinic case, for each $\eta_0 \in Z$ there is a unique bounded solution η to the initial value problem

$$\begin{aligned} \dot{x}(t) &= -(Df_0(h(t)))^T x(t), \\ x(0) &= \eta_0. \end{aligned} \tag{4.35}$$

This solution $\eta(t)$ is perpendicular to both $W^{ss,s}(p)$ and $W^{u,uu}(p)$ along the homoclinic orbit $h(t)$. This is recognized by observing that for a solution ξ of the first variation equation $\dot{x}(t) = Df_0(h(t))x(t)$,

$$\frac{d}{dt}\langle \xi(t), \eta(t) \rangle = 0.$$

As before in (4.6), we let

$$d(\lambda) = h^u_\lambda(0) - h^s_\lambda(0).$$

Lemma 4.19. *Let η be the solution of the initial value problem* (4.35). *Then*

$$\langle \eta(0), d(\lambda) \rangle = \lambda \int_{-\infty}^{\infty} \langle \eta(t), D_\lambda f(h(t), 0) \rangle \, dt + \mathcal{O}(\lambda^2).$$

Proof. The proof follows the reasoning of the planar case in Lemma 4.7 and is left to the reader (Exercise 4.16). □

4.1.2.3. *Local cross coordinates.* We start with an existence result on orbit pieces near p with, instead of initial conditions, data involving coordinates at the beginning and end points and the transition time. This is called the Shilnikov problem, and is a method developed by Leonid Shilnikov in his homoclinic bifurcation studies [**90, 92**]. Following the result, we will consider orbit pieces that start and end in given cross sections, and we will compute asymptotic expansions for such orbit pieces.

Lemma 4.20. *Take local coordinates near p from Lemma 4.17. Then there is an $R > 0$ such that for sufficiently large τ and $|x^0_{ss,s}| < R/2$, $|x^\tau_{u,uu}| < R/2$, there is a unique orbit $x(t)$ with $x_{ss,s}(0) = x^0_{ss,s}$ and $x_{u,uu}(\tau) = x^\tau_{u,uu}$.*

Proof. Similar to the $\mathbb{R}^2$-case, we find that on a compact neighborhood of the origin there is $K > 0$ so that

$$|f^{ss}(x)| \leq K\big(|x_{ss}||x| + x_s^2\big), \tag{4.36}$$

$$|f^{s}(x)| \leq K\big(|x_s|^2|x_{u,uu}| + |x_{ss}|\,|x_{u,uu}|\big), \tag{4.37}$$

$$|f^{u}(x)| \leq K\big(|x_u|^2|x_{ss,s}| + |x_{s,ss}|\,|x_{uu}|\big), \tag{4.38}$$

$$|f^{uu}(x)| \leq K\big(x_u^2 + |x_{uu}||x|\big). \tag{4.39}$$

By the variation of constants formula, an orbit $x(t)$ with boundary conditions

$$x_{ss,s}(0) = x^0_{ss,s},$$
$$x_{u,uu}(\tau) = x^\tau_{u,uu}$$

satisfies

$$x_{ss}(t) = e^{A^{ss}t}x^0_{ss} + \int_0^t e^{A^{ss}(t-s)}f^{ss}(x(s))\,ds, \tag{4.40}$$

$$x_{s}(t) = e^{\mu^{s}t}x^0_{s} + \int_0^t e^{\mu^{s}(t-s)}f^{s}(x(s))\,ds, \tag{4.41}$$

$$x_{u}(t) = e^{\mu^{u}(t-\tau)}x^\tau_{u} - \int_t^\tau e^{\mu^{u}(t-s)}f^{u}(x(s))\,ds, \tag{4.42}$$

$$x_{uu}(t) = e^{A^{uu}(t-\tau)}x^\tau_{uu} - \int_t^\tau e^{A^{uu}(t-s)}f^{uu}(x(s))\,ds. \tag{4.43}$$

Let $\omega > 0$ be small and consider the space $\mathcal{B}_\tau$ of continuous functions $x(t) = (x_{ss,s}(t), x_{u,uu}(t))$ that are defined on $[0, \tau]$, equipped with the norm

$$|x|_\tau = \max\{|x_{ss}|_\tau, |x_s|_\tau, |x_u|_\tau, |x_{uu}|_\tau\},$$

where

$$|x_{ss}|_\tau = \sup_{0\leq t\leq\tau} |x_{ss}(t)|\,e^{-(\mu^s-\omega)t}, \qquad |x_{s}|_\tau = \sup_{0\leq t\leq\tau} |x_{s}(t)|\,e^{-\mu^s t},$$

$$|x_{u}|_\tau = \sup_{0\leq t\leq\tau} |x_{u}(t)|\,e^{-\mu^u (t-\tau)}, \qquad |x_{uu}|_\tau = \sup_{0\leq t\leq\tau} |x_{uu}(t)|\,e^{-(\mu^u+\omega)(t-\tau)}.$$

For given parameters $x^0_{ss,s}$, $x^\tau_{u,uu}$ and τ, the right-hand side of (4.40)–(4.43) defines a map $\Gamma = \Gamma_{(\tau, x^0_{ss,s}, x^\tau_{u,uu})}$ on $\mathcal{B}_\tau$. Write

$$B_{\mathcal{B}_\tau}(R) = \big\{x = (x_{ss,s}, x_{u,uu}) \in \mathcal{B}_\tau;\ |x|_\tau \leq R\big\}$$

for the closed ball centered at 0 with radius R in $\mathcal{B}_\tau$. We claim that under the assumptions of the lemma there is an R such that $\Gamma_{(\tau, x^0_{ss,s}, x^\tau_{u,uu})}$ is a contractive map on $B_{\mathcal{B}_\tau}(R)$ into itself. Then the lemma follows from the Banach fixed point theorem; see Appendix A.2.

In what follows we drop the parameter in the notation of Γ. We show that there exist $R > 0$ and $0 < \lambda < 1$, so that

(i) $|\Gamma(x^1) - \Gamma(x^2)| \leq \lambda |x^1 - x^2|$, for $x^1, x^2 \in B_{\mathcal{B}_\tau}(R)$,

(ii) $\Gamma\big(B_{\mathcal{B}_\tau}(R)\big) \subset B_{\mathcal{B}_\tau}(R)$.

First we note that $x \in B_{\mathcal{B}_\tau}(R)$ means

$$\begin{aligned}
|x_{ss}(t)| &\leq Re^{(\mu^s - \omega)t},\\
|x_s(t)| &\leq Re^{\mu^s t},\\
|x_u(t)| &\leq Re^{\mu^u (t-\tau)},\\
|x_{uu}(t)| &\leq Re^{(\mu^u + \omega)(t-\tau)}.
\end{aligned}$$

Further, according to the assumptions of the lemma, we have

$$|x_{ss}(0)|,\ |x_s(0)|,\ |x_u(\tau)|,\ |x_{uu}(\tau)| \leq R/2.$$

We proceed as follows. First we show that there is an $\hat{R}$ for which item (i) holds true. Afterwards we show that there is an $R \leq \hat{R}$ for which item (ii) also holds true. We start with checking item (i). Take ω small enough so that $\lambda^{ss} < \mu^s - 2\omega$. We may assume that $|e^{A^{ss}t}| \leq e^{(\mu^s - 2\omega)t}$. Let $x^1, x^2 \in B_{\mathcal{B}_\tau}(\hat{R})$. This implies the following for the strong stable coordinate of $\Gamma = \Gamma_{(x^0_{ss,s}, x^\tau_{u,uu}, \tau)}$,

$$|\Gamma_{ss}(x^1(t)) - \Gamma_{ss}(x^2(t))| \leq \int_0^t e^{(\mu^s - 2\omega)(t-s)} |f^{ss}(x^1(s)) - f^{ss}(x^2(s))|\, ds.$$

Further, choose $\tilde{R} > 0$ and let $B_{\mathbb{R}^n}(\tilde{R})$ be the closed ball in $\mathbb{R}^n$ centered at 0 with radius $\tilde{R}$. Define

$$D_i = \max_{x \in B_{\mathbb{R}^n}(\tilde{R})} |D_{x_i} f^{ss}(x)|,$$

where $i = ss, s, u, uu$. Invoking the mean value theorem, we find

$$
\begin{aligned}
&|\Gamma_{ss}(x^1(t)) - \Gamma_{ss}(x^2(t))| \\
&\quad \le \int_0^t e^{(\mu^s-2\omega)(t-s)}\Big[D_{ss}|x^1_{ss}(s) - x^2_{ss}(s)| + D_s|x^1_s(s) - x^2_s(s)| \\
&\qquad\qquad + D_u|x^1_u(s) - x^2_u(s)| + D_{uu}|x^1_{uu}(s) - x^2_{uu}(s)|\Big]\, ds \\
&\quad \le \int_0^t e^{(\mu^s-2\omega)(t-s)}\Big[D_{ss}|x^1_{ss} - x^2_{ss}|_\tau\, e^{(\mu^s-\omega)s} + D_s|x^1_s - x^2_s|_\tau\, e^{\mu^s s} \\
&\qquad\qquad + D_u|x^1_u - x^2_u|_\tau\, e^{\mu^u(s-\tau)} + D_{uu}|x^1_{uu} - x^2_{uu}|_\tau\, e^{(\mu^u+\omega)(s-\tau)}\Big]\, ds \\
&\quad \le \int_0^t e^{(\mu^s-2\omega)(t-s)}\Big[D_{ss}\, e^{(\mu^s-\omega)s} + D_s\, e^{\mu^s s} \\
&\qquad\qquad + D_u\, e^{\mu^u(s-\tau)} + D_{uu}\, e^{(\mu^u+\omega)(s-\tau)}\Big]\, ds\, |x^1 - x^2|_\tau.
\end{aligned}
$$

The following structure of f^{ss} results from Lemma 4.17:

$$
f^{ss}(x) = \big(B_{11}(x_{ss}, x_{ss}) + B_{12}(x_{ss}, x_{s,u,uu})\big) f_1^{ss}(x) + B_2(x_{ss}, x_{ss}) f_2^{ss}(x),
$$

where B_{11}, B_{12}, and B_2 are corresponding bilinear operators. Exploiting this structure, we find for $\hat{R} < \tilde{R}$ and with an appropriate constant $M > 0$ which does not depend on τ (but may change from line to line in the following),

$$
\begin{aligned}
&|\Gamma_{ss}(x^1(t)) - \Gamma_{ss}(x^2(t))| \\
&\quad \le M\hat{R} \int_0^t e^{(\mu^s-2\omega)(t-s)}\Big[\big(e^{\mu^s s} + e^{\mu^u(s-\tau)}\big) e^{(\mu^s-\omega)s} + \big(e^{(\mu^s-\omega)s} + e^{\mu^s s}\big) e^{\mu^s s} \\
&\qquad\qquad + \big(e^{(\mu^s-\omega)s} + e^{2\mu^s s}\big)\big(e^{\mu^u(s-\tau)} + e^{(\mu^u+\omega)(s-\tau)}\big)\Big]\, ds\, |x^1 - x^2|_\tau \\
&\quad \le M\hat{R}\, e^{(\mu^s-\omega)t} \int_0^t e^{-\omega(t-s)} e^{-(\mu^s-\omega)s}\Big[\big(e^{\mu^s s} + e^{\mu^u(s-\tau)}\big) e^{(\mu^s-\omega)s} \\
&\qquad\qquad + \big(e^{(\mu^s-\omega)s} + e^{\mu^s s}\big) e^{\mu^s s} \\
&\qquad\qquad + \big(e^{(\mu^s-\omega)s} + e^{2\mu^s s}\big)\big(e^{\mu^u(s-\tau)} + e^{(\mu^u+\omega)(s-\tau)}\big)\Big]\, ds\, |x^1 - x^2|_\tau \\
&\quad \le M\hat{R}\, e^{(\mu^s-\omega)t} \int_0^t e^{-\omega(t-s)}\Big[\big(e^{\mu^s s} + e^{\mu^u(s-\tau)}\big) + \big(e^{\mu^s s} + e^{(\mu^s+\omega)s}\big) \\
&\qquad\qquad + \big(1 + e^{(\mu^s+\omega)s}\big)\big(e^{\mu^u(s-\tau)} + e^{(\mu^u+\omega)(s-\tau)}\big)\Big]\, ds\, |x^1 - x^2|_\tau.
\end{aligned}
$$

Note that ω can be chosen small enough that $\mu^s + \omega < 0$. So the integral term in the latter inequality can be estimated by a constant I which does not depend on t or τ, respectively. This yields

$$\begin{aligned}|\Gamma_{ss}(x^1) - \Gamma_{ss}(x^2)|_\tau &= \sup_{t\in[0,\tau]} |\Gamma_{ss}(x^1(t)) - \Gamma_{ss}(x^2(t))|\, e^{-(\mu^s-\omega)t} \\ &\leq M\hat{R}I\,|x^1 - x^2|_\tau.\end{aligned}$$

Finally we can choose $\hat{R}$ small enough that $M\hat{R}I < 1$. This proves the contractivity of the strong stable coordinate of Γ. The other coordinates of Γ can be handled in a similar way.

Next we check item (ii). Consider first the strong stable coordinate x_{ss}. Now in accordance with (4.40) and (4.36) we find

$$\begin{aligned}&|\Gamma_{ss}(x)(t)| \\ &\leq e^{(\mu^s-2\omega)t}|x^0_{ss}| + \int_0^t e^{(\mu^s-2\omega)(t-s)}|f^{ss}(x(s))|\,ds \\ &\leq e^{(\mu^s-2\omega)t}R/2 + \int_0^t e^{(\mu^s-2\omega)(t-s)}K\Big(|x_{ss}(s)|^2 + |x_{ss}(s)||x_s(s)| \\ &\qquad + |x_{ss}(s)||x_u(s)| + |x_{ss}(s)||x_{uu}(s)| + |x_s(s)|^2\Big)\,ds \\ &\leq e^{(\mu^s-2\omega)t}R/2 \\ &\quad + \int_0^t e^{(\mu^s-2\omega)(t-s)}2KR^2\big(e^{(\mu^s-\omega)s}e^{\mu^s s} + e^{(\mu^s-\omega)s}e^{\mu^u(s-\tau)} + e^{2\mu^s s}\big)\,ds \\ &\leq e^{(\mu^s-\omega)t}R\Big[1/2e^{-\omega t} \\ &\quad + 2KR\int_0^t \big(e^{-\omega t}e^{(\mu^s+\omega)s} + e^{\omega(s-t)}e^{\mu^u(s-\tau)} + e^{-\omega t}e^{(\mu^s+2\omega)s}\big)\,ds\Big] \\ &\leq e^{(\mu^s-\omega)t}R\Big[1/2 + 2KRI\Big],\end{aligned}$$

where I represents an estimate of the integral term that does not depend on t and also does not depend on τ.

Hence

$$|\Gamma_{ss}(x)(t)|e^{-(\mu^s-\omega)t} \leq R \quad\Leftrightarrow\quad \big[1/2 + 2KRI\big] \leq 1 \quad\Leftrightarrow\quad R \leq 1/(4KI).$$

Now choose

$$R \leq \min\{\hat{R},\ 1/(4KI)\}$$

to prove item (ii) for the strong stable coordinate of the Γ-image. Corresponding estimates for the other coordinates are obtained similarly. □

Remark 4.21. Recall that $\Gamma = \Gamma_{(\tau, x^0_{ss,s}, x^\tau_{u,uu})}$. The map Γ depends differentiably on these parameters. Applying the uniform contraction theorem, Theorem A.16, we find that also the fixed point of Γ depends differentiably on these parameters. By considering formulas for the derivatives, one obtains exponential expansions not just for orbits, but also for their derivatives: there are positive constants C_k, $k \geq 0$, so that

$$|D^k_{\tau,x^0_{ss,s},x^\tau_{u,uu}} x_{ss}(t)| \leq C_k e^{(\mu^s-\omega)t},$$

$$|D^k_{\tau,x^0_{ss,s},x^\tau_{u,uu}} x_s(t)| \leq C_k e^{\mu^s t},$$

$$|D^k_{\tau,x^0_{ss,s},x^\tau_{u,uu}} x_u(t)| \leq C_k e^{\mu^u(t-\tau)},$$

$$|D^k_{\tau,x^0_{ss,s},x^\tau_{u,uu}} x_{uu}(t)| \leq C_k e^{(\mu^u+\omega)(t-\tau)}. \tag{4.44}$$

The solutions also depend smoothly on the parameter λ. ■

Take local coordinates near p from Lemma 4.17, and let R be in accordance with Lemma 4.20. Let

$$\Sigma_{in} \subset \{x_s = \sigma\}, \quad \Sigma_{out} \subset \{x_u = \sigma\},$$

with $\sigma < R/2$, be cross sections close to p, which we assume to intersect the homoclinic orbit. By a rescaling, we may assume $\sigma = 1$. Write $(x^{in}_{ss}, x^{in}_u, x^{in}_{uu})$ for the coordinate system on Σ_{in} inherited from the coordinates near p. Write similarly $(x^{out}_{ss}, x^{out}_s, x^{out}_{uu})$ for coordinates on Σ_{out}. Let $P_{loc} : \Sigma_{in} \to \Sigma_{out}$ be the local transition map given by the flow of f. We may write

$$P_{loc}(x^{in}_{ss}, x^{in}_u, x^{in}_{uu}) = (x^{out}_{ss}, x^{out}_s, x^{out}_{uu}). \tag{4.45}$$

We connect this with Lemma 4.20. For sufficiently large given τ and given

$$x_{ss}(0) = x^{in}_{ss}, \quad x_s(0) = 1, \quad x_u(\tau) = 1, \quad x_{uu}(\tau) = x^{out}_{uu},$$

we find assigned

$$x^{out}_{ss} = x_{ss}(\tau), \quad x^{out}_s = x_s(\tau), \quad x^{in}_u = x_u(0) \quad x^{out}_{uu} = x_{uu}(\tau).$$

The variation of constants formula gives expressions (which are easily obtained from (4.40)–(4.43))

$$x^{out}_{ss} = e^{A^{ss}\tau} x^{in}_{ss} + \int_0^\tau e^{A^{ss}(\tau-s)} f^{ss}(x(s))\, ds, \tag{4.46}$$

$$x^{out}_s = e^{\mu^s\tau} + \int_0^\tau e^{\mu^s(\tau-s)} f^s(x(s))\, ds, \tag{4.47}$$

$$x^{in}_u = e^{-\mu^u\tau} - \int_0^\tau e^{-\mu^u s} f^u(x(s))\, ds, \tag{4.48}$$

$$x^{in}_{uu} = e^{-A^{uu}\tau} x^{out}_{uu} - \int_0^\tau e^{-A^{uu}s} f^{uu}(x(s))\, ds. \tag{4.49}$$

Note that the x in the integral terms depend on the data x_{ss}^{in}, x_{uu}^{out} and τ. For given x_u^{in}, we will solve τ as function of $(x_{ss}^{in}, x_u^{in}, x_{uu}^{out})$, and also provide asymptotic expansions for τ. This will prove the following lemma providing asymptotic formulas for the local transition map (assuming cross sections sufficiently close to p) in terms of cross coordinates.

Lemma 4.22. *In coordinates near p as in Lemma 4.17, and for σ small enough, P_{loc} satisfies the following. We can solve $(x_{ss}^{out}, x_s^{out}, x_{uu}^{in})$ as function of $(x_{ss}^{in}, x_u^{in}, x_{uu}^{out})$,*

$$\begin{aligned} x_{ss}^{out} &= S^{ss}(x_{ss}^{in}, x_u^{in}, x_{uu}^{out}), \\ x_s^{out} &= (x_u^{in})^\beta + S^s(x_{ss}^{in}, x_u^{in}, x_{uu}^{out}), \\ x_{uu}^{in} &= S^{uu}(x_{ss}^{in}, x_u^{in}, x_{uu}^{out}), \end{aligned}$$

and there exists $\omega > 0$ so that $S = (S^{ss}, S^s, S^{uu})$ satisfies

$$\begin{aligned} \left|D^k_{x_u^{in}} D^l_{x_{ss}^{out}, x_{uu}^{in}} D^m S^{ss}(x_{ss}^{in}, x_u^{in}, x_{uu}^{out})\right| &\le C_{k+l+m} |x_u^{in}|^{\beta+\omega-k}, \\ \left|D^k_{x_u^{in}} D^l_{x_{ss}^{out}, x_{uu}^{in}} D^m S^{s}(x_{ss}^{in}, x_u^{in}, x_{uu}^{out})\right| &\le C_{k+l+m} |x_u^{in}|^{\beta+\omega-k}, \\ \left|D^k_{x_u^{in}} D^l_{x_{ss}^{out}, x_{uu}^{in}} D^m S^{uu}(x_{ss}^{in}, x_u^{in}, x_{uu}^{out})\right| &\le C_{k+l+m} |x_u^{in}|^{1+\omega-k} \end{aligned}$$

for positive constants C_{k+l+m}.

Remark 4.23. Consider linear differential equations

$$\begin{aligned} \dot{x}_{ss} &= A^{ss} x_{ss}, \\ \dot{x}_s &= \mu^s x_s, \\ \dot{x}_u &= \mu^u x_u, \\ \dot{x}_{uu} &= A^{uu} x_{uu}. \end{aligned}$$

Then the local transition map in cross coordinates is given by formulas

$$\begin{aligned} x_{ss}^{out} &= \left(x_u^{in}\right)^{A^{ss}/\mu^u} x_{ss}^{in}, \\ x_s^{out} &= (x_u^{in})^\beta, \\ x_{uu}^{in} &= \left(x_u^{in}\right)^{-A^{uu}/\mu^u} x_{uu}^{out} \end{aligned}$$

(with for instance $\left(x_u^{in}\right)^{A^{ss}/\mu^u} = e^{-\frac{A^{ss}}{\mu^u} \ln(x_u^{in})}$). We see that in the local normal form from Lemma 4.17, Lemma 4.22 provides in essence the same expressions for the nonlinear differential equations, apart from higher-order terms. ■

Proof of Lemma 4.22. Assume $\sigma < R/2$. The right-hand sides of the formulas (4.46)–(4.49) define a map

$$(\tau, x_{ss}^{in}, x_{uu}^{out}) \mapsto T(\tau, x_{ss}^{in}, x_{uu}^{out})$$

with $T = (T^{ss}, T^s, T^u, T^{uu})$ in the different coordinates. So for instance

$$T^{ss}(\tau, x_{ss}^{in}, x_{uu}^{out}) = e^{A^{ss}\tau} x_{ss}^{in} + \int_0^\tau e^{A^{ss}(\tau - s)} f^{ss}(x(s))\, ds,$$

and so on. The operator T depends differentiably on $(\tau, x_{ss}^{in}, x_{uu}^{out})$ by Remark 4.21.

Write

$$r = e^{-\mu^u \tau}. \tag{4.50}$$

Thus also $\tau = \tau(r) = -\frac{1}{\mu^u} \ln r$. Rewrite (4.46)–(4.49) after changing τ to r by (4.50). We end up with equations of the form

$$\begin{aligned} x_{ss}^{out} &= \hat{T}^{ss}(r, x_{ss}^{in}, x_{uu}^{out}), \\ x_s^{out} &= \hat{T}^s(r, x_{ss}^{in}, x_{uu}^{out}), \\ x_u^{in} &= T^u(r, x_{ss}^{in}, x_{uu}^{out}), \\ x_{uu}^{in} &= T^{uu}(r, x_{ss}^{in}, x_{uu}^{out}). \end{aligned}$$

Here $\hat{T}^{ss}(r, x_{ss}^{in}, x_{uu}^{out}) = T^{ss}(\tau(r), x_{ss}^{in}, x_{uu}^{out})$ and so on. Also write

$$x_s^{out} = r^\beta + \hat{T}_I^s(r, x_{ss}^{in}, x_{uu}^{out})$$

and

$$x_u^{in} = r - \hat{T}_I^u(r, x_{ss}^{in}, x_{uu}^{out}). \tag{4.51}$$

So $\hat{T}_I^s(r, x_{ss}^{in}, x_{uu}^{out})$ is related to the integral term in (4.47) and $\hat{T}_I^u(r, x_{ss}^{in}, x_{uu}^{out})$ to the integral term in (4.48). By (4.44) in Remark 4.21 and Lemma 4.17 we find that

$$\begin{aligned} \left| \int_0^\tau e^{-\mu^u s} f^u(x(s))\, ds \right| &\le \int_0^\tau e^{-\mu^u s} C \left[e^{2\mu^u (s-\tau)} e^{\mu^s s} + e^{(\mu^u + \omega)(s-\tau)} e^{\mu^s s} \right] ds \\ &\le \tilde{C} e^{-(\mu^u + \omega)\tau}, \end{aligned}$$

for some constants $C, \tilde{C} > 0$. Consequently,

$$\hat{T}_I^u(r, x_{ss}^{in}, x_{uu}^{out}) = \mathcal{O}(r^{1+\frac{\omega}{\mu^u}})$$

as $r \to 0$. Using this, a similar estimate for $\hat{T}_I^s(r, x_{ss}^{in}, x_{uu}^{out})$, and (4.44) in Remark 4.21, we get expansions for $\hat{T}^{ss}, \hat{T}_I^s, \hat{T}_I^u, \hat{T}^{uu}$ and their derivatives,

$$\begin{aligned} \left| D^k_{x_{ss}^{in}, x_{uu}^{out}} D_r^l \hat{T}^{ss}(r, x_{ss}^{in}, x_{uu}^{out}) \right| &\le C_{k+l} r^{\beta + \frac{\omega}{\mu^u} - l}, \\ \left| D^k_{x_{ss}^{in}, x_{uu}^{out}} D_r^l \hat{T}_I^s(r, x_{ss}^{in}, x_{uu}^{out}) \right| &\le C_{k+l} r^{\beta + \frac{\omega}{\mu^u} - l}, \\ \left| D^k_{x_{ss}^{in}, x_{uu}^{out}} D_r^l \hat{T}_I^u(r, x_{ss}^{in}, x_{uu}^{out}) \right| &\le C_{k+l} r^{1 + \frac{\omega}{\mu^u} - l}, \\ \left| D^k_{x_{ss}^{in}, x_{uu}^{out}} D_r^l \hat{T}_I^{uu}(r, x_{ss}^{in}, x_{uu}^{out}) \right| &\le C_{k+l} r^{1 + \frac{\omega}{\mu^u} - l}, \end{aligned}$$

for positive constants C_{k+l}.

The estimates for $\hat{T}^u$ allow us to extend the domain of definition of $\hat{T}^u$ to a neighborhood of $r = 0$ by

$$\hat{T}^u(r, x_{ss}^{in}, x_{uu}^{out}) = \begin{cases} r - \hat{T}_I^u(-r, x_{ss}^{in}, x_{uu}^{out}), & r < 0, \\ 0, & r = 0, \\ r - \hat{T}_I^u(r, x_{ss}^{in}, x_{uu}^{out}), & r > 0. \end{cases}$$

It is clear that $\hat{T}^u(\cdot, x_{ss}^{in}, x_{uu}^{out})$ has an inverse function $\left(\hat{T}^u(\cdot, x_{ss}^{in}, x_{uu}^{out})\right)^{-1}$ in an appropriate neighborhood of $r = 0$. Hence we can solve (4.51) for

$$r = r(x_{ss}^{in}, x_u^{in}, x_{uu}^{out}) = \left(\hat{T}^u(\cdot, x_{ss}^{in}, x_{uu}^{out})\right)^{-1}(x_u^{in}),$$

and get

$$r = r(x_{ss}^{in}, x_u^{in}, x_{uu}^{out}) = x_u^{in} + o(x_u^{in}).$$

The estimates provide in fact

$$\left|D_{x_u^{in}}^k D_{x_{ss}^{in}, x_{uu}^{out}}^l \left(r(x_{ss}^{in}, x_u^{in}, x_{uu}^{out}) - x_u^{in}\right)\right| \le C_{k+l+m} |x_u^{in}|^{1+\omega-k} \tag{4.52}$$

for constants $C_{k+l+m} > 0$ (Exercise 4.17). Plugging $r = r(x_{ss}^{in}, x_u^{in}, x_{uu}^{out})$ into the remaining equations from (4.46)–(4.49), proves the lemma. □

4.1.2.4. *Analysis of the return map.* Recall from (4.34) that Σ is a cross section perpendicular to the homoclinic orbit h at $h(0)$. We will provide and then analyze expressions, in cross coordinates, for orbits of the Poincaré return map on Σ. We first discuss the existence of continuous bundles of strong stable, strong unstable, and center directions along the homoclinic orbit. For a nondegenerate homoclinic orbit this is due to the no-inclination-flip condition and no-orbit-flip condition.

Consider the vector bundles F^{ss} and $F^{ss,s,u}$ along the stable manifold $W^{ss,s}(p)$, given by

$$F_x^{ss} = T_x \mathcal{F}_x^{ss},$$
$$F^{ss,s,u} = T_x W^{ss,s,u}(p).$$

Note that $F_p^{ss} = E^{ss}$ and $F_x^{ss} \subset T_x W^{ss,s}(p)$. Likewise take vector bundles F^{uu} and $F^{s,u,uu}$ along the unstable manifold $W^{u,uu}(p)$, given by

$$F_x^{uu} = T_x \mathcal{F}_x^{uu},$$
$$F^{s,u,uu} = T_x W^{s,u,uu}(p).$$

Here $F_p^{uu} = E^{uu}$ and $F_x^{uu} \subset T_x W^{u,uu}(p)$.

Lemma 4.24. *Take the assumptions in Theorem* 4.14. *Then the bundles* F^{ss}, F^{uu}, $F^{ss,s,u}$, *and* $F^{s,u,uu}$ *are continuous along the closure of the homoclinic orbit. The intersection* $F^{s,u} = F^{ss,s,u} \cap F^{s,u,uu}$ *is a continuous bundle of planes along the homoclinic orbit.*

Proof. It is convenient to take coordinates $x = (x_{ss}, x_s, x_u, x_{uu})$ near p from Lemma 4.17. As was made clear in the proof of that lemma, for $q \in W^{ss,s}(p)$ near p we have $T_q W^{ss,s,u}(p) = \{x_{uu} = 0\}$, and for $q \in W^{u,uu}(p)$ near p we have $T_q W^{s,u,uu}(p) = \{x_{ss} = 0\}$. Consider the bundle F^{ss} along $W^{ss,s}(p)$. For $x = h(0)$ on the homoclinic orbit and for sufficiently large negative t, $\varphi^t(x)$ is in the domain of this coordinate system. Then, using the no-inclination-flip condition, $D\varphi^t(x)F^{ss}_x$ is a line spanned by a vector $v = (v_{ss}, v_s, v_u, v_{uu})$ with $v_{ss} \neq 0$. This implies that, while $\varphi^t(x) \to p$ as $t \to -\infty$, also $D\varphi^t(x)F^{ss}_x$ converges to E^{ss} as $t \to -\infty$. Thus F^{ss} forms a continuous vector bundle along the closure of h. The other vector bundles are treated similarly (Exercise 4.18). □

Note that this lemma explains that, in the three-dimensional pictures in Figure 4.10, the stable manifold forms a surface near the homoclinic orbit that is homeomorphic to either a cylinder or a Möbius band. The continuous bundles of vector spaces along the homoclinic orbit allow the construction of suitable coordinate systems on the cross section Σ.

Lemma 4.25. *Take the assumptions in Theorem* 4.14. *One can construct two coordinate systems $v = (v_{ss}, v_u, v_{uu})$ and $w = (w_{ss}, w_s, w_{uu})$ on Σ with the following properties.*

The coordinate systems are equal up to a translation by $h^u_\lambda(0) - h^s_\lambda(0) \in Z$. The first coordinate system $v = (v_{ss}, v_u, v_{uu})$ on Σ has the origin at $h^s_\lambda(0)$ and satisfies

$$W^{ss,s}(p) \cap \Sigma = \{v_{u,uu} = 0\},$$
$$W^{ss,s,u}(p) \cap \Sigma \overline{\cap}_{W^{ss,s}(p)\cap\Sigma} \{v_{uu} = 0\}.$$

The second coordinate system $w = (w_{ss}, w_s, w_{uu})$ on Σ has the origin at $h^u_\lambda(0)$ and satisfies

$$W^{u,uu}(p) \cap \Sigma = \{w_{ss,u} = 0\},$$
$$W^{s,u,uu}(p) \cap \Sigma \overline{\cap}_{W^{u,uu}(p)\cap\Sigma} \{w_{ss} = 0\}.$$

Proof. Let $\lambda = 0$. We construct the coordinate system v, and let w equal v. A change of the time parametrization near Σ makes $\mathcal{F}^{ss}_x = W^{ss,s}(p) \cap \Sigma$ for $x \in \Sigma$, as well as $\mathcal{F}^{uu}_x = W^{u,uu}(p) \cap \Sigma$ for $x \in \Sigma$. We get that F^{ss}_x and F^{uu}_x are contained in Σ for $x \in \Sigma$. We may assume that the stable and unstable manifolds in a neighborhood of $h(0)$ are flat inside Σ:

$$W^{ss,s}(p) \cap \Sigma = \{v_{u,uu} = 0\},$$
$$W^{u,uu}(p) \cap \Sigma = \{v_{ss,u} = 0\}.$$

We use the subspaces F^{ss}, $F^{s,u}$, F^{uu} to define coordinates (v_{ss}, v_s, v_{uu}) on Σ. This is done by choosing parameters on the subspaces, such as v_{ss} on F^{ss}, and then the coordinates are given by linearity. Let (v_{ss}, v_u, v_{uu}) be the same coordinates. We may assume $Z = F^{s,u} \cap \Sigma$ (to stay in line with Lemma 4.18 we merely have to choose the inner product appropriately).

Now let $\lambda \neq 0$. Here we assume coordinates v and w so that, first,

$$W^{ss,s}(p) \cap \Sigma = \{v_{u,uu} = 0\},$$
$$W^{u,uu}(p) \cap \Sigma = \{w_{ss,u} = 0\}.$$

We have bundles F^{ss}, $F^{ss,s,u}$ along h^s_λ and bundles F^{uu}, $F^{s,u,uu}$ along h^u_λ. We use these to define coordinates (v_{ss}, v_s, v_{uu}) on Σ, where the origin lies at $h^u_\lambda(0)$, and by translation coordinates (w_{ss}, w_s, w_{uu}) on Σ, where the origin lies at $h^s_\lambda(0)$. □

Let $P_\lambda : \Sigma \to \Sigma$ be the first return map given by the flow of f_λ following orbits in a small neighborhood of the closure of h. We will provide expressions in cross coordinates for orbits of P_λ. For the proof of Theorem 4.14 we solve equations for fixed points of P_λ. In the following to reduce the amount of repetitive and long formulas, we will use notation $f(x, y) = \mathcal{O}(x^\alpha)$ for functions f that depends smoothly on y and on x for $x > 0$, to mean

$$|D^k_y D^l_x f(x, y)| \leq C_{k+l} x^{\alpha - l}$$

for positive constants C_{k+l}, $k, l \geq 0$.

Proof of Theorem 4.14. Write

$$P_\lambda = P_{out} \circ P_{loc} \circ P_{in},$$

where $P_{in} : \Sigma \to \Sigma_{in}$, $P_{out} : \Sigma_{out} \to \Sigma$ and $P_{loc} : \Sigma_{in} \to \Sigma_{out}$ are transition maps defined by the flow. Note that P_{in} and P_{out} are local diffeomorphisms. Write, similar to (4.45),

$$P_{in}(v_{ss}, v_u, v_{uu}) = (x^{in}_{ss}, x^{in}_s, x^{in}_{uu}),$$
$$P_{out}(x^{out}_{ss}, x^{out}_u, x^{out}_{uu}) = (w_{ss}, w_s, w_{uu}).$$

By the choice of coordinates in Σ, Lemma 4.25, we find

$$DP_{in}(0,0,0) = \begin{pmatrix} * & ? & ? \\ 0 & * & ? \\ 0 & 0 & * \end{pmatrix},$$

where "$*$" represents invertible quantities, and

$$P_{in}(v_{ss}, v_u, v_{uu}) = DP_{in}(0,0,0) \begin{pmatrix} v_{ss} \\ v_u \\ v_{uu} \end{pmatrix} + \begin{pmatrix} \mathcal{O}(|v|^2) \\ \mathcal{O}(|v_{u,uu}||v|) \\ \mathcal{O}(|v_{uu}||x| + |v_u|^2) \end{pmatrix}.$$

By the implicit function theorem there is a map $\mathcal{S}_{in}$ (defined on a small neighborhood of $(0,0,0)$) so that

$$(x_{ss}^{in}, x_u^{in}, v_{uu}) = \mathcal{S}_{in}(v_{ss}, v_u, x_{uu}^{in})$$

and

$$D\mathcal{S}_{in}(0,0,0) = \begin{pmatrix} * & ? & ? \\ 0 & * & ? \\ 0 & 0 & * \end{pmatrix}.$$

This yields

$$\begin{pmatrix} x_{ss}^{in} \\ x_u^{in} \\ v_{uu} \end{pmatrix} = D\mathcal{S}_{in}(0,0,0) \begin{pmatrix} v_{ss} \\ v_u \\ x_{uu}^{in} \end{pmatrix} + \begin{pmatrix} \mathcal{O}(|(v_{ss}, v_u, x_{uu}^{in})|^2) \\ \mathcal{O}(|(v_u, x_{uu}^{in})||(v_{ss}, v_u, x_{uu}^{in})|) \\ \mathcal{O}(|x_{uu}^{in}||(v_{ss}, v_u, x_{uu}^{in})| + |v_u|^2) \end{pmatrix}.$$

A similar result we get for P_{out} and a related map $\mathcal{S}_{out}$.

This leads to the following systems of equations interrelating v, x^{in}, x^{out}, and w. For P_{in},

$$\begin{aligned} x_{ss}^{in} &= \mathcal{S}_{in}^{ss}(v_{ss}, v_u, x_{uu}^{in}), \\ x_u^{in} &= \mathcal{S}_{in}^{u}(v_{ss}, v_u, x_{uu}^{in}), \\ v_{uu} &= \mathcal{S}_{in}^{uu}(v_{ss}, v_u, x_{uu}^{in}). \end{aligned}$$

For P_{loc},

$$\begin{aligned} x_{ss}^{out} &= S^{ss}(x_{ss}^{in}, x_u^{in}, x_{uu}^{out}), \\ x_s^{out} &= S^{s}(x_{ss}^{in}, x_u^{in}, x_{uu}^{out}), \\ x_{uu}^{in} &= S^{uu}(x_{ss}^{in}, x_u^{in}, x_{uu}^{out}). \end{aligned}$$

For P_{out},

$$\begin{aligned} w_{ss} &= \mathcal{S}_{out}^{ss}(x_{ss}^{out}, x_s^{out}, w_{uu}), \\ w_s &= \mathcal{S}_{out}^{u}(x_{ss}^{out}, x_s^{out}, w_{uu}), \\ x_{uu}^{out} &= \mathcal{S}_{out}^{uu}(x_{ss}^{out}, x_s^{out}, w_{uu}). \end{aligned}$$

This set of equations can be solved for $(x^{in}, x^{out}, w_{ss}, w_s, v_{uu})$ as function of (v_{ss}, v_u, w_{uu}), by the implicit function theorem (see Exercise 4.19). In particular, this yields an equation

$$(w_{ss}, w_s, v_{uu}) = \mathcal{S}(v_{ss}, v_u, w_{uu}). \tag{4.53}$$

It follows from the reasoning above and from Lemma 4.22 that $\mathcal{S}$ has the following asymptotics:

$$\begin{aligned} \mathcal{S}^{ss}(v_{ss}, v_s, w_{uu}) &= \mathcal{O}(v_u^{\beta+\omega}),\\ \mathcal{S}^{s}(v_{ss}, v_s, w_{uu}) &= \varphi(\lambda)v_u^{\beta} + \mathcal{O}(v_u^{\beta+\omega}),\\ \mathcal{S}^{uu}(v_{ss}, v_s, w_{uu}) &= \mathcal{O}(v_u^{1+\omega}). \end{aligned}$$

Further, $\beta > 1$ and φ is a smooth nonzero function of λ.

Use a single coordinate system $x = (x_{ss}, x_u, x_{uu})$ on Σ—say equal to (v_{ss}, v_u, v_{uu}). For periodic orbits that intersect Σ in a single point, one must solve the fixed point equations $\mathcal{S}(x) = x$:

$$\begin{aligned} x_{ss} - \mathcal{O}(x_u^{\beta+\omega}) &= 0,\\ x_u - a(\lambda) - \varphi(\lambda)x_u^{\beta} + \mathcal{O}(x_u^{\beta+\omega}) &= 0,\\ x_{uu} - \mathcal{O}(x_u^{1+\omega}) &= 0. \end{aligned} \tag{4.54}$$

Write this as $\mathfrak{S}(x_{ss}, x_u, x_{uu}) = 0$ with $\mathfrak{S} = (\mathfrak{S}^{ss}, \mathfrak{S}^{u}, \mathfrak{S}^{u})$ and consider the subsystem

$$\begin{aligned} \mathfrak{S}^{ss}(x_{ss}, x_u, x_{uu}) &= 0,\\ \mathfrak{S}^{uu}(x_{ss}, x_u, x_{uu}) &= 0, \end{aligned} \tag{4.55}$$

consisting of the first and third equation of (4.54). Note that $\mathfrak{S}^{ss/uu}(0) = 0$ and

$$D_{(x_{ss}, x_{uu})}\left(\mathfrak{S}^{ss}(0), \mathfrak{S}^{uu}(0)\right) = \begin{pmatrix} \mathrm{id}_{\mathbb{R}^{n_{ss}}} & 0\\ 0 & \mathrm{id}_{\mathbb{R}^{n_{uu}}} \end{pmatrix}.$$

Using the implicit function theorem, (4.55) can be solved for $(x_{ss}, x_{uu})(x_u)$. For a single-round periodic orbit that intersects Σ once, this leads to a reduced bifurcation equation

$$x_u = a(\lambda) + \varphi(\lambda)x_u^{\beta} + \mathcal{O}(x_u^{\beta+\omega}).$$

The bifurcation theorem is now readily proved, noting that the absence of multiround periodic orbits (which intersect Σ multiple times) and also hyperbolicity of the periodic orbits is discussed in Section 4.1.2.5. □

Remark 4.26. For a nondegenerate homoclinic orbit, under the assumption of no-inclination-flip and no-orbit-flip conditions, one can prove the existence of a nonlocal two-dimensional homoclinic center manifold near the homoclinic orbit, in analogy to a local center manifold near an equilibrium, that contains the maximal invariant set of the flow in a neighborhood of the homoclinic orbit. Papers that develop this result are [**165**, **315**, **326**, **333**].

One can use this homoclinic center manifold reduction as a starting point to derive the bifurcation theorem in much the same way as the planar homoclinic bifurcation in Theorem 4.3. One must take into account the smoothness of the homoclinic center manifold—it is in general only continuously differentiable depending on spectral conditions at the equilibrium. Nonexistence of multiround periodic orbits can be concluded from a homoclinic center manifold reduction. ■

4.1.2.5. *Multiround periodic orbits and hyperbolicity of periodic orbits.* It remains to study hyperbolicity of the periodic orbit, and to establish the absence of multiround periodic orbits. We start with the latter. For $k \geq 1$ we speak of a k-periodic orbit if it has k intersection points with Σ. A single-round periodic orbit can thus also be referred to as a 1-periodic orbit.

Multiround periodic orbits. We take up the discussion from (4.53). Points

$$x(j) = (x_{ss}(j), x_u(j), x_{uu}(j))$$

in Σ lie on the same orbit of P_λ precisely if

$$(x_{ss}(j+1), x_u(j+1), x_{uu}(j)) - \mathcal{S}(x_{ss}(j), x_u(j), x_{uu}(j+1)) = 0 \tag{4.56}$$

for $j \in \mathbb{Z}$. These equations have asymptotic expansions

$$\begin{aligned} x_{ss}(j+1) - \mathcal{O}(x_u(j)^{\beta+\omega}) &= 0, \\ x_u(j+1) - a(\lambda) - \varphi(\lambda)x_u(j)^\beta + \mathcal{O}(x_u(j)^{\beta+\omega}) &= 0, \\ x_{uu}(j) - \mathcal{O}(x_u(j+1)^{1+\omega}) &= 0. \end{aligned} \tag{4.57}$$

Instead of writing $l^\infty(\mathbb{Z}, \mathbb{R}^k)$, we use abbreviated notation $l^\infty(\mathbb{R}^k)$ for the space of bi-infinite sequences of elements of $\mathbb{R}^k$ equipped with the supremum norm. Denote by n_{ss} and n_{uu} the dimensions of the strong stable and strong unstable directions. Then (4.56) can be considered as an equation $\mathfrak{S} = 0$, for $\mathfrak{S}$: $l^\infty(\mathbb{R}^{n_{ss}}) \times l^\infty(\mathbb{R}) \times l^\infty(\mathbb{R}^{n_{uu}}) \to l^\infty(\mathbb{R}^{n_{ss}}) \times l^\infty(\mathbb{R}) \times l^\infty(\mathbb{R}^{n_{uu}})$. Here $\mathfrak{S} = (\mathfrak{S}_i)_{i\in\mathbb{Z}}$ with

$$\mathfrak{S}_i = (x_{ss}(i+1), x_u(i+1), x_{uu}(i)) - \mathcal{S}(x_{ss}(i), x_u(i), x_{uu}(i+1)). \tag{4.58}$$

Consider the subsystem

$$\begin{aligned} \mathfrak{S}^{ss}\left((x_{ss}(j))_{j\in\mathbb{Z}}, (x_u(j))_{j\in\mathbb{Z}}, (x_{uu}(j))_{j\in\mathbb{Z}}\right) &= 0, \\ \mathfrak{S}^{uu}\left((x_{ss}(j))_{j\in\mathbb{Z}}, (x_u(j))_{j\in\mathbb{Z}}, (x_{uu}(j))_{j\in\mathbb{Z}}\right) &= 0, \end{aligned} \tag{4.59}$$

consisting of the first and third equation of (4.57). Note that $\mathfrak{S}^{ss/uu}(0) = 0$ and

$$D_{\left((x_{ss}(j))_{j\in\mathbb{Z}}, (x_{uu}(j))_{j\in\mathbb{Z}}\right)}(\mathfrak{S}^{ss}(0), \mathfrak{S}^{uu}(0)) = \begin{pmatrix} D\sigma^{ss} & 0 \\ 0 & id_{l^\infty(\mathbb{R}^{n_{uu}})} \end{pmatrix}.$$

Here σ^{ss} is the left shift on sequences in $l^\infty(\mathbb{R}^{n_{ss}})$. Using the implicit function theorem, (4.59) can be solved for

$$(x_{ss}(j), x_{uu}(j))_{j\in\mathbb{Z}}\left((x_u(i))_{i\in\mathbb{Z}}\right). \tag{4.60}$$

Plugging (4.60) into the second equation of (4.57) we arrive at

$$x_u(j+1) - a(\lambda) - \varphi x_u(j)^\beta + R\left((x_u(i))_{i\in\mathbb{Z}}\right) = 0,$$

with

$$\left|R\left((x_u(i))_{i\in\mathbb{Z}}\right)\right| \le C \sup_{i\in\mathbb{Z}} |x_u(i)|^{\beta+\omega},$$
$$\left|DR\left((x_u(i))_{i\in\mathbb{Z}}\right)\right| \le C \sup_{i\in\mathbb{Z}} |x_u(i)|^{\beta+\omega-1}.$$

Exercise 4.20 asks us to deduce the absence of multiround periodic orbits.

Hyperbolicity of periodic orbits. The above argument contains a derivation of bifurcation equations for orbits close to the homoclinic orbit. The approach we take now is to consider forward and backward orbits close to the periodic orbit, and to identify those forward and backward orbits that converge to the periodic orbit. We restrict the arguments below to forward orbits, but the corresponding statements for backward orbits follow similarly. Consider forward orbits $\left(x(j)\right)_{j\in\mathbb{N}_0}$ starting in $(x_{ss}^0, x_u^0, x_{uu}^0)$. As in the proof of Theorem 4.14, points $x(j) = (x_{ss}(j), x_u(j), x_{uu}(j))$, $j \in \mathbb{N}_0$, in Σ lie on the same forward orbit precisely if

$$(x_{ss}(j+1), x_u(j+1), x_{uu}(j)) - \mathcal{S}(x_{ss}(j), x_u(j), x_{uu}(j+1)) = 0,$$

where $j \in \mathbb{N}_0$. We write

$$l^\infty(\mathbb{R}^{n_{ss}}) = \{(x_{ss}(i))_{i\in\mathbb{N}}\},$$
$$l^\infty(\mathbb{R}) = \{(x_u(i))_{i\in\mathbb{N}}\},$$
$$l^\infty(\mathbb{R}^{n_{uu}}) = \{(x_{uu}(i))_{i\in\mathbb{N}_0}\}.$$

Similarly to how $\mathfrak{S}$ was defined in (4.58) we define

$$\mathfrak{S}^f : (\mathbb{R}^{n_{ss}} \times l^\infty(\mathbb{R}^{n_{ss}})) \times (\mathbb{R} \times l^\infty(\mathbb{R})) \times l^\infty(\mathbb{R}^{n_{uu}}) \to l^\infty(\mathbb{R}^{n_{ss}}) \times l^\infty(\mathbb{R}) \times l^\infty(\mathbb{R}^{n_{uu}}).$$

Here $\mathfrak{S}^f = \left(\mathfrak{S}_i^f\right)_{i\in\mathbb{N}_0}$ with

$$\mathfrak{S}_i^f = (x_{ss}(i), x_u(i), x_{uu}(i-1)) - \mathcal{S}\left(x_{ss}(i-1), x_u(i-1), x_{uu}(i)\right).$$

Forward orbits correspond to solutions of

$$\mathfrak{S}^f\left((x_{ss}^0, (x_{ss}(j))_{j\in\mathbb{N}}), (x_u^0, (x_u(j))_{j\in\mathbb{N}}), (x_{uu}(j))_{j\in\mathbb{N}_0}\right) = 0. \tag{4.61}$$

Let ζ_λ be the periodic orbit from Theorem 4.14 and let $x^p = \zeta_\lambda \cap \Sigma$. Write

$$x^p = \left(x_{ss}^p, x_u^p, x_{uu}^p\right).$$

Of course,

$$\mathfrak{S}^f\left((x_{ss}^p(0), (x_{ss}^p(j))_{j\in\mathbb{N}}), (x_u^p(0), (x_u^p(j))_{j\in\mathbb{N}}), (x_{uu}^p(j))_{j\in\mathbb{N}_0}\right) = 0.$$

Lemma 4.27. *Near*

$$\left((x_{ss}^p(0),(x_{ss}^p(j))_{j\in\mathbb{N}}\right),\left(x_u^p(0),(x_u^p(j))_{j\in\mathbb{N}}\right),\left(x_{uu}^p(j)\right)_{j\in\mathbb{N}_0}\right),$$

equation (4.61) can be solved for $\left((x_{ss}(j))_{j\in\mathbb{N}},(x_u(j))_{j\in\mathbb{N}},(x_{uu}(j))_{j\in\mathbb{N}_0}\right)$ *depending on* $\left(x_{ss}^0,x_u^0\right)$*. The resulting sequence* $(x(j))$*,* $x(j)=x(j)\left(x_{ss}^0,x_u^0\right)$ *tends exponentially fast to* x^p*, as* $j\to\infty$*.*

We use the following small lemma to prove the second part of Lemma 4.27.

Lemma 4.28. *Let* $(a_i^\mp)_{i\in\mathbb{N}_0}$ *be sequences of positive numbers such that for all* $j\in\mathbb{N}$*,* $a_j^-+a_j^+\le\frac{1}{2q}(a_{j-1}^-+a_{j+1}^+)$*, for some* $q>1$*. Then for any* $i\in\{0,\dots,j\}$

$$a_j^-+a_j^+\le\frac{1}{q^i}(a_{j-i}^-+a_{j+i}^+).$$

Proof. First we prove by induction in i that

$$\left(a_{j-i}^-+a_{j+i}^+\right)+\left(a_{j-i}^++a_{j+i}^-\right)\le\frac{1}{q}\left(a_{j-i-1}^-+a_{j+i+1}^+\right). \tag{4.62}$$

According to the assumption of the lemma we find for $i=0$ in (4.62)

$$2\left(a_j^-+a_j^+\right)\le\frac{1}{q}\left(a_{j-1}^-+a_{j+1}^+\right).$$

Now assume that (4.62) holds true for some i. Then, again applying the assumption of the lemma, we find

$$\begin{aligned}
&\left(a_{j-i-1}^-+a_{j+i+1}^+\right)+\left(a_{j-i-1}^++a_{j+i+1}^-\right)\\
&\quad\le\frac{1}{2q}\left(a_{j-i-2}^-+a_{j-i}^+\right)+\frac{1}{2q}\left(a_{j+i}^-+a_{j+i+2}^+\right)\\
&\quad=\frac{1}{2q}\left(a_{j-i-2}^-+a_{j+i+2}^+\right)+\frac{1}{2q}\left(a_{j+i}^-+a_{j-i}^+\right)\\
&\quad\le\frac{1}{2q}\left(a_{j-i-2}^-+a_{j+i+2}^+\right)+\frac{1}{2q^2}\left(a_{j-i-1}^-+a_{j+i+1}^+\right).
\end{aligned}$$

Therefore

$$\left(1-\frac{1}{2q^2}\right)\left(a_{j-i-1}^-+a_{j+i+1}^+\right)+\left(a_{j-i-1}^++a_{j+i+1}^-\right)\le\frac{1}{2q}\left(a_{j-i-2}^-+a_{j+i+2}^+\right),$$

and hence

$$\left(a_{j-i-1}^-+a_{j+i+1}^+\right)+\left(a_{j-i-1}^++a_{j+i+1}^-\right)\le\frac{1}{q}\left(a_{j-i-2}^-+a_{j+i+2}^+\right).$$

This proves (4.62).

Now, (4.62) yields in particular

$$\left(a_{j-i}^-+a_{j+i}^+\right)\le\frac{1}{q}\left(a_{j-i-1}^-+a_{j+i+1}^+\right). \tag{4.63}$$

For $i = 0$, this gives

$$(a_j^- + a_j^+) \le \frac{1}{q}(a_{j-1}^- + a_{j+1}^+).$$

Repeated application of (4.63) proves the lemma. □

Proof of Lemma 4.27. Observe

$$D_{\left((x_{ss}(j))_{j\in\mathbb{N}},(x_u(j))_{j\in\mathbb{N}},(x_{uu}(j))_{j\in\mathbb{N}_0}\right)}\mathfrak{S}^f(0)$$
$$= \begin{pmatrix} \mathrm{id}_{l^\infty(\mathbb{R}^{n_{ss}})} & 0 & 0 \\ 0 & \mathrm{id}_{l^\infty(\mathbb{R}^{n_u})} & 0 \\ 0 & 0 & \mathrm{id}_{l^\infty(\mathbb{R}^{n_{uu}})} \end{pmatrix}.$$

Since $\zeta_\lambda \cap \Sigma$ tends to zero as $\lambda \to 0$, we find that, for sufficiently small λ, also

$$D_{\left((x_{ss}(j))_{j\in\mathbb{N}},(x_u(j))_{j\in\mathbb{N}},(x_{uu}(j))_{j\in\mathbb{N}_0}\right)}\mathfrak{S}^f\left((x_{ss}^p)_{j\in\mathbb{N}}, (x_u^p)_{j\in\mathbb{N}}, (x_{uu}^p)_{j\in\mathbb{N}_0}\right)$$

is invertible. Now we can apply the implicit function theorem to prove the first part of the statement.

It remains to prove that $\left(x(j)(x_{ss}^0, x_u^0)\right)$ tends exponentially fast to x^p, as $j \to \infty$. In what follows we suppress the dependence on $\left(x_{ss}^0, x_u^0\right)$ from the notation. Clearly $\left(x(j)(x_{ss}^0, x_u^0)\right)$ tends exponentially fast to x^p if and only if $(\hat{x}(j))_{j\in\mathbb{N}}$ given by

$$\hat{x}(j) = (x_{ss}(j), x_u(j), x_{uu}(j-1)),$$

tends exponentially fast to x^p. Consider $\hat{x}(j) - x^p$. Since the points $x(j)$ lie on the same forward orbit, we find

$$\hat{x}(j+1) = \mathcal{S}(x_{ss}(j), x_u(j), x_{uu}(j+1)).$$

On the other hand we have

$$x^p = \mathcal{S}(x_{ss}^p, x_u^p, x_{uu}^p).$$

Therefore

$$\hat{x}(j+1) - x^p = \mathcal{S}(x_{ss}(j), x_u(j), x_{uu}(j+1)) - \mathcal{S}(x_{ss}^p, x_u^p, x_{uu}^p).$$

For the x_{ss}-component this yields, using the mean value theorem,

$$\begin{aligned} x_{ss}(j+1) - x_{ss}^p &= \mathcal{S}^{ss}(x_{ss}(j), x_u(j), x_{uu}(j+1)) - \mathcal{S}^{ss}(x_{ss}^p, x_u^p, x_{uu}^p) \\ &= \int_0^1 D\mathcal{S}^{ss}\big(x^p + t((x_{ss}(j), x_u(j), x_{uu}(j+1)) - x^p\big)dt \\ &\qquad\qquad ((x_{ss}(j), x_u(j), x_{uu}(j+1)) - x^p). \end{aligned}$$

So it follows from the reasoning in section 4.1.2 (see in particular p. 218) that there exist constants

$$a^{ss}, a^u, a^{uu} \in (0, 1/4)$$

such that

$$|x_{ss}(j+1) - x_{ss}^p| \leq a^{ss}|x_{ss}(j) - x_{ss}^p| + a^u|x_u(j) - x_u^p| + a^{uu}|x_{uu}(j+1) - x_{uu}^p|.$$

Note that $D\mathcal{S}(0) = 0$, $\zeta_\lambda \cap \Sigma = x^p \to 0$ as $\lambda \to 0$ and that $x(j)(\cdot,\cdot)$ is continuous and $x(j)(x_{ss}^p, x_u^p) = x^p$. For the x_u and x_{uu} components we find

$$\begin{aligned} &|x_u(j+1) - x_{ss}^p| \\ &\qquad \leq b^{ss}|x_{ss}(j) - x_{ss}^p| + b^u|x_u(j) - x_u^p| + b^{uu}|x_{uu}(j+1) - x_{uu}^p|, \\ &|x_{uu}(j) - x_{ss}^p| \\ &\qquad \leq c^{ss}|x_{ss}(j) - x_{ss}^p| + c^u|x_u(j) - x_u^p| + c^{uu}|x_{uu}(j+1) - x_{uu}^p| \end{aligned}$$

for some $b^{ss}, b^u, b^{uu}, c^{ss}, c^u, c^{uu} \in (0, 1/4)$. Define

$$\begin{aligned} a_j^- &= |x_{ss}(j+1) - x_{ss}^p| + |x_u(j+1) - x_u^p|, \\ a_j^+ &= |x_{uu}(j) - x_{ss}^p|. \end{aligned}$$

There is a $q > 1$ such that $a_j^- + a_j^+ \leq \frac{1}{2q}\left(a_{j-1}^- + a_{j+1}^+\right)$. The statement follows with Lemma 4.28. □

Let $\left((x_{ss}(j))_{j\in\mathbb{N}}, (x_u(j))_{j\in\mathbb{N}}, (x_{uu}(j))_{j\in\mathbb{N}_0}\right)\left((x_{ss}^0, x_u^0)\right)$ be solutions given by Lemma 4.27. Then

$$\left\{\left(x_{ss}(0), x_u(0), x_{uu}(0)(x_{ss}^0, x_u^0)\right) \;;\; |x_{ss}^0 - x_{ss}^p|, |x_u^0 - x_u^p| \text{ small}\right\}$$

is the intersection of the local stable manifold of ζ_λ and Σ. The local unstable manifold of ζ_λ in Σ is constructed similarly using backward orbits (Exercise 4.21). We conclude our study of the hyperbolicity of ζ_λ.

4.1.3. Saddle-focus homoclinic orbits. Consider a vector field on $\mathbb{R}^3$ with a hyperbolic equilibrium of saddle type so that the linearization about it has one real eigenvalue $\mu^u > 0$ and two complex conjugate eigenvalues $\mu^s \pm \phi^s i$. A homoclinic orbit to such an equilibrium is called a saddle-focus homoclinic orbit. Just as the homoclinic orbits studied in previous sections, it can arise in one-parameter families of differential equations $\dot{x} = f(x, \lambda)$; see Figure 4.13. The bifurcation scenarios are markedly different for $\mu^s + \mu^u < 0$ and $\mu^s + \mu^u > 0$. The number $\mu^s + \mu^u$ is called the saddle quantity. It turns out that the bifurcation for negative saddle quantity is similar to the bifurcation from a planar homoclinic loop: an attracting periodic orbit appears when the homoclinic loop breaks. We will focus solely on the case of a positive saddle quantity and in fact only consider the dynamics near a saddle-focus homoclinic orbit and not its bifurcations. A systematic study of the dynamics near such saddle-focus homoclinic orbits was pioneered by Leonid Shilnikov since the mid-1960s [**335**]. He found that saddle-focus homoclinic orbits can be accompanied by nearby chaotic dynamics including infinitely many periodic orbits. A geometric approach to the existence of suspensions of Smale horseshoes (see Section 2.5)

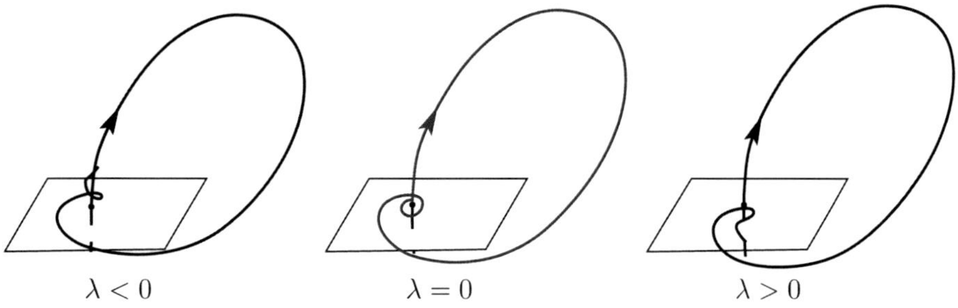

Figure 4.13. For a one-parameter family of differential equations $\dot{x} = f(x, \lambda)$ in $\mathbb{R}^3$, one can have a saddle-focus homoclinic orbit at a single bifurcation value $\lambda = 0$.

near the saddle-focus homoclinic orbits is contained in the work by Charles Tresser [**387**].

We restrict our inquiry here to vector fields in three-dimensional space and establish the existence of suspensions of horseshoe maps near a saddle-focus homoclinic orbit with positive saddle quantity. In Appendix C (see in particular Appendix C.6.3) we discuss such a result in $\mathbb{R}^n$ using Lin's method.

Theorem 4.29. *Let*

$$\dot{x} = f(x)$$

be a smooth vector field on $\mathbb{R}^3$. *Assume there is a hyperbolic saddle equilibrium* p *so that* $Df(p)$ *has a real eigenvalue* μ^u *and two complex conjugate stable eigenvalues* $\mu^s \pm \phi^s i$ *with* $\mu^s < 0 < \mu^u$. *Assume that* f *admits a homoclinic orbit* $h(t)$ *with*

$$\lim_{t \to \infty} h(t) = \lim_{t \to -\infty} h(t) = p.$$

Assume

$$\mu^s + \mu^u > 0.$$

In any neighborhood $\mathcal{U}$ *of the closure of* h, *there are invariant sets that are suspensions of Smale horseshoes.*

The proof starts with deriving a suitable normal form of the vector field near p that brings it to an almost linear form. Alternatively one may invoke C^1 linearization provided by [**31**].

Lemma 4.30. *The vector field* f *is locally smoothly equivalent to*

$$\begin{aligned}\dot{x} &= \mu^s x - \phi^s y + f(x, y, z),\\ \dot{y} &= \mu^s y + \phi^s x + g(x, y, z),\\ \dot{z} &= \mu^u z,\end{aligned}$$

where f *and* g *are of the order* $\mathcal{O}(|(x, y)|^2 z)$.

Proof. The reasoning from [**274**] is similar to the proof of Lemma 4.6, so we will be more brief. Take local coordinates (x, y, z) near the equilibrium p in which p becomes the origin $(0, 0, 0)$ and

$$Df(0,0,0) = \begin{pmatrix} \mu^s & -\phi^s & 0 \\ \phi^s & \mu^s & 0 \\ 0 & 0 & \mu^u \end{pmatrix}.$$

The differential equation is hence given by

$$\begin{aligned} \dot{x} &= \mu^s x - \phi^s y + f(x, y, z), \\ \dot{y} &= \mu^s y + \phi^s x + g(x, y, z), \\ \dot{z} &= \mu^u z + h(x, y, z), \end{aligned}$$

with f, g, h of quadratic order. A coordinate change that straightens the local stable and unstable manifolds, yields $f, g = \mathcal{O}(|(x, y)|)$ and $h = \mathcal{O}(z)$. A time reparametrization makes $h \equiv 0$. Moreover, we may assume that f restricted to the local stable manifold is linear, so that $f, g = \mathcal{O}(|(x, y)|z)$. One checks that a polynomial coordinate change removes monomials xz and yz from f and g, so that $f, g = \mathcal{O}(|(x, y)|z^2) + \mathcal{O}(|(x, y)|^2 z)$. We will remove the terms $\mathcal{O}(|(x, y)|z^2)$ from f and g. For this we consider a coordinate change of the form

$$\begin{aligned} u &= x + g_{11}(z)x + g_{12}(z)y, \\ v &= y + g_{21}(z)x + g_{22}(z)y, \\ w &= z. \end{aligned}$$

Write the differential equations for u, v, w as

$$\begin{aligned} \dot{u} &= \mu^s u - \phi^s v + F_{11}(u, v, w)u + F_{12}(u, v, w)v, \\ \dot{v} &= \mu^s y + \phi^s x + F_{12}(u, v, w)u + F_{22}(u, v, w)v, \\ \dot{w} &= \mu^u w. \end{aligned}$$

With $g = (g_{11}, g_{12}, g_{21}, g_{22})$ we get

$$\begin{aligned} F_{11}(0, 0, w) &= g_{11}'\mu^u w + \phi^s g_{12} + \phi^s g_{21} + \mathcal{O}(|(g(w), w)|^2), \\ F_{12}(0, 0, w) &= g_{12}'\mu^u w - \phi^s g_{11} + \phi^s g_{22} + \mathcal{O}(|(g(w), w)|^2), \\ F_{21}(0, 0, w) &= g_{21}'\mu^u w + \phi^s g_{22} - \phi^s g_{11} + \mathcal{O}(|(g(w), w)|^2), \\ F_{22}(0, 0, w) &= g_{22}'\mu^u w - \phi^s g_{21} - \phi^s g_{12} + \mathcal{O}(|(g(w), w)|^2). \end{aligned}$$

If these terms vanish, the differential equations have the form

$$\begin{aligned} \dot{u} &= \mu^s u - \phi^s v + \mathcal{O}(|(u, v)|^2 w), \\ \dot{v} &= \mu^s y + \phi^s x + \mathcal{O}(|(u, v)|^2 w), \\ \dot{w} &= \mu^u w, \end{aligned}$$

as desired. The demand that F_{ij}, $i, j = 1, 2$ vanish at $(u, v) = (0, 0)$, yields differential equations for w and $h_{ij}(t) = g_{ij}(w(t))$:

$$\dot{w} = \lambda_u w, \tag{4.64}$$

$$\begin{pmatrix} \dot{h}_{11} \\ \dot{h}_{12} \\ \dot{h}_{21} \\ \dot{h}_{22} \end{pmatrix} = \omega_s \begin{pmatrix} 0 & -1 & -1 & 0 \\ 1 & 0 & 0 & -1 \\ 1 & 0 & 0 & -1 \\ 0 & 1 & 1 & 0 \end{pmatrix} \begin{pmatrix} h_{11} \\ h_{12} \\ h_{21} \\ h_{22} \end{pmatrix} + \mathcal{O}(|(h, w)|^2). \tag{4.65}$$

The spectrum of the above antisymmetric matrix consists of four zero eigenvalues. The one-dimensional strong unstable manifold of the set of differential equations (4.64) and (4.65), provides the functions $g_{11}, \ldots, g_{22}$. □

For some small $\delta > 0$, take local cross sections

$$\Sigma_{in} \subset \{x^2 + y^2 = \delta^2, |z| \le \delta\},$$
$$\Sigma_{out} = \{x^2 + y^2 \le \delta^2, z = \delta\},$$

that we may assume to intersect the homoclinic orbit h transversely. Let Π be the first return map on Σ_{in}. Take coordinates (θ, z) on Σ_{in}, where θ is an angle in the (x, y)-plane. Choose the coordinates so that h intersects Σ_{in} in $z = 0$ and $\theta = 0$. Write $\beta = -\mu^s/\mu^u$. The eigenvalue condition $\mu^s + \mu^u > 0$ is equivalent to $0 < \beta < 1$.

Lemma 4.31. *In the local normal form of Lemma* 4.30, Π *has the following asymptotic expansion:*

$$\Pi(\theta, z) = \begin{pmatrix} \phi_1(\theta) z^\beta \sin\left(-\frac{\phi^s}{\mu^u} \ln z\right) + \phi_2(\theta) z^\beta \cos\left(-\frac{\phi^s}{\mu^u} \ln z\right) + R_1(\theta, z) \\ \phi_3(\theta) z^\beta \sin\left(-\frac{\phi^s}{\mu^u} \ln z\right) + \phi_4(\theta) z^\beta \cos\left(-\frac{\phi^s}{\mu^u} \ln z\right) + R_2(\theta, z) \end{pmatrix}.$$

The functions ϕ_i, $i = 1, 2, 3, 4$, *are smooth functions of* θ *and satisfy*

$$\det \begin{pmatrix} \phi_1 & \phi_2 \\ \phi_3 & \phi_4 \end{pmatrix} \ne 0.$$

Furthermore, for some $\omega > 0$, *one has estimates*

$$\left| \frac{\partial^{k+l}}{\partial \theta^k \partial z^l} R_i(\theta, z) \right| \le C_{k+l} z^{\beta + \omega - l}.$$

Proof. This is derived using the variation of constants formula, as before for planar homoclinic orbits in Lemma 4.11 (Exercise 4.22). □

The first return map Π is a perturbation from $\Pi_0 : \Sigma_{in} \to \Sigma_{in}$ given by

$$\Pi_0(\theta, z) = \begin{pmatrix} \phi_1(0) z^\beta \sin\left(-\frac{\phi^s}{\mu^u} \ln z\right) + \phi_2(0) z^\beta \cos\left(-\frac{\phi^s}{\mu^u} \ln z\right) \\ \phi_3(0) z^\beta \sin\left(-\frac{\phi^s}{\mu^u} \ln z\right) + \phi_4(0) z^\beta \cos\left(-\frac{\phi^s}{\mu^u} \ln z\right) \end{pmatrix},$$

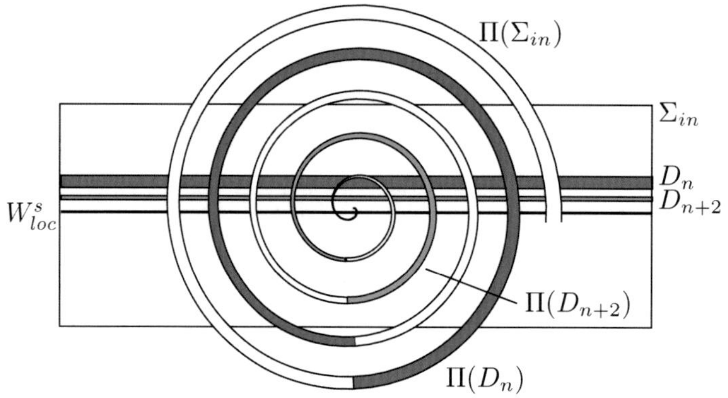

Figure 4.14. Strips D_n in the cross section Σ_{in} that accumulate onto $W^s_{loc} \cap \Sigma_{in}$ are mapped over itself in a horseshoe shape by Π.

where Π_0 is obtained from Π by removing the higher-order terms and computing the coefficients $\phi_1, \dots, \phi_4$ in $\theta = 0$. The image under Π_0 of a line piece $L = \{z > 0, \theta = 0\}$ is a spiral centered at $(0,0)$. More precisely, it is the image under a linear map of a logarithmic spiral. Take a sequence of points $\hat{z}_n > 0$ converging to 0, where $\Pi_0(L)$ has a local minimum z-coordinate. A calculation shows $\hat{z}_n \sim \alpha^n$ for some $\alpha < 1$, where the notation $\hat{z}_n \sim \alpha^n$ stands for $0 < \liminf_{n\to\infty} \hat{z}_n/\alpha^n \leq \limsup_{n\to\infty} \hat{z}_n/\alpha^n < \infty$. This indicates that Π maps strips

$$D_n = \{(\theta, z) \in \Sigma^{in} \; ; \; \hat{z}_{n+1} \leq z \leq \hat{z}_n\}$$

to parts of a thickened spiral as indicated in Figure 4.14. From $\beta < 1$ it is seen that the image $\Pi_0(D_n)$ intersects D_n as in a horseshoe map. To prove Theorem 4.29, we must make this intuitive picture rigorous. We follow arguments from Section 2.5; alternatively one can make use of cone field constructions as mentioned in Section 2.5 and in Remark 5.12.

Proof of Theorem 4.29. To analyze the action of the return map Π on a strip D_n for high n, we rescale coordinates by $(\theta, z) = (\hat{z}_n^\beta x, \hat{z}_n y)$. This gives a rescaled map

$$F(x,y) = \begin{pmatrix} \phi_1(0) y^\beta \sin\left(-\frac{\phi^s}{\mu^u} \ln \hat{z}_n y\right) + \phi_2(0) y^\beta \cos\left(-\frac{\phi^s}{\mu^u} \ln \hat{z}_n y\right) \\ \phi_3(0) \hat{z}_n^{\beta-1} y^\beta \sin\left(-\frac{\phi^s}{\mu^u} \ln \hat{z}_n y\right) + \phi_4(0) \hat{z}_n^{\beta-1} y^\beta \cos\left(-\frac{\phi^s}{\mu^u} \ln \hat{z}_n y\right) \end{pmatrix}$$

plus higher-order terms. Consider F defined on a square $D = [-K, K] \times [Y_1, Y_2]$ for suitable $K, Y_1, Y_2 > 0$. In the original coordinates this corresponds to a small region $E_n = [-K\hat{z}_n^\beta, K\hat{z}_n^\beta] \times [Y_1 \hat{z}_n, Y_2 \hat{z}_n]$.

For a suitable choice of the square D we have a setup as in Section 2.5 (with strong contraction and expansion rates for high n). The inverse image $F^{-1}(D)$ is contained in two horizontal strips of width $\sim \hat{z}_n^{1-\beta}$. We find that $F(D) \cap D$

consists of two connected components that we denote by V_0 and V_1. Likewise we write $H_0 = F^{-1}(V_0)$ and $H_1 = F^{-1}(V_1)$. The map F consists of two maps $F_0 : H_0 \to V_0, F_1 : H_1 \to V_1$. Write

$$DF_i = \begin{pmatrix} a(x,y) & b(x,y) \\ c(x,y) & d(z,y) \end{pmatrix}.$$

The coefficients depend only on (x, y).

For Π_0 we get $a = c = 0$. For the perturbation Π we get a bound $a, c = \mathcal{O}(\hat{z}_n^{\omega})$. This bound is uniform on D. Moreover, $b \sim \hat{z}_n^{-1}$ and $d \sim \hat{z}_n^{\beta-2}$, uniformly in (x, y). This means that for instance $b/\hat{z}_n^{-1}$ is bounded and bounded away from zero as $n \to \infty$, for all $(x, y) \in D$.

The implicit function theorem provides smooth maps G_i, $i = 0, 1$, with

$$G_i(x_0, y_1) = (x_1, y_0)$$

if $F_i(x_0, y_0) = (x_1, y_1)$. Note that

$$DG_i = \begin{pmatrix} a - bd^{-1}c & bd^{-1} \\ -d^{-1}c & d^{-1} \end{pmatrix}$$

calculated in (x_0, y_0). Note also that for Π_0, the coefficients in the left column of this matrix are 0.

Following the arguments of Theorem 2.58 finishes the proof. We copy the arguments. Denote by $l^\infty(\mathbb{Z}, D)$ the space of bounded sequences $\xi : \mathbb{Z} \to D$ endowed with the supremum norm

$$||\xi|| = \sup_{i \in \mathbb{Z}} |\xi_i|.$$

Fix an element $\omega \in \Sigma$. Define $\mathcal{H}_\omega : l^\infty(\mathbb{Z}, D) \to l^\infty(\mathbb{Z}, D)$ as follows: If $\gamma_i = (x_i, y_i)$ and $\mathcal{H}_\omega(\gamma) = \eta$ with $\eta_i = (u_i, v_i)$, then

$$(u_{i+1}, v_i) = G_{\omega_{i+1}}(x_i, y_{i+1})$$

for $i \in \mathbb{Z}$. For n large, the map $\mathcal{H}_\omega$ is a contraction,

$$||\mathcal{H}_\omega(\gamma) - \mathcal{H}_\omega(\eta)|| \le \lambda ||\gamma - \eta||$$

for some $0 < \lambda < 1$. The map $\mathcal{H}_\omega$ therefore possesses a unique fixed point. By uniqueness, the fixed point $\zeta = \zeta(\omega)$ of $\mathcal{H}_\omega$ satisfies $\zeta_{k+1} = F_{\omega_k}(\zeta_k)$. Thus ζ_k is an orbit for F. By Lemma A.13, the fixed point depends continuously on $\omega \in \Sigma$ in the product topology. We find that $\omega \to \zeta(\omega)$ defines a homeomorphism. The correspondence $\omega \to \zeta(\omega)_0$ defines a topological conjugacy since $\sigma\omega$ is mapped to the shifted sequence $\{\zeta_{k+1}\}$, $k \in \mathbb{Z}$. □

Remark 4.32. The suspensions of the Smale horseshoes are hyperbolic invariant sets; see Section 5.1.2. ■

The dynamics near saddle-focus homoclinic orbits is considerably more involved than hinted at by the existence of suspended horseshoes [**130**, **166**, **274**]. The maximal invariant set for the Poincaré return map Π on a strip D_n is a hyperbolic horseshoe, but the maximal invariant set on a union $D_n \cup D_m$ may be larger than the union of two horseshoes; there may be orbits that move from one strip to another and then back.

4.1.4. Homoclinic orbit at a neutral saddle.

If one of the generic conditions from Theorem 4.14 is not satisfied, a homoclinic bifurcation of higher codimension arises. Some of these bifurcations create multiround homoclinic orbits in the unfolding. Given is a differential equation $\dot{u} = f(u)$ with a homoclinic orbit $h(t)$ to an equilibrium p and a small tubular neighborhood $\mathcal{U}$ of the closure of h. Let S be a cross section through $h(0)$. A k-homoclinic orbit is a homoclinic orbit inside $\mathcal{U}$ that intersects S precisely k times.

We will briefly comment upon one such homoclinic bifurcation, of codimension 2, involving a homoclinic orbit to a hyperbolic equilibrium with simple real leading eigenvalues $\mu^s < 0$, $\mu^u > 0$, where the assumption $\mu^s + \mu^u \neq 0$ is violated (so, where $\mu^s + \mu^u = 0$ at the bifurcation). We want to make clear how the analysis of the sections on homoclinic orbits to equilibria with simple real leading eigenvalues, can be used to analyze such bifurcations as well. Some of the details are however omitted.

4.1.4.1. *Planar homoclinic orbit at a neutral saddle.* Bifurcations from homoclinic orbits to a neutral saddle in the plane have been studied in [**222**, **272**, **314**]. We present the codimension-2 bifurcation theorem.

Theorem 4.33. *Let*

$$\dot{u} = f_\lambda(u)$$

with $\lambda = (\lambda_1, \lambda_2)$ *be a two-parameter family of vector fields on* $\mathbb{R}^2$ *with a homoclinic solution* $h(t)$ *to the hyperbolic equilibrium* p *at* $\lambda = 0$*. We assume that the real eigenvalues* $\mu^s(\lambda) < 0 < \mu^u(\lambda)$ *satisfy*

$$\mu^s(0) = \mu^u(0).$$

Assume the following.

(i) *(Generic separatrix value) The separatrix value* $d_1(0)$ *appearing in* (4.66) *is different from* 1.

(ii) *(Generic unfolding) The derivative* $d_0'(0)$ *of* d_0 *appearing in* (4.66) *is nonzero.*

(iii) *(Generic unfolding)*

$$\partial_{\lambda_2}\mu^s(0) \neq \partial_{\lambda_2}\mu^u(0).$$

Figure 4.15. Bifurcation set of a planar homoclinic bifurcation with a neutral saddle.

The bifurcation set is as shown in Figure 4.15*: a one-sided curve of saddle-node bifurcations of periodic orbits emerges from the curve of homoclinic orbits at* $\lambda = 0$ *in the parameter plane.*

Sketch of proof. The analysis of the codimension-1 planar homoclinic orbit can be followed verbatim. This leads to the expression for a Poincaré return map Π on a cross section Σ as derived in Section 4.1.1,

$$\Pi(y, \lambda) = d_0(\lambda) + d_1(\lambda) y^{\beta} + \mathcal{O}(y^{\beta+\omega}). \tag{4.66}$$

After a reparametrization, in new parameters $\nu = (\nu_1, \nu_2)$, we find an expression

$$(y, \nu) \mapsto \nu_1 + d_1(\nu) y^{1+\nu_2} + \mathcal{O}(y^{1+\omega}).$$

The coefficient $d_1(0)$ is positive and, by assumption (i), different from 1. One can now easily analyze this expression to prove the bifurcation theorem. □

Remark 4.34. One can show that $d_1(0)$ equals the integral of the divergence of f along the homoclinic orbit,

$$d_1(0) = e^{\int_{-\infty}^{\infty} \operatorname{div} f(h(t))\, dt}. \tag{4.67}$$

To see this, use Theorem B.30 to take local coordinates (x, y) near the equilibrium in which the system appears linear $\dot{x} = \mu^s x$, $\dot{y} = \mu^u y$. Take cross sections $\Sigma^{in} \subset \{x = \delta\}$ and $\Sigma^{out} \subset \{y = \delta\}$, transverse to the homoclinic orbit. If $\varphi^t(x, \delta) = (\delta, y)$, then

$$\det D\varphi^t((x, \delta)) = \frac{|\mu^s \delta|}{|\mu^u \delta|} e^{\int_0^t \operatorname{div} f(\varphi^t((x,\delta)))\, dt};$$

see [**17**, § 28]. This formula is comparable to the formula for the derivative of the Poincaré return map in Theorem 2.27. From this we can derive (4.67) (Exercise 4.23). ■

4.1.4.2. *Higher-dimensional homoclinic orbit at a neutral saddle.* We treat the higher-dimensional resonant homoclinic bifurcation with real leading eigenvalues, where we shall assume that the homoclinic orbit is nondegenerate and not in an inclination-flip or an orbit-flip configuration. This bifurcation was investigated by Shui-Nee Chow, Bo Deng, and Bernold Fiedler [**68**].

Theorem 4.35. *Let*

$$\dot{u} = f_\lambda(u)$$

with $\lambda = (\lambda_1, \lambda_2)$ *be a two-parameter family of vector fields on* $\mathbb{R}^n$ *with a homoclinic solution* $h(t)$ *to the hyperbolic equilibrium* p *at* $\lambda = 0$. *We assume that the simple real leading eigenvalues* $\mu^s(\lambda) < 0 < \mu^u(\lambda)$ *satisfy*

$$\mu^s(0) = \mu^u(0).$$

Assume the following.

(i) *(No-inclination-flip, no-orbit-flip) See conditions* (ii), (iii) *of Theorem* 4.14.

(ii) *(Generic separatrix value) The separatrix value* $\varphi(0)$ *appearing in* (4.68) *is different from* ± 1.

(iii) *(Generic unfolding) The derivative* $a'(0)$ *of* a *appearing in* (4.66) *is nonzero.*

(iv) *(Generic unfolding)*

$$\partial_{\lambda_2}\mu^s(0) \neq \partial_{\lambda_2}\mu^u(0).$$

If $\varphi(0) > 0$, *then the bifurcation set is as shown in Figure* 4.16(i)*: a one-sided curve of saddle-node bifurcations of periodic orbits emerges from the curve of homoclinic orbits at* $\lambda = 0$ *in the parameter plane.*

If $\varphi(0) < 0$, *then the bifurcation set is as shown in Figure* 4.16(ii)*: a one-sided curve of period-doubling bifurcations of periodic orbits and a one-sided curve of 2-homoclinic orbits emerge from the curve of primary homoclinic orbits at* $\lambda = 0$ *in the parameter plane.*

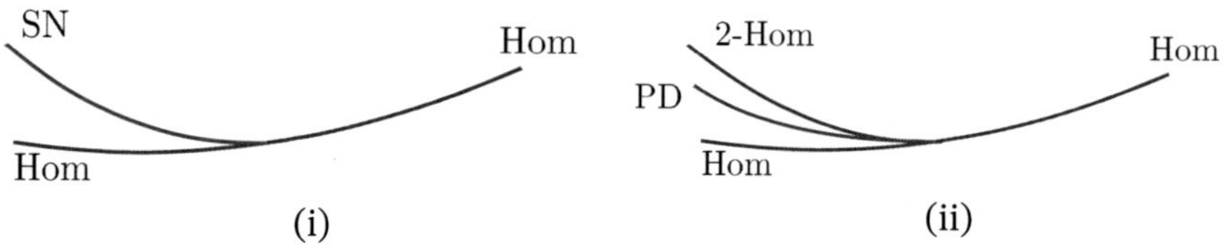

Figure 4.16. Bifurcation set of a homoclinic bifurcation with a neutral saddle, for orientable (left panel) and nonorientable (right panel) homoclinic orbits.

Sketch of proof. The analysis of the codimension-1 homoclinic orbit in $\mathbb{R}^n$ can be followed verbatim. This leads to equations for orbits $x(j) = (x_{ss}(j), x_u(j), x_{uu}(j))$ in cross coordinates,

$$\begin{aligned} x_{ss}(j+1) &= \mathcal{O}(x_u(j)^{\beta+\omega}), \\ x_u(j+1) &= a(\lambda) + \varphi(\lambda)x_u(j)^\beta + \mathcal{O}(x_u(j)^{\beta+\omega}), \\ x_{uu}(j) &= \mathcal{O}(x_u(j+1)^{1+\omega}). \end{aligned} \tag{4.68}$$

After a reparametrization, in new parameters $\nu = (\nu_1, \nu_2)$ we find an expression

$$\begin{aligned} x_{ss}(j+1) &= \mathcal{O}(x_u(j)^{1+\omega}), \\ x_u(j+1) &= \nu_1 + \varphi(\nu)x_u(j)^{1+\nu_2} + \mathcal{O}(x_u(j)^{1+\omega}), \\ x_{uu}(j) &= \mathcal{O}(x_u(j+1)^{1+\omega}). \end{aligned}$$

The coefficient $\varphi(0)$ is nonzero and, by assumption (ii), $|\varphi(0)| \neq 1$. It can be of positive or negative sign, which yields the two cases. We leave further analysis to the reader. □

Remark 4.36. In Remark 4.26 we mentioned the existence of a homoclinic center manifold. Such a manifold is two dimensional and either orientable and thus homeomorphic to an annulus, or nonorientable and homeomorphic to a Möbius band. A positive separatrix value corresponds to an orientable homoclinic center manifold. A negative separatrix value corresponds to a nonorientable homoclinic center manifold. The existence of a homoclinic center manifold makes clear that k-periodic orbits or k-homoclinic orbits do not exist for $k > 1$ (for orientable homoclinic center manifolds) or $k > 2$ (for nonorientable homoclinic center manifolds).

Of the papers that consider more degenerate cases of a homoclinic orbit with neutral saddle, we mention [**315**] and [**393**]. This last reference gives an example of a bifurcation that leads to an unbounded number of periodic orbits arising in the bifurcation.

Bifurcation problems in which the no-inclination-flip or no-orbit-flip condition is violated are more involved. Several cases occur and in some of the cases, k-homoclinic orbits for all k and suspended horseshoes appear. To stress that the notion of bifurcation depends on the topology, [**257**] shows how C^1-small perturbations from a system with an orbit-flip homoclinic orbit can produce systems with an inclination-flip homoclinic orbit, while this is not true for small smooth perturbations. We refer to the review paper [**172**] and the research literature mentioned in there. ■

4.2. Homoclinic orbits to periodic orbits

The following can be seen as a generalization of Definition 4.2.

Definition 4.37. Given a periodic orbit γ for a differential equation $\dot{x} = f(x)$ in $\mathbb{R}^n$, a nontrivial orbit $h(t)$ whose ω and α-limit set coincide with γ, that means

$$\omega(h(0)) = \alpha(h(0)) = \gamma$$

is called a *homoclinic orbit* to the periodic orbit γ.

A homoclinic orbit h to the periodic orbit γ is called a *transverse homoclinic orbit* if the stable and unstable manifolds of γ intersect transversely along h.

So a homoclinic orbit to a periodic orbit γ is situated in the intersection of the stable and unstable manifolds of γ.

A flow in $\mathbb{R}^n$ with $n \geq 3$ can have homoclinic orbits to periodic orbits. In this section we discuss some of the consequences for the dynamics, and some associated bifurcations.

4.2.1. Transverse homoclinic orbits.

The goal of this section is to demonstrate that transverse homoclinic orbits to periodic orbits force the existence of suspensions of horseshoes. Henri Poincaré was aware of the complicated geometry of transversely intersecting stable and unstable manifolds (or homoclinic tangles). The work of George Birkhoff [**39**], Stephen Smale [**353**], and Leonid Shilnikov [**336**] made clear that the transverse intersections imply the existence of complicated dynamics nearby.

We restrict our study to three-dimensional flows. A saddle periodic orbit γ of a differential equation in $\mathbb{R}^3$ has a two-dimensional stable manifold $W^s(\gamma)$ and a two-dimensional unstable manifold $W^u(\gamma)$. An intersection of $W^s(\gamma)$ and $W^u(\gamma)$ different from γ itself, is a homoclinic orbit to γ. Let h be a homoclinic orbit to γ, and take a local cross section S_1 through the point $h(0)$. Then $W^s(\gamma)$ and $W^u(\gamma)$ each intersect S_1; the connected components that contain $h(0)$ are two curves. These curves can have a transverse intersection at $h(0)$ as indicated in Figure 4.17, in which case one speaks of a transverse homoclinic orbit, or a tangency at $h(0)$, in which case one speaks of a homoclinic tangency.

Theorem 4.41 below gives that a transverse homoclinic orbit to a saddle periodic orbit implies the existence of infinitely many periodic orbits and, in

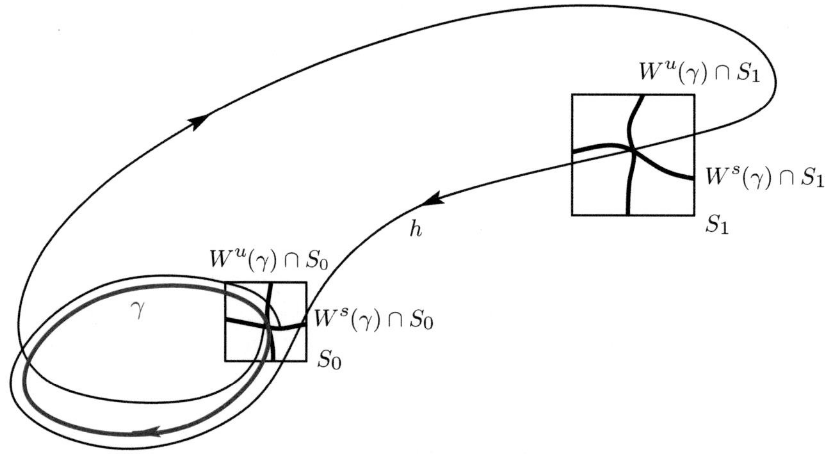

Figure 4.17. A transverse homoclinic orbit h to a saddle periodic orbit γ arises from a transverse intersection of $W^s(\gamma)$ with $W^u(\gamma)$.

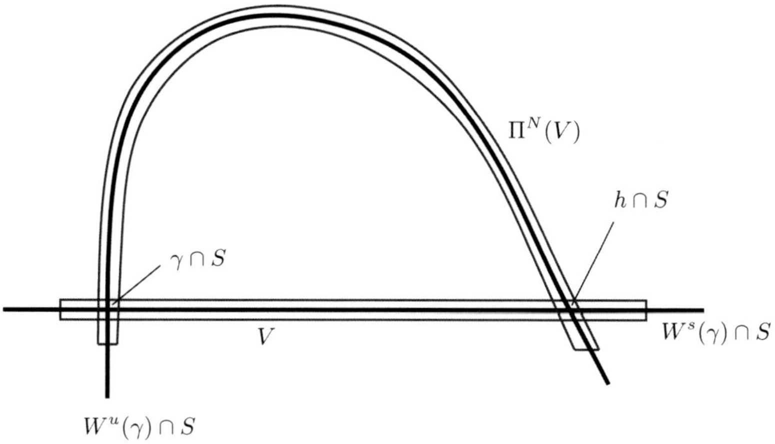

Figure 4.18. For a flow with a global cross section S, this picture explains how a transverse homoclinic orbit implies the existence of a horseshoe for the Poincaré return map Π on S.

fact, a suspension of a horseshoe. Figure 4.18 depicts the geometry in the easier to visualize case of a flow with a global cross section S. Compact parts of $W^s(\gamma) \cap S$ and $W^u(\gamma) \cap S$ are drawn in the picture.

Consider a thin neighborhood V of a compact part of $W^s(\gamma) \cap S$, containing both the point $\gamma \cap S$ on the periodic orbit and $h \cap S$ on the homoclinic orbit. For suitable regions V, a high iterate of the Poincaré return map $\Pi : S \to S$ will map V in a horseshoe shape over itself. A thinner region V means that more iterates of Π are needed. This will improve estimates needed to conclude the existence of a horseshoe, using reasoning following that in Section 2.5. As the computations involve a high number of iterates of Π near its fixed point $\gamma \cap S$, we will resort to a local normal form to obtain manageable expansions for these high iterates. Our analysis has a more analytical flavor compared to geometrical arguments of the result in [**198**, Section 6.5], [**282**, Chapter 2] and [**48**, Section 5.8]. These geometrical arguments make use of invariant cone fields [**259**].

In the general case, where a global cross section may not exist, we proceed as follows. Take a local cross section S_0 through $\gamma(0)$. Let $\mathcal{U}$ be a small open neighborhood of $\gamma \cup h$. Write $S = S_0 \cup S_1$ for the union of the two local cross sections through γ and h. Define the Poincaré return map $\Pi : S \to S$ by

$$\Pi(x) = \varphi^t(x),$$

where

$$t = \min\{s > 0 \; ; \; \varphi^s(x) \in S \text{ and } \varphi^u(x) \in \mathcal{U}, 0 \leq u \leq s\}.$$

So for Π we only consider orbits inside $\mathcal{U}$. Observe that Π is defined on an open subset $\mathcal{V}$ of S. We will nonetheless write $\Pi : S \to S$. The domain $\mathcal{V}$ contains $\gamma(0)$ and $h(0)$. Write $\Pi_0 : S_0 \to S_0$ for the return map following orbit pieces near γ. Note that $\gamma(0)$ is a fixed point of Π_0. In order to study the dynamics of Π, we need asymptotic expansions for iterates of Π_0. First we give a normal form lemma. The following steps can be replaced by the use of C^1 linearizing coordinates (see Theorem B.30) and ensuing computations.

Lemma 4.38. *There are smooth local coordinates (x, y) on S_0 near $\gamma(0)$ so that $(x_1, y_1) = \Pi_0(x_0, y_0)$ has the following expression. Let $\lambda < 1$, $\nu > 1$ be the Floquet multipliers of γ. Then*

$$x_1 = \lambda x_0 + e(x_0, y_0),$$
$$y_1 = \nu y_0 + f(x_0, y_0),$$

where e, f are smooth functions satisfying

$$e(x_0, y_0) = \mathcal{O}(x_0 y_0),$$
$$f(x_0, y_0) = \mathcal{O}(x_0 y_0).$$

Proof. The expressions hold in coordinates that satisfy the following properties. Take local coordinates (x, y) for which

$$W^u_{loc}(p_s) = \{y = 0\},$$
$$W^s_{loc}(p_s) = \{x = 0\}.$$

It follows that $\{x = 0\}$ and $\{y = 0\}$ are invariant. By a smooth coordinate change, Π, restricted to $V^u_{loc}(p_s)$ and to $V^s_{loc}(p_s)$, is linear:

$$\Pi(x, 0) = \lambda x,$$
$$\Pi(0, y) = \nu y.$$

See Theorem B.27 for this (note that the proof considers maps). □

Remark 4.39. Analysis along the lines of the proof of Lemma 4.6 enables an improved normal form as in [**127**] and [**339**]. With notation as in the above Lemma 4.38, we can achieve

$$e(x_0, y_0) = \mathcal{O}(x_0^2 y_0),$$
$$f(x_0, y_0) = \mathcal{O}(x_0 y_0^2).$$

■

The following lemma provides estimates for iterates of Π_0 in cross-coordinates, using the normal form from Lemma 4.38. Compare [**339**, Section 3.7].

Lemma 4.40. *For every $\sigma > 0$ there is $\varepsilon > 0$ so that the following holds. Assume $(x_i, y_i) = \Pi_0^i(x_0, y_0)$, $0 \le i \le N$, are in an ε ball around $(0,0)$. Then $(x_N, y_N) = \Pi_0^N(x_0, y_0)$ can be solved for (x_N, y_0) as function of (x_0, y_N), with the following expression:*

$$x_N = R_x(x_0, y_N),$$
$$y_0 = R_y(x_0, y_N),$$

where, for some $C > 0$ independent of N,

$$|R_x(x_0, y_N)|, |DR_x(x_0, y_N)| \le C(\lambda + \sigma)^N,$$
$$|R_y(x_0, y_N)|, |DR_y(x_0, y_N)| \le C\left(\frac{1}{\nu} + \sigma\right)^N.$$

Proof. We use coordinates from Lemma 4.38. Write $(x_1, y_1) = f(x_0, y_0)$ as

$$x_1 = \lambda x_0 + \mathcal{O}(x_0 y_0),$$
$$y_1 = \nu y_0 + \mathcal{O}(x_0 y_0).$$

The implicit function theorem allows us to solve (x_1, y_0) in terms of (x_0, y_1) if (x_0, y_0) is near $(0,0)$. We obtain

$$(x_1, y_0) = g(x_0, y_1)$$

of the form

$$x_1 = \lambda x_0 + \mathcal{O}(x_0 y_1),$$
$$y_0 = \nu^{-1} y_1 + \mathcal{O}(x_0 y_1). \tag{4.69}$$

The higher-order terms are order $x_0 y_1$ (Exercise 4.26).

Let $\mathfrak{B}(\{0, \dots, N\}, \mathbb{R}^2)$ be the space of bounded sequences $\{0, \dots, N\} \to \mathbb{R}^2$, endowed with the supremum norm

$$|\gamma| = \sup_{0 \le j \le N} |\gamma_j|,$$

where $|(x, y)| = \max\{|x|, |y|\}$ is the box norm on $\mathbb{R}^2 = E^s(0) \times E^u(0)$. Write $D_\delta^s = \{x_0 \in E^s \; ; \; |x_0| \le \delta\}$ and $\mathfrak{B}_\delta = \{\gamma \in \mathfrak{B}(\{1, \dots, N\}, \mathbb{R}^2) \; ; \; |\gamma| \le \delta\}$.

Write an element $\gamma \in \mathfrak{B}(\{1, \dots, N\}, \mathbb{R}^2)$ as $\gamma(j) = (\gamma_s(j), \gamma_u(j))$. Define the map $\Gamma : D_\delta^s \times D_\delta^u \times \mathfrak{B}_\delta \to \mathfrak{B}(\{1, \dots, N\}, \mathbb{R}^2)$ by $\Gamma(x_0, y_N, \gamma) = \eta$ with

$$\eta_s(0) = x_0,$$
$$(\eta_s(j+1), \eta_u(j)) = g(\eta_s(j), \eta_u(j+1)), \text{ for } 0 \le j < N,$$
$$\eta_u(n) = y_N.$$

The following is a direct consequence of the formulas for g, if δ is small enough:

(i) $\Gamma(D^s_\delta \times D^u_\delta \times \mathfrak{B}_\delta) \subset \mathfrak{B}_\delta$,

(ii) $\Gamma(x_0, y_N, \cdot)$ is a contraction on $\mathfrak{B}_\delta$.

By the implicit function theorem the fixed point of $\Gamma(x_0, y_N, \cdot)$ depends differentiably on x_0, y_N. Let η_{x_0,y_N} be the fixed point of $\Gamma(x_0, y_N, \cdot)$. Write $\eta_{x_0,y_N}(j) = (x_j, y_j)$. Then $(x_{j+1}, y_j) = g(x_j, y_{j+1})$ so that $(x_{j+1}, y_{j+1}) = f(x_j, y_j)$ and $\{(x_j, y_j)\}$, $0 \le j \le N$, is a finite orbit. It also follows from the expression for g that $x_N \le C(\lambda + \sigma)^N$ and $y_0 \le C\left(\frac{1}{\nu} + \sigma\right)^N$.

Derivatives with respect to x_0, y_N are treated by formally differentiating Γ and studying iterates of the resulting map. Consider for instance the derivatives $u_i = \frac{\partial}{\partial x_0} x_i$ and $v_i = \frac{\partial}{\partial x_0} y_i$. Considering x_i, y_i as functions of x_0, y_N and differentiating the formulas $\Gamma(x_0, y_N, \eta_{x_0,y_N})(i)$, $0 \le i \le N$, with respect to x_0 yields formulas for u_i, v_i.

This defines a map

$$\Gamma^1 : D^s_\delta \times D^u_\delta \times \mathfrak{B}_\delta \times \mathfrak{B}(\{1, \ldots, N\}, \mathbb{R}^2) \to \mathfrak{B}_\delta \times \mathfrak{B}(\{1, \ldots, N\}, \mathbb{R}^2)$$

given by $\Gamma^1(x_0, y_N, \gamma, \nu) = (\eta, \zeta)$ with $\eta = \Gamma(x_0, y_N, \gamma)$ and

$$\begin{aligned} \zeta_s(0) &= 1, \\ \zeta_u(N) &= 0, \\ \begin{pmatrix} \zeta_s(i+1) \\ \zeta_u(i) \end{pmatrix} &= Dg(\gamma_s(i+1), \gamma_u(i)) \begin{pmatrix} \nu_s(i) \\ \nu_u(i+1) \end{pmatrix}. \end{aligned}$$

A sequence $(x_i, y_i, \frac{\partial}{\partial x_0} x_i, \frac{\partial}{\partial x_0} y_i)$ is a fixed point of Γ^1. Now the map $\nu \mapsto \Gamma^1(x_0, y_N, \gamma, \nu)$ acts as a contraction in the last coordinate. The formulas, and similar formulas for the derivatives with respect to y_N, imply the estimates in the formulation of the lemma. □

Let $\Sigma^2 = \{0, 1\}^{\mathbb{Z}}$ be the space of infinite sequences of symbols 0, 1 endowed with product topology. Denote by $\sigma : \Sigma^2 \to \Sigma^2$ the left shift operator $(\sigma\omega)_i = \omega_{i+1}$; see also Section 2.5.

Theorem 4.41. *There are arbitrarily small domains $\mathcal{D}_N \subset S$ and integers $k(N)$ so that $\Pi^{k(N)}$ when restricted to the maximal invariant set in $\mathcal{D}_N$ is topologically conjugate to $\sigma|_{\Sigma^2}$.*

Proof. On S_0 take coordinates (x, y) given in Lemma 4.38. By rescaling we may assume that the local coordinates contain $\{|x| \le 2, |y| \le 2\}$. We can find arbitrarily large integers N and sets $V_2 = \Pi^N(V_1)$ satisfying

$$V_1 \subset \{|x| \le 1, |y| \le C(1/\nu)^N\},$$
$$V_2 \subset \{|x| \le C\lambda^N, |y| \le 1\}$$

for some uniform constant $C > 0$. There is $l_2 > 0$ so that $h(0) \in \Pi^{l_2}(V_2)$. There is $l_1 > 0$ so that $h(0) \in \Pi^{-l_1}(V_1)$. The numbers l_1, l_2 do not depend on N; see Figure 4.19. So $\Pi^{l_1+N+l_2}$ maps $\Pi^{-l_1}(V_1)$ to $\Pi^{l_2}(V_2)$. We find that $\Pi^{l_1+N+l_2}$ maps $\Pi^{-l_1}(V_1)$ to a set that intersects $\Pi^{-l_1}(V_1)$ in two components.

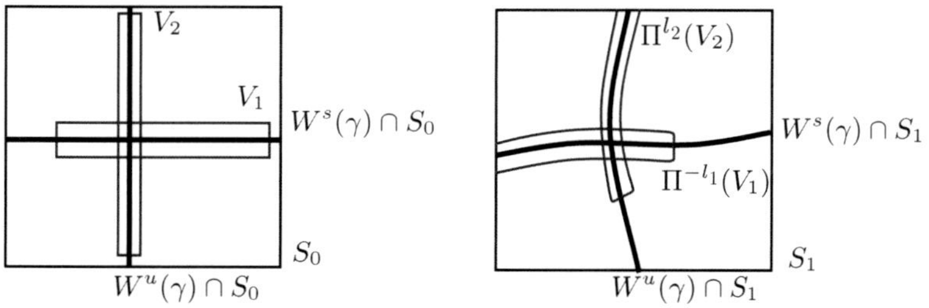

Figure 4.19. The horseshoe of a Poincaré return map for a transverse homoclinic orbit.

Denote $q = h(0)$ and write $W^s_{loc}(q)$ for the component of the intersection $W^s(\gamma) \cap S_1$ that contains q. Let $W^u_{loc}(q)$ be the component of the intersection $W^u(\gamma) \cap S_1$ that contains q. The two curves $W^s_{loc}(q)$ and $W^u_{loc}(q)$ intersect transversely in q. On S_1 take coordinates (x, y) in which q is $(0, 0)$ and with

$$W^s_{loc}(q) = \{y = 0\},$$
$$W^u_{loc}(q) = \{x = 0\}.$$

The map $\Pi^{l_1+N+l_2}$ consists of maps $\Pi_{0,0} : S_0 \cap \Pi^{-1}(S_0) \to S_0$, $\Pi_{0,1} : S_0 \cap \Pi^{-1}(S_1) \to S_1$, $\Pi_{1,0} : S_1 \cap \Pi^{-1}(S_0) \to S_0$ and $\Pi_{1,1} : S_1 \cap \Pi^{-1}(S_1) \to S_1$. All the maps are written in local coordinates (x, y). In cross coordinates we get maps $\Psi_{i,j}$ with $\Psi_{i,j}(x_0, y_k) = (x_k, y_0)$ if $\Pi_{i,j}(x_0, y_0) = (x_k, y_k)$. Recall that by Lemma 4.40 we have for $i, j = 0, 0$,

$$\Psi_{0,0}(x_0, y_1) = \begin{pmatrix} S_{0,0,x}(x_0, y_k) \\ S_{0,0,y}(x_0, y_k) \end{pmatrix}.$$

For some $C > 0$ independent of k,

$$|S_{0,0,x}(x_0, y_k)|, |DS_{0,0,x}(x_0, y_k)| \le C(\lambda + \sigma)^k,$$
$$|S_{0,0,y}(x_0, y_k)|, |DS_{0,0,y}(x_0, y_k)| \le C\left(\frac{1}{\nu} + \sigma\right)^k.$$

Similar estimates hold for $\Psi_{i,j}$ with other pairs i, j. For instance $\Psi_{0,1}$ is obtained as a composition $G \circ \Pi^{N+l_1}$ of a local diffeomorphism $G : S_0 \to S_1$ and a high iterate Π^{N+l_1} on S_0. Recall that G maps $W^u_{loc}(p_0)$ to $W^u_{loc}(q_0)$, thus G maps $\{x = 0\}$ to $\{x = 0\}$. So it has an expression

$$G((x, y) - \Pi^{-l_1}(q_0)) = \begin{pmatrix} ax + \mathcal{O}(x)\mathcal{O}(|(x, y|) \\ dx + ey + \mathcal{O}(|x, y|^2) \end{pmatrix}.$$

From this we get

$$\Psi_{0,1}(x_0, y_1) - \Pi^{-l_1}(q_0) = \begin{pmatrix} S_{0,1,x}(x_0, y_k) \\ S_{0,1,y}(x_0, y_k) \end{pmatrix}.$$

For some $C > 0$ independent of k,

$$|S_{0,1,x}(x_0, y_k)|, |DS_{0,1,x}(x_0, y_k)| \leq C(\lambda + \sigma)^k,$$

$$|S_{0,1,y}(x_0, y_k)|, |DS_{0,1,y}(x_0, y_k)| \leq C\left(\frac{1}{\nu} + \sigma\right)^k.$$

Similar estimates hold for $\Psi_{1,0}$ and $\Psi_{1,1}$.

Denote by $l^\infty(\mathbb{Z}, \mathbb{R}^2)$ the space of bounded sequences $\xi : \mathbb{Z} \to \mathbb{R}^2$ endowed with the supremum norm. Fix an element $\omega \in \Sigma^2$. Define $\mathcal{H} : l^\infty(\mathbb{Z}, \mathbb{R}^2) \to l^\infty(\mathbb{Z}, \mathbb{R}^2)$ as follows: if $\gamma_i = (x_i, y_i)$ and $\mathcal{H}(\gamma) = \eta$ with $\eta_i = (u_i, v_i)$, then

$$(u_{i+1}, v_i) = \Psi_{\omega_i, \omega_{i+1}}(x_i, y_{i+1})$$

for $i \in \mathbb{Z}$.

The map $\mathcal{H}$ is a contraction. The map $\mathcal{H}$ therefore possesses a unique fixed point. By uniqueness, the fixed point ζ of $\mathcal{H}$ satisfies $\zeta(k+1) = \Pi^{l_1+N+l_2}(\zeta(k))$. Thus $\zeta(k)$ is an orbit for $\Pi^{l_1+N+l_2}$. The fixed point depends continuously on $\eta \in \Sigma^2$ and defines a homeomorphism. The correspondence $\eta \to \zeta(0)$ defines a topological conjugacy since $\sigma\eta$ is mapped to $\zeta(1)$. □

The two references [**55, 173**] contain similar results without assuming transversality of the intersecting stable an unstable manifolds. Anatole Katok [**197**] proved a fundamental result connecting the existence of horseshoes to positive topological entropy (see for instance [**48**] for the notion of topological entropy).

4.2.2. Homoclinic tangencies. Homoclinic tangencies stand for the occurrence of nontransverse homoclinic orbits to periodic orbits. This is a research field in itself, with early results by Nikolai Gavrilov and Leonid Shilnikov [**120, 121**] and presented in [**282, 339, 340**]. We restrict our inquiry to a rescaling result that connects the study of homoclinic tangencies to the study of unimodal interval maps, such as logistic maps and Hénon-like diffeomorphisms (compare [**126, 402**] and see Section 5.2.4). As one highlight we mention the result by Leonardo Mora and Marcelo Viana [**256**] that adapts a theorem by Michael Benedicks and Lennart Carleson [**34**] on attractors in Hénon maps (see Theorem 5.63) to a context of unfoldings of quadratic homoclinic tangencies, and proves the occurrence of strange attractors (in particular attractors different from periodic orbits) in this context. The term *strange attractor* refers to a fractal attractor (for instance a non-integer Hausdorff dimension) with chaotic motion on it (sensitive dependence on initial conditions).

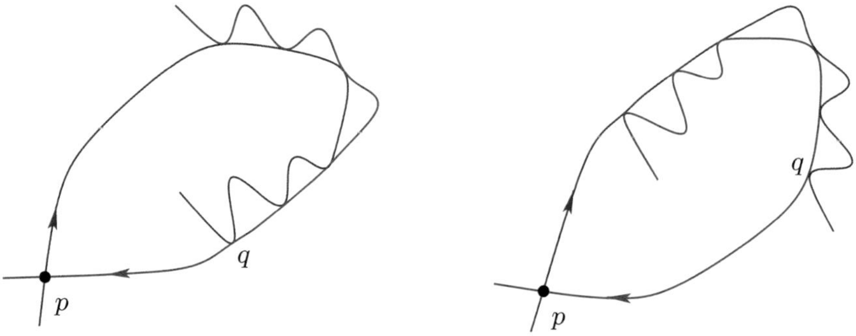

Figure 4.20. Quadratic homoclinic tangencies in two geometric configurations.

To inform our thinking, we will treat diffeomorphisms on $\mathbb{R}^2$. Let f be a diffeomorphism on the plane with a saddle fixed point p. Assume that the saddle fixed point is dissipative, meaning that the absolute value of the determinant of the Jacobian of f computed at the fixed point is less than one. A point q in the intersection of $W^s(p)$ and $W^u(p)$ is called a homoclinic point. We will consider the case where $W^s(p)$ and $W^u(p)$ are tangent at a homoclinic point q. Figure 4.20 provides an illustration with two pictures that are related by taking the inverse map. The tangency is called quadratic if the tangency gives a transverse intersection of $TW^s(p)$ and $TW^u(p)$ inside $T\mathbb{R}^2 = \mathbb{R}^4$. In this case one can take local coordinates (u, v) near q in which $W^s(p) = \{(u, v)\ ;\ v = 0\}$ and $W^u(p) = \{(u, v)\ ;\ v = au^2 + \mathcal{O}(u^3)\}$ for some $a \neq 0$.

The following rescaling result can be found in [**129**] where a proof using cross coordinates is presented. An approach that uses a C^2 local linearization is in [**282**, § 3.4]. This requires assuming additional conditions on eigenvalues. We follow this approach, but apply a partial linearization (Theorem B.31) that does not require additional conditions on eigenvalues.

Theorem 4.42. *Let f_μ be a one-parameter family of diffeomorphisms on the plane with a hyperbolic saddle fixed point p_μ. Assume that for $\mu = 0$, the stable and unstable manifold $W^s(p_0)$, $W^u(p_0)$ are tangent at a point q, with a quadratic tangency. Assume that the eigenvalues λ, ν with $0 < \lambda < 1 < \nu$ of the linearized map at p_0 satisfy*

$$\lambda\nu < 1.$$

Then there are a constant N and, for each positive integer n, a reparametrization

$$\mu = M_n(\bar{\mu})$$

and a $\bar{\mu}$-dependent coordinate change

$$(x, y) = \Psi_{n,\bar{\mu}}(\bar{x}, \bar{y})$$

such that

(i) *for each compact set K in $(\bar{\mu}, \bar{x}, \bar{y})$ space, the image of K under the map*

$$(\bar{\mu}, \bar{x}, \bar{y}) \mapsto (M_n(\bar{\mu}), \Psi_{n,\bar{\mu}}(\bar{x}, \bar{y}))$$

converges as $n \to \infty$ to $(0, q)$ in (μ, x, y) space; and

(ii) *the domains of the maps*

$$(\bar{\mu}, \bar{x}, \bar{y}) \mapsto (\bar{\mu}, \Psi_{n,\bar{\mu}}^{-1} \circ f_{M_n(\bar{\mu})}^{n+N} \circ \Psi_{n,\bar{\mu}})$$

converge for $n \to \infty$ to all of $\mathbb{R}^3$ and the maps converge in the C^2 topology to

$$(\bar{\mu}, \bar{x}, \bar{y}) \mapsto (\bar{\mu}, \bar{y}^2 + \bar{\mu}).$$

Proof. Take local coordinates near the fixed point given by Theorem B.31. We obtain a formula

$$f_\mu(x, y) = (\lambda x(1 + \mathcal{O}(y)), \nu y).$$

Note that ν and λ depend on μ although this is not expressed in the formulas. A calculation shows that, assuming that $(x_i, y_i) = f_\mu^i(x_0, y_0)$ is in the local coordinate system for $0 \leq i \leq n$,

$$f_\mu^n(x_0, y_0) = (\lambda^n x_0(1 + \mathcal{O}(y_0)), \nu^n y_0); \tag{4.70}$$

see Exercise 4.27.

Let q be a point in the orbit of tangency in the local stable manifold and let r be a point in the local unstable manifold. By rescaling, we may assume $q = (1, 0)$ and $r = (0, 1)$. Since q and r are in the orbit of tangency, there is $N > 0$ with $f_0^N(r) = q$. We reparametrize μ so that the y coordinate of $f_\mu^N(0, 1)$ is μ. After these preliminary steps we can write f_μ^N near $(0, 1)$ as

$$(u, 1 + v) \mapsto (1 + au + bv + \tilde{H}_1(\mu, u, v), \mu + cu + dv^2 + \tilde{H}_2(\mu, u, v)).$$

Here a, b, c, d are constants with $b, c, d \neq 0$ and

$$\begin{aligned}
\tilde{H}_1, D_u\tilde{H}_1, D_v\tilde{H}_1, D_\mu\tilde{H}_1 &= 0,\\
\tilde{H}_2, D_u\tilde{H}_2, D_v\tilde{H}_2, D_\mu\tilde{H}_2 &= 0,\\
D_v^2\tilde{H}_2, D_\mu^2\tilde{H}_2, D_{v\mu}^2\tilde{H}_2 &= 0,
\end{aligned}$$

all terms computed in $(0, 0, 0)$. Next we define reparametrizations of μ and a μ-dependent coordinate transformations by the following formulas:

$$\begin{aligned}
\mu &= \nu^{-2n}\bar{\mu} - c\lambda^n + \nu^{-n},\\
x &= 1 + \nu^{-n}\bar{x},\\
y &= \nu^{-n} + \nu^{-2n}\bar{y}.
\end{aligned}$$

The inverse transformation is given by

$$\begin{aligned}\bar{\mu} &= \nu^{2n}\mu + c\lambda^n\nu^{2n} - \nu^n,\\ \bar{x} &= \nu^n(x-1),\\ \bar{y} &= \nu^{2n}y - \nu^n.\end{aligned} \tag{4.71}$$

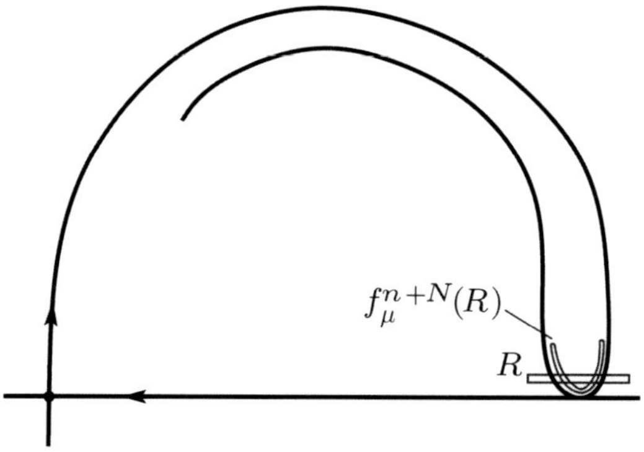

Figure 4.21. Rescalings of high iterates of f on a suitable rectangle R near a point of quadratic homoclinic tangency are perturbations of quadratic maps.

We start with the calculation to express f_μ^{n+N} in terms of $\bar{\mu}, \bar{x}, \bar{y}$; compare Figure 4.21. Consider a point (x_0, y_0) and $(x_i, y_i) = f_\mu^i(x_0, y_0)$ near the origin for $0 \le i \le n$, with x_0 near 1 and y_n near 1. In rescaled coordinates we write for instance $(\bar{x}_0, \bar{y}_0)$ as given by (4.71). After applying f_μ^n to (x_0, y_0), we get

$$\begin{aligned}x_n &= \lambda^n(1 + \nu^{-n}\bar{x}_0)(1 + \mathcal{O}(\nu^{-n} + \nu^{-2n}\bar{y}_0)),\\ y_n &= 1 + \nu^{-n}\bar{y}_0.\end{aligned}$$

Next we apply f_μ^N and find

$$\begin{aligned}x_{n+N} &= 1 + a\lambda^n(1 + \nu^{-n}\bar{x}_0)(1 + \mathcal{O}(\nu^{-n} + \nu^{-2n}\bar{y}_0)) + b\nu^{-n}\bar{y}_0 + \tilde{H}_1,\\ y_{n+N} &= (\nu^{-2n}\bar{\mu} - c\lambda^n + \nu^{-n}) + c\lambda^n(1 + \nu^{-n}\bar{x}_0)(1 + \mathcal{O}(\nu^{-n} + \nu^{-2n}\bar{y}_0))\\ &\quad + d\nu^{-2n}\bar{y}_0^2 + \tilde{H}_2,\end{aligned}$$

with $\tilde{H}_1, \tilde{H}_2$ calculated in

$$(\mu, x_n, y_n - 1) = (\mu, \lambda^n(1 + \nu^{-n}\bar{x}_0)(1 + \mathcal{O}(\nu^{-n} + \nu^{-2n}\bar{y}_0)), \nu^{-n}\bar{y}_0).$$

Transforming this back to the $(\bar{x}, \bar{y})$ coordinates, we have

$$\begin{aligned}\bar{x}_{n+N} &= a\lambda^n\nu^n(1 + \nu^{-n}\bar{x}_0)(1 + \mathcal{O}(\nu^{-n} + \nu^{-2n}\bar{y}_0)) + b\bar{y}_0 + \nu^n\tilde{H}_1,\\ \bar{y}_{n+N} &= \bar{\mu} + c\lambda^n\nu^n\bar{x}_0 + d\bar{y}_0^2 + \tilde{H}_2.\end{aligned}$$

In the expressions, terms with a factor $\lambda^n\nu^n\bar{x}_0$ go to zero as $n \to \infty$ because $\lambda\nu < 1$. When $(\bar{\mu}, \bar{x}_0, \bar{y}_0)$ remains bounded, the corresponding values of $(\mu, x_n, y_n - 1)$, which are substituted in $\tilde{H}_1, \tilde{H}_2$, satisfy

$$\mu = \mathcal{O}(\nu^{-n}), \quad x_n = \mathcal{O}(\lambda^n), \quad y_n - 1 = \mathcal{O}(\nu^{-n})$$

as $n \to \infty$. Define

$$\begin{aligned}\bar{H}_1(\bar{\mu}, \bar{x}_0, \bar{y}_0) &= \nu^n \tilde{H}_1(\mu, x_n, y_n - 1)\\ &= \nu^n \tilde{H}_1(\nu^{-2n}\bar{\mu} - c\lambda^n + \nu^{-n}, \lambda^n(1 + \nu^{-n}\bar{x}_0)(1 + \mathcal{O}(\nu^{-n})), \nu^{-n}\bar{y}_0).\end{aligned}$$

Then

$$\bar{H}_1(0,0,0) = \nu^n \tilde{H}_1(-c\lambda^n + \nu^{-n}, \lambda^n(1 + \mathcal{O}(\nu^{-n})), 0) = \nu^n \mathcal{O}(\lambda^n)$$

converges to zero for $n \to \infty$. Likewise, the first and second derivatives of $\bar{H}_1(\bar{\mu}, \bar{x}_0, \bar{y}_0)$ converge to zero, uniformly on compact sets. The same procedure works for the expressions in the formula for $\bar{y}_{n+N}$. So, for $n \to \infty$, the transformation formulas converge to

$$\begin{aligned}\bar{x}_{n+N} &= b\bar{y}_0,\\ \bar{y}_{n+N} &= \bar{\mu} + d\bar{y}_0^2.\end{aligned}$$

By a final substitution

$$\bar{\mu} = \tilde{\mu}/d, \quad \bar{x} = b\tilde{x}/d, \quad \bar{y} = \tilde{y}/d,$$

the limiting transformation becomes

$$(\tilde{x}, \tilde{y}) \mapsto (\tilde{y}, \tilde{\mu} + \tilde{y}^2). \qquad \square$$

Remark 4.43. A proof using cross coordinates [**129**] proceeds along the following lines. We adopt notation from the above proof. Start with the local normal form from Remark 4.39. Use this to prove expansions for iterates $(x_n, y_n) = f_\mu^n(x_0, y_0)$ near the fixed point, in cross coordinates. So write $(x_n, y_0) = g_\mu(x_0, y_n)$ and obtain the following expansions for g_μ:

$$\begin{aligned}x_n &= \lambda^n x_0 + \mathcal{O}(\lambda^n\nu^{-n}),\\ y_0 &= \nu^{-n} y_n + \mathcal{O}(\nu^{-2n}).\end{aligned}$$

Compose with the global map f_μ^N from a neighborhood of r to a neighborhood of q, as in the above proof. Use also expansions for $(x_{2n+N}, y_{n+N}) = g_\mu(x_{n+N}, y_{2n+N})$. Combine all these formulas to obtain expressions that relate (x_{n+N}, y_{n+N}) and (x_0, y_{2n+N}). An application of the implicit function theorem allows us to write (x_{n+N}, y_{2n+N}) as a function of (x_0, y_{n+N}), and a rescaling by a factor $\sim \nu^{-n}$ proves the above theorem. A possible way to interpret the formulas is by viewing (x_0, y_{n+N}) as coordinates on a box R near q. ■

4.2.3. Melnikov method. This section is devoted to an analytical method that allows us to prove homoclinic tangles and suspended horseshoes in a setting of nonautonomous differential equations. We consider a specific setup of a smooth nonautonomous differential equation

$$\dot{x} = f(x) + g(x,t,\lambda) \tag{4.72}$$

with $x \in \mathbb{R}^n$, $\lambda \in \mathbb{R}$, and where g is periodic with period $T > 0$ in t. We also assume that

$$g(x,t,0) \equiv 0,$$

so that (4.72) is, for small values of λ, a perturbation from $\dot{x} = f(x)$. We connect to the setup of Section 4.1.2, so that we can use results from there, and assume that $\dot{x} = f(x)$ admits a hyperbolic saddle equilibrium p with simple real leading eigenvalues and a nondegenerate homoclinic orbit h to p.

Adding an equation $\dot{t} = 1$, we obtain a system of equations

$$\begin{aligned} \dot{x} &= f(x) + g(x,t,\lambda), \\ \dot{t} &= 1, \end{aligned} \tag{4.73}$$

with variables $(x,t) \in \mathbb{R}^n \times R$. As the function g is T-periodic, we may also consider this as a system on $\mathbb{R}^n \times (\mathbb{R}/T\mathbb{Z})$. For each λ the Poincaré return map $\Pi_\lambda : \mathbb{R}^n \times \{t = 0\} \to \mathbb{R}^n \times \{t = 0\}$ is then a stroboscopic map given as the time T flow of the system. We want to note that $\mathbb{R}^n \times \{t = 0\}$ is a global cross section for the flow of (4.73). An application of the implicit function theorem gives a saddle periodic orbit $p_\lambda(t)$ continuing p for λ near 0. This defines a fixed point $(p_\lambda, 0)$ for Π_λ. We are interested in determining conditions that guarantee transverse intersections of stable and unstable manifolds of p_λ for Π_λ. As explained in Section 4.2.1 this would imply the existence of horseshoes for Π. Note that due to the existence of a global cross section, a transverse intersection of the stable and unstable manifolds of the periodic orbit $p_\lambda(\cdot)$ with respect to the flow of (4.73) is manifested by a transverse intersection of the stable and unstable manifolds of the fixed point p_λ of Π_λ.

Given a real number τ, take a cross section $S_\tau \subset \mathbb{R}^n$ through $h(-\tau)$, perpendicular to the homoclinic orbit h of $\dot{x} = f(x)$; see also right panel in Figure 4.22. As in Section 4.1.2.2, consider the line

$$Z_\tau = \left(T_{h(-\tau)} W^{ss,s}(p) + T_{h(-\tau)} W^{u,uu}(p)\right)^\perp$$

inside S_τ. Consider the solutions $h^s_\lambda(\cdot,\tau)$ in $W^s(p_\lambda)$ with $h^s_\lambda(0,\tau) \in S_\tau$ and $h^u_\lambda(\cdot,\tau)$ in $W^u(p_\lambda)$ with $h^u_\lambda(0,\tau) \in S_\tau$, as given in Lemma 4.18. In particular, $h^s_\lambda(0,\tau) - h^u_\lambda(0,\tau) \in Z_\tau$.

To make a better connection to Section 4.1.2.2, let us make it clear that with h also h_τ, $h_\tau(t) = h(t-\tau)$ describes the same homoclinic orbit (of $\dot{x} = f(x)$) to p. Note that $h_\tau(0) = h(-\tau)$.

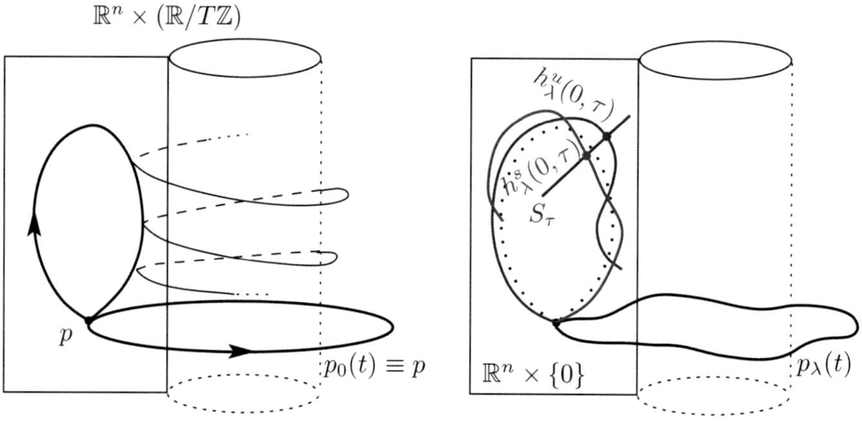

Figure 4.22. Invariant manifolds of (4.73) in the state space $\mathbb{R}^n \times (\mathbb{R}/T\mathbb{Z})$. Left picture: for $\lambda = 0$, part of the stable and unstable manifolds of the periodic solution $\{(p,t)\}$ coincide to form a *homoclinic manifold.* Right picture: for $\lambda \neq 0$, the periodic orbit $\{(p_\lambda(t),t)\}$ has unstable (blue) and stable (red) manifolds that may have transverse intersections within $\mathbb{R} \times \{0\}$.

Now, let $\hat{\eta}_\tau \in Z$. There is a unique bounded solution η_τ to the initial value problem

$$\dot{x}(t) = -(Df_0(h_\tau(t)))^T x(t), \quad x(0) = \hat{\eta}_\tau.$$

This solution $\eta_\tau(t)$ is perpendicular to both $W^{ss,s}(p)$ and $W^{u,uu}(p)$ along the homoclinic orbit $h(t)$. Then

$$d(\tau,\lambda) = h^u_\lambda(0,\tau) - h^s_\lambda(0,\tau)$$

measures the signed distance between stable and unstable manifolds of p_λ inside S_τ.

Lemma 4.44.

$$\langle \eta_\tau(0), d(\tau,\lambda)\rangle = \lambda\Big(\int_{-\infty}^{\infty} \langle \eta_\tau(t), D_\lambda g(h_\tau(t),t,0)\rangle\, dt\Big) + \mathcal{O}(\lambda^2).$$

Proof. One can copy the reasoning in the proof of Lemma 4.7 (Exercise 4.28). □

The function M with

$$M(\tau) = \int_{-\infty}^{\infty} \langle \eta_\tau(t), D_\lambda g(h_\tau(t),t,0)\rangle\, dt, \tag{4.74}$$

the integral appearing in Lemma 4.44, is known as the Melnikov function after Viktor Melnikov [**250**]. The following theorem is known as the Melnikov method for the detection of transverse homoclinic orbits. From those research papers that develop the theory and can be consulted for further information and extensions, we mention [**57**, **140**, **164**, **283**, **308**, **330**, **366**]. Examples of papers that apply the Melnikov method in a bifurcation analysis are [**109**, **156**, **213**].

Theorem 4.45. *Consider (4.72) and assume that for $\lambda = 0$ the resulting autonomous equation $\dot{x} = f(x)$ has a hyperbolic saddle equilibrium p and $Df(p)$ has simple real leading eigenvalues μ^s, μ^u with $\mu^s < 0 < \mu^u$ and a homoclinic orbit $h(t)$ with*

$$\lim_{t\to\infty} h(t) = \lim_{t\to-\infty} h(t) = p.$$

Assume the homoclinic orbit is nondegenerate:

$$T_{h(0)}W^s(p) \cap T_{h(0)}W^u(p) = T_{h(0)}\,\mathrm{span}\{f(h(0))\}.$$

Suppose that the Melnikov function M given by (4.74) has a zero $M(\tau) = 0$ with $M'(\tau) \neq 0$. Then (4.72) admits a transverse homoclinic orbit to the periodic orbit p_λ, for small, nonzero values of λ. Hence (4.72) admits invariant sets that are suspensions of horseshoes.

Proof. The assumptions on the Melnikov function imply that $W^s(p_\lambda)$ and $W^u(p_\lambda)$ have a transverse intersection for small, nonzero values of λ. The horseshoes exist by the results in Section 4.2.1. □

Simplified formulas for the Melnikov function exist in special cases. Following Remark 4.8 and Remark 4.9, consider $\dot{x} = f(x) + \lambda g(x,t)$ with x in the plane $\mathbb{R}^2$ and with $\mathrm{div}\, f \equiv 0$. Suppose $\dot{x} = f(x)$ admits a homoclinic orbit h. In this case M can be written as

$$M(\tau) = \frac{1}{|f(h(0))|}\int_{-\infty}^{\infty} f(h(t-\tau)) \wedge g(h(t-\tau),t)\,dt. \tag{4.75}$$

The following two examples treat nonautonomous perturbations to the inverted Duffing oscillator

$$\ddot{x} - x + x^3 = 0. \tag{4.76}$$

We refer to [**143**, Section 2.2] and [**381**, Chapter 6] for background on this differential equation.

Example 4.46. Consider the Hamiltonian function $H(x,y) = \frac{1}{2}y^2 - \frac{1}{2}x^2 + \frac{1}{4}x^4$ and the corresponding Hamiltonian differential equation $\dot{x} = \frac{\partial H}{\partial y}$, $\dot{y} = -\frac{\partial H}{\partial y}$:

$$\begin{aligned} \dot{x} &= y, \\ \dot{y} &= x - x^3. \end{aligned} \tag{4.77}$$

This system is equivalent to (4.76). It admits homoclinic orbits to the saddle equilibrium at the origin, inside the level set $\{H = 0\}$; see Figure 4.23.

The equation $H = 0$ is solved by $y^2 = x^2 - \frac{1}{2}x^4$, so that $y = \pm x\sqrt{1 - \frac{1}{2}x^2}$. The differential equation gives $\dot{x} = \pm x\sqrt{1 - \frac{1}{2}x^2}$. Solving for the homoclinic orbit in $\{x > 0\}$, this gives

$$h(t) = (\sqrt{2}\,\mathrm{sech}(t), -\sqrt{2}\,\mathrm{sech}(t)\tanh(t)).$$

Note that the second component from h follows from $y = \dot{x}$. Recall that the hyperbolic secant $\mathrm{sech}(t)$ is defined by $\mathrm{sech}(t) = 1/\cosh(t)$. This gives $h(0) = (\sqrt{2}, 0)$.

Now take the differential equations with a small nonautonomous forcing term added,

$$\begin{aligned}\dot{x} &= y,\\ \dot{y} &= x - x^3 + \lambda\cos(t).\end{aligned}$$

For λ small there is a periodic orbit with period $T = 2\pi$ near the origin. Adopting the notation from above, we find $g((x,y),t,\lambda) = (0, \lambda\cos(t))$. With the Melnikov method we can study homoclinic orbits to this periodic orbit. According to (4.75), the Melnikov function is given by

$$\begin{aligned}M(\tau) &= -\int_{-\infty}^{\infty} \mathrm{sech}(t-\tau)\tanh(t-\tau)\cos(t)\,dt\\ &= -\int_{-\infty}^{\infty} \mathrm{sech}(t)\tanh(t)\cos(t+\tau)\,dt.\end{aligned}$$

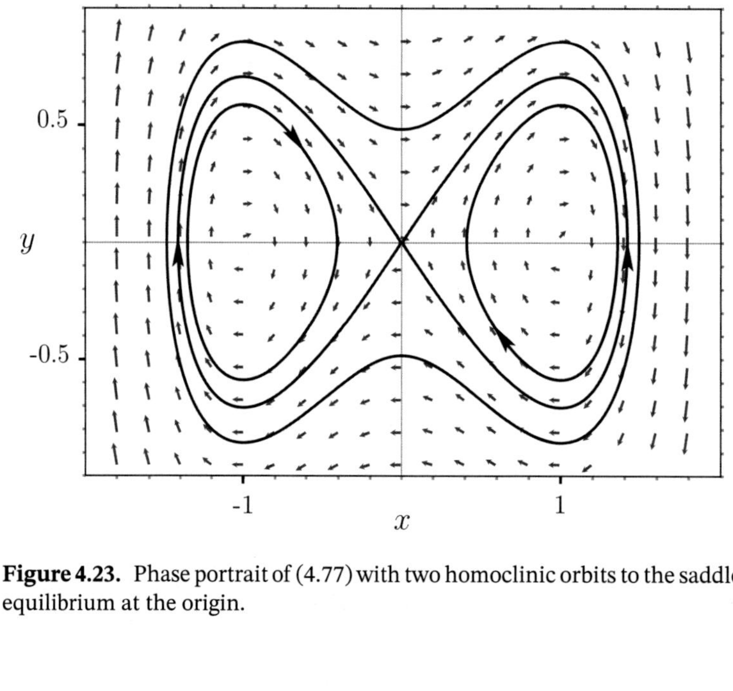

Figure 4.23. Phase portrait of (4.77) with two homoclinic orbits to the saddle equilibrium at the origin.

Now

$$\begin{aligned}
M(\tau) &= -\int_{-\infty}^{\infty} \operatorname{sech}(t)\tanh(t)\cos(t+\tau)\,dt \\
&= \operatorname{sech}(t)\tanh(t)\cos(t+\tau)|_{-\infty}^{\infty} + \int_{-\infty}^{\infty} \operatorname{sech}(t)\sin(t+\tau)\,dt \\
&= \int_{-\infty}^{\infty} \operatorname{sech}(t)\left(\sin(t)\cos(\tau)+\cos(t)\sin(\tau)\right)\,dt \\
&= \sin(\tau)\int_{-\infty}^{\infty} \operatorname{sech}(t)\cos(t)\,dt.
\end{aligned}$$

This final integral can be evaluated by residue calculus (see for instance [**118**]). To do this, take $R > 0$ and let D be the rectangle in the complex plane with edges $-R, R, R + \pi i, -R + \pi i$. The singularities of $z \mapsto \operatorname{sech}(z)$ in are $z_n = \pi i(n + \frac{1}{2})$, $n \in \mathbb{Z}$: the rectangle D contains a single singularity $z_0 = \frac{1}{2}\pi i$. Note that

$$M(\tau) = \operatorname{Re}\, \sin(\tau)\int_{-\infty}^{\infty} \operatorname{sech}(t)e^{it}\,dt.$$

Residue calculus gives $\operatorname{Res}\left[\operatorname{sech}(z), z_0\right] = -i$ and

$$\begin{aligned}
\int_{\partial D} \operatorname{sech}(z)e^{iz}\,dz &= 2\pi i \operatorname{Res}\left[\operatorname{sech}(z)e^{iz}, z_0\right] \\
&= 2\pi i\left(-ie^{-\pi/2}\right) \\
&= 2\pi e^{-\pi/2},
\end{aligned}$$

traversing ∂D counterclockwise. The integral over ∂D decomposes as a sum of four integrals over the four sides of D. The integrals over the two vertical sides, $\int_{-R}^{-R+\pi i} \operatorname{sech}(z)e^{iz}\,dz$ and $\int_{R}^{R+\pi i} \operatorname{sech}(z)e^{iz}\,dz$, converge to 0 as $R \to \infty$. Further, $\int_{-R+\pi i}^{R+\pi i} \operatorname{sech}(z)e^{iz}\,dz = \int_{-R}^{R} \operatorname{sech}(z+\pi i)e^{iz}e^{-\pi}\,dz$ is equal to $-e^{-\pi}\int_{-R}^{R} \operatorname{sech}(z)e^{iz}\,dz$. We conclude that

$$\begin{aligned}
\int_{-\infty}^{\infty} \operatorname{sech}(z)e^{iz}\,dz &= \frac{1}{1+e^{-\pi}}\int_{\partial D} \operatorname{sech}(z)e^{iz}\,dz \\
&= \frac{1}{1+e^{-\pi}}2e^{-\pi/2}.
\end{aligned}$$

Rewriting $\frac{1}{1+e^{-\pi}}2e^{-\pi/2} = \operatorname{sech}\left(\frac{\pi}{2}\right)$, we obtain

$$M(\tau) = \pi\operatorname{sech}\left(\frac{\pi}{2}\right)\sin(\tau).$$

From Theorem 4.45 we conclude that for small nonzero λ, stable and unstable manifolds of the saddle periodic orbit near $x = 0, y = 0$ intersect transversely.
■

Melnikov's method can also be used to detect homoclinic tangencies. We won't pursue this, but we include a brief description of an example in which this arises. The example continues the previous example and treats the inverted Duffing oscillator with nonautonomous forcing and friction terms,

$$\ddot{x} + \lambda\kappa\dot{x} - x + x^3 = \lambda\gamma\cos(t). \tag{4.78}$$

See [**143**, Section 4.5] for more information.

Example 4.47. Equation (4.78) is equivalent to the nonautonomous system of differential equations

$$\begin{aligned}\dot{x} &= y,\\ \dot{y} &= x - x^3 - \lambda\kappa y + \lambda\gamma\cos(t).\end{aligned}$$

The Melnikov function introduced in Example 4.46 is here given by

$$\begin{aligned}M(\tau) &= -\int_{-\infty}^{\infty} \operatorname{sech}(t)\tanh(t)(-\kappa\operatorname{sech}(t)\tanh(t) + \gamma\cos(t+\tau))\,dt\\ &= \kappa\int_{-\infty}^{\infty} \operatorname{sech}^2(t)\tanh^2(t)\,dt - \gamma\int_{-\infty}^{\infty} \operatorname{sech}(t)\tanh(t)\cos(t+\tau)\,dt\\ &= \kappa\int_{-\infty}^{\infty} \operatorname{sech}^2(t)\tanh^2(t)\,dt - \gamma\sin(\tau)\int_{-\infty}^{\infty} \operatorname{sech}(t)\cos(t)\,dt.\end{aligned}$$

Evaluating the integrals gives

$$M(\tau) = \frac{2}{3}\kappa - \pi\gamma\operatorname{sech}\left(\frac{1}{2}\pi\right)\sin(\tau).$$

Assuming that $\kappa > 0, \gamma > 0, M(\tau) = 0$ will be met for some τ if

$$\frac{2\kappa}{3\pi\gamma}\cosh\left(\frac{1}{2}\pi\right) \leq 1.$$

If κ is fixed, a homoclinic tangency will first occur for increasing forcing amplitude γ when

$$\gamma = \gamma_c = \frac{2\kappa}{3\pi}\cosh\left(\frac{1}{2}\pi\right),$$

and transverse homoclinic orbits will be present if γ exceeds this value (Exercise 4.29). ■

4.3. Exercises

Exercise 4.1. Consider Fisher's equation: the partial differential equation

$$\frac{\partial u}{\partial t} = \frac{\partial^2 u}{\partial x^2} + ru(1-u)$$

for functions $u : \mathbb{R}\times\mathbb{R} \to \mathbb{R}$ and a constant $r > 0$. Ronald Fisher proposed this equation to describe the spatial spread of an advantageous allele and explored its traveling wave solutions—solutions of the form $u(x,t) = v(x - ct)$.

Show that a traveling wave must satisfy the second-order ordinary differential equation

$$v'' + cv' + rv(1 - v) = 0.$$

Show that, for every $c > 2\sqrt{r}$, there is a traveling wave solution satisfying $v(s) \to 1$ as $s \to -\infty$ and $v(s) \to 0$ as $s \to \infty$, with $v' < 0$.
Hint: Consider the corresponding first-order system and discuss stability properties of the equilibrium at $(1, 0)$. Then show that there is a triangular region in the (v, v')-plane bounded by the lines $v' = 0$, $v = 1$, $v' = -\mu v$, μ appropriate, which is positively invariant.

Exercise 4.2. Consider the system

$$\dot{x} = y,$$
$$\dot{y} = -2x - ay - 3x^2$$

with $a > 0$.

(i) Show that (0,0) is asymptotically stable and (−2/3,0) is a saddle point.

(ii) Draw typical level sets of $V(x, y) = y^2/2 + x^2 + x^3$. This function is conserved when $a = 0$. Notice especially that $V(x, y) = 0$ contains a homoclinic orbit for $a = 0$.

(iii) For every initial condition $(x_0, y_0) \in \mathbb{R}^2$ for which the positive orbit is bounded, show that the ω-limit set is one of the equilibria.

(iv) Estimate the basin of attraction of the origin.

(v) Show that for (x_0, y_0) in the stable manifold $W^s((-2/3, 0))$, the negative orbit of (x_0, y_0) diverges to infinity.

(vi) Observe that there are orbits that are unbounded for positive as well as negative time.

(vii) Sketch the phase portrait of the system in the plane.

Exercise 4.3. Consider the two-dimensional system

$$\dot{x} = \mu + x^2 - xy,$$
$$\dot{y} = y^2 - x^2 - 1. \tag{4.79}$$

(i) Take $\mu = 0$. Show that (4.79) has two saddle points $P^+(0)$ and $P^-(0)$ and these points are connected by a heteroclinic orbit. Give a sketch of the phase portrait.

(ii) Now consider $\mu \neq 0$ and small. Determine a Taylor expansion of the saddles $P^+(\mu)$ and $P^-(\mu)$ up to quadratic terms in μ. What happens to the heteroclinic orbit? Give sketches of the phase portraits for $\mu < 0$ and $\mu > 0$.

Exercise 4.4. Consider the integrable system (that is, the system has a first integral)

$$\begin{aligned} \dot{x} &= y, \\ \dot{y} &= -x + x^3 - C, \end{aligned} \tag{4.80}$$

with $C \in \mathbb{R}$.

(i) Determine the set I_{hom} such that (4.80) has a homoclinic orbit if $C \in I_{\text{hom}}$. For which values of $C = C_{\text{het}}$ does (4.80) have heteroclinic orbits? Give sketches of the phase portraits of (4.80) for C such that $C_{\text{het}} > C \in I_{\text{hom}}$, $C = C_{\text{het}}$, $C_{\text{het}} < C \in I_{\text{hom}}$, and $C_{\text{het}} \neq C \notin I_{\text{hom}}$.

(ii) Now consider a more general version of (4.80),

$$\begin{aligned} \dot{x} &= y, \\ \dot{y} &= -x + Ax^2 + Bx^3 - C, \end{aligned} \tag{4.81}$$

where $A, B, C \in \mathbb{R}$. For which A, B, C does (4.81) have heteroclinic orbits.

Exercise 4.5. Let $V : \mathbb{R}^2 \to \mathbb{R}$ be a smooth function and consider the associated gradient flow

$$\dot{x} = -\nabla V(x). \tag{4.82}$$

Prove that (4.82) cannot have a homoclinic orbit.

Exercise 4.6. Consider the two-dimensional system

$$\begin{aligned} \dot{x} &= 1 + y - x^2 - y^2, \\ \dot{y} &= 1 - x - x^2 - y^2. \end{aligned} \tag{4.83}$$

(i) Determine the equilibria of (4.83) and their local character. Show that the flow generated by (4.83) is symmetric with respect to the line $\{x + y = 0\}$.

(ii) Show that (4.83) is integrable by constructing an integral $K(x, y)$. *Hint*: Introduce new variables $u = x - y$ and $v = x + y$ that exploit the symmetry, write (4.83) as a system in u and v, and determine an integral $\tilde{K}(u, v)$ for this by introducing $w = v^2$ and solving the equation for $\frac{dw}{du}$.

(iii) Sketch the phase portrait associated to (4.83) and conclude that (4.83) has a homoclinic orbit.

Now consider a more general version of (4.83),

$$\begin{aligned} \dot{x} &= 1 + y - x^2 - y^2 + h(x, y), \\ \dot{y} &= 1 - x - x^2 - y^2 + h(x, y), \end{aligned} \tag{4.84}$$

with $h : \mathbb{R}^2 \to \mathbb{R}$, $h(0, 0) = 0$, a smooth function.

(iv) Take $h(x, y) = \varepsilon(x + y)$ with $\varepsilon > 0$ small. Show that the homoclinic orbit of (4.83) does not survive the perturbation of (4.84).
Hint: Determine $\dot{K}$ or $\dot{\tilde{K}}$.

(v) Take $h(x, y) = \alpha(x - y)^3$, $\alpha \in \mathbb{R}$. Show that (4.84) is integrable by deriving an integral $K_\alpha(x, y)$ (or $\tilde{K}_\alpha(u, v)$) such that $K_0(x, y) = K(x, y)$.

(vi) Again take $h(x, y) = \alpha(x - y)^3$, now with $\alpha > 0$ small. Show that (4.84) has a homoclinic orbit and give a sketch of the phase portrait.

(vii) Again take $h(x, y) = \alpha(x - y)^3$, now with $\alpha > 0$ large. Show that (4.84) does not have a homoclinic orbit and give a sketch of the phase portrait.

Exercise 4.7. Consider a planar differential equation $\dot{x} = f_a(x)$ with, for $a = 0$, a homoclinic orbit γ to a hyperbolic equilibrium p. Writing $\mu < 0 < \lambda$ for the eigenvalues at p, assume $\mu + \lambda < 0$. Prove that there is a neighborhood U of $\gamma \cup \{p\}$ and $a_0 > 0$, so that for $|a| < a_0$ there is at most one periodic orbit in U. Such a periodic orbit is attracting.
Hint: Suppose η is a periodic orbit of f_a, of period T. The nonzero Floquet exponent ℓ of it satisfies

$$\ell = \frac{1}{T} \int_0^T \operatorname{tr} \frac{\partial f_a}{\partial x}(\eta(t))\, dt.$$

Show that $\ell \to \operatorname{tr} \frac{\partial f_a}{\partial x}(0) < 0$ as $a \to 0$. Conclude with an application of the Poincaré-Bendixson theorem.

Exercise 4.8. Consider the context of Section 4.1.1. Show that

$$e^{-\int_0^t \operatorname{div} f_0(h(s))\, ds}(f_0^2(h(t)), -f_0^1(h(t)))$$

is a bounded solution of (4.5).

Exercise 4.9. For $\alpha > 0$ and $I \geq 0$, consider the system

$$\begin{aligned} \dot{\phi} &= y, \\ \dot{y} &= I - \sin(\phi) - \alpha y \end{aligned} \tag{4.85}$$

on the cylinder $\mathbb{R}/2\pi\mathbb{Z} \times \mathbb{R}$.

(i) Analyze the existence and stability of equilibria.

(ii) Prove the existence of a periodic solution for $I > 1$ by following these steps:
  (a) Find an invariant strip $S = \mathbb{R}/2\pi\mathbb{Z} \times (y_1, y_2)$ with $0 < y_1 < y_2$.
  (b) Consider the first return map P on $\Sigma = \{0\} \times (y_1, y_2)$; $P(y_0) = (y_1)$ where $(0, y_1)$ is the first point on Σ from the positive orbit with

initial condition $(0, y_0)$. Prove that P is the time 2π map of

$$\frac{dy}{d\phi} = \frac{I - \sin(\phi) - \alpha y}{y}. \tag{4.86}$$

(c) Apply the intermediate value theorem to find a fixed point of P and thus a periodic solution of (4.85).

(iii) Prove uniqueness of the periodic solution by following these steps:

(a) Consider the function $E = \frac{1}{2}y^2 - \cos(\phi)$ along solutions of (4.86). Show that

$$\int_0^{2\pi} \frac{dE}{d\phi}\, d\phi = 0$$

along periodic solutions.

(b) Prove $\frac{dE}{d\phi} = I - \alpha y$.

(c) Combine the two previous steps to show

$$\int_0^{2\pi} y(\phi)\, d\phi = 2\pi I/\alpha$$

along periodic solutions.

(d) Derive a contradiction from the assumption that two periodic solutions exist.

Exercise 4.10. Derive the homoclinic bifurcation curve given by (4.15) for the Josephson junction model in Example 4.12, using Lemma 4.7. Analyze also the other homoclinic orbit

$$\gamma(t) = (-2\arctan(\sinh(t)), -2\,\mathrm{sech}(t))$$

and show that this does not give homoclinic orbits in perturbations with $\alpha > 0$.

Exercise 4.11. Consider the differential equations

$$\begin{aligned}
\dot{u} &= x,\\
\dot{x} &= uv^2 - \lambda(1-u),\\
\dot{v} &= y,\\
\dot{y} &= \lambda\left(v - uv^2\right).
\end{aligned}$$

Prove that for $\lambda > 9/2$, the system has a homoclinic solution to $(1, 0, 0, 0)$ given by

$$u(t) = 1 - \frac{3/\lambda}{1 + \sqrt{1 - \frac{9}{2\lambda}\cosh(\sqrt{\lambda}t)}}, \qquad v(t) = \frac{3}{1 + \sqrt{1 - \frac{9}{2\lambda}\cosh(\sqrt{\lambda}t)}}.$$

What happens at $\lambda = 9/2$? See [**149**].

Exercise 4.12. Consider the differential equations

$$\dot{x} = y,$$
$$\dot{y} = z,$$
$$\dot{z} = 18 - y + 4z - \frac{1}{2}x^2.$$

Show that the system has a homoclinic orbit to $(6, 0, 0)$ given by

$$x(t) = -9 - 15\tanh(t/2) + 15\tanh^2(t/2) + 15\tanh^3(t/2)$$

and $y(t) = \dot{x}(t), z(t) = \ddot{x}(t)$. Investigate the type of the equilibrium and the approach of the homoclinic orbit along leading directions. See [**12**].

Exercise 4.13. Give a self-contained proof of Theorem 4.14 in the case of a homoclinic orbit to an equilibrium with one-dimensional unstable direction.

Exercise 4.14. This exercise connects to Example 4.16. Analyze intersections of $(x, \lambda_1 + \lambda_3 x, \lambda_2 + x^2)$ with $(x, 0, 0)$.

Exercise 4.15. Derive (4.21).

Exercise 4.16. Prove Lemma 4.19.

Exercise 4.17. Prove (4.52).

Exercise 4.18. To finish the proof of Lemma 4.24, prove that F^{uu}, $F^{ss,s,u}$, and $F^{s,u,uu}$ are continuous bundles along the closure of the homoclinic orbit.

Exercise 4.19. Discuss how to obtain (4.53) from the implicit function theorem. Treat the set of equations also for $\beta < 1$.

Exercise 4.20. Finish the proof of Theorem 4.14. In particular, the existence of multiround periodic orbits must be excluded. Prove that there are no N-periodic orbits for $N > 1$, in a small but uniform neighborhood of the homoclinic orbit, for λ from a small but uniform neighborhood of 0. In other words, prove that there is a neighborhood $\mathcal{U}$ of $\overline{h}$, and an interval $I \ni 0$, so that for $\lambda \in I$, there are no N-periodic orbits, $N > 1$, in $\mathcal{U}$.

Exercise 4.21. Work out the construction of the local unstable manifold of ζ_λ in Σ, analogous to the local stable manifold in the proof of Lemma 4.27.

Exercise 4.22. Prove Lemma 4.31.

Exercise 4.23. Prove (4.67) in Remark 4.34.

Exercise 4.24. Consider the time-periodic Hamiltonian

$$H(q, p, t) = \frac{1}{2}(q^2 + p^2) - \frac{1}{3}q^3 - \varepsilon q \sin(t),$$

where ε is a small parameter.

(i) For $\varepsilon = 0$, sketch the phase diagram for the corresponding Hamiltonian system $\dot{q} = \frac{\partial H}{\partial p}$, $\dot{p} = -\frac{\partial H}{\partial q}$. For this, determine equilibria together with their type, and possible homoclinic or heteroclinic orbits.

(ii) Determine an expression in terms of p and q for all homoclinic and heteroclinic solutions that exist for $\varepsilon = 0$.
Hint: Use the Hamiltonian.

(iii) Determine the Melnikov function. For this you can use that

$$\int_{-\infty}^{\infty} \frac{\cos(t)}{\cosh^2(t/2)}\, dt = \frac{4\pi}{\sinh(\pi)}.$$

When do transverse homoclinic orbits exist?

(iv) Assume that the transverse intersection exists for $t = t^*$. Sketch the stable and unstable manifolds in (q, p)-space for $t < t^*$, $t = t^*$ and $t > t^*$.

Exercise 4.25. Consider the equation

$$\begin{aligned} \dot{\theta} &= v, \\ \dot{v} &= -\sin(\theta) + \varepsilon(\alpha + \gamma\cos(t)), \end{aligned}$$

where ε is small and positive.

(i) Determine the corresponding Hamiltonian.

(ii) Sketch the phase diagram for $\varepsilon = 0$. For this, determine equilibria together with their type, and possible homoclinic or heteroclinic orbits.

(iii) For $\varepsilon = 0$, determine an expression in terms of θ and v for all homoclinic and heteroclinic solutions that satisfy $-\frac{3}{2}\pi < \theta < \frac{3}{2}\pi$.
Hint: Substitute $\theta = 4\phi$.

(iv) Use the Melnikov method to determine bifurcation curves near which quadratic homoclinic tangencies occur.
Hint: Use

$$\int_{-\infty}^{\infty} \frac{\cos(t)^n}{\cosh(t)}\, dt = \frac{\pi}{\cosh(\pi/2)^n}$$

for $n = 0, 1$.

Exercise 4.26. Prove equation (4.69).

Exercise 4.27. Prove equation (4.70).

Exercise 4.28. Prove Lemma 4.44.

Exercise 4.29. Perform the calculations and work out the details of Example 4.47.

Chapter 5

Global bifurcations

A local bifurcation may not only affect dynamics near an equilibrium or periodic orbit but trigger other changes in the dynamics as well. If, for instance, a local bifurcation leads to the disappearance of an attractor, points will move to other attractors. It also happens that other attractors are created since orbits move through neighborhoods of the former attractors. The structure of the attractors and basins of attraction may thus have changed. The same remark holds for the effect of nonlocal bifurcations.

One may also wish to understand the geometric structure of the bifurcation set (the set of bifurcation values) in a large part of parameter space, instead of near a single bifurcation value. One problem is understanding through which bifurcations or sequences of bifurcations the dynamics can change from being simple dynamics to complex dynamics. This is referred to as *routes to chaos.*

In this chapter we show various ideas and results from such a global point of view. Unlike previous chapters we will give complete proofs only for some of the results, while providing sketches of proofs for other results or simply referring to research literature.

5.1. Global structural stability

Before an analysis of bifurcations can start, one must know the conditions that lead to bifurcations. Put another way, one must be able to classify the stable systems that do not lead to bifurcations. This section discusses notions of stability and bifurcation in a global setting and presents theory to appreciate these notions.

We develop a global point of view in a context of differential equations on manifolds. Appendix A.3 contains a brief recap of background on manifolds and the vector fields on manifolds. Let M be a compact manifold. A vector field or differential equation on M gives rise to a flow $\varphi^t : M \to M$ with $t \in \mathbb{R}$. Note that on open manifolds such as $\mathbb{R}^n$, orbits of differential equations may not be defined for all $t \in \mathbb{R}$. To avoid having to discuss intervals of existence is one reason to work on compact manifolds. In this section we work with vector fields on compact manifolds, denoted by M.

5.1.1. Topological equivalence and bifurcation. In Section 2.3 we introduced topological equivalence for the study of local bifurcations. Here we introduce and comment upon the notions for vector fields on manifolds. Similar to Definition 2.29 for flows in $\mathbb{R}^n$ we define an equivalence relation, topological equivalence, for vector fields f, g. Let φ^t, ψ^t be the flows of f and g, respectively.

Definition 5.1. Two vector fields f and g are *topologically equivalent* if there exists a homeomorphism $h : M \to M$ that sends orbits of f to orbits of g preserving the sense of orbits. That is, for all $x \in M$ and $t \in \mathbb{R}$ there is $t' \in \mathbb{R}$ with the same sign as t such that

$$h(\varphi^t(x)) = \psi^{t'}(h(x)).$$

Here φ^t and ψ^t are the flows of the vector fields f and g, respectively.

One can also consider a notion of topological conjugacy; compare Definition 2.30.

Definition 5.2. Two vector fields f and g are *topologically conjugate* if there exists a homeomorphism $h : M \to M$ such that

$$h(\varphi^t(x)) = \psi^t(h(x)).$$

Here φ^t and ψ^t are the flows of the vector fields f and g, respectively.

This seems a too restrictive definition for purposes of a qualitative study of dynamics. For instance periods of periodic orbits cannot be changed by a topological conjugacy. There are more restrictions as pointed out in the following result by Jacob Palis [**276**].

Theorem 5.3. *Let f be a vector field on a surface with a heteroclinic orbit $\gamma \subset W^u(p) \cap W^s(q)$ between two hyperbolic saddle equilibria p and q. Denote by μ^s the stable eigenvalue of $Df(p)$ and by ν^u the unstable eigenvalue of $Df(q)$. Let $\tilde{f}$ be a second vector field on the surface with a heteroclinic orbit $\tilde{\gamma}$ between hyperbolic saddle equilibria $\tilde{p}$ and $\tilde{q}$ with corresponding eigenvalues and write $\tilde{\mu}^s$ and $\tilde{\nu}^u$.*

If h is a topological conjugacy between f and $\tilde{f}$, with $h(\gamma) = \tilde{\gamma}$, then

$$-\mu^s/\nu^u = -\tilde{\mu}^s/\tilde{\nu}^u.$$

Proof. By Theorem B.30 we may take C^1 coordinates near the saddle equilibria in which the flows are linear. Let U_p, U_q, $\tilde{U}_{\tilde{p}}$, $\tilde{U}_{\tilde{q}}$ be neighborhoods in which linearizing coordinates exist. Writing $\varphi^t, \tilde{\varphi}^t$ for the flows of f and $\tilde{f}$, the topological conjugacy h satisfies

$$h \circ \varphi^t = \tilde{\varphi}^t \circ h.$$

Take a sequence of points $x_i \in W^s_{loc}(p)$ converging to $x \in U_p$ as $i \to \infty$. Take a sequence of points $y_i = \varphi^{t_i}(x_i) \in W^u_{loc}(p)$ converging to $y \in U_p$. Further take $z_i = \varphi^s(y_i)$ converging to $z = \varphi^s(y)$ in U_q. Finally, take points $w_i = \varphi^{s_i}(z_i)$ converging to a point $w \in U_q$. Note $w \in W^u_{loc}(q)$. Take similar points $\tilde{x}_i = h(x_i)$, $\tilde{y}_i = h(y_i)$, and so on, for the second vector field. Note that for instance $\tilde{y}_i = \tilde{\varphi}^{t_i}(\tilde{x}_i)$. We may assume $\tilde{x}_i \in \tilde{U}_{\tilde{p}}$ and so on; see Figure 5.1.

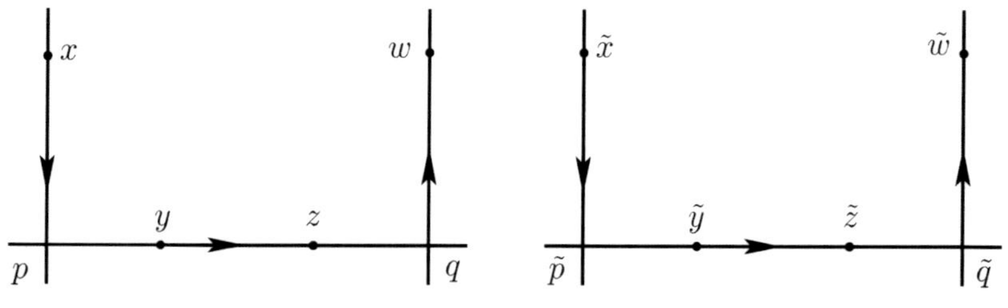

Figure 5.1. A heteroclinic orbit gives rise to an invariant for topological conjugacy.

Let a_i be the vertical coordinate of $\tilde{x}_i$ measured in the linearizing coordinates in U_p. Write a for the vertical coordinate of x. Likewise we have vertical coordinates b_i and b for the points w_i and w, measured in the linearizing coordinates in U_q. For the vector field $\tilde{f}$ we get coordinates $\tilde{a}_i$ and so on.

A straightforward calculation using the linearizing coordinates yields

$$b_i = a_i e^{\mu^s t_i} k_i e^{\nu^u s_i} \tag{5.1}$$

for some $k_i \to k$ as $i \to \infty$. Here k_i arises from the flow φ^s. For the vector field $\tilde{f}$ we get

$$\tilde{b}_i = \tilde{a}_i e^{\tilde{\mu}^s t_i} \tilde{k}_i e^{\tilde{\nu}^u s_i}$$

for some $\tilde{k}_i \to \tilde{k}$ as $i \to \infty$. From (5.1) we obtain that

$$\lim_{i\to\infty} s_i/t_i = -\mu^s/\nu^u.$$

As also $\lim_{i\to\infty} s_i/t_i = -\tilde{\mu}^s/\tilde{\nu}^u$, the theorem is proved. □

So in Theorem 5.3, the value of $-\mu^s/\nu^u$ is invariant under topological conjugacy. The next result from [**384**] gives an example of an invariant quantity under topological equivalence. Such an invariant quantity is called a *modulus of stability* (or a modulus of topological equivalence). The result features saddle-focus homoclinic orbits, which were introduced in Section 4.1.3.

Theorem 5.4. *Let f be a vector field on a three-dimensional manifold with a saddle-focus homoclinic orbit to an equilibrium p. Write $\mu^u, \mu^s \pm i\,\alpha$ for the eigenvalues of $Df(p)$, with $\mu^s < 0 < \mu^u$. Then $-\mu^s/\mu^u$ is invariant under topological equivalence.*

The space $C^k(M)$ of C^k vector fields on M is endowed with the uniform C^k topology, explained in Appendix A.3.

Definition 5.5. A vector field $f \in C^k(M)$, $1 \leq k$ or $k = \infty$, is called C^k-*structurally stable* if there is an open neighborhood U of f in $C^k(M)$ so that each $g \in U$ is topologically equivalent to f.

We remark that for vector fields on $\mathbb{R}^n$ it would make sense to use the compact-open topology described in Appendix A.1. If a vector field f is not C^k-structurally stable, then f is not an interior point of its equivalence class under topological equivalence. One can then find arbitrarily close to it a vector field g such that f and g are not topologically equivalent. The notion of bifurcation refers to this situation. We formalize a notion of bifurcation in a slightly more specific setting of a given family of vector fields, depending on finitely many parameters. Bifurcation values for local bifurcations were defined in Definition 2.33.

Definition 5.6. Let $\{f_\lambda\}$ be a family of vector fields depending on a parameter $\lambda \in \mathbb{R}^l$. If arbitrarily close to a parameter value λ_0, there are values of λ so that f_λ is not topologically equivalent to f_{λ_0}, we say that $\{f_\lambda\}$ has a *bifurcation* at $\lambda = \lambda_0$, and λ_0 is a *bifurcation value*.

It makes sense to include in the definition of structural stability the demand that the homeomorphism providing the topological equivalence is close to identity. A vector field $f \in C^k(M)$, $1 \leq k$ or $k = \infty$, would then be called C^k-structurally stable if there is an open neighborhood U of f in $C^k(M)$ so that each $g \in U$ is topologically equivalent to f using a homeomorphism that is close to the identity: for all $\varepsilon > 0$ there exists $\delta > 0$ so that if $d_{C^k}(f, g) < \delta$, then f and g are topologically equivalent using a homeomorphism h with $d_{C^0}(h, \mathrm{id}) < \varepsilon$. This additional demand is included for instance in the presentation in [**21**] and discussed in the tutorial [**338**]. If a vector field f is not C^r-structurally stable, one can then find arbitrarily close to it a vector field g such that f and g are not topologically equivalent, at least not using near identity homeomorphisms.

For a local version of the following definition we refer to Definition 2.38.

Definition 5.7. Two families of vector fields $\{f_\lambda\}$ and $\{g_\lambda\}$, $\lambda \in \mathbb{R}^l$, are *weakly topologically equivalent families* if there exists a homeomorphism k so that f_λ is topologically equivalent to $g_{k(\lambda)}$. That is, there is a homeomorphism h_λ on the state space that maps orbits of f_λ to orbits of $g_{k(\lambda)}$, preserving the sense of orbits. If h_λ depends continuously on λ, the families are *topologically equivalent families.*

Define the C^r distance $d_{C^r}(\{f_\lambda\}, \{g_\lambda\})$ between two families f_λ, g_λ as $\sup_\lambda d_{C^r}(f_\lambda, g_\lambda)$, if this supremum exists. We give a possible definition of C^r-structurally stable families; see also **[268]** for other approaches.

Definition 5.8. A family of vector fields $f_\lambda \in C^r(M)$ is called a *C^r-structurally stable family* if there are open neighborhoods U_λ of f_λ in $C^r(M)$ so that for each $g_\lambda \in U_\lambda$, g_λ and f_λ are topologically equivalent families using homeomorphisms that are close to the identity: for all $\varepsilon > 0$ there exists $\delta > 0$ so that if $d_{C^r}(\{f_\lambda\}, \{g_\lambda\}) < \delta$, then f_λ and g_λ are topologically equivalent using homeomorphisms k, h_λ with $d_{C^0}(\{h_\lambda\}, \text{id}) < \varepsilon$, $d_{C^0}(k, \text{id}) < \varepsilon$.

5.1.2. Hyperbolic sets. Recall from Definition 2.41 that an equilibrium p of a vector field f is hyperbolic if the spectrum of $Df(p)$ is disjunct from the imaginary axis. A periodic orbit is hyperbolic if its Floquet multipliers have modulus different from 1. The notion of hyperbolicity extends to general invariant sets. We introduce the notion of a hyperbolic set in this section, and we develop some of the ensuing theory. Hyperbolic equilibria and periodic orbits survive perturbations (compare Example A.19) and do not give rise to local bifurcations by the Grobman-Hartman theorem (Theorem 2.42). In this direction we provide a stability result for hyperbolic sets.

Consider a vector field f and its flow φ^t. Let Λ be a compact invariant set of the flow φ^t; $\varphi^t(\Lambda) = \Lambda$ for all $t \in \mathbb{R}$. We define the notion of hyperbolicity of Λ.

Definition 5.9. A compact invariant set Λ of a vector field f is called a *(uniform) hyperbolic set* if there is a splitting $T_xM = E^s(x) \oplus \mathbb{R}f(x) \oplus E^u(x)$, depending continuously on $x \in \Lambda$, and constants $C \geq 1$, $\lambda < 0$, $\mu > 0$ so that for $t > 0$,

$$\|D\varphi^t(x)v\| \leq Ce^{\lambda t}\|v\|, \ v \in E^s(x),$$
$$\|D\varphi^t(x)v\| \geq \frac{1}{C}e^{\mu t}\|v\|, \ v \in E^u(x).$$

The vector bundle $\{E^s(x) \; ; \; x \in \Lambda\}$ is called the *stable bundle* of the hyperbolic set, likewise $\{E^u(x) \; ; \; x \in \Lambda\}$ the *unstable bundle* of the hyperbolic set.

This definition without the flow direction also applies to diffeomorphisms. Let $f : M \to M$ be a diffeomorphism, and let Λ be a compact invariant set. Then Λ is called (uniformly) hyperbolic if there is a splitting $T_xM = E^s(x) \oplus E^u(x)$, depending continuously on $x \in \Lambda$, and constants $C \geq 1$, $0 < \lambda < 1$,

$\mu > 1$, with

$$\|Df^n(x)v\| \le C\lambda^n \|v\|, \ v \in E^s(x),$$
$$\|Df^n(x)v\| \ge \frac{1}{C}\mu^n \|v\|, \ v \in E^u(x).$$

A fixed point of a diffeomorphism is hyperbolic if the spectrum of the linearization about it is disjoint from the unit circle in the complex plane. Continuity of the splitting $E^s(x) \oplus E^u(x)$ follows from the other properties; see for instance [**48**, Section 5.2].

Consider a diffeomorphism $f : M \to M$ on a compact manifold M. For $x \in M$, define the stable set $W^s(x)$ and the unstable set $W^u(x)$ by

$$W^s(x) = \{y \in M \,;\, d(f^n(y), f^n(x)) \to 0 \text{ as } n \to \infty\},$$
$$W^u(x) = \{y \in M \,;\, d(f^n(y), f^n(x)) \to 0 \text{ as } n \to -\infty\}.$$

The distance $d(f^n(y), f^n(x))$ is defined using charts similar to the C^0-distance of vector fields; see Appendix A.3.

We state the stable manifold theorem for points in a hyperbolic set. We provide a hands-on approach that gives the existence of stable manifolds of points in the hyperbolic set, but does not contain a statement on how these stable manifolds vary with the points. See for instance [**347**, Chapter 6] or [**48**, Section 5.6].

Theorem 5.10. *Let $f : M \to M$ be a diffeomorphism with a hyperbolic set Λ. Let $x \in \Lambda$. Then $W^s(x)$ is a manifold, injectively immersed in M, with $T_xW^s(x) = E^s(x)$. We call $W^s(x)$ the stable manifold of x. Likewise, $W^u(x)$ is a manifold, injectively immersed in M, with $T_xW^u(x) = E^u(x)$. We call $W^u(x)$ the unstable manifold of x.*

Sketch of proof. We construct the stable manifold of x. The proof of its existence is a nonautonomous version of the proof for a hyperbolic fixed point in Theorem B.1. As in that proof we will construct a local stable manifold $W^s_{loc}(x)$, here given by

$$W^s_{loc}(x) = \Big\{y \in M \,;\, d(f^n(y), f^n(x)) \to 0 \text{ as } n \to \infty \text{ and } f^i(y) \in B_\delta(x_i) \text{ for all } i \in \mathbb{N}_0\Big\}$$

for $\delta > 0$ small. Then

$$W^s(x) = \bigcup_{i \in \mathbb{N}_0} f^{-i}(W^s_{loc}(x_i)). \tag{5.2}$$

Take the orbit $x_{i+1} = f(x_i)$, $i \in \mathbb{Z}$, with $x_0 = x$. For simplicity assume $C = 1$ in the definition of hyperbolicity. Observe that for $x \in M$ and $\delta > 0$ small, the ball $B_\delta(x)$ of radius δ about x is well defined. Let $U_i = B_\delta(x_i)$.

Using charts, we may assume $U_i \subset \mathbb{R}^m$ is the ball of radius δ around 0. Now f maps a neighborhood of x_i into a neighborhood of x_{i+1}, so written in the charts U_i, U_{i+1} it maps a neighborhood of 0 in U_i into a neighborhood of 0 in U_{i+1}. This defines a sequence of maps

$$f_i : U_i \to \mathbb{R}^m$$

with $f_i(0) = 0$ for all $i \in \mathbb{Z}$.

Use coordinates $E^s_{x_i} \times E^u_{x_i}$ in U_i, and write

$$(x^s_{i+1}, x^u_{i+1}) = f_i(x^s_i, x^u_i).$$

Using Taylor expansion, we have

$$\begin{aligned} x^s_{i+1} &= A^s_i x^s_i + \mathcal{O}(2), \\ x^u_{i+1} &= A^u_i x^u_i + \mathcal{O}(2), \end{aligned}$$

where $|A^s_i v| < |v|$, $|A^u_i w| > |w|$ and where $\mathcal{O}(2)$ stands for terms in (x^s_i, x^u_i) of order 2. By the implicit function theorem we obtain (x^s_{i+1}, x^u_i) as smooth function of (x^s_i, x^u_{i+1}):

$$(x^s_{i+1}, x^u_i) = g_i(x^s_i, x^u_{i+1}).$$

This expression has asymptotics

$$\begin{aligned} x^s_{i+1} &= A^s_i x^s_i + \mathcal{O}(2), \\ x^u_i &= (A^u_i)^{-1} x^u_{i+1} + \mathcal{O}(2), \end{aligned}$$

with $\mathcal{O}(2)$ standing for terms in (x^s_i, x^u_{i+1}) of order 2.

Write $l^\infty(\mathbb{N}_0, \mathbb{R}^m)$ for the space of bounded sequences $\mathbb{N}_0 \mapsto \mathbb{R}^m$ endowed with the supremum norm, and let $\mathfrak{B} = \{\gamma \in l^\infty(\mathbb{N}_0, \mathbb{R}^m)\ ;\ \gamma(i) \in U_i\}$. Write an element $\gamma \in \mathfrak{B}$ as $\gamma(n) = (\gamma^s(n), \gamma^u(n)) \in E^s_{x_n} \times E^u_{x_n}$, and write $D^s_{x,\delta} = \{y^s_0 \in E^s(x)\ ;\ |y^s_0| \le \delta\}$. Define the map $\Gamma : D^s_{x,\delta} \times \mathfrak{B} \to l^\infty(\mathbb{N}_0, \mathbb{R}^m)$ by $\Gamma(y^s_0, \gamma) = \eta$ with

$$\begin{aligned} \eta^s(0) &= y^s_0, \\ (\eta^s(n+1), \eta^u(n)) &= g_n(\gamma^s(n), \gamma^u(n+1)) \end{aligned}$$

for $n \ge 0$. As Γ is a contraction on $\mathfrak{B}$ for δ small, and Γ depends smoothly on the parameter y^s_0, it admits a fixed point η that depends smoothly on y^s_0. The fixed point $\eta = \Gamma(y^s_0, \eta)$ is the orbit in the stable manifold of x starting at a point $\eta(0)$ with $\eta^s(0) = y^s_0$. Compare the proof of Theorem B.1. This gives the local stable manifold $W^s_{loc}(x_0)$. The stable manifold $W^s(x_0)$ is obtained from $W^s_{loc}(x_0)$ and the similarly constructed local stable manifolds $W^s_{loc}(x_i)$, $i \in \mathbb{N}$, by (5.2).

For the unstable manifold consider the space $l^\infty(-\mathbb{N}_0, \mathbb{R}^m)$ of bounded sequences $-\mathbb{N}_0 \mapsto \mathbb{R}^m$ endowed with the supremum norm and let $\mathfrak{B} = \{\gamma \in l^\infty(-\mathbb{N}_0, \mathbb{R}^m)\ ;\ \gamma(i) \in U_i\}$, and accordingly let $D^u_{x,\delta} = \{y^u_0 \in E^u(x)\ ;\ |y^u_0| \le \delta\}$.

Define the map $\Gamma : D^u_\delta \times \mathfrak{B} \to l^\infty(-\mathbb{N}_0, \mathbb{R}^m)$ by $\Gamma(y^u_0, \gamma) = \eta$ with

$$\eta^u(0) = y^u_0,$$
$$(\eta^s(n+1), \eta^u(n)) = g_n(\gamma^s(n), \gamma^u(n+1))$$

for $n < 0$. With this the reasoning for the stable manifold can be followed. □

The hyperbolic set Λ of a diffeomorphism $f : M \to M$ is called maximal invariant if $\Lambda = \bigcap_{n\in\mathbb{Z}} f^n(U)$ for some open neighborhood U of Λ.

Theorem 5.11. *Let $f : M \to M$ be a diffeomorphism with a maximal invariant hyperbolic set Λ: there is an open neighborhood U of Λ so that*

$$\Lambda = \bigcap_{n\in\mathbb{Z}} f^n(U).$$

Then there is a neighborhood V of f in the C^1 topology, so that for any $g \in V$,

$$\Lambda(g) = \bigcap_{n\in\mathbb{Z}} g^n(U)$$

is a hyperbolic set of g.

Sketch of Proof. The theorem follows by finding a robust way of constructing the stable and unstable subspaces $E^s(x), E^u(x)$. Take an orbit $x_{i+1} = f(x_i)$, $i \in \mathbb{Z}$, inside Λ. For simplicity assume $C = 1$ in the definition of hyperbolicity. Observe that for $x \in M$ and $\delta > 0$ small, the ball $B_\delta(x)$ of radius δ about x is well defined. Let $U_i = B_\delta(x_i)$. Using charts, we may assume $U_i \subset \mathbb{R}^m$ is the ball of radius δ around 0.

Use coordinates $E^s_{x_i} \times E^u_{x_i}$ in U_i. Denote by $f_i : U_i \to \mathbb{R}^m$ the map f restricted to U_i and write

$$(x^s_{i+1}, x^u_{i+1}) = f_i(x^s_i, x^u_i).$$

The linearized dynamics is given by

$$(v^s_{i+1}, v^u_{i+1}) = Df_i(x^s_i, x^u_i)(v^s_i, v^u_i).$$

Note that

$$v^s_{i+1} = A^s_i v^s_i,$$
$$v^u_{i+1} = A^u_i v^u_i,$$

where $|A^s_i v| < |v|$, $|A^u_i w| > |w|$. We obtain (v^s_{i+1}, v^u_i) as smooth function of (v^s_i, v^u_{i+1}):

$$v^s_{i+1} = A^s_i v^s_i,$$
$$v^u_i = (A^u_i)^{-1} v^u_{i+1}.$$

Write $l^\infty(\mathbb{N}_0, \mathbb{R}^m)$ for the space of bounded sequences $\mathbb{N}_0 \mapsto \mathbb{R}^m$ endowed with the supremum norm and let $\mathfrak{B} = \{\gamma \in l^\infty(\mathbb{N}_0, \mathbb{R}^m) \ ; \ \gamma(i) \in U_i\}$. Write an element $\gamma \in \mathfrak{B}$ as $\gamma(n) = (\gamma^s(n), \gamma^u(n))$. Define the map $\Gamma : \mathfrak{B} \to l^\infty(\mathbb{N}_0, \mathbb{R}^m)$ by $\Gamma(\gamma) = \eta$ with

$$\eta^s(0) = v_0^s,$$
$$(\eta^s(n+1), \eta^u(n)) = (A_n^s \gamma^s(n), (A_n^u)^{-1}\gamma^u(n+1))$$

for $n \geq 0$. Then Γ defines a contraction on $\mathfrak{B}$ when δ is small. The fixed point of Γ is the orbit of the linearized equation starting at a point $\eta(0)$ with $\eta^s(0) = v_0^s$. The span of all solutions for varying v_0^s gives the stable directions.

Unstable directions are obtained as stable directions for the inverse diffeomorphism. Alternatively one may follow the above reasoning using instead the spaces $l^\infty(-\mathbb{N}_0, \mathbb{R}^m)$ of bounded sequences $-\mathbb{N}_0 \mapsto \mathbb{R}^m$ endowed with the supremum norm and $\mathfrak{B} = \{\gamma \in l^\infty(-\mathbb{N}_0, \mathbb{R}^m) \ ; \ \gamma(i) \in U_i\}$. Now, define the map $\Gamma : \mathfrak{B} \to l^\infty(-\mathbb{N}_0, \mathbb{R}^m)$ by $\Gamma(\gamma) = \eta$ with

$$\eta^u(0) = v_0^u,$$
$$(\eta^s(n), \eta^u(n-1)) = (A_n^s \gamma^s(n-1), (A_n^u)^{-1}\gamma^u(n))$$

for $n \leq 0$. The fixed point of Γ is the (negative) orbit of the linearized equation starting at a point $\eta(0)$ with $\eta^u(0) = v_0^u$. The span of all solutions for varying v_0^u gives the unstable directions.

Stable and unstable directions $E^s(x), E^u(x)$ depend continuously on x by [**48**, Proposition 5.2.1]. We may extend directions $E^s(x), E^u(x)$ in a continuous way to the neighborhood U of Λ, possibly taking a smaller neighborhood U of Λ. Then we can follow the above procedure for orbits of g that stay inside U, for g sufficiently to f in the C^1 topology. □

Remark 5.12. We sketch a second proof of Theorem 5.11 that is both more traditional and more geometric. Details can be found in [**48**] or [**198**]. The idea is again to prove the theorem by finding a robust way of constructing the stable and unstable subspaces $E^s(x), E^u(x)$. This is done using invariant (stable and unstable) cone fields. For simplicity we assume $C = 1$ in the definition of hyperbolicity. For $x \in \Lambda$, write $v \in T_xM$ as $v = v_s + v_u$ with $v_s \in E^s(x), v_u \in E^u(x)$. It is convenient to work with a box norm $|v| = \max\{|v_s|, |v_u|\}$ for given norms on $E^s(x), E^u(x)$. For $\alpha > 0$ and $x \in \Lambda$ define cones

$$K_\alpha^s(x) = \{v \in T_xM \ ; \ |v_u| \leq \alpha |v_s|\},$$
$$K_\alpha^u(x) = \{v \in T_xM \ ; \ |v_s| \leq \alpha |v_u|\}.$$

As Λ is a hyperbolic set, the linearizations $Df(x)$ are linear maps mapping $E^s(x)$ and $E^u(x)$ to $E^s(f(x))$ and $E^u(f(x))$. So $Df(x)v = A^s v_s + A^u v_u$ for $A^s : E^s(x) \to E^s(f(x))$ and $A^u : E^u(x) \to E^u(f(x))$. There exists therefore $\nu < 1$ so that for α small enough, $x \in \Lambda$,

$$Df(x)K^u_\alpha(x) \subset K^u_{\nu\alpha}(f(x)), \tag{5.3}$$

$$|Df(x)v| \geq \frac{1}{\nu}|v| \text{ for } v \in K^u_\alpha(f(x)). \tag{5.4}$$

Similarly,

$$Df^{-1}(f(x))K^s_\alpha(f(x)) \subset K^s_{\nu\alpha}(x), \tag{5.5}$$

$$|Df(x)v| \leq \nu|v| \text{ for } v \in K^s_\alpha. \tag{5.6}$$

Let the diameter of a cone K inside $K^u_\alpha(x)$ be defined by

$$\operatorname{diam} K = \sup\{|v_s - w_s| \; ; \; v_u + v_s, v_u + w_s \in K, |v_u| = 1\}.$$

Using the box norm it is clear that properties (5.3)–(5.6) imply that for any $x \in \Lambda$ and cone $K \subset K^u_\alpha(x)$, we have $\operatorname{diam} Df(x)K < \operatorname{diam} K$. It follows that $E^u(x)$ is obtained as

$$E^u(x) = \bigcap_{n \geq 0} Df^n(f^{-n}(x))K^u_\alpha(f^{-n}(x))$$

for some small $\alpha > 0$. Likewise,

$$E^s(x) = \bigcap_{n \geq 0} Df^{-n}(f^n(x))K^u_\alpha(f^n(x))$$

for some small $\alpha > 0$. We may extend the cones K^s_α, K^u_α to cone fields in $T_U M$, possible taking a smaller neighborhood U of Λ. Properties (5.3)–(5.6) also apply for f replaced by a map g that is sufficiently close to f in the C^1 topology, with $x \in \Lambda(g)$. We get that $\bigcap_{n\geq 0} Dg^n(g^{-n}(x))K^u_\alpha(g^{-n}(x))$ gives unstable directions for g and $\bigcap_{n\geq 0} Dg^{-n}(g^n(x))K^u_\alpha(g^n(x))$ gives stable directions for g. ■

Example 5.13. The solenoid or Smale-Williams attractor is the maximal invariant set for

$$F(\theta, z) = \left(2\theta \bmod 1, \lambda z + \frac{1}{2}e^{2\pi i\theta}\right)$$

on $\mathbb{T} \times D$, the product of the circle $\mathbb{T} = \mathbb{R}/\mathbb{Z}$ and the unit disk $D \subset \mathbb{C}$. In the above expression, $0 < \lambda < \frac{1}{2}$. The map F wraps the filled torus $\mathbb{T} \times D$ injectively into itself, acting as the angle doubling map $\theta \mapsto 2\theta \bmod 1$ in the first coordinate. See also [**48**] and the constructions in [**355, 419**]. Exercise 5.8 asks us to prove that the solenoid is a maximal hyperbolic set. One way to do this is by finding invariant cone fields as explained in the above remark. ■

Example 5.14. Consider a diffeomorphism f with a hyperbolic saddle fixed point p and assume the stable manifold $W^s(p)$ and the unstable manifold $W^u(p)$ intersect transversely in a homoclinic point q. Then the union of p and the orbit $\{f^n(q)\}, n \in \mathbb{Z}$ forms a hyperbolic invariant set. In the same spirit, consider a differential equation $\dot{x} = f(x)$ with a saddle hyperbolic periodic orbit γ. Assume that the stable and unstable manifolds $W^s(\gamma)$ and $W^u(\gamma)$ intersect transversely in a homoclinic orbit η. Then the union of γ and η is a hyperbolic set for the differential equation $\dot{x} = f(x)$. Exercise 5.9 asks us to prove these statements. ■

The next result yields structural stability of diffeomorphisms restricted to maximal invariant hyperbolic sets.

Theorem 5.15. *Let $f : M \to M$ be a diffeomorphism with a maximal invariant hyperbolic set Λ: there is an open neighborhood U of Λ so that*

$$\Lambda = \bigcap_{n \in \mathbb{Z}} f^n(U).$$

There exists $\varepsilon > 0$ so that any $\hat{f}$ which is ε-close to f in the C^1 topology, possesses a maximal invariant hyperbolic set $\Lambda(\hat{f})$ in U. Moreover, $f|_\Lambda$ and $\hat{f}|_{\Lambda(\hat{f})}$ are topologically conjugate: there exists a homeomorphism $h = h(\hat{f}) : \Lambda \to \Lambda(\hat{f})$ with

$$\hat{f} \circ h = h \circ f.$$

The dependence $\hat{f} \mapsto h(\hat{f})$ is continuous in the C^0 topology and $h(f) = \mathrm{id}$.

Proof. Fix an orbit $(x_i)_{i \in \mathbb{Z}}$, $x_{i+1} = f(x_i)$, of f in Λ. We start by describing a construction to recover the orbit x_i when starting with a sequence of points u_i close to x_i: the orbit arises as a fixed point of a contraction on a space of sequences. This construction will then be applied to perturbations of f to find orbits of these perturbations.

Along Λ, there is a continuous splitting $T_xM = E^s_x \oplus E^u_x$, $x \in \Lambda$, in stable and unstable subspaces. For simplicity assume $C = 1$ in the definition of hyperbolicity. Observe that for $x \in M$ and $\delta > 0$ small, the ball $B_\delta(x)$ of radius δ about x is well defined. Let $U_i = B_\delta(x_i)$. Using charts, we may assume $U_i \subset \mathbb{R}^m$ is the ball of radius δ around 0. Use coordinates $E^s_{x_i} \times E^u_{x_i}$ in U_i. Denote the map f restricted to U_i by $f_i : U_i \to \mathbb{R}^m$, and write

$$(x^s_{i+1}, x^u_{i+1}) = f_i(x^s_i, x^u_i).$$

Note that

$$\begin{aligned} x^s_{i+1} &= A^s_i x^s_i + \mathcal{O}(2), \\ x^u_{i+1} &= A^u_i x^u_i + \mathcal{O}(2), \end{aligned}$$

where $|A^s_i v| < |v|$, $|A^u_i w| > |w|$ and where $\mathcal{O}(2)$ stands for terms in (x^s_i, x^u_i) of order 2. By the implicit function theorem we obtain (x^s_{i+1}, x^u_i) as a smooth function of (x^s_i, x^u_{i+1}):

$$(x^s_{i+1}, x^u_i) = g_i(x^s_i, x^u_{i+1}).$$

This expression has asymptotics

$$\begin{aligned} x^s_{i+1} &= A^s_i x^s_i + \mathcal{O}(2), \\ x^u_i &= (A^u_i)^{-1} x^u_{i+1} + \mathcal{O}(2), \end{aligned}$$

with $\mathcal{O}(2)$ standing for terms in (x^s_i, x^u_{i+1}) of order 2.

Write $l^\infty(\mathbb{Z}, \mathbb{R}^m)$ for the space of bounded sequences $\mathbb{Z} \mapsto \mathbb{R}^m$ endowed with the supremum norm and let $\mathfrak{B} = \{\gamma \in l^\infty(\mathbb{Z}, \mathbb{R}^m)\ ;\ \gamma(i) \in U_i\}$. Write an element $\gamma \in \mathfrak{B}$ as $\gamma(n) = (\gamma^s(n), \gamma^u(n))$. Define the map $\Gamma : \mathfrak{B} \to l^\infty(\mathbb{Z}, \mathbb{R}^m)$ by $\Gamma(\gamma) = \eta$ with

$$(\eta^s(n+1), \eta^u(n)) = g_n(\gamma^s(n), \gamma^u(n+1))$$

for $n \in \mathbb{Z}$. The following is a direct consequence of the formulas for g_n, if δ is small enough:

(i) $\Gamma(\mathfrak{B}) \subset \mathfrak{B}$,

(ii) Γ is a contraction on $\mathfrak{B}$.

The fixed point of Γ is the constant zero sequence and corresponds to the orbit (x_i) of f which was fixed at the beginning.

We will now use the construction for perturbations of f. To stress the dependence on f we write Γ_f for the map Γ above. For a nearby diffeomorphism $\hat{f}$ we obtain a map $\Gamma_{\hat{f}}$.

Keep using the coordinates $E^s_{x_i} \times E^u_{x_i}$ in U_i and consider a sequence of points $(x^s_i, x^u_i) \in U_i$. Then for sufficiently small $\varepsilon > 0$, for any diffeomorphism $\hat{f} : M \to M$ that is ε-close to f in the C^1 topology, equations

$$(x^s_{i+1}, x^u_{i+1}) = \hat{f}_i(x^s_i, x^u_i)$$

can be solved by

$$(x^s_{i+1}, x^u_i) = \hat{g}_i(x^s_i, x^u_{i+1}).$$

Let $\Gamma_{\hat{f}} : \mathfrak{B} \to l^\infty(\mathbb{Z}, \mathbb{R}^m)$ be given by $\Gamma_{\hat{f}}(\gamma) = \eta$ with

$$(\eta^s(n+1), \eta^u(n)) = g_n(\gamma^s(n), \gamma^u(n+1))$$

for $n \in \mathbb{Z}$. For sufficiently small $\varepsilon > 0$, for any diffeomorphism $\hat{f} : M \to M$ that is ε-close to f in the C^1 topology,

(i) $\Gamma_{\hat{f}}(\mathfrak{B}) \subset \mathfrak{B}$,

(ii) $\Gamma_{\hat{f}}$ is a contraction on $\mathfrak{B}$,

(iii) the fixed point of $\Gamma_{\hat{f}}$ is the orbit $(z_i)_{i \in \mathbb{Z}}$, $z_{i+1} = \hat{f}(z_i)$, of $\hat{f}$ with $z_i \in U_i$.

Define a map $h : \Lambda \to U$ that maps $x_k \in \Lambda$ to the fixed point of $\Gamma_{\hat{f}}(\{x_i\})(k)$. The construction shows that $h \circ f = \hat{f} \circ h$. We leave it to the reader to show that h is continuous. Conversely, recall that the maximal invariant set of $\hat{f}$ in U is hyperbolic by Theorem 5.11. Given an orbit $\{y_i\}$ of $\hat{f}$ in $h(\Lambda)$ for $\hat{f}$ sufficiently close to f, $\Gamma_f(\{y_i\})$ provides a nearby orbit of f in Λ. So the map $j : \hat{f}(\Lambda) \to M$ that maps $y_k \in \hat{f}(\Lambda)$ to the fixed point of $\Gamma_f(\{y_i\})(k)$ is the inverse of h and is continuous. It follows that h is a homeomorphism. □

Remark 5.16. The construction yields as a byproduct a shadowing property for orbits in maximal invariant hyperbolic sets: for any sequence of points y_i with y_{i+1} close to $f(y_i)$ and close to Λ, there is a nearby real orbit x_i with $x_{i+1} = f(x_i)$. We say that y_i is shadowed by x_i. See for instance [**48**]. ■

Example 5.17. A diffeomorphism $f : M \to M$ is called Anosov diffeomorphism if M is a hyperbolic set of f. If M is a torus, one speaks of a toral Anosov diffeomorphism.

Toral Anosov diffeomorphisms can be constructed as follows: Consider a matrix $A \in \mathrm{GL}(2, \mathbb{Z})$, that is an invertible 2×2 matrix with integer coefficients. Assume further that $\det A = \pm 1$ (note that then also its inverse has integer coefficients) and that A has no eigenvalues on the unit circle. A matrix $A = \begin{pmatrix} a & b \\ c & d \end{pmatrix} \in \mathrm{GL}(2, \mathbb{Z})$ induces an automorphism on the torus $\mathbb{T}^2 = \mathbb{R}^2/\mathbb{Z}^2$. The induced map on $\mathbb{T}^2$, also denoted by A, is given by

$$A(x, y) = (ax + by, cx + dy) \bmod 1.$$

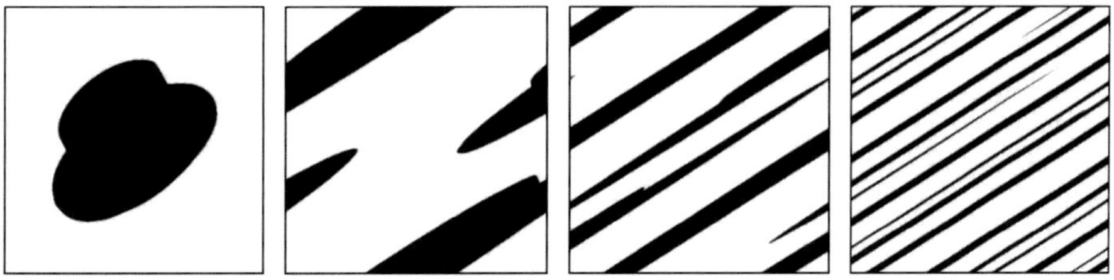

Figure 5.2. The hyperbolic automorphism of the torus provided by the linear map (5.7): using the projection of a hat on the torus as a picture, the images under the first, second, and third iterates are shown.

Suppose that $\mathbb{R}^2 = E^s \oplus E^u$ is an invariant splitting for A. For any $x \in \mathbb{R}^2$, we let $x = x^s + x^u$ with $x^s \in E^s$ and $x^u \in E^u$. We suppose that the eigenvalue of $A_s = A|_{E^s}$ has modulus less than one and that the eigenvalue of $A_u = A|_{E^u}$ has modulus greater than one. Hence

$$|A_s|, |A_u^{-1}| < 1.$$

The induced map on $\mathbb{T}^2$ is called a hyperbolic torus automorphism. Periodic points of A lie dense in $\mathbb{T}^2$, in fact, every point in $\mathbb{T}^2$ with rational coordinates is periodic; see [**309**]. An example of a hyperbolic torus automorphism is provided by the matrix

$$A = \begin{pmatrix} 2 & 1 \\ 1 & 1 \end{pmatrix} \tag{5.7}$$

with eigenvalues $\frac{1}{2}(3 + \sqrt{5})$ and its reciprocal. This example is known as the Arnold cat map; its dynamics was illustrated using the picture of a cat in [**24**].

The term "cat" can also be understood as an acronym for continuous automorphism of the torus. Figure 5.2 illustrates the effect of iterating using the picture of a hat. ■

Theorem 5.18. *Let $f : \mathbb{T}^2 \to \mathbb{T}^2$ be a hyperbolic diffeomorphism. There exists $\varepsilon > 0$ so that any $\hat{f}$ which is ε-close to f in the C^1 topology, is topologically conjugate to f: there exists a homeomorphism $h = h(\hat{f}) : \mathbb{T}^2 \to \mathbb{T}^2$ with*

$$\hat{f} \circ h = h \circ f.$$

The dependence $\hat{f} \mapsto h(\hat{f})$ is continuous in the C^0 topology and $h(f) = \mathrm{id}$.

Proof. The result is obtained as an application of Theorem 5.15 to hyperbolic torus automorphisms. For a different proof see [**21**, §13]. □

5.1.3. Global stability theorems. We collect a number of results that characterize or classify structurally stable systems. For flows on surfaces, Peixoto's theorem [**286**] (see also [**271**]) stated below classifies structurally stable systems. The earlier Andronov-Pontryagin theorem characterizes structural stability of flows on bounded regions in the plane, involving the first three conditions from Peixoto's theorem. We refer to [**16–18, 89, 215, 285**] for the development and results.

Example 5.19. An example of a torus flow that is not structurally stable is a translation field. For $\alpha \in \mathbb{R}$ consider the differential equation on $\mathbb{T}^2 = \mathbb{R}^2/\mathbb{Z}^2$ given by

$$\dot{x} = x + (1, \alpha) \bmod 1.$$

The flow φ^t is given by $\varphi^t(u, v) = (u + t, v + \alpha t) \bmod 1$. Orbits are periodic if $\alpha \in \mathbb{Q}$. If $\alpha \in \mathbb{R} \setminus \mathbb{Q}$ the flow admits no periodic orbits and no equilibria. The flow in this case is called quasiperiodic. This explains the need for a condition in Peixoto's theorem that addresses such flows. ■

Theorem 5.20 (Peixoto's theorem). *Let M be a compact orientable surface. Let $r \geq 1$. The C^r-structurally stable flows are those which satisfy the following properties:*

(i) *all equilibria are hyperbolic,*
(ii) *all periodic solutions are hyperbolic,*
(iii) *there are no orbits that converge to saddle equilibria for both positive and negative time,*
(iv) *the α- and ω-limit sets of every orbit can only be equilibria or periodic orbits.*

The set of C^r-structurally stable flows is open and dense in $C^r(M)$.

An orbit that converges to saddle equilibria for both positive and negative time is called a saddle connection. It is called a heteroclinic orbit if the two equilibria are different, and a homoclinic orbit if they are the same. Just as for differential equations on the plane, also for a flow on a surface we speak of stable and unstable separatrices of a saddle equilibrium. A homoclinic orbit to a saddle equilibrium thus arises if a stable separatrix of the equilibrium equals one of its unstable separatrices. Figure 5.3 illustrates the effect of breaking a heteroclinic orbit.

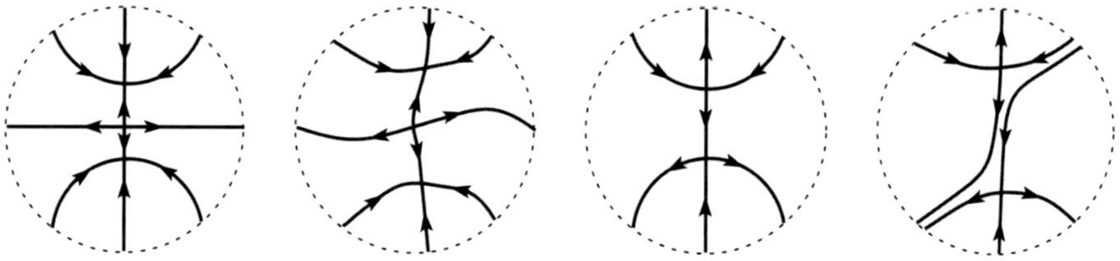

Figure 5.3. The two panels on the left show part of a phase diagram of a vector field and a small perturbation which is qualitatively the same. In contrast, the two panels on the right show part of a phase diagram of a vector field, with a saddle connection, and a small perturbation which is qualitatively different.

Theorem 5.20 is known to apply to flows on certain nonorientable surfaces, such as the Klein bottle. Example 5.21 illustrates flows on a Klein bottle yielding global bifurcations involving periodic attracting orbits of arbitrarily large arc length.

Example 5.21. Figure 5.4 illustrates bifurcations on surfaces that involve periodic attractors of arbitrarily large arc length. For the saddle-node bifurcation, points in the unstable set of the saddle-node periodic orbit return to a neighborhood of saddle-node periodic orbit and converge to it. In the unfolding of the saddle-node periodic orbit, one encounters sequences of period-doubling bifurcations converging to the saddle-node bifurcation [**184**].

For the homoclinic orbit one unstable separatrix of a hyperbolic saddle forms the homoclinic orbit while the other unstable separatrix converges to the closure of the homoclinic orbit. In the unfolding of the homoclinic bifurcation one gets a sequence of homoclinic bifurcations involving periodic attractors with large arc length [**165**]. ∎

To give the flavor of the argumentation in the proof of Theorem 5.20, we prove a simpler one-dimensional case in Theorem 5.23. It relies on Lemma 5.22 which says that for a smooth function $f : U \subset \mathbb{R} \to \mathbb{R}$ of a single real variable, the image under f of its set of singular points is small. This is the one-dimensional version of Sard's theorem, by Arthur Sard [**328**]. To enable comparison, we state the higher-dimensional version in Appendix A.3.2. Recall that to prove that a subset of the real line has zero Lebesgue measure, we

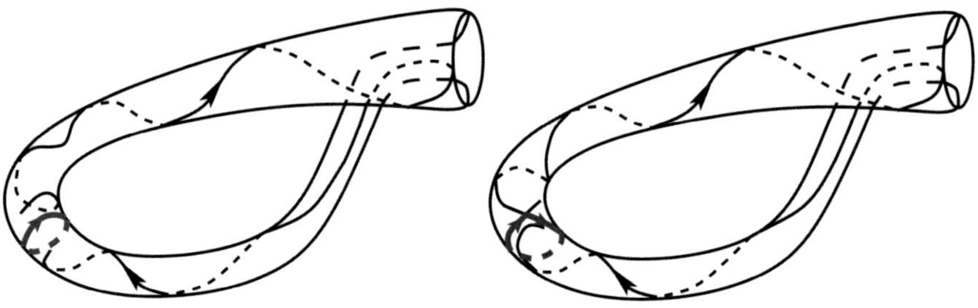

Figure 5.4. Left frame: A saddle-node bifurcation of a periodic orbit on a Klein bottle. The existence of nonhyperbolic periodic orbit violates (ii) in Theorem 5.20. Right frame: A homoclinic bifurcation on a Klein bottle. The existence of a homoclinic orbit violates (iii) in Theorem 5.20.

must show it can be covered by a union of intervals of arbitrarily small total length.

Lemma 5.22. *Let $f : U \to \mathbb{R}$, where $U \subset \mathbb{R}$, be a smooth function. Let*

$$W = \{x \in U\ ;\ f'(x) = 0\}.$$

Then $f(W)$ has Lebesgue measure zero.

Proof. Let I be an interval in U of length $a > 0$. There exists $K > 0$ so that for all $x \in W \cap I$ and $y \in I$,

$$|f(x) - f(y)| \leq K|x - y|^2. \tag{5.8}$$

Subdivide I into k intervals J_i, $1 \leq i \leq k$, of length a/k. Then (5.8) gives

$$|f(x) - f(y)| \leq K(a/k)^2$$

if $x \in W \cap J_i$, $y \in J_i$. Thus $f(W \cap I)$ is contained in a union of intervals of length at most $Kk(a/k)^2$. Letting k go to infinity shows that $f(W \cap I)$ has Lebesgue measure zero. Thus also $f(W)$ has Lebesgue measure zero. □

Theorem 5.23. *Let M be the circle. The C^1-structurally stable flows are those that satisfy the following property:*

(i) *all equilibria are hyperbolic.*

The set of C^1-structurally stable flows is open and dense in $C^1(M)$.

Proof. We first prove that a vector field f with only hyperbolic equilibria is C^1-structurally stable. Identifying the circle with $\mathbb{R}/\mathbb{Z}$, we can consider f as a periodic function on $\mathbb{R}$.

Suppose first f has no equilibria. Without loss of generality, $f > 0$. Then f has a positive minimum. Any g sufficiently close to f in the C^1 topology is also positive. So $g(x) = t(x)f(x)$ for a positive function t. It follows that f and g are topologically equivalent.

Next suppose that f does have hyperbolic equilibria. Since hyperbolic equilibria are isolated, there is a finite number of them by compactness of the circle. Denote the hyperbolic equilibria of f by $x_1, \dots, x_n$. Between two equilibria, f does not change sign. By the implicit function theorem, for any x_k, $k \in \{1, \dots, n\}$, there is an interval neighborhood U_k of x_k and a neighborhood V of f in $C^1(\mathbb{R}/\mathbb{Z})$, so that if $g \in V$, then g has a unique hyperbolic equilibrium y_k in U_k. Outside the intervals U_k, f is nonzero. Any g sufficiently C^1-close to f is also nonzero outside the U_k's.

We get the existence of a neighborhood V of f in $C^1(\mathbb{R}/\mathbb{Z})$ so that if $g \in V$, then g has precisely n equilibria y_k, each $y_k \in U_k$. Given f with equilibria x_k and nearby $g \in V$ with equilibria y_k, we can define a homeomorphism $h : \mathbb{R}/\mathbb{Z} \to \mathbb{R}/\mathbb{Z}$ with $h(x_k) = y_k$ and which is increasing (for instance piecewise affine) in between. It is clear that h defines a topological equivalence between f and g.

We establish that the set of C^1-structurally stable systems is dense in $C^1(\mathbb{R}/\mathbb{Z})$. By an arbitrarily C^1-small perturbation we may assume that f is smooth (compare [**160**, Chapter 2, Theorem 2.6]). Consider the family of vector fields $x \mapsto f(x) + \varepsilon$ depending on a real parameter ε. By Lemma 5.22 (a version of Sard's theorem) there are values of ε arbitrarily close to 0, for which $f + \varepsilon$ has no critical value at 0. The vector field $f + \varepsilon$ then has only hyperbolic equilibria.

It remains to show that if the hypothesis on hyperbolic fixed points is not satisfied, then f is not structurally stable. Sard's theorem shows that a system with infinitely many equilibria is not C^1-structurally stable. A homeomorphism defining topological equivalence must map equilibria onto equilibria, and by Sard's theorem there are arbitrarily small perturbations with only finitely many equilibria. So assume that f has a finite number of isolated equilibria, with a nonhyperbolic equilibrium x_1. Observe that x_1 is a singular point of f.

Suppose f has the same sign on either side of x_1, say $f > 0$ on $U \setminus \{x_1\}$ for a small neighborhood U of x_1. Let $\chi : \mathbb{R} \to [0,1]$ be a bump function: χ is a smooth nonnegative function with $\chi(x) = 1$ on $[-1,1]$ and $\chi = 0$ on $\mathbb{R} \setminus [-2,2]$. For $\varepsilon > 0$, let

$$j_\varepsilon(x) = \varepsilon^2 \chi(x/\varepsilon).$$

Note that j_ε converges to 0 in the C^1 topology if $\varepsilon \to 0$. For $\varepsilon > 0$ small, $f + j_\varepsilon > 0$ on U. That is, $f + j_\varepsilon$ has no equilibria in U.

If f has different signs on both sides of x_1, we apply a different perturbation. Assume $f(x) > 0$ for $x > x_1$, $x \in U$, and $f < 0$ for $x < x_1$, $x \in U$. Here U is a small interval neighborhood of x_1. Now define, for $\varepsilon > 0$,

$$j_\varepsilon(x) = -2\varepsilon^2 x \chi(x/\varepsilon).$$

Note that j_ε converges to 0 in the C^1 topology if $\varepsilon \to 0$. As $j'_\varepsilon(0) = -2\varepsilon^2$, it is easily seen that $f(x) + j_\varepsilon(x - x_1)$ possesses three equilibria close to x_1, for $\varepsilon > 0$ small. □

Among the class of structurally stable systems are Morse-Smale systems with simple dynamics.

Definition 5.24. A vector field f is *Morse-Smale* if it satisfies the following properties:

(i) f has a finite number of critical elements, all of which are hyperbolic;
(ii) If σ_1, σ_2 are critical elements of f, then the invariant manifolds $W^s(\sigma_1)$ and $W^u(\sigma_2)$ are transversal;
(iii) The nonwandering set of f equals the union of the critical elements.

The structurally stable vector fields on orientable surfaces from Peixoto's theorem, Theorem 5.20, give Morse-Smale systems. Structural stability of Morse-Smale vector fields was proved by Stephen Smale and Jacob Palis [**280**].

Theorem 5.25. *A Morse-Smale vector field is structurally stable in $C^r(M)$.*

Example 5.26. Gradient vector fields are a source of examples of Morse-Smale systems. We follow [**278**, Chapter 1, §1]. Consider a compact manifold M embedded in a Euclidean space $\mathbb{R}^k$. At each point $x \in M$ we can take an inner product $\langle \cdot, \cdot, \rangle_x$ on T_xM induced by the standard inner product on $\mathbb{R}^k$. Let $h : M \to \mathbb{R}$ be a smooth map. The gradient ∇h is defined by

$$\langle \nabla h(p), v \rangle_x = Dh(x)v$$

for each $v \in T_xM$. The gradient of h defines a smooth vector field $f = \nabla h$ which is called the gradient vector field of h.

Gradient Morse-Smale flows have only hyperbolic equilibria, transversal intersections of their stable and unstable manifolds, and no periodic orbits. They form an open and dense subset of the space of C^r gradient flows [**280, 351**]. We refer to Exercises 5.13 and 5.14 for more on gradient flows. ■

Exercise 5.15 discusses Morse-Smale diffeomorphisms. Also for systems that do not have the simple dynamics of Morse-Smale systems, hyperbolicity of critical elements and transversality of their stable and unstable manifolds is an important characteristic.

Definition 5.27. A vector field f is *Kupka-Smale* if it satisfies the following properties:

(i) The critical elements, meaning the equilibria and periodic orbits of f, are hyperbolic;

(ii) If σ_1, σ_2 are critical elements of f, then the invariant manifolds $W^s(\sigma_1)$ and $W^u(\sigma_2)$ are transversal.

The Kupka-Smale theorem by Ivan Kupka [**214**] and Stephen Smale [**352**] states that any smooth vector field can be perturbed to a Kupka-Smale vector field. A proof can be found in [**278**] or [**4**].

Theorem 5.28. *For any compact manifold M, the set of Kupka-Smale vector fields is dense in* $C^r(M)$.

Attempts to characterize structurally stable systems, including those with nonsimple dynamics, led Smale to the notion of the *Axiom A* vector field [**355**]. Hyperbolic invariant sets were discussed in Section 5.1.2, examples are suspensions of horseshoes as in Section 2.5 and hyperbolic torus automorphisms. See Exercise 5.7.

Definition 5.29. A vector field f satisfies Axiom A if

(i) The nonwandering set $\Omega(f)$ is hyperbolic;
(ii) Equilibria are isolated in $\Omega(f)$;
(iii) The critical elements are dense in $\Omega(f)$.

The following result by Stephen Smale [**355**] (see also [**198**]) characterizes the nonwandering set of a vector field that satisfies Axiom A.

Theorem 5.30 (Spectral decomposition theorem). *Let f be a* C^1 *vector field that satisfies Axiom A. The nonwandering set* $\Omega(f)$ *is a finite union*

$$\Omega(f) = \Omega_1 \cup \cdots \cup \Omega_n$$

of topologically transitive hyperbolic sets, that is they contain a dense orbit, called basic sets.

Morse-Smale vector fields satisfy Axiom A and the corresponding basic sets are hyperbolic equilibria and periodic orbits. But Axiom A vector fields may admit other basic sets including suspensions of horseshoes. It is also important to know the structure of connecting orbits between basic sets. This gives rise to the following definitions.

Definition 5.31. Suppose the vector field f satisfies Axiom A. A *cycle* is a sequence of points x_i, $0 \leq i < n$, in different basic sets, such that with $x_n = x_0$,

$$W^u(x_i) \cap W^s(x_{i+1}) \neq \emptyset, \qquad 0 \leq i < n.$$

A vector field f is said to satisfy the *no-cycle property* if no cycles exist. A vector field f that satisfies Axiom A is said to satisfy the *strong transversality property* if for any $x, y \in \Omega(f)$, the stable and unstable manifolds $W^s(x)$ and $W^u(y)$ are transversal.

Besides Axiom A, Morse-Smale vector fields satisfy the strong transversality condition. Although structural stability (Definition 5.5) is a central notion that one wishes to characterize, one can think of other notions of stability for instance by restricting the flow to invariant sets. Looking at nonwandering sets leads to the notion of Ω-stability.

Definition 5.32. A vector field $f \in C^k(M)$, $1 \leq k$ or $k = \infty$, is called C^k *Ω-stable* if there is an open neighborhood U of f in $C^k(M)$ so that for each $g \in U$, g restricted to $\Omega(g)$ is topologically equivalent to f restricted to $\Omega(f)$.

The combined efforts of Welington de Melo [**84**], Joel Robbin [**303**], Clark Robinson [**304,305**], Ricardo Mañé [**238**], Jacob Palis [**277**], Sen Hu [**181**], Shuhei Hayashi [**154**] yield the following characterizations of Ω-stability and structural stability.

Theorem 5.33. *A vector field is C^1 Ω-stable if and only if it satisfies Axiom A and the no-cycle property.*

Theorem 5.34. *A vector field is C^1-structurally stable if and only if it satisfies Axiom A and the strong transversality property.*

These results are restricted to the C^1 topology. Similar characterizations in higher degrees of regularity are unknown. An elegant formulation of these classical stability results is obtained by using the notion of a chain recurrent set. Charles Conley [**74, 75**] introduced the chain recurrent set to characterize the part of state space on which the flow is not similar to a gradient flow.

Definition 5.35. A point x of M is called *chain recurrent* for the flow φ^t of f provided that corresponding to any ε, $T > 0$ there exist points $x_0 = x, x_1, \ldots, x_n = x$ and real numbers $t_0, t_1, \ldots, t_{n-1}$ all greater than T such that $d(\varphi^{t_i}(x_i), x_{i+1}) < \varepsilon$ for all $0 \leq i \leq n-1$. The set of all such points is called the *chain recurrent set* $\mathcal{R}(f)$.

The chain recurrent set $\mathcal{R}(f)$ is a compact invariant set containing $\Omega(f)$. The following result from [**117**] allows for alternative formulations of the above stability results.

Theorem 5.36. *Let f be a C^1 vector field. Then $\mathcal{R}(f)$ is a hyperbolic set if and only if f satisfies Axiom A and the no-cycle property.*

One may extend these ideas for single vector fields to parametrized families of vector fields. Some key references that have explored this direction are [**52, 53, 216, 281, 292, 357, 378**]. See also the discussion of surface flows in Section 5.2.1.

Example 5.37. One of the questions that arises is what bifurcations occur on the boundary of structurally stable vector fields in typical one-parameter families. One can think of a one-parameter family of vector fields $\dot{x} = f_\lambda(x)$ that has a first bifurcation at some value λ_0, that is, the dynamics is structurally stable for $\lambda < \lambda_0$. In this context, Sir Christopher Zeeman [**423**] asked the question which additional bifurcations occur if, as a first bifurcation, a periodic orbit in a suspended horseshoe undergoes a saddle-node bifurcation. This is a nontrivial question that has been explored for instance in [**77, 80, 96**]. Other bifurcation scenarios in which suspended horseshoes are destroyed after a first bifurcation are possible as well, for instance through a homoclinic bifurcation of a periodic orbit in it [**91, 165**], homoclinic tangencies [**59, 301**], or certain heteroclinic bifurcations [**95**]. ■

5.1.4. Robust structural instability. The previous section contained a number of stability results. In particular, Theorem 5.20 and Theorem 5.23 show that structurally stable systems are open and dense among vector fields on orientable surfaces and simple closed curves. In higher dimensions structurally stable systems are not dense, and there are open sets of systems, none of which is structurally stable. This phenomenon is called robust structural instability. We discuss the example by Stephen Smale [**354**] on the four-dimensional torus, following [**21**, § 3.15].

Theorem 5.38. *There is an open set of vector fields in $C^2(\mathbb{T}^4)$ that are not C^1-structurally stable.*

Sketch of proof. The construction involves diffeomorphisms on the three-dimensional torus $\mathbb{T}^3 = \mathbb{R}^3/\mathbb{Z}^3$. By using a suspension, this gives an example of a flow on the four-dimensional torus.

On $\mathbb{T}^3$ we have coordinates (x, y, z). Let f be a diffeomorphism on $\mathbb{T}^3$ with the following properties:

(i) On a small neighborhood U of the two-torus $\{z = 0\}$, we have
$$f(x, y, z) = (2x + y, x + y, z/3);$$

(ii) On a small neighborhood V of $p = (0, 0, \frac{1}{2})$,
$$f(x, y, z) = (x/3, y/3, -1 + 3z).$$

We leave to the reader to show that a diffeomorphism with these properties exists: one can start with a diffeomorphism of the form $(x, y, z) \mapsto (2x + y, x + y, g(z))$ for some function g satisfying the first property, and then make a local perturbation near p to satisfy the second property. Note that the dynamics on the two-torus $M = \{z = 0\}$ is given by the hyperbolic torus automorphism
$$\begin{pmatrix} x \\ y \end{pmatrix} \mapsto \begin{pmatrix} 2 & 1 \\ 1 & 1 \end{pmatrix} \begin{pmatrix} x \\ y \end{pmatrix}.$$

The eigenvalues of the matrix $\begin{pmatrix} 2 & 1 \\ 1 & 1 \end{pmatrix}$ are $\frac{3}{2} \pm \frac{1}{2}\sqrt{5}$. On M there is a foliation $\mathcal{F}^s$ of the curves that are projections from $\mathbb{R}^2$ to $M = \mathbb{R}^2/\mathbb{Z}^2$ of lines parallel to the stable eigendirection of $\begin{pmatrix} 2 & 1 \\ 1 & 1 \end{pmatrix}$. Write $W^s(q)$ for the stable manifold of $q \in M$. Inside U there is a stable foliation with two-dimensional leaves $W^s(q)$, $q \in M$. The fixed point p has a one-dimensional unstable manifold $W^u(p)$. Assume that $W^u(p)$ has a quadratic tangency to $W^s(q)$ for some $q \in M$. The geometry is indicated in Figure 5.5.

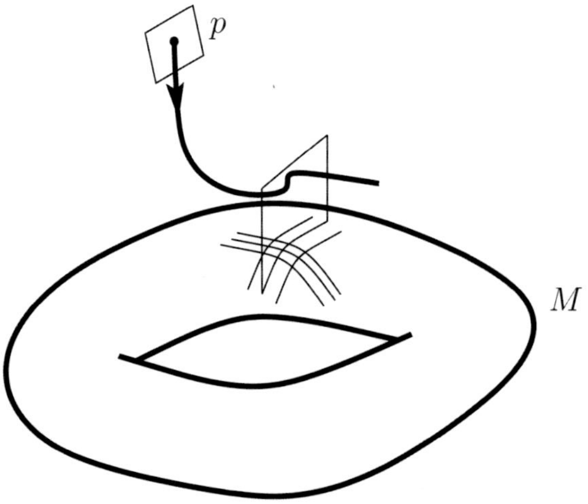

Figure 5.5. The unstable manifold of p is tangent to the stable manifold of some point in M.

If we perturb f to a nearby diffeomorphism g, then g admits an invariant two-torus M_g which is close to M. Note that we can consider g on $\mathbb{R}^2 \times \mathbb{R}$ and replace g by a map that is equal to the given map g on a small neighborhood of $\mathbb{R}^2 \times \{0\}$ and globally close to $(x, y, z) \mapsto (2x + y, x + y, z/3)$. The same for f. Because $\frac{1}{3} < \frac{3}{2} - \frac{1}{2}\sqrt{5}$, the surface M is normally hyperbolic (see Appendix B.1.4). Since M is normally hyperbolic, we find that for g sufficiently near f, M_g is a continuously differentiable manifold. Further, g has a stable foliation inside U, with leaves close to the ones for f.

By the implicit function theorem, g has a saddle fixed point near p. For f as well as for g, both stable manifolds of periodic points and stable manifolds of nonperiodic points are dense in the stable foliation in U. An arbitrarily small perturbation will make $W^u(p)$ tangent to either a strong stable manifold of a periodic point or a stable manifold of a nonperiodic point. However, the property that $W^u(p)$ is tangent to a stable manifold of a periodic point is an invariant under topological conjugacy. So any diffeomorphism sufficiently close to f is not structurally stable. □

A vector field f that is not structurally stable is said to have k moduli of stability if k is the minimal number of parameters needed in an unfolding of f to parametrize topological equivalence classes in a neighborhood U of f. If such k exists, we say that f has finite modulus of stability. A stream of research is devoted to moduli of stability, also for diffeomorphisms where topological conjugacy replaces topological equivalence. Early references on infinite moduli of stability are [**310**] and [**85**]. See [**32, 86, 403**] for examples of results characterizing finite modulus of stability.

Example 5.39. A variant of the example used to prove Theorem 5.38 yields a vector field that does not have finite modulus of stability. We sketch the construction, which again uses the setting of a diffeomorphism on the torus $\mathbb{T}^3$. Compare also [**137**, Theorem 5]. On $\mathbb{T}^3$ we have coordinates (x, y, z). Let f be a diffeomorphism on $\mathbb{T}^3$ with the following properties.

(i) On a small neighborhood U of the two-torus $M = \{z = 0\}$, we have
$$f(x, y, z) = (2x + y, x + y, z/3).$$
(ii) On a small neighborhood V of the two-torus $N = \{z = \frac{1}{2}\}$,
$$f(x, y, z) = (2x + y, x + y, -1 + 3z).$$

Consider g near f.

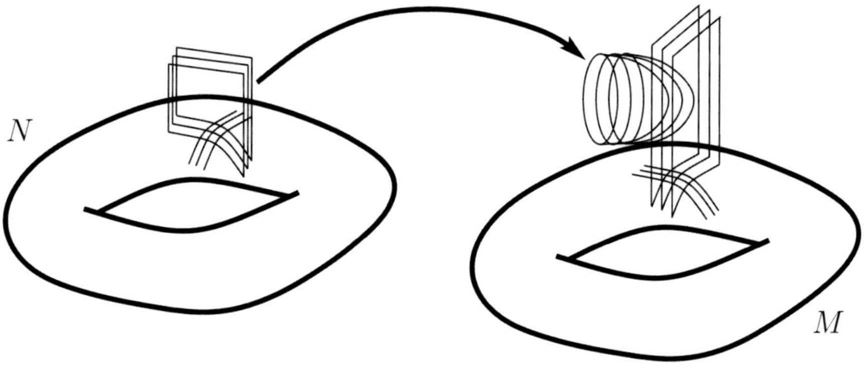

Figure 5.6. Unstable manifold of points in N are tangent to stable manifolds of points in M.

Since M and N are normally hyperbolic manifolds of f, we find for g sufficiently near f an invariant torus M_g of G near M and an invariant torus N_g of g near N. The torus M_g is attracting and points r in M_g have stable manifolds $W_g^s(r)$ of dimension 2. The different stable manifolds give a stable foliation of a neighborhood U of M_g. The torus N_g is repelling, and points r in it have two-dimensional unstable manifolds $W_g^u(r)$. The different unstable manifolds give a unstable foliation of a neighborhood V of N_g.

Assume that an unstable manifold $W_f^u(q)$ for a point $q \in N$ has a quadratic tangency with a stable manifold $W_f^s(p)$ for a point $p \in M$. Near the point of tangency there is a curve ℓ_f of tangencies of unstable manifolds of points in N with stable manifolds of points in M; see Figure 5.6. If g is a diffeomorphism near f, then g restricted to M_g is topologically conjugate to f restricted to M. Likewise, g restricted to N_g is topologically conjugate to f restricted to N. There is therefore a homeomorphism $h_g : M \cup N \to M_g \cup N_g$ with $h_g(M) = M_g$ and $h_g(N) = N_g$ and

$$g \circ h_g = h_g \circ f.$$

The existence of the curve ℓ of tangencies persists for small perturbations of f, hence the nearby diffeomorphism g has a curve of tangencies ℓ_g.

Parametrize local unstable manifolds $W^u_{f,loc}(r)$, r near q, by a coordinate in the local stable manifold $W^s_{f,loc}(q)$ of q. The unstable manifolds $W^u_f(r)$ define a map $i : W^s_{f,loc}(q) \to \ell$. Likewise, parametrize local stable manifolds $W^s_{f,loc}(r)$, r near p, by a coordinate in the local unstable manifold $W^u_{f,loc}(p)$ of p. The stable manifolds $W^s_f(r)$ define a map $j : W^u_{f,loc}(q) \to \ell$. This gives a continuous map $\phi : W^s_{f,loc}(q) \to W^u_{f,loc}(p)$ defined by $\phi = j^{-1} \circ i$. This map has the property that $W^u_f(r)$ is tangent to $W^s_f(\phi(r))$.

We can do the same for a diffeomorphism g near f. A diffeomorphism g near f has a local unstable manifold $W^s_{g,loc}(h_g(p))$ of $h_g(p)$. We get a coordinate on $W^u_{g,loc}(h_g(p))$ by using the correspondence $h_g : W^u_{f,loc}(p) \to W^u_{g,loc}(h_g(p))$. Likewise we get a coordinate on $W^s_{g,loc}(h_g(q))$ by using the correspondence $h_g : W^s_{f,loc}(q) \to W^s_{g,loc}(h_g(q))$.

The unstable manifolds $W^u_g(r)$ define a map $i_g : W^s_{g,loc}(h_g(q)) \to \ell_g$. The stable manifolds $W^s_g(r)$ define a map $j_g : W^u_{g,loc}(h_g(p)) \to \ell_g$. The map $\psi_g : W^s_{f,loc}(q) \to W^u_{f,loc}(p)$,

$$\psi_g = j_g^{-1} \circ i_g,$$

has the property that $W^u_g(h_g(r))$ is tangent to $W^s_g(\phi_g(h_g(r)))$. By a conjugation we get a map $\phi_g = h_g^{-1} \circ \psi_g \circ h_g$ from $W^s_{f,loc}(q)$ to $W^u_{f,loc}(p)$, which is thus better suited to compare with $\phi = \phi_f$.

The topological conjugacy between f restricted to the manifold M with g restricted to M_g maps the fixed point of f on M to the fixed point of g on M_g and also maps stable manifold to stable manifold and unstable manifold to unstable manifold. The topological conjugacy restricted to the manifold M is therefore unique. The topological conjugacy restricted to the manifold N is likewise unique. A conjugacy between f and g maps the heteroclinic tangencies to heteroclinic tangencies. Therefore f and g are not topologically conjugate if $\phi_g \neq \phi$. This shows that f does not have a finite modulus of stability. ∎

Examples of robust structurally unstable systems exist for flows on three-dimensional manifolds. One such example is given by Lorenz attractors; see Section 5.2.2 and [**44**, Section 9.1.1]. Persistent tangencies can also occur for

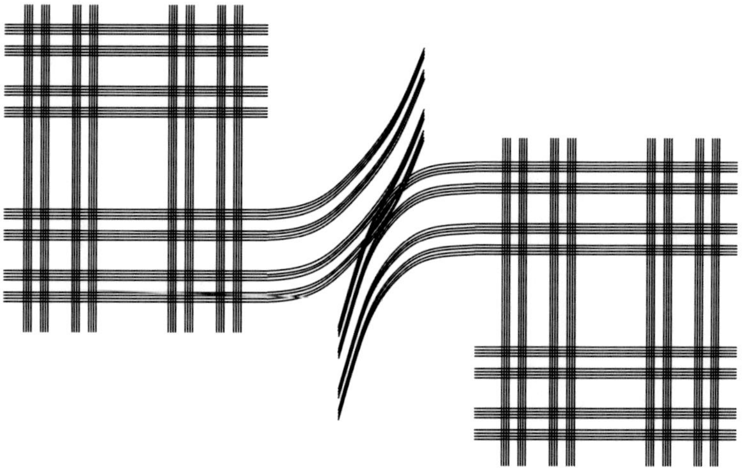

Figure 5.7. Robust heteroclinic tangencies between stable and unstable manifolds of hyperbolic sets.

stable and unstable manifolds of hyperbolic sets of saddle type in three-dimensional flows. This result is due to Sheldon Newhouse [**265**]. A rough sketch of the geometry in a context of planar diffeomorphisms is in Figure 5.7; depicted are local stable and unstable manifolds of two horseshoe invariant sets, and tangencies of unstable manifolds of one set with stable manifolds of the other set. Depending on metric properties of the invariant sets, such a geometry may lead to persistent heteroclinic tangencies. We will not discuss this here but instead refer to [**282**, Section 6.1] for an exposition of the theory. The two invariant sets can be the same and persistent tangencies of stable and unstable manifolds of one hyperbolic set of saddle type are possible, depending on metric properties of the invariant set. This leads to bifurcations of the nonwandering set. In the following remark we modify Example 5.39 to an example with persistent tangencies that give bifurcations of the nonwandering set.

Remark 5.40. Both constructions, in the proof of Theorem 5.38 and Example 5.39, focus on heteroclinic orbits and force persistent heteroclinic tangencies. The vector fields are Ω-stable. One can also construct examples with a similar flavor that do affect the nonwandering set. An early example is by Ralph Abraham and Stephen Smale [**5**], other examples are [**265**], [**349**], [**162**, Theorem (8.1)] and [**43**]. We leave to the reader the task of investigating the extension of Example 5.39 that we now sketch. We essentially take the system from Example 5.39 and add an extra dimension to obtain a diffeomorphism $f : \mathbb{T}^4 \to \mathbb{T}^4$. Use coordinates (x, y, z, u) on $\mathbb{T}^4$ and assume the following properties.

(i) On a small neighborhood U of the two-torus $M = \{z = 0, u = 0\}$, we have

$$f(x, y, z, u) = (2x + y, x + y, z/3, 3u).$$

(ii) On a small neighborhood V of the two-torus $N = \{z = \frac{1}{2}, u = 0\}$,

$$f(x, y, z) = (2x + y, x + y, -1 + 3z, u/3).$$

So f still has normally hyperbolic manifolds M and N. The extra direction for M is repelling. The extra direction for N is attracting. The manifolds M, N have stable and unstable manifolds $W^s(M), W^u(M), W^s(N), W^u(N)$, all of them three dimensional.

Assume a transverse intersection of $W^u(N)$ with $W^s(M)$, containing a quadratic tangency of a two-dimensional unstable manifold $W^u(q)$ of a point $q \in N$ with a two-dimensional stable manifold $W^s(p)$ of a point $p \in M$. Near the point of tangency in $W^u(q) \cap W^s(p)$, we may take coordinates (x_1, x_2, x_3, x_4) in which

$$W^s(M) = \{x_4 = 0\},$$
$$W^u(N) = \{x_3 = 0\}.$$

Inside $W^s(M) \cap W^u(N) = \{x_4 = 0, x_3 = 0\}$, we may assume $W^s(p) \cap W^s(M) \cap W^u(N) = \{x_1 = 0, x_4 = 0, x_3 = 0\}$, $W^u(q) \cap W^s(M) \cap W^u(N) = \{x_1 = -x_2^2, x_4 = 0, x_3 = 0\}$. The manifold $W^s(M)$ is foliated by stable manifolds of points in M, containing $W^s(p)$ as a leaf. Likewise, $W^u(N)$ is foliated by unstable manifolds of points in N, containing $W^u(q)$. Now perturb the diffeomorphism f slightly and observe that persistent heteroclinic tangencies arise.

Assume a transverse intersection of $W^u(p)$ with $W^s(q)$, inside a transverse intersection of $W^u(M)$ with $W^s(N)$. The nonwandering set of f contains the orbit of heteroclinic tangency [**5**]. When perturbing f, one finds persistent heteroclinic tangencies that are part of the nonwandering set. ■

Sheldon Newhouse [**266, 267**] established that persistent homoclinic tangencies involve the phenomenon of infinitely many coexisting periodic attractors (see also [**129, 307**] and the exposition in [**282**]). There are various works that explore aspects of this phenomenon and also how frequently it occurs. We mention [**37, 73, 131, 134, 375, 377, 394**]. For a connection with moduli of stability we refer to [**128**]. The reader is referred to the textbooks [**44, 282**] for more on dynamics that is not hyperbolic.

5.2. Bifurcation scenarios

In the sections below we showcase a choice of results and examples to illustrate global aspects of bifurcation theory. The sections on surface flows and torus flows give assorted results on structural stability of vector fields and families of vector fields in these contexts. We offer brief sections on the Lorenz family and also on the logistic and the Hénon families; their studies guided the research of properties of chaotic dynamics and bifurcations thereof. We discuss *routes to chaos* in the sections on period-doubling cascades and intermittency.

5.2.1. Surface flows. We continue with a discussion meant to illustrate issues that arise in the study of (weak) topological equivalence of families in global dynamics. The following material is written in a loose fashion. We sketch some ideas and wc describe underlying geometries, but we do not provide all of the technical details.

Observe first that a diffeomorphism near a hyperbolic fixed point on the line can be written as the time one map of a flow; this is clear from the existence of smooth linearization (Theorem B.27). The same is true for a diffeomorphism near a nondegenerate saddle-node equilibrium [**368**]. However, this has consequences for equivalence of families unfolding the saddle-node fixed point. We refer to [**184**] for the following result providing an embedding in a flow of local diffeomorphisms unfolding a saddle-node fixed point. We state the result in the context of flows with a saddle-node periodic orbit, using first return maps on a cross section.

Proposition 5.41. *Let f_λ be a family of vector fields on a compact surface with a generic unfolding of a nondegenerate saddle-node periodic orbit γ_0 at $\lambda = 0$ (we assume that the periodic orbit disappears for $\lambda > 0$). Let S be a local cross section through γ_0 and let Π_λ be the first return map on S. There is a smooth flow ψ_λ^t on S whose time one map ψ_λ^1 equals Π_λ. For $\lambda = 0$ the flow is unique.*

The following result can be found in [**268**] by Sheldon Newhouse, Jacob Palis, and Floris Takens. We will not include a proof.

Theorem 5.42. *Let f_λ be a family of vector fields on a compact surface with a generic unfolding of a nondegenerate saddle-node periodic orbit γ_0 at $\lambda = 0$. Let S be a local cross section through γ_0 and let Π_λ be the first return map on S. Let g_λ be a second family of vector fields on the same surface with a generic unfolding of a nondegenerate saddle-node periodic orbit η_0 at $\lambda = 0$. Let T be a local cross section through η_0 and let Ψ_λ be the first return map on T. We assume that the periodic orbits disappear for $\lambda > 0$.*

Write φ_λ^t and ψ_λ^t for corresponding flows on S and T given by Proposition 5.41, *so that in particular $\varphi_0^1 = \Pi_0$ and $\psi_0^1 = \Psi_0$.*

Let h_λ be a topological equivalence between the families f_λ and g_λ and let H_λ be a conjugacy between Π_λ and Ψ_λ induced by it. Then H_0 conjugates φ_0^t and ψ_0^t:

$$H_0 \circ \varphi_0^t = \psi_0^t \circ H_0.$$

The theorem states that the conjugacy H_0 is strongly restricted and determined by the images of two points. Take coordinates on S so that $\Pi_0(0) = 0$

and $\Pi_0(x) > x$ elsewhere. Likewise for coordinates on T. The statement of the theorem holds because, if we take a point $x < 0$ it will be mapped, if $\lambda > 0$, to a point with positive coordinate by a high iterate. We can take $\lambda_i \to 0$ from above so that $\Pi^i_{\lambda_i}(x)$ equals points y_i that converge to a point $y > 0$. Also $\Psi^i_{\lambda_i}(H_0(x))$ converges. The demand that H_λ depends continuously on λ forces that H_λ conjugates the flows φ^t_0 and ψ^t_0.

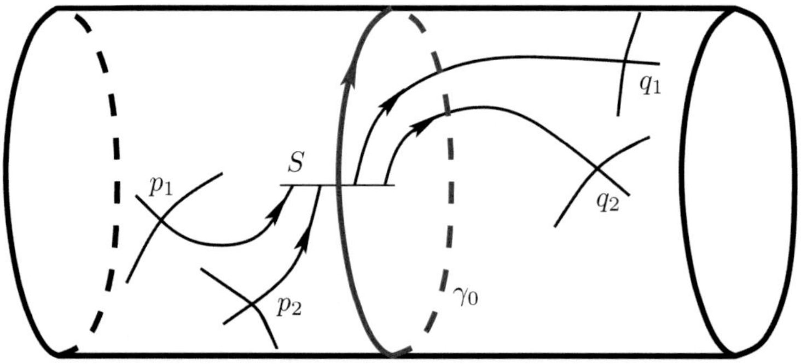

Figure 5.8. After disappearance of the saddle-node periodic orbit, heteroclinic connections can occur. The possible number of coexisting connections depends on the number of connections to the saddle-node periodic orbit, but also on their relative positions.

The following paragraph refers to the global bifurcation scenario depicted in Figure 5.8. Consider a family of vector fields f_λ on a surface with the following properties. For $\lambda = 0$ there is a saddle-node periodic orbit γ_0 unfolding generically as in Theorem 3.58. Suppose there are two hyperbolic saddle equilibria p_1, p_2 with unstable separatrices that accumulate onto γ_0. Suppose further that there are two hyperbolic saddle equilibria q_1, q_2 with stable separatrices that accumulate onto γ_0. Take a local cross section S transverse to γ_0 and let Π_λ denote the first return map on S. By Theorem 5.42 there is a vector field X on S such that the time one map φ^1_0 of the flow equals Π_0. Take intersections x_1^- of $W^u(p_1)$ with S and x_2^- of $W^u(p_2)$ with S such that x_2^- lies in between x_1^- and $\Pi_0(x_1^-)$. Likewise, take intersections x_1^+ of $W^s(q_1)$ with S and x_2^+ of $W^s(q_2)$ with S such that x_2^+ lies in between x_1^+ and $\Pi_0(x_1^+)$. Define times $t_-, t_+ \in (0,1)$ so that

$$x_2^- = \varphi_0^{t_-}(x_1^-),$$
$$x_2^+ = \varphi_0^{t_+}(x_1^+).$$

Iaci Malta and Jacob Palis [**237**] sketch a theory to arrive at a description of equivalence classes under equivalence of families of flows on compact surfaces. Because of Theorem 5.42 saddle-node bifurcations of periodic orbits can give rise to invariants for topologically equivalent families. The family f_λ introduced above, if $t_- = t_+$ or $t_- = 1 - t_+$, is not a structurally stable family.

The following theorem that implies that this follows [**185**] by Yulij Ilyashenko and Sergei Yakovenko.

Theorem 5.43. *With a family f_λ as above assume that either $t_- = t_+$ or $t_- = 1 - t_+$. There are families g_λ that are arbitrarily small perturbations of f_λ so that g_λ has two distinct saddle connections for some value of λ.*

Sketch of proof. We may assume that $t_- = t_+$ (we can relabel the points x_1^+, x_2^+ to achieve this). Consider a smooth two-parameter family f_{λ_1,λ_2} with $f_{\lambda_1} = f_{\lambda_1,0}$. Below we state conditions on the dependence on λ_2. Continue the points x_1^-, x_2^-, x_1^+, x_2^+ in the parameters λ_1, λ_2. These points then depend smoothly on both parameters. Also the times t_-, t_+ become smooth functions of the parameters. All these functions are defined for $\lambda_1 \geq 0$, but can be extended as smooth functions into $\lambda_1 < 0$. Take the family f_{λ_1,λ_2} so that

$$\frac{\partial}{\partial \lambda_2}(t_+(\lambda_1,\lambda_2) - t_-(\lambda_1,\lambda_2)) \neq 0.$$

This can for instance be achieved by making local perturbations near q_2. The curve

$$C = \{(\lambda_1,\lambda_2)\ ;\ t_-(\lambda_1,\lambda_2) = t_+(\lambda_1,\lambda_2)\}$$

is a smooth curve given as the graph of a function that expresses λ_2 in terms of λ_1. Along curves

$$C_{1,n} = \{(\lambda_1,\lambda_2)\ ;\ x_1^+(\lambda_1,\lambda_1) = \varphi_n(x_1^-(\lambda_1,\lambda_2))\}$$

for $n \in \mathbb{N}$ large, a heteroclinic connection from p_1 to q_1 exists. On intersection points in $C \cap C_{1,n}$ there is a second heteroclinic connection for p_2 to q_2. Such intersection points accumulate onto $(0,0)$ in the parameter plane. The theorem now easily follows. □

Above we sketched consequences for global bifurcations arising from saddle-node bifurcations of periodic orbits in flows on surfaces. Examples exist of bifurcations of planar vector fields involving only hyperbolic equilibria and homoclinic and heteroclinic orbits, where the bifurcation diagram varies with eigenvalues of the linearized vector fields at the equilibria. We present one such example due to Nataliya Goncharuk, Yury Kudryashov, and Nikita Solodnikov [**125**] in an illustrated description, and leave out precise statements and mathematical details. Examples like this arise in studies of stability of families of planar vector fields as in [**183**]. The upper left picture in Figure 5.9 shows a phase diagram of a planar vector field known as the glasses. It consists of two homoclinic orbits to different equilibria P and Q and a heteroclinic orbit from P to Q. Such a vector field can occur robustly in three-parameter families of vector fields (a configuration of glasses formed by two homoclinic orbits and a

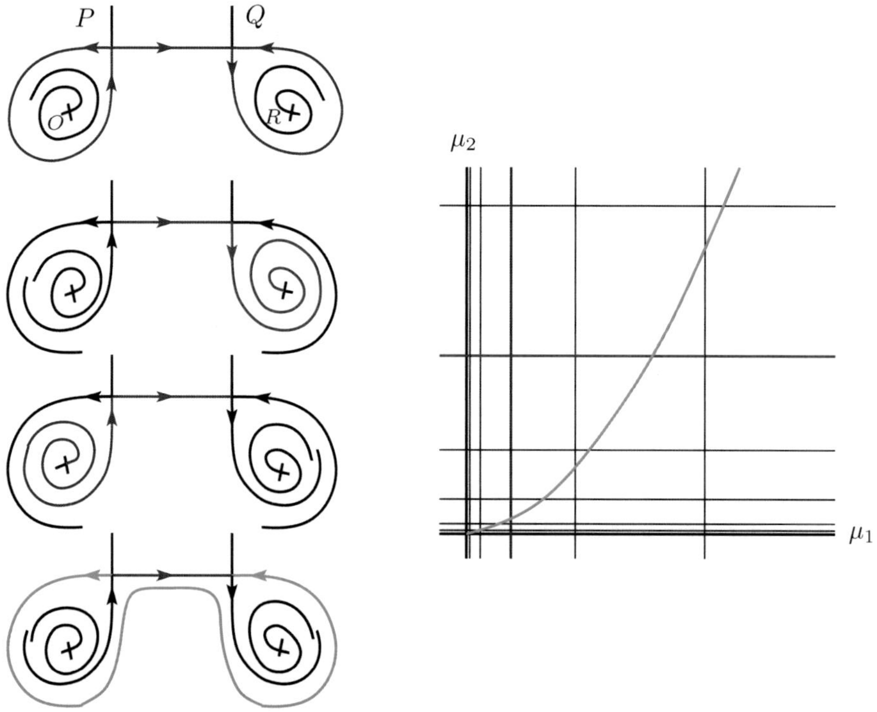

Figure 5.9. The glasses is a vector field containing two homoclinic orbits to saddles P and Q and a heteroclinic orbit from P to Q. The bifurcation set depends on eigenvalues of linearizations at P and Q.

heteroclinic orbit would still arise in slightly perturbed families). Inside the homoclinic orbit to P there is a hyperbolic saddle O with an unstable separatrix converging to the homoclinic orbit to P. Likewise, inside the homoclinic orbit to Q there is a hyperbolic saddle R with stable separatrix converging to the homoclinic orbit to Q. Consider now two-parameter families of vector fields that unfold both homoclinic bifurcations, while keeping the heteroclinic orbit from P to Q. The three phase diagrams below the glasses show perturbations in such two-parameter families. Take two parameters (μ_1, μ_2) with the glasses occuring at $(0, 0)$, as follows. Imagine that changing a parameter μ_1 changes the vector field in a neighborhood of the homoclinic orbit to P and keeps the vector field in a neighborhood of the homoclinic orbit to Q unchanged. And imagine that changing a parameter μ_2 changes the vector field in a neighborhood of the homoclinic orbit to Q and keeps the vector field in a neighborhood of the homoclinic orbit to P unchanged. There is a sequence of bifurcation parameters $\mu_{1,n}$ converging to 0 of heteroclinic orbits from O to P. Write $\lambda_P < 0 < \nu_P$ for the eigenvalues of the linearized vector fields at P. We assume $-\lambda_P/\nu_P > 1$. As in [**165**, Chapter 3] or [**183**, Lemma 4], one gets

$$\ln(\mu_{1,n+1})/\ln(\mu_{1,n}) \to -\lambda_P/\nu_P$$

as $n \to \infty$. The sequence appears as a sequence of vertical lines converging to the μ_2-axis in Figure 5.9. There is also a sequence of bifurcation parameters $\mu_{2,n}$ converging to 0 of heteroclinic orbits to Q. Here we have

$$\ln(\mu_{2,n+1})/\ln(\mu_{2,n}) \to -\nu_Q/\lambda_Q$$

as $n \to \infty$, where $\lambda_Q < 0 < \nu_Q$ are the eigenvalues of the linearized vector fields at Q and where we assume $-\lambda_Q/\nu_Q < 1$. The sequence appears as the sequence of horizontal lines in Figure 5.9 that converges to the μ_1-axis. There are other bifurcations as well. In particular there is a curve of a second heteroclinic orbit from P to Q as in the phase diagram depicted in the lower left in Figure 5.9. Such a curve, depicted in the bifurcation diagram in Figure 5.9, satisfies a formula $\mu_2 = a\mu_1^{(\lambda_P\lambda_Q)/(\nu_P\nu_Q)}$ plus higher-order terms, for some constant a. Now one can study how the geometry of intersections of this bifurcation curve with the horizontal and vertical bifurcation curves depends on ratios of eigenvalues, and how small perturbations that vary ratios of eigenvalues lead to four coexisting heteroclinic orbits.

5.2.2. Bifurcations in the Lorenz system. The Lorenz attractor, a strange attractor for the Lorenz equations, has become the standard visualization of chaos. The Lorenz equations are given by

$$\begin{aligned} \dot{x} &= \sigma(y - x), \\ \dot{y} &= -xz + \rho x - y, \\ \dot{z} &= xy - \beta z. \end{aligned} \tag{5.9}$$

The differential equations depend on three parameters β, σ, and ρ. Figure 5.10 depicts the Lorenz attractor for often used parameter values $\sigma = 10$, $\beta = 8/3$, $\rho = 28$. It is important to realize that the Lorenz system is symmetric under the reflection $R(x, y, z) = (-x, -y, z)$. This means that if $(x(t), y(t), z(t))$ is a solution, then also $(-x(t), -y(t), z(t))$ is a solution.

Following similar constructions as described in [**322**], Edward Lorenz derived the equations as a simplified mathematical model for convection of a liquid between two plates that is subject to gravity and heated from below [**231**]. The derivation is explained in the textbooks [**35**, Appendix D] and [**51**, Appendix D]. See also [**244**] and [**365**, Chapter 9] for a connection to the Malkus water wheel. A study of the Lorenz system can fill books [**358**]; we restrict our discussion to a descriptive tour of some bifurcation aspects.

Much theoretical progress concerns geometric Lorenz models, which are models of differential equations that are thought to explain the dynamics of the actual Lorenz system [**7, 144, 420**]. More generally a large body of theoretical

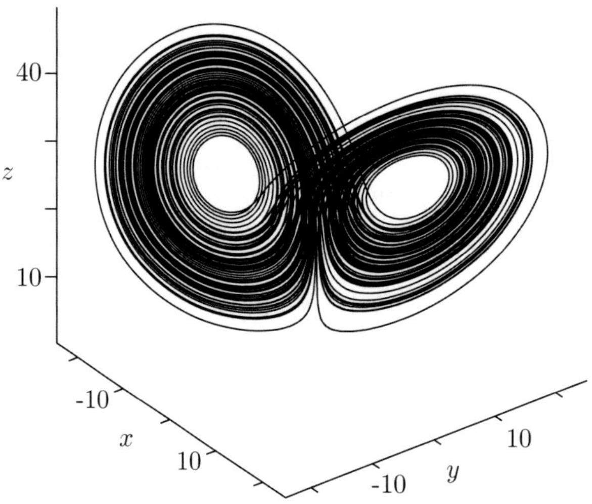

Figure 5.10. The Lorenz attractor.

work concerns singular hyperbolic dynamics, for which we refer to [**44**, Chapter 9]. A key property is the existence of a hyperbolic equilibrium inside a persistent attractor, or recurrent set. Warwick Tucker [**391, 392**] proved that the Lorenz attractor from Figure 5.10 is indeed a strange attractor with properties as predicted by analysis of proposed geometric models.

Figure 5.11 illustrates the flow of a geometric Lorenz model. There is a saddle equilibrium at the origin O with a one-dimensional unstable manifold. A cross section S is shown together with the image of the return map $P : S \to S$. The two-dimensional stable manifold $W^s(O)$ splits S into two parts that both return; $P(S)$ consists of two connected components. Geometric Lorenz models have the property that they are topologically equivalent to differential

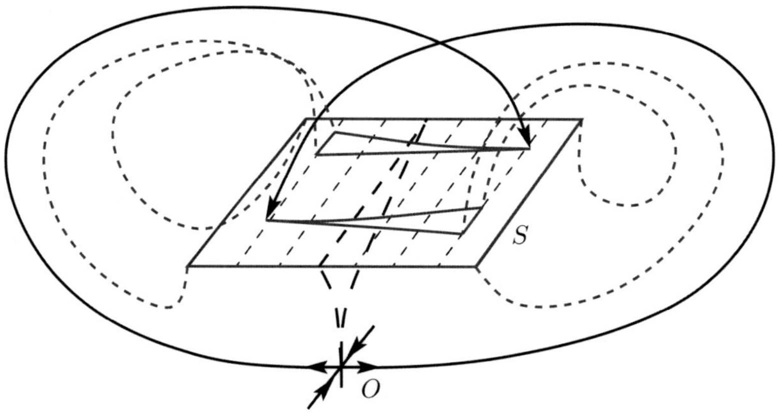

Figure 5.11. The geometric Lorenz model. The action of the return map P.

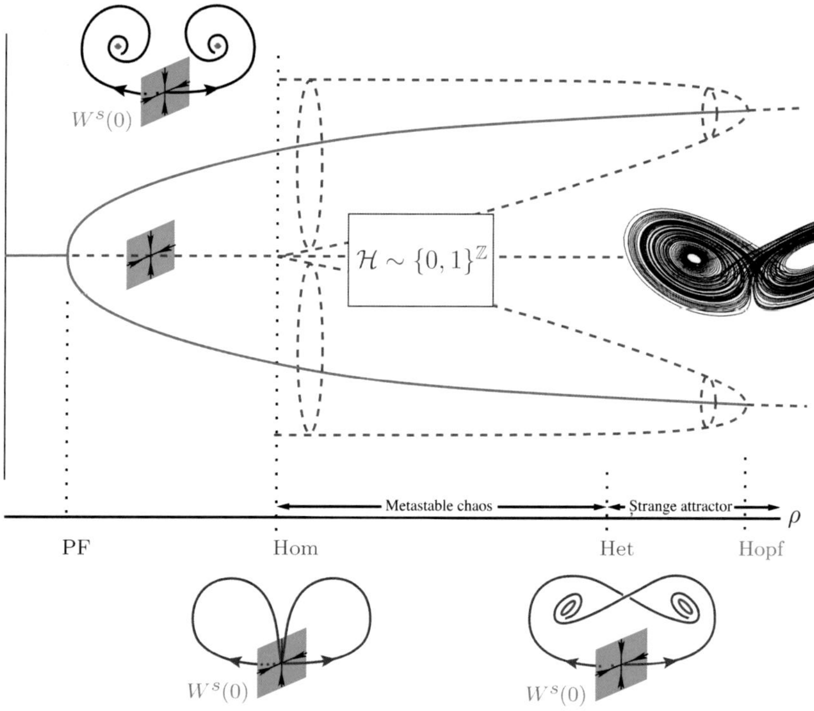

Figure 5.12. An artistic impression of bifurcations in the Lorenz system for varying ρ, fixing $\sigma = 10$ and $\beta = 8/3$.

equations whose return map becomes a map $P : [-1,1]^2 \to [-1,1]^2$ of the form $P(x,y) = (f(x), g(x,y))$ with

(i) $f(x) = -f(-x)$;

(ii) $f'(x) > 1$;

(iii) $\left|\frac{\partial}{\partial y} g(x,y)\right| < 1$.

The dynamics of the x-coordinate is given by the interval map f. As the map $g(x,y)$ in the y-coordinate contracts distance between points with identical x-coordinates, the dynamics is largely determined by the interval map f. We therefore refer to f as the reduced interval map. That this defines an open class of models (that is, that a small smooth perturbation of a geometric Lorenz model is again a geometric Lorenz model) is a technical issue that involves the construction of invariant strong stable foliations. We just refer to some key references that extend the original work [**19, 306, 332**].

Now take again the Lorenz equations (5.9). Fix $\sigma = 10$ and $\beta = 8/3$. If we take $\rho < 1$, the Lorenz system admits an attracting fixed point at the origin. We describe a postulated bifurcation diagram, when increasing ρ, that changes the system from trivial to the one with a strange attractor. Figure 5.12 gives an

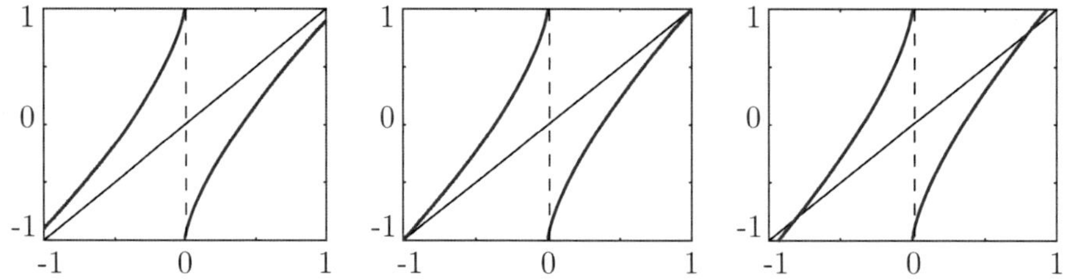

Figure 5.13. Reduced interval maps before, at, and after the heteroclinic bifurcation that creates the Lorenz attractor.

illustration. The numerically calculated bifurcation diagram for the Lorenz system, confirming this description, is contained in [**98**].

At $\rho = 1$, the origin undergoes a pitchfork bifurcation, which is indeed a local bifurcation of codimension 1 for differential equations that are equivariant under a reflection. For $\rho > 1$, the origin has one-dimensional unstable direction and two-dimensional stable directions. Two other stable equilibria have been created.

At ρ near 13.93, there are two symmetry related homoclinic orbits to the origin. For ρ larger than this homoclinic bifurcation value, there are periodic orbits of saddle type near the homoclinic orbit. One can show that in fact there is an invariant hyperbolic set $\mathcal{H}$ that can be coded by $\{0,1\}^{\mathbb{Z}}$ near the union of the two homoclinic orbits. The dynamics has been called metastable chaos. Orbits starting near the invariant set move erratically for some time, but eventually converge to one of the two stable equilibria that were created in the pitchfork bifurcation.

At ρ near 24.06, heteroclinic orbits exist from the origin to the periodic orbits created in the homoclinic bifurcation. The Lorenz attractor exists for ρ larger than this value. The reduced interval map is such that it maps $[-1,1]$ inside itself and orbits for P cannot escape $[-1,1]^2$. At the heteroclinic bifurcation which marks the starting point of the existence of the Lorenz attractor, the interval map maps $[-1,1]$ precisely twice onto itself, as indicated in Figure 5.13. At ρ near 24.74 the periodic orbits that were created in the homoclinic bifurcation disappear in a subcritical Hopf bifurcation. This does not affect the strange attractor.

5.2.3. Circle diffeomorphisms and torus flows.

In the Neimark-Sacker bifurcation described in Section 3.3.3, an invariant torus is created from a bifurcating periodic orbit. The first return map on a cross section transverse to the periodic orbit shows a bifurcation in which an invariant circle is created from a bifurcating fixed point. The study of the flow on the invariant torus thus leads to a study of diffeomorphisms on circles.

5.2.3.1. *Circle maps.* Here we copy results from the more elementary theory of the dynamics of circle diffeomorphisms. We follow the presentation in [**48**], but refer also to [**93, 309**] for more details.

Throughout this section we consider the circle as the quotient $\mathbb{T} = \mathbb{R}/\mathbb{Z}$. We will only look at orientation preserving homeomorphisms (or diffeomorphisms) f on $\mathbb{T}$. Those maps preserve the order (according to the orientation of the circle) of points on the circle. This means that the f image of any interval $[a, b]$ is contained in $[f(a), f(b)]$.

Orientation preserving homeomorphisms will be studied using a lift of f, which is defined as follows. Consider a covering map $\pi : \mathbb{R} \to \mathbb{T}$, $\pi(t) = t \bmod 1$. A lift F of f is a continuous map $\mathbb{R} \to \mathbb{R}$ with

$$\pi \circ F = f \circ \pi.$$

Every continuous circle map has a lift [**245, 260**]. An orientation preserving homeomorphism $f : \mathbb{T} \to \mathbb{T}$ has an monotonically increasing lift $F : \mathbb{R} \to \mathbb{R}$ with

$$F(x + k) = F(x) + k$$

for $k \in \mathbb{Z}$. Two lifts differ by an integer constant.

Example 5.44. Consider the rigid rotation $f(x) = x + \alpha \bmod 1$ on $\mathbb{T}$. Take the lift $F(x) = x + \alpha$ on $\mathbb{R}$. For $\alpha = \frac{p}{q} \in \mathbb{Q}$ (with p and q relatively prime) all points are periodic points and have period q. We find $F^q(x) = x + p$ for all x. If $\alpha \in \mathbb{R} \setminus \mathbb{Q}$, then all positive orbits are dense in $\mathbb{T}$. Indeed, if this were not true, then a positive orbit $\{f^i(x_0)\}$, $i \in \mathbb{N}$, would avoid an interval J. Take J of maximal length. The positive orbit of x_0 would also have empty intersection with images $f^i(J)$, $i > 0$. The intervals $f^i(J)$ all have the same length. As $\alpha \in \mathbb{R} \setminus \mathbb{Q}$, it cannot happen that $f^k(J) = J$ for some k. The intervals can also not be all disjoint. So some iterate $f^k(J)$ intersects J, contradicting the maximal length of J. ■

The key notion in the study of dynamics of orientation preserving circle homeomorphisms is the rotation number which is the average rotation per iterate. The rotation number of a point $x \in \mathbb{T}$ would thus be equal to $\rho(x, f) = \rho(x, F) \bmod 1$ with

$$\rho(x, F) = \lim_{n \to \infty} \frac{1}{n}(F^n(x) - x)$$

if the limit exists. Observe that if the limit exists for one lift F, then it exists for all lifts. Indeed, $\rho(x, F + k) = \rho(x, F)$. So the rotation number (the limit taken modulo 1) is independent of the lift.

Theorem 5.45. *Let $f : \mathbb{T} \to \mathbb{T}$ be an orientation preserving homeomorphism. Then for each $x \in \mathbb{T}$, the rotation number $\rho(x, f)$ exists and is independent of x.*

Proof. Let F be a lift of f. Take $x \in [0,1)$. Suppose first that

$$F^q(y) = y + p \tag{5.10}$$

for some $y \in [0,1)$ and $p \in \mathbb{Z}$, $q \in \mathbb{N}$. The point y gives a periodic point for f. Write $n = kq + r$ for $0 \le r < q$. Then $F^n(y) = F^r(F^{kq}(y)) = F^r(y) + kp$. Hence

$$\begin{aligned}\lim_{n\to\infty} \frac{F^n(y) - y}{n} &= \lim_{n\to\infty} \frac{F^r(y) - y}{n} + \frac{kp}{n} \\ &= \frac{p}{q}\end{aligned}$$

since $\lim_{n\to\infty} \frac{F^r(y)-y}{n} = 0$. Thus $\rho(y, F) = \frac{p}{q}$. Keeping assumption (5.10), take another point $x \in [0,1)$. Then

$$|F^n(x) - F^n(y)| \le 1,$$

since F maps an interval of length 1 to an interval of length 1. We thus also find $|(F^n(x) - x) - (F^n(y) - y)| \le |F^n(x) - F^n(y)| + |x - y| \le 2$ and hence

$$\lim_{n\to\infty} \frac{F^n(x) - x}{n} = \lim_{n\to\infty} \frac{F^n(y) - y}{n}.$$

The same holds for any $x \in \mathbb{R}$, not necessarily in $[0,1)$, as $F^n(x+k) = F^n(x)+k$.

The above reasoning shows that a circle diffeomorphism that possesses a periodic point ((5.10) holds) has a rotation number that is the same for each point.

Now suppose $F^n(x) \ne x + p$ for all $x \in \mathbb{R}$, $p \in \mathbb{Z}$, $q \in \mathbb{N}$. By continuity we have that either $F^n(x) > x + p$ for all $x \in \mathbb{R}$, or $F^n(x) < x + p$ for all $x \in \mathbb{R}$. For $n \in \mathbb{N}$ let p_n be so that $p_n - 1 < F^n(x) - x < p_n$ for all $x \in \mathbb{R}$. Then

$$m(p_n - 1) < F^{nm}(x) - x = \sum_{k=0}^{m-1} F^n(F^{kn}(x)) - F^{kn}(x) < mp_n,$$

which implies that

$$\frac{p_n}{n} - \frac{1}{n} < \frac{F^{mn}(x) - x}{mn} < \frac{p_n}{n}.$$

Interchanging the roles of m and n, we also have

$$\frac{p_n}{m} - \frac{1}{m} < \frac{F^{mn}(x) - x}{mn} < \frac{p_m}{m}.$$

Thus $|\frac{p_m}{m} - \frac{p_n}{n}| < |\frac{1}{m} - \frac{1}{n}|$ and therefore $\{\frac{p_n}{n}\}$, $n \in \mathbb{N}$, is a Cauchy sequence. It follows that $\frac{F^n(x)-x}{n}$ converges as $n \to \infty$. By the same reasoning for case (5.10) above, we get that the rotation number is constant. □

We write $\rho(f) = \rho(F) \bmod 1$ for the rotation number of an orientation preserving circle homeomorphism f, which we now know to be well defined.

The rotation number depends continuously on the circle homeomorphism in the C^0 topology. To see this, assume

$$\frac{p}{q} < \rho(f) < \frac{p'}{q'}.$$

Given $x \in [0,1)$, take a lift F of f so that $p < F^q(x) - x < p+1$. The bound $p < F^q(x) - x < p+1$ holds for all $x \in \mathbb{R}$ since otherwise the rotation number equals $\frac{p}{q}$. For g sufficiently close to f, we can take a lift G of g so that $p < G^q(x) - x < p+1$ for all $x \in \mathbb{R}$. Thus $\rho(g) > \frac{p}{q}$. As likewise $\rho(g) < \frac{p'}{q'}$ for g sufficiently close to f, continuous dependence of $\rho(f)$ on f follows.

The following results classifies possible dynamics of orientation preserving diffeomorphisms. See for instance [**48, 93**] or [**309**].

Theorem 5.46. *Let $f : \mathbb{T} \to \mathbb{T}$ be a C^2 orientation preserving circle diffeomorphism. The following holds.*

(i) *$\rho(f)$ is rational if and only if f has a periodic point. If $\rho(f) = \frac{p}{q}$ with $p, q \in \mathbb{N}$ relatively prime, then every periodic point x of f has period q and $F^q(x) = x + p$ for the unique lift F with $\rho(F) = \frac{p}{q}$.*

(ii) *$\rho(f)$ is irrational if and only if the dynamics of f is minimal (all orbits are dense in $\mathbb{T}$). In this case, f is topologically conjugate to the rigid rotation $x \mapsto x + \rho(f)$* mod 1.

A circle diffeomorphism with hyperbolic periodic orbits has a rational rotation number. Moreover, sufficiently small perturbations of the circle diffeomorphism have nearby periodic orbits and thus the same rotation number. Only when the periodic orbits disappear in saddle-node bifurcations can the rotation number change. The occurrence of rational versus irrational rotation numbers in unfoldings of saddle-node bifurcations in circle diffeomorphisms is considered in [**9**]. A model family of circle diffeomorphisms in which the change of rotation number is investigated is the standard family treated in the next example.

Example 5.47. The standard family of circle maps is given by

$$f(x) = x + a + b\sin(2\pi x) \bmod 1.$$

The map $f(x)$ is an orientation preserving diffeomorphism for any b with $|b| < \frac{1}{2\pi}$. We also write $f_{a,b}(x)$ to stress dependence on parameters. Observe that $f_{a,0}(x) = x + a \bmod 1$ is a rigid rotation with rotation number a.

For fixed b with $|b| < \frac{1}{2\pi}$, the rotation number $\rho_{a,b}$ is monotone increasing in a. See the left panel of Figure 5.14. Rational rotation numbers occur on intervals in a. For small b, the set

$$R = \{a \in [0,1]\ ;\ \rho_{a,b} \in \mathbb{Q}\}$$

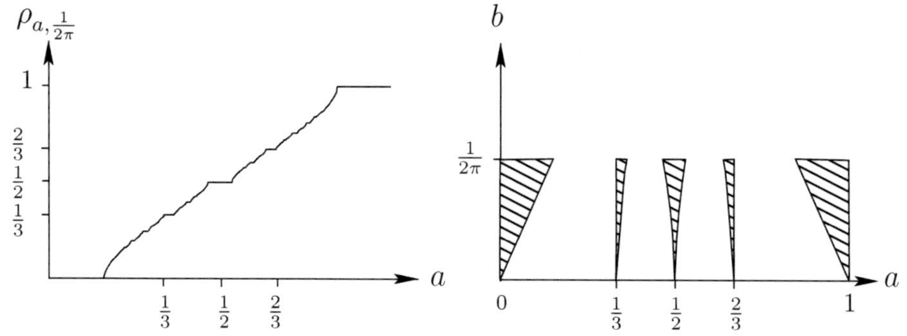

Figure 5.14. Left panel: Graph of the rotation number $\rho_{a,b}$ for $0 \le a \le 1$ and $b = \frac{1}{2\pi}$. For any fixed positive value of b, such a graph is called a devil's staircase because of its shape. Right panel: Arnold tongues for values $a \in \{0, \frac{1}{3}, \frac{1}{2}, \frac{2}{3}, 1\}$, and for $0 \le b \le \frac{1}{2\pi}$ in each case.

is open and dense in $[0, 1]$. However, its Lebesgue measure converges to zero as $b \to 0$. This was proved by Vladimir Arnold [**20**] (translated in [**1**]). The components of R in the parameter plane (a, b) that give a fixed rational rotation number are called Arnold tongues. See the right panel of Figure 5.14. ■

5.2.3.2. *Bifurcations of torus flows.* Following the work by David Ruelle and Floris Takens [**319**] we conduct a thought experiment. Consider a family of differential equations $\dot{x} = f_\lambda(x)$ on a high-dimensional Euclidean space $\mathbb{R}^{2m}$ with an equilibrium at the origin for all λ. Assume that for some λ, all eigenvalues of $Df(0, \lambda)$ have negative real parts and that, as λ increases, successive pairs of complex conjugate eigenvalues of $Df(0, \lambda)$ cross the imaginary axis, for $\lambda = \lambda_1, \lambda_2, \lambda_3, \ldots$. Assume first that the vector field f near 0 is of the special form $f(x, \lambda) = f_1(x_1, \lambda) + f_2(x_2, \lambda) + \cdots$, where $f_i(x_i, \lambda)$ gives the components in E_i. Here E_i is the two-dimensional linear space associated with the ith pair of eigenvalues of $Df(0, \lambda)$. For $\lambda > \lambda_1$ the equilibrium at the origin is no longer attracting. When λ moves through λ_1, the system undergoes a Hopf bifurcation and will develop, assuming the appropriate conditions, a stable periodic orbit γ_1 inside E_1. If λ is in the interval $(\lambda_k, \lambda_{k+1})$, the vector field leaves invariant a manifold T, which is the Cartesian product of k attracting periodic orbits $\gamma_1, \ldots, \gamma_k$ in the spaces $E_1, \ldots, E_k$. The manifold T is diffeomorphic to a k-dimensional torus $\mathbb{T}^k = \mathbb{R}^k/\mathbb{Z}^k$ and is attracting. By a suitable choice of coordinates on T the vector field may be written as

$$\dot{\theta}_1 = a_1,$$
$$\vdots$$
$$\dot{\theta}_k = a_k,$$

on the torus $\mathbb{T}^k$ with incommensurable a_i (the a_i are not rationally related). The related orbits are called quasi-periodic—they are generated by a superposition of incommensurable frequencies. The related flow is called quasi-periodic flow. Quasi-periodic flow means that orbits $x(t)$ on T can be written as $x(t) = \varphi(\omega_1 t, \dots, \omega_k t)$ where φ is periodic of period 1 in each of its arguments separately and the frequencies $\omega_1, \dots, \omega_k$ are not rationally related. Quasi-periodic motion is a natural generalization of the idea of periodic orbit, for which one has an expression $x(t) = \varphi(\omega_1 t)$ with one frequency ω_1. For a small perturbation of f one expects an invariant manifold that is close to T (using the theory of normally hyperbolic invariant manifolds [**162**]) with a flow on it that is typically no longer quasi-periodic. The first two bifurcations in this thought experiment would be a Hopf bifurcation of the equilibrium (Section 3.2.4) and a Neimark-Sacker bifurcation of the periodic orbit created in the Hopf bifurcation (Section 3.3.3).

If we take a quasi-periodic motion on a two-dimensional torus, then there are arbitrarily small perturbations that give stable periodic orbits in the torus. That is, consider the differential equation

$$\begin{aligned}\dot{\theta}_1 &= a_1,\\ \dot{\theta}_2 &= a_2,\end{aligned}$$

on the torus $\mathbb{T}^2 = \mathbb{R}^2/\mathbb{Z}^2$. There are arbitrarily small perturbations of it having a periodic attractor. To see this, consider an appropriate Poincaré map which describes a rigid rotation $x + \alpha$ on $\mathbb{T}$ with an irrational rotation number α. Then embed this map in the standard family.

On higher-dimensional tori, small perturbations of constant vector fields can create nontrivial dynamics. We quote the following result by Sheldon Newhouse, David Ruelle, and Floris Takens [**269**]. A nontrivial attractor refers to an attractor different from an equilibrium or periodic orbit.

Theorem 5.48. *Consider the differential equation*

$$\begin{aligned}\dot{\theta}_1 &= a_1,\\ \dot{\theta}_2 &= a_2,\\ \dot{\theta}_3 &= a_3,\end{aligned}$$

on the three-dimensional torus $\mathbb{T}^3 = \mathbb{R}^3/\mathbb{Z}^3$. There are arbitrarily C^2-small perturbations of this constant vector field having a nontrivial attractor.

Sketch of proof. Using a suspension, it suffices to prove a corresponding result for diffeomorphisms on the torus $\mathbb{T}^2 = \mathbb{R}^2/\mathbb{Z}^2$. We start with a translation $f(x, y) = (x + \alpha, y + \beta) \bmod 1$ on the torus $\mathbb{T}^2 = \mathbb{R}^2/\mathbb{Z}^2$. We must show that there are arbitrarily C^2-small perturbations of f that yield diffeomorphisms with a nontrivial attractor.

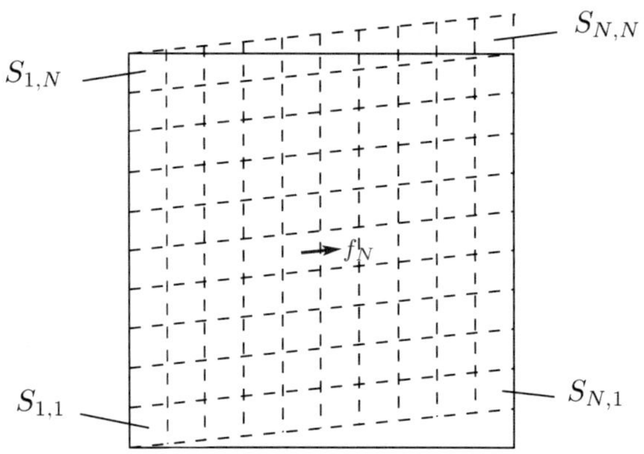

Figure 5.15. f_N permutes cyclically N^2 parallelograms that partition the torus.

We describe the general idea behind the construction of the perturbation. Consider a diffeomorphism ϕ on $\mathbb{T}^2 = \mathbb{R}^2/\mathbb{Z}^2$, such that its lift Φ on $\mathbb{R}^2$ leaves the square $[0,1]^2$ invariant. Assume moreover that ϕ is isotopic to the identity, so that there exists a curve ϕ_t, $t \in [0,1]$, of diffeomorphisms with $\phi_0 = \text{id}$ and $\phi_1 = \phi$.

Partition the torus $\mathbb{T}^2$ by parallelograms

$$S_{i,j} = \left\{ \frac{i-1}{N} \le x \le \frac{i}{N}, \frac{j-1}{N} \le y - \frac{x}{N} \le \frac{j}{N} \right\},$$

$1 \le i \le N, 1 \le j \le N$, as shown in Figure 5.15. Take $h_N : [0,1]^2 \to S_{1,1}$,

$$h_N(x,y) = \left(\frac{x}{N}, \frac{y}{N} + \frac{x}{N^2} \right).$$

Note that

$$h_N^{-1}(x,y) = (Nx, Ny - x).$$

Write $t(i,j) = \frac{i}{N^2} + \frac{j-1}{N}$, so that $t(1,1) = 0$ and $t(N,N) = 1$. Take a torus map $f_N : \mathbb{T}^2 \to \mathbb{T}^2$, on $S_{i,j}$ given by

$$f_N = h_N \circ \phi_{t(i,j)} \circ \phi_{t(i-1,j)}^{-1} \circ h_N^{-1} \left(x - \frac{i-1}{N}, y - \frac{j-1}{N} - \frac{i-1}{N^2} \right)$$
$$+ \left(\frac{i}{N}, \frac{j-1}{N} + \frac{i}{N^2} \right) \bmod 1.$$

The map f_N maps a parallelogram $S_{i,j}$ to the next parallelogram $S_{i+1,j}$ if $i < N$ (and $S_{N,j}$ to $S_{1,j+1}$ if $j < N$ and $S_{N,N}$ to $S_{1,1}$).

The iterate f_N^N maps $S_{1,1}$ onto itself, and on $S_{1,1}$ it is topologically conjugate to ϕ. Now observe that f_N converges in the C^2 topology to the identity map as $N \to \infty$. To see this, consider the composition $\phi_{t(i,j)} \circ \phi_{t(i-s,j)}^{-1}$ that appears with $s = 1$ in the definition of f_N. This map and its derivatives depend smoothly on the parameter s, and the map equals the identity map if $s = 0$. From the chain rule it follows that the first derivative is close to the identity, and converges to it, if $N \to \infty$, for $0 \leq s \leq 1$. The second derivative is small, and goes to 0 if $N \to \infty$, for $0 \leq s \leq 1$. This proves that f_N converges in the C^2 topology to the identity map as $N \to \infty$.

To complete the proof of the theorem, we choose ϕ so that it possesses a nontrivial attractor. Such maps exist—one can for instance use a Hénon map with a nontrivial attractor [**34**] (see Section 5.2.4) and alter accordingly. □

A system of n independent linear oscillators is given by equations

$$\begin{aligned}\dot{\theta}_1 &= a_1,\\ &\vdots\\ \dot{\theta}_n &= a_n,\end{aligned}$$

where $\theta_i \in \mathbb{T}$, $1 \leq i \leq n$. A variant of Theorem 5.48 in three and more dimensions (see [**269**]) shows that for $n \geq 3$, there are arbitrarily C^2-small functions $f_i(\theta_1, \dots, \theta_n)$ so that the weakly coupled oscillators,

$$\begin{aligned}\dot{\theta}_1 &= a_1 + f_1(\theta_1, \dots, \theta_n),\\ &\vdots\\ \dot{\theta}_n &= a_n + f_n(\theta_1, \dots, \theta_n),\end{aligned}$$

form a system of differential equations with a nontrivial attractor.

Bifurcation scenarios in which a torus is destroyed are also a possibility. This has been described by James Curry and James Yorke [**82**]; see also [**35**, Chapter VII] and [**8**, Section 5.5]. See further the bifurcation study in [**28**] and the bifurcation theory for a quasi-periodic flow on tori developed in [**50**].

5.2.4. Logistic and Hénon families. Our goal in this section is to present some of the research on logistic maps and Hénon maps with a connection to bifurcation theory. Logistic maps are quadratic maps and as such the simplest noninvertible maps on the real line. Their dynamics serves as paradigm for the dynamics of noninvertible maps on the line. Hénon maps are in the same sense representatives of planar diffeomorphisms.

5.2.4.1. *Logistic maps.* We start with the logistic maps. For a proper treatment and much more information than we include, we refer to the textbooks [**93**] and [**133**], and to the research monographs [**70**] and [**87**]. We refer to [**246**] for an interpretive review of the role of interval maps in biological sciences.

The logistic family (also known as quadratic family) is the one-parameter family of maps

$$f_\lambda(x) = f(x, \lambda) = \lambda x(1 - x)$$

on the real line.

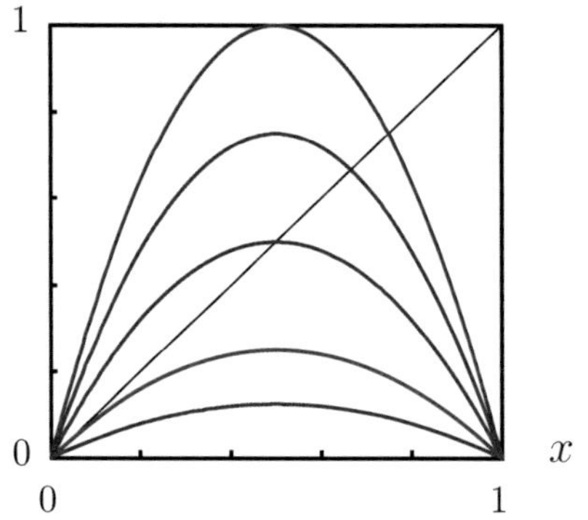

Figure 5.16. Graphs of f_λ for $\lambda = 0.5, 1$ (red), $2, 3, 4$ (purple).

A logistic map is a unimodal map with a unique critical point and an increasing and a decreasing branch. For $0 \leq \lambda \leq 4$ the unit interval $[0,1]$ is invariant. Figure 5.16 shows the graph of f_λ on $[0,1]$ for a few characteristic values of λ. Iterates of an initial point outside the unit interval diverge to minus infinity. We note that f_λ is not an diffeomorphism. Thus only forward iterates are meaningful to consider. However, the terms introduced in Chapter 2 can be easily applied to this case.

For $1 < \lambda < 3$, f_λ possesses a unique attracting fixed point that attracts all points in $(0,1)$; see [**93**]. More complicated dynamics, and various bifurcations, occurs for larger values of λ. Figure 5.17 shows a numerically computed bifurcation diagram of the logistic family. The parameter runs on the horizontal axis from 2.5 to 4. On the vertical axis is the x-coordinate of a numerically computed attractor.

At $\lambda_0 = 3$ a period-doubling bifurcation occurs in which an attracting period 2 orbit is created. A second period-doubling bifurcation is at $\lambda_1 = 1 + \sqrt{6}$ and results in an attracting period 4 orbit for parameter values directly beyond λ_1. This goes on and there is a sequence of period-doubling bifurcations λ_n resulting in attracting periodic orbits of period 2^{n+1}. The bifurcation values λ_n accumulate to some value λ_∞. This phenomenon of infinitely many period-doubling bifurcations is discussed in Section 5.2.5.

A special case and the last bifurcation value is given by the map f_4 that maps $[0,1]$ precisely twice onto itself. Its dynamics can be well investigated using a suitable topological conjugacy. To prepare for this, consider first $h : [0,1] \to [0,1]$ given by

$$h(x) = \sin^2(\pi x).$$

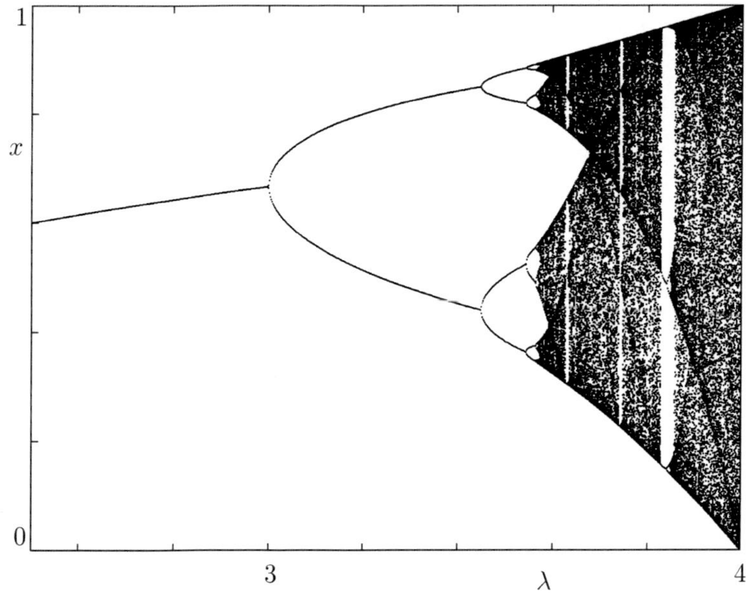

Figure 5.17. Numerically computed bifurcation diagram of the logistic family $f_\lambda(x) = \lambda x(1-x)$ with $\lambda \in [2.5, 4]$.

Using the double angle formula $\sin(2\theta) = 2\sin(\theta)\cos(\theta)$, we find

$$\begin{aligned} h(2x) &= \sin^2(2\pi x) \\ &= 4\sin^2(\pi x)\cos^2(\pi x) \\ &= f_4(h(x)). \end{aligned}$$

For iterates we find $h(2^n x \pmod 1) = f_4^n(h(x))$. So if $x_n = f_4^n(x_0)$, and $x_0 = \sin^2(\pi\theta_0)$, then we have a simple expression for x_n:

$$x_n = \sin^2(\pi\theta_n)$$

with

$$\theta_n = 2^n\theta_0 \pmod 1.$$

The function h is not a homeomorphism and therefore does not provide a conjugacy between f_4 and $x \mapsto 2x \pmod 1$. A topological conjugacy with the tent map exists, as the following result tells. An example where this result is used is in Exercise 5.16.

Proposition 5.49. *The map $f_4(x) = 4x(1-x)$ is topologically conjugate to the tent map $T : [0,1] \to [0,1]$ given by*

$$T(x) = \begin{cases} 2x, & 0 \le x \le 1/2, \\ 2(1-x), & 1/2 \le x \le 1. \end{cases}$$

Proof. Let $h : [0,1] \to [0,1]$ be given by

$$h(x) = \sin^2(\pi x/2).$$

Then h is an increasing homeomorphism with $h(0) = 0, h(1) = 1$. Using $\sin(2\theta) = 2\sin(\theta)\cos(\theta)$, one checks that for $x \in [0, 1/2]$,

$$h(2x) = 4h(x)(1 - h(x)). \tag{5.11}$$

For $x \in [1/2, 1]$, the equation

$$h(2(1-x)) = 4h(x)(1 - h(x)) \tag{5.12}$$

holds. Indeed,

$$\begin{aligned} h(2(1-x)) = \sin^2(\pi(1-x)) &= \sin^2(\pi x) \\ &= 4\sin^2(\pi x/2)\cos^2(\pi x/2) = 4h(x)(1-h(x)). \end{aligned}$$

Equations (5.11) and (5.12) together prove that h is a conjugacy between f_4 and the tent map T. □

Exercise 5.18 asks us to prove the following statements. First, that the tent map T on $[0, 1]$ is chaotic in the sense of Devaney. And second, that as a consequence of the above proposition, f_4 restricted to $[0, 1]$ is chaotic in the sense of Devaney. We remark that [**29**] observes that sensitive dependence on initial conditions follows from topological transitivity plus dense periodic orbits. In fact, for continuous interval maps, topological transitivity implies both sensitive dependence on initial conditions and dense periodic orbits [**40, 410**]. As f_λ for $1 < \lambda < 3$ has just fixed points, varying λ from 1 to 4 will show bifurcations in which infinitely many periodic orbits are created.

The study of the dynamics of f_λ is helped by using the Schwarzian derivative and in particular the minimum principle, which applies to maps with negative Schwarzian derivative.

Definition 5.50. For a smooth function $g : \mathbb{R} \to \mathbb{R}$, the *Schwarzian derivative* Sg is defined by

$$Sg(x) = \frac{g'''(x)}{g'(x)} - \frac{3}{2}\left(\frac{g''(x)}{g'(x)}\right)^2,$$

defined for all x with $g'(x) \neq 0$.

It follows from a calculation using the chain rule that $S(f \circ g) < 0$ if both $Sf < 0$ and $Sg < 0$; see [**93**] or [**133**]. Therefore, if $Sg(x) < 0$ for all $x \in \mathbb{R}$ with $g'(x) \neq 0$, then also $Sg^n(x) < 0$ for all x with $(g^n)'(x) \neq 0$. By a simple calculation one verifies that $Sf_\lambda < 0$ for all $x \neq \frac{1}{2}$: logistic maps have negative Schwarzian derivative. As just observed, also $Sf_\lambda^n < 0$ wherever defined.

Lemma 5.51 (Minimum principle). *If $g' \neq 0$ on an interval (a, b) and $Sg < 0$, then g' cannot have a positive local minimum or a negative local maximum on (a, b). Moreover, $|g'|$ takes its minimum value at a or b.*

Proof. If g' has a local minimum at a point $x \in (a, b)$, then $g''(x) = 0$ and $g'''(x) \geq 0$. If $g'(x) > 0$, this implies that $Sg \geq 0$ which contradicts the assumption that $Sg < 0$. Likewise g' cannot have a negative local maximum on (a, b). As a consequence, $|g'|$ takes its minimum value at a or b. □

The following result is known as Singer's theorem [**350**], valid in particular for logistic maps.

Theorem 5.52. *Let $g : [0, 1] \to [0, 1]$ be a unimodal map with $g(0) = g(1) = 0$ and with a negative Schwarzian derivative. Suppose $g'(0) > 1$. Then g can possess at most one periodic attractor, since a periodic attractor contains the critical point in its basin of attraction.*

Sketch of proof. We refer to [**93**] or [**133**] for more detailed reasoning. We will use the statement from Lemma 5.51 that if $Sg < 0$ on an interval, then g' cannot have a positive local minimum or a negative local maximum on that interval.

Now suppose g has an attracting periodic orbit of period d that does not contain the critical point c in its basin of attraction. Take a periodic point $p = g^d(p)$ from the orbit and the maximal interval (a, b) in its basin of attraction. Then $\{a, b\}$ is invariant under g^d. So $g(a)$ is either a or b and likewise $g(b)$ is either a or b. In all possible cases that arise, one checks, using the observation on extremal values of $(g^d)'$, that g^d has a critical point in (a, b). This implies that c is contained in the basin of attraction of the orbit of p. □

We will state and sketch proofs of a number of results that use the negative Schwarzian derivative of the logistic maps. First we note that there are no further bifurcations occurring for $\lambda > 4$; the maximal invariant set of f_λ in $[0, 1]$ is a Cantor set, and iterates of points outside of it escape to infinity. In the present context of subsets of the real line, a set is a Cantor set if it is closed, without isolated points, and without intervals.

Proposition 5.53. *For $\lambda > 4$, let Ω_λ be the maximal invariant set of f_λ in $[0, 1]$. For every $\lambda > 4$, Ω_λ is a Cantor set.*

Sketch of proof. A detailed version of the following reasoning can be found in [**209**]; see also [**26**]. Let D_λ be the open central interval in $[0, 1]$ that is mapped outside $[0, 1]$ by f_λ. Then

$$\Omega_\lambda = [0, 1] \setminus \bigcup_{i=0}^{\infty} f_\lambda^{-i}(D_\lambda). \tag{5.13}$$

An easier case occurs for $\lambda > 2+\sqrt{5}$. Namely, as a calculation confirms, for $\lambda > 2+\sqrt{5}$ we have $|f_\lambda'| > 1$ on $[0,1]\setminus D_\lambda$. This implies there cannot be a subinterval of $[0,1]$ whose iterates remain in $[0,1]$; the length of iterates of such a subinterval would increase and get longer than one. It follows from (5.13) that Ω_λ is closed. An isolated point r in Ω_λ, should it exist, would be mapped to q_λ or $\hat{q}_\lambda$ by some iterate. It is easy to see that q_λ and $\hat{q}_\lambda$ are accumulated by other points in Ω_λ, so also r cannot be isolated in Ω_λ. The proposition follows in this case (see also [**93**] or [**363**]).

For $4 < \lambda \le 2+\sqrt{5}$ we will replace the expansion property $|f_\lambda'| > 1$ by an eventual expansion property:

(5.14) $$\text{there exists } C > 0, \eta > 1 \text{ with } \left| f_\lambda'|_{\Omega_\lambda} \right| \ge C\eta^n, n \in \mathbb{N}.$$

By compactness of Ω_λ, this is equivalent to the following statement:

(5.15) $$\text{for every } x \in \Omega_\lambda, \text{there is } n_x \in \mathbb{N} \text{ with } |(f_\lambda^{n_x})'(x)| > 1.$$

See Exercise 5.19.

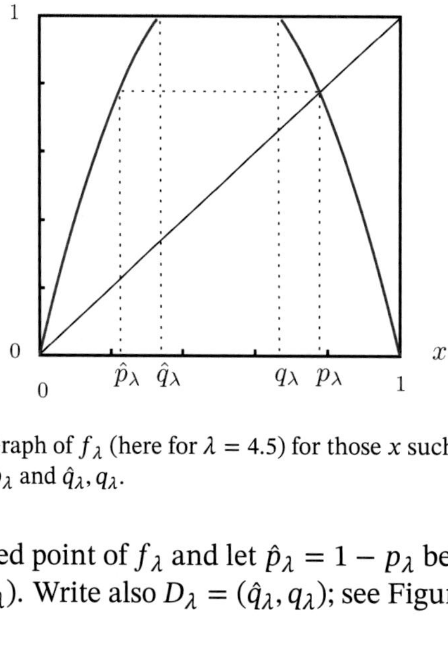

Figure 5.18. Graph of f_λ (here for $\lambda = 4.5$) for those x such that $f_\lambda(x) \le 1$, indicating $\hat{p}_\lambda, p_\lambda$ and $\hat{q}_\lambda, q_\lambda$.

Let p_λ be the fixed point of f_λ and let $\hat{p}_\lambda = 1 - p_\lambda$ be the symmetric point with $f_\lambda(p_\lambda) = f_\lambda(\hat{p}_\lambda)$. Write also $D_\lambda = (\hat{q}_\lambda, q_\lambda)$; see Figure 5.18. A calculation shows

(5.16) $$\begin{aligned} \hat{q}_\lambda - \hat{p}_\lambda &< \hat{p}_\lambda, \\ p_\lambda - q_\lambda &< 1 - p_\lambda. \end{aligned}$$

These inequalities compare lengths of intervals and say that $[0,\hat{p}_\lambda]$ is longer than $[\hat{q}_\lambda,\hat{p}_\lambda]$ and likewise $[p_\lambda, 1]$ is longer than $[q_\lambda, p_\lambda]$.

Now take $x \in \Omega_\lambda$. We will prove that for some $n_x \in \mathbb{N}$, $|(f_\lambda^{n_x})'(x)| > 1$. There is no loss of generality in assuming $x > 1/2$. For $x \in [p_\lambda, 1]$ we can take $n_x = 1$. For $x = q_\lambda$, as $f_\lambda^2(q_\lambda) = 0$ and $f_\lambda'(0) > 1$, one has $|(f_\lambda^n)'(q_\lambda)| > 1$

for n large enough. Assume that $x \in (q_\lambda, p_\lambda)$. Let I_n be the interval containing x that is mapped monotonically onto $[0,1]$ by f_λ^n. We claim that for n high enough, $I_n \subset (q_\lambda, p_\lambda)$. This can be seen as follows. The fixed point p_λ is repelling: $|f_\lambda'(p_\lambda)| > 1$. There is a unique orbit of period 2 for f_λ with $\lambda > 4$, and this has orbit has one point in $(\hat{p}_\lambda, \hat{q}_\lambda)$ and the other point in $(p_\lambda, 1)$. These statements can be checked by straightforward calculations and solving equations. It follows that iterates of points in $(q_\lambda, 1)$, different from p_λ, eventually leave the interval $(q_\lambda, 1)$. In particular, p_λ is accumulated by points that are mapped into D_λ by high iterates of f_λ. And as a consequence, for n large enough, $I_n \subset (q_\lambda, p_\lambda)$.

Now iterates of points in Ω_λ will always enter $[\hat{p}_\lambda, p_\lambda]$. We may therefore also assume $f_\lambda^n(x) \in [\hat{p}_\lambda, p_\lambda]$. Let $L_\lambda, M_\lambda, R_\lambda$ be disjoint intervals with $I_n = L_\lambda \cup M_\lambda \cup R_\lambda$ and

$$f_\lambda^n(M_\lambda) = [\hat{p}_\lambda, p_\lambda].$$

So $x \in M_\lambda$ and for the side intervals $L_\lambda \cup R_\lambda$ we have

$$f_\lambda^n(L_\lambda \cup R_\lambda) = [0, \hat{p}_\lambda) \cup (p_\lambda, 1].$$

By (5.16) we have, using $I_n \subset (q_\lambda, p_\lambda)$, that

$$|f_\lambda^n(L_\lambda)| > |L_\lambda|,$$
$$|f_\lambda^n(R_\lambda)| > |R_\lambda|.$$

There exist therefore $l \in L_\lambda$ and $r \in R_\lambda$ with $|(f_\lambda^n)'(l)| > 1$ and $|(f_\lambda^n)'(r)| > 1$. Using the minimum principle and noting $x \in M_\lambda$, we deduce

$$|(f_\lambda^n)'(x)| > 1. \qquad \square$$

For each $\lambda > 4$ there exist $C > 0$ and $\zeta > 1$, so that $|(f_\lambda^n)'| \geq C\zeta^n$ on Ω_λ. Because of this property, Ω_λ is called a hyperbolic set; compare Section 5.1.2, which develops the theory of hyperbolic sets for flows and diffeomorphisms. Using this, one sees that the dynamics of f_λ on the Cantor set Ω_λ is topologically conjugate to a one-sided left shift operator on two symbols; see Exercise 5.21. In particular, the map f_λ restricted to Ω_λ is chaotic in the sense of Devaney.

The saddle-node bifurcation of an interval map was treated in Theorem 3.58. Recall that we speak of a nondegenerate saddle-node bifurcation if the assumption of a nonvanishing second derivative in that theorem applies. The bifurcation is generically unfolding if the condition of the nonzero derivative with respect to the parameter holds. It is similar for the period-doubling bifurcation for interval maps treated in Theorem 3.63. This is nondegenerate and generically unfolding if the assumptions stated in that theorem on the third derivative and the derivative of a multiplier with respect to the parameter hold.

Proposition 5.54. *A saddle-node bifurcation of a periodic orbit in the logistic family is nondegenerate. A period-doubling bifurcation of a periodic orbit in the logistic family is nondegenerate and supercritical in the sense that a bifurcating periodic orbit of twice the period is attracting near the bifurcation value.*

Sketch of proof. If a logistic map f_{λ_0} has a degenerate saddle-node bifurcation (a bifurcation of codimension at least 2), one can find a unimodal map g arbitrarily C^3 near f_{λ_0} (so also with negative Schwarzian derivative) that has two periodic attractors. This is impossible according to Theorem 5.52. See [**87**, Section III.3, Exercise 3.1]. Exercise 5.22 asks us to give a detailed proof.

Suppose f_λ has a period-doubling bifurcation of a period-d periodic point p at $\lambda = \lambda_0$. The result follows by noting that the condition for a nondegenerate period-doubling bifurcation,

$$2(f^d_{\lambda_0})'''(p) + 3\left((f^d_{\lambda_0})''(p)\right)^2 \neq 0$$

from Remark 3.64, is equivalent to

$$-2\frac{(f^d_{\lambda_0})'''(p)}{(f^d_{\lambda_0})'(p)} + 3\left(\frac{(f^d_{\lambda_0})''(p)}{(f^d_{\lambda_0})'(p)}\right)^2 \neq 0,$$

because $(f^d_{\lambda_0})'(p) = -1$. This holds true since the Schwarzian derivative of f^d at p is nonzero. We see in fact that

$$2(f^d_{\lambda_0})'''(p) + 3\left((f^d_{\lambda_0})''(p)\right)^2 > 0,$$

which means that the bifurcation is supercritical in the stated sense. □

We point at [**87**, Section III.4, Exercises 4.5,4.6,4.7] for more on the bifurcation diagram of the logistic family that can be derived using the above result. A bifurcation analysis of classes of unimodal maps beyond the logistic maps was started in [**142, 193, 194**].

Note that the above proposition does not discuss generic unfolding conditions (see Section 2.3) for the bifurcations. This requires more advanced theory. The following result provides such a statement plus monotonicity of the bifurcations. Generic unfolding of bifurcations was considered by Adrien Douady and John Hubbard [**100**]. We refer to [**226**] for an explicit formulation and extensions to other families then the logistic family. One example of this is the family $x \mapsto \lambda \sin(x)$ on the real line, for which pitchfork bifurcations of periodic orbits also occur. The next theorem is the first of some celebrated results with which we conclude the brief overview of dynamics and bifurcations of the logistic family.

Theorem 5.55. *The only bifurcations of periodic orbits in the logistic family f_λ are saddle-node and period-doubling bifurcations. Both are nondegenerate and* *generically unfolding. For each fixed k, the number of periodic points of f_λ of period k is nondecreasing as a function of λ.*

The following related result is found in [**254**] by John Milnor and William Thurston. It expresses an increasing complexity of the dynamics of f_λ for increasing λ. See also [**225, 389, 390**], which discuss generic unfolding conditions involving the orbit of the critical point. We refer to [**48**] for an explanation of topological entropy.

Theorem 5.56. *The topological entropy of f_λ is a nondecreasing function of λ.*

The following result on density of hyperbolicity is proved by Jacek Graczyk and Grzegorz Świątek [**135**] and independently by Mikhail Lyubich [**234**]. It implies that the set of bifurcation values of the logistic family is nowhere dense.

Theorem 5.57. *For the logistic family f_λ, the set of parameter values λ with a hyperbolic periodic attractor is open and dense in* $[0,4]$.

The set of bifurcation values of the logistic family however has positive Lebesgue measure, as implied by the following result of Michael Jakobson [**191**]. We take the formulation from [**33**].

Theorem 5.58. *For the logistic family f_λ, the set of parameter values λ without a periodic attractor has positive Lebesgue measure.*

One has in fact that $\liminf_{n\to\infty} \frac{1}{n} \ln |(f_\lambda^n)'(f_\lambda(1/2))| > 0$ for a set of parameter values λ with positive Lebesgue measure [**33, 34, 71**]. Note that the standard family of circle maps also shows a bifurcation set that is nowhere dense, yet of positive Lebesgue measure (Example 5.47).

Remark 5.59. Exercise 5.20 gives a conjugation of the logistic map to the quadratic map $x \mapsto x^2 + c$ depending on a parameter c. This connects the study of the logistic map to the study of complex quadratic maps $Q_c(z) = z^2 + c$ on $\mathbb{C}$, where also c is taken from $\mathbb{C}$. The key to understanding its dynamics is the Mandelbrot set

$$\mathcal{M} = \left\{ c \in \mathbb{C} \; ; \; \sup_{n\geq 0} |Q_c^n(0)| < \infty \right\}$$

of parameter values for which the positive orbit of the critical point at the origin remains bounded. See also [**93**]. Adrien Douady and John Hubbard showed that the Mandelbrot set is a connected set [**99**]. Its boundary is a bifurcation set. A main result on the size of the boundary (establishing full Hausdorff dimension) is obtained by Mitsuhiro Shishikura [**344**]. Some textbooks exploring dynamics of holomorphic functions are [**60, 253**]. ■

5.2.4.2. *Hénon maps.* Motivated by studies of the Lorenz system, Michel Hénon [**157**] introduced planar maps, now called Hénon maps. The goal was to have a simpler setting than the differential equations setting of the Lorenz system in which to study strange attractors. Recall that a Hénon map is given by

$$H_{a,b}(x,y) = (y + 1 - ax^2, bx).$$

For $b \neq 0$ this is a diffeomorphism with

$$H_{a,b}^{-1}(x,y) = (y/b, x - 1 + ay^2/b^2).$$

The determinant of the Jacobian $\det DH_{a,b}$ is constant and equals $-b$. For values of b with $|b| < 1$ the Hénon maps are therefore dissipative in the sense that they contract areas. For values of b close to 0 the Hénon maps are strongly dissipative. We see that for $b = 0$, $H_{a,0}$ is not a diffeomorphism. As $H_{a,0}(x,0) = (1 - ax^2, 0)$, it can be viewed as an embedding of the one-dimensional map $x \mapsto 1 - ax^2$ in a planar map. For small values of b, $H_{a,b}$ can be seen as a perturbation of $H_{a,0}$. This is the point of view we take here.

Note that

$$q_a(x) = 1 - ax^2$$

is affinely conjugate to some f_λ (affinely conjugate means topologically conjugate with an affine map for the conjugacy). Namely, let

$$s_\pm = \frac{1}{2a}\left(-1 \pm \sqrt{1+4a}\right)$$

denote the fixed points of q_a. Let $h : \mathbb{R} \to \mathbb{R}$ be given by

$$h(x) = \frac{1}{2s_-}x + \frac{1}{2}.$$

Then q_a restricted to $[s_-, -s_-]$ and f_λ restricted to $[0,1]$ are conjugate by h:

$$f_\lambda \circ h = h \circ q_a$$

for $4\lambda = h(1) = \frac{1}{2s_-} + \frac{1}{2}$ when $s_- < -1$. Compare also [**133**] or [**363**], and see Exercise 5.20. This connects logistic maps and strongly dissipative Hénon maps.

Several features of q_a can be extended to the Hénon map $H_{a,b}$ with small b; compare [**59, 81, 402**]. The following two theorems are devoted to this. The first result discusses hyperbolic sets, the second result discusses bifurcations of periodic orbits. Figure 5.19 shows a numerically computed horseshoe for $a = 3$ and a small value of b, close to the maximal invariant set of $H_{a,0}$ inside the x-axis. The algorithm that is used to compute it is described in Example 2.60.

Theorem 5.60. *Suppose Λ_a is a hyperbolic maximal invariant set for q_a, so that there exists $C > 0$ and $\eta > 1$ with $|Dq_a^n(x)| \geq C\eta^n$ for $x \in \Lambda_a$. Then for b small,*

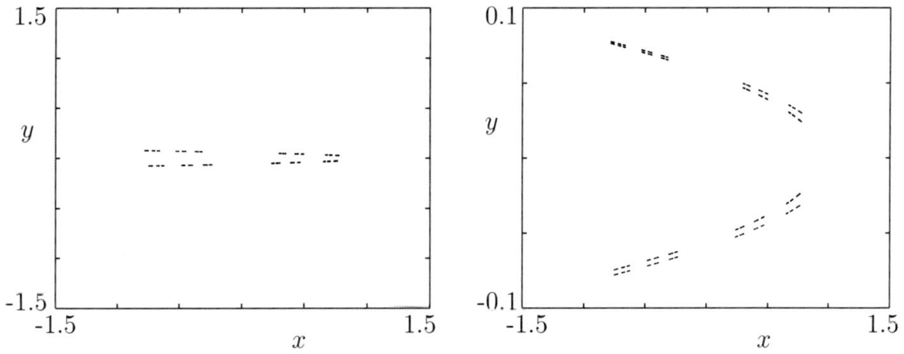

Figure 5.19. A numerically computed picture of a horseshoe in the Hénon map for $a = 3$ and $b = 0.1$. The left frame shows the horseshoe close to the x-axis, the right frame shows a scaled version.

$H_{a,b}$ admits an invariant hyperbolic set $\Lambda_{a,b}$ that converges in the Hausdorff metric to Λ_a as $b \to 0$ (here Λ_a is considered to lie in the x-axis in $\mathbb{R}^2$).

Sketch of proof. In essence the result follows from the theory in Section 5.1.2 since modifications of the proofs of Theorems 5.11 and 5.15 apply, even though they were formulated for diffeomorphisms and we start with an endomorphism and not a diffeomorphism.

For clarity we will comment on this using the original coordinates of the system. Below we will take a slightly easier situation with specific conditions on a. From Proposition 5.53 we know that the logistic family $f_\lambda(x) = \lambda x(1-x)$ admits an invariant Cantor set Ω_λ as maximal bounded invariant set for $\lambda > 4$. The inequality $\lambda > 4$ corresponds, through the affine conjugacy of f_λ to q_a, with $a > 2$. The inequality $\lambda > 2 + \sqrt{5}$ that appeared in the proof of Proposition 5.53 implies that $|Df_\lambda| > 1$ on Ω_λ. The corresponding bound for q_a is given by $a > 5/4 + \sqrt{5}/2$; this implies $|Dq_a| > 1$ on the maximal bounded invariant set of q_a. For simplicity we will go a little further and assume that Λ_a is the maximal bounded invariant set of q_a with $a > 2 + \sqrt{2}$, which implies that $|Dq_a| > 2$ on Λ_a. As a consequence we can take the constant C in the formulation of the theorem equal to one and $\eta > 2$. In general however one can take any maximal invariant hyperbolic set and replace $H_{a,0}$ with a sufficiently high iterate to get sufficient expansion already after one iterate.

Consider the Hénon map $H_{a,0}$ for $b = 0$. The invariant set Λ_a corresponds to an invariant set $\Lambda_{a,0}$ for $H_{a,0}$ contained in the x-axis. Note

$$DH_{a,0}(x, y) = \begin{pmatrix} -2ax & 1 \\ 0 & 0 \end{pmatrix}. \tag{5.17}$$

Let U be a small neighborhood of $\Lambda_{a,0}$ so that $\Lambda_{a,0}$ is the maximal invariant set of $H_{a,0}$ in U. We will adapt the arguments of Theorem 5.11 to show that for small b, the maximal invariant set of $H_{a,b}$ in U is hyperbolic. We start by finding an invariant splitting $E^s_p \oplus E^u_p$, $p = (x, 0) \in \Lambda_{a,0}$, for $H_{a,0}$. As E^u_p is in the direction of the x-axis, it suffices to construct E^s_p.

We follow the setup of Theorem 5.11 and will construct a sequence of vectors $\begin{pmatrix} u_i \\ v_i \end{pmatrix}$ in $E^s_{H^i_{a,0}(p)}$ with

$$\begin{pmatrix} u_{i+1} \\ v_{i+1} \end{pmatrix} = DH_{a,0}(H^i_{a,0}(p)) \begin{pmatrix} u_i \\ v_i \end{pmatrix}.$$

The vectors are uniformly bounded and determined by a choice of $v(0)$.

Take an orbit $p_i = (x_i, 0)$ with $p_i = H^i_{a,0}(p_0)$ for $i \geq 0$. Note that by (5.17) and the assumption on $\Lambda_{a,0}$ we can write

$$\begin{pmatrix} u_{i+1} \\ v_{i+1} \end{pmatrix} = \begin{pmatrix} \lambda & 1 \\ 0 & 0 \end{pmatrix} \begin{pmatrix} u_i \\ v_i \end{pmatrix},$$

where $\lambda = -2ax_i$ depends on p_i and satisfies $|\lambda| > 2$. Solving the equations, this can be written as

$$\begin{pmatrix} u_i \\ v_{i+1} \end{pmatrix} = \begin{pmatrix} \frac{1}{\lambda} & -\frac{1}{\lambda} \\ 0 & 0 \end{pmatrix} \begin{pmatrix} u_{i+1} \\ v_i \end{pmatrix}.$$

As in the proof of Theorem 5.11 we can construct the bundle E^s from here, by a contraction argument. Fix for instance $v_0 = 1$. We will necessarily get $v_i = 0$ for $i > 0$. The u_i's are therefore determined by $u_0 = \frac{1}{\lambda}u_1 - \frac{1}{\lambda}$ and $u_i = \frac{1}{\lambda}u_{i+1}$ for $i > 0$. This is a fixed point of a contraction Γ, defined on the space of bounded sequences of real numbers and given by $\Gamma((u_i)_{i\geq 0}) = (\hat{u}_i)_{i\geq 0}$ with

$$\hat{u}_i = \begin{cases} \frac{1}{\lambda}u_1 - \frac{1}{\lambda}, & i = 0, \\ \frac{1}{\lambda}u_{i+1}, & i > 0. \end{cases}$$

It is in fact straightforward to find the solution explicitly: $u_0 = -1/\lambda$ and $u_i = 0$ for $i > 0$.

Next we must construct, for b sufficiently small and $\Lambda_{a,b}$ an invariant set of $H_{a,b}$ in U, stable and unstable bundles E^s and E^u for $H_{a,b}$ over $\Lambda_{a,b}$. Taking $b \neq 0$ small, we find a perturbation of the matrix $DH_{a,0}$. We follow the above sketched procedure to construct a sequence of vectors $\begin{pmatrix} u_i \\ v_i \end{pmatrix}$ in $E^s_{H^i_{a,b}(\hat{p}_0)}$ with $\hat{p}_0 \in \Lambda_{a,b}$ and

$$\begin{pmatrix} u_{i+1} \\ v_{i+1} \end{pmatrix} = DH_{a,b}(H^i_{a,b}(\hat{p}_0)) \begin{pmatrix} u_i \\ v_i \end{pmatrix}. \tag{5.18}$$

Write $\hat{p}_0 = (\hat{x}_0, \hat{y}_0)$ and $(\hat{x}_i, \hat{y}_i) = H^i_{a,b}(\hat{p}_0)$ for $i > 0$. Now (5.18) becomes

$$\begin{pmatrix} u_{i+1} \\ v_{i+1} \end{pmatrix} = \begin{pmatrix} \lambda & 1 \\ b & 0 \end{pmatrix} \begin{pmatrix} u_i \\ v_i \end{pmatrix}$$

with $\lambda = -2a\hat{x}_i$. Rewrite this as

$$\begin{pmatrix} u_i \\ v_{i+1} \end{pmatrix} = \begin{pmatrix} \frac{1}{\lambda} & -\frac{1}{\lambda} \\ \frac{b}{\lambda} & -\frac{b}{\lambda} \end{pmatrix} \begin{pmatrix} u_{i+1} \\ v_i \end{pmatrix}. \tag{5.19}$$

Again as in the proof of Theorem 5.11 we can construct the bundle E^s over $\Lambda_{a,b}$ from here. Take $l^\infty(\mathbb{N}_0, \mathbb{R}^2)$ to be the space of bounded sequences indexed by $\mathbb{N}_0$ and with values in $\mathbb{R}^2$. Use the box norm $|(u, v)| = \sup\{|u|, |v|\}$ on $\mathbb{R}^2$ and the corresponding supremum norm on $l^\infty(\mathbb{N}_0, \mathbb{R}^2)$. For given $v_0 \in \mathbb{R}$, define $\Gamma : l^\infty(\mathbb{N}_0, \mathbb{R}^2) \to l^\infty(\mathbb{N}_0, \mathbb{R}^2)$ by $(\hat{u}_i, \hat{v}_i)_{i\in\mathbb{N}_0} = \Gamma((u_i, v_i)_{i\in\mathbb{N}_0})$ with

$$\begin{aligned} \hat{u}_i &= \frac{1}{\lambda} u_{i+1} - \frac{1}{\lambda} v_i, \\ \hat{v}_0 &= v_0, \\ \hat{v}_{i+1} &= \frac{b}{\lambda} u_{i+1} - \frac{b}{\lambda} v_i \end{aligned}$$

for $i \geq 0$. Since $1/|\lambda| < 1/2$ by assumption, Γ is a contraction. The unique fixed point defines the desired sequence of vectors $\begin{pmatrix} u_i \\ v_i \end{pmatrix}$. Varying $v_0 \in \mathbb{R}$ and $p_0 \in \Lambda_{a,b}$ provides the bundle E^s.

The bundle E^u may not be parallel to the x-axis and must also be constructed. To construct the unstable bundle E^u, one uses the same procedure, but with sequences indexed by $-\mathbb{N}_0$. See the proof of Theorem 5.11.

As an aside we mention that one can allow for general perturbations and write (5.18) as

$$\begin{pmatrix} u_{i+1} \\ v_{i+1} \end{pmatrix} = \begin{pmatrix} \lambda + \alpha & 1 + \beta \\ \gamma & \delta \end{pmatrix} \begin{pmatrix} u_i \\ v_i \end{pmatrix},$$

where $\alpha, \beta, \gamma, \delta$ go to zero as b goes to zero. Then continue from here. There is no additional difficulty in this more general setup.

We now know that any invariant set $\Lambda_{a,b}$ inside U is hyperbolic. To actually prove the existence of an invariant hyperbolic set $\Lambda_{a,b}$ near $\Lambda_{a,0}$ for small values of b, the proof of Theorem 5.15 can be followed and adapted. Take an orbit $(x_i, 0) \subset \Lambda_{a,0}$ with $i \in \mathbb{Z}$ for $H_{a,0}$: x_i is a sequence of points with $(x_{i+1}, 0) = H_{a,0}(x_i, 0)$. Let b be small. We wish to find a sequence (u_i, v_i) so that $(\hat{x}_i, \hat{y}_i) = (x_i + u_i, y_i + v_i)$ is an orbit of $H_{a,b}$. We look for u_i and v_i so that the supremum of $|u_i|$ and $|v_i|$ is small if b is small. We comment on the procedure and the ensuing formulas still under the assumption that $a > 2 + \sqrt{2}$. As said above this implies that we can take $C = 1$ and have $|2ax_i| > 2$ for any $x_i \in \Lambda_a$.

A calculation shows

$$u_{i+1} = -2ax_iu_i - au_i^2 + v_i,$$
$$v_{i+1} = bx_i + bu_i.$$

Rewrite to get

$$u_i = -x_i + \sqrt{x_i^2 - u_{i+1}/a + v_i/a},$$
$$v_{i+1} = bx_i + b\left(-x_i + \sqrt{x_i^2 - u_{i+1}/a + v_i/a}\right).$$

Consider the map $\Gamma((u_i, v_i)_{i\in\mathbb{Z}}) = (\hat{u}_i, \hat{v}_i)_{i\in\mathbb{Z}}$ with

$$\begin{pmatrix}\hat{u}_i\\ \hat{v}_{i+1}\end{pmatrix} = \begin{pmatrix}-x_i + \sqrt{x_i^2 - u_{i+1}/a + v_i/a}\\ b\sqrt{x_i^2 - u_{i+1}/a + v_i/a}\end{pmatrix}. \tag{5.20}$$

Given $d > 0$, let $\mathfrak{B}$ be the ball of radius d in $l^\infty(\mathbb{Z}, \mathbb{R}^2)$. The derivative of the right-hand side of (5.20) equals (5.19). Therefore, one has that for d sufficiently small, Γ maps $\mathfrak{B}$ into itself and is a contraction on $\mathfrak{B}$, provided b is small. The conclusion follows as in the proof of Theorem 5.15. □

Theorem 5.61. *Suppose that for $a = a_0$, q_a admits a generically unfolding and nondegenerate saddle-node bifurcation of a periodic orbit. Then there exists $b_0 > 0$ so that $H_{a,b}(x, y)$ admits a generically unfolding nondegenerate saddle-node bifurcation along a smooth curve $a(b)$ defined for $|b| < b_0$ and with $a(0) = a_0$. Such a statement also holds for generically unfolding nondegenerate period-doubling bifurcations.*

Sketch of proof. For $b = 0$ the bifurcation in $H_{a,0}$ follows from the bifurcation result for q_a. By a center manifold reduction as explained in Appendix B.1.2 one obtains the result for small values of b. This works even though $H_{a,0}$ is not a diffeomorphism.

To fix thoughts, consider the case of a saddle-node bifurcation of a periodic orbit. By replacing $H_{a,0}$ with an iterate, we may assume the bifurcation is of a fixed point. Let a_0 denote the bifurcation value. A translation and a linear coordinate change brings the fixed point to the origin and the linearization to a diagonal form. We thus find a family $f_{a,b} : \mathbb{R}^2 \to \mathbb{R}^2$ with $f_{a_0,0}(0, 0) = (0, 0)$ and $Df_{a_0,0}(0, 0) = \begin{pmatrix}1 & 0\\ 0 & 0\end{pmatrix}$. By using a bump function, one obtains a map $f_{a,b}$ that is unaltered near $(0, 0)$ and globally close to the linearization about $(0, 0)$. Further, the x-axis is invariant and $x \mapsto \pi f_{a,0}(x, 0)$, where π denotes the coordinate projection to the x-axis, admits a generically unfolding nondegenerate saddle-node bifurcation. The notation E^c and E^s from Theorem B.11 here stands for the x-axis and the y-axis, respectively. Now $f_{a,b}$ depends smoothly on parameters a and b. Theorem B.11 provides a one-dimensional center manifold $W^c_{a,b}$ that is C^k and also C^k depends on a, b, for a high value of k. For $b = 0$ we have a generic unfolding of a nondegenerate saddle-node bifurcation at some parameter value a_0. As the center manifold C^k depends on the parameters a, b, so does the reduced map on the center manifold. Therefore one finds a generic unfolding of a nondegenerate saddle-node bifurcation for all small values of b; compare Exercise 3.8. The implicit function theorem gives that these bifurcations occur along curves $a(b)$ with b small and $a(0) = a_0$.

This concludes the proof. To clarify the construction of a center manifold we will add a description specific to this case with only a center and a strong stable direction and the strong unstable direction being absent. This construction, which adapts the reasoning to prove Theorem B.11, avoids mentioning strong unstable directions, and employs one-sided sequences of points instead of the two-sided sequences that are used to prove Theorem B.11. One can view this as the construction of a center-unstable manifold, noting that a center manifold can be obtained as an intersection of a center-stable and a center-unstable manifold; compare [**347**] and [**404**].

Consider the equation $f_{a,b}(x_{-1}, y_{-1}) = (x_0, y_0)$ and solve (x_{-1}, y_0) as a smooth function of (x_0, y_{-1}). This is done by first solving x_{-1} as function of x_0 and y_{-1} from the equation for the x-coordinate, and plugging this into the equation for the y-coordinate. Note that this works even though $Df_{a,b}(0,0)$ is not invertible. We get

$$(x_{-1}, y_0) = h(x_0, y_{-1})$$

with $h(0,0) = (0,0)$ and $Dh(0,0) = \begin{pmatrix} 1 & 0 \\ 0 & 0 \end{pmatrix}$. The map h is globally close to its linearization about $(0,0)$.

For $\eta > 1$, let $l^{\infty,\eta}(-\mathbb{N}_0, \mathbb{R}^2)$ be the space of sequences $-\mathbb{N}_0 \to \mathbb{R}^2$ with

$$\|\gamma\|_\eta = \sup_{n \in -\mathbb{N}_0} \eta^{-|n|} |\gamma_n| < \infty$$

(compare with (B.3)) and is endowed with the norm $\|\cdot\|_\eta$. Here $|(x,y)|$ is the box norm $\max\{|x|, |y|\}$. We abbreviate notation and write $l^{\infty,\eta}$. Write an element $\gamma \in l^{\infty,\eta}$ as $\gamma(n) = (\gamma_x(n), \gamma_y(n))$. Define the map $\Gamma : E^c \times l^{\infty,\eta} \to l^{\infty,\eta}$ by $\Gamma(x_0^c, \gamma) = \zeta$ with

$$\begin{aligned} \zeta_c(0) &= x_0^c, \\ (\zeta_x(n-1), \zeta_y(n)) &= h(\gamma_x(n), \gamma_y(n-1)), \quad \text{for } n \le 0. \end{aligned}$$

One can verify that

(i) $\Gamma(E^c \times l^{\infty,\eta}) \subset l^{\infty,\eta}$;

(ii) $\Gamma(x_0^c, \cdot)$ is a uniform contraction on $l^{\infty,\eta}$.

A fixed point $\gamma = \Gamma(x_0^c, \gamma)$ is an orbit in $l^{\infty,\eta}$ with $\pi_c \gamma(0) = x_0^c$. The rest of the center manifold construction follows the proof of Theorem B.5. □

Also nonlocal bifurcations extend into nonzero values of b; see Exercise 5.23. We note that the bifurcation scenario of $H_{a,b}$ for fixed small values of b is different from that of q_a: period-doubling cascades (see the next section and compare Theorem 5.56) do not always occur in increasing order in a [**195**]. As mentioned in Section 5.1.4, Sheldon Newhouse proved that there can be infinitely many coexisting attractors; see [**282**].

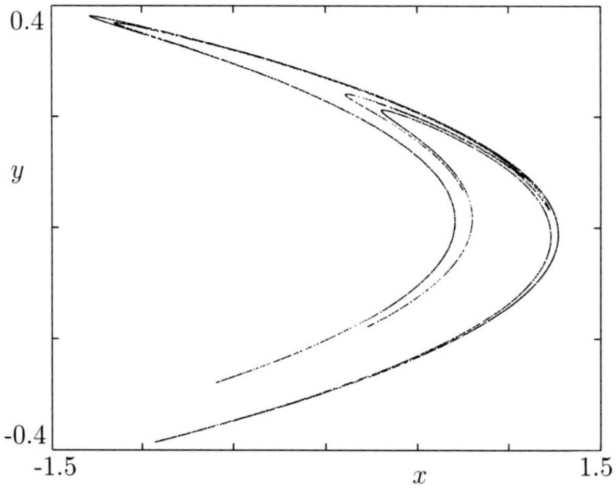

Figure 5.20. A numerically computed picture of a Hénon attractor for $a = 1.4$ and $b = 0.3$.

Numerical calculations in [**157**] indicated the existence of a strange attractor. Figure 5.20 shows the Hénon attractor which appears to be a strange attractor. The attractor looks like the closure of the unstable manifold of a saddle fixed point. Although this is not proven for the parameter values $a = 1.4, b = 0.3$, it is known that strange attractors do exist in the Hénon family. Before stating this celebrated result, we include the following observation which can be found in [**282**, Appendix IV].

Proposition 5.62. *Let $f : \mathbb{R}^2 \to \mathbb{R}^2$ be a diffeomorphism with a hyperbolic saddle fixed point p and a transverse homoclinic point $q \in W^u(p) \cap W^s(p)$. Assume $|\det(Df(x))| < 1$ for all $x \in \mathbb{R}^2$, and assume that $W^u(p)$ remains in a bounded region of $\mathbb{R}^2$. Then there is a nonempty open set $U \subset \mathbb{R}^2$ such that for $x \in U$,*

$$\omega(x) \subset \overline{W^u(p)}.$$

Proof. Take for U a bounded open set whose boundary consists of segments of $W^u(p)$ and $W^s(p)$. Now consider $f^n(U)$ for $n \geq 0$. Its boundary consists of segments of $W^u(p)$ and $W^s(p)$. The segments from $W^s(p)$ here have length converging to 0 as $n \to \infty$. As $W^u(p)$ is in a bounded region, $f^n(U)$ stays in a bounded region V in $\mathbb{R}^2$. As $\sup_{x\in V} |\det(Df(x))| < 1$, the area of $f^n(U)$ goes to zero as $n \to \infty$.

For $x \in U$ we therefore find that $f^n(x)$ converges to the boundary of $f^n(U)$. As segments in $W^s(p)$ shrink when applying f^n, this proves the proposition. □

This result applies to the Hénon map. One can in fact show that for the Hénon map, U may be taken to be an open neighborhood of $\overline{W^u(p)}$ [**58, 413**]. There is an open region in parameter space, for which $H_{a,b}$ satisfies the assumptions of the above proposition. The attractors that one finds in $\overline{W^u(p)}$ can be periodic attractors. However, a generalization of the result from Theorem 5.58 for Hénon maps by Michael Benedicks and Lennart Carleson [**34**], shows that strange attractors also occur.

Theorem 5.63. *Let $0 < c < \ln(2)$. For sufficiently small $b > 0$, there is a set $E(b)$ of positive Lebesgue measure so that for $a \in E(b)$, the following holds. For the saddle fixed point p in $\{(x, y) \in \mathbb{R}^2\ ;\ x, y > 0\}$ there is a point $z_0 \in W^u(p)$, so that*

(i) *$\{H^n_{a,b}(z_0)\}$, $n \in \mathbb{N}_0$, is dense in $W^u(p)$;*

(ii) *for some nonzero vector $v \in \mathbb{R}^2$, $\left|DH^n_{a,b}(z_0)v\right| \geq e^{cn}$, $n \in \mathbb{N}_0$.*

5.2.5. Period-doubling cascades. By a *route to chaos* we mean a bifurcation or sequence of bifurcations in a family $\dot{x} = f(x, \lambda)$ of differential equations depending on a single real parameter λ, where for $\lambda = 0$ the dynamics is trivial or Morse-Smale, and for $\lambda = 1$ the dynamics is chaotic and possesses, for instance, nontrivial hyperbolic invariant sets.

A well known route to chaos is through a cascade of period-doubling bifurcations. The phenomenon is best understood in the context of the logistic family, which we consider in the next example. Following it, we discuss similar bifurcations in the Rössler system, a family of differential equations in $\mathbb{R}^3$.

Example 5.64. Recall from Section 5.2.4 that the logistic family is given by $f_\lambda(x) = \lambda x(1 - x)$. The numerically computed bifurcation diagram in Figure 5.17 reveals a sequence of period-doubling bifurcations at bifurcation values λ_n to periodic attractors of period 2^{n+1} starting at $\lambda_0 = 3$, $\lambda_1 = 1 + \sqrt{6}$.

An explanation of the occurrence of infinitely many period-doubling bifurcations is obtained by using the technique of renormalization. We give a brief intuitive description and refer to [**87**] for more information. With a central interval we mean an interval $[1/2 - a, 1/2 + a] \subset [0, 1]$. Renormalization in the current context means taking a central interval strictly inside $[0,1]$, considering a first return map on it, and conjugate the central interval by a linear map to $[0,1]$. Let R_1 stand for the parameter value where $f_{R_1}^2$ maps a central interval exactly twice onto itself; see Figure 5.21. Using that the critical point $1/2$ is mapped to $1/\lambda$ in two iterates, one can check that R_1 is a solution to $\lambda^3 - 2\lambda^2 - 4\lambda - 8 = 0$ and has the expression $R_1 = \frac{2}{3}\left(1 + \sqrt[3]{19 + 3\sqrt{33}} + \sqrt[3]{19 - 3\sqrt{33}}\right) = 3.67857\cdots$. For $\lambda \in [3, R_1]$ one can take a central interval I_λ and an orientation reversing linear map $L_\lambda : I_\lambda \to [0,1]$, so that

$$\mathcal{R}f_\lambda = L_\lambda \circ f_\lambda^2 \circ L_\lambda^{-1}$$

is a unimodal map with $\mathcal{R}f_\lambda(1) = \mathcal{R}f_\lambda(0) = 0$. Figure 5.21 indicates the procedure. The unimodal map $\mathcal{R}f_\lambda$ is the renormalized map. The family $\mathcal{R}f_\lambda$ with $\lambda \in [3, R_1]$ is similar to the original family f_λ with $\lambda \in [1,4]$. Both families f_λ, $\lambda \in [1,4]$, and $\mathcal{R}f_\lambda$, $\lambda \in [3, R_1]$, go under increasing λ from a map with a single fixed point at 0 to a map with infinitely many periodic points. Both families must contain a period-doubling bifurcation of a fixed point. Note that a fixed point of $\mathcal{R}f_\lambda$ is a periodic point of period 2 of f_λ. So a period-doubling bifurcation of a fixed point of $\mathcal{R}f_\lambda$ is a period-doubling bifurcation of a periodic orbit of period 2 of f_λ. One can iterate the renormalization procedure and conclude the existence of infinitely many period-doubling bifurcations of periodic orbits of period 2^n, $n \in \mathbb{N}$.

The period-doubling bifurcations λ_n converge to a limit value, at which the map has an invariant Cantor set which is a Milnor attractor [**252**], but it is not asymptotically stable. A nontrivial analysis of the renormalization procedure

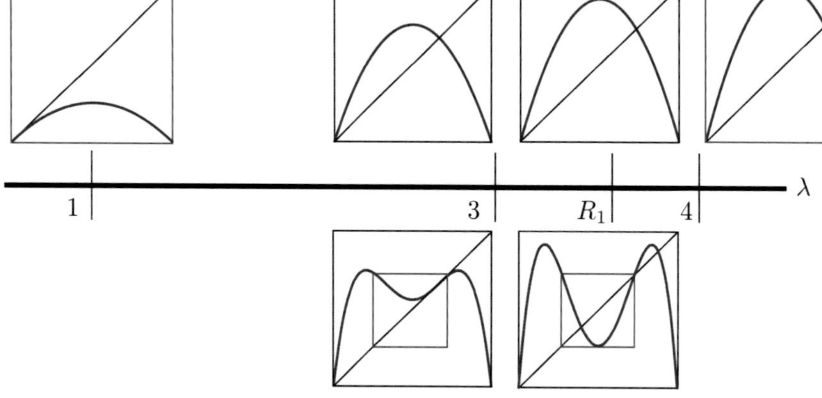

Figure 5.21. Period-doubling cascades in the logistic family. Above the line with λ-values graphs of f_λ for $\lambda = 1, 3, R_1, 4$ are shown. Below the line graphs of f_λ^2 for $\lambda = 3, R_1$ are shown.

reveals that the bifurcation values λ_n converge exponentially and one has

$$\lim_{n\to\infty} \frac{\lambda_{n+1} - \lambda_n}{\lambda_n - \lambda_{n-1}} = \frac{1}{\delta}$$

for a number

$$\delta = 4.6692016091\cdots.$$

The number δ is universal in the sense that it is the convergence speed of period-doubling cascades not just for the logistic family but for perturbed families as well. The explanation lies in the fact that δ arises as the unstable eigenvalue at a fixed point of the renormalization operator $\mathcal{R}$. From the large collection of research articles on this universal bifurcation phenomenon, we mention the articles [**110**] by Mitchell Feigenbaum and [**388**] by Charles Tresser and Pierre Coullet, that observed it and provided the ideas of using renormalization to study it, and [**107, 217, 235**] for proofs. ■

Example 5.65. The Rössler equations are differential equations in $\mathbb{R}^3$, depending on parameters a, b, c, given by

$$\begin{aligned}
\dot{x} &= -y - z,\\
\dot{y} &= x + ay,\\
\dot{z} &= b + z(x - c).
\end{aligned}$$

Otto Rössler constructed the differential equations in order to have a system simpler than the Lorenz equations, but also with chaotic dynamics [**312**]. He did not have a physical interpretation in mind.

For the one-parameter family obtained by fixing $a = 0.2$ and $b = 0.2$ and varying c, numerical experiments show a cascade of period-doubling bifurcations of periodic attractors. The first bifurcations of the cascade occur at $c = 2.832445\ldots$ and $c = 3.837358\ldots$. Figure 5.22 shows periodic attractors arising in the period-doubling bifurcations. For larger values of c there appear to be strange attractors as depicted in Figure 5.23.

Given a time series of the x-coordinate of orbits in the attractor, one writes down a list x_n, $n \in \mathbb{N}$ of x-coordinates that are local maxima of the time series.

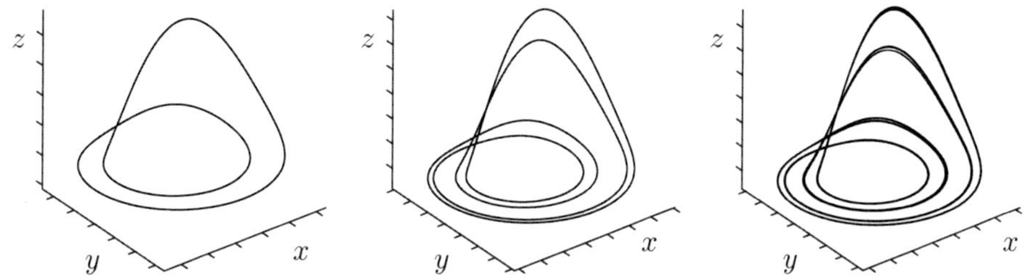

Figure 5.22. Numerically computed periodic attractors of the Rössler system with $a = b = 0.2$ and varying c: from left to right $c = 3.3, 4.0, 4.15$.

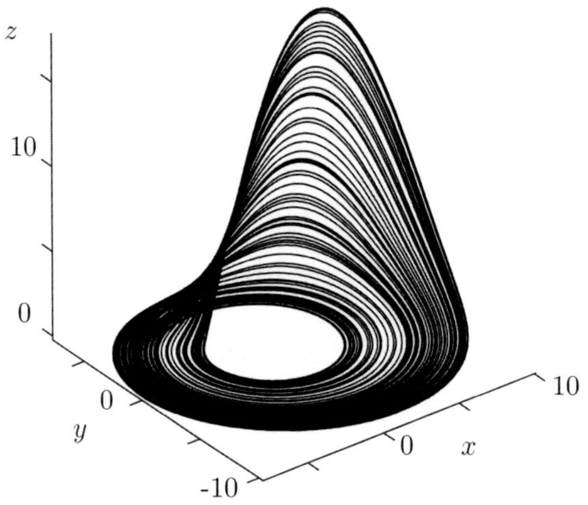

Figure 5.23. The Rössler attractor for $a = b = 0.2$ and $c = 5$.

Note that this can only occur when the orbit hits the plane $\{y+z = 0\}$ where $\dot{x} = 0$. Following an approach that is also present in the study of the Lorenz system by Edward Lorenz [**231**], one can consider pairs (x_n, x_{n+1}), $n \in \mathbb{N}$, to see if there is a relation between subsequent maximum values. This is an instance of a general idea called reconstruction, whose development starts from [**6**, **275**, **372**]. This idea is executed in Figure 5.24 that plots numerically calculated ordered pairs of subsequent maximum x-coordinates of a long orbit piece starting from a large positive time. It is calculated for the Rössler system with parameters $a = b = 0.2$ and $c = 5$. The figure looks like the graph of a unimodal interval map. Similar pictures are obtained for other, at least nearby, values of a, b, c.

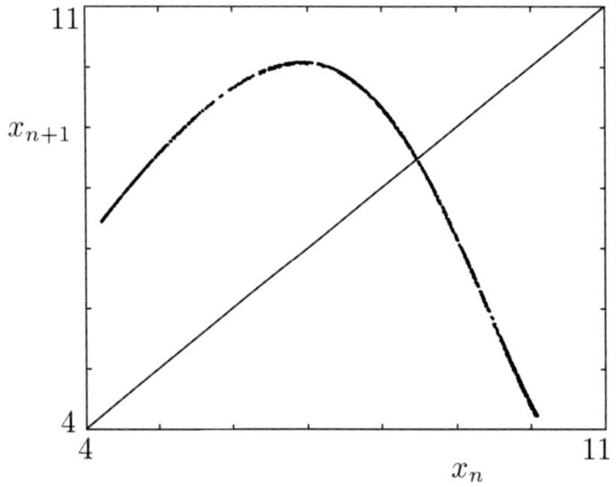

Figure 5.24. The Rössler system for $a = 0.2$, $b = 0.2$, and $c = 5$: ordered pairs of subsequent maximum x-coordinates of an orbit lie on a set that resembles the graph of a unimodal map.

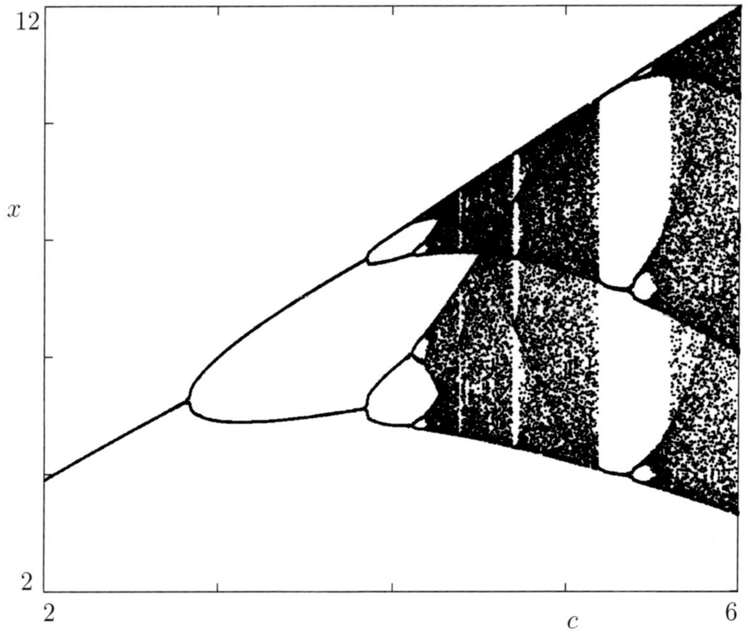

Figure 5.25. Numerically computed bifurcation diagram of the Rössler system, for $a = b = 0.2$ and $c \in [2, 6]$. The vertical axis shows local maximum values of the x-variable in long orbit pieces.

This procedure of listing local maximum values of the x-coordinate of time series can also be used to compute numerically a bifurcation diagram for the Rössler system; compare the presentation in [**284**, Section 12.3]. The result is shown in Figure 5.25. The bifurcation diagram is computed for a grid of parameter values c ranging from 2 to 6, while fixing $a = b = 0.2$. For each considered parameter value, local maximum values of a long orbit piece starting from a large positive time are calculated and plotted. Note that the thus obtained picture is strikingly similar to the bifurcation diagram of the logistic family and shows in particular a period-doubling cascade.

The Rössler system returns in Example 5.70. ■

We present a topological theory of period-doubling cascades in a context of two-dimensional diffeomorphisms on the plane in which the dynamics evolves from a trivial to a hyperbolic horseshoe under the variation of a parameter. We follow the work by Kathleen Alligood and James Yorke in [**422**]. Corresponding results for flows hold by looking at first return maps. This may give a handle to study systems such as the Rössler system from Example 5.65.

The picture we have in mind is depicted in Figure 5.26. This is formalized in the list of hypotheses which we now pose. We will look at invariant sets in a

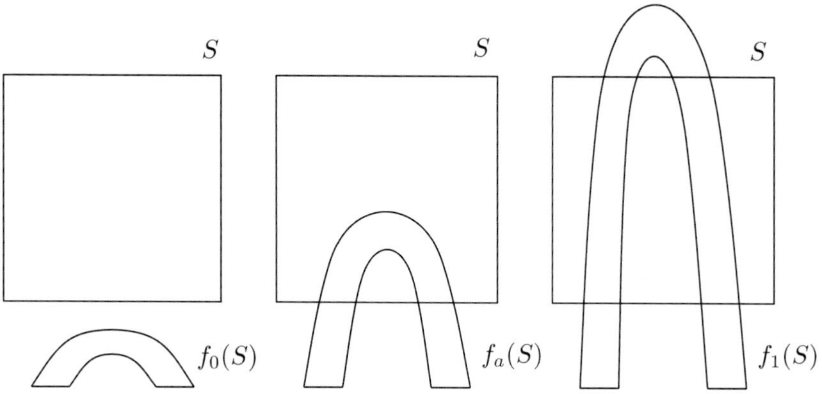

Figure 5.26. Cascades of period-doubling bifurcations occur in the creation of a horseshoe.

square S. The square with edge, top, and bottom are defined by

$$\begin{aligned} S &= \{(x,y) \in \mathbb{R}^2 \ ; \ 0 \le x \le 1, 0 \le y \le 1\}, \\ E &= \{(x,y) \ ; \ x = 0 \text{ or } x = 1\}, \\ T &= \{(x,y) \ ; \ 0 \le x \le 1, y = 1\}, \\ B &= \{(x,y) \ ; \ 0 \le x \le 1, y = 0\}. \end{aligned}$$

Consider the following hypotheses for a family of planar diffeomorphisms f_a, $0 \le a \le 1$.

(H1) $\det(Df_a) \le \theta < 1$;

(H2) $f_0(S) \cap S = \emptyset$;

(H3) f_1 is a horseshoe map (see Section 2.5) with a hyperbolic invariant set;

(H4) $f_a(T) \cap S = \emptyset$, $f_a(B) \cap S = \emptyset$ for all $0 \le a \le 1$;

(H5) $f_a(S) \cap E = \emptyset$ for all $0 \le a \le 1$.

A family f_a that satisfies (H1)–(H5) can undergo saddle-node and period-doubling bifurcations of periodic orbits, but Neimark-Sacker bifurcations are not possible. Let P_a denote the set of periodic points ($f_a^k(p) = p$ for some $k \ge 1$) inside S of f_a. Let

$$P = \{(x,a) \ ; \ x \in P_a\}.$$

Theorem 5.66. *Let f_a satisfy hypotheses* (H1)–(H5). *Let p be a saddle periodic point of f_1 with period k, so that $Df_1^k(p)$ has positive eigenvalues. The component of P containing $(p,1)$ has attracting periodic orbits of period $2^n k$ for each $n \in \mathbb{N}$.*

The proof of this theorem makes use of the fact that one can approximate the family f_a with families for which bifurcations unfold generically. We will state this result and then prove Theorem 5.66 using it. We call a family g_a satisfying (H1)–(H5) a generic family if

(i) For each $a \in [0,1]$, g_a has at most one nonhyperbolic periodic orbit;

(ii) Each saddle-node bifurcation of a periodic orbit is nondegenerate and generically unfolding;

(iii) Each period-doubling bifurcation of a periodic orbit is nondegenerate and generically unfolding.

The following approximation theorem has a similar flavor to the Kupka-Smale theorem, Theorem 5.28, and can be viewed as a generalization to parametrized families of dynamical systems. The result can be found in [**13**].

Theorem 5.67. *There exist arbitrarily C^1-small perturbations g_a of f_a that are generic families.*

The key to the proof of Theorem 5.66 is the introduction of an orbit index that allows us to pathfollow periodic orbits with varying parameters. The exclusion of Neimark-Sacker bifurcations aids since for these bifurcations the appearance of periodic orbits is a more subtle phenomenon. To fix thoughts, suppose that f_a is a generic family satisfying hypotheses (H1)–(H5). Bifurcations of periodic orbits occur in the product $S \times [0,1]$ of state and parameter space as curves. An index allows us to associate a direction to the bifurcation curves of periodic orbits.

Let $\tilde{P} = P/\sim$, where the equivalence relation $\sim$ is the identification of points in the same orbit. This is a topological space in which periodic orbits form continuous curves except at period-doubling bifurcations where it branches. Assign a function $\varphi : \tilde{P} \to \{-1, 0, 1\}$ by

$$\varphi(x,a) = \begin{cases} -1, & x \text{ is a saddle orbit with a multiplier in } (1,\infty), \\ 0, & x \text{ is a Möbius orbit with a multiplier in } (-\infty,-1), \\ 1, & x \text{ is an attracting periodic orbit.} \end{cases}$$

We call φ the orbit index. It is meant to orient curves of periodic orbits: we follow curves of periodic orbits through increasing a values if $\varphi = 1$ and through decreasing a values if $\varphi = -1$. Curves of Möbius orbits are avoided.

Proof of Theorem 5.66. We first consider the case of a generic family f_a that satisfies hypotheses (H1)–(H5). Take a point $(x,1) \in \tilde{P}$ with x a saddle orbit. Follow the path Γ in $\tilde{P}$ that contains $(x,1)$. We follow Γ through decreasing a values. We must reach a bifurcation since we cannot follow Γ up to $a = 0$. Figure 5.27 depicts bifurcation curves near possible occurring bifurcations, either saddle-node or period-doubling bifurcations. In all cases the curve Γ can be continued in a well defined way. In particular Γ cannot return to itself. The

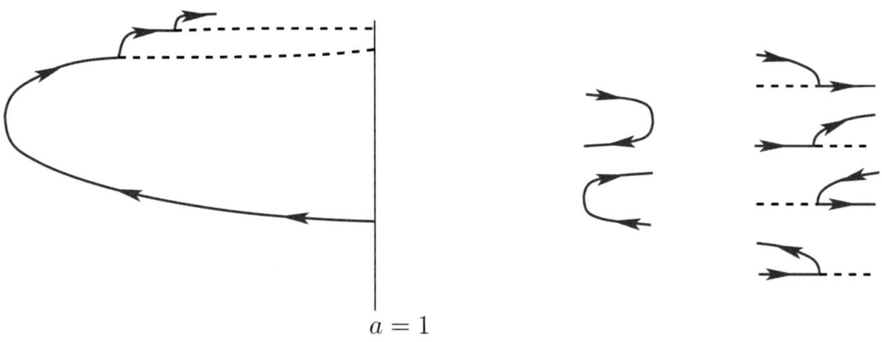

Figure 5.27. The left panel indicates a curve of periodic orbits given a direction using the orbit index, which goes through infinitely many period-doubling bifurcations. The right panel shows curves of periodic orbits near bifurcations (saddle-node and sub- or supercritical period-doubling bifurcations) together with direction. Dashed curves are curves of Möbius orbits that are not assigned a direction.

curve Γ thus continued cannot reach back to $a = 1$ since there are no sinks at $a = 1$.

We cannot terminate in $S \times [0, 1]$ if we go through finitely many bifurcations. Since f_a is a generic family, we could then prolong Γ. It is also not possible that we terminate after infinitely many bifurcations with bounded periods. Indeed, consider a sequence $(x_i, a_i) \in P$ that converges to $(\tilde{x}, \tilde{a})$. If the periods of x_i are bounded, then $(\tilde{x}, \tilde{a}) \in P$. But then the corresponding point in $\tilde{P}$ lies on a curve that extends to smaller and larger values of a. The curve Γ must thus go through infinitely many bifurcations with unbounded periods. This is only possible with infinitely many period-doubling bifurcations.

Now take any family f_a that satisfies hypotheses (H1)–(H5). Consider generic families $g_{i,a}$ converging to f_a in the C^1 topology. We may assume $g_{i,a}$ equals f_a near $a = 0$ and $a = 1$. If p_i is a periodic orbit of g_{i,a_i} of fixed period l and (p_i, a_i) converges to (p, a), then p is a periodic orbit of f_a. If p is hyperbolic, it can be continued in a (Theorem 2.43). Then also p_i for large values of i is a hyperbolic orbit since derivatives $Dg^l_{i,a}(x_i)$, $x_i \in p_i$, and $Df^l_a(x)$, $x_i \to x \in p$, are close. The periods of p_i and p are then the same. If p is nonhyperbolic then, by continuity of eigenvalues, there is an eigenvalue μ_i of $Dg^l_{i,a}(p_i)$ that converges to ± 1. If m denotes the period of p, then $m = l$ or $l/2$.

Recall that $(p, 1)$ is a saddle periodic orbit of f_1 and therefore also of $g_{i,1}$. Write Γ_i for the continuous path of periodic orbits of $g_{i,a}$ containing $(p, 1)$ with nonzero orbit index. As it shows infinitely many period-doublings, we can take the first points $\beta_{i,m}$ (when pathfollowing from $(p, 1)$ on) where the periods jump from $2^m k$ to $2^{m+1} k$. Fixing m, let G_i be the part of the path Γ_i in between $\beta_{i,m}$ and $\beta_{i,m+1}$. Parametrize the path by t, $0 \le t \le 1$. Write $\mu_1(t), \mu_2(t)$

for the multipliers of $G_i(t)$. Then one of the multipliers goes to 1 as $t \downarrow 0$. And one of the multipliers goes to -1 as $t \uparrow 1$. We claim there exist orbits on G_i with $|\mu_1|, |\mu_2| \leq \sqrt{\theta}$. Suppose not. Then for each $t \in [0,1]$, $|\mu_j(t)| > \sqrt{\theta}$ for $j = 1$ or 2, but not both. Say this holds for $j = 1$. But then $|\mu_1(t)| > \sqrt{\theta}$ for all $t \in [0,1]$ since the other multiplier cannot cross the circle with radius $\sqrt{\theta}$ in the complex plane. So $\mu_1(t)$ goes to -1 as $t \uparrow 0$ and to 1 as $t \downarrow 1$. Now $|\mu_1(t)| > 0$ for all t means that μ_1 cannot be real for all $t \in [0,1]$. So $\mu_2(t) = \overline{\mu_1(t)}$ are complex conjugate for some $t \in (0,1)$ and both $|\mu_1(t)|, |\mu_2(t)|$ would be larger than $\sqrt{\theta}$. This is a contradiction.

Let $\nu_{i,m}$ be an orbit on G_i of period $2^{m+1}k$, such that $|\mu_1|, |\mu_2| \leq \sqrt{\theta}$ for both multipliers. Take a converging subsequence $\nu_{i,m}$ as $i \to \infty$, that converges to ν_m. Then ν_m is an attractor of an f_a. It has period $2^{m+1}k$. Let $\Gamma_{i,m}$ be the segment of Γ_i with endpoints $(p,1)$ and $\nu_{i,m}$. All of its periodic orbits have period at most $2^{m+1}k$. Let Γ_m be the set of limit points x of sequences x_i in $\Gamma_{i,m}$. Then Γ_m is a compact and connected set of orbits containing $(p,1)$ and ν_m. Hence we conclude that ν_m is in the component of period orbits of the family f_a containing $(p,1)$. □

A theory of renormalization in two and more dimensions, that extends the theory for unimodal maps mentioned in Example 5.64, is considered in [**72**]. A selection of research that contributes to the development of such a theory of renormalization is [**62–64, 155, 236**].

Example 5.68. Section 4.1.4 describes one instance of a codimension-2 homoclinic bifurcation in which a double homoclinic orbit branches. A double homoclinic orbit here is a homoclinic orbit that makes two rounds through a small tubular neighborhood of the original homoclinic orbit. There are two more codimension-2 homoclinic bifurcations in which a double homoclinic orbit branches [**421**]: an orbit-flip with additional conditions on eigenvalues at the equilibrium and an inclination-flip, also with additional conditions on eigenvalues. Several researchers contributed to the bifurcation theory; we refer to the review paper [**172**]. The bifurcation diagrams of these two other codimension-2 homoclinic bifurcations differ somewhat from the bifurcation diagram of the resonant homoclinic bifurcation. They are as depicted in the left panel of Figure 5.28.

Homoclinic-doubling cascades are a mechanism for the disappearance of period-doubling sequences in vector fields in which each periodic orbit in the period-doubling cascade collides with a homoclinic orbit to a hyperbolic equilibrium. A homoclinic-doubling cascade consists of a cascade of homoclinic-doubling bifurcations, consisting of a connected set of homoclinic bifurcations in the parameter plane in which each double homoclinic orbit is the primary homoclinic orbit of its own homoclinic-doubling bifurcation. The existence of

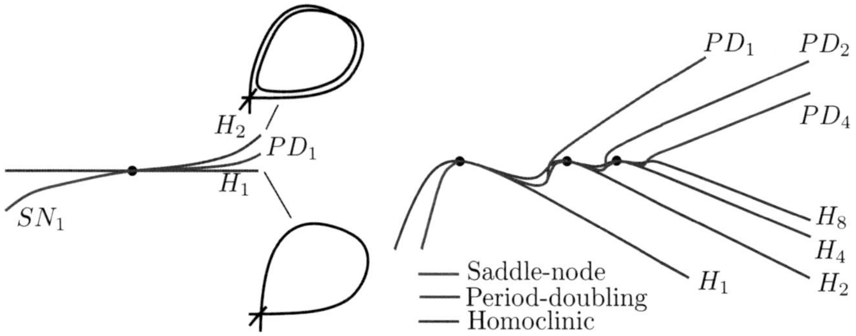

Figure 5.28. Left panel: the homoclinic-doubling bifurcation. SN_1 is a curve of saddle-node bifurcations of periodic orbits, PD_1 of period-doubling bifurcations, and H_1, H_2 of homoclinic bifurcations. Right panel: the postulated bifurcation set with a cascade of homoclinic-doubling bifurcations.

a cascade of homoclinic-doubling bifurcations in certain two-parameter vector fields in $\mathbb{R}^3$ has been proved in [**171**], using a continuation theory for homoclinic orbits in two parameters reminiscent of the continuation of periodic orbits in one parameter used to prove Theorem 5.66. A renormalization analysis, restricted however to model interval maps with both a critical point and a singularity (a point with infinite derivative) is discussed in [**174**]. It entails the existence of two unstable eigenvalues, in contrast with the single unstable eigenvalue in the renormalization theory for period-doubling cascades mentioned in Example 5.64. We note here that similar model interval maps appear in the study [**334**] of the Shimizu-Morioka model [**343**]. A numerical investigation of a homoclinic-doubling cascade in Sandstede's model described in Section 1.3 is in [**273**]. Figure 5.28 shows the postulated bifurcation set deducted from these references. Moving along a line from left to right in the top part of the parameter plane, one encounters a period-doubling cascade. Continuing along such a line in the bottom part of the parameter plane, one gets a cascade of homoclinic bifurcations. Systems in the right part of the parameter plane are not Morse-Smale. ■

5.2.6. Intermittency. In the supercritical Hopf bifurcation, the attractor changes from an equilibrium to a small limit cycle. Although this is an important change in the dynamics as it is the moment that oscillations are created, the attractor changes little in the sense that close to the bifurcation it is close to the equilibrium. In contrast, in the saddle-node bifurcation, the attractor disappears altogether. Following these examples one can distinguish between hard and soft bifurcations (references [**21,23**] speak of hard and soft loss of stability). The saddle-node bifurcation and the subcritical Hopf bifurcation are examples of hard bifurcations. The supercritical Hopf bifurcation is an example of a soft bifurcation. Hard bifurcations alter the dynamics on a global scale.

Example 5.69. Consider a one-parameter family of vector fields on the circle that unfolds a saddle-node bifurcation of a unique equilibrium. This creates periodic motion on the circle; see Figure 5.29. Motion near the vanished equilibrium is slow, so that the period is large and the flow has a slow passage through a neighborhood of the vanished equilibrium and a relatively fast part outside. Such bifurcations are ingredients in models for spiking in neuron dynamics, and they appear for instance in the Wilson-Cowan model from Example 3.46 [**178**, Section 2.7.1].

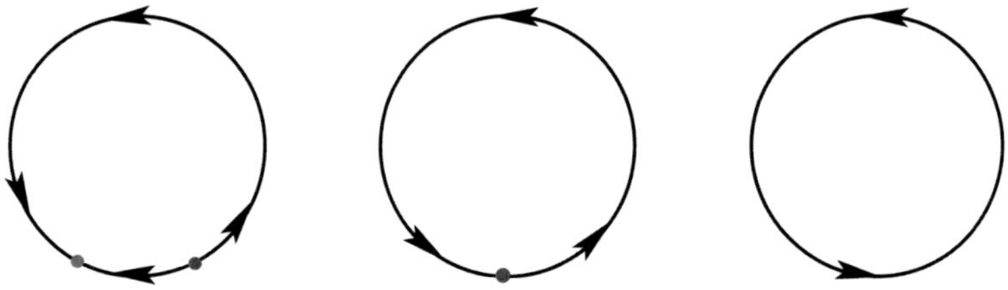

Figure 5.29. A saddle-node bifurcation of a unique equilibrium on a circle creates period motion. The pictures are phase diagrams of before, at, and after the bifurcation.

To make the slow passage explicit, consider the model family of differential equations $\dot{x} = \lambda + ax^2$, $a > 0$, on the line with a saddle-node bifurcation of the equilibrium 0 for $\lambda = 0$. Let $x_l < 0 < x_r$ be two points near 0 and consider for $\lambda > 0$ the time $\tau(\lambda)$ of the flow φ_λ^t needed to go from x_l to x_r. Solving the differential equation, we find

$$\varphi_\lambda^t(x_l) = \sqrt{\frac{\lambda}{a}} \tan\left(\sqrt{a\lambda}t + \arctan\left(\sqrt{\frac{a}{\lambda}}x_l\right)\right).$$

Hence

$$\sqrt{a\lambda}\tau(\lambda) = \arctan\left(\sqrt{\frac{a}{\lambda}}x_r\right) - \arctan\left(\sqrt{\frac{a}{\lambda}}x_l\right).$$

We deduce

$$\lim_{\lambda\to 0} \frac{\sqrt{a\lambda}\tau(\lambda)}{\pi} = 1. \tag{5.21}$$

■

5.2.6.1. *Concept and first examples.* The phenomenon of intermittency was first described by Yves Pomeau and Paul Manneville ([**297**]; see also the textbook [**35**]). It was introduced as the alternation of phases of apparently periodic and nonperiodic dynamics. Phases with nearly periodic dynamics are referred to as laminar phases. In the other phase, the relaminarization phase, the orbit makes an excursion away from the periodic region. We will mainly look at intermittency as a result of a saddle-node bifurcation of a periodic orbit. Mechanisms of intermittency caused by subcritical Hopf bifurcations, subcritical period-doubling bifurcations of periodic orbits, or homoclinic bifurcations are not treated.

Example 5.70. Recall from Example 5.65 that the Rössler equations are given by

$$\begin{aligned}\dot{x} &= -y - z,\\ \dot{y} &= x + ay,\\ \dot{z} &= b + z(x - c).\end{aligned}$$

Figure 5.30 shows phase portraits and time series from the Rössler equations. Numerical experiments show the following. With $a = b = 0.2$ fixed and varying c, a periodic attractor occurs for c near 5.19, such as $c = 5.191$ in the figure. More complicated dynamics exists for somewhat smaller values of c, $c = 5.182$

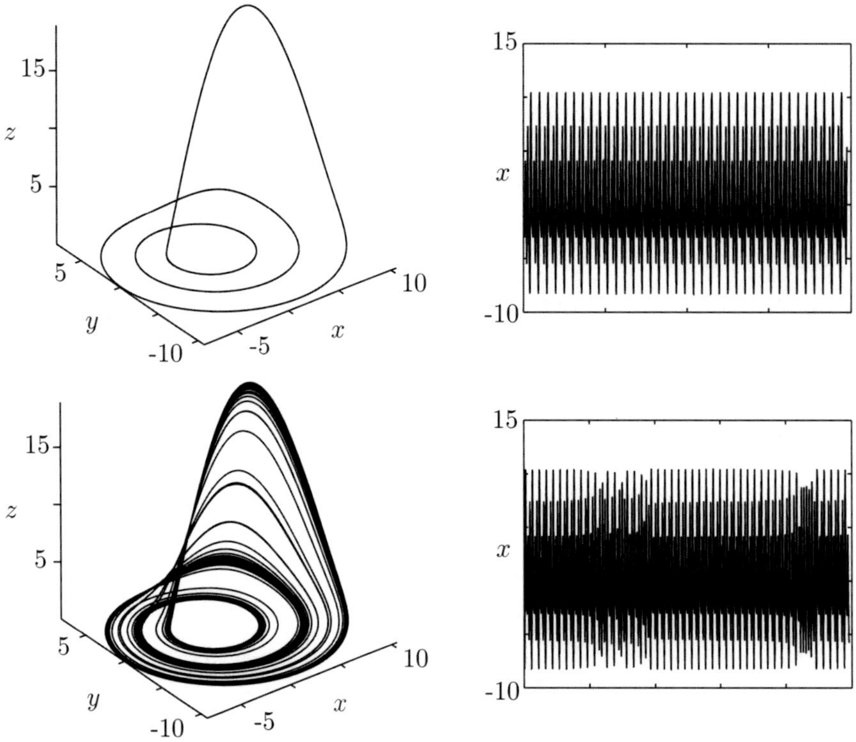

Figure 5.30. Dynamics of the Rössler equations for varying c and fixed $a = b = 0.2$. The upper panels show a periodic orbit and periodic time series of the x-coordinate for $c = 5.191$. The lower panels show a long orbit piece which appears periodic most of the time, and intermittent time series of the x-coordinate, for $c = 5.182$.

in the figure, where time series are not periodic but appear periodic for long stretches.

The explanation lies in the saddle-node bifurcation between these two values of c in which the periodic attractor is created. This bifurcation induces intermittency just before the bifurcation value. The reader may compare with intermittency in the logistic family discussed below. ■

As reported in [**297**], similar dynamics as in Example 5.70 arises in the Lorenz equations. To see how a saddle-node bifurcation of a periodic orbit may cause intermittent dynamics, let f_λ be a one-parameter family of vector fields unfolding a saddle-node bifurcation of a periodic orbit at $\lambda = \lambda_0$. For $\lambda < \lambda_0$, say, the family possesses an attracting periodic orbit. This has disappeared for $\lambda > \lambda_0$. Let U be a small neighborhood of the periodic orbit at $\lambda = \lambda_0$. For λ slightly larger than λ_0, an orbit starting in U will take a long time to leave U. Intermittent dynamics occurs if orbits that leave U return to U at a later time, creating other periods of almost periodic dynamics.

For functions $h(\lambda)$, $g(\lambda)$ with λ from an interval bounded by 0, we write $h(\lambda) \sim g(\lambda)$ if $\lim_{\lambda \to 0} \frac{h(\lambda)}{g(\lambda)} = 1$. So for instance (5.21) reads $\tau(\lambda) \sim \frac{\pi}{\sqrt{a\lambda}}$. Now consider a map $f_\lambda(x) = x + \lambda + ax^2 + \mathcal{O}(x^3)$ near $x = 0$. This map has a saddle-node bifurcation of the fixed point 0 for $\lambda = 0$. For definiteness assume $a > 0$. Let $x_l < 0 < x_r$ be two points near 0 and consider for $\lambda > 0$ the number of iterates $l = l(\lambda, x_l, x_r)$ of f_λ needed to map x_l to the right of x_r. That is, for $\lambda > 0$ we define

$$l(\lambda, x_l, x_r) = \min\{l \in \mathbb{N}\ ;\ f_\lambda^l(x_l) > x_r\}; \tag{5.22}$$

compare Figure 5.31. The next lemma is a statement on the duration of laminar phases.

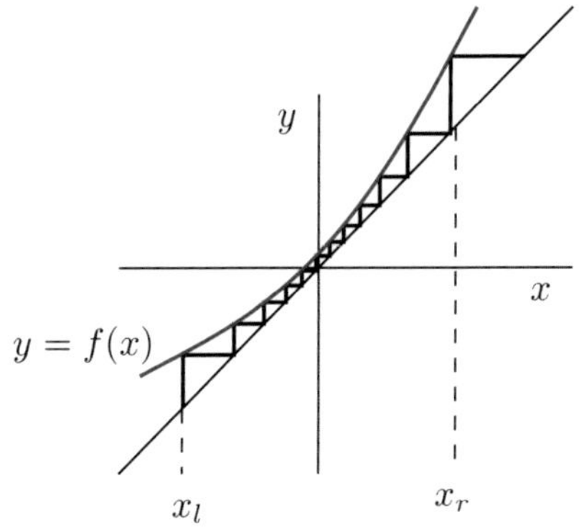

Figure 5.31. Depicted is the graph of $f_\lambda : \mathbb{R} \to \mathbb{R}$ for small positive λ so that the graph almost touches the diagonal, and iterates of a point that passes through the region.

Lemma 5.71. *Let $f_\lambda(x) = x + \lambda + ax^2 + \mathcal{O}(x^3)$, $a > 0$, and let x near 0 be a smooth map. The transition time l from (5.22) satisfies, for $\lambda \to 0$,*

$$l(\lambda) \sim \frac{\pi}{\sqrt{a\lambda}}.$$

Proof. As follows from Example 5.69, the time 1 map of the flow of $\dot{x} = \lambda + ax^2 =: f_{a,\lambda}(x)$ is given by

$$\begin{aligned}\varphi^1_{a,\lambda}(x) &= \sqrt{\frac{\lambda}{a}}\tan\left(\sqrt{a\lambda} + \arctan\left(\sqrt{\frac{a}{\lambda}}x\right)\right)\\ &= \lambda + x + ax^2 + \mathcal{O}(\lambda^2) + \mathcal{O}(\lambda x) + \mathcal{O}(x^3)\end{aligned}$$

for $x, \lambda \to 0$.

Given $\lambda > 0$ and $\varepsilon > 0$ small, we calculate transition times for the flows of $f_{a,\lambda}$, from x_l to $-\varepsilon$, from $-\varepsilon$ to ε, and from ε to x_r. Write $\tau(u, v)$ for the time needed to flow from u to v: $\varphi^{\tau(u,v)}_{a,\lambda}(u) = v$. Recall from Example 5.69 that

$$\sqrt{a\lambda}\tau(x_l, x_r) = \arctan\left(x_r\sqrt{\frac{a}{\lambda}}\right) - \arctan\left(x_l\sqrt{\frac{a}{\lambda}}\right).$$

Asymptotics for small λ are derived using $\lim_{x\to-\infty} \frac{\arctan(x)+\frac{1}{2}\pi}{1/x} = -1$. This yields

$$\begin{aligned}\lim_{\lambda\to 0}\tau(x_l, -\varepsilon) &= \lim_{\lambda\to 0}\frac{\arctan\left(-\varepsilon\sqrt{\frac{a}{\lambda}}\right) - \arctan\left(x_l\sqrt{\frac{a}{\lambda}}\right)}{\sqrt{a\lambda}}\\ &= \frac{1}{a\varepsilon} - \frac{1}{ax_l}.\end{aligned} \tag{5.23}$$

Likewise

$$\lim_{\lambda\to 0}\tau(\varepsilon, x_r) = \frac{1}{ax_r} - \frac{1}{a\varepsilon}. \tag{5.24}$$

We also have

$$\begin{aligned}\lim_{\lambda\to 0}\tau(-\varepsilon, \varepsilon) - \frac{\pi}{\sqrt{a\lambda}} &= \lim_{\lambda\to 0}\frac{\arctan\left(\varepsilon\sqrt{\frac{a}{\lambda}}\right) - \arctan\left(-\varepsilon\sqrt{\frac{a}{\lambda}}\right) - \pi}{\sqrt{a\lambda}}\\ &= \frac{-2}{a\varepsilon}.\end{aligned} \tag{5.25}$$

A reparametrization would bring $\varphi^1_{a,\lambda}$ to the form $\psi^1_{a,\lambda}(x) = \lambda + x + ax^2 + \mathcal{O}(\lambda x) + \mathcal{O}(x^3)$. This does not alter the asymptotics of the transition time.

We can take $b^- < a < b^+$ so that $\psi^1_{b^-,\lambda} < f_\lambda < \psi^1_{b^+,\lambda}$ on $[x_l, x_r]$. Using this and (5.23) and (5.24), we get the existence of a positive constant C with $l(\lambda, x_l, -\varepsilon) \le C/\varepsilon$ and $l(\lambda, \varepsilon, x_r) \le C/\varepsilon$ for all small λ. Given a^-, a^+ near a with

$a^- < a < a^+$, take $\varepsilon > 0$ small enough so that $\psi^1_{a^-,\lambda} < f_\lambda < \psi^1_{a^+,\lambda}$ on $[-\varepsilon, \varepsilon]$, for small λ. Combining this with (5.25) gives

$$\frac{\pi}{\sqrt{a^-}} \leq \liminf_{\lambda\to 0} l(\lambda, x_l, x_r)\sqrt{\lambda} \leq \limsup_{\lambda\to 0} l(\lambda, x_l, x_r)\sqrt{\lambda} \leq \frac{\pi}{\sqrt{a^+}}.$$

Letting a^-, a^+ go to a, we get the desired asymptotics $l \sim \pi/\sqrt{a\lambda}$. □

We attempt to formulate a definition of intermittency bifurcations, following [**96, 374**], that includes the examples listed in this section. We allow for a laminar phase that is more complicated than periodic. A sequence of compact sets A_n converges to a compact set A in the Hausdorff sense if the distance between A_n and A in the Hausdorff metric goes to zero as $n \to \infty$. A compact invariant set C is called an attracting set if for any neighborhood U of A, there exists an open neighborhood $V \subset U$ that is forward invariant and C is the maximal invariant set in V.

Definition 5.72. A one-parameter family $\dot{x} = f_\lambda(x)$ of differential equations has an *intermittency bifurcation* for $\lambda = \lambda_0$ at a compact invariant set K, if the following holds. Let $\mathcal{U}$ be a small open neighborhood of K. There is $\varepsilon > 0$ so that for $|\lambda - \lambda_0| < \varepsilon$,

(i) For $\lambda < \lambda_0$ the system has an attracting set $K_\lambda \subset \mathcal{U}$ converging to K in the Hausdorff sense;
(ii) For $\lambda > \lambda_0$ there is a uniformly positive Lebesgue measure set of initial points in $\mathcal{U}$ whose positive orbits leave and enter $\mathcal{U}$ infinitely often.

We note that Example 5.21 of saddle-node and homoclinic bifurcations on the Klein bottle (and similar examples on other surfaces such as the torus) and Example 5.69 provide examples of intermittency bifurcations. So does the following example of a blue sky catastrophe.

Example 5.73. The question about the possibility for a periodic orbit to remain in a bounded region of the phase space while the period and arc length of the orbit increase with no bound as it approaches its existence boundary was raised by Jacob Palis and Charles Pugh in 1974 (see [**279**, problem 37]. The problem was code-named a *blue sky catastrophe* as the orbit, while getting longer and longer, would be virtually vanishing in the space. For flows on surfaces the phenomenon was investigated in [**247, 248**].

A construction of a blue sky catastrophe was given by Dmitry Turaev and Leonid Shilnikov [**341, 342**] and is illustrated in Figure 5.32. At the bifurcation value the three-dimensional flow possesses a saddle-node periodic orbit with normal strong stable directions, so that the unstable part of the center manifold converges to the periodic orbit as depicted. On the side of the bifurcation where

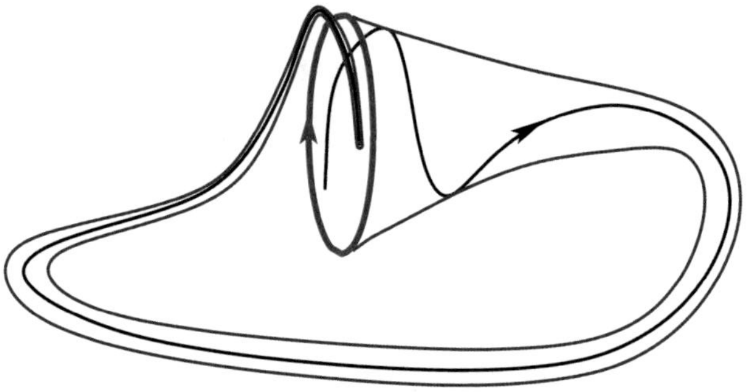

Figure 5.32. A periodic attractor develops unbounded arc length and disappears at a saddle-node bifurcation of a second periodic orbit.

the saddle-node periodic is gone, a periodic attractor with large arc length appears. An explicit example of a family of differential equations with a blue sky catastrophe was given by Nikolai Gavrilov and Andrey Shilnikov [**119**]. ■

5.2.6.2. *Intermittency in the logistic family.* We discuss intermittent dynamics in the context of the logistic family $f_\lambda(x) = \lambda x(1-x)$. A lot of complexity in the dynamics that can come with intermittency is visible in this context. Similar phenomena to the ones sketched here can be expected in systems such as Hénon maps and Rössler differential equations. The presentation here focuses on numerical experiments to indicate ideas and types of questions.

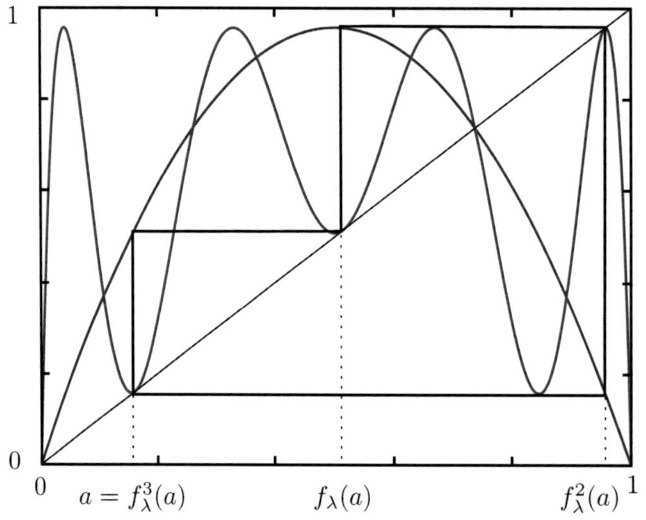

Figure 5.33. The graph of the logistic map f_λ (blue) and its third iterate f_λ^3 (red) for $\lambda = 1+\sqrt{8}$ at the saddle-node bifurcation of a period 3 periodic orbit.

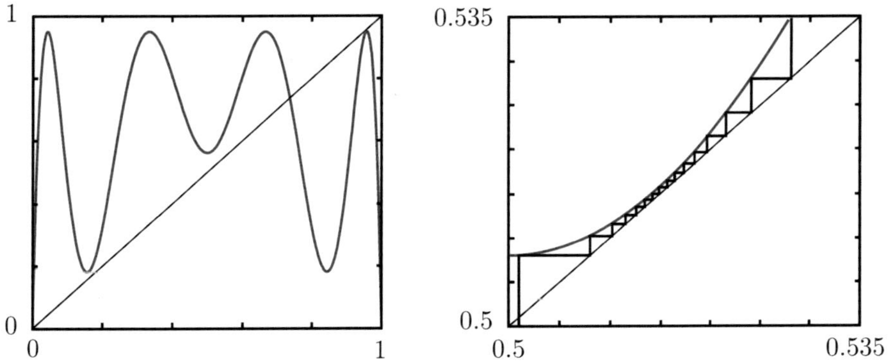

Figure 5.34. The graph of the third iterate of the logistic map f_λ for $\lambda = 3.8$ (left panel) and an image section for $\lambda = 3.828$ (right panel). Compare also Figure 5.31.

Consider λ near the bifurcation value $\lambda_0 = 1 + \sqrt{8}$ of the saddle-node bifurcation of the period-3 orbit $\mathcal{O}(a) = \{a, f_{\lambda_0}(a), f^2_{\lambda_0}(a)\}$; see Figure 5.33. For λ just larger than λ_0, f_λ admits an attracting periodic orbit of period 3. Orbits of f, for almost all initial points, converge to this periodic attractor. For λ just smaller than λ_0 there is no period 3 periodic orbit; see Figure 5.34.

The left panel in Figure 5.35 shows intermittent time series with nearly periodic laminar phases and chaotic bursts. Ideally one would like to know the distribution of lengths of laminar and relaminarization phases as a function of the parameter. An experimental way to investigate the relative frequency of iterates in the laminar phase is as follows. Let U be a small neighborhood of $\mathcal{O}(a)$ for $f^3_{\lambda_0}$. Let 1_U be the indicator function

$$1_U(x) = \begin{cases} 0, & x \notin U, \\ 1, & x \in U. \end{cases}$$

Consider the average χ_U defined as

$$\chi_U(x, \lambda) = \lim_{n\to\infty} \frac{1}{n} \sum_{i=0}^{n-1} 1_U(f^i_\lambda(x)), \tag{5.26}$$

whenever the limit exists. That is, $\chi_U(x, \lambda)$ is the relative frequency with which the orbit $\{f^i_\lambda(x)\}_{i\in\mathbb{N}_0}$ visits U. The right panel in Figure 5.35 depicts a numerical computation of $\chi_U(x, \lambda)$ for a choice of U. The numerical computation is necessarily imperfect as a grid of parameter values are taken and finitely many iterates of f_λ. We quote the following result from [**176**]. There exists a set Λ of parameter values with positive density at $\lambda = \lambda_0$, that is

$$\liminf_{d\downarrow 0} \frac{\text{Leb}(\Lambda \cap (\lambda_0 - d, \lambda_0))}{d} > 0$$

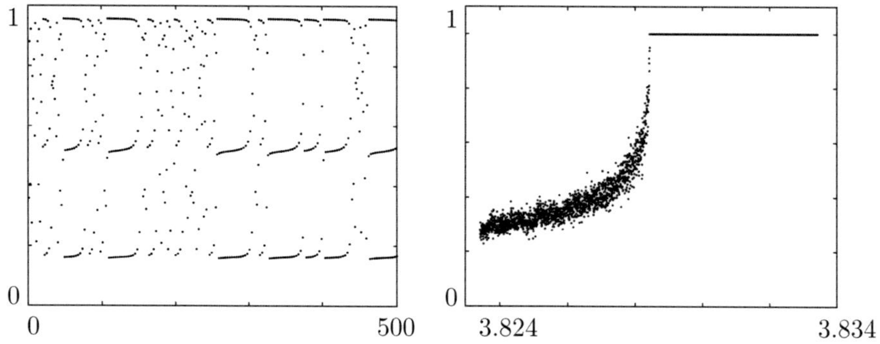

Figure 5.35. Left panel: time series for the logistic map $x \mapsto \lambda x(1-x)$ for $\lambda = 3.8279$ near the saddle-node bifurcation of the period-3 orbit. Right panel: as a function of λ, the frequency of visits of orbits to a small neighborhood U of the period-3 orbit at λ_0.

(here $\mathrm{Leb}(\cdot)$ stands for Lebesgue measure), with the following properties. When restricting λ to Λ, $\chi_U(x,\lambda)$ is a constant, $\chi_U(\lambda)$, almost everywhere on $[0,1]$, and $\chi_U(\lambda)$ depends continuously on λ at λ_0. Moreover, there exist $K_1, K_2 > 0$ so that

$$K_1 \leq \lim_{\lambda \in \Lambda, \lambda \uparrow \lambda_0} \frac{1 - \chi_U(\lambda)}{\sqrt{\lambda}} \leq K_2.$$

Restricting λ to a subset Λ is necessary for such a quantitative result [**175**].

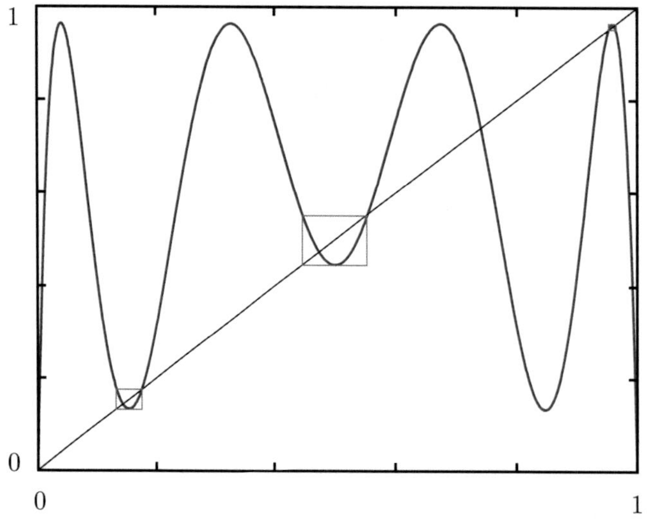

Figure 5.36. The graph of the third iterate of the logistic map f_λ at a crisis bifurcation value λ_1. The union of the indicated three intervals is invariant for f_{λ_1}.

We finish with a brief description of a second type of intermittency bifurcation in the logistic family. There is a bifurcation value $\lambda_1 > \lambda_0$, depicted in Figure 5.36, for which there is a set I_{λ_1} of three intervals so that the third iterate $f_{\lambda_1}^3$ maps each of these three intervals twice onto itself, similar to f_4 and the interval $[0,1]$. The bifurcation at $\lambda = \lambda_1$ is an example of a crisis bifurcation [**136**] and it is an intermittency bifurcation in the sense of Definition 5.72, with $K = I_{\lambda_1}$. For λ near λ_1, there is a set I_λ of three intervals that continues I_{λ_1} and is bounded by periodic and preperiodic points. Intermittent time series occur for parameter values slightly larger than λ_1. For such values of λ, orbits alternate between being inside I_λ for, typically, long stretches (the laminar phase) or outside I_λ (the relaminarization phase). Similar to the saddle-node bifurcation, numerical experiments give insight in the frequency of iterates in laminar phases; see [**175**] for such experiments and accompanying theoretical explanations.

The intricacies of intermittency bifurcations in logistic families are due to discontinuous parameter dependence of *natural measures*; see [**383**] and the review paper [**382**].

5.3. Exercises

Exercise 5.1. Let f_λ be a one-parameter family of vector fields. Assume that for each $\lambda \in [a,b]$, f_λ is structurally stable. Prove that f_a and f_b are topologically equivalent.

Exercise 5.2. Show the following invariance properties under conjugacies for flows.

(i) The period of a periodic orbit is invariant under a topological conjugacy.

(ii) Eigenvalues of the linearization about an equilibrium are invariant under a C^1 conjugacy.

(iii) Floquet multipliers of a periodic solution are invariant under a C^1 conjugacy.

Exercise 5.3. Consider the constant differential equation $\dot{x} = f(x) = 1$ on $\mathbb{R}$. Show that there exists $\varepsilon > 0$ so that each $g : \mathbb{R} \to \mathbb{R}$ that is ε-close in the uniform C^1 topology ($|f(x) - g(x)| < \varepsilon$ and $|f'(x) - g'(x)| < \varepsilon$ for all $x \in \mathbb{R}$), then the differential equations given by f and g are differentiably conjugate. That is, there is a C^1 diffeomorphism $h : \mathbb{R} \to \mathbb{R}$ that conjugates the flows.

Exercise 5.4. Consider an automorphism of $\mathbb{T}^2 = \mathbb{R}^2/\mathbb{Z}^2$ corresponding to a matrix in $\mathrm{GL}(2,\mathbb{Z})$ whose eigenvalues are not roots of 1.

(i) Prove that every point with rational coordinates is periodic.

(ii) Prove that every periodic point has rational coordinates.

Exercise 5.5. Let 0 be a hyperbolic stable equilibrium for a vector field f. Give an example where $Df(0)$ has only one eigenvalue $\lambda < 0$ (with multiplicity larger than 1) but $\|e^{Df(0)t}\| > e^{\lambda t}$ for $t > 0$. For this example, provide $\tilde{\lambda} < 0$, $C > 0$, so that $\|e^{Df(0)t}\| < Ce^{\tilde{\lambda}t}$.

Exercise 5.6. What are necessary and sufficient conditions, in terms of Floquet multipliers, for a periodic orbit to be a hyperbolic set?

Exercise 5.7. Prove that a small perturbation from a linear horseshoe map as in Theorem 2.58 is a hyperbolic invariant set.

Exercise 5.8. Prove that the solenoid from Example 5.13 is a maximal hyperbolic set.

Exercise 5.9. Example 5.14 describes two invariant sets, one for a diffeomorphism and one for a differential equation, which are both the closures of a homoclinic orbit. Prove that these invariant sets are hyperbolic.

Exercise 5.10. Let Λ be a hyperbolic invariant set of a diffeomorphism f. Adjust the statement and proof of Theorem 5.10 to include continuous dependence of local stable manifolds $W^s_{loc}(x)$, $x \in \Lambda$, on x.

Exercise 5.11. Consider a differential equation on a compact manifold. Prove that the nonwandering set is closed and invariant. Provide an example to show that the nonwandering and the limit set (the union of the ω-limit sets of points) can be different. Is one always contained in the other?

Exercise 5.12. Given is a smooth differential equation $\dot{x} = f(x)$ on the plane, such that orbits are transverse to the unit circle. Suppose that inside the unit disk the system has only finitely many equilibria, which are all hyperbolic, only finitely many periodic orbits, all hyperbolic, and no heteroclinic orbits that connect saddle equilibria. Prove that a small perturbation of the system satisfies the same properties and has its equilibria and periodic orbits in the unit disk close to those of f.

Exercise 5.13. Let $V : M \to \mathbb{R}$ be a C^2 function on a compact manifold M such that each singular point is nondegenerate, that is, at each point where $\nabla V(x) = 0$, the Hessian matrix of partial derivatives of second order is nonsingular. Prove that all fixed points of the gradient vector field are hyperbolic. Prove that the gradient vector field has no periodic orbits.

Exercise 5.14. For $0 < r < R$, consider the torus $(\sqrt{y^2 + z^2} - R)^2 + x^2 = r^2$ in $\mathbb{R}^3$. Let $V : \mathbb{R}^3 \to \mathbb{R}$ be the height function $V(x, y, z) = z$. Show that the gradient vector field ∇V is not Morse-Smale.

Exercise 5.15. Morse-Smale diffeomorphisms are defined in an analogous way as Morse-Smale flows: they are diffeomorphisms with a finite number of hyperbolic periodic points and transversely intersecting stable and unstable manifolds. Let φ^t be a Morse-Smale flow for a vector field. Suppose φ^t has no periodic solutions. Prove that φ^1 is a Morse-Smale diffeomorphism.

Exercise 5.16. Use the topological conjugacy of $f_4(x) = 4x(1-x)$ with the tent map

$$T(x) = \begin{cases} 2x, & 0 \le x \le 1/2, \\ 2(1-x), & 1/2 \le x \le 1, \end{cases}$$

both on $[0,1]$, to find period-k points, $k \ge 2$, for f_4.

Exercise 5.17. Let $T_2 : [-1,1] \to [-1,1]$ be the piecewise affine map given by

$$T_2(x) = \begin{cases} 2x-1, & x \ge 0, \\ -2x-1, & x \le 0. \end{cases}$$

The quadratic map $Q_2 : [-1,1] \to [-1,1]$ is given by

$$Q_2(x) = 2x^2 - 1.$$

(i) Show that the homeomorphism $h(x) = \sin(\pi x/2)$ on $[-1,1]$ conjugates T_2 and Q_2:

$$h \circ T_2 = Q_2 \circ h.$$

Now consider the piecewise affine map $T_3 : [-1,1] \to [-1,1]$ given by

$$T_3(x) = \begin{cases} 3x+2, & -1 \le x \le -1/3, \\ -3x, & -1/3 \le x \le 1/3, \\ 3x-2, & 1/3 \le x \le 1. \end{cases}$$

and the cubic map $Q_3 : [-1,1] \to [-1,1]$ given by

$$Q_3(x) = 4x^3 - 3x.$$

(ii) Show that the two maps T_3 and Q_3 are topologically conjugate.
(iii) Show that periodic points for Q_3 are dense in $[-1,1]$.
(iv) Similarly, give the formulas of a fourth-order polynomial and a piecewise affine map that are topologically conjugate on $[-1,1]$.

Exercise 5.18. Prove that the tent map $T : [0,1] \to [0,1]$ given by

$$T(x) = \begin{cases} 2x, & 0 \le x \le 1/2, \\ 2(1-x), & 1/2 \le x \le 1, \end{cases}$$

is chaotic in the sense of Devaney. Use Proposition 5.49 to conclude that the logistic map $f_4(x) = 4x(1-x)$ is chaotic in the sense of Devaney.

Exercise 5.19. Show that two conditions providing an expansion property on a compact invariant set for interval maps, (5.14) and (5.15), are equivalent.

Exercise 5.20. Prove that a quadratic map $f(x) = Ax^2 + Bx + C$ is affinely conjugate to a map of the form $Q_c(x) = x^2 + c$. Relate the coefficients A, B, C to c.

Exercise 5.21. Prove that the logistic map f_λ for $\lambda > 4$, restricted to the maximal invariant Cantor set $\Omega_\lambda \subset [0,1]$, is topologically conjugate to the left shift operator on the space $\{0,1\}^{\mathbb{N}}$ endowed with the product topology.

Exercise 5.22. Proposition 5.54 states that saddle-node bifurcations of periodic orbits in the logistic family are nondegenerate. Provide the details of the arguments to prove this statement.

Exercise 5.23. Consider the Hénon map $H_{a,b}(x,y) = (y + 1 - ax^2, bx)$ for parameter values $(a,b) = (a_0, 0)$ at which $x \mapsto 1 - ax^2$ has a crisis bifurcation with a preperiodic critical point, such as depicted in Figure 5.36. Establish and discuss the following statement, comparable to Theorem 5.61: there is a curve $a(b)$ defined for small values of b, with $a(0) = a_0$, of homoclinic tangencies to a hyperbolic periodic point for $b \neq 0$.

Appendix A

Elements of nonlinear analysis

In this appendix we present results and techniques from analysis that are used in bifurcation theory. We offer a recap of differentiable calculus on Banach spaces including a section on the fundamental uniform contraction theorem and the implicit function theorem. The method of Lyapunov-Schmidt reduction, which is derived from the implicit function theorem and which is a tool for solving equations, is explained. This appendix contains a brief part recalling definitions and elementary properties of manifolds.

A.1. Calculus on Banach spaces

We collect results from differentiable calculus on Banach spaces, mostly without proof. A detailed account can be found, for instance, in [**218**] or [**425**].

Let X be a Banach space. The norm in X we will denote by $||\cdot||$, or $||\cdot||_X$ if any confusion could occur, or to emphasize the relation of the norm to this space. If $X = \mathbb{R}^n$, we denote its norm by $|\cdot|$.

A.1.1. Derivatives. Let X and Y be Banach spaces. We let $L(X,Y)$ be the Banach space of bounded linear operators from X to Y with the operator topology. For given norms on X and Y, both denoted by $||\cdot||$, the norm $||A||$ for $A \in L(X,Y)$ is the infimum of those $K \geq 0$ for which

$$||Av|| \leq K||v||.$$

Let U be an open subset of X. A function $f : U \to Y$ is said to be (Fréchet) differentiable at x_0 if there is a bounded linear operator $Df(x_0) : X \to Y$ such that

$$\|f(x_0+h)-f(x_0)-Df(x_0)h\| = o(\|h\|)$$

as $\|h\| \to 0$. The operator $Df(x_0)$ is called the derivative or Fréchet derivative of f at x_0.

The Fréchet derivative has properties very similar to the derivative in finite dimensions. For example, if $f : X \to Y, g : Y \to Z$ are Fréchet differentiable, then the chain rule holds for $g \circ f$:

$$Dg \circ f(x) = Dg(f(x))Df(x).$$

If $f : X \to Y$, $Y = \prod_{i=1}^n Y_i$, $f = (f_1, \dots, f_n)$ with each f_i being Fréchet differentiable, then f is Fréchet differentiable and

$$Df(x) = (Df_1(x), \dots, Df_n(x)).$$

If $X = \prod_{i=1}^N X_i$, $f : X \to Y$, $f(x) = f(x_1, \dots, x_N)$, $x_i \in X_i$, then one can define partial Fréchet derivatives $D_i f(x) \in L(X_i, Y)$ with respect to x_i in the usual way:

$$\|f(x_1, \dots, x_i + h, \dots, x_N) - f(x_1, \dots, x_i, \dots, x_N) - D_i f(x)h\| = o(\|h\|)$$

as $\|h\| \to 0$. If $Df(x), D_i f(x)$ exist and $h = (h_1, \dots, h_N) \in X$ with $h_i \in X_i$, then

$$Df(x)h = \sum_{i=1}^N D_i f(x)h_i.$$

In the main text we often write $D_{x_i} f(x_1, \dots, x_N)$ for the partial derivative with respect to x_i.

To define higher derivatives (also termed derivatives of higher order) we need the concept of a multilinear operator. Let X_j, $j \in \{1, \dots, n\}$ be Banach spaces. An operator $f : \prod_{j=1}^n X_j \to Y$ is called multilinear if for each $x = (x_1, \dots, x_n) \in \prod_{j=1}^n X_j$ and each integer $k = 1, 2, \dots, n$, $f(x_1, \dots, x_n)$ is linear in x_k for all other variables fixed. The norm $\|f\|$ of a multilinear map f from $\prod_{j=1}^n X_j$ to Y is the infimum of those $K \geq 0$ satisfying

$$\|f(x_1, \dots, x_n)\| \leq K \prod_{i=1}^n \|x_i\|_{X_i},$$

where $\|\cdot\|_{X_i}$ denotes the norm on X_i. The set of bounded multilinear maps from $X = \prod_{j=1}^n X_j$ to Y will be denoted by $L(X_1, \dots, X_n, Y)$. This is a Banach space with the usual rules for addition and scalar multiplication and the above norm. If $X_1 = \cdots = X_n = X$, we let $L(X, \dots, X, Y) = L^n(X, Y)$. There is an isomorphism between the Banach spaces $L(X_1, \dots, X_n, Y)$ and $L(X_1, L(X_2, L(X_3, \dots, L(X_n, Y))))$.

A multilinear form $f \in L^n(X, Y)$ is symmetric if $f(x_1, \dots, x_n)$ is invariant under any permutation $\sigma(1, 2, \dots, n)$ of the integers $1, 2, \dots, n$ giving the indices. If U is an open set in X and $f : U \to Y$ has a Fréchet derivative $Df(x)$ for $x \in U$, then we say that f has a second Fréchet derivative $D^2f(x_0)$ at x_0 if $Df(\cdot) : U \to L(X,Y)$ has a Fréchet derivative at x_0. In this case, $D^2f(x_0) \in L(X, L(X,Y)) = L^2(X,Y)$. It is possible to show that, if f is twice differentiable on U and $x \mapsto D^kf(x)$, $0 \le k \le 2$, is continuous, $D^2f(x_0)$ is a symmetric bilinear form; that is

$$D^2f(x_0)(h_1,h_2) = D^2f(x_0)(h_2,h_1)$$

for all $(h_1,h_2) \in X \times X$. By induction one can define higher Fréchet derivatives with the Nth derivative $D^Nf(x_0) \in L^N(X,Y)$. If f is N times differentiable on U and $x \mapsto D^kf(x)$ is continuous for each $0 \le k \le N$, then $D^Nf(x_0)$ is symmetric.

A.1.2. Function spaces. If X and Y are Banach spaces and U is an open subset of X, the space $C^N(U,Y)$, $N \ge 0$, is the space of functions $f : U \to Y$ such that the jth derivative $D^jf(x)$ exists for each $x \in U$, $0 \le j \le N$, and the mapping $x \mapsto D^jf(x)$ of U into $L^j(X,Y)$ is continuous for each $x \in U$. If $f \in C^N(U,Y)$ for all integers $N \ge 0$, we say $f \in C^\infty(U,Y)$. For the maps from $C^N(U,Y)$ with uniformly bounded derivatives up to order N, we can use the norm

$$\|f\|_{C^N} = \sup_{x\in U}\left\{\|f(x)\|, \|Df(x)\|, \dots, \|D^Nf(x)\|\right\}.$$

The following lemma is encountered in the proof of the uniform contraction theorem below.

Lemma A.1. *Let X,Y be Banach spaces, and let U be an open set in X. Let g_n, $n \in \mathbb{N}$, be a sequence in $C^1(U,Y)$ that converges to $g \in C^0(U,Y)$ uniformly. Assume also that Dg_n in $C^0(U,L(X,Y))$ converges uniformly to $w \in C^0(U,L(X,Y))$. Then g_n converges to g in $C^1(U,V)$ and $Dg = w$.*

Proof. Write

$$g_n(x+h) = g_n(x) + \int_0^1 Dg_n(x+sh)h\,ds.$$

For $\|h\|$ small we have that Dg_n converges to w uniformly on $\{x+sh \ ; \ 0 \le s \le 1\}$. Taking the limit $n \to \infty$ we thus get

$$g(x+h) = g(x) + \int_0^1 w(x+sh)h\,ds.$$

Then

$$\begin{aligned}\|g(x+h)-g(x)-w(x)h\| &= \left\| \int_0^1 w(x+sh)h - w(x)h\,ds \right\| \\ &\le \int_0^1 \|w(x+sh)-w(x)\|\|h\|\,ds \\ &= o(\|h\|)\end{aligned}$$

as $\|h\| \to 0$. So $Dg = w$. □

Corollary A.2. *Let X, Y be Banach spaces, and let U be an open set in X. Let $k \geq 1$. Let g_n, $n \in \mathbb{N}$, be a sequence in $C^k(U,Y)$ that converges to g in $C^{k-1}(U,Y)$. Assume also that $D^k g_n$ converges in $C^0(U, L^k(X,Y))$ to $w \in C^0(U, L^k(X,Y))$. Then g_n converges to g in $C^k(U,V)$ and $D^k g = w$.*

Proof. Apply the theorem to $D^{k-1}g_n$ replacing g_n. □

For Banach spaces X, Y, and $0 < \varepsilon < 1$, write $C^{k,\varepsilon}(X,Y)$ for the space of C^k maps $f : X \to Y$, whose derivative of order k is (uniformly) ε-Hölder continuous:

$$\|D^k f(x_1) - D^k f(x_2)\| \le C\|x_1 - x_2\|^\varepsilon$$

for some $C > 0$. This is also defined for $\varepsilon = 1$, in which case the derivative of order k is (uniformly) Lipschitz continuous.

The following lemma, stating that a bounded closed ball in $C^{k,\varepsilon}(X,Y)$ gives a closed subset of $C^0(X,Y)$, can be found in [**158**, Lemma 6.1.6].

Lemma A.3. *Let X, Y be Banach spaces. Let $0 < \varepsilon \le 1$. For $k \ge 0$ and given positive constants $M_0, M_1, \ldots, M_k$ and M_{k+1}, let*

$$\begin{aligned}&B(M_0,\ldots,M_{k+1}) \\ &\quad = \Big\{ f \in C^{k,\varepsilon}(X,Y)\ ;\ \|f\| \le M_0, \|D^i f\| \le M_i, \\ &\qquad \|D^k f(x_1) - D^k f(x_2)\| \le M_{k+1}\|x_1 - x_2\|^\varepsilon, 1 \le i \le k, x_1, x_2 \in X \Big\}.\end{aligned}$$

Then $B(M_0,\ldots,M_{k+1})$ is closed in $C^0(X,Y)$.

Proof. The statement is clear for $k = 0$, that is, for Hölder continuous functions (if $0 < \varepsilon < 1$) or Lipschitz continuous functions (if $\varepsilon = 1$). Consider $k = 1$ and take a sequence of functions $f_n \in B(M_0, M_1, M_2)$ converging in $C^0(X,Y)$ to f. Using $g(x+h) - g(x) - Dg(x)h = \int_0^1 Dg(x+sh)h\,ds$ with $g = f_n - f_m$,

we can write

$$\begin{aligned}
&\|Df_n(x)h - Df_m(x)h\| \\
&\quad = \Big\| f_n(x+h) - f_m(x+h) - f_n(x) + f_m(x) \\
&\qquad - \int_0^1 Df_n(x+sh)h - Df_n(x)h - Df_m(x+sh)h + Df_m(x)h\, ds \Big\| \\
&\quad \le 2\|f_n - f_m\|_0 + \int_0^1 \|Df_n(x+sh)h - Df_n(x)\|\, \|h\|\, ds \\
&\qquad + \int_0^1 \|Df_m(x+sh)h - Df_m(x)\|\, \|h\|\, ds \\
&\quad \le 2\|f_n - f_m\|_0 + 2M_2 \int_0^1 s^\varepsilon \|h\|^{1+\varepsilon}\, ds \\
&\quad \le 2\|f_n - f_m\|_0 + 2M_2\|h\|^{1+\varepsilon}.
\end{aligned}$$

So

$$\|Df_n(x) - Df_m(x)\| \le \frac{2}{\|h\|}\|f_n - f_m\|_0 + 2M_2\|h\|^\varepsilon.$$

As this holds for all values of $\|h\|$,

$$\|Df_n(x) - Df_m(x)\| \le \min_{y\in\mathbb{R}} \left\{ \frac{2}{|y|}\|f_n - f_m\|_0 + 2M_2|y|^\varepsilon \right\}.$$

Plugging in the minimum value gives

$$\|Df_n(x) - Df_m(x)\| \le \frac{2}{(\varepsilon M_2)^{\varepsilon/(1+\varepsilon)}} \frac{1}{1+\varepsilon}\|f_n - f_m\|_0^{\varepsilon/(1+\varepsilon)}.$$

We conclude that Df_n is a Cauchy sequence. So Df_n converges uniformly and hence, by Lemma A.1, f_n converges to a C^1 function f. Clearly, $f \in B(M_0, M_1, M_2)$. Higher derivatives are handled by induction. □

The compact-open topology. An often used topology on $C^k(\mathbb{R}^n, \mathbb{R}^m)$, $0 \le k$, is the compact-open topology of convergence of all derivatives up to order k on compact sets. The topology is generated by open sets of the form

$$V_{f,K,i,\varepsilon} = \{g \in C^k(\mathbb{R}^n, \mathbb{R}^m) \;;\; \sup_{x\in K} \|D^i g(x) - D^i f(x)\| < \varepsilon\},$$

where $f \in C^k(\mathbb{R}^n, \mathbb{R}^m)$, $K \subset \mathbb{R}^n$ a compact set, $0 \le i \le k$, $\varepsilon > 0$ (here $D^0 f = f$). This topology is metrizable. For $0 \le i \le k$, write

$$d_{r,i}(f, g) = \sup_{\|x\|\le r} \|D^i g(x) - D^i f(x)\|.$$

A metric for the compact-open topology on $C^k(\mathbb{R}^n, \mathbb{R}^m)$ is

$$d_k(f, g) = \sum_{\substack{r\in\mathbb{N}, r>0 \\ 0\le i\le k}} \frac{1}{2^{r+i}} \frac{d_{r,i}(f, g)}{1 + d_{r,i}(f, g)}.$$

For $k = \infty$, on $C^\infty(\mathbb{R}^n, \mathbb{R}^m)$, there is the compact-open topology of convergence of all derivatives on compact sets. This topology is likewise generated by open sets

$$V_{f,K,i,\varepsilon} = \{g \in C^\infty(\mathbb{R}^n, \mathbb{R}^m) \,;\, \sup_{x\in K} \|D^i g(x) - D^i f(x)\| < \varepsilon\},$$

where $f \in C^\infty(\mathbb{R}^n, \mathbb{R}^m)$, $K \subset \mathbb{R}^n$ a compact set, $i \in \mathbb{N}$, $\varepsilon > 0$. A metric for the compact-open topology on $C^\infty(\mathbb{R}^n, \mathbb{R}^m)$ is

$$d_\infty(f, g) = \sum_{\substack{r\in\mathbb{N}, r>0 \\ i\in\mathbb{N}}} \frac{1}{2^{r+i}} \frac{d_{r,i}(f, g)}{1 + d_{r,i}(f, g)}.$$

A.1.3. Power series expansions. We start this part on the mean value theorem, Taylor's theorem, and Borel's theorem with an elementary lemma.

Lemma A.4. *Let $f \in C^\infty(\mathbb{R}^n, \mathbb{R})$ with $f(0) = 0$. Then there exist smooth functions $g_1, \ldots, g_n : \mathbb{R}^n \to \mathbb{R}$ such that $g_i(0) = \frac{\partial f}{\partial x_i}(0)$ for every i, and*

$$f(x_1, \ldots, x_n) = \sum_{i=1}^n x_i g_i(x_1, \ldots, x_n).$$

Proof. Consider the function $f(tx_1, \ldots, tx_n)$ with the parameter t. Compute

$$\begin{aligned} f(x_1, \ldots, x_n) &= \int_0^1 \frac{df}{dt}(tx_1, \ldots, tx_n)\, dt \\ &= \int_0^1 \sum_{i=1}^n x_i \frac{\partial f}{\partial x_i}(tx_1, \ldots, tx_n)\, dt. \end{aligned}$$

The lemma follows with $g_i(x_1, \ldots, x_n) = \int_0^1 \frac{\partial f}{\partial x_i}(tx_1, \ldots, tx_n)\, dt$. □

We formulate a mean value theorem for Banach space valued functions.

Theorem A.5 (Mean value theorem). *Let X, Y be Banach spaces, and let U be an open set in X. Let $f : U \to Y$ be continuously differentiable. If the line segment connecting x and $x + h$ is in U, then*

$$f(x + h) - f(x) = \left(\int_0^1 Df(x + sh)\, ds \right) h.$$

In particular,

$$\|f(x+h)-f(x)\| \leq \sup_{s\in(0,1)} \|Df(x+sh)\|\|h\|.$$

Proof. The theorem follows from $\frac{d}{ds}f(x+sh) = Df(x+sh)h$ together with the fundamental theorem of calculus; see [**218**]. □

We state Taylor's theorem; see for instance [**97**] or [**218**]. This generalizes the mean value theorem to higher-order approximations. The power series expansion obtained is called a Taylor expansion (of a given order). Write x^k for the k-tuple $(x,\dots,x)$ in order to simplify notation such as $D^2f(x)(h,h) = D^2f(x)h^2$.

Theorem A.6 (Taylor's theorem). *If* $f \in C^n(U,Y)$*, then*

$$f(x+h) = f(x) + Df(x)h + \cdots + \frac{1}{n!}D^nf(x)h^n + R_n(x,h)$$

for $x \in U$, $x+sh \in U$, $0 \leq s \leq 1$, *where*

$$R_n(x,h) = \frac{1}{(n-1)!}\int_0^1 (1-s)^{n-1}\left[D^nf(x+sh) - D^nf(x)\right]h^n\,ds$$

and $R_n(x,h) = o(\|h\|^n)$ *as* $\|h\| \to 0$.

In particular this yields expansions such as

$$f(x+h) = f(x) + \left(\int_0^1 Df(x+sh)\,ds\right)h,$$

$$f(x+h) = f(x) + Df(x)h + \left(\int_0^1 (1-s)D^2f(x+sh)\,ds\right)h^2,$$

and so forth, extending the mean value theorem with remainder terms of increasing order $\|h\|, \|h\|^2, \dots$. Assume $X, Y = \mathbb{R}^m$ and consider a Taylor expansion around the origin,

$$f(h) = f(0) + Df(0)h + \cdots + \frac{1}{n!}D^nf(0)h^n + R_n(0,h).$$

In coordinates $h = (h_1,\dots,h_m)$, $f = (f_1,\dots,f_m)$, and $x = (x_1,\dots,x_m)$, one has

$$(Df(0)h)_i = \sum_{j=1}^m \frac{\partial}{\partial x_j}f_i(0)h_j,$$

$$(D^2f(0)h^2)_i = \sum_{j,k=1}^m \frac{\partial^2}{\partial x_j\partial x_k}f_i(0)h_jh_k,$$

$$(D^3f(0)h^3)_i = \sum_{j,k,l=1}^m \frac{\partial^3}{\partial x_j\partial x_k\partial x_l}f_i(0)h_jh_kh_l,$$

and so on.

Borel's theorem states that any formal Taylor series occurs as the Taylor series of a C^∞ function. Note the contrast with real analytic functions, where convergence is required. We state the result for functions on $\mathbb{R}^n$; see [**212**, Theorem 15.4] for a version for maps between Banach spaces.

Theorem A.7 (Borel's theorem). *Given any sequence of symmetric multilinear maps $c_k \in L^k(\mathbb{R}^n, \mathbb{R})$, there exists a C^∞ function $f : \mathbb{R}^n \to \mathbb{R}$ with*

$$D^k f(0) = k!\, c_k.$$

A.1.4. Superposition operators. We discuss differentiability of superposition operators, operators acting on Banach spaces of, for instance, sequences with values in $\mathbb{R}^n$, defined by applying a map $f : \mathbb{R}^n \to \mathbb{R}^m$ to these sequences. The results are used to obtain smoothness of invariant manifolds, in particular stable, unstable, and center manifolds in Appendix B. They are also used in the analysis of Lin's method in Appendix C. Superposition operators are sometimes called Nemytskii operators. The reader may also consult the discussion of the Nemytskii operator in [**69**]. We provide the results that we need further on. We start with two similar theorems of which we prove the second one. The proof of the first result follows identical reasoning.

Theorem A.8. *Let $f : \mathbb{R}^n \to \mathbb{R}^m$ be C^1. Define*

$$F : C^0([0,1], \mathbb{R}^n) \to C^0([0,1], \mathbb{R}^m)$$

by $F(\phi)(t) = f(\phi(t))$. Then F is C^1.

Denote by $l^\infty(\mathbb{N}_0, \mathbb{R}^n)$ the space of bounded sequences $\phi : \mathbb{N}_0 \to \mathbb{R}^n$ equipped with the supremum norm $\|\phi\| = \sup_{n\geq 0} |\phi(n)|$.

Theorem A.9. *Let $f : \mathbb{R}^n \to \mathbb{R}^n$ be C^k, $k \geq 0$. Define*

$$F : l^\infty(\mathbb{N}_0, \mathbb{R}^n) \to l^\infty(\mathbb{N}_0, \mathbb{R}^n)$$

by $F(\phi)(n) = f(\phi(n))$. Then F is C^k.

Proof. It is clear that F is continuous. We will first show that F is C^1 if f is C^1. We claim that for $\phi \in l^\infty(\mathbb{N}_0, \mathbb{R}^n)$, $DF(\phi) \in L(l^\infty(\mathbb{N}_0, \mathbb{R}^n), l^\infty(\mathbb{N}_0, \mathbb{R}^n))$ is given by

$$DF(\phi)\psi(n) = Df(\phi(n))\psi(n).$$

Write $\mathcal{T}F(\phi, \psi) = Df(\phi)\psi$. By the mean value theorem,

$$\begin{aligned} &\|(F(\phi + \psi) - F(\phi) - \mathcal{T}F(\phi, \psi))(n)\| \\ &= |f(\phi(n) + \psi(n)) - f(\phi(n)) - Df(\phi(n))\psi(n)| \\ &\leq |Df(\xi(n)) - Df(\phi(n))||\psi(n)| \end{aligned}$$

for some $\xi(n)$ on the line piece in between $\phi(n)$ and $\phi(n) + \psi(n)$.

Since the closure of $\phi(\mathbb{N}_0)$ is compact, Df is uniformly continuous on $\phi(\mathbb{N}_0)$. For $\varepsilon > 0$, there exists $\delta > 0$ such that if $x_1 \in \phi(\mathbb{N}_0)$ and $|x_2 - x_1| < \delta$, then $|Df(x_2) - Df(x_1)| < \varepsilon$. Therefore, for $|\psi| < \delta$,

$$||(F(\phi+\psi) - F(\phi) - \mathcal{J}F(\phi,\psi))(n)|| \le \varepsilon|\psi(n)| \le \varepsilon||\psi||.$$

Taking the supremum over $n \in \mathbb{N}_0$, we get $||F(\phi+\psi) - F(\phi) - \mathcal{J}F(\phi,\psi)|| \le \varepsilon||\psi||$.

Finally we establish that $DF : l^\infty(\mathbb{N}_0, \mathbb{R}^n) \to L(l^\infty(\mathbb{N}_0,\mathbb{R}^n), l^\infty(\mathbb{N}_0,\mathbb{R}^n))$ is continuous. Let $\phi_1 \in l^\infty(\mathbb{N}_0,\mathbb{R}^n)$. We will show that DF is continuous at ϕ_1. Note that

$$(DF(\phi_2) - DF(\phi_1))\psi(n) = (Df(\phi_2(n)) - Df(\phi_1(n)))\psi(n).$$

Let E be a compact neighborhood of $\phi_1(\mathbb{N}_0)$. Let $\varepsilon > 0$. As above, there is $\delta > 0$ such that if $x_2, x_1 \in E$, $|x_2 - x_1| < \delta$, then $|Df(x_2) - Df(x_1)| < \varepsilon$. Then, if $||\phi_2 - \phi_1|| < \delta$,

$$\begin{aligned}||(DF(\phi_2) - DF(\phi_1))\psi(n)|| &\le |Df(\phi_2(n)) - Df(\phi_1(n))||\psi(n)| \\ &\le \varepsilon||\psi||.\end{aligned}$$

Taking the supremum over $n \in \mathbb{N}_0$, we get $||(DF(\phi_2) - DF(\phi_1))\psi|| \le \varepsilon||\psi||$. Therefore $||DF(\phi_2) - DF(\phi_1)|| \le \varepsilon$ when $||\phi_2 - \phi_1|| < \delta$. Since ε is arbitrary, this shows that DF is continuous at ϕ_1.

Higher differentiability is by an induction argument. Suppose f is C^k, $k > 1$, so $D^{k-1}f : \mathbb{R}^n \to L^{k-1}(\mathbb{R}^n, \mathbb{R}^m)$ is C^1. By induction F is C^{k-1}, so $D^{k-1}F$ is continuous. The above argument shows that $D^{k-1}F$ is C^1 and so F is C^k. □

For $\eta > 0$, let $l^{\infty,\eta}(\mathbb{N}_0, \mathbb{R}^n)$ be the space of sequences $\mathbb{N}_0 \to \mathbb{R}^n$ with

$$||\gamma||_\eta = \sup_{n\in\mathbb{N}_0} \eta^{-n}|\gamma_n| < \infty$$

and it is equipped with the norm $||\cdot||_\eta$. Note $l^{\infty,\eta'}(\mathbb{N}_0,\mathbb{R}^n) \subset l^{\infty,\eta}(\mathbb{N}_0,\mathbb{R}^n)$ for $0 < \eta' < \eta$. Moreover, $||\gamma||_\eta \le ||\gamma||_{\eta'}$ for $\gamma \in l^{\infty,\eta'}(\mathbb{N}_0,\mathbb{R}^n)$, so that this is a continuous embedding.

Theorem A.10. *Let $f : \mathbb{R}^n \to \mathbb{R}^m$ be C^k. Assume $D^i f$, $1 \le i \le k$, are bounded. For $\eta > 1$, assume that the formula $F(\phi)(n) = f(\phi(n))$ defines a map $F : l^{\infty,\eta}(\mathbb{N}_0,\mathbb{R}^n) \to l^{\infty,\eta}(\mathbb{N}_0,\mathbb{R}^m)$. Then F is continuous. If $1 < \eta' < \eta$ satisfies $(\eta')^k < \eta$, then $F : l^{\infty,\eta'}(\mathbb{N}_0,\mathbb{R}^n) \to l^{\infty,\eta}(\mathbb{N}_0,\mathbb{R}^m)$ is C^k.*

Proof. We abbreviate $l^{\infty,\eta}(\mathbb{N}_0,\mathbb{R}^m)$ by $l^{\infty,\eta}$ and $l^{\infty,\eta'}(\mathbb{N}_0,\mathbb{R}^n)$ by $l^{\infty,\eta'}$. We follow the proof of Theorem A.9 and adapt where needed.

As f is uniformly Lipschitz continuous, we have $\|F(\phi + \psi) - F(\phi)\|_\eta \leq L\|\psi\|_\eta$ for some $L > 0$, implying continuity of F. By the mean value theorem,

$$|f(\phi(n) + \psi(n)) - f(\phi(n)) - Df(\phi(n))\psi(n)| \leq \int_0^1 |Df(\phi(n) + s\psi(n)) - Df(\phi(n))|\, ds|\psi(n)|.$$

Write $\mathcal{T}F(\phi,\psi)(n) = Df(\phi(n))\psi(n)$. Let $[0,\psi(n)]$ denote the line segment between 0 and $\psi(n)$ and estimate

$$\begin{aligned}
&\|F(\phi + \psi) - F(\phi) - \mathcal{T}F(\phi,\psi)\|_\eta \\
&\quad = \sup_{n\in\mathbb{N}_0} \eta^{-n}|f(\phi(n) + \psi(n)) - f(\phi(n)) - Df(\phi(n))\psi(n)| \\
&\quad \leq \sup_{n\in\mathbb{N}_0} \sup_{y\in[0,\psi(n)]} \eta^{-n}|Df(\phi(n) + y) - Df(\phi(n))||\psi(n)| \\
&\quad \leq \sup_{n\in\mathbb{N}_0} \sup_{y\in[0,\psi(n)]} \eta^{-n}(\eta')^n|Df(\phi(n) + y) - Df(\phi(n))|\|\psi\|_{\eta'}.
\end{aligned}$$

Using that Df is bounded, we will have the following statement. For any $\varepsilon > 0$ there is $\delta > 0$ so that $\|\psi\|_{\eta'} < \delta$ implies

$$\sup_{n\in\mathbb{N}_0} \sup_{y\in[0,\psi(n)]} \eta^{-n}(\eta')^n|Df(\phi(n) + y) - Df(\phi(n))| < \varepsilon.$$

Using this claim in the above estimate implies that $DF(\phi)\psi = \mathcal{T}F(\phi,\psi)$.

To get the claim, fix $\varepsilon > 0$. Since Df is bounded, we can take N such that

$$(\eta'/\eta)^n \sup_{x,y} |Df(x + y) - Df(x)| < \varepsilon \tag{A.1}$$

for $n > N$. Then note that Df restricted to a ball of radius R is uniformly continuous. As $\|\phi\|_\eta < \infty$, there exists $R \geq 0$ so that $|\phi(n)| \leq R$ for $n \leq N$. If $\|\psi\|_{\eta'}$ is small, also $\max_{0\leq i\leq N} |\psi(i)|$ is small. Therefore, there is $\delta > 0$ so that for $\|\psi\|_{\eta'} < \delta$,

$$\sup_{n\leq N} \sup_{y\in[0,\psi(n)]} (\eta'/\eta)^n|Df(\phi(n) + y) - Df(\phi(n))| < \varepsilon. \tag{A.2}$$

Estimates (A.2) and (A.1) together prove the claim. Continuity of $DF(x)$ with x follows similarly; compare the proof of Theorem A.9.

Higher differentiability is treated by an induction argument. Suppose f is C^k. By induction, F is C^{k-1}. To prove that F is C^k, we will show

$$\|D^{k-1}F(\phi + \psi) - D^{k-1}F(\phi) - \mathcal{T}^kF(\phi,\psi)\| = o(\|\psi\|_{\eta'})$$

in $L^{k-1}(l^{\infty,\eta'}, l^{\infty,\eta})$, with $\mathcal{J}^k F(\phi,\psi)(n) = D^k f(\phi(n))(\psi(n),\cdot)$. This follows from the following estimates, in which $\chi = (\chi_1,\ldots,\chi_{k-1}) \in \left(l^{\infty,\eta'}\right)^{k-1}$:

$$\frac{1}{\eta^n}\left|\left(D^{k-1}f(\phi(n)+\psi(n)) - D^{k-1}f(\phi(n))\right)\chi(n) - D^k f(\phi(n))(\psi(n),\chi(n))\right|$$
$$\leq \frac{1}{\eta^n}\sup_{y\in[0,\psi(n)]}\left|D^k f(\phi(n)+y) - D^k f(\phi(n))\right| |\psi(n)||\chi_1(n)|\cdots|\chi_{k-1}(n)|$$
$$\leq \frac{(\eta')^{kn}}{\eta^n}\sup_{y\in[0,\psi(n)]}\left|D^k f(\phi(n)+y) - D^k f(\phi(n))\right| \|\psi\|_{\eta'}\|\chi_1\|_{\eta'}\cdots\|\chi_{k-1}\|_{\eta'}.$$

□

Example A.11. This example comes from [47]. Consider a smooth function $g : \mathbb{R} \to \mathbb{R}$ with $g(x) = x^2$ for $x \leq \varepsilon$ and $g(x) = 0$ for $x \geq 2\varepsilon$. For $\eta > 1$, let $l^{\infty,\eta}(\mathbb{N}_0,\mathbb{R}^m)$ be the space of sequences $y : \mathbb{N}_0 \to \mathbb{R}$, with $\sup_{n\in\mathbb{N}_0}|y(n)|/\eta^n < \infty$ and it is endowed with the norm

$$\|y\|_\eta = \sup_{n\in\mathbb{N}_0}|y(n)|/\eta^n.$$

Consider the superposition operator $G : l^{\infty,\eta}(\mathbb{N}_0,\mathbb{R})$ given by

$$G(y)(n) = g(y(n)).$$

We claim that $DG(0)$ does not exist. If it did, it would be equal to zero. However, if we take sequences $y_m(n) = 0$ for $n \neq m$ and $y_m(m) = \varepsilon$, then $\|y_m\|_\eta$ goes to zero as $m \to \infty$ and

$$\|G(y_m) - G(0)\|_\eta/\|y_m\|_\eta = (\varepsilon^2/\eta^m)/(\varepsilon/\eta^m) = \varepsilon.$$

This shows that $DG(0)$ does not exist.

Now consider $1 < \eta' < \eta$, note that $l^{\infty,\eta'} \subset l^{\infty,\eta}$ and consider $G : l^{\infty,\eta'} \to l^{\infty,\eta}$. Then a similar calculation shows

$$\|G(y_m) - G(0)\|_\eta/\|y_m\|_{\eta'} = (\varepsilon^2/\eta^m)/(\varepsilon/\eta'^m) = \varepsilon(\eta/\eta')^m,$$

which goes to zero. This indicates that $DG(0) = 0$. Theorem A.10 confirms differentiability of G. ■

A.2. Uniform contractions and the implicit function theorem

A contraction has a global attracting fixed point. For contractions depending on a parameter one wishes to know the dependence of the fixed point on the parameter. This can be done for uniform contractions where the contraction rate is uniform in the parameter. The implicit function theorem is used to find local solutions to equations. Under the conditions of the implicit function theorem the equation to be solved can be rewritten as a fixed point problem for a uniform contraction.

A.2.1. Uniform contractions. Recall that a continuous map $T : S \to S$ on a metric space is a contraction if, for some $0 < \lambda < 1$,

$$d(T(x), T(y)) \leq \lambda d(x, y)$$

for all $x, y \in S$. The following theorem is also known as the Banach fixed point theorem.

Theorem A.12 (Contraction mapping theorem). *Let (S, d) be a complete metric space, and let $T : S \to S$ be a contraction. Then there is a unique fixed point $\bar{x}$ in S. Moreover, for any $x_0 \in S$, $T^n(x_0) \to \bar{x}$ as $n \to \infty$.*

Proof. If $x = T(x)$ and $y = T(y)$ are fixed points, then

$$d(x, y) = d(T(x), T(y)) \leq \lambda d(x, y)$$

shows that $x = y$: the fixed point is unique if it exists.

Take any $x_0 \in S$. Then, for $n \geq 1$

$$d(T^{n+1}(x_0), T^n(x_0)) \leq \lambda d(T^n(x_0), T^{n-1}(x_0)) \leq \cdots \leq \lambda^n d(T(x_0), x_0).$$

So, for $m > n > 0$,

$$\begin{aligned}
&d(T^m(x_0), T^n(x_0)) \\
&\quad \leq d(T^m(x_0), T^{m-1}(x_0)) + \cdots + d(T^{n+1}(x_0), T^n(x_0)) \\
&\quad \leq (\lambda^{m-1} + \cdots + \lambda^n) d(T(x_0), x_0) \\
&\quad \leq \frac{\lambda^n}{1-\lambda} d(T(x_0), x_0).
\end{aligned}$$

The sequence $\{T^n(x_0)\}$ is therefore a Cauchy sequence. Since S is complete, it converges to a point $\bar{x} \in S$ as $n \to \infty$. Also,

$$d(T(\bar{x}), \bar{x}) = \lim_{n \to \infty} d(T^{m+1}(x_0), T^m(x_0)) = 0,$$

so that $T(\bar{x}) = \bar{x}$. □

To treat dependence of the fixed point on parameters, consider a metric space (S, d), a set A, and a map $T : S \times A \to S$. We say that T is a uniform contraction if it is continuous and there is $0 < \lambda < 1$ with

$$d(T(x, a), T(y, a) \leq \lambda d(x, y)$$

for all $x, y \in S$, $a \in A$. The following lemma states continuous dependence of the fixed point of a uniform contraction on a parameter.

Lemma A.13. *Let (S, d) be a complete metric space, let A be a metric space, and suppose $T : S \times A \to S$ is a uniform contraction. Then for each $a \in A$ the map $T(\cdot, a)$ has a unique fixed point $x_a \in S$, and x_a depends continuously on a.*

Proof. Take $a_0 \in S$ and consider

$$\begin{aligned} d(x_a, x_{a_0}) &= d(T(x_a, a), T(x_{a_0}, a_0)) \\ &\leq d(T(x_a, a), T(x_a, a_0)) + d(T(x_a, a_0), T(x_{a_0}, a_0)) \\ &\leq d(T(x_a, a), T(x_a, a_0)) + \lambda d(x_a, x_{a_0}). \end{aligned}$$

Hence $d(x_a, x_{a_0}) \leq (1-\lambda)^{-1} d(T(x_a, a), T(x_a, a_0)) \to 0$ as $a \to a_0$. □

The following result is a form of the fiber contraction theorem. The result implies that a map of the form $(x, y) \mapsto (T(x, y), g(y))$ admits a globally attracting fixed point, if T is a uniform contraction and g has a globally attracting fixed point.

Theorem A.14 (Fiber contraction theorem). *Let U, V be open sets in Banach spaces X, Y, and let $T : \bar{U} \times V \to \bar{U}$ be a uniform contraction on $\bar{U}$. Let $g(y)$ be the fixed point of $T(\cdot, y)$ in $\bar{U}$. Consider a converging sequence $y_i \to \hat{y}$, $i \geq 0$, in V. Then for any $x_0 \in \bar{U}$ the iterates $x_{i+1} = T(x_i, y_i)$ converge to $g(\hat{y})$.*

Proof. Note that $d_i = \|T(g(\hat{y}), y_i) - T(g(\hat{y}), \hat{y})\|$ goes to zero as $i \to \infty$. Since T is a uniform contraction,

$$\begin{aligned} \|x_{i+1} - g(\hat{y})\| &= \|T(x_i, y_i) - T(g(\hat{y}), \hat{y})\| \\ &\leq \|T(x_i, y_i) - T(g(\hat{y}), y_i)\| + \|T(g(\hat{y}), y_i) - T(g(\hat{y}), \hat{y})\| \\ &\leq \lambda \|x_i - g(\hat{y})\| + d_i \end{aligned}$$

with $0 < \lambda < 1$. Hence

$$\|x_i - g(\hat{y})\| \leq \lambda^i \|x_0 - g(\hat{y})\| + \sum_{j=0}^{i-1} \lambda^{i-1-j} d_j.$$

Since $d_j \to 0$ as $j \to \infty$, we find for any $\varepsilon > 0$ a number $N \in \mathbb{N}$ so that $d_j < \varepsilon$ for $j > N$. Now for $i > N$,

$$\begin{aligned} \sum_{j=0}^{i-1} \lambda^{i-1-j} d_j &< \sum_{j=0}^{N-1} \lambda^{i-1-j} d_j + \sum_{j=N}^{i-1} \lambda^{i-1-j} \varepsilon \\ &< \frac{\lambda^{i-N}}{1-\lambda} \sup_{j \geq 0} d_j + \frac{1}{1-\lambda} \varepsilon, \end{aligned}$$

from which we get that $x_i \to g(\hat{y})$ as $i \to \infty$. □

Remark A.15. To find convergence in the above theorem of the iterates $x_{i+1} = T(x_i, y_i)$ to $g(\hat{y})$, it suffices to demand the following conditions: take a map

$T : \bar{U} \times V \to \bar{U}$ as above but not necessarily continuous in y, and assume

(i) There exists $0 < \lambda < 1$ with $\|T(x,y) - T(\hat{x},y)\| \leq \lambda\|x - \hat{x}\|$ for all $y \in V$;

(ii) $\lim_{i\to\infty} T(g(\hat{y}), y_i) = T(g(\hat{y}), \hat{y})$.

This follows directly from the above proof. The last condition is fulfilled if $y \mapsto T(g(\hat{y}), y)$ is continuous at $\hat{y}$. Such a formulation is also found in [**404**]. The fiber contraction theorem under these conditions will be applied in the proof of the center manifold theorem. ■

The next theorem is the uniform contraction theorem which discusses smooth dependence of the fixed point of a uniform contraction on parameters.

Theorem A.16 (Uniform contraction theorem). *Let U, V be open sets in Banach spaces X, Y, and let $T : \bar{U} \times V \to \bar{U}$ be a uniform contraction on $\bar{U}$. Let $g(y)$ be the fixed point of $T(\cdot, y)$ in $\bar{U}$. If $T \in C^k(\bar{U} \times V, X)$, $0 \leq k < \infty$, then $g \in C^k(V, X)$.*

Proof. Take $g_0 \equiv x_0$ for some $x_0 \in \bar{U}$ and define recursively

$$g_{i+1}(y) = T(g_i(y), y).$$

From the contraction mapping theorem we know that $g_i(y)$ converges to $g(y)$ as $i \to \infty$. Now

$$\begin{aligned} &\|g_{i+1}(y+h) - g_{i+1}(y)\| \\ &\quad = \|T(g_i(y+h), y+h) - T(g_i(y), y)\| \\ &\quad \leq \lambda\|g_i(y+h) - g_i(y)\| + \|T(g_i(y), y+h) - T(g_i(y), y)\|. \end{aligned} \tag{A.3}$$

As $g_i(y)$ converges we have for all $i \in \mathbb{N}$ and for all $\varepsilon > 0$, that there is $\delta > 0$ with $\|T(g_i(y), y+h) - T(g_i(y), y)\| < \varepsilon$ if $\|h\| < \delta$. From (A.3) it now follows that for all $i \in \mathbb{N}$,

$$\|g_i(y+h) - g_i(y)\| \leq \frac{1}{1-\lambda}\varepsilon.$$

Taking the limit $i \to \infty$, we find that $\|g(y+h) - g(y)\| \leq \frac{1}{1-\lambda}\varepsilon$. Thus g_i converges to g in $C^0(V, X)$.

Assume that T is continuously differentiable. Let $w_i = Dg_i$ so that

$$w_{i+1}(y) = D_xT(g_i(y), y)w_i(y) + D_yT(g_i(y), y).$$

Since $\|T(x_1, y) - T(x_2, y)\| \leq \lambda\|x_1 - x_2\|$ for all $x_1, x_2 \in U$, $y \in V$, it follows that $\|D_xT(x,y)\| \leq \lambda < 1$ for $(x,y) \in U \times V$. By Theorem A.14, $w_i(y)$ converges as $i \to \infty$. Now

$$\begin{aligned}
&\|w_{i+1}(y+h) - w_{i+1}(y)\| \\
&\quad \le \|D_xT(g_i(y+h), y+h)w_i(y+h) - D_xT(g_i(y),y)w_i(y)\| \\
&\qquad + \|D_yT(g_i(y+h), y+h) - D_yT(g_i(y),y)\| \\
&\quad \le \|D_xT(g_i(y+h), y+h)\|\|w_i(y+h) - w_i(y)\| \\
&\qquad + \|D_xT(g_i(y+h), y+h) - D_xT(g_i(y),y)\|\|w_i(y)\| \\
&\qquad + \|D_yT(g_i(y+h), y+h) - D_yT(g_i(y),y)\| \\
&\quad \le \lambda\|w_i(y+h) - w_i(y)\| \\
&\qquad + \|D_xT(g_i(y+h), y+h) - D_xT(g_i(y),y)\|\|w_i(y)\| \\
&\qquad + \|D_yT(g_i(y+h), y+h) - D_yT(g_i(y),y)\|.
\end{aligned}$$

As $g_i(y)$ and $w_i(y)$ converge we have for all $i \in \mathbb{N}$ and for all $\varepsilon > 0$, that there is $\delta > 0$ with $\|D_xT(g_i(y+h), y+h) - D_xT(g_i(y),y)\|\|w_i(y)\| + \|D_yT(g_i(y+h), y+h) - D_yT(g_i(y),y)\| < \varepsilon$ if $\|h\| < \delta$. From this we see, as above, that w_i converges in $C^0(V, L(Y,X))$. Lemma A.1 implies that g_i converges to g in $C^1(V,X)$.

Suppose the result holds for $k-1$ and $k > 1$. Thus, if T is C^k, then g is C^{k-1} at least and the fact that $Dg(y)$ satisfies

$$M - D_xT(g(y),y)M = D_yT(g(y),y),$$

implies that g is C^k. □

A.2.2. Implicit function theorem. The implicit function theorem is an essential tool to find solutions to equations and a central tool in bifurcation theory. The history of the theorem is described in [**210**]. A version on Banach spaces that we will also make use of was developed in [**159**]. The implicit function theorem can be obtained as a corollary of the uniform contraction theorem. We follow the exposition in [**69**].

Theorem A.17 (Implicit function theorem). *Suppose that X, Y, Z are Banach spaces, that $U \subset X, V \subset Y$ are open, and that $F : U \times V \to Z$ is a C^k map, $k \ge 1$. Assume $F(x_0, y_0) = 0$ for some $(x_0, y_0) \in U \times V$ and $D_xF(x_0, y_0)$ has bounded inverse. Then there is a neighborhood $U_1 \times V_1 \subset U \times V$ of (x_0, y_0) and a C^k function $f : V_1 \to U_1$, $f(y_0) = x_0$ so that $F(x,y) = 0$ for $(x,y) \in U_1 \times V_1$ if and only if $x = f(y)$.*

Proof. If $L = (D_xF(x_0, y_0))^{-1}$, $G(x,y) = x - LF(x,y)$, then the fixed points of G are solutions of $F = 0$. The function G has the same smoothness properties as F, $G(x_0, y_0) = x_0$, $D_xG(x_0, y_0) = 0$. Therefore, $\|D_xG(x,y)\| \le \theta < 1$ for all x, y in a neighborhood $U_1 \times V_1$ of (x_0, y_0). One can choose this neighborhood so that $G : U_1 \times V_1 \to U_1$. The result now follows from the uniform contraction theorem. □

Remark A.18. The proof also gives the following formulation of the implicit function theorem from [**36**, Section 3.1B]. In the context of the theorem, assume $F : U \times V \to Z$ is a C^0 map with $F(x_0, y_0) = 0$ for some $(x_0, y_0) \in U \times V$. Assume that $D_x F(x, y) \in L(X, Z)$ exists and is continuous in y.

Then there is a neighborhood $U_1 \times V_1 \subset U \times V$ of (x_0, y_0) and a C^0 function $f : V_1 \to U_1$, $f(y_0) = x_0$ so that $F(x, y) = 0$ for $(x, y) \in U_1 \times V_1$ if and only if $x = f(y)$. ■

The following example discusses finding equilibria of families of differential equations using the implicit function theorem.

Example A.19. Consider a family of differential equations $\dot{x} = f_\lambda(x)$, $x \in \mathbb{R}^n$, $\lambda \in \mathbb{R}^m$. Let x_0 be an equilibrium for $\lambda = \lambda_0$. Suppose $Df_{\lambda_0}(x_0)$ has no eigenvalue 0. Then there exist a neighborhood U of x_0 and $\varepsilon > 0$ so that for any λ with $|\lambda - \lambda_0| < \varepsilon$, f_λ has a unique equilibrium in U. This statement is proved by the implicit function theorem. Indeed, the equation $f_\lambda(x) = 0$ can be solved near (λ_0, x_0) for $x = \bar{\lambda}$ with $\bar{x}(\lambda_0) = x_0$ since $Df_{\lambda_0}(x_0)$ is invertible.

An application of the implicit function theorem yields the following similar statement. Let x_0 be an equilibrium of a differential equation $\dot{x} = f(x)$ on $\mathbb{R}^n$. Suppose $Df(x_0)$ has no eigenvalue 0. Then there exist a neighborhood U of x_0 and $\varepsilon > 0$ so that any $g : \mathbb{R}^n \to \mathbb{R}^n$ with $\sup_{\in \mathbb{R}^n} |g(x) - f(x)|$, $|Dg(x) - Df(x)| < \varepsilon$ has a unique equilibrium in U. To obtain this statement, consider the equation $F(g, x) = g(x) = 0$ for $F : \mathbb{R}^n \times C^1(\mathbb{R}^n, \mathbb{R}^n) \to \mathbb{R}^n$ and note that F is continuously differentiable and that $D_x F(f, x_0) = Df(x_0)$ is invertible. The implicit function can thus be applied to yield the statement, as above for the family f_λ. ■

Following [**302**], we use the version of the implicit function theorem presented in Remark A.18 to prove the existence and uniqueness theorem for ordinary differential equations. We include parameter dependence. Suppose Λ is a Banach space, $\Omega \subset \mathbb{R} \times \mathbb{R}^n$, $G \subset \Lambda$ are open sets, $f : \Omega \times G$ is continuous, $D_x f(t, x, \lambda)$ is continuous for $(t, x) \in \Omega$, $\lambda \in \Lambda$, and consider the initial value problem

$$\dot{x} = f(t, x, \lambda), \qquad x(\sigma) = \xi, \tag{A.4}$$

where $(\sigma, \xi) \in \Omega$.

Theorem A.20. *Under the above hypotheses, there is a solution $x(\sigma, \xi, \lambda)(t)$ of (A.4) which is unique and continuous in $(\sigma, \xi, \lambda, t)$ in its domain of definition. If $f \in C^k(\Omega \times G, \mathbb{R}^n)$, then $x(\sigma, \xi, \lambda)(t)$ is C^k in $(\sigma, \xi, \lambda, t)$ in its domain of definition.*

Proof. If x is a solution of (A.4) on $[\sigma-\alpha,\sigma+\alpha]$, $t-\sigma=\alpha\tau$, $z(\tau)=x(\alpha\tau+\sigma)-\xi$, then z must satisfy

$$\frac{dz(\tau)}{d\tau}-\alpha f(\alpha\tau+\sigma,\xi+z,\lambda)=0,$$
$$z(0)=0,$$

and conversely. Let

$$X=\{\phi\in C^1([-1,1],\mathbb{R}^n)\ ;\ \phi(0)=0\},$$
$$Y=C^0([-1,1],\mathbb{R}^n),$$

and let $F:\mathbb{R}\times\mathbb{R}\times\Lambda\times X\to Y$ be given by

$$F(\alpha,\sigma,\xi,\lambda,\phi)(\tau)=\frac{d\phi(\tau)}{d\tau}-\alpha f(\alpha\tau+\sigma,\xi+\phi,\lambda),$$

$\tau\in[-1,1]$. Then $F(0,\sigma_0,\xi_0,\lambda_0,0)=0$ and $D_\phi F(0,\sigma_0,\xi_0,\lambda_0,0)\psi=d\psi/d\tau$ for any $(\sigma_0,\xi_0,\lambda_0)$. If $\psi\in X$, $d\psi/d\tau=y\in Y$, then $\psi(\tau)=\int_0^\tau y(s)ds$ and ψ is continuous and linear in y. The implicit function theorem implies the existence of a unique solution $\phi^*(\alpha,\sigma,\xi,\lambda)$ of $F(\alpha,\sigma,\xi,\lambda,\phi)=0$ in a neighborhood of $(0,\sigma_0,\xi_0,\lambda_0,0)$, and this function has the same smoothness properties as f. This proves the theorem locally. The global theorem is obtained by the process of continuation. □

Example A.21. Consider a smooth map $f:\mathbb{R}^n\times\mathbb{R}^m\to\mathbb{R}^n$ and an equation $f(x,y)=0$. Assume that for some small $\varepsilon>0$, $f(x,y)=Ax+R(x,y)$ with A invertible and $\sup_{(x,y)\in\mathbb{R}^n\times\mathbb{R}^m}|R(x,y)|,|DR(x,y)|<\varepsilon$. In other words, f is globally C^1-close to an invertible linear map. To solve $f(x,y)=0$, rewrite it as $G(x,y)=x$ with $G(x,y)=x-A^{-1}f(x,y)$. Note that for ε small enough, $G:\mathbb{R}^n\times\mathbb{R}^m\to\mathbb{R}^n$ is a uniform contraction, uniform for $y\in\mathbb{R}^m$. One can therefore, if ε is sufficiently small, solve the equation $f(x,y)=0$ with a smooth function $\hat{x}:\mathbb{R}^m\to\mathbb{R}^n$; $f(\hat{x}(y),y)=0$. ■

A.2.3. Lyapunov-Schmidt reduction. The Lyapunov-Schmidt reduction is a way to solve, from a set of equations, a subset of equations by the implicit function theorem to be left with a smaller set of equations to be studied by other means. We follow the exposition in [**69**]. We refer also to [**202**] for the theory and for its use in bifurcation theory, in particular in infinite dimensional settings. Let us start with a motivating example.

Example A.22. Consider the equation

$$y^2-\lambda-f(\lambda,y,z)=0,$$
$$Bz-g(\lambda,y,z)=0,$$

where $\lambda\in\mathbb{R}$, $y\in\mathbb{R}$, $z\in\mathbb{R}^{n-1}$, B a nonsingular matrix, $f=O(|y|^3+|yz|+|z|^2)$, $g=O(|y|^2+|z|^2)$ as $|y|,|z|\to 0$, $|\lambda|<\lambda_0$. For λ,y,z small, the second equation has a unique solution $z = z^*(\lambda, y)$, $z^*(\lambda, y) = O(|y|^2)$ as $y \to 0$. Putting this into the first equation gives

$$y^2 - \lambda - f(\lambda, y, z^*(\lambda, y)) = 0$$

and $f(\lambda, y, z^*(\lambda, y)) = O(|y|^3)$ as $|y| \to 0$, $|\lambda| < \lambda_0$. This equation arises in the study of the saddle-node bifurcation; see Section 3.2.1. ■

In spite of the simplicity of this example, its method can be systematically generalized to equations with multidimensional state space coordinates and parameters. We develop the theory for equations on Euclidean spaces only, but it applies likewise to equations on Banach spaces. Let $A : \mathbb{R}^n \to \mathbb{R}^n$ be a linear map, and let $N : \mathbb{R}^n \to \mathbb{R}^n$ be a map with $N(0) = 0$ and $DN(0) = 0$. The problem is to determine the solutions of the equation

$$Ax - N(x) = 0 \tag{A.5}$$

for $x \in X$.

The null space of A is denoted by $\mathcal{N}(A)$, the range by $\mathcal{R}(A)$. Let $Q : \mathbb{R}^n \to \mathcal{N}(A)$ be a projection to the kernel of A. Let $P : \mathbb{R}^n \to \mathcal{R}(A)$ be a projection to the range of A.

Lemma A.23. *There is a linear map $K : \mathcal{R}(A) \to \mathcal{R}(A)$, called the right inverse of A, such that $AK = I$ on $\mathcal{R}(A)$, $KA = I - Q$ on $\mathbb{R}^n$ and* (A.5) *is equivalent to the equation*

$$z - KPN(y + z) = 0, \tag{A.6}$$

$$(I - P)N(y + z) = 0, \tag{A.7}$$

where $y \in \mathcal{N}(A)$, $z \in (I - Q)\mathbb{R}^n$ and $x = y + z$.

Proof. The map A is one-to-one from $(I-Q)\mathbb{R}^n$ onto $\mathcal{R}(A)$. Thus, the existence of a right inverse is clear. Equation (A.5) is equivalent to

$$P(A - N)(y + z) = 0,$$
$$(I - P)(A - N)(y + z) = 0.$$

The second equation gives $(I-P)N(y+z) = (I-P)A(y+z)$. Since $(I-P)A = 0$, this yields (A.7). The first equation gives $PA(y + z) = PN(y + z)$. As $PA = A$ and $KA(y + z) = (I - Q)(y + z) = z$, this yields (A.6). □

If it is possible to find a solution $z^*(y)$ for (A.6), then (A.5) is equivalent to

$$(I - P)N(y + z^*(y)) = 0.$$

In bifurcation theory this reduction method often arises in the following context. For parameters $\lambda \in \Lambda$, assume that for $N : \mathbb{R}^n \times \Lambda \to \mathbb{R}^n$ we have

$$N(0, 0) = 0, \ D_xN(0, 0) = 0.$$

Consider the equation

$$Ax - N(x, \lambda) = 0 \tag{A.8}$$

for (x, λ) near $(0, 0)$. This equation is equivalent to

$$\begin{aligned} z - KPN(y + z, \lambda) &= 0, \\ (I - P)N(y + z, \lambda) &= 0 \end{aligned} \tag{A.9}$$

for $x = y + z$ with $y \in \mathcal{N}(A), z \in (I - Q)\mathbb{R}^n$. Apply the implicit function theorem to the first equation of (A.9). This provides a neighborhood $V \subset \mathcal{N}(A) \times \Lambda$ of $(0, 0)$ and a function $z^* : V \to (I - Q)\mathbb{R}^n$, $z^*(0, 0) = 0$, such that $z^*(y, \lambda)$ satisfies the first equation of (A.9) and is the only solution in a neighborhood of 0. Thus (A.8) has a solution near $(x, \lambda) = (0, 0)$ if and only if $(y, \lambda) \in V$ satisfy the reduced bifurcation equations

$$(I - P)N(y + z^*(y, \lambda), \lambda) = 0.$$

This method to obtain reduced bifurcation equations is called the Lyapunov-Schmidt reduction.

A.3. Manifolds and transversality

We recall the notions of manifold and transverse intersection, and state Sard's theorem on the set of singular values of maps. For a more detailed introduction to the theory of manifolds and vector fields on manifolds, we refer to [**45**]. This is also the starting point of further global results including Thom's transversality theorem, which we do not include, but see for instance [**123**], [**4**], or [**362**].

A.3.1. Manifolds.

Definition A.24. Let $U \subset \mathbb{R}^n$ open, and let $f \in C^1(U, \mathbb{R}^k)$. A point $x \in U$ is called a *regular point* for f if $Df(x) : \mathbb{R}^n \to \mathbb{R}^k$ is surjective. A point $x \in U$ is called a *singular point* for f if x is not a regular point, so if $\operatorname{rank} Df(x) < k$. A point $y \in Z$ is called a *regular value* for f if each point in $f^{-1}(y)$ is a regular point. Otherwise it is called a *singular value*. Instead of singular point or singular value, also the terms *critical point* and *critical value* are used.

A set $M \subset \mathbb{R}^n$ is said to be a C^r-manifold of dimension m if, for each $x \in M$, there is an open neighborhood U of x and a map $F \in C^r(U, \mathbb{R}^{n-m})$ which is regular at each point of U and $M \cap U = \{x \in U\ ;\ F(x) = 0\}$. We call $n - m$ the codimension of M.

Theorem A.25. *A C^r-manifold of dimension m in $\mathbb{R}^n$ is locally the graph of a C^r map. More precisely, one can express $\mathbb{R}^n$ as the product $\mathbb{R}^m \times \mathbb{R}^{n-m}$ so that, if $x = (u, v)$, $u \in \mathbb{R}^m$, $v \in \mathbb{R}^{n-m}$, and $x_0 = (u_0, v_0) \in M$, then there is a neighborhood U of x_0, a neighborhood V of u_0, and $f \in C^r(V, \mathbb{R}^{n-m})$ such that $M \cap U = \{(u, v)\ ;\ v = f(u), u \in V\}$.*

A manifold M is thus obtained by gluing together pieces of $\mathbb{R}^m$; there are open sets $U_i \subset M$, open sets $V_i \subset \mathbb{R}^m$, and homeomorphisms $\psi_i : U_i \to \mathbb{R}^m$, such that ψ_i identifies U_i with V_i. The open sets U_i with the maps ψ_i are called charts. A collection of charts covering the manifold is an atlas. For a C^r manifold M, charts $\psi_i : U_i \to M$ and $\psi_j : U_j \to M$ with $U_i \cap U_j \neq \emptyset$ are such that $\psi_i \circ \psi_j^{-1}$ is C^r on $\psi_j^{-1}(U_j \cap U_i)$.

A submanifold $N \subset M$ is simply a manifold N that is contained in M. We will also use the concept of an injectively immersed manifold in a manifold M; this is the image of an injective map $N \to M$ from a manifold N into M for which the derivative is injective at every point. An injectively immersed manifold can accumulate onto itself.

Suppose M is a manifold of dimension m in $\mathbb{R}^n$. For $x_0 \in M$ and a neighborhood U of x_0, if $M \cap U = \{x \in U \,;\, F(x) = 0\}$ and x_0 is a regular point of F, then the tangent space $T_{x_0}M$ is defined by

$$T_{x_0}M = \{x \in \mathbb{R}^n \,;\, DF(x_0)x = 0\}.$$

The collection of tangent spaces forms the tangent bundle [**45**]. One can also consider other vector bundles, in particular subbundles of the tangent bundle. We refer to [**221**] or [**160**] for treatments of these notions.

A vector field on M is a function X that assigns a vector $X(x) \in T_xM$ for each $x \in M$. Let (U_i, ψ_i) be a chart. For a vector field X on M, there will be functions $Y_i : \psi_i(U_i) \to \mathbb{R}^m$ such that

$$X(\psi_i^{-1}(y)) = D\psi_i^{-1}(y)Y_i(y).$$

A vector field X on M is thus replaced by vector fields Y_i on $\mathbb{R}^m$. A vector field X on M is of class C^k if the Y_i are C^k functions and the manifold M is C^{k+1}.

A vector field X on M gives rise to a flow $\varphi^t : M \to M$ built from solutions of the differential equation

$$\dot{\varphi}^t(x) = X(\varphi^t(x)).$$

Using charts, we see that a differential equation on M is locally the same as a differential equation on $\mathbb{R}^m$. We therefore have local existence and uniqueness. Global existence and uniqueness on a compact manifold is obtained by continuation.

For a compact manifold M, consider the space $C^k(M)$ of C^k vector fields on M, endowed with the uniform C^k topology: A sequence of vector fields (X_n) converges to X, $X_n \to X$, if $D^iX_n \to D^iX$ uniformly on M for $0 \le i \le k$. For finite k one can put a norm compatible with this topology on $C^k(M)$. Namely, cover M with a finite collection of open sets V_i, such that each V_i is contained in the domain of a local chart U_i with coordinates h_i that map V_i onto $D^m(0)$, the unit disc in $\mathbb{R}^m$. Then, for $X \in C^k(M)$, define

$$\|X\|_k = \max_i \max_{0\le j\le k} \left\{ \sup_{u\in D^n(0)} |D^j Y_i \circ h_i^{-1}(u)| \right\},$$

where Y_i are the local representations of X as introduced above. With that we define a distance of two vector fields X and Y by

$$d_{C^k}(X,Y) = \|X - Y\|_k.$$

Lemma A.26. *$\|\cdot\|_k$ is a complete norm on $C^k(M)$.*

For $k = \infty$, we have a complete metric d_∞, compatible with the topology, given by

$$d_\infty(X,Y) = \sum_{j=1}^{\infty} 2^{-j} \frac{\|X-Y\|_j}{1+\|X-Y\|_j}.$$

Consider the space of C^k maps between compact manifolds $M \subset \mathbb{R}^n$ and $N \subset \mathbb{R}^p$. As N is a compact subset of $\mathbb{R}^p$, we get $C^k(M,N)$ as a closed subset of $C^k(M,\mathbb{R}^p)$. The textbook [**160**] contains detailed information on spaces of maps on manifolds.

Complete metric spaces are Baire spaces, meaning that every set that contains a countable intersection of open and dense sets is dense. A subset containing a countable intersection of open and dense sets is residual. A property shared by all members of a residual set is called generic.

Two manifolds M, N in $\mathbb{R}^n$ are said to be transverse if either $M \cap N = \emptyset$ or, for every $p \in M \cap N$, $T_pM + T_pN = \mathbb{R}^n$. Note that the sum is not necessarily a direct sum. In this case, $M \cap N$ is a manifold of codimension equal to the sum of the codimensions of M and N in $\mathbb{R}^n$. To see this, let $p \in M \cap N$ and suppose that near p, $M = F^{-1}(0)$ for $F : \mathbb{R}^n \to \mathbb{R}^{n-\dim(M)}$ and $N = G^{-1}(0)$ for $G : \mathbb{R}^n \to \mathbb{R}^{n-\dim(N)}$. Consider the function $H : \mathbb{R}^n \times \mathbb{R}^n \to \mathbb{R}^n \times \mathbb{R}^{n-\dim(M)} \times \mathbb{R}^{n-\dim(N)}$,

$$H(x,y) = (y - x, F(x), G(y)).$$

The transversality condition gives that p is a regular point for H, so that $M \cap N$ is a manifold.

A foliation $\mathcal{F}$ of M consists of a union of manifolds, called leaves, that fill M. More precisely, a foliation of an m-dimensional manifold M with d-dimensional leaves, is given by charts U_i of M as follows. There are rectangular open sets $V_i \subset \mathbb{R}^d \times \mathbb{R}^{m-d}$ and maps $\psi_i : U_i \to \mathbb{R}^d \times \mathbb{R}^{m-d}$ such that ψ_i identifies U_i with V_i, and the images $\psi_i^{-1}(V_i \cap \mathbb{R}^d \times \{x\})$ are the leaves of $\mathcal{F}$ intersected with U_i. Such local leaves are called plaques. Different charts $\psi_i : U_i \to \mathbb{R}^m$ and $\psi_j : U_j \to \mathbb{R}^m$ with $U_i \cap U_j \neq \emptyset$ are compatible in the sense that plaques coincide in $U_i \cap U_j$. For $p \in M$, one writes $\mathcal{F}_p$ for the leaf containing the point p.

A.3.2. Sard's theorem. Consider a smooth map $f : M \to N$ from a smooth manifold M of dimension n to a smooth manifold N of dimension p. A point x is singular if the differential at x,

$$Df(x) : T_x M \to T_{f(x)} N,$$

has rank less than p, that is, is not surjective. In Lemma 5.22 we encountered the one-dimensional version of Sard's theorem. For the convenience of the reader we state here the higher-dimensional version of Sard's theorem by Arthur Sard [**328**]. A proof can be found in [**69**].

Theorem A.27 (Sard's theorem). *Let $U \subset \mathbb{R}^n$ be open, and let $f : U \to \mathbb{R}^p$ be a smooth map. If $W \subset U$ is the set of singular points of f, then $f(W)$ has Lebesgue measure zero. In particular, the set of regular values of f is dense in $\mathbb{R}^p$.*

Using charts, we also get the following formulation of Sard's theorem.

Theorem A.28. *Let $f : M \to N$ be a smooth map between manifolds M, N. Then the set of regular values is dense.*

Appendix B

Invariant manifolds and normal forms

This appendix introduces tools specifically tailored to the study of dynamical systems and bifurcation theory in particular: invariant manifold theory and normal form theory. We state and prove existence results on stable, unstable, and center manifolds, and we cover some adjacent results in the first part of the appendix. Normal forms is about the art of simplifying expressions of vector fields and maps by applying coordinate changes. We collect results that we use in this book, ranging from statements on linearization to the general normal form theorem in the second part of this appendix.

B.1. Invariant manifolds

Invariant manifolds are basic objects in the study of dynamical systems. For hyperbolic critical elements, orbits that converge towards them form manifolds called stable manifolds. Orbits that diverge away from them form manifolds called unstable manifolds. The critical elements and their stable and unstable manifolds organize the geometry of the dynamics. In local bifurcation theory one constructs invariant manifolds, the center manifolds, that contain recurrent dynamics. They enable a dimension reduction as one can restrict a study of the dynamics to these center manifolds. In this appendix we develop the necessary theory and provide proofs of the stable manifold theorem and the center manifold theorem.

B.1.1. Stable and unstable manifolds. In this section we state and prove the stable manifold theorem, also called the Hadamard-Perron theorem. The theorem originates with work of Jacques Hadamard [**145**], Émile Cotton [**78**], and Oskar Perron [**290, 291**]. A number of textbooks give detailed expositions which we recommend for additional reading. A geometrical approach to the stable manifold theorem using the graph transform is explained, for instance, in [**48, 347**]. Cotton and Perron use a more functional analytic approach in which orbits that make up the stable manifold are found as fixed points, which is presented in [**189**]. Our approach is a combination of Perron's method with the method of cross coordinates from Shilnikov.

We start with diffeomorphisms, after which we consider vector fields. Consider a diffeomorphism f on $\mathbb{R}^m$. A fixed point $p = f(p)$ is hyperbolic if there are a splitting $\mathbb{R}^m = E^s(p) \oplus E^u(p)$ and constants $C \geq 1, 0 < \lambda < 1, \mu > 1$, with

$$|Df^n(p)v| \leq C\lambda^n |v|, \qquad v \in E^s(p),$$
$$|Df^n(p)v| \geq \frac{1}{C}\mu^n |v|, \qquad v \in E^u(p),$$

for all $n \geq 0$.

Define the stable set $W^s(p)$ and the unstable set $W^u(p)$ by

$$W^s(p) = \{x \in \mathbb{R}^m \; ; \; f^n(x) \to p \text{ as } n \to \infty\},$$
$$W^u(p) = \{x \in \mathbb{R}^m \; ; \; f^n(x) \to p \text{ as } n \to -\infty\}.$$

Theorem B.1 (Stable manifold theorem for maps). *Suppose p is a hyperbolic fixed point of a diffeomorphism f. Then $W^s(p)$ is an injectively immersed manifold with $T_pW^s(p) = E^s(p)$. We call $W^s(p)$ the stable manifold of p. Likewise, $W^u(p)$ is an injectively immersed manifold with $T_pW^u(p) = E^u(p)$. We call $W^u(p)$ the unstable manifold of p.*

Proof. We may assume that p is the origin in $\mathbb{R}^m$. For a given small $\delta > 0$, define the local stable manifold W^s_{loc},

$$W^s_{loc} = \{x \in \mathbb{R}^m \; ; \; f^n(x) \to 0 \text{ as } n \to \infty \text{ and } |f^n(x)| < \delta \text{ for all } n \in \mathbb{N}_0\}.$$

We will construct

$$V^s_{loc} = \{x \in \mathbb{R}^m \; ; \; |f^n(x)| < \delta \text{ for all } n \in \mathbb{N}_0\}.$$

It will follow from the construction that this is identical to W^s_{loc}. Then

$$W^s(p) = \bigcup_{i \in \mathbb{N}_0} f^{-i}(W^s_{loc}).$$

Take coordinates $x = (x^s, x^u) \in E^s(0) \times E^u(0)$ and a box norm

$$|(x^s, x^u)| = \max\{|x^s|, |x^u|\}$$

on $\mathbb{R}^m = E^s(0) \times E^u(0)$ for given norms on $E^s(0)$, $E^u(0)$. Let λ be a bound for the eigenvalues of $A_s = Df(0)|_{E^s(0)}$; $|\mathrm{spec}\, A_s| < \lambda < 1$. Likewise, let $1 < \mu < |\mathrm{spec}\, A_u|$ with $A_u = Df(0)|_{E^u(0)}$. Using a linear conjugation, we may assume $|Df(0)v_s| < \lambda |v_s|$ for all $v_s \in E^s(0)$ and $|Df(0)v_u| > \mu |v_u|$ for all $v_u \in E^u(0)$.

Write $(y^s, y^u) = f(x^s, x^u)$ as

$$\begin{aligned} y^s &= A_s x^s + \mathcal{O}(2), \\ y^u &= A_u x^u + \mathcal{O}(2), \end{aligned}$$

where $\mathcal{O}(2)$ stands for terms in (x^s, x^u) of order 2. The implicit function theorem allows us to solve (y^s, x^u) in terms of (x^s, y^u) if (x^s, x^u) is near $(0, 0)$. We obtain

$$(y^s, x^u) = g(x^s, y^u)$$

of the form

$$\begin{aligned} y^s &= A_s x^s + \mathcal{O}(2), \\ x^u &= A_u^{-1} y^u + \mathcal{O}(2), \end{aligned}$$

where now $\mathcal{O}(2)$ stands for terms in (x^s, y^u) of order 2.

Let $l^\infty(\mathbb{N}_0, \mathbb{R}^m)$ be the space of bounded sequences $\gamma = (\gamma(n))_{n \in \mathbb{N}_0}$ in $\mathbb{R}^m$, endowed with the supremum norm

$$\|\gamma\| = \sup_{n \in \mathbb{N}_0} |\gamma(n)|.$$

Write $D^s_\delta = \{x^s \in E^s(0) \,;\, |x^s| \le \delta\}$ and $l^\infty_\delta = \{\gamma \in l^\infty(\mathbb{N}_0, \mathbb{R}^m) \,;\, \|\gamma\| \le \delta\}$.

Write an element $\gamma \in l^\infty(\mathbb{N}_0, \mathbb{R}^m)$ as $\gamma(n) = (\gamma^s(n), \gamma^u(n))$. Define the map $\Gamma : D^s_\delta \times l^\infty_\delta \to l^\infty(\mathbb{N}_0, \mathbb{R}^m)$ by $\Gamma(x^s, \gamma) = \eta$ with

$$\begin{aligned} \eta^s(0) &= x^s, \\ (\eta^s(n+1), \eta^u(n)) &= g(\gamma^s(n), \gamma^u(n+1)), \end{aligned}$$

for $n \ge 0$. The following is a direct consequence of the properties of g, if δ is small enough:

(i) $\Gamma(D^s_\delta \times l^\infty_\delta) \subset l^\infty_\delta$,

(ii) $\Gamma(x^s, \cdot)$ is a contraction on l^∞_δ.

The map Γ is a composition $M \circ G \circ L$ of the superposition operator $G(\gamma)(n) = g(\gamma(n))$ (see Appendix A.1.4) and maps L, M with $L\gamma(n) = (\gamma^s(n), \gamma^u(n+1))$, M defined by $M\eta(0) = (x^s, \eta^u(0))$ and $M\eta(n) = (\eta^s(n-1), \eta^u(n))$ for $n > 0$. Using Theorem A.9, Γ is differentiable, so that by the implicit function theorem the fixed point of $\Gamma(x^s, \cdot)$ depends differentiably on x^s. Let η_{x^s} be the fixed point of $\Gamma(x^s, \cdot)$. Then the correspondence $x^s \mapsto \eta_{x^s}(0)$ defines a smooth manifold and we have

$$V^s_{loc} = \bigcup_{x^s \in D^s_\delta} \eta_{x^s}(0).$$

We will establish that $W^s_{loc} = V^s_{loc}$. Write $\eta_{x^s}(n) = (x^s_n, x^u_n)$. Then

$$(x^s_{n+1}, x^u_n) = g(x^s_n, x^u_{n+1})$$

so that $(x^s_{n+1}, x^u_{n+1}) = f(x^s_n, x^u_n)$ and $\{(x^s_n, x^u_n)\}$ is an orbit. We conclude that η_{x^s} is a positive orbit of f that stays in a δ-neighborhood of 0. For the points (x^s_n, x^u_n), we find that x^u_n is determined by x^s_n as $x^u_n = \eta_{x^s_n}(0)$ and $|x^u_n| \le C|x^s_n|$ for some $C > 0$. It now follows from the expression for f that, for δ small, $x^s_n \to 0$ as $n \to \infty$. Necessarily, also $x^u_n \to 0$ as $n \to \infty$ so that (x^s_n, x^u_n) converges to 0 as $n \to \infty$. So $W^s_{loc} = V^s_{loc}$.

The unstable manifold is the stable manifold of f^{-1}. □

Remark B.2. The above stable manifold theorem also applies to diffeomorphisms on manifolds M, where a stable manifold of a hyperbolic equilibrium is an injectively immersed manifold in M [**189**]. ■

Remark B.3. A local unstable manifold can be constructed as local stable manifold of f^{-1}, but also directly by a similar construction as the local stable manifold. Instead of the space $l^\infty(\mathbb{N}_0, \mathbb{R}^m)$ and the map Γ defined on a δ-ball around the origin in it, as in the above proof consider the space $l^\infty(-\mathbb{N}_0, \mathbb{R}^m)$ of bounded sequences $-\mathbb{N}_0 \to \mathbb{R}^m$ endowed with the supremum norm, and now write l^∞_δ for the δ-ball around the origin in $l^\infty(-\mathbb{N}_0, \mathbb{R}^m)$. Write $D^u_\delta = \{x^u \in E^u \; ; \; |x^u| \le \delta\}$ and define the map $\Gamma : D^u_\delta \times l^\infty_\delta \to l^\infty(-\mathbb{N}_0, \mathbb{R}^m)$ by $\Gamma(x^u, \gamma) = \eta$ with

$$\eta^u(0) = x^u,$$
$$(\eta^s(n+1), \eta^u(n)) = g(\gamma^s(n), \gamma^u(n+1))$$

for $n < 0$. Proceed by finding a fixed point of Γ just as for the stable manifold. ■

As a corollary we obtain the stable manifold theorem for vector fields on $\mathbb{R}^m$. Recall that an equilibrium p of a vector field f is hyperbolic if the spectrum of $Df(p)$ is disjoint from the imaginary axis. Then there are a splitting $\mathbb{R}^m = E^s(p) \oplus E^u(p)$ and constants $C \ge 1, \lambda < 0, \mu > 0$, with

$$|D\varphi^t(x)v| \le Ce^{\lambda t}|v|, \qquad v \in E^s(p),$$
$$|D\varphi^t(x)v| \ge \frac{1}{C}e^{\mu t}|v|, \qquad v \in E^u(p),$$

for all $t > 0$. Define the stable set $W^s(p)$ and the unstable set $W^u(p)$ by

$$W^s(p) = \{x \in \mathbb{R}^m \; ; \; \varphi^t(x) \to p \text{ as } t \to \infty\},$$
$$W^u(p) = \{x \in \mathbb{R}^m \; ; \; \varphi^t(x) \to p \text{ as } t \to -\infty\}.$$

Theorem B.4 (Stable manifold theorem for flows). *Suppose p is a hyperbolic equilibrium of a vector field f. Then $W^s(p)$ is an injectively immersed manifold with $T_pW^s(p) = E^s(p)$. We call $W^s(p)$ the stable manifold. Likewise, $W^u(p)$ is an injectively immersed with $T_pW^u(p) = E^u(p)$. We call $W^u(p)$ the unstable manifold.*

Proof. Consider the time 1 map $F = \varphi^1$ of the flow. We show that the local stable manifold $W^s_{loc}(p)$ of the fixed point p for the diffeomorphism F is the local stable manifold of the equilibrium p for the flow φ^t of the vector field f. If x on $W^s_{loc}(p)$ is near p, then also $\varphi^s(x)$ for $0 \le s \le 1$ is near p. For integers k, $\varphi^{k+s}(x) = \varphi^s \circ \varphi^k(x)$ goes to p as $k \to \infty$. The point $\varphi^s(x)$ therefore lies on $W^s_{loc}(p)$. □

As mentioned, the graph transform technique [**48**, **347**] provides a more geometric strategy of proof for the stable manifold theorem, allowing various generalizations [**162**]. A sketch of another proof of the stable manifold theorem can be found in [**360**]. See [**251**] for a proof of the stable manifold theorem tailored to analytic diffeomorphisms and analytic differential equations. An approach called the parameterization method, which considers a fixed point equation for the local stable manifold and projected dynamics on the stable subspace together, is described in [**56**].

B.1.2. Center manifolds. Center manifolds reduce the dimension of local bifurcation problems. We state and prove a center manifold theorem for local diffeomorphisms. A corresponding result for vector fields is obtained as a corollary. Original constructions of center manifolds are by Aleksandr Lyapunov [**233**] (in a special case with pure imaginary center eigenvalues, the Russian original manuscript is from 1892) and in more general cases by Viktor Pliss [**293**] and Al Kelley [**199**] (see also an appendix to [**4**]). The result by Aleksandr Shoshitaishvili [**345**, **346**] (see also an English translation [**2**] or textbooks [**21**, § 32C], [**215**, Thm. 5.4]) includes a conjugation to a normal form. Our proof of the center manifold theorem is a sophisticated variant of our proof of the stable manifold theorem with several adaptations, in which we combine elements of [**188**, **404**, **408**, **415**] (in particular [**404**] contains a detailed discussion of the center manifold theorem). It follows the strategy of Perron's proof for the local stable manifold using a contraction on a space of sequences to obtain orbits.

We start with a global center manifold theorem. Consider a diffeomorphism f on $\mathbb{R}^m$ with a fixed point $f(0) = 0$ at the origin and assume a splitting $\mathbb{R}^m = E^s \times E^c \times E^u$, invariant under $Df(0)$, so that $|\operatorname{spec} Df(0)|_{E^s}| < 1$, $\operatorname{spec} Df(0)|_{E^c}$ lies on the unit circle in the complex plane and $|\operatorname{spec} Df(0)|_{E^u}| > 1$. There are constants $C \ge 1, 0 < \lambda < 1, \mu > 1, q > 1$ with $\lambda < 1/q$, $q < \mu$, so that

$$|Df^n(0)v| \le C\lambda^n|v|, \qquad v \in E^s,$$

$$\frac{1}{C}q^{-n}|v| \le |Df^n(0)v| \le Cq^n|v|, \qquad v \in E^c,$$

$$|Df^n(0)v| \ge \frac{1}{C}\mu^n|v|, \qquad v \in E^u, \tag{B.1}$$

for all $n \ge 0$. By a linear transformation we may assume $C = 1$, and we can take q arbitrarily close to 1. Take coordinates $u = (x^s, x^c, x^u) \in E^s \times E^c \times E^u$ and write

$$Df(0)(x^s, x^c, x^u) = (A_s x^s, A_c x^c, A_u x^u).$$

Write π_s, π_c, π_u for the coordinate projections onto E^s, E^c, E^u:

$$\pi_s(x^s, x^c, x^u) = x^s,$$
$$\pi_c(x^s, x^c, x^u) = x^c,$$
$$\pi_u(x^s, x^c, x^u) = x^u.$$

Let $C^r(\mathbb{R}^m, \mathbb{R}^m)$ denote the Banach space of all C^r functions whose derivatives up to order r are uniformly bounded on $\mathbb{R}^m$ and $\|\cdot\|_{C^r}$ denotes the norm on $C^r(\mathbb{R}^m, \mathbb{R}^m)$. For $\varepsilon > 0$ let

$$B^1_\varepsilon = \{w \in C^1(\mathbb{R}^m, \mathbb{R}^m)\ ;\ \|w\|_{C^1} < \varepsilon\}$$

be the open ε-ball in $C^1(\mathbb{R}^m, \mathbb{R}^m)$ centered at 0.

From now on we consider more specific diffeomorphisms $f : \mathbb{R}^m \to \mathbb{R}^m$ of the form

$$f(x^s, x^c, x^u) = (A_s x^s, A_c x^c, A_u x^u) + R(x^s, x^c, x^u) \tag{B.2}$$

with $R \in C^r(\mathbb{R}^m, \mathbb{R}^m) \cap B^1_\varepsilon$, $r \ge 1$, $\varepsilon > 0$.

A center manifold of the fixed point 0 is an invariant manifold $W^c(0)$ which is tangent to the center eigenspace E^c, that is $T_0W^c(0) = E^c$. The following result is the center manifold theorem for diffeomorphisms.

Theorem B.5 (Global center manifold theorem for maps). *Consider a diffeomorphism f as in* (B.2) *with $R \in C^r(\mathbb{R}^m, \mathbb{R}^m) \cap B^1_\varepsilon$. For any $r > 0$ there is $\varepsilon_0 > 0$ so that for $\varepsilon < \varepsilon_0$ the following holds.*

There exists a C^r function $H : E^c \to E^s \times E^u$ such that

(i) *$H(0) = 0$ and $DH(0) = 0$.*

(ii) *The set*

$$M_c = \{(x^s, x^c, x^u)\ ;\ (x^s, x^u) = H(x^c), x^c \in E^c\}$$

is a C^r manifold and is invariant under f.

(iii) *M_c contains all bounded orbits of f.*

Proof. First we prove the existence of a center manifold. The proof involves a contraction Γ on a space of double sided sequences. Following the existence proof, we verify the differentiability of the center manifold. Since the mapping Γ is not differentiable, the verification of the differentiability does not follow from the uniform contraction theorem, and requires additional reasoning.

EXISTENCE OF THE CENTER MANIFOLD. For $\eta \in \left(1, \min\{\lambda^{-1}, \mu\}\right)$, let $l^{\infty,\eta} = l^{\infty,\eta}(\mathbb{Z}, \mathbb{R}^m)$ be the space of double sided sequences $\gamma = (\gamma(n))_{n\in\mathbb{Z}}$ in $\mathbb{R}^m$ with

$$\|\gamma\|_\eta = \sup_{n\in\mathbb{Z}} \eta^{-|n|}|\gamma(n)| < \infty, \tag{B.3}$$

and it is endowed with the norm $\|\cdot\|_\eta$. Here $|(x^c, x^s, x^u)|$ is the box norm $\max\{|x^s|, |x^c|, |x^u|\}$ for given norms on E^s, E^c, E^u.

Consider $y = f(x)$, or in coordinates

$$(y^s, y^c, y^u) = f(x^s, x^c, x^u).$$

An implicit function theorem argument allows us to solve (y^s, y^c, x^u) as a smooth function of (x^s, x^c, y^u). So we may write

$$(y^s, y^c, x^u) = g(x^s, x^c, y^u) \tag{B.4}$$

with $g(0,0,0) = (0,0,0)$ and $Dg(0,0,0) = (A_s, A_c, A_u^{-1})$. Likewise, take

$$(z^s, z^c, z^u) = f^{-1}(x^s, x^c, x^u)$$

and solve (x^s, z^c, z^u) as a smooth function of (z^s, x^c, x^u). This gives

$$(x^s, z^c, z^u) = h(z^s, x^c, x^u) \tag{B.5}$$

with $h(0,0,0) = (0,0,0)$ and $Dh(0,0,0) = (A_s, A_c^{-1}, A_u^{-1})$. For any $\sigma > 0$ we can find ε_0 so that

$$\|g - Dg(0)\|_{C^1} \le \sigma, \qquad \|h - Dh(0)\|_{C^1} \le \sigma. \tag{B.6}$$

Note that if E^s or E^u is zero-dimensional, then always the s-coordinate or the u-coordinate is equal to zero, or in other words $h = f^{-1}$ or $g = f$, respectively. In the following, we assume that both $E^s \neq \{0\}$ and $E^u \neq \{0\}$. The adaptations to the cases that one of these spaces is zero-dimensional are straightforward.

Write an element $\gamma \in l^{\infty,\eta}$ as $\gamma(n) = (\gamma_s(n), \gamma_c(n), \gamma_u(n))$. Define the map $\Gamma : E^c \times l^{\infty,\eta} \to l^{\infty,\eta}$ by $\Gamma(x^c, \gamma) = \zeta$ with

$$\begin{aligned}
\zeta_c(0) &= x^c, \\
(\zeta_s(n+1), \zeta_c(n+1), \zeta_u(n)) &= g(\gamma_s(n), \gamma_c(n), \gamma_u(n+1)), \text{ for } n \ge 0, \\
(\zeta_s(n), \zeta_c(n-1), \zeta_u(n-1)) &= h(\gamma_s(n-1), \gamma_c(n), \gamma_u(n)), \text{ for } n \le 0.
\end{aligned}$$

This defines a continuous map on $E^c \times l^{\infty,\eta}$ by Theorem A.10. A fixed point $\gamma = \Gamma(x^c, \gamma)$ is an orbit in $l^{\infty,\eta}$ with $\pi_c\gamma(0) = x^c$. From the estimates for g and

h one can verify that

(i) $\Gamma(E^c \times l^{\infty,\eta}) \subset l^{\infty,\eta}$;

(ii) $\Gamma(x^c, \cdot)$ is a uniform contraction on $l^{\infty,\eta}$.

The estimates to prove this are straightforward if g and h are linear, and they extend to small perturbations thereof. Write $\zeta = \Gamma(x^c, \gamma)$. Recall $\|\zeta\|_\eta = \sup_{n\in\mathbb{Z}} \eta^{-|n|}|\zeta(n)|$. Now $|\zeta(n)|$ can be bounded separately for the stable, center, and unstable coordinates. For example, consider the center coordinate for $n > 0$:

$$|\zeta_c(n)| = |\pi_c g(\gamma_s(n-1), \gamma_c(n-1), \gamma_u(n))|.$$

Now taking into consideration (B.1) and (B.6) (compare also the representation of $Dg(0,0,0)$) yields

$$\begin{aligned}|\zeta_c(n)| &\le q|\gamma_c(n-1)| + \sigma|(\gamma_s(n-1), \gamma_c(n-1), \gamma_u(n))| \\ &\le q\eta^{n-1}\|\gamma\|_\eta + \sigma\eta^n\|\gamma\|_\eta.\end{aligned}$$

So also $\eta^{-n}|\zeta_c(n)| \le \left(\frac{q}{\eta} + \sigma\right)\|\gamma\|_\eta$. We can get $\frac{q}{\eta} + \sigma < 1$ by taking ε_0 small. Similar estimates for the other coordinates and for $n \le 0$ prove that $\Gamma(x^c, \gamma) \in l^{\infty,\eta}$ for $\gamma \in l^{\infty,\eta}$. Estimates to prove that Γ is a uniform contraction run accordingly. With $\tilde{\zeta} = \Gamma(x^c, \tilde{\gamma})$, we have $\|\zeta - \tilde{\zeta}\|_\eta = \sup_{n\in\mathbb{Z}} \eta^{-|n|}|\zeta(n) - \tilde{\zeta}(n)|$, and $|\zeta(n) - \tilde{\zeta}(n)|$ can be bounded separately for the stable, center, and unstable coordinates. Taking, as above, the center coordinate,

$$\begin{aligned}&|\zeta_c(n) - \tilde{\zeta}_c(n)| \\ &\quad = |\pi_c g(\gamma_s(n-1), \gamma_c(n-1), \gamma_u(n)) - \pi_c g(\tilde{\gamma}_s(n-1), \tilde{\gamma}_c(n-1), \tilde{\gamma}_u(n))| \\ &\quad \le q|\gamma_c(n-1) - \tilde{\gamma}_c(n-1)| \\ &\qquad\quad + \sigma|(\gamma_s(n-1), \gamma_c(n-1), \gamma_u(n)) - (\tilde{\gamma}_s(n-1), \tilde{\gamma}_c(n-1), \tilde{\gamma}_u(n))| \\ &\quad \le q\eta^{n-1}\|\gamma - \tilde{\gamma}\|_\eta + \sigma\eta^n\|\gamma - \tilde{\gamma}\|_\eta.\end{aligned}$$

So also $\eta^{-n}|\zeta_c(n) - \tilde{\zeta}_c(n)| \le \left(\frac{q}{\eta} + \sigma\right)\|\gamma - \tilde{\gamma}\|_\eta < \|\gamma - \tilde{\gamma}\|_\eta$. Similar estimates for the other coordinates and for $n < 0$ prove that $\Gamma(x^c, \cdot)$ is a uniform contraction on $l^{\infty,\eta}$.

For any $x^c \in E^c$ the construction gives a unique fixed point $\hat{\gamma}(x^c)$ of $\Gamma(x^c, \cdot)$. The mapping $x^c \mapsto \Gamma(x^c, \hat{\gamma}(x^c))$ belongs to $C^0(E^c, l^{\infty,\eta})$. The function H is defined by

$$H(x^c) = (\pi_s \times \pi_u)\hat{\gamma}(x^c)(0)$$

and is continuous. In particular all globally bounded orbits are contained in the graph of H. In [**404**, Lemma 2.6] an argument is given that shows that H is bounded.

Differentiability of the center manifold. Differentiability of the center manifold cannot be proved by a direct application of the uniform contraction theorem as the map $\Gamma : E^c \times l^{\infty,\eta} \to l^{\infty,\eta}$ is not differentiable. However, we will make use of the fact that for $1 < \eta' < \eta$, $l^{\infty,\eta'}$ is continuously embedded in $l^{\infty,\eta}$ and the map $\Gamma : E^c \times l^{\infty,\eta'} \to l^{\infty,\eta}$ is C^1. This is seen as in the proof of Theorem B.1 but now invoking Theorem A.10 instead of Theorem A.9. The differentiability allows to follow the arguments of the uniform contraction theorem and prove differentiability of the center manifold.

Fix some $x^c \in E^c$ and define a sequence of maps $m_i : E^c \to l^{\infty,\eta}$ by $m_0 \equiv 0$ and

$$m_{i+1}(x^c) = \Gamma(x^c, m_i(x^c)).$$

As a consequence of the above procedure (an application of the uniform contraction theorem), we know that m_i converges to $\hat{\gamma}$ in $C^0(E^c, l^{\infty,\eta})$ as $i \to \infty$. We will establish that Dm_i converges in $C^0(E^c, L(E^c, l^{\infty,\eta}))$. Then Lemma A.1 gives that m_i converges to $\hat{\gamma}$ in $C^1(E^c, l^{\infty,\eta})$, so that the fixed point $\hat{\gamma}$ is C^1.

Let $1 < \eta' < \eta$. Considering Γ acting on $E^c \times l^{\infty,\eta'}$ we find, for ε_0 small, that it defines a uniform contraction on $l^{\infty,\eta'}$ (we can get $\frac{q}{\eta'} + \sigma < 1$ which, as we have seen above, appears in the estimates). So we have $m_i \in C^0(E^c, l^{\infty,\eta'})$ and $m_i \to \hat{\gamma}$ in $C^0(E^c, l^{\infty,\eta'})$.

For $\gamma \in C^1(E^c, l^{\infty,\eta'})$ and considering $D_\gamma \Gamma \in L(l^{\infty,\eta'}, l^{\infty,\eta})$, we have

$$\frac{d}{dx^c}(\Gamma(x^c, \gamma(x^c))) = D_{x^c}\Gamma(x^c, \gamma(x^c)) + D_\gamma \Gamma(x^c, \gamma(x^c)) D\gamma(x^c)$$

in $L(E^c, l^{\infty,\eta})$. For given $\gamma \in l^{\infty,\eta}$, write $\mathcal{T}\Gamma(\gamma)$ for the linear map in $L(l^{\infty,\eta}, l^{\infty,\eta})$ given by $\chi = \mathcal{T}\Gamma(\gamma)\zeta$ with

$$\chi_c(0) = 0$$

and

$$\begin{aligned}
&(\chi_s(n+1), \chi_c(n+1), \chi_u(n)) \\
&\qquad = Dg(\gamma_s(n), \gamma_c(n), \gamma_u(n+1))(\zeta_s(n), \zeta_c(n), \zeta_u(n+1)) \text{ for } n \geq 0, \\
&(\chi_s(n), \chi_c(n-1), \chi_u(n-1)) \\
&\qquad = Dh(\gamma_s(n-1), \gamma_c(n), \gamma_u(n))(\zeta_s(n-1), \zeta_c(n), \zeta_u(n)) \text{ for } n \leq 0.
\end{aligned}$$

When considering $\mathcal{T}\Gamma(\gamma)$ as a linear map in $L(l^{\infty,\eta'}, l^{\infty,\eta})$, it is equal to $D_\gamma \Gamma(x^c, \gamma)$ (this follows from the proof of Theorem A.10). It is then in particular continuous in γ.

Define

$$\Gamma^{(1)} : E^c \times l^{\infty,\eta} \times L(E^c, l^{\infty,\eta}) \to l^{\infty,\eta} \times L(E^c, l^{\infty,\eta})$$

by

$$\Gamma^{(1)}(x^c,\gamma,\psi)=(\Gamma(x^c,\gamma),D_{x^c}\Gamma(x^c,\gamma)+\mathcal{T}\Gamma(\gamma)\psi).$$

Write $\Gamma_f^{(1)}(x^c,\gamma,\psi)$ for the fiber coordinate $D_{x^c}\Gamma(x^c,\gamma)+\mathcal{T}\Gamma(\gamma)\psi$.

We may consider $\Gamma^{(1)}$ on $E^c\times l^{\infty,\eta'}\times L(E^c,l^{\infty,\eta'})$. As for Γ we find the following property. If ε_0 is small, for fixed $x^c\in E^c$ and $\gamma\in l^{\infty,\eta'}$ we have $\mathcal{T}\Gamma(\gamma)\in L(l^{\infty,\eta'},l^{\infty,\eta'})$ and $\Gamma_f^{(1)}$ contracts distances in $L(E^c,l^{\infty,\eta'})$ with a contraction factor that is uniform in x^c and γ:

$$||\Gamma_f^{(1)}(x^c,\gamma,\psi)-\Gamma_f^{(1)}(x^c,\gamma,\tilde{\psi})||\le\kappa||\psi-\tilde{\psi}||.$$

So, in the fixed fiber $\{(x^c,\hat{\gamma}(x^c))\}\times L(E^c,l^{\infty,\eta'})$, $\Gamma_f^{(1)}(x^c,\hat{\gamma}(x^c))$ admits a unique fixed point $\hat{\zeta}(x^c)\in L(E^c,l^{\infty,\eta'})$, and we have

$$\Gamma^{(1)}(x^c,\hat{\gamma}(x^c),\hat{\zeta}(x^c))=(\hat{\gamma}(x^c),\hat{\zeta}(x^c)).$$

We remark that one can check that $\psi\mapsto\Gamma_f^{(1)}(x^c,\hat{\gamma}(x^c),\psi)$ maps a ball of some large enough radius R into itself, for all $x^c\in E^c$, to get that $\hat{\zeta}$ is a bounded function.

Recalling $m_{i+1}(x^c)=\Gamma(x^c,m_i(x^c))$, let $w_0\equiv 0$ and

$$(m_{i+1}(x^c),w_{i+1}(x^c))=\Gamma^{(1)}(x^c,m_i(x^c),w_i(x^c)).$$

From $\hat{\zeta}(x^c)\in L(E^c,l^{\infty,\eta'})$ and considering $\mathcal{T}\Gamma\in L(l^{\infty,\eta'},l^{\infty,\eta})$, we find that

$$\begin{aligned}\lim_{i\to\infty}\Gamma_f^{(1)}(x^c,m_i(x^c),\hat{\zeta}(x^c))&=\lim_{i\to\infty}D_{x^c}\Gamma(x^c,m_i(x^c))+\mathcal{T}\Gamma(m_i(x^c))\hat{\zeta}(x^c)\\&=\lim_{i\to\infty}D_{x^c}\Gamma(x^c,m_i(x^c))+D_\gamma\Gamma(x^c,m_i(x^c))\hat{\zeta}(x^c)\\&=\Gamma_f^{(1)}(x^c,\hat{\gamma}(x^c),\hat{\zeta}(x^c)).\end{aligned}$$

The fiber contraction theorem (Theorem A.14) in combination with Remark A.15 yields that $w_i(x^c)$ converges in $L(E^c,l^{\infty,\eta})$ to $\hat{\zeta}(x^c)$.

Reasoning as in the proof of Theorem A.16 shows that w_i converges in $C^0(E^c, L(E^c, l^{\infty,\eta}))$. Namely,

$$\begin{aligned}
&|w_{i+1}(x^c + h) - w_{i+1}(x^c)| \\
&\quad \le |\mathcal{T}\Gamma(m_i(x^c + h))w_i(x^c + h) - \mathcal{T}\Gamma(m_i(x^c))w_i(x^c)| \\
&\qquad\quad + |D_{x^c}\Gamma(x^c + h, m_i(x^c + h)) - D_{x^c}\Gamma(x^c, m_i(x^c))| \\
&\quad \le |\mathcal{T}\Gamma(m_i(x^c + h))||w_i(x^c + h) - w_i(x^c)| \\
&\qquad\quad + |(T\Gamma(m_i(x^c + h)) - \mathcal{T}\Gamma(m_i(x^c)))w_i(x^c)| \\
&\qquad\quad + |D_{x^c}\Gamma(x^c + h, m_i(x^c + h)) - D_{x^c}\Gamma(x^c, m_i(x^c))| \\
&\quad \le \kappa|w_i(x^c + h) - w_i(x^c)| \\
&\qquad\quad + |(\mathcal{T}\Gamma(m_i(x^c + h)) - \mathcal{T}\Gamma(m_i(x^c)))w_i(x^c)| \\
&\qquad\quad + |D_{x^c}\Gamma(x^c + h, m_i(x^c + h)) - D_{x^c}\Gamma(x^c, m_i(x^c))|.
\end{aligned}$$

As m_i converges in $C^0(E^c, l^{\infty,\eta'})$, $w_i(x^c)$ converges to $\hat{\zeta}(x^c) \in L(E^c, l^{\infty,\eta'})$, we have for all $i \in \mathbb{N}_0$ and for all $\varepsilon > 0$, that there is $\delta > 0$ with

$$\begin{aligned}
&|(T\Gamma(m_i(x^c + h)) - \mathcal{T}\Gamma(m_i(x^c)))w_i(x^c)| \\
&\qquad\qquad + |D_{x^c}\Gamma(x^c + h, m_i(x^c + h)) - D_{x^c}\Gamma(x^c, m_i(x^c))| < \varepsilon
\end{aligned}$$

if $|h| < \delta$. As in the proof of Theorem A.16 we find that w_i converges in $C^0(E^c, L(E^c, l^{\infty,\eta}))$. As said, Lemma A.1 gives that m_i converges to $\hat{\gamma}$ in $C^1(E^c, l^{\infty,\eta})$, so that the fixed point $\hat{\gamma}$ is C^1. Recall that the center manifold is obtained as the graph of $x^c \mapsto (\pi_s \times \pi_u)\hat{\gamma}(x^c)(0)$, it is therefore the graph of a C^1 map. We remark that, as $\hat{\gamma}$ and $\hat{\zeta}$ are bounded, $x^c \mapsto (\pi_s \times \pi_u)\hat{\gamma}(x^c)(0)$ is bounded in $C^1(E^c, E^s \times E^u)$.

HIGHER DIFFERENTIABILITY. Higher differentiability is handled with an induction argument, using reasoning similar as above. We will use that for $1 < \eta' < \eta$ satisfying $(\eta')^k < \eta$ (which we assume), the map $\Gamma : E^c \times l^{\infty,\eta'} \to l^{\infty,\eta}$ is C^k. Starting from

$$\frac{d}{dx^c}(\Gamma(x^c, \gamma(x^c))) = D_\gamma\Gamma(x^c, \gamma(x^c))D\gamma(x^c) + D_{x^c}\Gamma(x^c, \gamma(x^c))$$

for the first derivative, we obtain by a repeated application of the chain rule an expression of the form

$$\begin{aligned}
&\left(\frac{d}{dx^c}\right)^k (\Gamma(x^c, \gamma(x^c))) \\
&\qquad\qquad = D_\gamma\Gamma(x^c, \gamma(x^c))D^k\gamma(x^c) + \Phi(x^c, \gamma(x^c), \dots, D^{k-1}\gamma(x^c))
\end{aligned}$$

for some map Φ, assuming the derivatives up to order k of γ exist. The map Φ features derivatives of Γ up to order k (it contains in particular a term $D^k_\gamma\Gamma(x^c, \gamma(x^c))(D\gamma(x^c))^k$ and other terms that all include derivatives of Γ with respect to x^c). For $k > 1$ define

$$\Gamma^{(k)} : E^c \times l^{\infty,\eta} \times L(E^c, l^{\infty,\eta}) \times \cdots \times L^k(E^c, l^{\infty,\eta}) \\ \to l^{\infty,\eta} \times L(E^c, l^{\infty,\eta}) \times \cdots \times L^k(E^c, l^{\infty,\eta})$$

recursively by

$$\Gamma^{(k)}(x^c, \gamma, \psi^{(1)}, \dots, \psi^{(k)}) \\ = \left(\Gamma^{(k-1)}(x^c, \gamma, \psi^{(1)}, \dots, \psi^{(k-1)}), \mathcal{T}\Gamma(\gamma)\psi^{(k)} + \Phi(x^c, \gamma, \psi^{(1)}, \dots, \psi^{(k-1)})\right).$$

Write $\Gamma_f^{(k)}$ for the fiber coordinate,

$$\Gamma_f^{(k)}(x^c, \gamma, \psi^{(1)}, \dots, \psi^{(k)}) = \mathcal{T}\Gamma(\gamma)\psi^{(k)} + \Phi(x^c, \gamma, \psi^{(1)}, \dots, \psi^{(k-1)}).$$

For ε_0 small, there is $\kappa < 1$ so that

$$\|\Gamma_f^{(k)}(x^c, \gamma, \psi^{(1)}, \dots, \psi^{(k-1)}, \nu) - \Gamma_f^{(k)}(x^c, \gamma, \psi^{(1)}, \dots, \psi^{(k-1)}, \tilde{\nu})\| \le \kappa\|\nu - \tilde{\nu}\|$$

in $L^k(E^c, l^{\infty,\eta'})$, for all $(x^c, \gamma, \psi^{(1)}, \dots, \psi^{(k-1)}) \in E^c \times l^{\infty,\eta'} \times L(E^c, l^{\infty,\eta'}) \times \dots \times L^{k-1}(E^c, l^{\infty,\eta'})$.

Recall that for ε_0 small we get the fixed point $\hat{\gamma} \in C^0(E^c, l^{\infty,\eta'})$. By induction we have for ε_0 small that $\hat{\gamma} \in C^{k-1}(E^c, l^{\infty,\eta'})$ and m_i converges in $C^{k-1}(E^c, l^{\infty,\eta'})$ as $i \to \infty$. Write $\hat{\zeta}^{(k)}(x^c)$ for the fixed point

$$\hat{\zeta}^{(k)}(x^c) = \mathcal{T}\Gamma(\hat{\gamma}(x^c))\hat{\zeta}^{(k)}(x^c) + \Phi(x^c, \hat{\gamma}(x^c), D\hat{\gamma}(x^c), \dots, D^{k-1}\hat{\gamma}(x^c))$$

in $L^k(E^c, l^{\infty,\eta'})$. By the choice of η',

$$\lim_{i\to\infty} \Gamma_f^{(k)}(x^c, m_i(x^c), Dm_i(x^c), \dots, D^{k-1}m_i(x^c), \hat{\zeta}^{(k)}(x^c)) \\ = \Gamma_f^{(k)}(x^c, \hat{\gamma}(x^c), \dots, D^{k-1}\hat{\gamma}(x^c), \hat{\zeta}^{(k)}(x^c)).$$

From Theorem A.14 and Remark A.15 we find that $D^k m_i(x^c)$ converges in $L^k(E^c, l^{\infty,\eta})$. As above $D^k m_i$ converges in $C^0(E^c, L^k(E^c, l^{\infty,\eta}))$. By Lemma A.1 and Corollary A.2, the fixed point $\hat{\gamma}$ is C^k. The center manifold is obtained as the graph of $x^c \mapsto (\pi_s \times \pi_u)\hat{\gamma}(x^c)(0)$ and is thus the graph of a C^k map. We note that as above one can conclude that $x^c \mapsto (\pi_s \times \pi_u)\hat{\gamma}(x^c)(0)$ is bounded in $C^k(E^c, E^s \times E^u)$. □

Remark B.6. The proof of the theorem reveals that M_c consists of all f-orbits satisfying (B.3). Moreover, M_c is the only f-invariant manifold with this property. ■

We continue with a local center manifold theorem, on which the explanations in Section 3.1.2.2 are based. Assume a local diffeomorphism $\tilde{f} : U \subset \mathbb{R}^m \to \mathbb{R}^m$ with $0 \in U$ and $\tilde{f}(0) = 0$ and the spectrum $\sigma D\tilde{f}(0)$ of $D\tilde{f}(0)$ intersects the unit circle in the complex plane. Let E^s, E^c, and E^u be the corresponding stable, center, and unstable subspaces, respectively.

Theorem B.7 (Local center manifold theorem for maps). *Consider $\tilde{f}$ as above. Then there exist open neighborhoods V of $0 \in \mathbb{R}^m$, $\tilde{V}$ of $0 \in E^c$ and a C^r-function $\tilde{H} : \tilde{V} \to E^s \oplus E^u$ such that*

(i) *$\tilde{H}(0) = 0$ and $D\tilde{H}(0) = 0$.*

(ii) *The (local) C^r manifold*
$$W^c_{loc} = \{(x^s, x^c, x^u) \; ; \; (x^s, x^u) = \tilde{H}(x^c), x^c \in \tilde{V}\}$$
is invariant under f.

(iii) *If $x \in V$ and all f-iterates of x exist and belong to V, then $x \in W^c_{loc}$.*

Proof. We extend $\tilde{f}$ to a diffeomorphism on all of $\mathbb{R}^m$ that is globally close to the linearization at the origin. Let $\phi : \mathbb{R}^m \to \mathbb{R}$ be a smooth bump function: a nonnegative function ϕ with $\phi \equiv 1$ on a neighborhood of 0 and of compact support. For $\delta > 0$, let
$$\phi_\delta(x) = \phi(x/\delta).$$
Replace $\tilde{f}$ by the map
$$f(x) = \phi_\delta(x)\tilde{f}(x) + (1 - \phi_\delta(x))D\tilde{f}(0)x. \tag{B.7}$$
The new map f is then C^1-close to its linearization $Df(0)$ at 0,
$$|f(x) - Df(0)x|, |Df(x) - Df(0)| \leq C\delta$$
for some $C > 0$ and all $x \in \mathbb{R}^m$. For any $\varepsilon > 0$ we may find $\delta > 0$ so that (B.7) is of the form (B.2). In other words f satisfies the assumptions of Theorem B.5 and therefore has a unique global center manifold M_c.

Further, note that f is equal to $\tilde{f}$ on a small (order δ) neighborhood Ω of 0. The intersection of $\Omega \cap M_c$ defines the local center manifold. The last statement of the theorem follows from Theorem B.5 (iii). □

Finally we state a corresponding center manifold theorem for differential equations, which is basically obtained as the center manifold for the time 1 flow of a related vector field. Consider the system of differential equations on $U \subset \mathbb{R}^m$,
$$\dot{x} = Ax + \tilde{u}(x, y),$$
$$\dot{y} = By + \tilde{v}(x, y),$$
where $(x, y) \in U \subset \mathbb{R}^m$, $(\tilde{u}, \tilde{v}) \in C^r(U, \mathbb{R}^m)$, and A and B are constant matrices. Assume that all eigenvalues of A have zero real parts and all eigenvalues of B have nonzero real parts. Accordingly we write $U = U^c \times U^h \subset E^c \times E^h$, with the center eigenspace E^c and the hyperbolic eigenspace E^h.

Theorem B.8 (Local center manifold theorem for flows). *Consider a differential equation as above. Then there exist open neighborhoods V of $0 \in \mathbb{R}^m$, $\tilde{V}$ of $0 \in E^c$, and a C^r-function $\tilde{H} : \tilde{V} \to E^s \oplus E^u$ such that*

(i) $\tilde{H}(0) = 0$ *and* $D\tilde{H}(0) = 0$.

(ii) *The (local)* C^r *manifold*

$$W^c_{loc} = \{(x^c, x^h)\ ;\ (x^h) = \tilde{H}(x^c), x^c \in \tilde{V}\}$$

is invariant under the flow of the differential equation.

(iii) *If* $x \in V$ *and the orbit of* x *does exist for all times and belongs to* V*, then* $x \in W^c_{loc}$.

Proof. Similar to the procedure in the proof of Theorem B.7 we extend $(\tilde{u}, \tilde{v})$ to functions $(u, v) \in C^r(\mathbb{R}^m, \mathbb{R}^m) \cap C^1_\varepsilon(\mathbb{R}^m, \mathbb{R}^m)$, $r \geq 1$, $\varepsilon > 0$. Since (u, v) are bounded, the related flow φ^t exists for all times. In particular φ^1 does exist.

Applying the variation of constants formula reveals that there is a $\hat{\varepsilon} > 0$ such that $\varphi^1 \in C^r(\mathbb{R}^m, \mathbb{R}^m) \cap C^1_{\hat{\varepsilon}}(\mathbb{R}^m, \mathbb{R}^m)$. Moreover $\hat{\varepsilon} > 0$ can be chosen arbitrarily small if ε is sufficiently small. So the diffeomorphism φ^1 has a unique global center manifold M_c in accordance with Theorem B.5. Then according to Remark B.6 there is an $\eta \in (0, \min\{\alpha_s^{-1}, \alpha_u\}$ such that

$$M_c = \{x \in \mathbb{R}^m; \sup_{n \in \mathbb{Z}} e^{-\eta|n|}|\varphi^n(x)| < \infty\}.$$

Similar to the proof of Theorem B.4 we find

$$M_c = \{x \in \mathbb{R}^m; \sup_{t \in \mathbb{R}} e^{-\eta|t|}|\varphi^t(x)| < \infty\}.$$

This proves the invariance of M_c with respect to the flow φ^t. Since the flow φ^t coincides with the flow $\tilde{\varphi}^t$ of the original differential equation on a neighborhood of the origin, restricting to this neighborhood yields the theorem. □

Local center manifolds may not be unique as the construction depends on the choice of bump function in (B.7).

Example B.9. Consider the system

$$\text{(B.8)} \qquad \begin{aligned} \dot{x} &= -x^3, \\ \dot{y} &= -y \end{aligned}$$

with $x, y \in \mathbb{R}$. Let c_1, c_2 be real numbers, and let

$$h(x; c_1, c_2) = \begin{cases} -c_1 e^{-1/(2x^2)}, & x < 0, \\ 0, & x = 0, \\ c_2 e^{-1/(2x^2)}, & x > 0. \end{cases}$$

For any c_1, c_2, the curve $y = h(x; c_1, c_2)$ is an invariant manifold of (B.8) and provides a local center manifold because

$$h(0, c_1, c_2) = 0,\ Dh(0; c_1, c_2) = 0.$$

■

It is known that center manifolds may not be C^∞; [**401**] contains explicit examples (see also [**116**, Section 3.3]). An extensive study of (non)uniqueness and regularity of local center manifolds is in [**348**].

Example B.10. One might think that in cases where local center manifolds are unique, they are C^∞. But also this is not true. We give a geometric description of a unique local center manifold that is not C^∞.

For this consider equations of a pitchfork bifurcation,

$$\begin{aligned} \dot{x} &= -\lambda x + x^3, \\ \dot{y} &= -y \end{aligned} \tag{B.9}$$

in $\mathbb{R}^2$ depending on a real parameter λ. In an extended phase space one includes an equation

$$\dot{\lambda} = 0. \tag{B.10}$$

The center manifold of the equations (B.9) and (B.10), depicted in Figure B.1, equals $\{y = 0\}$. It is unique since it contains unstable manifolds of the *saddle* fixed points indicated by red dashed curves. Now if one adds generic perturbations to the equations (B.9), (B.10), the plane $\{y = 0\}$ will no longer be invariant. The center manifold will still consist of the unstable manifolds of the saddle fixed points and thus be unique. The unstable manifolds of the fixed points for $\lambda > 0$ are weak stable manifolds of the *stable nodes* in the center manifold indicated by a green line piece. These weak stable manifolds will, for generic perturbations, be only finitely often differentiable [**167**].

In the above example it is true that the center manifold has higher differentiability if one restricts their inquiry to a smaller neighborhood of the origin.

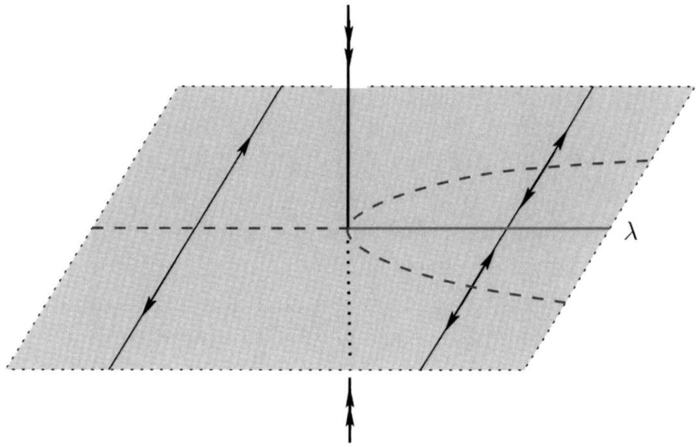

Figure B.1. The phase diagram of the pitchfork bifurcation as it appears in the extended (λ, x, y)-phase plane.

But also such a property is not true in general: [**373**] constructs examples of C^k center manifolds that are not C^{k+1} and thus restrictions to smaller neighborhoods of the origin are still not C^{k+1}. ■

See [**83,327,347**] for a proof of the center manifold theorem using the graph transform (in Section 3.3.3 we apply a graph transform method in a related setting to obtain an invariant simple closed curve for the Neimark-Sacker bifurcation). An approach using the parameterization method is in [**398**]. Infinite-dimensional settings are considered in [**150, 407**].

Center manifolds for endomorphisms. Theorem B.7 on local center manifolds for maps is stated for diffeomorphisms. The arguments however work for smooth maps that have a fixed point with a linearization that has 0 as eigenvalue. The following result takes the setting of Theorem B.5 with a map f of the form (B.2), but allows for a matrix A_s that is noninvertible and has an eigenvalue 0. An orbit is here a sequence x_n defined for $n \in \mathbb{Z}$, not just $n \in \mathbb{N}_0$, and satisfying $x_{n+1} = f(x_n)$ for $n \in \mathbb{Z}$. An explicit example where the need to include noninvertible maps arises is in Theorem 5.61 on bifurcations in Hénon maps $H_{a,b}$, which are noninvertible for $b = 0$.

Theorem B.11 (Global center manifold theorem for endomorphisms). *Consider a smooth map f as in* (B.2) *with $R \in C^r(\mathbb{R}^m, \mathbb{R}^m) \cap B^1_\varepsilon$ and A_s not necessarily invertible. For any $r > 0$ there is $\varepsilon_0 > 0$ so that for $\varepsilon < \varepsilon_0$ the following holds.*

There exists a C^r function $H : E^c \to E^s \times E^u$ such that

(i) *$H(0) = 0$ and $DH(0) = 0$.*

(ii) *The set*

$$M_c = \{(x^s, x^c, x^u)\ ;\ (x^s, x^u) = H(x^c), x^c \in E^c\}$$

is a C^r manifold and is invariant under f.

(iii) *M_c contains all bounded orbits of f.*

Proof. We follow the proof of Theorem B.5 and go through the reasoning that gives the existence of a center manifold. The only part that needs to be considered is the construction of the maps g and h in (B.4) and (B.5), the remainder will go through unaltered. Consider $y = f(x)$, or in coordinates $(y^s, y^c, y^u) = f(x^s, x^c, x^u)$. An implicit function theorem argument allows us to solve (y^s, y^c, x^u) as a smooth function of (x^s, x^c, y^u). So we may write

$$(y^s, y^c, x^u) = g(x^s, x^c, y^u)$$

with $g(0,0,0) = (0,0,0)$ and $Dg(0,0,0) = (A_s, A_c, A_u^{-1})$.

Instead of $(z^s, z^c, z^u) = f^{-1}(x^s, x^c, x^u)$, we write

$$f(z^s, z^c, z^u) = (x^s, x^c, x^u).$$

From this we solve (x^s, z^c, z^u) as a smooth function of (z^s, x^c, x^u). We get

$$(x^s, z^c, z^u) = h(z^s, x^c, x^u)$$

with $h(0,0,0) = (0,0,0)$ and $Dh(0,0,0) = (A_s, A_c^{-1}, A_u^{-1})$. From here the proof of Theorem B.5 can be followed verbatim. Note that the fixed point $\hat{\gamma}(x^c) = \Gamma(x^c, \hat{\gamma}(x^c))$ satisfies $\hat{\gamma}(x^c)(n+1) = f(\hat{\gamma}(x^c)(n))$ not just for $n \in \mathbb{N}_0$ (as one usually considers forward orbits for endomorphisms), but for $n \in \mathbb{Z}$. □

B.1.3. Strong stable manifolds and foliations. The manifolds in this section are locally defined, so we consider a diffeomorphism $f : \mathbb{R}^m \to \mathbb{R}^m$ with a hyperbolic attracting fixed point at the origin. Suppose there are $Df(0)$ invariant subspaces $\mathbb{R}^m = E^{ss} \oplus E^s$ such that for some constants $C \geq 1, 0 < \lambda < \mu < 1$,

$$|Df^n(0)v| \leq C\lambda^n |v|, \ v \in E^{ss},$$

$$|Df^n(0)v| \geq \frac{1}{C}\mu^n |v|, \ v \in E^s$$

for all $n \geq 0$. The subspace E^{ss} are strong stable directions, consisting of vectors v so that $Df^n(0)v$ converges at a strong rate to 0.

There exists an invariant manifold $W^{ss}(0)$ that is tangent to E^{ss} at 0, and so that points in it converge fast to 0 under iteration by f. Such a manifold is called a strong stable manifold. What is stated about strong stable manifolds also applies to strong unstable manifolds with obvious changes.

Theorem B.12. *Suppose 0 is a fixed point of a diffeomorphism $f : \mathbb{R}^m \to \mathbb{R}^m$ with a $Df(0)$-invariant splitting $E^{ss} \oplus E^s$ as above. Let η be such that $\lambda < \eta < \mu$. Then there exists a local invariant manifold $W^{ss}_{loc}(0)$ that is tangent to E^{ss} at 0. For $x \in W^{ss}_{loc}(0)$,*

$$\lim_{n \to \infty} \eta^{-n} |f^n(x)| = 0.$$

Sketch of proof. As in the section on center manifolds, using a bump function we can alter the definition of f in such a way that f equals $Df(0)$ outside a small ball of 0 and f is globally C^1-close to $Df(0)$,

$$\|f - Df(0)\|_{C^1} < \varepsilon$$

for a given small $\varepsilon > 0$.

For η as in the statement of the theorem, let $l^{\infty,\eta}(\mathbb{N}_0, \mathbb{R}^m)$ be the space of sequences $\gamma = (\gamma(n))_{n \in \mathbb{N}_0}$ in $\mathbb{R}^m$ with

$$\|\gamma\|_\eta = \sup_{n \in \mathbb{N}_0} \eta^{-|n|} |\gamma(n)| < \infty$$

and endowed with the norm $\|\cdot\|_\eta$.

Write $y = f(x)$, or in coordinates $(y^{ss}, y^s) = f(x^{ss}, x^s)$. Again we use the box norm $|(x^{ss}, x^s)| = \max\{|x^{ss}|, |x^s|\}$ on $E^{ss} \times E^s$. The implicit function theorem allows us to solve (y^{ss}, x^s) as a smooth function of (x^{ss}, x^s). So we may write

$$(y^{ss}, x^s) = g(x^{ss}, x^s)$$

with $g(0,0) = (0,0)$ and $Dg(0,0) = (A_{ss}, A_s^{-1})$ where $A_{ss} = Df(0)|_{E^{ss}}$ and $A_s = Df(0)|_{E^s}$. For any $\sigma > 0$ we can find ε so that

$$\|g - Dg(0)\|_{C^1} \leq \sigma.$$

Write an element $\gamma \in l^\infty(\mathbb{N}_0, \mathbb{R}^m)$ as $\gamma(n) = (\gamma_{ss}(n), \gamma_s(n))$. Define the map $\Gamma : E^{ss} \times l^{\infty,\eta}(\mathbb{N}_0, \mathbb{R}^m) \to l^{\infty,\eta}(\mathbb{N}_0, \mathbb{R}^m)$ by $\Gamma(x^{ss}, \gamma) = \zeta$ with

$$\zeta_{ss}(0) = x^{ss},$$

$$(\zeta_{ss}(n+1), \zeta_s(n)) = g(\gamma_{ss}(n), \gamma_s(n+1)) \text{ for } n \geq 0.$$

This defines a continuous map on $E^{ss} \times l^{\infty,\eta}(\mathbb{N}_0, \mathbb{R}^m)$. From the estimates for g with σ sufficiently small we get

(i) $\Gamma(E^{ss} \times l^{\infty,\eta}(\mathbb{N}_0, \mathbb{R}^m)) \subset l^{\infty,\eta}(\mathbb{N}_0, \mathbb{R}^m)$;

(ii) $\Gamma(x^{ss}, \cdot)$ is a uniform contraction on $l^{\infty,\eta}(\mathbb{N}_0, \mathbb{R}^m)$.

By the uniform contraction theorem there is a unique fixed point

$$\Gamma(x^{ss}, \gamma_{x^{ss}}) = \gamma_{x^{ss}}$$

with $\gamma_{x^{ss}} = \gamma(x^{ss})$ depending continuously on x^{ss}. For any x^{ss}, the construction gives that the orbit through $\gamma_{x^{ss}}(0)$ belongs to $l^{\infty,\eta}(\mathbb{N}_0, \mathbb{R}^m)$. The manifold $W^{ss}_{loc}(0)$ is the set $\{\gamma_{x^{ss}}(0); x^{ss} \in E^{ss}\}$ or in other words the graph of the function $x^{ss} \mapsto \pi_{ss}\gamma_{x^{ss}}(0)$, where π_{ss} is the projection $\pi_{ss}(x^{ss}, x^s) = x^{ss}$. Smoothness follows from the implicit function theorem. □

Remark B.13. Strong stable manifolds can likewise be constructed for fixed points that are not hyperbolic. Needed is a $Df(0)$ invariant splitting $\mathbb{R}^m = E^{ss} \oplus E^{cu}$ such that for some constants $C \geq 1, 0 < \lambda < \mu < 1$,

$$|Df^n(0)v| \leq C\lambda^n |v|, \; v \in E^{ss},$$

$$|Df^n(0)v| \geq \frac{1}{C}\mu^n |v|, \; v \in E^{cu}$$

for all $n \geq 0$. The argument of Theorem B.12 provides an invariant manifold tangent to E^{ss} at 0. ■

We continue with the setting of Theorem B.12, and look at invariant foliations. We refer to [**3**] for an introduction to the theory of foliations. A strong stable foliation of a neighborhood U of 0 is a disjoint decomposition of U into leaves that are graphs of maps $w : E^{ss} \to E^s$. Writing $\mathcal{F}^{ss}$ for the foliation and

$\mathcal{F}_x^{ss}$ for the leaf containing the point x, the foliation is invariant in the sense that

$$f(\mathcal{F}_x^{ss}) \subset \mathcal{F}_{f(x)}^{ss}.$$

For points x_1, x_2 in the same leaf,

$$\lim_{n\to\infty} \frac{|f^n(x_1) - f^n(x_2)|}{\eta^n} = 0.$$

The foliation is said to be a C^k foliation if there is a C^k foliation box $\xi : U \mapsto E^{ss} \times E^s$ so that for $y \in E^s$, $\xi^{-1}(E^{ss} \times \{y\})$ is contained in a single leaf.

Theorem B.14. *Let f be a C^{k+1} diffeomorphism with an attracting hyperbolic fixed point 0 with a $Df(0)$-invariant splitting $E^{ss} \bigoplus E^s$ as before. Then there exists a C^k strong stable foliation $\mathcal{F}^{ss}$ with $T_0\mathcal{F}_0^{ss} = E^{ss}$.*

Sketch of proof. Given $x_0 \in U$, the positive orbit of x_0 converges to 0. We want to obtain the strong stable manifold $\mathcal{F}_{x_0}^{ss}$ of x_0 as the collection of points x_1 so that

$$\lim_{n\to\infty} \eta^{-n} \, |f^n(x_1) - f^n(x_0)| = 0.$$

The proof of Theorem B.12 can be adapted to construct $\mathcal{F}_{x_0}^{ss}$. For this, work with the space $l_{x_0}^{\infty,\eta}(\mathbb{N}_0, \mathbb{R}^m)$ of sequences $\gamma = (\gamma(n))_{n\in\mathbb{N}_0}$ in $\mathbb{R}^m$ with

$$\|\gamma\|_\eta = \sup_{n\in\mathbb{N}_0} \eta^{-n} \, |\gamma(n) - f^n(x_0)| < \infty.$$

Replacing $l^{\infty,\eta}(\mathbb{N}_0, \mathbb{R}^m)$ by $l_{x_0}^{\infty,\eta}(\mathbb{N}_0, \mathbb{R}^m)$, the procedure of Theorem B.12 gives the smooth manifold $\mathcal{F}_{x_0}^{ss}$. The collection of the leaves $\mathcal{F}_{x_0}^{ss}$ over $x_0 \in U$ gives the strong stable foliation of U.

This proves the existence of a C^0 strong stable foliation (with smooth leaves) but does not prove the existence of a C^k strong stable foliation. This can be done by showing that the bundle $x \mapsto T_x\mathcal{F}_x^{ss}$ is C^k, since $\mathcal{F}^{ss}$ is obtained from these tangent spaces by integration. A tangent space $T_x\mathcal{F}_x^{ss}$ can be viewed as the graph of a linear map in $L(E^{ss}, E^s)$. Consider an induced map $Gf : \mathbb{R}^m \times L(E^{ss}, E^s) \to \mathbb{R}^m \times L(E^{ss}, E^s)$ defined by

$$Gf(x_0, \alpha_0) = (f(x_0), \alpha_1)$$

with

$$\operatorname{graph} \alpha_1 = Df(x_0) \operatorname{graph} \alpha_0.$$

Note that $Gf(0,0) = (0,0)$ and

$$D(Gf)(0,0)(v,w) = Df(0)v \times Df(0)|_{E^s} \, w \left(Df(0)|_{E^{ss}}\right)^{-1}.$$

From this formula we get

$$\left|D(Gf)^n(0,0)|_{\{0\}\times L(E^{ss},E^s)} \, w\right| \geq \frac{1}{C} \left(\frac{\mu}{\lambda}\right)^n |w|$$

for some $C > 1$. Because $\frac{\mu}{\lambda} > 1$, the bundle $T\mathcal{F}^{ss}$ is obtained from the stable manifold of $(0, 0)$ for Gf. It is therefore C^k since Gf is C^k. By integration we obtain the C^k strong stable foliation. □

B.1.4. Center stable and center unstable manifolds. We briefly discuss some other invariant manifolds that are relevant to bifurcation theory. Only diffeomorphisms are treated, noting that corresponding results hold for differential equations.

The center manifolds for diffeomorphisms constructed in the previous section correspond to the part of the spectrum of $Df(0)$ that lies on the unit circle (or has zero real part in the case of differential equations). This is the context needed for local bifurcation theory. The spectrum is thus split into three sets: inside, on, or outside the unit circle. One can generalize to splittings in three parts where the middle part is not just the unit circle but an annulus bounded by two circles around the origin in the complex plane.

Motivated by the previous discussion, we start with a diffeomorphism $f : \mathbb{R}^m \to \mathbb{R}^m$ with $f(0) = 0$ that is globally C^1-close to its linearization $Df(0)$ at 0,

$$\|f - Df(0)\|_{C^1} \le C\varepsilon$$

for some $C > 0$.

Given numbers $r_i < r_o$, consider circles R_i and R_o around the origin in the complex plane with radius r_i and r_o. Assume a splitting $\mathbb{R}^m = \mathcal{E}^s \times \mathcal{E}^c \times \mathcal{E}^u$, invariant under $Df(0)$, so that $\operatorname{spec} Df(0)|_{\mathcal{E}^s}$ lies strictly inside R_i, $\operatorname{spec} Df(0)|_{\mathcal{E}^c}$ lies in the open annulus bounded by R_i and R_o, and $\operatorname{spec} Df(0)|_{\mathcal{E}^u}$ lies strictly outside R_o. There are constants $C \ge 1, \sigma > 0$, with

$$|Df^n(x)v| \le C(r_i - \sigma)^n |v|, \; v \in \mathcal{E}^s,$$

$$\frac{1}{C}(r_i + \sigma)^n |v| \le |Df^n(x)v| \le C(r_o - \sigma)^n |v|, \; v \in \mathcal{E}^c,$$

$$|Df^n(x)v| \ge \frac{1}{C}(r_o + \sigma)^n |v|, \; v \in \mathcal{E}^u,$$

for all $n \ge 0$. Take coordinates $(x^s, x^c, x^u) \in \mathcal{E}^s \times \mathcal{E}^c \times \mathcal{E}^u$ and write

$$Df(0)(x^s, x^c, x^u) = (A_s x^s, A_c x^c, A_u x^u).$$

For $\varepsilon > 0$ consider diffeomorphisms

$$f(x^s, x^c, x^u) = (A_s x^s, A_c x^c, A_u x^u) + R(x^s, x^c, x^u), \tag{B.11}$$

with $R \in C^r(\mathbb{R}^m, \mathbb{R}^m) \cap C^1_\varepsilon(\mathbb{R}^m, \mathbb{R}^m)$, $r \ge 1$, $\varepsilon > 0$, and with $R(u) = \mathcal{O}(|u|^2)$, $u \to 0$.

Arguments akin to those used in the proof of Theorem B.5 allow us to prove the following result.

Theorem B.15. *Consider* (B.11). *There is* $\varepsilon_0 > 0$ *so that for* $\varepsilon < \varepsilon_0$ *the following holds.*

There exists a C^1 *function* $h : \mathcal{E}^c \to \mathcal{E}^s \times \mathcal{E}^u$ *such that*

(i) $h(0) = 0$ *and* $Dh(0) = 0$.

(ii) *The set*

$$M_c = \{(x^s, x^c, x^u) \,;\, (x^s, x^u) = h(x^c), x^c \in \mathcal{E}^c\}$$

is a C^1 *manifold and is invariant under* (B.11).

Remark B.16. The manifold M_c from Theorem B.15 is continuously differentiable but may still have a higher degree of differentiability: its smoothness depends on gap conditions on the spectra of $Df(0)$ restricted to the invariant spaces $\mathcal{E}^s, \mathcal{E}^c, \mathcal{E}^u$. ■

Consider a diffeomorphism $f : \mathbb{R}^m \to \mathbb{R}^m$ with a hyperbolic fixed point at the origin 0, such that $Df(0)$ admits an invariant splitting $E^{ss} \oplus E^s \oplus E^u$ in strong stable, weak stable, and unstable directions. So there is a circle R around the origin in the complex plane, with radius $r < 1$, so that $\operatorname{spec} Df(0)|_{E^{ss}}$ lies strictly inside R, $\operatorname{spec} Df(0)|_{E^s}$ lies in the open annulus bounded by R and the unit circle, and $\operatorname{spec} Df(0)|_{E^u}$ lies strictly outside the unit circle. Theorem B.15 implies the existence of an invariant manifold $W^{s,u}(0)$ for f that is tangent to $E^s \oplus E^u$ at 0. This is called a center unstable manifold. Such a manifold is not unique. However, its tangent bundle along the unstable manifold $W^u(0)$ is unique.

Proposition B.17. *Let* $f : \mathbb{R}^m \to \mathbb{R}^m$ *be a diffeomorphism with a hyperbolic fixed point as above. Let* $W^{s,u}(0)$ *be a center unstable manifold with* $T_0 W^{s,u}(0) = E^s \oplus E^u$. *Then* $T_{W^u(0)} W^{s,u}(0)$ *is a unique smooth bundle.*

Sketch of proof. Near the origin, a tangent space $T_x W^{s,u}(0)$ can be viewed as the graph of a linear map in $L(E^{s,u}, E^{ss})$ (where we denote $E^{s,u} = E^s \oplus E^u$). Consider an induced map $Gf : \mathbb{R}^m \times L(E^{s,u}, E^{ss}) \to \mathbb{R}^m \times L(E^{s,u}, E^{ss})$ defined by

$$Gf(x_0, \alpha_0) = (f(x_0), \alpha_1)$$

with

$$\operatorname{graph} \alpha_1 = Df(x_0) \operatorname{graph} \alpha_0.$$

Note that $Gf(0,0) = (0,0)$ and

$$D(Gf)(0,0)|_{0 \times L(E^{s,u}, E^{ss})}\, w = Df(0)|_{E^{ss}}\, w \left(Df(0)|_{E^{s,u}}\right)^{-1}.$$

This makes clear that the spectrum of $D(Gf)(0,0)$ is inside the unit circle in the complex plane. The unstable manifold of $(0,0)$ for Gf is a unique smooth manifold, which provides a vector bundle along the unstable manifold of 0 for

f. By identifying linear maps in $L(E^{s,u}, E^{ss})$ with their images inside $\mathbb{R}^m$, this gives the tangent bundle of $W^{s,u}(0)$, which is therefore unique and smooth. □

There is a general definition of a normally hyperbolic manifold, which is a starting point of global reduction results.

Definition B.18. Let f be a diffeomorphism on $\mathbb{R}^m$. A compact invariant manifold N of F is called a *normally hyperbolic manifold* if there is a Df-invariant splitting

$$\mathbb{R}^m = E^s(x) \oplus T_x N \oplus E^u(x), \qquad x \in N,$$

with the following properties. There are constants $C \geq 1, \nu_s < \nu_1 < 1 < \nu_2 < \nu_u$ with

$$\begin{aligned} &|Df^n(x)v| \leq C(\nu_s)^n|v|,\ v \in E^s(x), \\ &\frac{1}{C}(\nu_1)^n|v| \leq |Df^n(x)v| \leq C(\nu_2)^n|v|,\ v \in T_x N, \\ &|Df^n(x)v| \geq \frac{1}{C}(\nu_u)^n|v|,\ v \in E^u(x), \end{aligned}$$

for all $n \geq 0$.

The monograph [**162**] (and the earlier [**161**]) contains a wealth of information on invariant manifolds in great generality, based on graph transform techniques. Similar ideas were developed in [**111, 112, 114**]. In particular it is established in these references that normally hyperbolic manifolds are persistent under perturbations: a C^1-small perturbation g of a vector field f with a normally hyperbolic manifold N possesses a normally hyperbolic manifold close to N.

B.2. Normal forms

The study of differential equations frequently involves coordinate transformations which simplify the expression of a vector field. The resulting simplified vector fields are called normal forms. In the main text we performed normal form calculations on an ad hoc basis. The treatment of essentially every bifurcation theorem, whether local or nonlocal, starts with normal form computations. An improved normal form often eases the bifurcation analysis.

B.2.1. The normal form theorem. We recall the Jordan normal form theorem for matrices and present the normal form theorem for equilibria of vector fields. Recall that any $n \times n$ matrix can be transformed into a simple form, the Jordan normal form, by a linear coordinate transformation; see for instance [**163**].

Theorem B.19 (Jordan normal form theorem). *Let A be a complex $n \times n$ matrix. Then there exists a linear transformation U that transforms A to a block matrix*

$$U^{-1}AU = \begin{pmatrix} J_1 & 0 & 0 \\ 0 & \ddots & 0 \\ 0 & 0 & J_m \end{pmatrix}$$

with each block of the form

$$J_i = \alpha I + N = \begin{pmatrix} \alpha & 1 & 0 & 0 & 0 \\ 0 & \alpha & 1 & 0 & 0 \\ 0 & 0 & \alpha & \ddots & 0 \\ 0 & 0 & 0 & \ddots & 1 \\ 0 & 0 & 0 & 0 & \alpha \end{pmatrix}.$$

Here I is the identity matrix and N is a nilpotent matrix with ones above the diagonal and zeros elsewhere.

For real matrices there is a real Jordan normal form. Here, the block matrices for real eigenvalues are the same as for the Jordan normal form. Complex conjugate eigenvalues give rise to block matrices

$$\begin{pmatrix} R & I & 0 & 0 & 0 \\ 0 & R & I & 0 & 0 \\ 0 & 0 & R & \ddots & 0 \\ 0 & 0 & 0 & \ddots & I \\ 0 & 0 & 0 & 0 & R \end{pmatrix}$$

with $R = \begin{pmatrix} a & -b \\ b & a \end{pmatrix}$ for real a, b and $I = \begin{pmatrix} 1 & 0 \\ 0 & 1 \end{pmatrix}$. Versions for smooth families of matrices are obtained in the same way: as long as geometric and algebraic multiplicities of eigenvalues do not change, the linear transformations used to put the system to Jordan normal form can be chosen to vary smoothly with parameters.

A linear map $x \mapsto Lx$ induces a map $\operatorname{ad} L$ on the linear space H_k of vector fields whose coefficients are homogeneous polynomials of degree k. The map ad is referred to as adjoint action and $\operatorname{ad} L$ is defined by

$$\operatorname{ad} L(Y)(x) = [L, Y](x) = DY(x)Lx - LY(x). \tag{B.12}$$

In component form, with $L = (L_{ij})_{i,j \in \{1,\dots,n\}}$ and $x = (x_1, \dots, x_n)$, we have

$$[L, Y]_i = \sum_{j=1}^{n} \left(\frac{\partial Y_i}{\partial x_j} L_j - L_{ij} Y_j \right).$$

Normal form theorems go back to Henri Poincaré and Henri Dulac. The following fundamental result can be found in [**371**], we follow [**143**, Theorem 3.3.1].

Theorem B.20 (Normal form theorem). *Let $\dot{x} = f(x)$ be a C^r differential equation with $f(0) = 0$ and $Df(0) = L$. Choose a complement G_k for $\operatorname{ad} L(H_k)$ in H_k, so that $H_k = \operatorname{ad} L(H_k) \oplus G_k$. Then there is an analytic change of coordinates in a neighborhood of the origin which transforms the system $\dot{x} = f(x)$ to*

$$\dot{y} = g(y) = Ly + g^{(2)}(y) + \cdots + g^{(r)}(y) + R_r(y)$$

with $g^{(k)} \in G_k$ for $2 \le k \le r$ and $R_r(y) = o(|y|^r)$ as $|y| \to 0$.

Proof. We use induction and assume that $\dot{x} = f(x)$ has been transformed so that the terms of degree smaller than s lie in the complementary subspace G_i, $2 \le i < s$. We introduce a coordinate transformation of the form $x = h(y) = y + P(y)$, where P is a homogeneous polynomial of degree s whose coefficients are to be determined. Substitution gives the equation

$$(\mathrm{id} + DP(y))\dot{y} = Ly + f^{(2)}(y) + \cdots + f^{(s)}(y) + LP(y) + o(|y|^s)$$

as $|y| \to 0$. The terms of degree smaller than s are unchanged by this transformation, while the new terms of order s are

$$f^{(s)}(y) + LP(y) - DP(y)Ly = f^{(s)}(y) - \operatorname{ad} L(P)(y).$$

A suitable choice of P will make $f^{(s)}(y) - \operatorname{ad} L(P)(y)$ lie in G_s, as desired. □

Remark B.21. An explicit choice for the complementary subspaces is worked out in [**108**]. Consider an inner product $\langle \cdot, \cdot \rangle_k$ on H_k given by

$$\left\langle \sum_{|\sigma|=k} a_\sigma x^\sigma, \sum_{|\sigma|=k} b_\sigma x^\sigma \right\rangle_k = \sum_{|\sigma|=k} \langle a_\sigma, b_\sigma \rangle.$$

With $\left(\operatorname{ad} L|_{H_k}\right)^T$ defined by $\langle \left(\operatorname{ad} L|_{H_k}\right)^T (g), h \rangle_k = \langle g, \operatorname{ad} L(h) \rangle_k$, we have

$$\left(\operatorname{ad} L|_{H_k}\right)^T = \operatorname{ad} L^T|_{H_k}$$

and

$$H_k = \operatorname{ad} L(H_k) \oplus \ker \left(\operatorname{ad} L|_{H_k}\right)^T = \operatorname{ad} L(H_k) \oplus \ker \operatorname{ad} L^T|_{H_k}.$$

A natural choice for G_k is therefore $\ker \operatorname{ad} L^T|_{H_k}$. ■

By applying the procedure of the normal form theorem, we will prove the Poincaré linearization theorem on formal linearization.

Theorem B.22. *Let $\dot{x} = f(x)$ be a smooth differential equation on $\mathbb{R}^m$ with $f(0) = 0$ and $Df(0) = A$. If the eigenvalues λ_i of A are nonresonant, i.e.,*

$$\lambda_s \neq \sum_{i=1}^{n} m_i \lambda_i$$

for $m_i \in \mathbb{N}_0$, $\sum_{i=1}^{n} m_i \ge 2$, then $\dot{x} = f(x)$ can be reduced to $\dot{x} = Ax + r^\infty(x)$ by a smooth change of coordinates. Here r^∞ is a flat function, and $D^i r^\infty(0) = 0$ for all $i \ge 0$.

Proof. Assume that A is diagonal. We claim that $\operatorname{ad} L$ acting on H_k is diagonal and has eigenvectors $x^m e_s = x_1^{m_1} \cdots x_n^{m_n} e_s$, $1 \le s \le n$, with eigenvalues $\langle m, \lambda \rangle - \lambda_s$. Here e_s is the sth standard basis vector and $\lambda = (\lambda_1, \dots, \lambda_n)$. Namely, calculate

$$\operatorname{ad} L(Y) = \sum_{i=1}^{n} \frac{m_i}{x_i} x^m \lambda_i x_i - \lambda_s x^m = (\langle m, \lambda \rangle - \lambda_s) x^m e_s.$$

If all eigenvalues of $\operatorname{ad} L$ are different from zero, then it is invertible. This holds by assumption. So we can successively kill terms of order $2, 3, \dots$ in the Taylor expansion of f. This defines a sequence of substitutions, which for all substitutions together give an infinite Taylor expansion of a coordinate change. By Borel's theorem, Theorem A.7, we obtain a smooth coordinate transformation as in the statement of the theorem.

If A is not diagonal but has Jordan blocks, then also $\operatorname{ad} L$ has Jordan blocks. The eigenvalues are however the same as in the diagonal case. Therefore, $\operatorname{ad} L$ is invertible on H_k. The theorem therefore holds in the nondiagonal case as well. □

We continue with two examples that relate to the planar Hopf bifurcation and the planar Bogdanov-Takens bifurcation. Planar vector fields $(f_1(x, y), f_2(x, y))$ are written as

$$f_1(x, y)\frac{\partial}{\partial x} + f_2(x, y)\frac{\partial}{\partial y}.$$

Example B.23. Following [**49**, Section 7.6], we illustrate the normal form procedure for a planar system $(\dot{x}, \dot{y}) = f(x, y)$ which has an equilibrium with eigenvalues $\pm i$. After a linear coordinate change,

$$L = Df(0) = \begin{pmatrix} 0 & -1 \\ 1 & 0 \end{pmatrix}.$$

For calculations it is advantageous to work with complex coordinates. In complex coordinates $z = x + i\,y$ and $\bar{z} = x - i\,y$, we have

$$\frac{\partial}{\partial z} = \frac{1}{2}\left(\frac{\partial}{\partial x} - i\frac{\partial}{\partial y}\right), \qquad \frac{\partial}{\partial \bar{z}} = \frac{1}{2}\left(\frac{\partial}{\partial x} + i\frac{\partial}{\partial y}\right).$$

Note that

$$x\frac{\partial}{\partial y} - y\frac{\partial}{\partial x} = i\left(z\frac{\partial}{\partial z} - \bar{z}\frac{\partial}{\partial \bar{z}}\right), \qquad x\frac{\partial}{\partial y} + y\frac{\partial}{\partial x} = \left(z\frac{\partial}{\partial z} + \bar{z}\frac{\partial}{\partial \bar{z}}\right).$$

A calculation shows

$$\left[z\frac{\partial}{\partial z} - \bar{z}\frac{\partial}{\partial \bar{z}}, z^k \bar{z}^l \frac{\partial}{\partial z}\right] = (k - l - 1) z^k \bar{z}^l \frac{\partial}{\partial z},$$

$$\left[z\frac{\partial}{\partial z} - \bar{z}\frac{\partial}{\partial \bar{z}}, z^k \bar{z}^l \frac{\partial}{\partial \bar{z}}\right] = (k - l + 1) z^k \bar{z}^l \frac{\partial}{\partial \bar{z}}.$$

Consequently, ker $\operatorname{ad} A|_{H_{2m}} = \{0\}$ and ker $\operatorname{ad} A|_{H_{2m+1}}$ is spanned by

$$\left\{(z\bar{z})^m z\frac{\partial}{\partial z}, (z\bar{z})^m \bar{z}\frac{\partial}{\partial \bar{z}}\right\},$$

and thus by

$$\left\{(z\bar{z})^m i\left(z\frac{\partial}{\partial z} - \bar{z}\frac{\partial}{\partial \bar{z}}\right), (z\bar{z})^m\left(z\frac{\partial}{\partial z} + \bar{z}\frac{\partial}{\partial \bar{z}}\right)\right\},$$

or in real coordinates by

$$\left\{(x^2+y^2)^m\left(x\frac{\partial}{\partial y} - y\frac{\partial}{\partial x}\right), (x^2+y^2)^m\left(x\frac{\partial}{\partial x} + y\frac{\partial}{\partial y}\right)\right\}.$$

Since ker $\operatorname{ad} A|_{H_m}$ = ker $\operatorname{ad} A^T|_{H_m}$, by a smooth coordinate transformation the vector field can be brought to a normal form

$$\dot{u} = -v + \sum_{k=1}^{N}(a_k u - b_k v)\left(u^2+v^2\right)^k + \mathcal{O}\left(|(u,v)|^{2N+2}\right),$$

$$\dot{v} = u + \sum_{k=1}^{N}(a_k v + b_k u)\left(u^2+v^2\right)^k + \mathcal{O}\left(|(u,v)|^{2N+2}\right),$$

for constants a_k, b_k and any given $N \geq 1$. Compare also [**143**, Section 3.3] and (3.48) which results from a normal form transformation in the context of Hopf bifurcations. ■

Example B.24. Consider a differential equation

$$(\dot{x}, \dot{y}) = f(x,y)$$

on the plane with $f(0,0) = (0,0)$ and

$$D_{x,y}f(0,0) = \begin{pmatrix} 0 & 1 \\ 0 & 0 \end{pmatrix}.$$

The linearization has a double eigenvalue 0 and is nilpotent. Such a vector field is the starting point of the analysis of the Bogdanov-Takens bifurcation in Section 3.2.5.

Normal form calculations as below are found in [**49**, Section 7.6] and [**143**, Section 7.2]. The adjoint action introduced in (B.12) is here $\operatorname{ad} A(X) = [y\frac{\partial}{\partial x}, X]$.

Consider the action of $\operatorname{ad} A$ on H_2 and calculate, for $i = 0, 1, 2$,

$$\left[y\frac{\partial}{\partial x}, x^i y^{2-i}\frac{\partial}{\partial x}\right] = ix^{i-1}y^{3-i}\frac{\partial}{\partial x},$$

$$\left[y\frac{\partial}{\partial x}, x^i y^{2-i}\frac{\partial}{\partial y}\right] = ix^{i-1}y^{3-i}\frac{\partial}{\partial y} - x^i y^{2-i}\frac{\partial}{\partial x}.$$

It follows that $\operatorname{ad} A(H_2)$ is four dimensional and is spanned by

$$xy\frac{\partial}{\partial x},\ y^2\frac{\partial}{\partial x},\ y^2\frac{\partial}{\partial y} - xy\frac{\partial}{\partial x},\ 2xy\frac{\partial}{\partial y} - x^2\frac{\partial}{\partial x}.$$

Note that $\operatorname{ad} A^T(X) = [x\frac{\partial}{\partial y}, X]$. For its action on H_2 we find, for $i = 0, 1, 2$,

$$\left[x\frac{\partial}{\partial y}, x^i y^{2-i}\frac{\partial}{\partial x}\right] = (2-i)x^{i+1}y^{1-i}\frac{\partial}{\partial x} - x^i y^{2-i}\frac{\partial}{\partial y},$$
$$\left[x\frac{\partial}{\partial y}, x^i y^{2-i}\frac{\partial}{\partial y}\right] = (2-i)x^{i+1}y^{1-i}\frac{\partial}{\partial y}.$$

We find that $\ker \operatorname{ad} A^T|_{H_2}$ is spanned by $x^2\frac{\partial}{\partial y}$ and $xy\frac{\partial}{\partial y} + x^2\frac{\partial}{\partial x}$. Instead of taking these vector fields as a basis for G_2, one can take G_2 as the space spanned by

$$x^2\frac{\partial}{\partial y},\ xy\frac{\partial}{\partial y}.$$

Then by applying the normal form theorem, Theorem B.20, we find that near the origin the vector field f is smoothly equivalent to a vector field

$$y\frac{\partial}{\partial x} + \left(ax^2 + bxy\right)\frac{\partial}{\partial y} + Q_1\frac{\partial}{\partial x} + Q_2\frac{\partial}{\partial y},$$

where a, b are constants and

$$Q_1, Q_2 = \mathcal{O}\left(|(x,y)|^3\right).$$

Further calculations gives that $\ker \operatorname{ad} A^T|_{H_m}$ is two dimensional for all $m \geq 2$ and is spanned by $x^m\frac{\partial}{\partial y}$ and $x^{m-1}y\frac{\partial}{\partial y} + x^m\frac{\partial}{\partial x}$. Now $\operatorname{ad} A\left(x^m\frac{\partial}{\partial y}\right) = mx^{m-1}y\frac{\partial}{\partial y} - x^m\frac{\partial}{\partial x}$. We find that $x^{m-1}y\frac{\partial}{\partial y} \notin \operatorname{ad} A(H_m)$. Combining, we can choose G_m as the space spanned by

$$\left\{x^m\frac{\partial}{\partial y}, x^{m-1}y\frac{\partial}{\partial y}\right\}.$$

By the normal form theorem the vector field is smoothly equivalent to a vector field

$$y\frac{\partial}{\partial x} + (G(x) + H(x)y)\frac{\partial}{\partial y} + Q_1\frac{\partial}{\partial x} + Q_2\frac{\partial}{\partial y},$$

where

$$Q_1, Q_2 = \mathcal{O}\left(|(x,y)|^{N+1}\right),$$

G is a polynomial of degree at most N, and H is a polynomial of degree at most $N-1$. ■

A detailed exposition on normal forms can be found in [**404**]. A number of textbooks dig deeper into normal form theory and related theory. We mention [**21**,**184**,**261**], and also [**104**] for blowing up techniques and [**323**] for averaging.

B.2.2. Linearization. Local bifurcation theory involves equilibria that are nonhyperbolic: this is a consequence of the Grobman-Hartman theorem, Theorem 2.42. The Grobman-Hartman theorem is stated below in the two contexts of hyperbolic fixed points of diffeomorphisms and hyperbolic equilibria of differential equations. Proofs can be found for instance in [**69**], [**21**], or [**198**]. We add other results on linearizing coordinates, results that are used frequently in the research literature on nonlocal bifurcation theory.

Consider the differential equations on $\mathbb{R}^m$,

$$\dot{x} = Lx, \tag{B.13}$$

$$\dot{x} = Lx + r(x), \tag{B.14}$$

where $r \in C^1$. Assume there are L invariant subspaces $E^s, E^u \subset \mathbb{R}^m$ such that the restrictions $L|_{E^s}$ and $L|_{E^u}$ have all their eigenvalues with negative and positive part, respectively. Let $\varphi^t(x)$ and $\psi^t(x)$ be the flows generated by (B.13) and (B.14), respectively.

Let C^j be the space of maps from $\mathbb{R}^m$ to $\mathbb{R}^m$ whose derivatives up to order j are bounded and uniformly continuous. The norm $\|\cdot\|_{C^j}$ on C^j is the sup norm of all derivatives up through order j;

$$\|r\|_{C^j} = \sup\{|r(x)|, |Dr(x)|, \ldots, |D^j r(x)| \; ; \; x \in \mathbb{R}^m\}.$$

Write

$$B^1_{\mu_0} = \{r \in C^1 \; ; \; \|r\|_{C^1} < \mu_0\}.$$

Theorem B.25 (Grobman-Hartman theorem for flows). *There is a $\mu_0 > 0$ such that, for any $r \in B^1_{\mu_0}$, there exists a unique homeomorphism $h \in C^0$, depending continuously on r, such that, for all $x \in \mathbb{R}^m$ and $t \in \mathbb{R}$,*

$$h \circ \psi^t(x) = \varphi^t(h(x)).$$

Sketch of proof. The detailed version of the following argument can be found in [**198**]. The stable manifold theorem gives continuously differentiable stable and unstable manifolds. Take coordinates in which these manifolds are the linear subspaces E^s and E^u. Consider the flow restricted to the stable subspace E^s. Write B^s for the unit sphere $\{x \in E^s \; ; \; |x| = 1\}$ in E^s. By writing L in a suitable normal form, we may assume $\langle Lx, x\rangle < 0$ for $x \neq 0$, so that $|\varphi^t(x)| < 1$ for $x \in B^s$. Likewise, if μ_0 is small enough, $\langle Lx + r(x), x\rangle < 0$ for $x \in B^s$, so that $|\psi^t(x)| < 1$ for $x \in B^s$. Define $h : \mathbb{R}^m \to \mathbb{R}^m$ as follows. If $y = \psi^t(x)$ for $x \in B^s$, let

$$h(y) = \varphi^t(x).$$

Then $h(x) = x$ on B^s and maps orbits of ψ^t to orbits of φ^t, preserving time parametrization. A similar conjugation can be found on E^u. We may hence assume that $\varphi^t = \psi^t$ on E^s and on E^u.

The conjugation is extended to all of $\mathbb{R}^m$ through the construction of stable and unstable foliations. Similar to Theorem B.14 one can find a stable foliation $\mathcal{F}^s$: a disjoint family of leaves $\mathcal{F}^s_{x^u}$, $x^u \in E^u$, with $\lim_{t\to\infty} |\varphi^t(u) - \varphi^t(v)| = 0$ whenever $u, v \in \mathcal{F}^s_{x^u}$. The leaves form the stable foliation and contain the stable manifold as the leaf through the origin. The proof of Theorem B.1 can be adapted to construct $\mathcal{F}^s_{x^u}$. For this, work with the space $l^\infty_{x^u}(\mathbb{N}_0, \mathbb{R}^m)$ of sequences $\gamma = (\gamma_n)_{n\in\mathbb{N}_0}$ in $\mathbb{R}^m$ with

$$\|\gamma\| = \sup_{n\in\mathbb{N}_0} |\gamma_n - f^n(x^u)| < \infty.$$

Replacing $l^\infty(\mathbb{N}_0, \mathbb{R}^m)$ by $l^\infty_{x^u}(\mathbb{N}_0, \mathbb{R}^m)$, the procedure of Theorem B.1 gives the smooth manifold $\mathcal{F}^s_{x^u}$. The collection of the leaves $\mathcal{F}^s_{x^u}$ over $x^u \in E^u$ gives the stable foliation of $\mathbb{R}^m$. Likewise there is an unstable foliation $\mathcal{F}^u$ with leaves $\mathcal{F}^u_{x^s}$, $x^s \in E^s$. Each point x in $\mathbb{R}^m$ is a unique intersection point $x = \mathcal{F}^s_{x^u} \cap \mathcal{F}^u_{x^s}$, where both x^s and x^u depend continuously on x. With $h(x) = x^s + x^u$, we have the required topological conjugation. □

Let A be a nonsingular $m \times m$ matrix. Suppose that $\mathbb{R}^m = E^s \oplus E^u$ is an invariant splitting for A. For any $x \in \mathbb{R}^m$, we let $x = x^s + x^u$ with $x^s \in E^s$ and $x^u \in E^u$. On $\mathbb{R}^m$ we can take a product norm $|x| = \max\{|x^s|, |x^u|\}$, for given norms on E^s, E^u. We suppose that the eigenvalues of $A_s = A|_{E^s}$ have modulus less than one and that the eigenvalues of $A_u = A|_{E^u}$ have modulus larger than one.

Theorem B.26 (Grobman-Hartman theorem for maps). *There is $\mu_0 > 0$ such that, for any $R \in B^1_{\mu_0}$, there is a unique homeomorphism h with $R \mapsto h - \mathrm{id} \in C^0$ depending continuously on R, $h(0) = \mathrm{id}$, and $h \circ (A + R) = A \circ h$.*

We continue with results on differentiable coordinate changes that linearize a vector field near a hyperbolic equilibrium. We emphasize parameter dependence as that is the typical setting of bifurcation theory.

Theorem B.27. *Assume $f : \mathbb{R} \to \mathbb{R}$ is a C^∞ vector field with a hyperbolic equilibrium at the origin. Then there is a smooth diffeomorphism h on $\mathbb{R}$ that conjugates the flow of f and the flow of $Df(0)$ on a neighborhood of 0.*

For a smooth family of vector fields $f(x, \lambda)$ depending on a parameter λ, there is a smooth family of diffeomorphisms h_λ conjugating the flow of f and the flow of $Df(0)$ on a neighborhood of 0.

Sketch of proof. The idea of the construction comes from [**359, 360**] and is applicable in a wider variety of linearization problems. We first consider diffeomorphisms on the line with a hyperbolic fixed point. So let $g : \mathbb{R} \to \mathbb{R}$ be a smooth diffeomorphism with a hyperbolic fixed point at the origin.

Let $Dg(0) = \mu$. We may assume $0 < \mu < 1$. By normal form computations (see Theorem B.22) we may assume $g(x) = \mu x + r(x)$ with $r(x) = O(x^\ell)$ for

$\ell \in \mathbb{N}_0$ arbitrarily large. From $Dg(0) \circ h = h \circ g$ we get $h = Dg(0)^{-1} \circ h \circ g = \frac{1}{\mu} \cdot h \circ g$. Denote

$$\mathcal{R}(h) = \frac{1}{\mu} \cdot h \circ g.$$

Let B_ε be the interval $(-\varepsilon, \varepsilon)$. Consider the space

$$\mathfrak{D}^k(B_\varepsilon, \mathbb{R}) = \{j \in C^k(B_\varepsilon, \mathbb{R})\ ;\ j(0) = 0, \dots, D^{k-1}j(0) = 0\}$$

endowed with the C^k norm

$$\|j\| = \sup_{x \in B_\varepsilon} |D^k j(x)|.$$

Note that $\|j\| < \varepsilon$ implies $\sup_{x \in B_\varepsilon} |D^i j(x)| < \varepsilon$ for all $0 \le i \le k$.

Define a map $\mathcal{S}$ on $\mathfrak{D}^k(B_\varepsilon, \mathbb{R})$ by

$$\mathcal{S}(j) = \mathcal{R}(\mathrm{id} + j) - \mathrm{id}.$$

We find

$$\mathcal{S}(j)(x) = \frac{1}{\mu} r(x) + \frac{1}{\mu} j(\mu x + r(x)).$$

The following statements follow easily from this expression: taking ℓ much bigger than k, there is a ball $\mathfrak{B}^k = \{h \in \mathfrak{D}^k(B_\varepsilon, \mathbb{R})\ ;\ \|h\| \le \delta\}$ so that

(i) $\mathcal{S}$ maps $\mathfrak{B}^k$ into itself;

(ii) $\mathcal{S}$ is a contraction on $\mathfrak{B}^k$.

The unique fixed point is a C^k local diffeomorphism that conjugates g to $Dg(0)$.

For families $g(x, \lambda)$ of diffeomorphisms, start by bringing the diffeomorphisms to a form $g(x, \lambda) = \mu(\lambda)x + r(x, \lambda)$ with $r(x) = O(x^\ell)$ for $\ell \in \mathbb{N}_0$ large. The map $\mathcal{S}$ is then a uniform contraction, and its fixed point C^k depends on the parameter λ by the uniform contraction theorem.

The case of vector fields is obtained from the case of diffeomorphisms by the following argument. Assume we have a flow φ^t and the linearized flow $D\varphi^t(0)$. Assume $\varphi^k = D\varphi^k(0)$ for $k \in \mathbb{Z}$: the time 1 map has been linearized. Then set

$$h = \int_0^1 D\varphi^{-\alpha}(0)\varphi^\alpha \, d\alpha.$$

With this we get

$$\begin{aligned} D\varphi^{-t}(0)h &= \int_0^1 D\varphi^{-\alpha-t}(0)\varphi^{\alpha}\,d\alpha \\ &= \int_{-t}^{1-t} D\varphi^{-\alpha}(0)\varphi^{\alpha+t}\,d\alpha \\ &= \int_{-t}^{0} D\varphi^{-\alpha}(0)\varphi^{\alpha+t}\,d\alpha + \int_0^{1-t} D\varphi^{-\alpha}(0)\varphi^{\alpha+t}\,d\alpha \end{aligned}$$

which equals $h\varphi^t$ since

$$\begin{aligned} \int_{-t}^{0} D\varphi^{-\alpha}(0)\varphi^{\alpha+t}\,d\alpha &= \int_{-t}^{0} D\varphi^{-\alpha}(0)D\varphi^{-1}(0)\varphi^{1}\varphi^{\alpha+t}\,d\alpha \\ &= \int_{1-t}^{1} D\varphi^{-\alpha}(0)\varphi^{\alpha+t}\,d\alpha. \end{aligned}$$ □

Remark B.28. The variation of constants formula for $g(x) = \mu x + r(x)$ provides the formula

$$g^n(x_0) = \mu^n x_0 + \sum_{i=0}^{n-1} \mu^{n-i} r(x_i).$$

Given h_0 introduce $h_{i+1} = \mathcal{R}(h_i)$, $i \geq 0$. Thus

$$h_i = \mathcal{R}^i(h_0) = \mathcal{S}^i(h_0 - \mathrm{id}) + \mathrm{id} = \frac{1}{\mu^i} \cdot h_0 \circ g^i.$$

The limit $\bar{h} = \lim_{i\to\infty} h_i$ exists and satisfies $\bar{h} = \frac{1}{\mu} \cdot \bar{h} \circ g$. We find the formula

$$\bar{h}(x) = x + \sum_{i=0}^{\infty} \mu^{-i} r(x_i).$$

For vector fields $f(x) = \mu x + r(x)$, $\mu < 0$,

$$\bar{h}(x) = x + \int_0^{\infty} e^{-\mu s} r(x(s))\,ds.$$

■

Remark B.29. The proof of Theorem B.27 works, with small adaptations, to prove the following result in higher dimensions [**360**]. Assume $f : \mathbb{R}^m \to \mathbb{R}^m$ is a C^∞ vector field with a hyperbolic attracting equilibrium at the origin. Let

$$\begin{aligned} M &= \max_{\mu \in \mathrm{spec}\,(Df(0))} |\mathrm{Re}\,\mu|, \\ m &= \min_{\mu \in \mathrm{spec}\,(Df(0))} |\mathrm{Re}\,\mu|, \end{aligned}$$

where spec $(Df(0))$ stands for the collection of eigenvalues of $Df(0)$. Then for $k < M/m$ there is a C^k diffeomorphism h on $\mathbb{R}^m$ that conjugates the flow of f and the flow of $Df(0)$ on a neighborhood of 0. ∎

Differentiable linearization in the plane was first done by Philip Hartman [**151**].

Theorem B.30. *Let f be a diffeomorphism on $\mathbb{R}^2$ with a hyperbolic saddle fixed point at the origin. Then there is a C^1 local diffeomorphism h so that $h \circ f = Df(0) \circ h$.*

If f_λ is a C^1 family of diffeomorphisms, $\lambda \in \mathbb{R}$, with $f_0 = f$, then for λ near 0 there is a C^1 local diffeomorphism h_λ, depending C^1 on λ so that $h_\lambda \circ f_\lambda = Df_\lambda(0) \circ h_\lambda$.

Sketch of proof. Write μ^s with $|\mu| < 1$ and μ^u with $|\mu^u| > 1$ for the eigenvalues of $Df(0)$. Denote by E^s and E^u the one-dimensional stable and unstable directions (the stable and unstable eigenspaces of $Df(0)$). Take coordinates in $E^s \times E^u$. Now

$$Df(0) = \begin{pmatrix} \mu^s & 0 \\ 0 & \mu^u \end{pmatrix}.$$

An initial smooth coordinate change straightens the local stable and local unstable manifold so that they are contained in E^s and E^u, respectively. By Theorem B.27 one can take coordinates in which the diffeomorphism is linear on the local stable and local unstable manifold.

The remaining coordinate change is by constructing stable and unstable foliations near the origin and straighten them by a C^1 coordinate change. The following is a construction of the stable and unstable foliations akin to the proof of Theorem B.14. An unstable foliation of a neighborhood U of 0 is a disjoint decomposition of U into leaves that are graphs of maps $w : E^u \to E^s$. Writing $\mathcal{F}^u$ for the foliation and $\mathcal{F}^u_x$ for the leaf containing the point x, the foliation is invariant in the sense

$$f(\mathcal{F}^u_x) \subset \mathcal{F}^u_{f(x)}.$$

The leaf $\mathcal{F}_0$ containing the origin is the local unstable manifold E^u. The unstable foliation is determined by the bundle of tangent lines $T\mathcal{F}^u$. A tangent space $T_x\mathcal{F}^u_x$ can be viewed as the graph of a linear map in $L(E^u, E^s)$. Consider an induced map $Gf : \mathbb{R}^2 \times L(E^u, E^s) \to \mathbb{R}^2 \times L(E^u, E^s)$ defined by

$$Gf(x_0, \alpha_0) = (f(x_0), \alpha_1)$$

with

$$\operatorname{graph} \alpha_1 = Df(x_0) \operatorname{graph} \alpha_0.$$

Note that $Gf(0, 0) = (0, 0)$ and

$$D(Gf)(0,0)|_{\{0 \times L(E^u, E^s)\}}\, w = Df(0)|_{E^s}\, w \left(Df(0)|_{E^u}\right)^{-1}.$$

From this formula we get

$$D(Gf)(0,0)|_{\{0\times L(E^u,E^s)\}}\, w = \frac{\mu^s}{\mu^u} w.$$

Note that $\frac{|\mu^s|}{|\mu^u|} < |\mu^s|$. Construct the two-dimensional center unstable manifold of $(0,0)$ for Gf; see Appendix B.1.4. This corresponds to a bundle $x \mapsto E_x$ of lines that is invariant under Df: $Df(x)E_x = E_{f(x)}$. The line bundle can be integrated to yield an unstable foliation.

A C^1 coordinate change maps the unstable foliation to an affine foliation with leaves parallel to E^u. One can similarly construct a stable foliation and straighten its leaves by a C^1 coordinate change. Together this defines the C^1 linearizing coordinates. Inclusion of a parameter is possible by extending the system to $(x,\lambda) \mapsto (f_\lambda(x),\lambda)$, and we proceed from there. □

One can derive other normal forms, possible under further eigenvalue conditions. The following result is an example for dissipative saddle fixed points.

Theorem B.31. *Let f be a diffeomorphism on $\mathbb{R}^2$ with a hyperbolic saddle fixed point at the origin. Let $\mu^s < 1$, $\mu^u > 1$ be the eigenvalues of $Df(0)$. Assume $\mu^s\mu^u < 1$. Then there is a C^2 local diffeomorphism h so that $h \circ f = g \circ h$ for a diffeomorphism $g(x,y) = (\mu^s x + R(x,y), \mu^u y)$ with $R(x,y) = \mathcal{O}(xy)$.*

Let f_λ be a family of diffeomorphisms, $\lambda \in \mathbb{R}$, with $f_0 = f$. Write $\mu^s(\lambda)$ and $\mu^u(\lambda)$ for the eigenvalues of $Df_\lambda(0)$. Then for λ near 0 there is a C^2 local diffeomorphism h_λ, depending C^2 on λ so that $h_\lambda \circ f_\lambda = g_\lambda \circ h_\lambda$ for a diffeomorphism $g(x,y) = (\mu^s(\lambda)x + R(x,y,\lambda), \mu^u(\lambda)y)$ with $R(x,y,\lambda) = \mathcal{O}(xy)$.

Sketch of proof. Lemma 4.38 gives an initial coordinate change. The reasoning for Theorem B.30 gives the existence of a C^2 stable foliation. □

Various papers study differentiable and smooth linearizations. We single out [**31**] by Genrikh Belitskii, [**364**] by Dennis Stowe, and [**360, 361**] by Shlomo Sternberg.

Appendix C

Lin's method

Purpose of this appendix is an exposition of results, with proofs, and the use of Lin's method in homoclinic bifurcation theory.

Lin's method gives a functional analytic approach to the study of homoclinic and heteroclinic bifurcations. The method originates with work of Xiao-Biao Lin [**229**] and was developed further by, in particular, André Vanderbauwhede and Bernold Fiedler [**406**] and Björn Sandstede [**324**]. Many papers have since discussed extensions that enlarged its applicability. These extensions include, among many others, studies of higher codimension homoclinic bifurcations [**324**], bifurcations in systems possessing a symmetry [**169, 200, 400**], homoclinic and heteroclinic bifurcations involving periodic orbits [**207, 211, 300**], and homoclinic bifurcations in discrete systems [**204**]. The method has also proved successful in the study of homoclinic bifurcations in infinite-dimensional systems [**122, 182**].

This exposition is structured as follows. In Appendix C.1 we present the general idea of the method and formulate the main statements which are needed to detect particular orbits, such as periodic orbits, in a neighborhood of a given homoclinic orbit. In the following sections we first develop some of the theory of exponential dichotomies, which discusses asymptotics of solutions of classes of nonautonomous differential equations. We will then proceed to an exposition of Lin's method, with proofs, applied to the codimension-1 homoclinic bifurcation with real leading eigenvalues; we will re-examine the homoclinic bifurcation studied in Section 4.1. Proofs of Lin's method are contained in Appendix C.4. Appendix C.3 that precedes it contains full proofs of Lin's method restricted to the detection of 1-periodic orbits near a homoclinic orbit. These proofs serve as a blueprint for the procedure in the general case. A homoclinic bifurcation analysis with Lin's method is presented in Appendix C.6.

The bifurcation analysis restricted to the detection of 1-periodic orbits is presented in Appendix C.6.1.

Readers who want an impression of statements, proofs, and use of Lin's method can restrict their inquiry to the existence of 1-periodic orbits, and read the following parts:

(i) Appendix C.1 outlining Lin's method;
(ii) Appendix C.3 giving full proofs for the detection of 1-periodic orbits (this uses material on exponential dichotomies from Appendix C.2);
(iii) Appendix C.6.1 for a bifurcation analysis of 1-periodic orbits.

That would give a complete account of Lin's method restricted to the detection of 1-periodic orbits in codimension-1 homoclinic bifurcations with real leading eigenvalues. The reader can compare this with the analysis in Section 4.1.2. A link between Lin's method for deriving the bifurcation equations, and the method described in Section 4.1.2 for deriving bifurcation equations for the same homoclinic bifurcation, is explained in [**170**, Appendix B].

Lin's method as developed in Appendices C.3 and C.4 provides the existence of bifurcating periodic orbits but yields no information on stability. In spirit this is similar to the Lyapunov-Schmidt method in local bifurcation analysis, which yields reduced bifurcation equations and also does not entail stability information. A stability analysis with Lin's method is possible, but more effort is needed. The necessary extensions of the method to forward and backward Lin orbits are developed in Appendix C.5. These results will be applied in Appendix C.6.2 to determine stable and unstable manifolds of periodic orbits.

We include a brief bifurcation analysis of the saddle-focus homoclinic orbit in Appendix C.6.3. For this we adapt Lin's method to homoclinic orbits with complex eigenvalues. Of particular interest are Shilnikov saddle-focus homoclinic orbits, as studied in Section 4.1.3. We discuss the existence of various 1-periodic orbits and shift dynamics.

C.1. Outline of Lin's method

Lin's method can be viewed as a concept for analyzing the dynamics near a heteroclinic chain. A heteroclinic chain is a double infinite sequence of connecting orbits h_i, $i \in \mathbb{Z}$, so that $\omega(h_{i-1}) = \alpha(h_i)$; see Section 2.1 for the notion of limit set.

We will now restrict our inquiry to connecting orbits between hyperbolic equilibria. Write

$$p_i = \omega(h_{i-1}) = \alpha(h_i),$$

where p_i are hyperbolic equilibria. So for each fixed index $i \in \mathbb{Z}$, h_i lies in the intersection of the unstable manifold of p_i and the stable manifold of p_{i+1}.

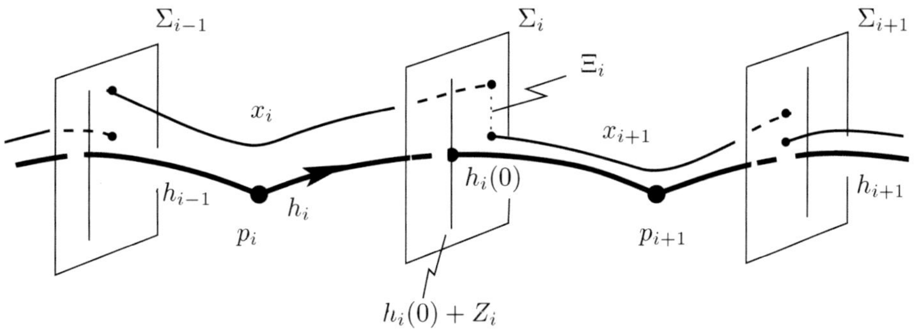

Figure C.1. Lin's method involves the construction of piecewise continuous orbits following a heteroclinic chain with jumps in a fixed direction at points in cross sections.

The basic idea of the method is to construct a sequence $(x_i)_{i\in\mathbb{Z}}$ of partial orbits shadowing the original heteroclinic chain. A visualization is in Figure C.1. The partial orbit x_i starts in a cross section Σ_{i-1} of h_{i-1} and terminates in a cross section Σ_i of h_i. The jump Ξ_i between two consecutive partial orbits x_i and x_{i+1} has to lie in a certain subspace Z_i. We refer to such sequences of partial orbits as Lin orbits. The analysis of Lin's method is divided into two parts, a statement on the existence and uniqueness of Lin orbits, and a derivation of formulas for the jumps in the cross sections. One finds orbits near the heteroclinic chain by solving for the jumps to vanish.

We consider a parameter-dependent differential equation

$$\dot{x} = f_\lambda(x) = f(x, \lambda), \quad x \in \mathbb{R}^n, \lambda \in \mathbb{R}.$$

In what follows we restrict our inquiry to a bifurcation analysis near a homoclinic orbit h, so that in the setting of Lin's method all connecting orbits and equilibria coincide. So we choose

$$h = h_i, \quad p = p_i, \quad \Sigma = \Sigma_i, \quad Z = Z_i,$$

for all $i \in \mathbb{Z}$. The situation is depicted in Figure C.2. We assume a codimension-1 unfolding of a nondegenerate homoclinic orbit, with simple real leading eigenvalues, as in Section 4.1.2. The case of a saddle-focus homoclinic orbit will be briefly discussed in Appendix C.6.3. Compared to Section 4.1.2, eigenvalue conditions will be reversed, and we thus have the following list of assumptions with notation borrowed from Section 4.1.2.

(i) For $\lambda = 0$ there is hyperbolic saddle equilibrium p and $Df_0(p)$ has simple real leading eigenvalues μ^s, μ^u with $\mu^s < 0 < \mu^u$ and a homoclinic orbit $h(t)$ with

$$\lim_{t\to\infty} h(t) = \lim_{t\to-\infty} h(t) = p.$$

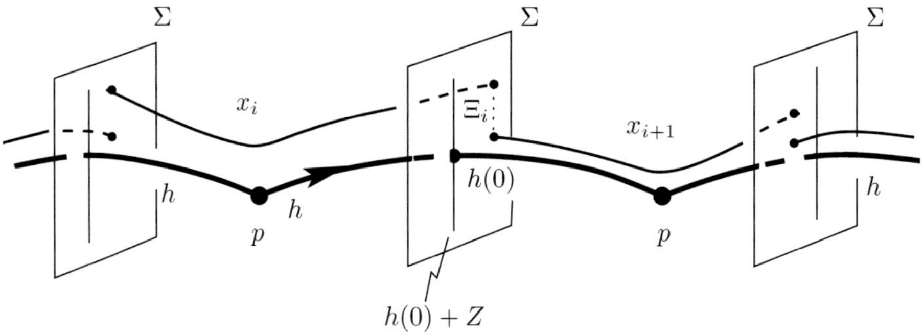

Figure C.2. Lin's method for homoclinic orbits.

For the saddle quantity we assume

$$\mu^s + \mu^u > 0. \tag{C.1}$$

(ii) The homoclinic orbit h is nondegenerate,

$$T_{h(0)}W^{ss,s}(p) \cap T_{h(0)}W^{u,uu}(p) = T_{h(0)}\text{span}\{f(h(0))\}. \tag{C.2}$$

(iii) There is no inclination-flip,

$$\begin{aligned} &W^{ss,s,u}(p) \pitchfork_h W^{u,uu}(p), \\ &W^{s,u,uu}(p) \pitchfork_h W^{ss,s}(p). \end{aligned} \tag{C.3}$$

(iv) The homoclinic orbit h approaches p along leading directions (no orbit-flip),

$$\begin{aligned} &\lim_{t\to\infty} \dot{h}(t)/\|\dot{h}(t)\| \in E^s, \\ &\lim_{t\to-\infty} \dot{h}(t)/\|\dot{h}(t)\| \in E^u. \end{aligned} \tag{C.4}$$

(v) The homoclinic orbit unfolds generically,

$$M = \int_{-\infty}^{\infty} \langle \eta(t), D_\lambda f(h(t), 0)\rangle \, dt \neq 0, \tag{C.5}$$

where η is a bounded solution of the adjoint variational equation $\dot{x} = -Df_0(h(t))^T x$ along h.

Before formulating the results on existence and uniqueness of Lin orbits, we start by making the setting, in particular the definition of the cross section Σ and the jump direction Z, precise. Let $\langle\cdot,\cdot\rangle$ be an inner product on the state space $\mathbb{R}^n$ so that $T_pW^{ss,s}(p) \perp T_pW^{u,uu}(p)$. Write

$$X = \text{span}\{f(h(0), 0)\}$$

for the tangent space to the orbit $h(t)$ at $t = 0$. Then define a hyperplane Σ, as before in (4.34), by

$$\Sigma = h(0) + X^\perp.$$

As in Lemma 4.18 we denote

$$Z = \left(T_{h(0)}W^{ss,s}(p) + T_{h(0)}W^{u,uu}(p)\right)^{\perp}.$$

Note that $Z \subset X^{\perp}$ and so $h(0) + Z \subset \Sigma$. As the homoclinic orbit is assumed to be nondegenerate, we find

$$\dim Z = 1.$$

We can thus take a unit vector $\psi \in Z$ spanning Z. More in particular, with $h^{s/u}(\lambda) = h^{s/u}_{\lambda}$ defined in Lemma 4.18, we choose ψ such that

$$\frac{\partial}{\partial \lambda}\langle \psi, h^s(\lambda)(0) - h^u(\lambda)(0)\rangle > 0. \tag{C.6}$$

Consider the following orthogonal direct sum decomposition

$$\mathbb{R}^n = X \oplus W^+ \oplus W^- \oplus Z, \tag{C.7}$$

where $W^+ = T_{h(0)}W^{ss,s}(p) \cap X^{\perp}$ and $W^- = T_{h(0)}W^{u,uu}(p) \cap X^{\perp}$.

Next we consider the construction of Lin orbits in the setting as just described with assumptions (i) to (v). Given a sequence $\omega = (\omega_i)_{i\in\mathbb{Z}}$ of sufficiently large transition times $\omega_i > 0$, we will prove the existence of a unique piecewise continuous orbit $x = (x_i)_{i\in\mathbb{Z}}$ with the following properties.

(i) Each x_i is a partial orbit of the vector field, starting at a point $x_i(0)$ on Σ, staying close to h until it reaches a neighborhood of p, and then continuing close to h until it reaches Σ at time $2\omega_i$.

(ii) The jump Ξ_i, defined as the difference $x_{i+1}(0) - x_i(2\omega_i)$ between the initial point of x_{i+1} and the final point of x_i, belongs to the subspace Z.

Both the Lin orbit x and the corresponding sequence of jumps $\Xi = (\Xi_i)_{i\in\mathbb{Z}}$ depend on ω and λ, so that we can write $x = x(\omega, \lambda)$ and $\Xi = \Xi(\omega, \lambda)$. The following theorem ensures the existence of Lin orbits for a given sequence ω of transition times. Its proof is contained in Appendix C.4.1.

Theorem C.1. *There is an $\Omega > 0$, so that for each sequence $\omega = (\omega_i)_{i\in\mathbb{Z}}$ with $\inf_{i\in\mathbb{Z}} \omega_i > \Omega$ and each λ, $|\lambda|$ sufficiently small, there is a unique sequence $(x_i)_{i\in\mathbb{Z}}$ of partial orbits $x_i = x_i(\omega, \lambda)$ such that*

$$x_i(\omega,\lambda)(0),\, x_i(\omega,\lambda)(2\omega_i) \in \Sigma,$$
$$\Xi_i(\omega,\lambda) = x_{i+1}(\omega,\lambda)(0) - x_i(\omega,\lambda)(2\omega_i) \in Z.$$

The sequence $(x_i(\omega,\lambda))_{i\in\mathbb{Z}}$ and hence also $\Xi(\omega,\lambda)$ are differentiable with respect to λ.

The following corollary treats periodic sequences.

Corollary C.2. *Let $\omega = (\omega_i)_{i\in\mathbb{Z}}$ be a sequence as in Theorem C.1 which is k-periodic (meaning $\omega_{i+k} = \omega_i$ for all i). Then the sequence $(\Xi_i)_{i\in\mathbb{Z}}$ of jumps is k-periodic.*

Proof. Let $\omega = (\omega_i)_{i\in\mathbb{Z}}$ be a sequence as in Theorem C.1. The left shift operator σ maps ω to a sequence $\sigma\omega$ with $(\sigma\omega)_i = \omega_{i+1}$. Corresponding to ω, Theorem C.1 provides a Lin orbit $x = (x_i)_{i\in\mathbb{Z}}$. Likewise, corresponding to $\sigma^k\omega$, we get a Lin orbit $\sigma^k x$ with $(\sigma^k x)_i = x_{i+k}$. By uniqueness, if $\sigma^k\omega = \omega$, then the Lin orbits obtained are identical. The Lin orbits are therefore k-periodic. □

To obtain actual orbits, staying close to the homoclinic orbit h, one has to solve for the jumps to be equal to zero, $\Xi(\omega, \lambda) = 0$. We decompose the single jumps Ξ_i as

$$\Xi_i(\omega, \lambda) = \xi^\infty(\lambda) + \xi_i(\omega, \lambda), \tag{C.8}$$

where

$$\xi^\infty(\lambda) = h^s_\lambda(0) - h^u_\lambda(0).$$

The quantity $\xi^\infty(\lambda)$ measures the splitting of the stable and unstable manifolds of p; see Lemma 4.18. Since $\Xi_i \in Z$ and Z is spanned by ψ, we have

$$\Xi_i(\omega, \lambda) = \langle \psi, \Xi_i(\omega, \lambda)\rangle \psi.$$

Of course $\xi^\infty(0) = 0$, because for $\lambda = 0$ the unstable manifold $W^{u,uu}(p)$ intersects the stable manifold $W^{ss,s}(p)$ along h. By assumption (C.5), $D\langle \psi, \xi^\infty(0)\rangle \neq 0$. Recalling (C.6), after a reparametrization of the parameter, we may therefore assume

$$\langle \psi, \xi^\infty(\lambda)\rangle = \lambda.$$

As in Section 4.1 we denote by $p(\lambda) = p_\lambda$ the continuation of the equilibrium p for λ near 0. Accordingly, we write $\mu^s(\lambda)$ and $\mu^u(\lambda)$ for the (real) leading stable and unstable eigenvalues of $Df_\lambda(p_\lambda)$.

Theorem C.3. *Under the assumptions of this section there is a smooth reparametrization of the parameter λ, so that for sufficiently small $|\lambda|$ the bifurcation equations $\Xi_i = 0$ are equivalent to*

$$\langle \psi, \Xi_i(\omega, \lambda)\rangle = \lambda - e^{2\mu^s(\lambda)\omega_i}\mathcal{E}^s(\lambda) + R_i(\omega, \lambda) = 0, \qquad i \in \mathbb{Z}, \tag{C.9}$$

where $\mathcal{E}^s(0) \neq 0$. There is a $\delta > 1$ such that

$$R_i(\omega, \lambda) = \mathcal{O}(e^{2\mu^s(\lambda)\omega_i\delta}) + \mathcal{O}(e^{2\mu^s(\lambda)\omega_{i+1}\delta}) + \mathcal{O}(e^{2\alpha^s(\omega_{i-1}+\omega_i)}) + \mathcal{O}(e^{2\alpha^s(\omega_i+\omega_{i+1})}) + \mathcal{O}(e^{2\alpha^s(\omega_{i+1}+\omega_{i+2})}),$$

where $\alpha^s > \mu^s$ can be chosen arbitrarily close to μ^s.

The given expressions for leading and higher-order terms are under the assumption $\mu^s + \mu^u > 0$ on the saddle quantity. For an explicit representation for $\mathcal{E}^s$ we refer to (C.116) below.

Finally we state that the jump is differentiable with respect to ω and give estimates of the partial derivatives $D_{\omega_j} R_i$. To this end we consider Ξ as a mapping

$$\Xi(\cdot,\lambda) : l^\infty(\mathbb{Z},\mathbb{R}) \to l^\infty(\mathbb{Z},\mathbb{R})$$

and correspondingly

$$\langle \psi, \Xi_i(\cdot,\lambda)\rangle : l^\infty(\mathbb{Z},\mathbb{R}) \to \mathbb{R}.$$

Proposition C.4. *Under the conditions of Theorem* C.3 *the mapping*

$$\omega \mapsto (\langle \psi, \Xi_i(\omega,\lambda)\rangle)_{i\in\mathbb{Z}}$$

is differentiable, and with Ω *being a lower bound of* $\omega \in l^\infty(\mathbb{Z},\mathbb{R})$ *the following estimates of the partial derivatives hold. There is a* $\hat{\delta} < 0$ *such that*

$$D_{\omega_j}\langle \xi_i(\omega,\lambda), \psi\rangle = -D_{\omega_j} e^{2\mu^s(\lambda)\omega_i}\mathcal{E}^s(\lambda) + \mathcal{O}(e^{(2\mu^s(\lambda)+\hat{\delta})\Omega}).$$

More detailed estimates of the partial derivatives can be found in [**324**]. We conclude with a representation of $D\xi_i(\omega)$. Recall that the dual space of $l^\infty(\mathbb{Z},\mathbb{R})$ does not coincide with $l^1(\mathbb{Z},\mathbb{R})$. Indeed, the mapping

$$L : l^1(\mathbb{Z},\mathbb{R}) \to (l^\infty(\mathbb{Z},\mathbb{R}))', \qquad (x_i) \mapsto L(x_i),$$

where

$$L(x_i)(y_i) = \sum_i x_i y_i, \quad (x_i) \in l^1,\ (y_i) \in l^\infty,$$

is isomorphic but not surjective [**46**, Section 2.1]. The following proposition clarifies the structure of $D\xi_i(\omega)$.

Proposition C.5. *For each* $i \in \mathbb{Z}$ *one has* $\left(D_{\omega_j}\xi_i(\omega)\right)_{j\in\mathbb{Z}} \in l^1(\mathbb{Z},\mathbb{R})$, *and for* $\mathbf{h} = (h_j)_{j\in\mathbb{Z}} \in l^\infty(\mathbb{Z},\mathbb{R})$,

$$D\xi_i(\omega)\mathbf{h} = \sum_{j\in\mathbb{Z}} D_{\omega_j}\xi_i(\omega)h_j.$$

Further, there are a $\hat{\delta} < 0$ *and a constant* C *such that, with* Ω *a lower bound for* $\omega \in l^\infty(\mathbb{Z},\mathbb{R})$,

$$\|D_\omega\big(R_i(\omega,\lambda)\big)_{i\in\mathbb{Z}}\| \le Ce^{(2\mu^s(\lambda)+\hat{\delta})\Omega}.$$

The proofs of Theorem C.3 and of Propositions C.4 and C.5 will be given in Appendix C.4.2 and Appendix C.4.3, respectively.

C.2. Exponential dichotomies and asymptotic expansions

Proofs of Lin's method are started in Appendix C.3 below. It requires statements from the theory of exponential dichotomies, which are developed in this section.

C.2.1. Exponential dichotomies. Given a homoclinic orbit $h(t)$ of a differential equation $\dot{u} = f(u)$ to a hyperbolic equilibrium p, the first variation equation $\dot{v}(t) = Df(h(t))v(t)$ is a nonautonomous linear differential equation with a special feature. Namely, it has a form $\dot{v}(t) = A(t)v(t)$ with $A(t)$ converging to a hyperbolic matrix $Df(p)$ as $t \to \infty$. Linking solutions of $\dot{v}(t) = A(t)v(t)$ to those of the linear equation $\dot{v}(t) = Df(p)v(t)$ is a topic of the theory of exponential dichotomies. The resulting estimates play a role in Lin's method. The theory is broader than our presentation and is essential in a general study of nonautonomous differential equations. We refer to [**203**] for a comprehensive treatment of the theory of nonautonomous differential equations, which includes discussions of attractors and nonautonomous bifurcation theory. We refer to [**14**] for a discussion of nonautonomous bifurcation theory.

We start with a slight generalization of William Coppel's definition of an exponential dichotomy [**76**]. Consider the linear differential equation

$$\dot{x} = A(t)x, \quad x \in \mathbb{R}^n, \tag{C.10}$$

with transition matrix $\Phi(\cdot,\cdot)$. As with the principal matrix in Section 2.2.1 on Floquet theory, the transition matrix utilizes the linear structure of solutions of (C.10) and means that $x(t) = \Phi(t,t_0)\eta$ solves (C.10) with $x(t_0) = \eta$.

Definition C.6. Equation (C.10), or the transition matrix Φ, has an *exponential dichotomy* on $[t_0, \infty)$ with constants α, β, if there exist projections $P(t)$ on $\mathbb{R}^n$, $t \in [t_0, \infty)$, constants α and β with $\alpha < \beta$, and a positive constant C such that

$$\Phi(t,\tau)P(\tau) = P(t)\Phi(t,\tau)$$

for all $t, \tau \in [t_0, \infty)$, and

$$\begin{aligned} \|\Phi(t,\tau)P(\tau)\| &\le Ce^{\alpha(t-\tau)}, \\ \|\Phi(\tau,t)(\mathrm{id} - P(t))\| &\le Ce^{\beta(\tau-t)}, \end{aligned} \tag{C.11}$$

for $t \ge \tau \ge t_0$. The *projections* are said to be *associated to the exponential dichotomy*.

If $t_0 = 0$, we say that (C.10) has an exponential dichotomy on $\mathbb{R}^+$. In the same way we define exponential dichotomies on $(-\infty, t_0]$ or $\mathbb{R}^-$. In our further explanations we confine ourselves to exponential dichotomies on $[t_0, \infty)$. The only difference to Coppel's notion is that we do not require $\operatorname{sign}\alpha \neq \operatorname{sign}\beta$. More precisely, in the classical version one has $\alpha < 0 < \beta$. We will address this as a classical exponential dichotomy.

For $\xi \in \operatorname{im} P(\tau)$ the solution $\Phi(t,\tau)\xi$ can be bounded by

$$|\Phi(t,\tau)\xi| \le Ce^{\alpha(t-\tau)}|\xi|.$$

If on the other hand $\xi \in \operatorname{im}(\mathrm{id} - P(\tau))$, then with $\zeta = \Phi(t,\tau)\xi \in \operatorname{im}(\mathrm{id} - P(t))$, we find

$$\begin{aligned}|\xi| &= |\Phi(\tau,t)(\mathrm{id} - P(t))\zeta| \\ &\leq Ce^{\beta(\tau-t)}|\zeta| \\ &= Ce^{\beta(\tau-t)}|\Phi(t,\tau)\xi|,\end{aligned}$$

and hence

$$\frac{1}{C}|\xi|e^{\beta(t-\tau)} \leq |\Phi(t,\tau)\xi|.$$

In other words solutions of (C.10) starting at time τ in $\operatorname{im} P(\tau)$ have an exponential upper bound while solutions of (C.10) starting in $\operatorname{im}(\mathrm{id} - P(\tau))$ have an exponential lower bound. In the classical context with $\alpha < 0 < \beta$, solutions starting in $\operatorname{im} P(\tau)$ approach zero exponentially fast while solutions starting in $\operatorname{im}(\mathrm{id} - P(\tau))$ escape exponentially fast.

Plugging $t = \tau$ into the first estimate in (C.11), provides

$$\|P(t)\| \leq C \tag{C.12}$$

for all $t \geq t_0$. That means that the family of projections, which is associated with an exponential dichotomy, is bounded. From a more geometrical point of view this means that the *angle* between the spaces $\operatorname{im} P(t)$ and $\operatorname{im}(\mathrm{id} - P(t))$ remains bounded away from zero.

The next two lemmas are formulated in [**76**] for classical exponential dichotomies.

Lemma C.7. *Let $A(t) \in L(\mathbb{R}^n, \mathbb{R}^n)$. Assume that $\dot{x} = A(t)x$ with transition matrix Φ has an exponential dichotomy on $[t_0, \infty)$ with constants α, β and associated projections $P(t)$. Let $Q(t_0)$ be a projection on $\mathbb{R}^n$ with $\operatorname{im} P(t_0) = \operatorname{im} Q(t_0)$, and define projections $Q(t) = \Phi(t,t_0)Q(t_0)\Phi(t_0,t)$. Then there is a constant $\tilde{C}$ such that*

$$\|P(t) - Q(t)\| \leq \tilde{C}e^{(\alpha-\beta)(t-t_0)}.$$

Proof. Because $\operatorname{im} P(t_0) = \operatorname{im} Q(t_0)$, we have

$$P(t_0) - Q(t_0) = P(t_0)(P(t_0) - Q(t_0))(\mathrm{id} - P(t_0)).$$

Using (C.11), we get

$$\begin{aligned}\|P(t) - Q(t)\| &= \|\Phi(t,t_0)(P(t_0) - Q(t_0))\Phi(t_0,t)\| \\ &= \|\Phi(t,t_0)P(t_0)(P(t_0) - Q(t_0))(\mathrm{id} - P(t_0))\Phi(t_0,t)\| \\ &\leq \|\Phi(t,t_0)P(t_0)\|\,\|(P(t_0) - Q(t_0))\|\,\|(\mathrm{id} - P(t_0))\Phi(t_0,t)\| \\ &= \|\Phi(t,t_0)P(t_0)\|\,\|(P(t_0) - Q(t_0))\|\,\|\Phi(t_0,t)(\mathrm{id} - P(t))\| \\ &\leq C^2\|(P(t_0) - Q(t_0))\|\,e^{(\alpha-\beta)(t-t_0)}.\end{aligned}$$

□

Lemma C.8. *Let $A(t) \in L(\mathbb{R}^n, \mathbb{R}^n)$. Assume that the equation $\dot{x} = A(t)x$ with transition matrix Φ has an exponential dichotomy on $[t_0, \infty)$ with constants α, β and associated projections $P(t)$. Let $Q(t_0)$ be a projection on $\mathbb{R}^n$ with $\operatorname{im} P(t_0) = \operatorname{im} Q(t_0)$. Then the projections $Q(t) = \Phi(t, t_0)Q(t_0)\Phi(t_0, t)$ are associated to the exponential dichotomy.*

Proof. From the definition of $Q(t)$ it is clear that the projections $Q(t)$ commute with the transition matrix Φ. So it remains to verify the estimates (C.11).

First we note that by (C.12) and Lemma C.7, the norm $\|Q(t)\|$ remains bounded. Further, by construction we have $\operatorname{im} P(t) = \operatorname{im} Q(t)$. Therefore

$$P(t)Q(t) = Q(t)$$

and

$$(\mathrm{id} - Q(t))(\mathrm{id} - P(t)) = \mathrm{id} - Q(t).$$

Hence for all $t \geq \tau \geq t_0$,

$$\begin{aligned} \|\Phi(t, \tau)Q(\tau)\| &= \|\Phi(t, \tau)P(\tau)Q(\tau)\| \\ &\leq \|\Phi(t, \tau)P(\tau)\| \, \|Q(\tau)\|. \end{aligned}$$

Because of the estimate (C.11) for $\|\Phi(t, \tau)P(\tau)\|$, there is a constant $\hat{C}$ such that

$$\|\Phi(t, \tau)Q(\tau)\| \leq \hat{C}e^{\alpha(t-\tau)}.$$

Similarly

$$\begin{aligned} \|\Phi(\tau, t)(\mathrm{id} - Q(t))\| &= \|\Phi(\tau, t)(\mathrm{id} - Q(t))(\mathrm{id} - P(t))\| \\ &= \|(\mathrm{id} - Q(\tau))\Phi(\tau, t)(\mathrm{id} - P(t))\|. \end{aligned}$$

Now by estimate (C.11) for $\|\Phi(\tau, t)(\mathrm{id} - P(t))\|$, there is a $\tilde{C}$ with

$$\|\Phi(\tau, t)(\mathrm{id} - Q(t))\| \leq \tilde{C}e^{\beta(\tau-t)}.$$ □

Consider an autonomous equation

$$\dot{x} = Ax, \tag{C.13}$$

where $A \in L(\mathbb{R}^n, \mathbb{R}^n)$. Let the spectrum $\sigma(A)$ be composed of nonempty sets σ^1 and σ^2,

$$\sigma(A) = \sigma^1 \cup \sigma^2.$$

If there are constants α, β such that

$$\operatorname{Re} \mu^1 < \alpha < \beta < \operatorname{Re} \mu^2 \tag{C.14}$$

for all $\mu^1 \in \sigma^1$ and $\mu^2 \in \sigma^2$, then (C.13) has an exponential dichotomy on $\mathbb{R}^+$ with constants α, β. And vice versa, if (C.13) has an exponential dichotomy on $\mathbb{R}^+$ with constants α, β, then there exists a decomposition $\sigma(A) = \sigma^1 \cup \sigma^2$ of the spectrum of A such that (C.14) is true. Moreover the projections $P(t)$ can be chosen to be identically equal to the spectral projection P corresponding to the decomposition of the spectrum of A. If in particular $\alpha < 0 < \beta$, then σ^1 is the stable spectrum of A and σ^2 is the unstable spectrum of A.

One of the most important features of exponential dichotomies is a roughness property. This means that (certain) perturbations of systems having an exponential dichotomy remain having an exponential dichotomy. We restrict ourselves to perturbations from autonomous systems.

Theorem C.9. *Let $A \in L(\mathbb{R}^n, \mathbb{R}^n)$ and let α and β be in accordance with* (C.14). *For $t \in [t_0, \infty)$, let $B(t) \in L(\mathbb{R}^n, \mathbb{R}^n)$. Assume that there are positive constants K_B and δ such that*

$$\|B(t)\| \leq K_B e^{-\delta t}. \tag{C.15}$$

Then the equation

$$\dot{x} = (A + B(t))x \tag{C.16}$$

has an exponential dichotomy on $[t_0, \infty)$ with constants α and β.

Proof. We use ideas from [**324**]. Let $\Phi(\cdot, \cdot)$ and $\Phi_B(\cdot, \cdot)$ be the transition matrices of (C.13) and (C.16), respectively. Take the decomposition $\sigma(A) = \sigma^1 \cup \sigma^2$ of the spectrum of A such that (C.14) is true. Let Q denote the corresponding spectral projection onto the sum of generalized eigenspaces of σ^1.

First we construct projections $\hat{Q}_s(t)$ on $\mathbb{R}^n$ that satisfy the first inequality in (C.11). For this purpose we consider, for $\eta \in \mathbb{R}^n$, the fixed point equation

$$x(t, \tau) = T_s(x, \eta)(t, \tau), \tag{C.17}$$

where

$$\begin{aligned} T_s(x, \eta)(t, \tau) = \Phi(t, \tau)Q\eta &+ \int_\tau^t \Phi(t, s)QB(s)x(s, \tau)\, ds \\ &- \int_t^\infty \Phi(t, s)(\mathrm{id} - Q)B(s)x(s, \tau)\, ds. \end{aligned} \tag{C.18}$$

We consider $T_s(\cdot, \eta)$ acting on the Banach space

$$\mathbb{S}_\alpha = \{x\ ;\ [t_0, \infty) \times [t_0, \infty) \to \mathbb{R}^n\ ,\ \sup_{t \geq \tau \geq t_0} e^{\alpha(\tau - t)}|x(t, \tau)| < \infty\},$$

equipped with the norm

$$\|x\|_\alpha = \sup_{t \geq \tau \geq t_0} e^{\alpha(\tau - t)}|x(t, \tau)|.$$

The contraction mapping theorem can be applied to prove that (C.17) has a unique fixed point $x_s(\eta)(\cdot,\cdot)$. For this we exploit that for some constant K,

$$\|\Phi(t,s)Q\| \leq Ke^{\alpha(t-s)}, \qquad \text{for } t \geq s,$$

$$\|\Phi(t,s)(\mathrm{id}-Q)\| \leq Ke^{\alpha(t-s)}, \qquad \text{for } s \geq t,$$

$$|x(s,\tau)| \leq \|x\|_\alpha e^{\alpha(s-\tau)}, \qquad \text{for } s \geq \tau. \tag{C.19}$$

Together with (C.15) these estimates show that $T_s(\cdot,\eta)$ maps $\mathbb{S}_\alpha$ into itself, and that (for sufficiently large t_0) $T_s(\cdot,\eta)$ is a contraction. By differentiating, one can check that if $x(t,\tau) = T_s(x,\eta)(t,\tau)$, then $\frac{d}{dt}x(t,\tau) = (A + B(t))x(t,\tau)$.

Define projections $\hat{Q}_s(\tau) : \mathbb{R}^n \to \mathbb{R}^n$ by

$$\hat{Q}_s(\tau)\xi = x_s(Q\xi)(\tau,\tau).$$

This indeed defines projections. First $\hat{Q}_s(\tau)(\cdot)$ is linear, because $x_s(\eta)(\cdot,\cdot)$ depends linearly on η. And, since Q commutes with Φ and $Q(\mathrm{id}-Q) = 0$, we find from (C.18) that $\hat{Q}_s(\tau)(\cdot)$ is idempotent and thus a projection. So we have $x_s(Q\xi)(\tau,\tau) = \hat{Q}_s(\tau)\xi$, and we claim that

$$x_s(Q\xi)(t,\tau) = \Phi_B(t,\tau)\hat{Q}_s(\tau)\xi. \tag{C.20}$$

This is due to the fact that both $x_s(Q\xi)(\cdot,\tau)$ and $\Phi_B(\cdot,\tau)\hat{Q}_s(\tau)\xi$ solve the initial value problem

$$\dot{x} = (A + B(t))x,$$

$$x(\tau) = \hat{Q}_s(\tau)\xi.$$

(For $\Phi_B(\cdot,\tau)\hat{Q}_s(\tau)\xi$ this is clear as Φ_B is the transition matrix for this equation, for $x_s(Q\xi)(\cdot,\tau)$ this can be checked, as said, by differentiating the fixed point equation (C.17), (C.18).)

For $\hat{\tau} \geq t_0$ and $\xi \in \mathbb{R}^n$ consider $x(\xi)(t,\tau) = \Phi_B(t,\tau)\Phi_B(\tau,\hat{\tau})\xi$. We find that $x(\xi)(\cdot,\cdot)$ is a fixed point of $T_s(\cdot,\xi)$ in $\mathbb{S}_\alpha$ precisely if $\Phi_B(\tau,\hat{\tau})\xi \in \mathrm{im}\,\hat{Q}_s(\tau)$. Now $x(\xi)(\tau,\tau) = \Phi_B(\tau,\hat{\tau})\xi$. Doing the above analysis with τ replaced by $\hat{\tau}$, we find that $\Phi_B(t,\tau)\Phi_B(\tau,\hat{\tau})\xi = \Phi_B(t,\hat{\tau})\xi$ is in $\mathbb{S}_\alpha$ precisely if $\xi \in \mathrm{im}\,\hat{Q}_s(\hat{\tau})$. Hence

$$\Phi_B(\tau,\hat{\tau})\mathrm{im}\,\hat{Q}_s(\hat{\tau}) = \mathrm{im}\,\hat{Q}_s(\tau).$$

In words, the images of $\hat{Q}_s$ are invariant under Φ_B.

We can now construct projections $P(t)$ associated to the exponential dichotomy of (C.16). Consider the direct sum decompositions of $\mathbb{R}^n$

$$\mathbb{R}^n = \mathrm{im}\,\hat{Q}_s(t) \oplus \Phi_B(t,t_0)\ker\hat{Q}_s(t_0).$$

Let $P(t)$ be the corresponding projections with

$$\mathrm{im}\,P(t) = \mathrm{im}\,\hat{Q}_s(t).$$

Of course $P(t)$ commutes with Φ_B,

$$P(t)\Phi_B(t,\tau) = \Phi_B(t,\tau)P(\tau).$$

It remains to verify estimates (C.11). To do this, we consider solutions of (C.16) starting in $\ker P(\tau) = \operatorname{im}(\mathrm{id} - P(\tau))$ as solutions of the fixed point equation

$$x(t,\tau) = T_u(x,\eta)(\tau,t), \tag{C.21}$$

where

$$T_u(x,\eta)(\tau,t) = \Phi(\tau,t)(\mathrm{id} - Q)\eta + \int_{t_0}^{\tau} \Phi(\tau,s)QB(s)x(s,t)\,ds - \int_{\tau}^{t} \Phi(\tau,s)(\mathrm{id} - Q)B(s)x(s,t)\,ds. \tag{C.22}$$

We consider $T_u(\cdot,\eta)$ acting on the Banach space

$$\mathbb{S}^\beta = \{x\,;\ [t_0,\infty)\times[t_0,\infty) \to \mathbb{R}^n\,,\ \sup_{t\geq\tau\geq t_0} e^{\beta(t-\tau)}|x(\tau,t)| < \infty\}$$

equipped with the norm

$$\|x\|^\beta = \sup_{t\geq\tau\geq t_0} e^{\beta(t-\tau)}|x(\tau,t)|.$$

Similarly, the contraction mapping theorem can be applied to prove that (C.21) has a unique fixed point $x_u(\eta)(\cdot,\cdot)$. We can use estimates

$$\begin{aligned} \|\Phi(t,s)Q\| &\leq Ke^{\beta(t-s)}, &&\text{for } t \geq s,\\ \|\Phi(t,s)(\mathrm{id} - Q)\| &\leq Ke^{\beta(t-s)}, &&\text{for } s \geq t,\\ |x(s,t)| &\leq \|x\|^\beta e^{\beta(s-t)}, &&\text{for } t \geq s, \end{aligned} \tag{C.23}$$

to show that $T_u(\cdot,\eta)$ maps $\mathbb{S}^\beta$ into itself and is a contraction on $\mathbb{S}^\beta$. The contraction mapping theorem yields that for each $\eta \in \operatorname{im}(\mathrm{id} - Q)$, $T_u(\cdot,\eta)$ has a unique fixed point $x_u(\eta)(\cdot,\cdot)$. And again $\hat{Q}_u(\tau) : \mathbb{R}^n \to \mathbb{R}^n$, given by

$$\hat{Q}_u(\tau)\xi = x_u((\mathrm{id} - Q)\xi)(\tau,\tau),$$

defines projections. From the fixed point equation (C.21) we read that $\operatorname{im}\hat{Q}_u(t_0) = \operatorname{im}(\mathrm{id} - Q)$. Similarly, we find from (C.17) that $\ker\hat{Q}_s(t_0) = \operatorname{im}(\mathrm{id} - Q)$. This gives

$$\operatorname{im}\hat{Q}_u(t) = \Phi_B(t,t_0)\ker\hat{Q}_s(t_0) = \ker P(t).$$

The function $x_u(\eta)(\cdot,\tau)$ is a solution of (C.16). Therefore

$$\begin{aligned} x_u((\mathrm{id} - Q)\xi)(t,\tau) &= \Phi_B(t,\tau)x_u((\mathrm{id} - Q)\xi)(\tau,\tau)\\ &= \Phi_B(t,\tau)\hat{Q}_u(\tau)\xi. \end{aligned} \tag{C.24}$$

Because of $\operatorname{im} P(t) = \operatorname{im} \hat{Q}_s(t)$ and $\operatorname{im}(\mathrm{id} - P(t)) = \operatorname{im} \hat{Q}_u(t)$, we have for $t \geq \tau \geq t_0$,

$$\Phi_B(t,\tau)P(\tau) = \Phi_B(t,\tau)\hat{Q}_s(\tau)P(\tau),$$
$$\Phi_B(\tau,t)(\mathrm{id} - P(t)) = \Phi_B(\tau,t)\hat{Q}_u(t)(\mathrm{id} - P(t)).$$

If $\{||P(t)|| \ ; \ t \geq t_0\}$ is bounded (we will confirm this below), then with (C.27) and (C.28), we find a positive constant C such that

$$||\Phi_B(t,\tau)P(\tau)|| \leq Ce^{\alpha(t-\tau)},$$
$$||\Phi_B(\tau,t)(\mathrm{id} - P(t))|| \leq Ce^{\beta(\tau-t)},$$

for $t \geq \tau \geq t_0$. So, checking the requirements in Definition C.6, we conclude that (C.16) has an exponential dichotomy as stated in the theorem.

We conclude with the verification that $\{||P(t)|| \ ; \ t \geq t_0\}$ is bounded. For $\xi \in \mathbb{R}^n$ we define $\xi_s = P(t)\xi$ and $\xi_u = (\mathrm{id} - P(t))\xi$. Since $\operatorname{im} P(t) = \operatorname{im} \hat{Q}_s(t)$, we have

$$\begin{aligned} P(t)\xi &= \hat{Q}_s(t)P(t)\xi \\ &= \hat{Q}_s(t)\xi_s \\ &= x_s(Q\xi_s)(t,t). \end{aligned}$$

Then by (C.17) we find

$$\begin{aligned} &P(t)\xi \\ &\quad = Q\xi_s - \int_t^\infty \Phi(t,s)(\mathrm{id} - Q)B(s)x_s(Q\xi_s)(s,t)\,ds \\ &\quad = Q\xi - Q\xi_u - \int_t^\infty \Phi(t,s)(\mathrm{id} - Q)B(s)x_s(Q\xi_s)(s,t)\,ds \\ &\quad = Q\xi - Q\hat{Q}_u(t)\xi_u - \int_t^\infty \Phi(t,s)(\mathrm{id} - Q)B(s)x_s(Q\xi_s)(s,t)\,ds \\ &\quad = Q\xi - Qx_u((\mathrm{id} - Q)\xi_u)(t,t) - \int_t^\infty \Phi(t,s)(\mathrm{id} - Q)B(s)x_s(Q\xi_s)(s,t)\,ds. \end{aligned}$$

Now exploiting (C.21), we get

$$\begin{aligned} P(t)\xi = Q\xi &- \int_{t_0}^t \Phi(t,s)QB(s)x_u((\mathrm{id} - Q)\xi_u)(s,t)\,ds \\ &- \int_t^\infty \Phi(t,s)(\mathrm{id} - Q)B(s)x_s(Q\xi_s)(s,t)\,ds. \end{aligned} \tag{C.25}$$

Because of (C.20) and (C.24) it follows that

$$
\begin{aligned}
P(t)\xi = Q\xi &- \int_{t_0}^{t} \Phi(t,s)QB(s)\Phi_B(s,t)\hat{Q}_u(t)(\mathrm{id} - P(t))\xi \, ds \\
&- \int_{t}^{\infty} \Phi(t,s)(\mathrm{id} - Q)B(s)\Phi_B(s,t)\hat{Q}_s(t)P(t)\xi \, ds. \qquad \text{(C.26)}
\end{aligned}
$$

We will estimate the integral terms in the last equation.

First note that (C.20) and the third estimate in (C.19) yield that for some positive $\mathcal{K}_s$,

$$\|\Phi_B(t,\tau)\hat{Q}_s(\tau)\| \le \mathcal{K}_s e^{\alpha(t-\tau)}, \qquad \text{(C.27)}$$

for $t \ge \tau \ge t_0$. Similarly we have, for some positive $\mathcal{K}_u$,

$$\|\Phi_B(\tau,t)\hat{Q}_u(t)\| \le \mathcal{K}_u e^{\beta(\tau-t)}, \qquad \text{(C.28)}$$

for $t \ge \tau \ge t_0$. Now, by (C.15), (C.19), and (C.28),

$$
\begin{aligned}
&\left| \int_{t_0}^{t} \Phi(t,s)QB(s)\Phi_B(s,t)\hat{Q}_u(t)(\mathrm{id} - P(t))\xi ds \right| \\
&\qquad \le \int_{t_0}^{t} KK_B\mathcal{K}_u e^{(\alpha-\beta)(t-s)} e^{-\delta s}(1 + \|P(t)\|)|\xi| \, ds.
\end{aligned}
$$

As $\alpha - \beta < 0$ we get

$$
\begin{aligned}
&\left| \int_{t_0}^{t} \Phi(t,s)QB(s)\Phi_B(s,t)\hat{Q}_u(t)(\mathrm{id} - P(t))\xi \, ds \right| \qquad \text{(C.29)} \\
&\qquad \le \left(\int_{t_0}^{t} KK_B\mathcal{K}_u e^{-\delta s} \, ds + \int_{t_0}^{t} KK_B\mathcal{K}_u e^{-\delta s} \, ds \|P(t)\| \right) |\xi|.
\end{aligned}
$$

In the same way, but this time exploiting (C.15), (C.23), and (C.27),

$$
\begin{aligned}
&\left| \int_{t}^{\infty} \Phi(t,s)(\mathrm{id} - Q)B(s)\Phi_B(s,t)\hat{Q}_s(t)P(t)\xi \, ds \right| \qquad \text{(C.30)} \\
&\qquad \le \left(\int_{t}^{\infty} KK_B\mathcal{K}_s e^{-\delta s} \, ds \|P(t)\| \right) |\xi|.
\end{aligned}
$$

We choose t_0 large so that $KK_B \max\{\mathcal{K}_s, \mathcal{K}_u\} \int_{t_0}^{\infty} e^{-\delta s} \, ds \le \frac{1}{4}$. Combining (C.26), (C.29), (C.30), we find

$$\|P(t)\| \le 2\left(\|Q\| + KK_B\mathcal{K}_u \int_{t_0}^{\infty} e^{-\delta s} \, ds \right). \qquad \square$$

Under the assumptions of Theorem C.9, with the spectral projection Q associated to the exponential dichotomy of $\dot{x} = Ax$ as in its proof, and for projections $P(t)$ associated to the exponential dichotomy of the perturbed equation (C.16), the norm $\|P(t) - Q\|$ tends exponentially fast to zero as t tends to infinity. It turns out that the exponential rate depends on the spectral gap between σ^1 and σ^2 and on the exponential rate δ.

Lemma C.10. *Assume the hypotheses of Theorem C.9. Let Q be the spectral projection of A associated to the exponential dichotomy of $\dot{x} = Ax$, and let $P(t)$ be the projections obtained in the proof of Theorem C.9.*

Let $\gamma > 0$ satisfy

$$\begin{aligned} \alpha - \beta + \gamma &< 0, \\ \gamma - \delta &< 0, \\ \operatorname{Re} \mu^1 &< \alpha - \gamma, \end{aligned}$$

for all $\mu^1 \in \sigma^1$. Then there is a constant $\mathcal{K}$ such that

$$\|P(t) - Q\| \leq \mathcal{K} e^{-\gamma t}.$$

Proof. We use notation from the proof of Theorem C.9. To estimate $\|P(t) - Q\|$ we start from (C.25), which yields

$$\text{(C.31)} \quad \begin{aligned} |P(t)\xi - Q\xi| \leq & \left| \int_{t_0}^{t} \Phi(t,s) Q B(s) x_u((\mathrm{id} - Q)\xi_u)(s,t)\, ds \right| \\ & + \left| \int_{t}^{\infty} \Phi(t,s)(\mathrm{id} - Q) B(s) x_s(Q\xi_s)(s,t)\, ds \right|. \end{aligned}$$

From (C.22) we see that

$$\text{(C.32)} \quad \begin{aligned} Q x_u(\eta)(\tau, t) &= \int_{t_0}^{\tau} \Phi(\tau, s) Q B(s) x_u(\eta)(s,t)\, ds \\ &= \int_{t_0}^{\tau} \Phi(\tau, s) Q B(s) Q x_u(\eta)(s,t)\, ds \\ &\quad + \int_{t_0}^{\tau} \Phi(\tau, s) Q B(s)(\mathrm{id} - Q) x_u(\eta)(s,t)\, ds. \end{aligned}$$

Therefore we have

$$
\begin{aligned}
&|Qx_u(\eta)(\tau,t)|e^{\beta(t-\tau)}e^{\gamma\tau}\\
&\quad\leq e^{\beta(t-\tau)}e^{\gamma\tau}\Bigg(\int_{t_0}^{\tau}\|\Phi(\tau,s)Q\|\,\|B(s)\|\,|Qx_u(\eta)(s,t)|\,ds\\
&\qquad\qquad+\int_{t_0}^{\tau}\|\Phi(\tau,s)Q\|\,\|B(s)\|\,\|(\mathrm{id}-Q)\|\,|x_u(\eta)(s,t)|\,ds\Bigg).
\end{aligned}
$$

With (C.15) and (C.19) it follows that

$$
\begin{aligned}
&|Qx_u(\eta)(\tau,t)|e^{\beta(t-\tau)}e^{\gamma\tau}\\
&\quad\leq e^{\beta(t-\tau)}e^{\gamma\tau}\Bigg(\int_{t_0}^{\tau}KK_Be^{\alpha(\tau-s)}e^{-\delta s}\,|Qx_u(\eta)(s,t)|\,ds\\
&\qquad\qquad+\int_{t_0}^{\tau}KK_Be^{\alpha(\tau-s)}e^{-\delta s}\,\|(\mathrm{id}-Q)\|\,|x_u(\eta)(s,t)|\,ds\Bigg),
\end{aligned}
$$

and by inserting a *factor* 1,

$$
\begin{aligned}
&|Qx_u(\eta)(\tau,t)|e^{\beta(t-\tau)}e^{\gamma\tau}\\
&=e^{\beta(t-\tau)}e^{\gamma\tau}\Big(\int_{t_0}^{\tau}KK_Be^{\alpha(\tau-s)}e^{-\delta s}\,|Qx_u(\eta)(s,t)|e^{\beta(t-s)}e^{\gamma s}\,e^{-\beta(t-s)}e^{-\gamma s}\,ds\\
&+\int_{t_0}^{\tau}KK_Be^{\alpha(\tau-s)}e^{-\delta s}\,\|(\mathrm{id}-Q)\|\,|x_u(\eta)(s,t)|e^{\beta(t-s)}e^{\gamma s}\,e^{-\beta(t-s)}e^{-\gamma s}\,ds\Big).
\end{aligned}
$$

With (C.23) this yields

$$
\begin{aligned}
&|Qx_u(\eta)(\tau,t)|e^{\beta(t-\tau)}e^{\gamma\tau}\\
&\quad\leq\int_{t_0}^{\tau}KK_Be^{(\alpha-\beta+\gamma)(\tau-s)}e^{-\delta s}\,ds\left(\sup_{t_0\leq s\leq\tau}|Qx_u(\eta)(s,t)|e^{\beta(t-s)}e^{\gamma s}\right)\\
&\qquad\qquad+\int_{t_0}^{\tau}KK_Be^{(\alpha-\beta+\gamma)(\tau-s)}e^{(\gamma-\delta)s}\|(\mathrm{id}-Q)\|\|\|x_u(\eta)\|^{\beta}\,ds.
\end{aligned}
\tag{C.33}
$$

Consider the last inequality for $\tau\leq t$. Clearly we have that for fixed t,

$$
\sup_{t_0\leq\tau\leq t}|Qx_u(\eta)(\tau,t)|e^{\beta(t-\tau)}e^{\gamma\tau}<\infty.
\tag{C.34}
$$

For sufficiently large t_0 (independent of the choice of $\tau>t_0$), using $\alpha-\beta+\gamma<0$, we have

$$
\int_{t_0}^{\tau}KK_Be^{(\alpha-\beta+\gamma)(\tau-s)}e^{-\delta s}\,ds\leq\frac{1}{2}.
\tag{C.35}
$$

With (C.33) and (C.35) we can estimate

$$
\begin{aligned}
&\sup_{t_0\le\tau\le t} |Qx_u(\eta)(\tau,t)|e^{\beta(t-\tau)}e^{\gamma\tau}\\
&\le \frac{1}{2}\left(\sup_{t_0\le\tau\le t}\ \sup_{t_0\le s\le\tau} |Qx_u(\eta)(s,t)|e^{\beta(t-s)}e^{\gamma s}\right)\\
&\qquad + \sup_{t_0\le\tau\le t}\int_{t_0}^{\tau} KK_B e^{(\alpha-\beta+\gamma)(\tau-s)}e^{(\gamma-\delta)s}\|(\mathrm{id}-Q)\|\|x_u(\eta)\|^{\beta}\,ds\\
&= \frac{1}{2}\sup_{t_0\le\tau\le t} |Qx_u(\eta)(\tau,t)|e^{\beta(t-\tau)}e^{\gamma\tau}\\
&\qquad + \sup_{t_0\le\tau\le t}\int_{t_0}^{\tau} KK_B e^{(\alpha-\beta+\gamma)(\tau-s)}e^{(\gamma-\delta)s}\|(\mathrm{id}-Q)\|\|x_u(\eta)\|^{\beta}\,ds.
\end{aligned}
$$

By (C.34) and $\gamma-\delta<0$ this gives

$$
\sup_{t_0\le\tau\le t} |Qx_u(\eta)(\tau,t)|e^{\beta(t-\tau)}e^{\gamma\tau} \le 2\int_{t_0}^{t} KK_B e^{(\alpha-\beta+\gamma)(t-s)}\|(\mathrm{id}-Q)\|\|x_u(\eta)\|^{\beta}\,ds. \tag{C.36}
$$

The integral on the right-hand side in the last inequality remains bounded as $t\to\infty$; that is, there is a constant $\mathcal{K}^u$ such that for all $t\ge t_0$,

$$
\int_{t_0}^{t} KK_B e^{(\alpha-\beta+\gamma)(t-s)}\|(\mathrm{id}-Q)\|\|x_u(\eta)\|^{\beta}\,ds \le \mathcal{K}^u.
$$

In particular for $\tau=t$ the estimate (C.36) reads

$$
|Qx_u(\eta)(t,t)| \le e^{-\gamma t}2\mathcal{K}^u.
$$

We emphasize that the last estimate holds for all $\eta\in\mathbb{R}^n$. So, with the notation of (C.32), we arrive at

$$
\left|\int_{t_0}^{t}\Phi(t,s)QB(s)x_u(\eta)(s,t)\,ds\right| \le e^{-\gamma t}2\mathcal{K}^u \tag{C.37}
$$

for all $\eta\in\mathbb{R}^n$. Now we turn towards the estimate of the second integral term in (C.31). In principle these calculations run along the same lines as above. However the counterpart of (C.34) calls for an additional argument.

In the same way as above, but this time exploiting (C.18), we find

$$\begin{aligned}(\mathrm{id}-Q)x_s(\eta)(t,\tau) &= -\int_t^\infty \Phi(t,s)(\mathrm{id}-Q)B(s)x_s(\eta)(s,\tau)\,ds\\ &= -\Big(\int_t^\infty \Phi(t,s)(\mathrm{id}-Q)B(s)(\mathrm{id}-Q)x_s(\eta)(s,\tau)\,ds\\ &\quad+\int_t^\infty \Phi(t,s)(\mathrm{id}-Q)B(s)Qx_s(\eta)(s,\tau)\,ds\Big).\end{aligned}$$

By (C.15) and (C.23) we conclude

$$\begin{aligned}&|(\mathrm{id}-Q)x_s(\eta)(t,\tau)|\,e^{\alpha(\tau-t)}e^{\gamma t} \le e^{\alpha(\tau-t)}e^{\gamma t}\\ &\Big(\int_t^\infty KK_Be^{\beta(t-s)}e^{-\delta s}|(\mathrm{id}-Q)x_s(\eta)(s,\tau)|e^{\alpha(\tau-s)}e^{\gamma s}e^{-\alpha(\tau-s)}e^{-\gamma s}\,ds\\ &\quad+\int_t^\infty KK_Be^{\beta(t-s)}e^{-\delta s}\|Q\||x_s(\eta)(s,\tau)|e^{\alpha(\tau-s)}e^{\gamma s}\,e^{-\alpha(\tau-s)}e^{-\gamma s}\,ds\Big).\end{aligned}$$

With (C.19) we get

$$\begin{aligned}&|(\mathrm{id}-Q)x_s(\eta)(t,\tau)|\,e^{\alpha(\tau-t)}e^{\gamma t}\\ &\le \int_t^\infty KK_Be^{(\beta-\alpha+\gamma)(t-s)}e^{-\delta s}\,ds\Big(\sup_{t_0\le\tau\le t\le s}|(\mathrm{id}-Q)x_s(\eta)(s,\tau)|e^{\alpha(\tau-s)}e^{\gamma s}\Big)\\ &\quad+\int_t^\infty KK_Be^{(\beta-\alpha+\gamma)(t-s)}e^{(\gamma-\delta)s}\|Q\|\|x_s(\eta)\|_\alpha\,ds.\end{aligned}$$

Again we find that for sufficiently large t_0 (recall that $t \ge t_0$),

$$\int_t^\infty KK_Be^{(\beta-\alpha+\gamma)(t-s)}e^{-\delta s}\,ds \le \frac{1}{2}.$$

Therefore

$$\begin{aligned}&\sup_{t_0\le\tau\le t}|(\mathrm{id}-Q)x_s(\eta)(t,\tau)|e^{\alpha(\tau-t)}e^{\gamma t}\\ &\quad\le \frac{1}{2}\sup_{t_0\le\tau\le t}\ \sup_{t_0\le\tau\le t\le s}|(\mathrm{id}-Q)x_s(\eta)(s,\tau)|e^{\alpha(\tau-s)}e^{\gamma s}\\ &\qquad+\sup_{t_0\le\tau\le t}\int_t^\infty KK_Be^{(\beta-\alpha+\gamma)(t-s)}e^{(\gamma-\delta)s}\|Q\|\|x_s(\eta)\|_\alpha\,ds\\ &\quad=\frac{1}{2}\sup_{t_0\le\tau\le t}|(\mathrm{id}-Q)x_s(\eta)(t,\tau)|e^{\alpha(\tau-t)}e^{\gamma t}\\ &\qquad+\sup_{t_0\le\tau\le t}\int_t^\infty KK_Be^{(\beta-\alpha+\gamma)(t-s)}e^{(\gamma-\delta)s}\|Q\|\|x_s(\eta)\|_\alpha\,ds.\end{aligned}$$

There is a constant $\mathcal{K}^s$ such that

$$\sup_{t_0 \le \tau \le t} \int_t^\infty K K_B e^{(\beta-\alpha+\gamma)(t-s)} e^{(\gamma-\delta)s} \|Q\| \|x_s(\eta)\|_\alpha \, ds \le \mathcal{K}^s.$$

For τ fixed,

$$\sup_{t_0 \le \tau \le t} |(\mathrm{id} - Q) x_s(\eta)(t,\tau)| \, e^{\alpha(\tau - t)} e^{\gamma t}$$
$$= \sup_{t_0 \le \tau \le t} |(\mathrm{id} - Q) x_s(\eta)(t,\tau)| \, e^{(\alpha-\gamma)(\tau - t)} e^{\gamma \tau} < \infty,$$

by $\mathrm{Re}\,\mu^1 < \alpha - \gamma$. We can continue in the same way as for the estimate of Qx_u, to find

$$\sup_{t_0 \le \tau \le t} |(\mathrm{id} - Q) x_s(\eta)(t,\tau)| e^{\alpha(\tau - t)} e^{\gamma t} \le 2\mathcal{K}^s.$$

For $t = \tau$ we get, again independently of the choice of η,

$$\left| \int_t^\infty \Phi(t,s)(\mathrm{id} - Q) B(s) x_s(\eta)(s,t) \, ds \right| \le e^{-\gamma t} 2\mathcal{K}^s. \tag{C.38}$$

Combining the bounds (C.31), (C.37), and (C.38) proves the lemma. □

Corollary C.11. *Assume the hypotheses of Theorem* C.9. *Let* Q *and* $\tilde{P}(t)$ *be projections which are associated to the exponential dichotomy with constants* α, β *of the equation* $\dot{x} = Ax$ *and* $\dot{x} = (A + B(t))x$, *respectively. Then there are constants* C *and* $\gamma > 0$ *such that* $\|\tilde{P}(t) - Q\| \le Ce^{-\gamma(t-t_0)}$.

Proof. The proof follows by combining Lemma C.7 and Lemma C.10. □

C.2.2. Asymptotic expansions for orbits. We will apply the theory on exponential dichotomies to orbits converging to a hyperbolic equilibrium. Consider a differential equation $\dot{x} = f(x,\lambda)$ with a hyperbolic equilibrium $x = 0$ for all small $\lambda \in \mathbb{R}$ and corresponding stable and unstable manifolds W^s_λ and W^u_λ. Let $\phi(t,\cdot)$ be the flow of the differential equation.

Lemma C.12. *Let* $\zeta(\cdot)$ *be a solution of* $\dot{x} = f(x,\lambda)$ *inside the stable manifold* W^s_λ. *Then the variational equation along* ζ,

$$\dot{x} = D_x f(\zeta(t),\lambda) x, \tag{C.39}$$

has an exponential dichotomy on $\mathbb{R}^+$ *with projections* $P(t,\lambda)$. *Moreover,*

$$\mathrm{im}\, P(t,\lambda) = T_{\zeta(t)} W^s_\lambda.$$

Proof. The first observation we make is that the differential equation (C.39) can be written as

$$\dot{x} = D_x f(0,\lambda) x + (D_x f(\zeta(t),\lambda) - D_x f(0,\lambda)) x. \tag{C.40}$$

We can use the mean value theorem to show that the second term on the right-hand side of (C.40) tends to zero exponentially fast as $t \to \infty$. By Theorem C.9 this equation has an exponential dichotomy. The associated projections we denote by $P(t,\lambda)$.

It remains to show that $\operatorname{im} P(t,\lambda) = T_{\zeta(t)}W^s_\lambda$. In other words it remains to show that

$$T_{\zeta(0)}W^s_\lambda = \left\{x\ ;\ \sup_{t\in\mathbb{R}^+}|\Phi(t,0)x| < \infty\right\},$$

where $\Phi(\cdot,\cdot)$ is the transition matrix of the variational equation (C.39). The local stable manifold $W^s_{loc,\lambda}$ is the graph of a function h mapping from the stable subspace E^s to unstable subspace E^u. Let $H : E^s \to \mathbb{R}^n$ be defined by $H(\xi) = \xi + h(\xi)$, so that H parametrizes the local stable manifold and

$$W^s_{loc,\lambda} = \{\phi(0,H(\xi))\ ;\ \xi \in E^s, |\xi| \text{ small}\},$$

and therefore

$$\begin{aligned} T_{H(\xi)}W^s_{loc,\lambda} &= DH(\xi)E^s \\ &= \left\{\frac{d}{d\xi}\phi(0,H(\xi))\eta\ ;\ \eta \in E^s\right\}. \end{aligned}$$

For given ξ and all $\eta \in E^s$, the function ζ_η given by $\zeta_\eta(t) = \frac{d}{d\xi}\phi(t,H(\xi))\eta$ solves the differential equation

$$\dot{x} = D_x f(\phi(t,H(\xi)),\lambda)x.$$

We conclude that $\zeta_\eta(t) = \Phi(t,0)\zeta_\eta(0)$. Let $\Psi : E^s \to C^1_b(\mathbb{R}^+,\mathbb{R}^n)$ be the map $\Psi(\xi) = \phi(\cdot,H(\xi))$. Here $C^1_b(\mathbb{R}^+,\mathbb{R}^n)$ stands for the space of bounded and continuously differentiable maps from $\mathbb{R}^+$ to $\mathbb{R}^n$. Note that $\zeta_\eta(\cdot) = D\Psi(\xi)\eta \in C^1_b(\mathbb{R}^+,\mathbb{R}^n)$. Together this shows that

$$T_{H(\xi)}W^s_{loc,\lambda} \subset \{x\ ;\ \sup_{t\in\mathbb{R}^+}|\Phi(t,0)x| < \infty\} = \operatorname{im} P(0,\lambda).$$

Since the dimensions of $T_{H(\xi)}W^s_{loc,\lambda}$ and $\operatorname{im} P(0,\lambda)$ coincide, this shows

$$T_{\zeta(0)}W^s_{loc,\lambda} = \{x\ ;\ \sup_{t\in\mathbb{R}^+}|\Phi(t,0)x| < \infty\}. \qquad \square$$

In a similar way we find that variational equations along solutions in the unstable manifold have an exponential dichotomy on $\mathbb{R}^-$.

We will present two lemmas providing asymptotic expansions for solutions of certain nonlinear and autonomous linear equations involving real leading eigenvalues. The estimates are related to [**324**, Lemma 1.7]. Let the origin be an asymptotically stable equilibrium of a smooth family of differential equations

$$\dot{x} = f(x,\lambda)$$

with $x \in \mathbb{R}^n$ and $\lambda \in \mathbb{R}$ near 0. We assume a real leading stable eigenvalue $\mu^s(\lambda)$ at the origin. So we can write $\operatorname{spec}(D_x f(0,\lambda)) = \{\mu^s(\lambda)\} \cup \operatorname{spec}^{ss}(\lambda)$ and we can take numbers $\alpha^{ss} < \alpha^s < 0$ so that

$$\begin{aligned} \operatorname{Re}\mu &< \alpha^{ss} < \mu^s(\lambda) < \alpha^s < 0, \\ 2\alpha^s &< \mu^s(\lambda), \end{aligned}$$

for all $\mu \in \operatorname{spec}^{ss}(\lambda)$ and λ near 0. Let $E^s(\lambda)$ be the generalized eigenspace assigned to $\mu^s(\lambda)$, and let $E^{ss}(\lambda)$ be the sum of the generalized eigenspaces assigned to $\operatorname{spec}^{ss}(\lambda)$.

Lemma C.13. *Let $P_s(\lambda)$ be the projection on $E^s(\lambda)$ along $E^{ss}(\lambda)$. Then there is a $\delta > 0$ such that for all orbits $x(\cdot)$ of $\dot{x} = f(x,\lambda)$ with $\|x(0)\| < \delta$, the limit*

$$\eta(x(0),\lambda) = \lim_{t\to\infty} e^{-D_x f(0,\lambda)t} P_s(\lambda)x(t)$$

exists and lies in $E^s(\lambda)$. Furthermore, there is a constant c such that

$$|x(t) - e^{D_x f(0,\lambda)t}\eta(x(0),\lambda)| \le c e^{\max\{\alpha^{ss},2\alpha^s\}t}. \tag{C.41}$$

Proof. In order to prove this lemma, we use that any orbit within the stable manifold tends exponentially fast towards the equilibrium. More precisely, for each $\alpha^s < 0$ which is larger than the real leading stable eigenvalue, there is a C such that $\|x(t)\| < Ce^{\alpha^s t}$; see for instance [**411**].

Write

$$f(x,\lambda) = D_x f(0,\lambda)x + g(x,\lambda),$$

where $g(0,\lambda) = 0$ and $D_x g(0,\lambda) = 0$. Then $x(\cdot)$ is an orbit of $\dot{x} = f(x,\lambda)$ if and only if it solves

$$x(t) = e^{D_x f(0,\lambda)(t-s)}x(s) + \int_s^t e^{D_x f(0,\lambda)(t-\tau)} g(x(\tau),\lambda)\,d\tau. \tag{C.42}$$

As $P_s(\lambda)$ and $e^{D_x f(0,\lambda)}$ commute,

$$\begin{aligned} &e^{-D_x f(0,\lambda)t} P_s(\lambda)x(t) \\ &\qquad = e^{-D_x f(0,\lambda)s} P_s(\lambda)x(s) + \int_s^t e^{-D_x f(0,\lambda)\tau} P_s(\lambda) g(x(\tau),\lambda)\,d\tau. \end{aligned} \tag{C.43}$$

From this formula we see that there is a $K > 0$ so that for sufficiently small $|x(s)|$,

$$\begin{aligned} &|e^{-D_x f(0,\lambda)t_1} P_s(\lambda)x(t_1) - e^{-D_x f(0,\lambda)t_2} P_s(\lambda)x(t_2)| \\ &\qquad \le \int_{t_2}^{t_1} \|e^{-D_x f(0,\lambda)\tau} P_s(\lambda)\|\,|g(x(\tau),\lambda)|\,d\tau. \end{aligned}$$

The right-hand side can be estimated by

$$\int_{t_2}^{t_1} \|e^{-D_x f(0,\lambda)\tau} P_s(\lambda)\| |g(\tau,\lambda)|\, d\tau \le \int_{t_2}^{t_1} K e^{-\mu^s(\lambda)\tau} e^{2\alpha^s \tau}.$$

This shows that $\lim_{t\to\infty} e^{-D_x f(0,\lambda)t} P_s(\lambda)x(t)$ exists.

We turn to estimate (C.41). Write (C.42) as a system

$$\begin{aligned} P_s(\lambda)x(t) &= e^{D_x f(0,\lambda)(t-s)} P_s(\lambda)x(s) \\ &\quad + \int_s^t e^{D_x f(0,\lambda)(t-\tau)} P_s(\lambda) g(x(\tau),\lambda)\, d\tau, \\ (\mathrm{id} - P_s(\lambda))x(t) &= e^{D_x f(0,\lambda)(t-s)} (\mathrm{id} - P_s(\lambda))x(s) \\ &\quad + \int_s^t e^{D_x f(0,\lambda)(t-\tau)} (\mathrm{id} - P_s(\lambda)) g(x(\tau),\lambda)\, d\tau. \end{aligned}$$

We know from the first part of the proof that in the first equation the limit when $s \to \infty$ exists, and we get

$$P_s(\lambda)x(t) = e^{D_x f(0,\lambda)t} \eta(x(0),\lambda) - \int_t^\infty e^{D_x f(0,\lambda)(t-\tau)} P_s(\lambda) g(x(\tau),\lambda)\, d\tau.$$

Therefore we find

$$\begin{aligned} |x(t) - e^{D_x f(0,\lambda)t}\eta(x(0),\lambda)| &\le |e^{D_x f(0,\lambda)(t-s)} (\mathrm{id} - P_s(\lambda))x(s)| \\ &\quad + \left| \int_t^\infty e^{D_x f(0,\lambda)(t-\tau)} P_s(\lambda) g(x(\tau),\lambda)\, d\tau \right| \\ &\quad + \left| \int_s^t e^{D_x f(0,\lambda)(t-\tau)} (\mathrm{id} - P_s(\lambda)) g(x(\tau),\lambda)\, d\tau \right|. \end{aligned}$$

The different terms in the right-hand side of this inequality can be estimated as follows:

$$\begin{aligned} |e^{D_x f(0,\lambda)(t-s)} (\mathrm{id} - P_s(\lambda))x(s)| &\le c_1 e^{\alpha^{ss}(t-s)} |x(s)| \\ &\le c_2 e^{\alpha^{ss} t}, \\ \left| \int_t^\infty e^{D_x f(0,\lambda)(t-\tau)} P_s(\lambda) g(x(\tau),\lambda)\, d\tau \right| &\le \int_t^\infty e^{\alpha^s (t-\tau)} |x(\tau)|^2 \\ &\le c_3 e^{2\alpha^s t}, \\ \left| \int_s^t e^{D_x f(0,\lambda)(t-\tau)} (\mathrm{id} - P_s(\lambda)) g(x(\tau),\lambda)\, d\tau \right| &\le \int_s^t e^{\alpha^{ss}(t-\tau)} |x(\tau)|^2 \\ &\le c_4 (e^{\alpha^{ss} t} + e^{2\alpha^s t}). \end{aligned}$$

Together this proves (C.41). □

The lemma (although it is only formulated for asymptotically stable equilibria) shows that any orbit x in the stable manifold of an equilibrium with real leading stable eigenvalue, has an asymptotic expansion

$$x(t) = e^{D_x f(0,\lambda)t}\eta(x(0),\lambda) + \mathcal{O}(e^{\max\{\alpha^{ss},2\alpha^s\}t}).$$

Moreover, $\eta(x(0),\lambda) = 0$ if and only if $x(0)$ belongs to the strong stable manifold.

A corresponding assertion for linear nonautonomous differential equations is contained in the next lemma. The proof runs along the same lines.

Lemma C.14. *Consider a smooth family of linear nonautonomous differential equations*

$$\dot{x} = (A(\lambda) + B(t,\lambda))x,$$

and assume that

(i) $\operatorname{spec}(A(\lambda)) = \operatorname{spec}^{ss}(\lambda) \cup \{\mu^s(\lambda)\}$, *where* $\operatorname{Re}\mu < \alpha^{ss} < \mu^s(\lambda) < \alpha^s < 0$ *for all* $\mu \in \operatorname{spec}^{ss}(\lambda)$;

(ii) *The leading eigenvalue* $\mu^s(\lambda)$ *is real;*

(iii) *There is a* $\beta < 0$ *such that* $\|B(t,\lambda)\| < e^{\beta t}$ *and* $\alpha^s + \beta < \mu^s$.

Let $E^s(\lambda)$ *and* $E^{ss}(\lambda)$ *be the sums of the generalized eigenspaces of* $A(\lambda)$ *assigned to* $\mu^s(\lambda)$ *and* $\operatorname{spec}^{ss}(\lambda)$, *respectively, and let* $P_s(\lambda)$ *be the projection on* $E^s(\lambda)$ *along* $E^{ss}(\lambda)$. *Then the limit*

$$\eta(x(0),\lambda) = \lim_{t\to\infty} e^{-A(\lambda)t}P_s(\lambda)x(t)$$

exists and lies in $E^s(\lambda)$. *Furthermore, there is a constant* c *such that*

$$|x(t) - e^{A(\lambda)t}\eta(x(0),\lambda)| \le ce^{\max\{\alpha^{ss},\alpha^s+\beta\}t}.$$

For the linear nonautonomous differential equation $\dot{x} = (A(\lambda) + B(t,\lambda))x$ with an exponential dichotomy on $\mathbb{R}^+$, one can speak of stable and strong stable subspaces, which will depend on t as well as on λ. The lemma thus tells that orbits starting in the stable subspace at $t = 0$ can be written as

$$x(t) = e^{A(\lambda)t}\eta(x(0),\lambda) + \mathcal{O}(e^{\max\{\alpha^{ss},\alpha^s+\beta\}t}),$$

and $\eta(x(0),\lambda) = 0$ if and only if $\eta(x(0),\lambda)$ belongs to the strong stable subspace at $t = 0$.

C.3. Proofs of Lin's method—1-periodic orbits

This section prepares us for the bifurcation analysis in Appendix C.6.1 where we study 1-periodic orbits in a codimension-1 homoclinic bifurcation by means of Lin's method.

We adopt the setup and notation from Appendix C.1. Recall the assumption of simple real leading eigenvalues $\mu^s < 0$ and $\mu^u > 0$ and the eigenvalue condition (C.1) which says $\mu^s + \mu^u > 0$. Throughout we use quantities α^s and α^u satisfying

$$\mu^s < \alpha^s < 0 < \alpha^u < \mu^u. \tag{C.44}$$

Taking $\mu^s + \mu^u > 0$ into account, we see that α^s satisfies

$$-\min\{|\mu^s|, \mu^u\} < \alpha^s < 0.$$

We make a start with a restriction of the statements of Lin's method to 1-periodic Lin orbits. A simplification is that here and throughout Section C.3, ω stands for a single real value and not a sequence of values, as in Theorem C.1. Against the background of Corollary C.2 we formulate the following corollary to Theorem C.1.

Corollary C.15. *There is a $\Omega > 0$, so that for each ω with $\omega > \Omega$ and each λ, $|\lambda|$ sufficiently small, there is a unique partial orbit $x(\omega, \lambda)(\cdot)$ such that*

$$x(\omega, \lambda)(0), x(\omega, \lambda)(2\omega) \in \Sigma,$$
$$\Xi(\omega, \lambda) = x(\omega, \lambda)(0) - x(\omega, \lambda)(2\omega) \in Z.$$

The function $x(\omega, \lambda)$ and hence also $\Xi(\omega, \lambda)$ are differentiable with respect to λ.

The following corollary is implied by Theorem C.3.

Corollary C.16. *There is a smooth reparametrization of the parameter λ, so that the bifurcation equation $\Xi = 0$ is equivalent to*

$$\langle \psi, \Xi(\omega, \lambda) \rangle = \lambda - e^{2\mu^s(\lambda)\omega} \mathcal{E}^s(\lambda) + R(\omega, \lambda) = 0,$$

where $\mathcal{E}^s(0) \neq 0$. There is a $\delta > 1$ such that

$$R(\omega, \lambda) = \mathcal{O}(e^{2\mu^s(\lambda)\omega\delta}).$$

The expression $\langle \psi, \Xi(\omega, \lambda) \rangle$ is differentiable with respect to ω and

$$D_\omega R(\omega, \lambda) = \mathcal{O}(e^{2\mu^s(\lambda)\omega\delta}).$$

We will give the proof of Corollary C.15 in Appendix C.3.1 below. Appendices C.3.2 and C.3.3 then contain the proof of Corollary C.16. The arguments are the blueprint for the proofs of Theorem C.3 and Proposition C.4.

C.3.1. Existence of 1-periodic Lin orbits. This section is devoted to the proof of Corollary C.15. We start with an initial section that introduces various projections connected to exponential dichotomies, and which contains statements on exponential expansions for special orbits. These projections and formulas are frequently used in the following and also in Appendix C.4, which contains the proof of Lin's method without the restriction to 1-periodic orbits.

C.3.1.1. *Projections and asymptotic expansions for orbits.* In our analysis we use suitable coordinate systems near the equilibrium p and near the point $h(0)$. In particular we assume throughout that $p_\lambda \equiv p$, and we assume that for all λ, the local stable and unstable manifolds $W^{ss,s}_{loc}$ and $W^{u,uu}_{loc}$ are flat and coincide with the corresponding stable and unstable spaces for $\lambda = 0$:

$$\begin{aligned} W^{ss,s}_{loc}(p,\lambda) &\subset T_p W^{ss,s}_{loc}(p,0), \\ W^{u,uu}_{loc}(p,\lambda) &\subset T_p W^{u,uu}_{loc}(p,0). \end{aligned} \tag{C.45}$$

We can always use coordinates in which this holds.

Recall from Lemma 4.18 the choice of specific orbits $h^s_\lambda(t)$, $t \geq 0$, in $W^{ss,s}(p,\lambda)$ and $h^u_\lambda(t)$, $t \leq 0$, in $W^{u,uu}(p,\lambda)$. The orbits h^s_λ, h^u_λ were chosen so that $h^s_\lambda(0) - h^u_\lambda(0) \in Z$. As a consequence of (C.45) we have that for large t, the orbits $h^s_\lambda(t)$, $h^u_\lambda(-t)$ belong to the spaces $T_p W^{ss,s}_{loc}(p,0)$, $T_p W^{u,uu}_{loc}(p,0)$. For coordinates near $h(0)$ we demand that the stable and unstable manifolds in a neighborhood of $h(0)$ are flat within Σ. More precisely, with

$$\begin{aligned} W^+ &= T_{h(0)} W^{ss,s}(p,0) \cap X^\perp, \\ W^- &= T_{h(0)} W^{u,uu}(p,0) \cap X^\perp, \end{aligned}$$

we assume

$$\begin{aligned} W^{ss,s}(p,\lambda) \cap B(h(0),\epsilon) \cap \Sigma &\subset h^s_\lambda(0) + W^+, \\ W^{u,uu}(p,\lambda) \cap B(h(0),\epsilon) \cap \Sigma &\subset h^u_\lambda(0) + W^- \end{aligned} \tag{C.46}$$

as a standing assumption; see Figure C.3. We can always use coordinates in which this holds.

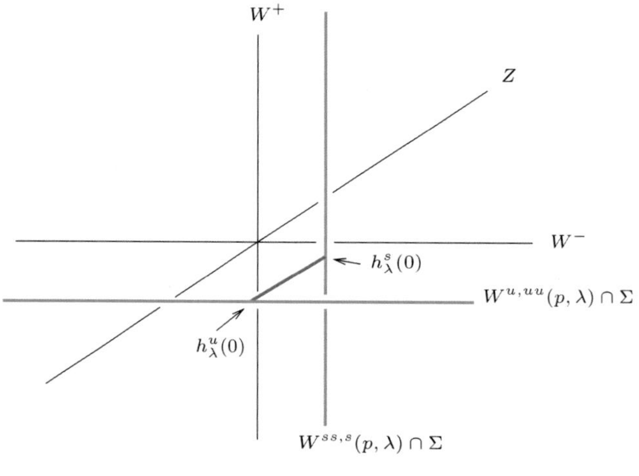

Figure C.3. A coordinate system is chosen so that inside $\Sigma = h(0) + X^\perp$, the stable and unstable manifolds of p are straightened. The directions of W^+, W^-, Z are indicated.

It follows from the no-orbit-flip condition that

$$e^s = \lim_{t\to\infty} h(t)/\|h(t)\| \tag{C.47}$$

is an eigenvector for the eigenvalue μ^s. To elucidate the symmetrical relation with the definition of a second vector e^- below, we provide an equivalent definition via the variational equation. Let $\zeta(t) = \dot{h}(t)$ be the solution to

$$\dot{v}(t) = D_x f(h(t), 0)v(t)$$

with $v(0) = -\dot{h}(0)$. Then e^s also satisfies

$$e^s = \lim_{t\to\infty} \zeta(t)/\|\zeta(t)\|.$$

Now let $\psi(t)$ be the solution to the adjoint variational equation,

$$\dot{w}(t) = -D_x f(h(t), 0)^T w(t)$$

with $w(0) = \psi$. Recall that the initial condition ψ is a unit vector spanning Z; see (C.6). This initial condition guarantees that $\psi(t)$ converges to 0 as $t \to \pm\infty$; see Lemma C.14. Define

$$e^- = \lim_{t\to-\infty} \psi(t)/\|\psi(t)\|. \tag{C.48}$$

The existence of the limit is guaranteed by Lemma C.14. By the no-inclination-flip condition, the vector e^- is contained in the leading unstable space E^- of $D_x f(p)^T$, which equals E^s by the choice of the inner product.

We consider projections and their asymptotics (for projections depending on time) involved in the theory of Lin's method. Consider the spectral projection P of $D_x f(p, \lambda)$. More precisely P is defined by

$$\begin{aligned} \operatorname{im} P &= T_p W^{ss,s}(p), \\ \ker P &= T_p W^{u,uu}(p). \end{aligned} \tag{C.49}$$

For the variational equations

$$\dot{v} = D_x f(h_\lambda^{s/u}(t), \lambda)v, \tag{C.50}$$

defined on $\mathbb{R}^\pm$, and corresponding transition matrices $\Phi^\pm(\lambda, \cdot, \cdot)$, we define projections $P^\pm(\lambda, t)$ related to the direct sum decomposition (C.7) and satisfying

$$\begin{aligned} \ker P^+(\lambda, 0) &= T_{h_\lambda^s(0)} W^{ss,s}(p), \\ \operatorname{im} P^+(\lambda, 0) &= W^- \oplus Z, \\ \ker P^-(\lambda, 0) &= T_{h_\lambda^u(0)} W^{u,uu}(p), \\ \operatorname{im} P^-(\lambda, 0) &= W^+ \oplus Z. \end{aligned} \tag{C.51}$$

The projections are commuting with $\Phi^\pm(\lambda, \cdot, \cdot)$,

$$P^\pm(\lambda, t)\Phi^\pm(\lambda, t, s) = \Phi^\pm(\lambda, t, s)P^\pm(\lambda, s). \tag{C.52}$$

In the limit $t \to \pm\infty$, $P^{\pm}(\lambda, t)$ converge to projections onto stable and unstable subspaces at the equilibria,

$$\begin{aligned} \ker \lim_{t\to\infty} P^+(\lambda,t) &= T_p W^{ss,s}(p), \\ \operatorname{im} \lim_{t\to\infty} P^+(\lambda,t) &= T_p W^{u,uu}(p), \\ \ker \lim_{t\to-\infty} P^-(\lambda,t) &= T_p W^{u,uu}(p), \\ \operatorname{im} \lim_{t\to-\infty} P^-(\lambda,t) &= T_p W^{ss,s}(p). \end{aligned}$$

The results of Appendix C.2.1 show that these projections are associated to exponential dichotomies of these variational equations. More precisely, write the variational equation $\dot{v} = D_x f(h_\lambda^{s/u}(t), \lambda)v$ as

$$\dot{v} = D_x f(p,\lambda)v + \left(D_x f(h_\lambda^{s/u}(t),\lambda) - D_x f(p,\lambda)\right) v.$$

The equation $\dot{v} = D_x f(p,\lambda)v$ has an exponential dichotomy on $\mathbb{R}^+$ with constants α^s, α^u satisfying (C.44). Recall that μ^s and μ^u are the leading stable and unstable eigenvalues associated to the equilibrium p. By Lemma C.13 we find that, for some constant c,

$$\|D_x f(h_\lambda^{s/u}(t),\lambda) - D_x f(p,\lambda)\| \le c e^{\alpha^s t}. \tag{C.53}$$

The roughness theorem, Theorem C.9, yields that also $\dot{v} = D_x f(h_\lambda^{s/u}(t), \lambda)v$ has an exponential dichotomy on $\mathbb{R}^{+/-}$ with constants α^s, α^u. Using Lemma C.12, we find that $\left(\mathrm{id} - P^{+/-}(\lambda, t)\right)$ are associated projections. From these considerations it follows that there is a positive constant C such that

$$\begin{aligned} |\Phi^+(\lambda,t,0)(\mathrm{id} - P^+(\lambda,0))x| &= |\Phi^+(\lambda,t,0)(\mathrm{id} - P^+(\lambda,0))^2 x| \\ &\le C e^{\alpha^s t} |(\mathrm{id} - P^+(\lambda,0))x| \end{aligned} \tag{C.54}$$

and

$$\begin{aligned} |\Phi^+(\lambda,t,\omega)P^+(\lambda,\omega)x| &= |\Phi^+(\lambda,t,\omega)P^+(\lambda,\omega)^2 x| \\ &\le C e^{\alpha^u (t-\omega)} |P^+(\lambda,\omega)x|. \end{aligned} \tag{C.55}$$

Corresponding estimates apply to Φ^- and P^-:

$$|\Phi^-(\lambda,t,0)(\mathrm{id} - P^-(\lambda,0))x| \le C e^{\alpha^u t} |(\mathrm{id} - P^-(\lambda,0))x| \tag{C.56}$$

and

$$|\Phi^-(\lambda,t,-\omega)P^-(\lambda,-\omega)x| \le C e^{\alpha^s (t+\omega)} |P^-(\lambda,\omega))x|. \tag{C.57}$$

According to Corollary C.11 (see also Lemma C.10 and use (C.53)), we have

$$\|(\mathrm{id} - P^+(\lambda,t)) - P\| \le C e^{\alpha^s t}. \tag{C.58}$$

Similarly, considering exponential dichotomies on $\mathbb{R}^-$, we find

$$\|\,(\mathrm{id} - P^-(\lambda,t)) - (\mathrm{id} - P)\| \le C e^{\alpha^u t}. \tag{C.59}$$

Lemma C.17. *For sufficiently large ω we get direct sum decompositions of $\mathbb{R}^n$ given by*

$$\mathbb{R}^n = \operatorname{im}(\operatorname{id} - P^+(\lambda,\omega)) \oplus \operatorname{im}(\operatorname{id} - P^-(\lambda,-\omega)),$$
$$\mathbb{R}^n = \operatorname{im} P^+(\lambda,\omega) \oplus \operatorname{im} P^-(\lambda,-\omega).$$

Proof. Both statements are proved similarly; we restrict our work to proving the second statement, for which we follow the proof of [**406**, Lemma 7]. We construct a projection $\tilde{P}(\lambda,\omega)$ with

$$\operatorname{im}\tilde{P}(\lambda,\omega) = \operatorname{im} P^+(\lambda,\omega) \quad \text{and} \quad \operatorname{im}(\operatorname{id} - \tilde{P}(\lambda,\omega)) = \operatorname{im} P^-(\lambda,-\omega).$$

Let $\tilde{M} = \max\{||P||, ||\operatorname{id} - P||\}$ and note that $\tilde{M} \geq 1$. By Lemma C.10, the projections P^- and P^+ converge to the projection P, and we have

$$\lim_{t\to-\infty} ||P^-(\lambda,t) - P|| = 0,$$
$$\lim_{t\to\infty} ||P^+(\lambda,t) - (\operatorname{id} - P)|| = 0. \tag{C.60}$$

Therefore we find c, Ω such that for all $\omega > \Omega$ and all $|\lambda| < c$, we have

$$||P^-(\lambda,-\omega) - P|| \leq 1/(4\tilde{M}) \qquad \text{and} \qquad ||P^+(\lambda,\omega) - (\operatorname{id} - P)|| \leq 1/(4\tilde{M}).$$

For each $\omega > \Omega$ we define

$$S(\lambda,\omega) = P^-(\lambda,-\omega)P + P^+(\lambda,\omega)(\operatorname{id} - P). \tag{C.61}$$

This mapping is invertible since

$$S(\lambda,\omega) = \operatorname{id} - \left[(\operatorname{id} - P^-(\lambda,-\omega))P + (\operatorname{id} - P^+(\lambda,\omega))(\operatorname{id} - P)\right],$$

where

$$||(\operatorname{id} - P^-(\lambda,-\omega))P|| + ||(\operatorname{id} - P^+(\lambda,\omega))(\operatorname{id} - P)|| \leq 1/2.$$

We find therefore

$$||S(\lambda,\omega)||, ||S(\lambda,\omega)^{-1}|| \leq 2. \tag{C.62}$$

Now we define

$$\tilde{P}(\lambda,\omega) = S(\lambda,\omega)(\operatorname{id} - P)S(\lambda,\omega)^{-1} \tag{C.63}$$

and show that $\tilde{P}$ is the claimed projection. It is obvious that $\tilde{P}^2 = \tilde{P}$, and so $\tilde{P}$ is a projection. From $\tilde{P}(\lambda,\omega)S(\lambda,\omega) = S(\lambda,\omega)(\operatorname{id} - P) = P^+(\lambda,\omega)(\operatorname{id} - P)$ we conclude that

$$\begin{aligned}\operatorname{im}\tilde{P}(\lambda,\omega) &= \operatorname{im} P^+(\lambda,\omega)(\operatorname{id} - P)\\ &= \operatorname{im} P^+(\lambda,\omega).\end{aligned}$$

The last equality is due to (C.60) since $P^+(\lambda,\omega)$ is injective on $\operatorname{im}(\operatorname{id} - P)$ for $\omega > \Omega$ sufficiently large and both projections $P^+(\lambda,\omega)$ and $(\operatorname{id} - P)$ have the same rank. Analogously we find from $(\mathrm{id} - \tilde{P}(\lambda,\omega))S(\lambda,\omega) = S(\lambda,\omega)P = P^-(\lambda,-\omega)P$ that

$$\begin{aligned}\mathrm{im}\,(\mathrm{id} - \tilde{P}(\lambda,\omega)) &= \mathrm{im}\,P^-(\lambda,-\omega)P\\ &= \mathrm{im}\,P^-(\lambda,-\omega).\end{aligned}$$

We obtain from (C.63) that

$$\begin{aligned}\|\tilde{P}(\lambda,\omega)\| &\le 4\|\mathrm{id} - P\| \le 4\tilde{M},\\ \|\mathrm{id} - \tilde{P}(\lambda,\omega)\| &\le 4\|P\| \le 4\tilde{M},\end{aligned}$$

which concludes the proof. □

The proof of the above lemma gives projections $\tilde{P}(\lambda,\omega)$ on $\mathbb{R}^n$ with

$$\text{(C.64)}\qquad \mathrm{im}\,\tilde{P}(\lambda,\omega) = \mathrm{im}\ P^+(\lambda,\omega) \quad\text{and}\quad \ker\tilde{P}(\lambda,\omega) = \mathrm{im}\,P^-(\lambda,-\omega).$$

In the following lemma we consider the asymptotics of $\tilde{P}$. Recall that for the saddle quantity we assume $\mu^s + \mu^u > 0$.

Lemma C.18. *Let α^s, α^u, $|\alpha^s| < |\alpha^u|$ be constants such that $\mu^s < \alpha^s < 0 < \alpha^u < \mu^u$. Then we have the following asymptotic expansion of $\tilde{P}$:*

$$\tilde{P}(\lambda,\omega) = (\mathrm{id} - P) + \mathcal{O}\left(e^{\alpha^s\omega}\right).$$

Proof. From the definition of $\tilde{P}$ in (C.63), we get

$$\begin{aligned}&\|\tilde{P}(\lambda,\omega) - (\mathrm{id} - P)\|\\ &\quad= \|\,(S(\lambda,\omega) - \mathrm{id} + \mathrm{id})\,(\mathrm{id} - P)\left(S(\lambda,\omega)^{-1} - \mathrm{id} + \mathrm{id}\right) - (\mathrm{id} - P)\|\\ &\quad\le \|\,(S(\lambda,\omega) - \mathrm{id})\,(\mathrm{id} - P)\left(S(\lambda,\omega)^{-1} - \mathrm{id}\right)\|\\ &\qquad\qquad + \|\,(S(\lambda,\omega) - \mathrm{id})\,(\mathrm{id} - P)\| + \|(\mathrm{id} - P)\left(S(\lambda,\omega)^{-1} - \mathrm{id}\right)\|.\end{aligned}$$

Using the definition of S in (C.61), we get

$$\begin{aligned}\|S(\lambda,\omega) - \mathrm{id}\,\| &\le \|(\mathrm{id} - P^-(\lambda,-\omega))P\| + \|(\mathrm{id} - P^+(\lambda,\omega))(\mathrm{id} - P)\|\\ &= \|\,((\mathrm{id} - P^-(\lambda,-\omega)) - (\mathrm{id} - P))\,P\|\\ &\qquad + \|\,((\mathrm{id} - P^+(\lambda,\omega)) - P)\,(\mathrm{id} - P)\|.\end{aligned}$$

Note that $S(\lambda,\omega)^{-1} - \mathrm{id} = S(\lambda,\omega)^{-1}\,(\mathrm{id} - S(\lambda,\omega))$. The statement follows by combining these estimates and using (C.58) and (C.59). □

We make use of Lemma C.13 on asymptotic expansions for solutions in the stable manifold and of Lemma C.14 on asymptotic expansions for solutions in the (t-dependent) stable subspaces of a nonautonomous linear differential equation. We start with the asymptotic expansions for the reference orbits $h_\lambda^{s/u}$. Lemma C.13 implies that there are $\delta > 1$ and uniquely defined vectors $\eta^s \in E^s$, $\eta^u \in E^u$ depending smoothly on λ, such that

$$\text{(C.65)}\qquad h_\lambda^s(t) = e^{\mu^s(\lambda)t}\eta^s(\lambda) + \mathcal{O}(e^{\mu^s(\lambda)t\delta})$$

for $t \geq 0$, and

(C.66) $$h_\lambda^u(t) = e^{\mu^u(\lambda)t}\eta^u(\lambda) + \mathcal{O}(e^{\mu^u(\lambda)t\delta})$$

for $t \leq 0$. By the no-orbit-flip condition, the vectors $\eta^s(0)$ and $\eta^u(0)$ are different from zero. By the definition of e^s in (C.47), $\eta^s(0)$ points in the same direction as the vector e^s.

Using Lemma C.14, there are $\delta > 1$ and uniquely defined vectors $\eta^- \in (E^u)^\perp$ and $\eta^+ \in (E^s)^\perp$ depending smoothly on λ, such that

(C.67) $$\Phi^-(\lambda, 0, t)^T P^-(\lambda, 0)^T \psi = e^{-\mu^s(\lambda)t}\eta^-(\lambda) + \mathcal{O}(e^{-\mu^s(\lambda)t\delta}), \quad t \leq 0,$$

and

(C.68) $$\Phi^+(\lambda, 0, t)^T P^+(\lambda, 0)^T \psi = e^{-\mu^u(\lambda)t}\eta^+(\lambda) + \mathcal{O}(e^{-\mu^u(\lambda)t\delta}), \quad t \geq 0.$$

The stable subspace (at time $s = 0$) of the flow $\Phi^+(\lambda, 0, t)^T$ is

$$\left(T_{h_\lambda^s(0)} W_\lambda^s(p)\right)^\perp = \operatorname{im} P^+(\lambda, 0)^T.$$

By the no-inclination-flip condition, the vectors $\eta^-(0)$ and $\eta^+(0)$ are different from zero. Also, by (C.48), $\eta^-(0)$ points in the same direction as the vector e^-. Figure C.7, where a bifurcation analysis is given, depicts the setting for planar differential equations.

C.3.1.2. *Existence of 1-periodic Lin orbits.* First we outline the arguments leading to Corollary C.15. In this outline we postpone the proofs of some of the steps, which are provided after the outline. The searched Lin orbit $x(\cdot)$ will be composed of orbits $x^+(\cdot)$ and $x^-(\cdot)$ defined on $[0, \omega]$ and $[-\omega, 0]$,

(C.69) $$x(t) = \begin{cases} x^+(t), & t \in [0, \omega], \\ x^-(t - 2\omega), & t \in [\omega, 2\omega]. \end{cases}$$

This requires the continuity condition

(C.70) $$x^+(\omega) = x^-(-\omega)$$

and the jump condition

(C.71) $$\Xi = x(0) - x(2\omega) = x^+(0) - x^-(0) \in Z.$$

Having in mind the decomposition (C.8), which reads here as

(C.72) $$\Xi(\omega, \lambda) = \xi^\infty(\lambda) + \xi(\omega, \lambda),$$

where $\xi^\infty(\lambda) = h_\lambda^s(0) - h_\lambda^u(0)$, we write $x^\pm$ in the form

(C.73) $$x^\pm(t) = h_\lambda^{s/u}(t) + v^\pm(t).$$

For $x^\pm$ close to the homoclinic orbit and λ small, the $v^\pm$ will be close to zero. We prove that there are unique functions $v^\pm(\omega, \lambda)(\cdot)$ such that $x^\pm$ satisfy conditions

(C.70) and (C.71). The functions $v^\pm$ solve the (nonlinear) variational equation along $h_\lambda^{s/u}$,

$$\dot{v}^\pm(t) = D_x f(h_\lambda^{s/u}(t), \lambda) v^\pm(t) + h^\pm(t, v^\pm(t), \lambda), \tag{C.74}$$

where

$$h^\pm(t, v, \lambda) = f(h_\lambda^{s/u}(t) + v, \lambda) - f(h_\lambda^{s/u}(t), \lambda) - D_x f(h_\lambda^{s/u}(t), \lambda) v. \tag{C.75}$$

The conditions (C.70) and (C.71) translate to conditions that $v^\pm$ must satisfy

$$v^+(0), v^-(0) \in W^+ \oplus W^- \oplus Z, \tag{C.76}$$

$$v^+(\omega) - v^-(-\omega) = h_\lambda^u(-\omega) - h_\lambda^s(\omega), \tag{C.77}$$

$$v^+(0) - v^-(0) \in Z. \tag{C.78}$$

To solve (C.74) with conditions (C.76)–(C.78), we perform several steps. First we simplify (C.74) by replacing h^+ and h^- with fixed functions $g^+ \in C[0, \omega]$ and $g^- \in C[-\omega, 0]$. So we get an equation

$$\dot{v}^\pm(t) = D_x f(h_\lambda^{s/u}(t), \lambda) v^\pm(t) + g^\pm(t, \lambda). \tag{C.79}$$

Simultaneously we replace the coupling condition (C.77) by prescribing projections a^+ and a^- of $v^+(\omega)$ and $v^-(-\omega)$:

(C.80)
$$a^+ = a^+(\lambda, \omega) = P^+(\lambda, \omega) v^+(\omega) \quad \text{and} \quad a^- = a^-(\lambda, \omega) = P^-(\lambda, -\omega) v^-(-\omega).$$

Lemma C.19 below provides a unique solution $\bar{v}(\omega, \lambda, g, a) = (\bar{v}^+, \bar{v}^-)$ for the variational equation (C.79) with boundary conditions (C.76), (C.78), (C.80), where $g = (g^+, g^-)$ and $a = (a^+, a^-)$.

We introduce notation

$$d(\omega, \lambda) = h_\lambda^u(-\omega) - h_\lambda^s(\omega) \tag{C.81}$$

(appearing in (C.77)).

In the next step we show that there exists $a(\omega, \lambda, g, d)$ so that $\hat{v}(\omega, \lambda, g, d)$, defined by

$$\hat{v}(\omega, \lambda, g, d) = \bar{v}(\omega, \lambda, g, a(\omega, \lambda, g, d)),$$

solves (C.79) with boundary conditions (C.76)–(C.78). This is the basis of Lemma C.23.

The original boundary value problem (C.74) with the boundary conditions (C.76)–(C.78) is now equivalent to a fixed point equation

$$v = \mathcal{F}_\omega(v, \lambda) = \hat{v}(\omega, \lambda, \mathcal{H}(v, \lambda), d(\omega, \lambda)) \tag{C.82}$$

in $C[0, \omega] \times C[-\omega, 0]$, where

$$\mathcal{H}(v, \lambda) = (H^+(v, \lambda), H^-(v, \lambda)) \tag{C.83}$$

and

$$H^{\pm}(v,\lambda)(t) = h^{\pm}(t, v^{\pm}(t), \lambda)). \tag{C.84}$$

Note that $\mathcal{H}$ is a mapping from $(C[0,\omega] \times C[-\omega,0]) \times \mathbb{R}$ to $C[0,\omega] \times C[-\omega,0]$. The statement of Corollary C.15 now follows from Lemma C.24 which provides a unique solution $v(\omega,\lambda)$ to equation (C.82).

We start executing the single steps that were described in the outline. Various estimates in the single steps make use of expressions for solutions obtained from the variation of constants formula, which we write down here. In terms of the transition matrices $\Phi^{\pm}$, a formula for solutions $v^{\pm}$ of (C.79) is given by

$$v^{+}(t) = \Phi^{+}(\lambda,t,0)v^{+}(0) + \int_0^t \Phi^{+}(\lambda,t,s)g^{+}(s)\,ds \tag{C.85}$$

and

$$v^{-}(t) = \Phi^{-}(\lambda,t,0)v^{-}(0) - \int_t^0 \Phi^{-}(\lambda,t,s)g^{-}(s)\,ds. \tag{C.86}$$

For solutions $v^{\pm}$ of (C.74) the variation of constants formula gives an expression solutions must satisfy, which is

$$v^{+}(t) = \Phi^{+}(\lambda,t,0)v^{+}(0) + \int_0^t \Phi^{+}(\lambda,t,s)h^{+}(s,v^{+}(s),\lambda)\,ds \tag{C.87}$$

and

$$v^{-}(t) = \Phi^{-}(\lambda,t,0)v^{-}(0) - \int_t^0 \Phi^{-}(\lambda,t,s)h^{-}(s,v^{-}(s),\lambda)\,ds. \tag{C.88}$$

Lemma C.19. *The variational equation* (C.79) *with boundary conditions* (C.76), (C.78), *and* (C.80) *has a unique solution* $\bar{v}(\omega,\lambda,g,a) = (\bar{v}^{+},\bar{v}^{-})$.

Proof. Using (C.52), (C.85), and (C.86), we have

$$\begin{aligned} &P^{+}(\lambda,0)v^{+}(0) \\ &\quad = \Phi^{+}(\lambda,0,\omega)\underbrace{P^{+}(\lambda,\omega)v^{+}(\omega)}_{a^{+}} - \int_0^{\omega} \Phi^{+}(\lambda,0,s)P^{+}(\lambda,s)g^{+}(s)\,ds \end{aligned} \tag{C.89}$$

and

$$\begin{aligned} &P^{-}(\lambda,0)v^{-}(0) \\ &\quad = \Phi^{-}(\lambda,0,-\omega)\underbrace{P^{-}(\lambda,-\omega)v^{-}(-\omega)}_{a^{-}} + \int_{-\omega}^{0} \Phi^{-}(\lambda,0,s)P^{-}(\lambda,s)g^{-}(s)\,ds. \end{aligned} \tag{C.90}$$

We indicated a^{+} and a^{-}, which are defined in (C.80).

In view of (C.76), (C.78) we may write

$$v^+(0) = w^+ + w^- + z^+, \tag{C.91}$$

and

$$v^-(0) = w^+ + w^- + z^-. \tag{C.92}$$

As we are using coordinates that satisfy (C.46), we find

$$w^- + z^+ = \Phi^+(\lambda, 0, \omega)a^+ - \int_0^\omega \Phi^+(\lambda, 0, s)P^+(\lambda, s)g^+(s)\,ds,$$

$$w^+ + z^- = \Phi^-(\lambda, 0, -\omega)a^- + \int_{-\omega}^0 \Phi^-(\lambda, 0, s)P^-(\lambda, s)g^-(s)\,ds. \tag{C.93}$$

We see that $w^\pm$, $z^\pm$, are uniquely determined by ω, g, a and depend linearly on g, a. Hence $v^\pm(0)$ are uniquely determined by ω, g, a by (C.91) and (C.92), respectively, and depend linearly on g, a. Now $\bar{v}(\omega, \lambda, g, a)$ is obtained from (C.85) and (C.86). □

The lemma provides maps $\bar{v}(\omega, \cdot, \cdot, \cdot) : \mathbb{R} \times (C[0,\omega] \times C[-\omega, 0]) \times (\mathbb{R}^n \times \mathbb{R}^n) \to (C[0,\omega] \times C[-\omega, 0])$ which are built from functions $\bar{v}^\pm$,

$$\bar{v}^\pm(\cdot) = \bar{v}^\pm(\omega, \lambda, (g^+, g^-), (a^+, a^-))(\cdot).$$

The spaces $C[0,\omega]$ and $C[-\omega, 0]$ are equipped with the supremum norm $\|\cdot\|$.

Lemma C.20. *Let the assumptions of Lemma* C.19 *be satisfied, and let* $\Omega > 0$ *be sufficiently large. Then for* $-\min\{|\mu^s|, \mu^u\} < \alpha^s < 0$, *there is a constant* C *such that for all* $\omega \geq \Omega$,

$$|(\mathrm{id} - P^+(\lambda, \omega))\bar{v}^+(\omega)| \leq Ce^{\alpha^s\omega}\left(e^{\alpha^s\omega}|a^-| + \|g^-\|\right) + C\|g^+\|,$$

$$|(\mathrm{id} - P^-(\lambda, -\omega))\bar{v}^-(-\omega)| \leq Ce^{\alpha^s\omega}\left(e^{\alpha^s\omega}|a^+| + \|g^+\|\right) + C\|g^-\|.$$

Proof. Starting from (C.85) we find

$$(\mathrm{id} - P^+(\lambda, t))v^+(t)$$
$$= \Phi^+(\lambda, t, 0)(\mathrm{id} - P^+(\lambda, 0))v^+(0) + \int_0^t \Phi^+(\lambda, t, s)(\mathrm{id} - P^+(\lambda, s))g^+(s)\,ds.$$

Recall that Φ^+ is the transition matrix of the variational equation (C.50), which has an exponential dichotomy with constants α^s and α^u and associated projection $(\mathrm{id} - P^+(\lambda, 0))$. This yields (see (C.54)) that there are constants $\bar{C}_a$ and $\bar{C}_g$ such that

$$|(\mathrm{id} - P^+(\lambda, \omega))\bar{v}^+(\omega)|$$
$$\leq \bar{C}_a e^{\alpha^s\omega}|(\mathrm{id} - P^+(\lambda, 0))\bar{v}^+(0)| + \bar{C}_g\|(\mathrm{id} - P^+(\lambda, 0))g^+\|.$$

Similarly, starting from (C.86), we find

$$|(\mathrm{id} - P^-(\lambda, -\omega))\bar{v}^-(-\omega)| \\ \le \bar{C}_a e^{\alpha^s \omega} |(\mathrm{id} - P^-(\lambda, 0))\bar{v}^-(0)| + \bar{C}_g \|(\mathrm{id} - P^-(\lambda, 0))g^-\|.$$

Next we estimate the terms $|(\mathrm{id} - P^\pm(\lambda, 0))\bar{v}^\pm(0)|$ appearing in these bounds. Using (C.46) and the definition of $P^\pm$ in (C.51), we find from (C.91), (C.92) that

$$(\mathrm{id} - P^\pm(\lambda, 0))\bar{v}^+(0) = w^\pm = (\mathrm{id} - P^\pm(\lambda, 0))(w^\pm + z^\mp).$$

With (C.93) this yields for $v^+(0)$,

$$(\mathrm{id} - P^+(\lambda, 0))\bar{v}^+(0) \\ = (\mathrm{id} - P^+(\lambda, 0)) \left(\Phi^-(\lambda, 0, -\omega)a^- + \int_{-\omega}^0 \Phi^-(\lambda, 0, s)P^-(\lambda, s)g^-(s)\, ds \right).$$

Exploiting the exponential dichotomy of Φ^- (see (C.57)) gives

$$|(\mathrm{id} - P^+(\lambda, 0))\bar{v}^+(0)| \le C(e^{\alpha^s \omega}|a^-| + \|g^-\|). \tag{C.94}$$

Combining this with the above estimate of $|(\mathrm{id} - P^+(\lambda, \omega))\bar{v}^+(\omega)|$ provides the statement of the lemma for v^+.

The proof so far shows that the constants appearing in the estimates are related to the exponential dichotomy of Φ^+ and the norm of the projection $\mathrm{id} - P^+(\lambda, 0)$. They do not depend on the particular choice of ω. In the same way one can verify the statement for v^-. □

The following lemma provides bounds for the solution $\bar{v}(\omega, \lambda, \cdot, \cdot)$ from Lemma C.19.

Lemma C.21. *Let $\Omega > 0$ be sufficiently large, and let $\omega > \Omega$. The function $\bar{v}(\omega, \lambda, \cdot, \cdot)$ is linear and there exists a constant $\bar{C}$ such that*

$$\|\bar{v}(\omega, \lambda, g, a)\| \le \bar{C}(\|g\| + |a|).$$

Proof. We show that the single terms $\bar{v}^\pm$ satisfy an estimate as stated in the lemma. We consider only $\bar{v}^+$. Write

$$\bar{v}^+(t) = P^+(\lambda, t)\bar{v}^+(t) + (\mathrm{id} - P^+(\lambda, t))\bar{v}^+(t).$$

We will give bounds for the single terms on the right-hand side. The term $(\mathrm{id} - P^+(\lambda, t))\bar{v}^+(t)$ can be bounded as in the proof of Lemma C.20. This gives the existence of a constant C such that

$$|(\mathrm{id} - P^+(\lambda, t))\bar{v}^+(t)| \le C(\|(g^-, g^+)\| + |a^-|). \tag{C.95}$$

Taking into consideration that $a^+ \in \operatorname{im} P^+(\lambda,\omega)$, we can write the term $P^+(\lambda,t)\bar{v}^+(t)$ as

(C.96)
$$P^+(\lambda,t)\bar{v}^+(t) = \Phi^+(\lambda,t,\omega)P^+(\lambda,\omega)a^+ - \int_t^\omega \Phi^+(\lambda,t,s)P^+(\lambda,s)g^+(s)\,ds,$$

similar to (C.89). Again exploiting exponential dichotomies of Φ^+, this time applying (C.55), we find that there is a constant C, such that

$$|P^+(\lambda,t)\bar{v}^+(t)| \le C(|a^+| + \|g^+\|).$$

Combining this with (C.95) proves the lemma.

As in the proof of Lemma C.20, we note that the constants appearing in the estimates are related to the exponential dichotomy of Φ^+ and the norm of the projection $\mathrm{id} - P^+(\lambda,0)$. They do not depend on the particular choice of ω. □

Remark C.22. From (C.96) we infer for $t = 0$ that

$$|P^+(\lambda,0)\bar{v}^+(0)| \le C(e^{\alpha^s\omega}|a^+| + \|g^+\|). \tag{C.97}$$

■

Lemma C.23. *Let $\Omega \in \mathbb{R}^+$ be sufficiently large, let $\omega > \Omega$, let $g \in C[0,\omega] \times C[-\omega,0]$, and let $d \in \mathbb{R}^n$. Then the variational equation* (C.79) *with boundary conditions* (C.76), *$v^+(\omega) - v^-(-\omega) = d$, and* (C.78) *has a unique solution $\hat{v}(\omega,\lambda,g,d) = (\hat{v}^+,\hat{v}^-)$.*

Proof. We will show that for given d, there is an $a = a(\omega,\lambda,g,d)$ such that

$$\bar{v}^+(\omega,\lambda,g,a)(\omega) - \bar{v}^-(\omega,\lambda,g,a)(-\omega) = d. \tag{C.98}$$

The lemma then results from $\hat{v}(\omega,\lambda,g,d) = \bar{v}(\omega,\lambda,g,a(\omega,\lambda,g,d))$.

Using the definition of a in (C.80), we rewrite equation (C.98) as

$$a^+ - a^- = d - (\mathrm{id} - P^+(\lambda,\omega))\bar{v}^+(\omega) + (\mathrm{id} - P^-(\lambda,-\omega))\bar{v}^-(-\omega). \tag{C.99}$$

By Lemma C.17, $\mathbb{R}^n = \operatorname{im} P^+(\lambda,\omega) \oplus \operatorname{im} P^-(\lambda,-\omega)$ for sufficiently large ω. This allows us to define, for large ω, a projection $\tilde{P}(\lambda,\omega)$ on $\mathbb{R}^n$ by

$$\operatorname{im}\tilde{P}(\lambda,\omega) = \operatorname{im} P^+(\lambda,\omega) \quad \text{and} \quad \ker\tilde{P}(\lambda,\omega) = \operatorname{im} P^-(\lambda,-\omega);$$

see (C.64). We use this projection to rewrite (C.99) as a fixed point equation for $a = a^+ + a^-$ to obtain

$$\begin{aligned} a = \big(2\tilde{P}(\lambda,\omega) - \mathrm{id}\big)\big(d &- (\mathrm{id} - P^+(\lambda,\omega))\bar{v}^+(\dots,a)(\omega) \\ &+ (\mathrm{id} - P^-(\lambda,-\omega))\bar{v}^-(\dots,a)(-\omega)\big). \end{aligned} \tag{C.100}$$

We know from Lemma C.21 that the functions $\bar{v}^\pm$ depend linearly on (g,a). This fixed point equation can therefore be written in the form

$$a = L_1(\lambda,\omega)a + L_2(\lambda,\omega)g + L_3(\lambda,\omega)d, \tag{C.101}$$

for linear bounded operators $L_j(\lambda,\omega)(\cdot)$, $j = 1,2,3$. By Lemma C.20, the linear operator $(\mathrm{id} - L_1(\lambda,\omega))$ is invertible for sufficiently large Ω. Hence equation (C.101) can be solved for a. □

We have obtained a map $\hat{v}(\omega,\cdot,\cdot,\cdot) : \mathbb{R}\times C[0,\omega]\times C[-\omega,0]\times\mathbb{R}^n \to C[0,\omega]\times C[-\omega,0]$. It follows from the derivation that $\hat{v}(\omega,\lambda,\cdot,\cdot)$ is linear and that there exists a constant $\hat{C}$ such that

$$\|\hat{v}(\omega,\lambda,g,d)\| \leq \hat{C}(\|g\| + |d|). \tag{C.102}$$

This estimate follows from Lemma C.21 together with an estimate

$$|a| \leq C(\|g\| + |d|)$$

for an appropriate constant C, which results from (C.101).

Lemma C.24. *Equation* (C.82) *has, for a given sequence ω and given sufficiently small λ, a unique solution $v(\omega,\lambda)$ in $C[0,\omega]\times C[-\omega,0]$. The solution $v(\omega,\cdot)$ of* (C.82) *is continuously differentiable.*

Proof. We will apply the uniform contraction theorem (Theorem A.16) on $\mathcal{F}_\omega(\cdot,\lambda)$ in the fixed point equation (C.82). To do so, we need to establish differentiability of $\mathcal{F}_\omega$. First we prove that $\mathcal{H}(\cdot,\lambda)$ from (C.83) is differentiable.

That the functions $H^\pm(\cdot,\lambda)$ are differentiable follows as in Appendix A.1.4 on superposition operators; see Theorem A.8. Consider the Nemytskii operator $H : C[0,\omega]\times\mathbb{R} \to C[0,\omega]$ given by $v \mapsto h^+(\cdot,v(\cdot),\lambda)$ for a function $(t,x,\lambda) \mapsto h^+(t,x,\lambda)$. We will show that $D_vH(v,\lambda)w = D_xh^+(\cdot,v(\cdot),\lambda)w(\cdot)$. Consider

$$\begin{aligned}
&\|H(v+w,\lambda) - H(v,\lambda) - D_xh^+(\cdot,v(\cdot),\lambda)w(\cdot)\| \\
&\quad = \max_{t\in[0,\omega]} |h^+(t,(v+w)(t),\lambda) - h^+(t,v(t),\lambda) - D_xh^+(t,v(t),\lambda)w(t)| \\
&\quad \leq \max_{t\in[0,\omega]} \int_0^1 |D_xh^+(t,(v+sw)(t),\lambda) - D_xh^+(t,v(t),\lambda)|\; ds\|w\|.
\end{aligned}$$

Since D_xh^+ is continuous it follows that

$$\lim_{w\to 0} \frac{\|H(v+w,\lambda) - H(v,\lambda) - D_xh^+(\cdot,v(\cdot),\lambda)w(\cdot)\|}{\|w\|} = 0.$$

This proves differentiability of $\mathcal{H}$ with respect to v. Differentiability of $\mathcal{H}$ with respect to λ follows directly from the differentiability of h^+. The differentiability with respect to v carries over to $\mathcal{F}_\omega$ since $\hat{v}(\omega,\lambda,\cdot,\cdot)$ is linear. The differentiability with respect to λ follows from the derivation of v; in each step all quantities are differentiable with respect to λ.

In order to apply the uniform contraction theorem, we first show that there is an $\epsilon > 0$ such that $\mathcal{F}_\omega(\cdot,\lambda)$ leaves the closed ball $B[0,\epsilon] \subset C[0,\omega]\times C[-\omega,0]$

invariant. The bound (C.102) gives

$$\begin{aligned}\|\mathcal{F}_\omega(v,\lambda)\| &= \|\hat{v}(\omega,\lambda,\mathcal{H}(v,\lambda),d(\omega,\lambda))\|\\ &\le \hat{C}(\|\mathcal{H}\|+|d|).\end{aligned} \tag{C.103}$$

Consider the term $\|\mathcal{H}\|$ appearing in this estimate. From its definition in (C.83) it follows that $\mathcal{H}(0,\lambda)=0$. The mean value theorem (see Theorem A.5) gives

$$\|\mathcal{H}(v,\lambda)\| \le \int_0^1 \|D_v\mathcal{H}(\tau v,\lambda)\|\,d\tau\|v\|.$$

Since $D_v\mathcal{H}$ is continuous and $D_v\mathcal{H}(0,\lambda)=0$, there is an $\epsilon>0$ such that for $\|v\|,|\lambda|\le\epsilon$, one has $\|D_v\mathcal{H}(\tau v,\lambda)\|\le\frac{1}{3\hat{C}}$. Hence, for $\|v\|,|\lambda|\le\epsilon$,

$$\|\mathcal{H}(v,\lambda)\| \le \frac{\epsilon}{3\hat{C}}.$$

Note that for $\lambda=0$ we find that $d(\omega,0)$ tends to 0 as $\omega\to\infty$. So, for sufficiently large Ω (note that $\omega\ge\Omega$) λ can be chosen small enough so that $\|d(\omega,\lambda)\|\le\frac{\epsilon}{3\hat{C}}$. We get from (C.103) that $\mathcal{F}_\omega(\cdot,\lambda,w_0^+)$ maps the closed ball $B[0,\epsilon]$ into itself.

The following estimate shows that for these λ, the operator $\mathcal{F}_\omega(\cdot,\lambda)$ is a contraction on $B[0,\epsilon]$:

$$\begin{aligned}\|D_v\mathcal{F}_\omega(v,\lambda)\| &\le \|D_g\hat{v}(\omega,\lambda,\mathcal{H}(v,\lambda),d(\omega,\lambda))\|\cdot\|D_v\mathcal{H}(v,\lambda)\|\\ &\le \hat{C}\frac{1}{3\hat{C}}\\ &< 1.\end{aligned} \tag{C.104}$$

Here we used that $\hat{v}(\omega,\lambda,\cdot,\cdot)$ is linear, as well as the estimate (C.103). Now apply the uniform contraction theorem. □

C.3.2. Estimates of the jumps. We begin the proof of Corollary C.16 by starting with an outline of the derivation of the representation of the jump and the estimate of the residual term. After it we prove a number of lemmas to which we refer in the outline.

C.3.2.1. *Estimate of the residual term.* With $\xi(\omega,\lambda)$ as in (C.8) defined by $\Xi(\omega,\lambda)=\xi^\infty(\lambda)+\xi(\omega,\lambda)$, where $\xi^\infty(\lambda)=h_\lambda^s(0)-h_\lambda^u(0)$, we will prove that

$$\langle\psi,\xi(\omega,\lambda)\rangle = -e^{2\mu^s(\lambda)\omega}\mathcal{E}^s(\lambda)+R(\omega,\lambda).$$

As a consequence of (C.45), we have that for sufficiently large t, $h_\lambda^s(t)$ and $h_\lambda^u(-t)$ belong to the stable and unstable eigenspaces of p.

With (C.73) we can write

$$\xi(\omega,\lambda) = v^+(\omega,\lambda)(0)-v^-(\omega,\lambda)(0), \tag{C.105}$$

where $v^\pm$ are given by the unique solution of the fixed point equation (C.82). Decompose the term $\langle\psi, \xi(\omega,\lambda)\rangle$ as

$$\langle\psi, \xi(\omega,\lambda)\rangle = T^1(\omega,\lambda) - T^2(\omega,\lambda), \tag{C.106}$$

with

$$T^1(\omega,\lambda) = \langle\psi, P^+(\lambda,0)v^+(\omega,\lambda)(0)\rangle,$$
$$T^2(\omega,\lambda) = \langle\psi, P^-(\lambda,0)v^-(\omega,\lambda)(0)\rangle.$$

Next we rewrite these expressions. The representations (C.89) and (C.90) yield

$$P^+(\lambda,0)v^+(\omega,\lambda)(0)$$
$$= \Phi^+(\lambda,0,\omega)a^+ - \int_0^\omega \Phi^+(\lambda,0,s)P^+(\lambda,s)h^+(s,v^+(\omega,\lambda)(s),\lambda)\,ds$$

and

$$P^-(\lambda,0)v^-(\omega,\lambda)(0)$$
$$= \Phi^-(\lambda,0,-\omega)a^- + \int_{-\omega}^0 \Phi^-(\lambda,0,s)P^-(\lambda,s)h^-(s,v^-(\omega,\lambda)(s),\lambda)\,ds.$$

Incorporating (C.99) and using the definition of $\tilde{P}$ in (C.64), we end up with

$$\begin{aligned} T^1(\omega,\lambda) =& \Big\langle \Phi^+(\lambda,0,\omega)^T P^+(\lambda,0)^T\psi, \\ & \tilde{P}(\lambda,\omega)\Big[h^u_\lambda(-\omega) - h^s_\lambda(\omega) + (\mathrm{id} - P^-(\lambda,-\omega))v^-(\omega,\lambda)(-\omega) \\ & - (\mathrm{id} - P^+(\lambda,\omega))v^+(\omega,\lambda)(\omega)\Big]\Big\rangle \\ & - \Big\langle \psi, \int_0^\omega \Phi^+(\lambda,0,s)P^+(\lambda,s)h^+(s,v^+(\omega,\lambda)(s),\lambda)\,ds\Big\rangle \end{aligned} \tag{C.107}$$

and

$$\begin{aligned} T^2(\omega,\lambda) =& \Big\langle \Phi^-(\lambda,0,-\omega)^T P^-(\lambda,0)^T\psi, \\ & (\mathrm{id} - \tilde{P}(\lambda,\omega))\Big[h^s_\lambda(\omega) - h^u_\lambda(-\omega) + (\mathrm{id} - P^+(\lambda,\omega))v^+_{i-1}(\omega,\lambda)(\omega) \\ & - (\mathrm{id} - P^-(\lambda,-\omega))v^-(\omega,\lambda)(-\omega)\Big]\Big\rangle \\ & - \Big\langle \psi, \int_{-\omega}^0 \Phi^-(\lambda,0,s)P^-(\lambda,s)h^-(s,v^-(\omega,\lambda)(s),\lambda)\,ds\Big\rangle. \end{aligned} \tag{C.108}$$

We must provide bounds for the separate terms that appear in (C.107) and (C.108). In what follows we use the notation

$$\Psi^\pm(\lambda,t,\tau) = \Phi^\pm(\lambda,\tau,t)^T. \tag{C.109}$$

First consider the expressions

$$T^{11} = \left\langle \Psi^+(\lambda,\omega,0)P^+(\lambda,0)^T\psi, \tilde{P}(\lambda,\omega)h_\lambda^u(-\omega)\right\rangle$$

and

$$T^{21} = \left\langle \Psi^-(\lambda,-\omega,0)P^-(\lambda,0)^T\psi, (\mathrm{id}-\tilde{P}(\lambda,\omega))h_\lambda^s(\omega)\right\rangle .$$

Equation (C.66) provides an asymptotic expansion for $h_\lambda^u(-\omega)$ and (C.68) gives an asymptotic expansion for $\Psi^+(\lambda,\omega,0)P^+(\lambda,0)^T\psi$. Using these and Lemma C.18 we find, for some $\delta > 1$,

$$\begin{aligned}(\text{C.110})\quad T^{11} &= \Big\langle e^{-\mu^u(\lambda)\omega}\eta^+(\lambda) + \mathcal{O}(e^{-\mu^u(\lambda)\omega\delta}),\\ &\qquad ((\mathrm{id}-P) + \mathcal{O}\left(e^{\alpha^s\omega}\right))(e^{-\mu^u(\lambda)\omega}\eta^u(\lambda) + \mathcal{O}(e^{-\mu^u(\lambda)\omega\delta}))\Big\rangle\\ &= e^{-2\mu^u(\lambda)\omega}\langle\eta^+(\lambda),\eta^u(\lambda)\rangle + \mathcal{O}\left(e^{-2\mu^u(\lambda)\omega\delta}\right).\end{aligned}$$

Likewise,

$$\begin{aligned}(\text{C.111})\quad T^{21} &= \Big\langle e^{\mu^s(\lambda)\omega}\eta^-(\lambda) + \mathcal{O}(e^{\mu^s(\lambda)\omega\delta}),\\ &\qquad \left(P + \mathcal{O}\left(e^{\alpha^s\omega}\right)\right)\left(e^{\mu^s(\lambda)\omega}\eta^s(\lambda) + \mathcal{O}(e^{\mu^s(\lambda)\omega\delta})\right)\Big\rangle\\ &= e^{2\mu^s(\lambda)\omega}\langle\eta^-(\lambda),\eta^s(\lambda)\rangle + \mathcal{O}\left(e^{2\mu^s(\lambda)\omega\delta}\right).\end{aligned}$$

Summarizing we have

$$\langle\psi,\Xi(\omega,\lambda)\rangle = \lambda + e^{-2\mu^u(\lambda)\omega}\langle\eta^+(\lambda),\eta^u(\lambda)\rangle - e^{2\mu^s(\lambda)\omega}\langle\eta^-(\lambda),\eta^s(\lambda)\rangle + \tilde{R}(\omega,\lambda).$$

In the remaining part of the proof we will derive appropriate bounds for the terms subsumed in $\tilde{R}$; we will see that these are of higher order. Write

$$\begin{aligned}T^{12} &= \left\langle \Phi^+(\lambda,0,\omega)^T P^+(\lambda,0)^T\psi, -\tilde{P}(\lambda,\omega)h_\lambda^s(\omega)\right\rangle,\\ T^{22} &= \left\langle \Phi^-(\lambda,0,-\omega)^T P^-(\lambda,0)^T\psi, -(\mathrm{id}-\tilde{P}(\lambda,\omega))h_\lambda^u(-\omega)\right\rangle .\end{aligned}$$

Since $h_\lambda^s(\omega)$ and $h_\lambda^u(-\omega)$ are in the local stable and the local unstable manifold, we find, using the same arguments as in the derivation of (C.110), (C.111), that

$$\begin{aligned}T^{12} &= \mathcal{O}\left(e^{(-\mu^u(\lambda)+\mu^s(\lambda))\omega\delta}\right),\\ (\text{C.112})\quad T^{22} &= \mathcal{O}\left(e^{(-\mu^u(\lambda)+\mu^s(\lambda))\omega\delta}\right).\end{aligned}$$

Consider the terms

$$\begin{aligned}T^{13} = \Big\langle &\Phi^+(\lambda,0,\omega)^T P^+(\lambda,0)^T\psi,\\ &\tilde{P}(\lambda,\omega)\big[(\mathrm{id}-P^-(\lambda,-\omega))v^-(\omega,\lambda)(-\omega) - (\mathrm{id}-P^+(\lambda,\omega))v^+(\omega,\lambda)(\omega)\big]\Big\rangle\end{aligned}$$

and

$$\begin{aligned}T^{23} = \Big\langle &\Phi^-(\lambda,0,-\omega)^T P^-(\lambda,0)^T\psi, (\mathrm{id}-\tilde{P}(\lambda,\omega))\\ &\big[(\mathrm{id}-P^+(\lambda,\omega))v^+(\omega,\lambda)(\omega) - (\mathrm{id}-P^-(\lambda,-\omega))v^-(\omega,\lambda)(-\omega)\big]\Big\rangle.\end{aligned}$$

We recognize terms of the form $(\mathrm{id} - P^{\pm}(\lambda,\omega))v^{\pm}(\omega,\lambda)(\pm\omega)$. By Lemma C.20 we find (replacing $g^{\pm}$ by $H^{\pm}$) that

$$|(\mathrm{id} - P^{+}(\lambda,\omega))v^{+}(\omega,\lambda)(\omega)| \leq Ce^{\alpha^s\omega}\left(e^{\alpha^s\omega}|a^-| + \|H^-(v^-)\|\right) + C\|H^+(v^+)\|$$

and

$$|(\mathrm{id} - P^{-}(\lambda,-\omega))v^{-}(\omega,\lambda)(-\omega)| \leq Ce^{\alpha^s\omega}\left(e^{\alpha^s\omega}|a^+| + \|H^+(v^+)\|\right) + C\|H^-(v^-)\|.$$

From the definition (C.83), (C.84) of $\mathcal{H}(\mathbf{v},\lambda) = (H^+(v^+,\lambda), H^-(v^-,\lambda))$, using the definition of $h^{\pm}$ in (C.75) and the proof of Lemma C.24, it follows that $H^{\pm}(0,\lambda) = 0$ and $D_v H^{\pm}(0,\lambda) = 0$. Hence we have

$$H^{\pm}(v^{\pm},\lambda) = \mathcal{O}(\|v^{\pm}\|^2), \tag{C.113}$$

uniformly in λ.

Now (C.118) (which is proved below using (C.81)) yields

$$\|v^{\pm}\|^2 \leq Ce^{2\alpha^s\omega}. \tag{C.114}$$

Estimates of $|a^{\pm}|$ are given in Lemma C.27. Combining these estimates with the asymptotic expansions (C.67), (C.68) for $\Phi^-(\lambda,0,-\omega)^T P^-(\lambda,0)^T\psi$ and $\Phi^+(\lambda,0,\omega)^T P^+(\lambda,0)^T\psi$ gives

$$|T^{13}| \leq Ce^{(-\mu^u(\lambda)+3\alpha^s)\omega},$$
$$|T^{23}| \leq Ce^{(\mu^s(\lambda)+3\alpha^s)\omega},$$

for an appropriate constant C.

The remaining terms are

$$T^{14} = -\left\langle \psi, \int_0^{\omega} \Phi^+(\lambda,0,s)P^+(\lambda,s)h^+(s,v^+(\omega,\lambda)(s),\lambda)\,ds \right\rangle,$$

$$T^{24} = -\left\langle \psi, \int_{-\omega}^{0} \Phi^-(\lambda,0,s)P^-(\lambda,s)h^-(s,v^-(\omega,\lambda)(s),\lambda)\,ds \right\rangle. \tag{C.115}$$

These are treated in Lemma C.30, which gives

$$|T^{14}| = \mathcal{O}\left(e^{3\alpha^s\omega}\right),$$
$$|T^{24}| = \mathcal{O}\left(e^{3\alpha^s\omega}\right).$$

Corollary C.16 follows by combining the bounds obtained for the terms T^{kl}, $k = 1,2$, $l = 1,\ldots,4$.

In the above outline we have obtained

$$\mathcal{E}^s(\lambda) = \langle \eta^-(\lambda), \eta^s(\lambda)\rangle, \tag{C.116}$$

with η^s from (C.65) and η^- from (C.67).

C.3.2.2. *Auxiliary lemmas.* Next we state and prove the lemmas to which we referred in the above outline. These are Lemmas C.26, C.27, and C.30.

First we show that v^+ and v^- are exponentially small as the lower bound Ω of ω tends to infinity. From (C.102) with g replaced by $\mathcal{H}(v, \lambda)$ we find

$$\|v\| \leq \hat{C}(\|\mathcal{H}\| + |d|). \tag{C.117}$$

Recall that by $|\cdot|$ we denote the Euclidean norm in $\mathbb{R}^n$ and by $\|\cdot\|$ the supremum norm. From (C.113) we infer

$$\|\mathcal{H}\| = \mathcal{O}(\|v\|^2).$$

Hence there is $\epsilon > 0$ such that for $\|v\| < \epsilon$ (see also the derivation of v in Lemma C.24),

$$\|\mathcal{H}\| \leq \frac{1}{2}\|v\|.$$

Together with (C.117) this shows that there is a constant C such that

$$\|v\| \leq C|d|. \tag{C.118}$$

By the definition of d in (C.81), this proves that $\|v\|$ becomes exponentially small as $\Omega \to \infty$.

Define projections of $v^\pm$ on stable and unstable directions:

$$\begin{aligned} v^{\pm,s}(t) &= (\mathrm{id} - P^\pm(t))v^\pm(t), \\ v^{\pm,u}(t) &= P^\pm(t)v^\pm(t). \end{aligned} \tag{C.119}$$

Likewise we write $h^+ = h^{+,s} + h^{+,u}$ and $f = f^s + f^u$ in components. By (C.60) and (C.118) we find that

$$\lim_{\Omega\to\infty} \|v^{\pm,s/u}\| = 0. \tag{C.120}$$

Before starting with the actual estimates we prove a preliminary lemma on estimates of $h^\pm$.

Lemma C.25. *There exist constants Ω and c such that for all $|\lambda| < c$ and $\omega > \Omega$, there exists a constant $M > 0$ such that*

$$|h^{+,s}(t, v^+(t), \lambda)| \leq M(e^{\alpha^s t}|v^{+,u}(t)| + |v^{+,s}(t)|)(|v^{+,s}(t)| + |v^{+,u}(t)|), \qquad t > 0,$$

and

$$|h^{-,s}(t, v^-(t), \lambda)| \leq M(e^{-\alpha^s t}|v^{-,u}(t)| + |v^{-,s}(t)|)(|v^{-,s}(t)| + |v^{-,u}(t)|), \qquad t < 0.$$

Proof. We only consider the first bound. In the notation below we omit dependence on λ. We use the convention that the constant C appearing in the estimates may vary from line to line.

Consider first the statement for $t \geq \Omega$. Applying Taylor's theorem and taking advantage of the fact that the chain rule yields

$$\begin{aligned}\frac{d}{d\tau} f^s(h^{+,s}(t) + \tau(v^{+,s}(t) + v^{+,u}(t))) \\ = Df^s(h^{+,s}(t) + \tau(v^{+,s}(t) + v^{+,u}(t)))\,(v^{+,s}(t) + v^{+,u}(t)),\end{aligned}$$

we get

$$\begin{aligned}&|h^{+,s}(t,(v^{+,s} + v^{+,u})(t))| \\ &\quad = \Big| f^s(h^{+,s}(t) + v^{+,s}(t) + v^{+,u}(t)) - f^s(h^{+,s}(t)) \\ &\qquad\qquad - Df^s(h^{+,s}(t))\,(v^{+,s}(t) + v^{+,u}(t)) \Big| \\ &\quad \leq \int_0^1 |Df^s(h^{+,s}(t) + \tau(v^{+,s}(t) + v^{+,u}(t))) - Df^s(h^{+,s}(t))|\, d\tau\ |v^{+,s}(t)| \\ &\quad + \left| \int_0^1 Df^s(h^{+,s}(t) + \tau(v^{+,s}(t) + v^{+,u}(t))) - Df^s(h^{+,s}(t))\, d\tau \right| |v^{+,u}(t)|\,.\end{aligned}$$

(Basically, this is nothing more than an application of the mean value theorem.) The first summand is of order $\mathcal{O}(|v^{+,s}(t)|(|v^{+,s}(t)| + |v^{+,u}(t)|))$. In order to treat the second summand, we take into consideration that

$$\begin{aligned}\text{(C.121)}\quad &\frac{d}{d\sigma} \int_0^1 Df^s(h^{+,s}(t) + \sigma\tau(v^{+,s}(t) + v^{+,u}(t)))\, d\tau \\ &= \int_0^1 D^2 f^s(h^{+,s}(t) + \sigma\tau(v^{+,s}(t) + v^{+,u}(t)))\, \tau(v^{+,s}(t) + v^{+,u}(t))\, d\tau.\end{aligned}$$

From that we infer

$$\begin{aligned}&\int_0^1 \int_0^1 D^2 f^s(h^{+,s}(t) + \tau_1\tau_2(v^{+,s}(t) + v^{+,u}(t)))\, \tau_1(v^{+,s}(t) + v^{+,u}(t))\, d\tau_1 d\tau_2 \\ &\quad = \int_0^1 \left(\frac{d}{d\tau_2} \int_0^1 Df^s(h^{+,s}(t) + \tau_2\tau_1(v^{+,s}(t) + v^{+,u}(t)))\, d\tau_1 \right) d\tau_2 \\ &\quad = \int_0^1 (Df^s(h^{+,s}(t) + \tau(v^{+,s}(t) + v^{+,u}(t))) - Df^s(h^{+,s}(t))\, d\tau.\end{aligned}$$

This leads eventually to the following estimate of $h^{+,s}$,

$$
\begin{aligned}
&|h^{+,s}(t,(v^{+,s}+v^{+,u})(t))| \\
&\quad \le C|v^{+,s}(t)|(|v^{+,s}(t)|+|v^{+,u}(t)|) \\
&\qquad + \left(\int_0^1\int_0^1 |D^2 f^s(h^{+,s}(t)+\tau_1\tau_2(v^{+,s}(t)+v^{+,u}(t)))|\, d\tau_1 d\tau_2\right) \\
&\qquad |v^{+,s}(t)|\,|v^{+,u}(t)| \\
&\qquad + \left(\int_0^1\int_0^1 |D^2 f^s(h^{+,s}(t)+\tau_1\tau_2(v^{+,s}(t)+v^{+,u}(t)))|\, d\tau_1 d\tau_2\right) \\
&\qquad |v^{+,u}(t)|\,|v^{+,u}(t)|\,.
\end{aligned}
$$

Estimating the second term as $\mathcal{O}(|v^{+,s}(t)|(|v^{+,s}(t)|+|v^{+,u}(t)|))$, we find

$$
\begin{aligned}
\text{(C.122)}\quad &|h^{+,s}(t,(v^{+,s}+v^{+,u})(t))| \\
&\quad \le C|v^{+,s}(t)|(|v^{+,s}(t)|+|v^{+,u}(t)|) \\
&\qquad + \int_0^1\int_0^1 |D^2 f^s(h^{+,s}(t)+\tau_1\tau_2(v^{+,s}(t)+v^{+,u}(t)))|\, d\tau_1 d\tau_2 \\
&\qquad |v^{+,u}(t)|\,|v^{+,u}(t)|\,.
\end{aligned}
$$

Because of (C.45), for x close to the equilibrium p the term $f^s(x)$ belongs to $T_pW^{ss,s}(p)$. Consequently $(\mathrm{id}-P)f^s(x)$ vanishes identically. Hence, $D^2(\mathrm{id}-P)f^s(x)=0$ for those x. In particular we have for $t \ge \Omega$

$$D^2(\mathrm{id}-P)f^s((\mathrm{id}-P)v^{+,u}(t)) = 0.$$

With this we write the integral term in (C.122) as

$$
\begin{aligned}
&\int_0^1\int_0^1 \left|D^2 f^s(h^{+,s}(t)+\tau_1\tau_2(v^{+,s}(t)+v^{+,u}(t)))\right| d\tau_1 d\tau_2 \\
&\quad = \int_0^1\int_0^1 \Big|D^2 f^s\,(h^{+,s}(t)+\tau_1\tau_2(v^{+,s}(t)+Pv^{+,u}(t)+(\mathrm{id}-P)v^{+,u}(t))) \\
&\qquad\qquad - D^2(\mathrm{id}-P)f^s((\mathrm{id}-P)v^{+,u}(t))\Big|\, d\tau_1 d\tau_2 \\
&\quad \le \int_0^1\int_0^1 \Big|D^2 f^s\,(h^{+,s}(t)+\tau_1\tau_2(v^{+,s}(t)+Pv^{+,u}(t)+(\mathrm{id}-P)v^{+,u}(t))) \\
&\qquad\qquad - D^2 f^s((\mathrm{id}-P)v^{+,u}(t))\Big|\, d\tau_1 d\tau_2 \\
&\qquad + \int_0^1\int_0^1 \left|D^2 P f^s((\mathrm{id}-P)v^{+,u}(t))\right| d\tau_1 d\tau_2.
\end{aligned}
$$

Again applying the mean value theorem, the first integral in this last expression can be estimated as $\mathcal{O}(|h^{+,s}(t)|+|v^{+,s}(t)|+|Pv^{+,u}(t)|)$. The integrand of the second integral we write as

$$\begin{aligned}D^2Pf^s((\operatorname{id}-P)v^{+,u}(t)) &= P(\operatorname{id}-P^+(t))D^2f((\operatorname{id}-P)v^{+,u}(t))\\ &= P(\operatorname{id}-P^+(t))(\operatorname{id}-P)D^2f((\operatorname{id}-P)v^{+,u}(t)).\end{aligned}$$

The latter equality follows from (C.45) which gives $f((\operatorname{id}-P)v^{+,u}(t)) \in T_pW_0^{u,uu}(p)$. Together this yields, for $t > \Omega$,

$$\begin{aligned}|h^{+,s}(t,(v^{+,s}+v^{+,u})(t))| &\le C|v^{+,s}(t)|(|v^{+,s}(t)| + |v^{+,u}(t)|)\\ &\quad + C(|h^{+,s}(t)| + |v^{+,s}(t)| + |Pv^{+,u}(t)|)|v^{+,u}(t)|^2\\ &\quad + C\|(\operatorname{id}-P^+(t))(\operatorname{id}-P)\|\,|v^{+,u}(t)|^2\\ &\le C(e^{\alpha^s t}|v^{+,u}(t)| + |v^{+,s}(t)|)(|v^{+,s}(t)| + |v^{+,u}(t)|),\end{aligned}$$

using $|h^{+,s}(t)| \le Ce^{\alpha^s t}$, $\|(\operatorname{id}-P^+(t))(\operatorname{id}-P)\| \le Ce^{\alpha^s t}$, $\|PP^+(t)\| \le Ce^{\alpha^s t}$.

It remains to consider $h^{+,s}$ for $t \in [0,\Omega]$. Since Ω is fixed this is simply done by choosing the constants adequately. To be more precise, we have for $t \in [0,\Omega]$, because $h^{+,s}(t, v^+(t)) = \mathcal{O}(|v^+(t)|^2)$, that

$$\begin{aligned}|h^{+,s}(t,v^+(t))| &\le C(|v^{+,s}(t)| + |v^{+,u}(t)|)^2\\ &\le Ce^{-\alpha^s(\Omega-t)}(|v^{+,s}(t)| + |v^{+,u}(t)|)^2\\ &\le C(e^{\alpha^s t}|v^{+,u}(t)| + |v^{+,s}(t)|)(|v^{+,s}(t)| + |v^{+,u}(t)|). \qquad \square\end{aligned}$$

Now we turn towards the actual estimates of $v^{\pm}$.

Lemma C.26. *There is a constant C such that*

$$\begin{aligned}\|v^{+,s}\| &\le Ce^{2\alpha^s\omega}, \quad \|v^{+,u}\| \le Ce^{\alpha^s\omega},\\ \|v^{-,s}\| &\le Ce^{2\alpha^s\omega}, \quad \|v^{-,u}\| \le Ce^{\alpha^s\omega}.\end{aligned}$$

Proof. In what follows the constants C may change from line to line. As in the proof of Lemma C.20 we use exponential dichotomies to find

$$\begin{aligned}\text{(C.123)}\quad |v^{+,s}(t)| &\le Ce^{\alpha^s t}|v^{-,u}(0)|\\ &\quad + C\int_0^t e^{(\alpha^s-\delta)(t-s)}|(\operatorname{id}-P^+(\lambda,s))h^+(s,v^+(s),\lambda)|\,ds.\end{aligned}$$

Here we exploit $(\operatorname{id}-P^+(\lambda,0))v^+(0) = (\operatorname{id}-P^+(\lambda,0))v^{-,u}(0)$, which follows from (C.91) and (C.92). Note that α^s and $\alpha^s - \delta$ are appropriate constants for the exponential dichotomy, if also $\mu^s < \alpha^s - \delta$.

Applying Lemma C.25, we get

$$\begin{aligned}|v^{+,s}(t)| &\le Ce^{\alpha^s t}|v^{-,u}(0)|\\ &\quad + C\int_0^t e^{(\alpha^s-\delta)(t-s)}(e^{\alpha^s s}|v^{+,u}(s)| + |v^{+,s}(s)|)(|v^{+,u}(s)| + |v^{+,s}(s)|)\,ds\\ &\le e^{\alpha^s t}\Big(C|v^{-,u}(0)|\\ &\quad + C\Big(\|v^{+,u}\| + \sup_{s\in[0,t]} e^{-\alpha^s s}|v^{+,s}(s)|\Big)(\|v^{+,u}\| + \|v^{+,s}\|)\int_0^t e^{-\delta(t-s)}\,ds\Big).\end{aligned}$$

Multiplication with $e^{-\alpha^s t}$ yields

$$|e^{-\alpha^s t}v^{+,s}(t)| \le C|v^{-,u}(0)| + C\left(\|v^{+,u}\| + \|e^{-\alpha^s t}v^{+,s}(t)\|\right)(\|v^{+,u}\| + \|v^{+,s}\|)\,.$$

Rewrite this as

$$\begin{aligned}(1 - C(\|v^{+,u}\| + \|v^{+,s}\|))\,\|e^{-\alpha^s t}v^{+,s}(t)\|&\\ \le C|v^{-,u}(0)| + C\|v^{+,u}\|\,&(\|v^{+,u}\| + \|v^{+,s}\|)\,.\end{aligned}$$

By (C.120) we have for sufficiently large Ω that $1 - C(\|v^{+,u}\| + \|v^{+,s}\|) > \frac{1}{2}$, with C as above, and we thus get an estimate of the form

$$|e^{-\alpha^s t}v^{+,s}(t)| \le C(|v^{-,u}(0)| + \|v^{+,u}\|(\|v^{+,u}\| + \|v^{+,s}\|)). \tag{C.124}$$

In the same way we find

$$|e^{\alpha^s t}v^{-,s}(t)| \le C(|v^{+,u}(0)| + \|v^{-,u}\|(\|v^{-,u}\| + \|v^{-,s}\|)). \tag{C.125}$$

Hence

$$\begin{aligned}|v^{+,s}(t)| &\le C(|v^{-,u}(0)| + \|v^{+,u}\|(\|v^{+,u}\| + \|v^{+,s}\|)),\\ |v^{-,s}(t)| &\le C(|v^{+,u}(0)| + \|v^{-,u}\|(\|v^{-,u}\| + \|v^{-,s}\|)).\end{aligned} \tag{C.126}$$

For sufficiently large Ω, we have $1 - C\|v^{\pm,u}\| > \frac{1}{2}$ (see again (C.120)) with C from (C.126). This leads to an estimate

$$\|v^{\pm,s}\| \le C(|v^{\mp,u}(0)| + \|v^{\pm,u}\|^2). \tag{C.127}$$

Now consider $v^{\pm,u}$. Starting from (C.89) and (C.90), similar to (C.87), (C.88) (with also the definition of $a^{\pm}$ from (C.80), and (C.52) for formulas of commuting flow and projections $P^{\pm}$), we write down expressions

$$\begin{aligned}
&P^+(\lambda,t)v^+(t)\\
&\quad= \Phi^+(\lambda,t,\omega)P^+(\lambda,\omega)v^+(\omega)\\
&\qquad\qquad\qquad - \int_t^{\omega} \Phi^+(\lambda,t,s)P^+(\lambda,s)h^+(s,v^+(s),\lambda)\,ds\\
&\quad= \Phi^+(\lambda,t,\omega)a^+ - \int_t^{\omega} \Phi^+(\lambda,t,s)P^+(\lambda,s)h^+(s,v^+(s),\lambda)\,ds,\\
&P^-(\lambda,t)v^-(t)\\
&\quad= \Phi^-(\lambda,t,-\omega)P^-(\lambda,-\omega)v^-(-\omega)\\
&\qquad\qquad\qquad + \int_{-\omega}^{t} \Phi^-(\lambda,t,s)P^-(\lambda,s)h^-(s,v^-(s),\lambda)\,ds\\
&\quad= \Phi^-(\lambda,t,-\omega)a^- + \int_{-\omega}^{t} \Phi^-(\lambda,t,s)P^-(\lambda,s)h^-(s,v^-(s),\lambda)\,ds.
\end{aligned}$$

The first of these gives

$$|v^{+,u}(t)| \le Ce^{\alpha^s(\omega-t)}|a^+| + C\int_t^{\omega} e^{-\alpha^s(t-s)}|h^{+,u}(s,v^+(s),\lambda)|\,ds.$$

With Lemma C.27 below this yields, exploiting $h^{+,u}(v) = \mathcal{O}(|v|^2)$,

$$|v^{+,u}(t)| \le Ce^{\alpha^s(\omega-t)}e^{\alpha^s\omega} + C(\|v^{+,s}\| + \|v^{+,u}\|)^2. \tag{C.128}$$

In the same way we proceed with $v^{-,u}$ and end up with

$$|v^{-,u}(t)| \le Ce^{\alpha^s(\omega+t)}e^{\alpha^s\omega} + C(\|v^{-,s}\| + \|v^{-,u}\|)^2. \tag{C.129}$$

As $\|v^{\pm,u}\|$ is small (see (C.120)), we conclude from these estimates that

$$\begin{aligned}
\|v^{+,u}\| &\le C(e^{\alpha^s\omega} + \|v^{+,s}\|^2),\\
\|v^{-,u}\| &\le C(e^{\alpha^s\omega} + \|v^{-,s}\|^2).
\end{aligned}\tag{C.130}$$

Equations (C.130) in combination with (C.127) yield

$$\begin{aligned}
\|v^{+,s}\| &\le C\left(e^{2\alpha^s\omega} + (\|v^{-,s}\| + \|v^{-,u}\|)^2 + (e^{\alpha^s\omega} + \|v^{+,s}\|^2)^2\right)\\
&\le C\left(e^{2\alpha^s\omega} + (\|v^{-,s}\| + \|v^{-,u}\|)^2 + e^{2\alpha^s\omega} + \epsilon^+(\Omega)\|v^{+,s}\|\right),
\end{aligned}$$

where $\epsilon^+(\Omega)$ tends to zero as $\Omega \to \infty$. Here we used that $|v^{\pm}(0)| \le \|v^{\pm}\|$ and that $\|v^{+,s}\|$ tends to zero as Ω tends to infinity; see (C.120). Similarly we find, with a corresponding $\epsilon^-(\Omega)$,

$$\|v^{-,s}\| \le C\left(e^{2\alpha^s\omega} + (\|v^{+,s}\| + \|v^{+,u}\|)^2 + e^{2\alpha^s\omega} + \epsilon^-(\Omega)\|v^{-,s}\|\right).$$

Hence

$$
\begin{aligned}
&\|v^{+,s}\| \le C\left(e^{2\alpha^s\omega} + (\|v^{-,s}\| + \|v^{-,u}\|)^2\right), \\
\text{(C.131)} \qquad &\|v^{-,s}\| \le C\left(e^{2\alpha^s\omega} + (\|v^{+,s}\| + \|v^{+,u}\|)^2\right).
\end{aligned}
$$

Plugging (C.130) into (C.131) yields

$$
\begin{aligned}
&\|v^{+,s}\| \le C\left(e^{2\alpha^s\omega} + \hat{\epsilon}^-(\Omega)\|v^{-,s}\|\right), \\
\text{(C.132)} \qquad &\|v^{-,s}\| \le C\left(e^{2\alpha^s\omega} + \hat{\epsilon}^+(\Omega)\|v^{+,s}\|\right),
\end{aligned}
$$

where $\hat{\epsilon}^{\pm}(\Omega)$ tends to zero as $\Omega \to \infty$.

Finally, the statement of the lemma for $\|v^{\pm,s}\|$ follows by plugging the estimates (C.132) into each other. In doing so, we take advantage of the fact that $\hat{\epsilon}^{\pm}(\Omega)$ tends to zero as $\Omega \to \infty$. Plugging the resulting estimates of $\|v^{\pm,s}\|$ into (C.130) yields the statement of the lemma for $\|v^{\pm,u}\|$. □

Lemma C.27. *There exists a constant C such that for sufficiently large Ω,*

$$
|a^+|, |a^-| \le Ce^{\alpha^s\omega}.
$$

Proof. Formulas for the quantities a^+ or a^- are obtained from (C.99) by applying $\tilde{P}(\lambda,\omega)$ or $(\mathrm{id} - \tilde{P}(\lambda,\omega))$, respectively. This yields

$$
\begin{aligned}
a^+ &= \tilde{P}(\lambda,\omega)d - \tilde{P}(\lambda,\omega)(\mathrm{id} - P^+(\lambda,\omega))\bar{v}^+(\omega) \\
&\quad + (\mathrm{id} - P^-(\lambda,-\omega))\bar{v}^-(-\omega), \\
-a^- &= (\mathrm{id} - \tilde{P}(\lambda,\omega))d - (\mathrm{id} - \tilde{P}(\lambda,\omega))(\mathrm{id} - P^+(\lambda,\omega))\bar{v}^+(\omega) \\
&\quad + (\mathrm{id} - P^-(\lambda,-\omega))\bar{v}^-(-\omega),
\end{aligned}
$$

from which we derive bounds

$$
\begin{aligned}
|a^+| &\le |\tilde{P}(\lambda,\omega)d| + C\|\tilde{P}(\lambda,\omega)\| \left(|v^{+,s}(\lambda)(\omega)| + |v^{-,s}(\lambda)(-\omega)|\right), \\
|a^-| &\le |(\mathrm{id} - \tilde{P}(\lambda,\omega))d| \\
&\qquad + C\|(\mathrm{id} - \tilde{P}(\lambda,\omega))\| \left(|v^{+,s}(\lambda)(\omega)| + |v^{-,s}(\lambda)(-\omega)|\right),
\end{aligned}
$$

where C is an appropriate constant related to the norm of the projections $\mathrm{id} - P^{\pm}(\lambda,\pm\omega)$.

Further, the necessary estimates of $|v^{\pm,s}(\lambda)(\pm\omega)|$ follow from Lemma C.26. The remaining terms $|\tilde{P}(\lambda,\omega)d|$ and $|(\mathrm{id}-\tilde{P}(\lambda,\omega))d|$ have been estimated when treating the terms T^{11}, T^{12} and T^{21}, T^{22}; see (C.110)–(C.112). □

Consider the integral terms appearing in the expressions for T^{14} and T^{24} defined in (C.115). First we estimate $P^{\pm}h^{\pm}$. To this end decompose $v^{\pm,s}(t)$ into

$$v^{\pm,s}(t) = v^{\pm,ss}(t) + v^{\pm,su}(t),$$

where

$$\begin{aligned} v^{\pm,ss}(t) &\in \Phi^{\pm}(\lambda,t,0)W^{\pm}, \\ v^{\pm,su}(t) &\in \Phi^{\pm}(\lambda,t,0)\mathrm{span}\{f(\gamma^{\pm}(\lambda)(0),\lambda)\}. \end{aligned}$$

Lemma C.28. *There exist constants Ω and c such that there exists a constant $M > 0$ such that for all $|\lambda| < c$ and $\omega > \Omega$,*

$$|P^{\pm}(\lambda,t)h^{\pm}(t,v^{\pm}(t),\lambda)| \le M(|v^{\pm,u}(t)| + |v^{\pm,su}(t)|)|v^{\pm}(t)|.$$

Proof. We give the proof only for "+". Again we adopt the notation defined in (C.119) for h^+ and f and write $h^{+,u} = P^+h^+$ and $f^u = P^+f$. We also suppress the dependency on λ from the notation. Finally we use the convention that the constant C appearing in the estimates may vary from line to line.

Applying Taylor's formula yields

$$\begin{aligned} &h^{+,u}(t,(v^{+,s}+v^{+,u})(t)) \\ &= f^u(h^{+,s}(t)+v^{+,s}(t)+v^{+,u}(t)) - f^u(h^{+,s}(t)) \\ &\quad - Df^u(h^{+,s}(t))\,(v^{+,s}(t)+v^{+,u}(t)) \\ &= \left(\int_0^1 Df^u(h^{+,s}(t)+\tau(v^{+,s}(t)+v^{+,u}(t))) - Df^u(h^{+,s}(t))\,d\tau\right) v^{+,ss}(t) \\ &\quad + \left(\int_0^1 Df^u(h^{+,s}(t)+\tau(v^{+,s}(t)+v^{+,u}(t))) - Df^u(h^{+,s}(t))\,d\tau\right) v^{+,su}(t) \\ &\quad + \left(\int_0^1 Df^u(h^{+,s}(t)+\tau(v^{+,s}(t)+v^{+,u}(t))) - Df^u(h^{+,s}(t))\,d\tau\right) v^{+,u}(t). \end{aligned}$$

Continuing by rewriting differences as integrals, introducing notation such as $v_2^{+,ss,ss} = (v^{+,ss}, v^{+,ss})$, $v_2^{+,ss,su} = (v^{+,ss}, v^{+,su})$,

$$
\begin{aligned}
\text{(C.133)}\quad & h^{+,u}(t,(v^{+,s}+v^{+,u})(t)) \\
&= \left(\int_0^1\int_0^1 D^2 f^u(h^{+,s}(t)+\tau_1\tau_2(v^{+,s}(t)+v^{+,u}(t)))\,d\tau_1 d\tau_2\right) v_2^{+,ss,ss} \\
&\quad +2\left(\int_0^1\int_0^1 D^2 f^u(h^{+,s}(t)+\tau_1\tau_2(v^{+,s}(t)+v^{+,u}(t)))\,d\tau_1 d\tau_2\right) v_2^{+,ss,su} \\
&\quad +\left(\int_0^1\int_0^1 D^2 f^u(h^{+,s}(t)+\tau_1\tau_2(v^{+,s}(t)+v^{+,u}(t)))\,d\tau_1 d\tau_2\right) v_2^{+,su,su} \\
&\quad +2\left(\int_0^1\int_0^1 D^2 f^u(h^{+,s}(t)+\tau_1\tau_2(v^{+,s}(t)+v^{+,u}(t)))\,d\tau_1 d\tau_2\right) v_2^{+,u,s} \\
&\quad +\left(\int_0^1\int_0^1 D^2 f^u(h^{+,s}(t)+\tau_1\tau_2(v^{+,s}(t)+v^{+,u}(t)))\,d\tau_1 d\tau_2\right) v_2^{+,u,u}.
\end{aligned}
$$

Recall from (C.46) that we work with coordinates in which stable and unstable manifolds are flat in Σ. So we may assume that

$$v^{+,ss}(t) \in h^{+,s}(t) + \Phi^+(t,0)W^+ \subset W^{ss,s}(p).$$

Hence, considered as a function in $v^{+,ss}$,

$$g(v^{+,ss}(t)) := P^+(t) f(h^{+,s}(t) + v^{+,ss}(t)) \equiv 0.$$

Therefore we have $D^2 g(v^{+,ss}(t))(\cdot,\cdot) = D^2 f^u(h^{+,s}(t) + v^{+,ss}(t))(\cdot,\cdot) = 0$. This allows us to write the first summand on the right-hand side of (C.133) as

$$
\begin{aligned}
\text{(C.134)}\quad & \int_{[0,1]^2} D^2 f^u(h^{+,s}(t)+\tau_1\tau_2(v^{+,s}(t)+v^{+,u}(t)))\,d(\tau_1,\tau_2) v_2^{+,ss,ss}(t) \\
&= \Bigg(\int_{[0,1]^2} D^2 f^u(h^{+,s}(t)+\tau_1\tau_2(v^{+,ss}(t)+v^{+,su}(t)+v^{+,u}(t))) \\
&\qquad - D^2 f^u(h^{+,s}(t)+\tau_1\tau_2 v^{+,ss}(t))\,d(\tau_1,\tau_2)\Bigg) v_2^{+,ss,ss}(t) \\
&= \int_{[0,1]^3} D^3 f^u(h^{+,s}(t)+\tau_1\tau_2(v^{+,ss}(t)+\tau_3(v^{+,su}(t)+v^{+,u}(t))))\,d(\tau_1,\tau_2,\tau_3) \\
&\qquad v_3^{+,ss,ss,su}(t) \\
&\quad + \int_{[0,1]^3} D^3 f^u(h^{+,s}(t)+\tau_1\tau_2(v^{+,ss}(t)+\tau_3(v^{+,su}(t)+v^{+,u}(t))))\,d(\tau_1,\tau_2,\tau_3) \\
&\qquad v_3^{+,ss,ss,u}(t).
\end{aligned}
$$

Here $\int_{[0,1]^2} \cdots$ and $\int_{[0,1]^3} \cdots$ stands for double and triple integrals and we abbreviate notation as $v_3^{+,ss,ss,u}(t) = (v^{+,ss}(t), v^{+,ss}(t), v^{+,u}(t))$. Now apply the mean value theorem to the terms in (C.133), replacing the first summand by (C.134). □

We proceed with estimating $v^{\pm,su}$.

Lemma C.29. *There exists a constant C such that*

$$|v^{+,su}(t)| \leq Ce^{\alpha^s t}\left(e^{\alpha^s(2\omega-t)} + e^{2\alpha^s\omega}\right)^2,$$
$$|v^{-,su}(t)| \leq Ce^{-\alpha^s t}\left(e^{\alpha^s(2\omega+t)} + e^{2\alpha^s\omega}\right)^2.$$

Proof. Plugging the bounds given in Lemma C.26 into (C.124) yields

$$\begin{aligned}|v^{+,u}(t)| &\leq C\left(e^{\alpha^s(2\omega-t)} + (e^{2\alpha^s\omega} + e^{\alpha^s\omega})^2\right)\\ &\leq C\left(e^{\alpha^s(2\omega-t)} + e^{\alpha^s\omega}e^{2\alpha^s\omega} + e^{4\alpha^s\omega}\right)\\ &\leq C\left(e^{\alpha^s(2\omega-t)} + e^{3\alpha^s\omega}\right).\end{aligned} \tag{C.135}$$

In the latter estimate we used that $t \in [0,\omega]$ and hence $e^{2\alpha^s\omega} \leq e^{2\alpha^s\omega-t}$ (recall that $\alpha^s < 0$). Similarly it follows from Lemma C.26 and (C.124), this time taking into account that $t \in [-\omega, 0]$, that

$$|v^{-,u}(t)| \leq C\left(e^{\alpha^s(2\omega+t)} + e^{3\alpha^s\omega}\right). \tag{C.136}$$

In the same way we proceed with $v^{\pm,s}$. Here we combine the estimates of Lemma C.26 with (C.128) and (C.129). Additionally, we use bounds of $|v^{\pm,u}(0)|$ which result from (C.135) and (C.136). We find

$$|v^{+,s}(t)| \leq Ce^{\alpha^s t}\left(e^{2\alpha^s\omega} + e^{2\alpha^s\omega}\right) \leq e^{\alpha^s(2\omega+t)},$$
$$|v^{-,s}(t)| \leq Ce^{-\alpha^s t}\left(e^{2\alpha^s\omega} + e^{2\alpha^s\omega}\right) \leq e^{\alpha^s(2\omega-t)}.$$

Using these bounds, we repeat the estimate of the integral term in (C.123). We find

$$\begin{aligned}&\int_0^t |\Phi^+(t,s)(\mathrm{id} - P^+(\lambda,s))h^{+,s}(s,v^+(s),\lambda)|\, ds\\ &\leq \int_0^t e^{(\alpha^s-\delta)(t-s)}\left(e^{\alpha^s s}|v^{+,u}(s)| + |v^{+,s}(s)|\right)\left(|v^{+,u}(s)| + |v^{+,s}(s)|\right) ds\\ &\leq Ce^{\alpha^s t}\left(e^{\alpha^s(2\omega-t)} + e^{2\alpha^s\omega}\right)^2.\end{aligned}$$

Similarly we obtain

$$\int_t^0 |\Phi^-(t,s)(\mathrm{id} - P^-(\lambda,s))h^{-,s}(s,v^-(s),\lambda)|\, ds$$
$$\leq Ce^{-\alpha^s t}\left(e^{\alpha^s(2\omega+t)} + e^{2\alpha^s\omega}\right)^2.$$

Now, since $v^{\pm,su}(0) = 0$ we have, using the variation of constants formula,

$$|v^{+,su}(t)| \leq \int_0^t |\Phi^+(t,s)(\mathrm{id} - P^+(\lambda,s))h^{+,s}(s,v^+(s),\lambda)|\,ds,$$

$$|v^{-,su}(t)| \leq \int_t^0 |\Phi^-(t,s)(\mathrm{id} - P^-(\lambda,s))h^{-,s}(s,v^-(s),\lambda)|\,ds.$$

Together this proves the lemma. □

Lemma C.30. *There exist constants Ω and c such that for all $|\lambda| < c$ and $\omega > \Omega$ the following estimates hold:*

$$\left|\int_0^\omega \Phi^+(\lambda,0,s)P^+(\lambda,s)h^+(s,v^+(s),\lambda)\,ds\right| = \mathcal{O}\left(e^{3\alpha^s\omega}\right),$$

$$\left|\int_{-\omega}^0 \Phi^-(\lambda,0,s)P^-(\lambda,s)h^-(s,v^-(s),\lambda)\,ds\right| = \mathcal{O}\left(e^{3\alpha^s\omega}\right).$$

Proof. We give the proof for the "+" sign. We adopt the notation defined in (C.119) for h^+ and write $h^{+,u} = P^+h^+$. The constant C appearing in the estimates may vary from line to line.

With Lemma C.28 we find, again using the exponential dichotomy of Φ^+,

$$\left|\int_0^\omega \Phi^+(\lambda,0,s)h^{+,u}(s,v^+(s),\lambda)\,ds\right|$$
$$\leq C\int_0^\omega \|\Phi^+(\lambda,0,s)P^+(\lambda,s)\|\left(|v^{+,u}(s)| + |v^{+,su}(s)|\right)|v^+(s)|\,ds$$
$$\leq C\int_0^\omega e^{(\alpha^s-\delta)s}\left(|v^{+,u}(s)| + |v^{+,su}(s)|\right)|v^+(s)|\,ds. \tag{C.137}$$

Here $\delta > 0$ can be chosen such that $-\alpha^s + \delta < \mu^u$ for all λ sufficiently small.

With the estimate of $|v^{+,su}(t)|$ given in Lemma C.29, and the estimates of $|v^{+,s}(t)|$ and $|v^{+,u}(t)|$ given in the beginning of the proof of Lemma C.29, we find

$$\left(|v^{+,u}(s)| + |v^{+,su}(s)|\right)|v^+(s)| \leq C\left(e^{\alpha^s(4\omega-2s)} + e^{\alpha^s(4\omega-s)}\right) + \mathcal{O}(e^{5\alpha^s\omega}).$$

Using this estimate in (C.137) gives the lemma. □

C.3.3. Derivatives of the jumps. We prove the statements on derivatives of the jumps in Corollary C.16, in short that $D_\omega R(\omega,\lambda) = \mathcal{O}(e^{2\mu^s(\lambda)\omega\delta})$.

C.3.3.1. *Differentiability of the jumps.* First we address the differentiability of the map $\Xi(\omega,\lambda)$ defined in (C.72) and more specifically the differentiability of the map $\xi(\omega,\lambda)$. This is equivalent to addressing the differentiability of $v(\omega,\lambda)$ from Lemma C.24. Differentiability of $v(\omega,\lambda)$ with respect to λ is contained in Lemma C.24. Differentiability with respect to ω calls for more effort.

In our presentation we follow the explanations in [**406**]. Let, for the moment, ω be fixed. Let $x(\omega,\lambda)$ be the partial orbit corresponding to (C.69). Note that $x(\omega,\lambda)(\cdot) \in C[0,2\omega]$. Define

$$\check{x}(\omega,\beta,\lambda)(t) = x((1+\beta)\omega,\lambda)((1+\beta)t),$$

where β is an additional parameter close to zero such that $(1+\beta)\omega > \Omega$. The functions $\check{x}(\omega,\beta,\lambda)(\cdot)$ solve the differential equation

$$\dot{x} = (1+\beta)f(x,\lambda).$$

By construction $\check{x}(\omega,\beta,\lambda)(\cdot) \in C[0,2\omega]$, and both

$$\check{x}(\omega,\beta,\lambda)(0) = x((1+\beta)\omega,\lambda)(0)$$

and

$$\check{x}(\omega,\beta,\lambda)(2\omega) = x((1+\beta)\omega,\lambda)(2(1+\beta)\omega)$$

are located in Σ. Further

$$\check{\Xi}(\omega,\beta,\lambda) = \Xi((1+\beta)\omega,\lambda) \in Z.$$

Note that

$$\check{\Xi}(\omega,\beta,\lambda) = \check{x}(\omega,\beta,\lambda)(0) - \check{x}(\omega,\beta,\lambda)(2\omega).$$

Consequently $\check{x}(\omega,\lambda,\beta)(\cdot)$ is the unique orbit given by Corollary C.15, related to the transition time 2ω and the parameters λ,β. Therefore $\check{\Xi}(\omega,\beta,\lambda)$ is differentiable with respect to β.

Now consider

$$\begin{aligned}\Xi(\omega+\beta\omega,\lambda) - \Xi(\omega,\lambda) &= \check{\Xi}(\omega,\beta,\lambda) - \check{\Xi}(\omega,0,\lambda)\\ &= D_\beta\check{\Xi}(\omega,0,\lambda)\beta + o(\beta)\\ &= D_\beta\check{\Xi}(\omega,0,\lambda)\frac{1}{\omega}\beta\omega + o(\beta\omega).\end{aligned}$$

This means that $\Xi(\cdot,\lambda)$ is differentiable, and

$$D_\omega\Xi(\omega,\lambda) = D_\beta\check{\Xi}(\omega,0,\lambda)\frac{1}{\omega}. \tag{C.138}$$

C.3.3.2. *Estimates of the derivatives of the jumps.* We start from (C.138). Recall from (C.72) that $\Xi(\omega,\lambda) = \xi^\infty(\lambda) + \xi(\omega,\lambda)$, $\xi^\infty(\lambda) = h^s_\lambda(0) - h^u_\lambda(0)$. Likewise we can write

$$\check{\Xi}(\omega,\beta,\lambda) = \check{\xi}^\infty(\lambda,\beta) + \check{\xi}(\omega,\beta,\lambda),$$

with

$$\check{\xi}^\infty(\lambda,\beta) = \check{h}^s_{\lambda,\beta}(0) - \check{h}^u_{\lambda,\beta}(0)$$

and

$$\begin{aligned}\check{h}^s_{\lambda,\beta}(t) &= h^s_\lambda((1+\beta)t),\\ \check{h}^u_{\lambda,\beta}(t) &= h^u_\lambda((1+\beta)t).\end{aligned}$$

Thus $\check{\xi}^\infty(\lambda,\beta) \equiv \xi^\infty(\lambda)$ and therefore

$$D_\beta \check{\Xi}(\omega,0,\lambda) = D_\beta \check{\xi}(\omega,0,\lambda).$$

For the computation of the latter derivative we start from the counterpart of the representation (C.106),

$$\big\langle \psi, \check{\xi}(\omega,\lambda,\beta)\big\rangle = \check{T}^1(\omega,\lambda,\beta) - \check{T}^2(\omega,\lambda,\beta),$$

where $\check{T}^i(\omega,\lambda,\beta) = T^i((1+\beta)\omega,\lambda)$, $i = 1,2$. As in Appendix C.3.2, where we wrote (C.107) and (C.108) as a sum of separate terms, we decompose

$$\check{T}^i(\omega,\lambda,\beta) = \sum_{j=1}^{4} \check{T}^{ij}(\omega,\lambda,\beta) = \sum_{j=1}^{4} T^{ij}((1+\beta)\omega,\lambda).$$

So, essentially we need to estimate $D_\beta \check{T}^{ij}(\omega,\lambda,0)$. Consider first $\check{T}^{11}$ given by

$$\begin{aligned}\check{T}^{11}(\omega,\lambda,\beta) &= T^{11}((1+\beta)\omega,\lambda)\\ &= \big\langle \Phi^+(\lambda,0,(1+\beta)\omega)^T P^+(\lambda,0)^T\psi, \tilde{P}(\lambda,(1+\beta)\omega)h^u_\lambda(-(1+\beta)\omega)\big\rangle .\end{aligned}$$

Differentiating with respect to β gives

$$\begin{aligned}&D_\beta \check{T}^{11}(\omega,\lambda,0)\\ &= \left\langle \frac{\partial}{\partial\beta}\left(\Phi^+(\lambda,0,(1+\beta)\omega)^T\right)\Big|_{\beta=0} P^+(\lambda,0)^T\psi, \tilde{P}(\lambda,\omega)h^u_\lambda(-\omega)\right\rangle\\ &\quad + \left\langle \Phi^+(\lambda,0,\omega)^T P^+(\lambda,0)^T\psi, \frac{\partial}{\partial\beta}\left(\tilde{P}(\lambda,(1+\beta)\omega)h^u_\lambda(-(1+\beta)\omega)\right)\Big|_{\beta=0}\right\rangle .\end{aligned}$$

Similarly we compute $D_\beta \check{T}^{ij}(\omega,\lambda,0)$ for other i,j. For $i = 1$ we find (the corresponding terms for $i = 2$ result in the same way)

$$\begin{aligned}&D_\beta \check{T}^{12}(\omega,\lambda,0)\\ &= \left\langle \frac{\partial}{\partial\beta}\left(\Phi^+(\lambda,0,(1+\beta)\omega)^T\right)\Big|_{\beta=0} P^+(\lambda,0)^T\psi,\right.\\ &\qquad\qquad \left. - \tilde{P}(\lambda,(1+\beta)\omega)h^s_\lambda((1+\beta)\omega)\right\rangle\\ &\quad + \left\langle \Phi^+(\lambda,0,(1+\beta)\omega)^T P^+(\lambda,0)^T\psi,\right.\\ &\qquad\qquad \left. - \frac{\partial}{\partial\beta}\left(\tilde{P}(\lambda,(1+\beta)\omega)h^s_\lambda((1+\beta)\omega)\right)\Big|_{\beta=0}\right\rangle,\end{aligned}$$

and

$$
\begin{aligned}
&D_\beta \check{T}^{13}(\omega,\lambda,0)\\
&= \Big\langle \frac{\partial}{\partial\beta}\left(\Phi^+(\lambda,0,(1+\beta)\omega)^T\right)\Big|_{\beta=0} P^+(\lambda,0)^T\psi,\\
&\qquad \tilde{P}(\lambda,(1+\beta)\omega)\big[(\mathrm{id}-P^-(\lambda,-(1+\beta)\omega))v^-((1+\beta)\omega,\lambda)(-(1+\beta)\omega)\\
&\qquad\qquad -(\mathrm{id}-P^+(\lambda,(1+\beta)\omega))v^+((1+\beta)\omega,\lambda)((1+\beta)\omega)\big]\Big\rangle\\
&+\Big\langle \Phi^+(\lambda,0,(1+\beta)\omega)^T P^+(\lambda,0)^T\psi,\\
&\frac{\partial}{\partial\beta}\Big(\tilde{P}(\lambda,(1+\beta)\omega)\big[(\mathrm{id}-P^-(\lambda,-(1+\beta)\omega))v^-((1+\beta)\omega,\lambda)(-(1+\beta)\omega)\\
&\qquad -(\mathrm{id}-P^+(\lambda,(1+\beta)\omega))v^+((1+\beta)\omega,\lambda)((1+\beta)\omega)\big]\Big)\Big|_{\beta=0}\Big\rangle
\end{aligned}
$$

and

$$D_\beta \check{T}^{14}(\omega,\lambda,0) = -\langle\psi, A\rangle,$$

where A stands for

$$\frac{\partial}{\partial\beta}\left(\int_0^{(1+\beta)\omega} \Phi^+(\lambda,0,s)P^+(\lambda,s)h^+(s,v^+((1+\beta)\omega,\lambda)(s),\lambda)\,ds\right)\Big|_{\beta=0}.$$

In the following parts we consider the separate terms that show derivatives with respect to β, in the expressions for $D_\beta\check{T}^{ij}(\omega,\lambda,0)$. We derive estimates for these terms. Note that estimates for the other terms in the expressions have been obtained earlier.

The term $\frac{\partial}{\partial\beta}\left(\Phi^+(\lambda,0,(1+\beta)\omega)^T\right)|_{\beta=0} P^+(\lambda,0)^T\psi$. Recall from (C.50) that

$$\Phi^+(\lambda,s,t)^T = \Psi^+(\lambda,t,s)$$

is the transition matrix of $\dot{x} = -(D_x f(h^s_\lambda(t),\lambda))^T x$. Hence

$$
\begin{aligned}
&\frac{\partial}{\partial\beta}\left(\Phi^+(\lambda,0,(1+\beta)\omega)^T\right)\Big|_{\beta=0} P^+(\lambda,0)^T\psi\\
&\qquad = -(D_x f(h^s_\lambda(\omega),\lambda))^T\Phi^+(\lambda,0,\omega)^T P^+(\lambda,0)^T\omega\psi.
\end{aligned}
$$

Applying (C.65) and (C.68) yields

$$
\begin{aligned}
\text{(C.139)}\quad &\frac{\partial}{\partial\beta}\left(\Phi^+(\lambda,0,(1+\beta)\omega)^T\right)\Big|_{\beta=0} P^+(\lambda,0)^T\psi\\
&\qquad = -\mu^u(\lambda)e^{-\mu^u(\lambda)\omega}\eta^+(\lambda)\omega + \mathcal{O}(e^{-\mu^u(\lambda)\omega\delta}),
\end{aligned}
$$

for some $\delta > 1$.

The term $\frac{\partial}{\partial\beta}\left(h_\lambda^u(-(1+\beta)\omega)\right)\big|_{\beta=0}$, $\frac{\partial}{\partial\beta}\left(h_\lambda^s((1+\beta)\omega)\right)\big|_{\beta=0}$. Similar as above we estimate the expression $\frac{\partial}{\partial\beta}\left(h_\lambda^u(-(1+\beta)\omega)\right)\Big|_{\beta=0}$. Here we exploit that h_λ^u solves $\dot{x} = f(x,\lambda)$. Hence

$$\dot{h}_\lambda^u(-\omega) = f(h_\lambda^u(-\omega),\lambda) = D_x f(0,\lambda) h_\lambda^u(-\omega) + \mathcal{O}((h_\lambda^u(-\omega))^2).$$

The expansion (C.66) for $h_\lambda^u(-\omega)$ yields

$$\text{(C.140)} \qquad \frac{\partial}{\partial\beta}\left(h_\lambda^u(-(1+\beta)\omega)\right)\big|_{\beta=0} = \mu^u(\lambda)e^{-\mu^u(\lambda)\omega}\omega\eta^u(\lambda) + \mathcal{O}(e^{-\mu^u(\lambda)\omega\delta}),$$

for some $\delta > 1$. For $\frac{\partial}{\partial\beta}\left(h_\lambda^s((1+\beta)\omega)\right)\big|_{\beta=0}$ we likewise get an estimate, now using (C.65),

$$\text{(C.141)} \qquad \frac{\partial}{\partial\beta}\left(h_\lambda^s((1+\beta)\omega)\right)\big|_{\beta=0} = \mu^s(\lambda)e^{\mu^s(\lambda)\omega}\omega\eta^s(\lambda) + \mathcal{O}(e^{\mu^s(\lambda)\omega\delta}).$$

The term $\frac{\partial}{\partial\beta}\left(\tilde{P}(\lambda,(1+\beta)\omega)\right)\big|_{\beta=0}$. Next we study the derivatives of the projections. To this end we first recall the definitions of $P^\pm(\lambda,t)$ given in (C.51), (C.52) and of $\tilde{P}(\lambda,t)$ given in (C.63), (C.64).

From (C.52) we infer

$$\begin{aligned}\dot{P}^\pm(\lambda,t) &= D_x f(h_\lambda^{s/u}(t),\lambda)P^\pm(\lambda,t) - P^\pm(\lambda,t)D_x f(h_\lambda^{s/u}(t),\lambda)\\ &= D_x f(h_\lambda^{s/u}(t),\lambda)P^\pm(\lambda,t) - D_x f(0,\lambda)P\\ &\qquad + PD_x f(0,\lambda) - P^\pm(\lambda,t)D_x f(h_\lambda^{s/u}(t),\lambda),\end{aligned}$$

using (C.49) to justify the latter equality. Using (C.53) and (C.58), respectively (C.59), we find

$$\begin{aligned}\left\|\frac{\partial}{\partial\beta}\left(P^+(\lambda,(1+\beta)\omega)\right)\big|_{\beta=0}\right\| &\le Ce^{\alpha^s\omega}\omega,\\ \left\|\frac{\partial}{\partial\beta}\left(P^-(\lambda,-(1+\beta)\omega)\right)\big|_{\beta=0}\right\| &\le Ce^{\alpha^s\omega}\omega,\end{aligned}$$

where $\alpha^s > \mu^s$ can be chosen arbitrarily close to μ^s.

To estimate the derivative of $\tilde{P}$ we start from (C.63).

$$(\tilde{P}(\lambda,t))^{\cdot} = (S(\lambda,t))^{\cdot}(\mathrm{id}-P)S(\lambda,t)^{-1} + S(\lambda,t)(\mathrm{id}-P)(S(\lambda,t)^{-1})^{\cdot}.$$

From (C.61) and the above estimates of $P^\pm$ we get

$$\|(S(\lambda,t))^{\cdot}\| \le Ce^{\alpha^s t}.$$

From $S(\lambda,t)\circ S(\lambda,t)^{-1} = \mathrm{id}$ it follows that

$$(S(\lambda,t)^{-1})^{\cdot} = -S(\lambda,t)^{-1}\circ(S(\lambda,t))^{\cdot}\circ S(\lambda,t)^{-1}.$$

With (C.62) it follows that also

$$\|(S(\lambda,t)^{-1})^{\cdot}\| \leq Ce^{\alpha^s t}.$$

Together this implies

$$\left\|\frac{\partial}{\partial\beta}\left(\tilde{P}(\lambda,(1+\beta)\omega)\right)\Big|_{\beta=0}\right\| \leq Ce^{\alpha^s\omega}\omega. \tag{C.142}$$

The term $\frac{\partial}{\partial\beta}\, v^{\pm}((1+\beta)\omega,\lambda)(\pm(1+\beta)\omega)|_{\beta=0}$. Calculate

$$\begin{aligned}\frac{\partial}{\partial\beta}&\left(v^{\pm}((1+\beta)\omega,\lambda)(\pm(1+\beta)\omega)\right)|_{\beta=0}\\ &= \frac{\partial}{\partial\beta}\left(v^{\pm}((1+\beta)\omega,\lambda)(\pm\omega)\right)|_{\beta=0} + \dot{v}^{\pm}(\omega,\lambda)(\pm\omega).\end{aligned} \tag{C.143}$$

First we consider $\dot{v}^{\pm}(\omega,\lambda)(\cdot)$, where we exploit that $v^{\pm}$ satisfy the variational equation (C.74),

$$\dot{v}^{\pm}(\omega,\lambda)(t) = D_x f(h_\lambda^{s/u}(t),\lambda)v^{\pm}(\omega,\lambda)(t) + h^{\pm}(t,v^{\pm}(\omega,\lambda)(t),\lambda). \tag{C.144}$$

From the estimates of $v^{\pm}$ and $h^{\pm}(t,v^{\pm}(t),\lambda)$ in Appendix C.3.2 (see (C.113)) we infer

$$|\dot{v}^{\pm}(\omega,\lambda)(\omega)| \leq Ce^{\alpha^s\omega}.$$

To obtain improved estimates (such as those in Appendix C.3.2 for $v^{\pm,s/u}$), we take the fixed point equations (C.87) and (C.88) for v^+, v^-, given by the variational equations

$$\begin{aligned}&v^+(\omega,\lambda)(t)\\ &\qquad= \Phi^+(\lambda,t,0)v^+(\omega,\lambda)(0) + \int_0^t \Phi^+(\lambda,t,s)h^+(s,v^+(\omega,\lambda)(s),\lambda)\,ds,\end{aligned}$$

and

$$\begin{aligned}&v^-(\omega,\lambda)(t)\\ &\qquad= \Phi^-(\lambda,t,0)v^-(\omega,\lambda)(0) - \int_t^0 \Phi^-(\lambda,t,s)h^-(s,v^-(\omega,\lambda)(s),\lambda)\,ds.\end{aligned}$$

From the definition of $v^{\pm,s/u}$ (see (C.119)) this yields (for instance) for $v^{+,s}$,

$$\begin{aligned}v^{+,s}(\omega,\lambda)(t) &= \Phi^+(\lambda,t,0)v^{+,s}(\omega,\lambda)(0)\\ &\qquad+ \int_0^t \Phi^+(\lambda,t,s)h^{+,s}(s,v^+(\omega,\lambda)(s),\lambda)\,ds.\end{aligned}$$

Here we use that Φ^+ commutes with the projection P^+ (see (C.52)). Differentiating with respect to t yields

$$\begin{aligned}\dot{v}^{+,s}(\omega,\lambda)(t) =& D_x f(h^s(t),\lambda)\Phi^+(\lambda,t,0)v^{+,s}(\omega,\lambda)(0) + h^{+,s}(t,v^+(\omega,\lambda)(t),\lambda)\\ &+ \int_0^t D_x f(h^s(t),\lambda)\Phi^+(\lambda,t,s)h^{+,s}(s,v^+(\omega,\lambda)(s),\lambda)\,ds.\end{aligned}$$

With the estimates provided in Appendix C.3.2 (see in particular Lemma C.26), we find

$$|\dot{v}^{+,s}(\omega,\lambda)(\omega)| \le Ce^{2\alpha^s\omega}.$$

Together we find, similar to Lemma C.26, the stricter estimates

$$\begin{aligned}||\dot{v}^{+,s}|| &\le Ce^{2\alpha^s\omega},\\ ||\dot{v}^{+,u}|| &\le Ce^{\alpha^s\omega},\\ ||\dot{v}^{-,s}|| &\le Ce^{2\alpha^s\omega},\\ ||\dot{v}^{-,u}|| &\le Ce^{\alpha^s\omega}.\end{aligned} \tag{C.145}$$

We continue with studying the other term in (C.143),

$$\frac{\partial}{\partial\beta}\left(v^{\pm}((1+\beta)\omega,\lambda)(\pm\omega)\right)\big|_{\beta=0},$$

or similarly $D_\omega v^{\pm}(\omega,\lambda)(t)$ at $t=\pm\omega$. From (C.144) we deduce

$$(D_\omega v^{\pm}(\omega,\lambda))^{\cdot}(t) = D_x f(h_\lambda^{s/u}(t),\lambda)D_\omega v^{\pm}(\omega,\lambda)(t) + \frac{\partial}{\partial\omega}h^{\pm}(t,v^{\pm}(\omega,\lambda)(t),\lambda).$$

We can write down fixed point equations for $D_\omega v^{\pm}$ similar those given in (C.87), (C.88). There are corresponding fixed point equations for $D_\omega v^{\pm,s/u}$. The one for $D_\omega v^{+,s}$ reads

$$\begin{aligned}D_\omega v^{+,s}(\omega,\lambda)(t) =& \Phi^+(\lambda,t,0)D_\omega v^{+,s}(\omega,\lambda)(0)\\ &+ \int_0^t \Phi^+(\lambda,t,s)\frac{\partial}{\partial\omega}h^{+,s}(s,v^+(\omega,\lambda)(s),\lambda)\,ds.\end{aligned} \tag{C.146}$$

Recall that $h^{+,s}(\cdot,v^+(\omega,\lambda)(\cdot),\lambda)$ is a Nemytskii operator (compare the proof of Lemma C.24).

Starting from (C.146), we can proceed, with some adaptions, as in the proof of Lemma C.26. To do so we first derive a counterpart of Lemma C.25. Starting from (C.75) we find

$$D_v h^{\pm}(t,v,\lambda) = D_x f(h_\lambda^{s/u}(t)+v,\lambda) - D_x f(h_\lambda^{s/u}(t),\lambda)$$

and accordingly

$$\frac{\partial}{\partial\omega}h^{+,s}(t, v^+(\omega,\lambda)(t),\lambda)$$
$$= \big(D_x f(h_\lambda^{s/u}(t) + v, \lambda) - D_x f(h_\lambda^{s/u}(t),\lambda)\big)D_\omega v^+(\omega,\lambda)(t).$$

Now decompose $v^+(\omega,\lambda)(t) = v^{+,s}(\omega,\lambda)(t) + v^{+,u}(\omega,\lambda)(t)$ and proceed along the lines of the proof of Lemma C.25. We arrive at a bound

$$\begin{aligned}&\left\|\frac{\partial}{\partial\omega}h^{+,s}(t, v^+(\omega,\lambda)(t),\lambda)\right\|\\ &\quad\le M\big((e^{\alpha^s t}|v^{+,u}(\omega,\lambda)(t)| + |v^{+,s}(\omega,\lambda)(t)|)|D_\omega v^{+,u}(\omega,\lambda)(t)|\\ &\qquad + |v^+(\omega,\lambda)(t)|\,|D_\omega v^{+,s}(\omega,\lambda)(t)|\big)\end{aligned}$$

for $t > 0$. Similarly we find

$$\begin{aligned}&\left\|\frac{\partial}{\partial\omega}h^{-,s}(t, v^-(\omega,\lambda)(t),\lambda)\right\|\\ &\quad\le M\big((e^{\alpha^s t}|v^{-,u}(\omega,\lambda)(t)| + |v^{-,s}(\omega,\lambda)(t)|)|D_\omega v^{-,u}(\omega,\lambda)(t)|\\ &\qquad + |v^-(\omega,\lambda)(t)|\,|D_\omega v^{-,s}(\omega,\lambda)(t)|\big)\end{aligned}$$

for $t > 0$.

Take up equation (C.146). Using (C.91), (C.92) we find for all ω the equality

$$(\mathrm{id} - P^+(\lambda,0))v^+(\omega,\lambda)(0) = (\mathrm{id} - P^+(\lambda,0))v^{-,u}(\omega,\lambda)(0).$$

This leads to the following counterpart of (C.123),

$$\begin{aligned}|D_\omega v^{+,s}(\omega,\lambda)(t)| &\le Ce^{\alpha^s t}|D_\omega v^{-,u}(\omega,\lambda)(0)|\\ &\quad + C\int_0^t e^{(\alpha^s-\delta)(t-s)}\left|\frac{\partial}{\partial\omega}h^{+,s}(s, v^+(\omega,\lambda)(s),\lambda)\right|\,ds.\end{aligned}$$

Based on (C.80) we find

$$\begin{aligned}D_\omega v^{+,u}(\omega,\lambda)(\omega) &= D_\omega a^+(\lambda,\omega) - \dot v^{+,u}(\omega,\lambda)(\omega),\\ D_\omega v^{-,u}(\omega,\lambda)(\omega) &= D_\omega a^-(\lambda,\omega) - \dot v^{-,u}(\omega,\lambda)(-\omega).\end{aligned}$$

To derive estimates of $D_\omega v^{\pm,u}$, we need the derivatives of $a^\pm$. In order to estimate $D_\omega a^\pm$, we start form (C.99) and apply the projection $\tilde P(\lambda,\omega)$ or $\mathrm{id} - \tilde P(\lambda,\omega)$, respectively. In this way we find

$$\begin{aligned}a^+(\lambda,\omega) &= \tilde P(\lambda,\omega)\big(d(\omega,\lambda) - v^{+,s}(\omega,\lambda)(\omega) + v^{-,s}(\omega,\lambda)(-\omega)\big),\\ a^-(\lambda,\omega) &= -(\mathrm{id} - \tilde P(\lambda,\omega))\big(d(\omega,\lambda) - v^{+,s}(\omega,\lambda)(\omega) + v^{-,s}(\omega,\lambda)(-\omega)\big).\end{aligned}$$

Using the already known estimates, we find that there is a positive constant C (not depending on (λ,ω)) such that

$$|D_\omega a^\pm(\lambda,\omega)| \le Ce^{\alpha^s\omega}. \tag{C.147}$$

Using (C.147) and following the lines of the proof of Lemma C.26, we end up with estimates

$$
\begin{aligned}
&\|D_\omega v^{+,s}(\omega,\lambda)\| \leq Ce^{2\alpha^s\omega},\\
&\|D_\omega v^{+,u}(\omega,\lambda)\| \leq Ce^{\alpha^s\omega},\\
&\|D_\omega v^{-,s}(\omega,\lambda)\| \leq Ce^{2\alpha^s\omega},\\
&\|D_\omega v^{-,u}(\omega,\lambda)\| \leq Ce^{\alpha^s\omega}.
\end{aligned}
\tag{C.148}
$$

Conclusion. Now we have all necessary ingredients (including (C.139), (C.140), (C.141), (C.142), (C.148), and earlier bounds obtained as well as similar bounds of terms arising in expressions for $D_\beta \check{T}^{2j}$, $j = 1, \dots, 4$) to estimate the terms $D_\beta \check{T}^{ij}(\omega, \lambda, 0)$. In particular we find, for some $\delta > 1$,

$$
D_\beta \check{T}^{21}(\omega, 0, \lambda) = 2\mu^s(\lambda)\omega e^{2\mu^s(\lambda)\omega}\langle \eta^-(\lambda), \eta^s(\lambda)\rangle + \mathcal{O}\left(e^{2\mu^s(\lambda)\omega\delta}\right). \tag{C.149}
$$

The execution of all the estimates establishes that the other terms are higher order and (recall (C.138)) provide a formula

$$
\frac{\partial}{\partial\omega}\langle \psi, \Xi(\omega,\lambda)\rangle = 2\mu^s(\lambda)e^{2\mu^s(\lambda)\omega}\langle \eta^-(\lambda), \eta^s(\lambda)\rangle + R(\omega,\lambda),
$$

with the desired bounds for the derivative of $R(\omega, \lambda)$. This completes the proof of Corollary C.16.

C.4. Proofs of Lin's method—general case

After having treated a special case of 1-periodic Lin orbits, we will now focus on the proofs of the general case: here we present the proofs of the statements of Lin's method from Appendix C.1. We distinguish different statements: an existence theorem for Lin orbits, estimates of the jumps in the Lin orbits, and differentiability of the jumps in the data with corresponding estimates of derivatives. Throughout we use setup and notation from Appendix C.3.1.

C.4.1. Existence of Lin orbits. Our aim here is to prove Theorem C.1 which we first recall.

There is a $\Omega > 0$, so that for each sequence $\omega = (\omega_i)_{i\in\mathbb{Z}}$ with $\inf_{i\in\mathbb{Z}} \omega_i > \Omega$ and each λ, $|\lambda|$ sufficiently small, there is a unique sequence $(x_i)_{i\in\mathbb{Z}}$ of partial orbits x_i such that

$$
\begin{aligned}
&x_i(0), x_i(2\omega_i) \in \Sigma,\\
&\Xi_i(\omega) = x_{i+1}(0) - x_i(2\omega_i) \in Z.
\end{aligned}
$$

The sequence $(x_i(\omega,\lambda))_{i\in\mathbb{Z}}$ and hence also $\Xi(\omega,\lambda)$ are differentiable with respect to λ.

To a large extent the proof runs along the lines of Appendix C.3.1. We adapt the procedure to the general case, and take the outline presented in Appendix C.3.1.2 as guideline. The main difference is that here a Lin orbit consists of a sequence of partial orbits related to a sequence $\omega = (\omega_i)_{i\in\mathbb{Z}}$ of transition times ω_i. We can adopt the notation from Appendix C.3.1, noting the difference that several quantities used there appear here with an additional index.

Assigned to a given sequence ω of transition times, we define the space of sequences

$$\mathcal{V}_\omega = \Big\{\mathbf{v} = (v_i^+, v_i^-)_{i\in\mathbb{Z}}\ ; \\ (v_i^+, v_i^-) \in C[0,\omega_{i+1}] \times C[-\omega_i, 0], \sup_{i\in\mathbb{Z}} \|v_i^+\|, \sup_{i\in\mathbb{Z}} \|v_i^-\| < \infty\Big\}.$$

Endowed with the norm

$$\|\mathbf{v}\| = \max\{\sup_{i\in\mathbb{Z}} \|v_i^+\|, \sup_{i\in\mathbb{Z}} \|v_i^-\|\},$$

$\mathcal{V}_\omega$ is a Banach space.

Partial orbits $x_i(\cdot)$ which make up the Lin orbits will be composed of orbits $x_{i-1}^+(\cdot)$ and $x_i^-(\cdot)$ which are defined on $[0,\omega_i]$ and $[-\omega_i, 0]$, respectively:

$$x_i(t) = \begin{cases} x_{i-1}^+(t), & t \in [0,\omega_i], \\ x_i^-(t - 2\omega_i), & t \in [\omega_i, 2\omega_i]. \end{cases}$$

Figure C.4 provides a visualization. Here and in the following, the index i runs through $\mathbb{Z}$. The continuity and jump conditions, analogous to (C.70) and (C.71), read

$$x_{i-1}^+(\omega_i) = x_i^-(-\omega_i), \tag{C.150}$$

and

$$\Xi_i := x_{i+1}(0) - x_i(2\omega_i) = x_i^+(0) - x_i^-(0) \in Z. \tag{C.151}$$

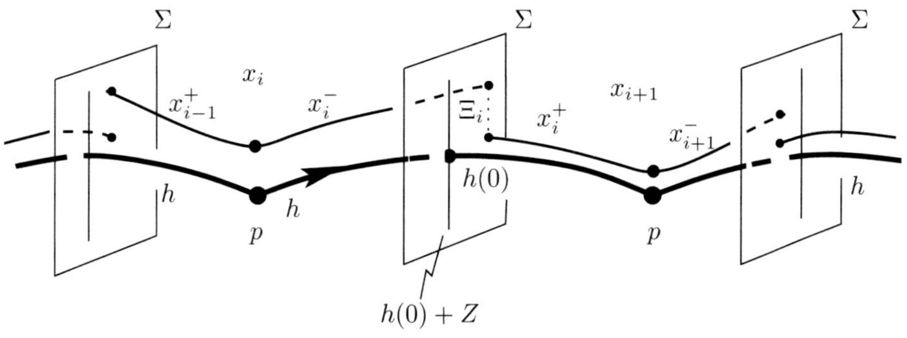

Figure C.4. The ingredients of Lin's method for homoclinic orbits.

Write $x_i^\mp$ in the form (as in (C.73)),

$$x_i^\mp(t) = h_\lambda^{s/u}(t) + v_i^\mp(t). \tag{C.152}$$

We will prove that there are unique functions $v_i^\mp(\omega,\lambda)(\cdot)$ such that $x_i^\pm$ satisfy conditions (C.150), (C.151).

For all $i \in \mathbb{Z}$ the functions $v_i^\pm$ solve the (nonlinear) variational equation (C.74) along $h_\lambda^{s/u}$. For easier reference we copy the variational equation,

$$\dot{v}^\pm(t) = D_x f(h_\lambda^{s/u}(t),\lambda)v^\pm(t) + h^\pm(t, v^\pm(t),\lambda), \tag{C.153}$$

where

$$h^\pm(t,v,\lambda) = f(h_\lambda^{s/u}(t) + v,\lambda) - f(h_\lambda^{s/u}(t),\lambda) - D_x f(h_\lambda^{s/u}(t),\lambda)v.$$

The conditions (C.150), (C.151) translate to conditions that $v_i^\mp$ must satisfy:

$$v_i^+(0), v_i^-(0) \in W^+ \oplus W^- \oplus Z, \tag{C.154}$$

$$v_i^+(\omega_{i+1}) - v_{i+1}^-(-\omega_{i+1}) = h_\lambda^u(-\omega_{i+1}) - h_\lambda^s(\omega_{i+1}), \tag{C.155}$$

$$v_i^+(0) - v_i^-(0) \in Z. \tag{C.156}$$

To solve (C.153) with conditions (C.154)–(C.156) we proceed as in Appendix C.3.1.2. First we replace the nonlinear terms in (C.153) by functions $g_i^+ \in C[0,\omega_{i+1}]$ and $g_i^- \in C[-\omega_i, 0]$ and arrive at the counterpart of (C.79) given by

$$\dot{v}_i^\mp(t) = D_x f(h_\lambda^{s/u}(t),\lambda)v_i^\mp(t) + g_i^\pm(t,\lambda), \quad i \in \mathbb{Z}. \tag{C.157}$$

The related projections by which we replace the coupling condition (C.155) read

$$a_i^+ = P^+(\lambda,\omega_i)v_{i-1}^+(\omega_i) \text{ and } a_i^- = P^-(\lambda,-\omega_i)v_i^-(-\omega_i) \tag{C.158}$$

(as in (C.80)). The corresponding sequences we denote by $\mathbf{g} = \left(g_i^+, g_i^-\right)_{i\in\mathbb{Z}}$ and $\mathbf{a} = (a_i^+, a_i^-)_{i\in\mathbb{Z}}$.

Now we consider the variational equation (C.157) with boundary conditions (C.154), (C.156), and (C.158). Since the single equations and boundary conditions are decoupled (with respect to i), we may apply Lemma C.19 to solve for all i the related boundary value problem. This provides a unique solution $\bar{\mathbf{v}}(\omega,\lambda,\mathbf{g},\mathbf{a}) = \left(\bar{v}_i^+, \bar{v}_i^-\right)_{i\in\mathbb{Z}}$ for the variational equation (C.157) with boundary conditions (C.154), (C.156), (C.158). Here $\bar{\mathbf{v}}(\omega,\cdot,\cdot,\cdot)$ is a map $\mathbb{R} \times \mathcal{V}_\omega \times l^\infty(\mathbb{Z},\mathbb{R}^n) \to \mathcal{V}_\omega$. The functions $\bar{v}_i^\mp$ that make up this map do not depend on the entire sequences $\mathbf{g}$ and $\mathbf{a}$. Indicating only relevant variables, we may write

$$\bar{v}_i^\mp(\cdot) = \bar{v}_i^\mp(\omega,\lambda,(g_i^+,g_i^-),(a_{i+1}^+,a_i^-))(\cdot).$$

We mention that

$$\left(\bar{v}_i^+(\cdot), \bar{v}_i^-(\cdot)\right) \in C[0,\omega_{i+1}] \times C[-\omega_i, 0].$$

If we again exploit that the boundary value problems are decoupled, we find, using Lemma C.21, that the function $\bar{\mathbf{v}}(\omega, \lambda, \cdot, \cdot)$ is linear and there exists a constant $\bar{C}$ such that

$$\|\bar{\mathbf{v}}(\omega, \lambda, \mathbf{g}, \mathbf{a})\| \leq \bar{C}(\|\mathbf{g}\| + \|\mathbf{a}\|). \tag{C.159}$$

Now we consider the linearized variational equation (C.157) with the original boundary conditions (C.154)–(C.156). To this end we introduce notation (as in (C.81))

$$d_{i+1}(\omega, \lambda) = h^u_\lambda(-\omega_{i+1}) - h^s_\lambda(\omega_{i+1}) \tag{C.160}$$

and write $\mathbf{d}(\omega, \lambda) = (d_i(\omega, \lambda))_{i \in \mathbb{Z}}$. Parallel to Lemma C.23 we can show that there exists $\mathbf{a}(\omega, \lambda, \mathbf{g}, \mathbf{d})$ so that $\hat{\mathbf{v}}(\omega, \lambda, \mathbf{g}, \mathbf{d})$ defined by

$$\hat{\mathbf{v}}(\omega, \lambda, \mathbf{g}, \mathbf{d}) = \bar{\mathbf{v}}(\omega, \lambda, \mathbf{g}, \mathbf{a}(\omega, \lambda, \mathbf{g}, \mathbf{d})) \tag{C.161}$$

solves (C.157) with boundary conditions (C.154)–(C.156). In what follows we sketch the necessary adaptions to the proof of Lemma C.23. Indexing the quantities properly, we start from (see also (C.98))

$$\bar{v}^+_{i-1}(\omega, \lambda, \mathbf{g}, \mathbf{a})(\omega_i) - \bar{v}^-_i(\omega, \lambda, \mathbf{g}, \mathbf{a})(-\omega_i) = d_i.$$

Via (compare (C.99))

$$a^+_i - a^-_i = d_i - (\mathrm{id} - P^+(\lambda, \omega_i))\bar{v}^+_{i-1}(\omega_i) + (\mathrm{id} - P^-(\lambda, -\omega_i))\bar{v}^-_i(-\omega_i),$$

we arrive at (compare (C.100))

$$\begin{aligned} a_i = \big(2\tilde{P}(\lambda, \omega_i) - \mathrm{id}\big)\big(d_i &- (\mathrm{id} - P^+(\lambda, \omega_i))\bar{v}^+_{i-1}(\dots, a)(\omega_i) \\ &+ (\mathrm{id} - P^-(\lambda, -\omega_i))\bar{v}^-_i(\dots, a)(-\omega_i)\big), \end{aligned}$$

where $i \in \mathbb{Z}$. This set of fixed point equations can therefore be written in the form

$$\mathbf{a} = L_1(\lambda, \omega)\mathbf{a} + L_2(\lambda, \omega)\mathbf{g} + L_3(\lambda, \omega)\mathbf{d}, \tag{C.162}$$

for linear bounded operators $L_j(\lambda, \omega)(\cdot)$, $j = 1, 2, 3$. By Lemma C.20, the linear operator $(\mathrm{id} - L_1(\lambda, \omega))$ is invertible for sufficiently large Ω (a lower bound for the ω_i's). Hence equation (C.162) can be solved for $\mathbf{a}$.

So we have obtained a map $\hat{\mathbf{v}}(\omega, \cdot, \cdot, \cdot) : \mathbb{R} \times V_\omega \times l^\infty(\mathbb{Z}, \mathbb{R}^n) \to V_\omega$. It follows from the derivation that $\hat{\mathbf{v}}(\omega, \lambda, \cdot, \cdot)$ is linear and that there exists a constant $\hat{C}$ such that (compare (C.102))

$$\|\hat{\mathbf{v}}(\omega, \lambda, \mathbf{g}, \mathbf{d})\| \leq \hat{C}(\|\mathbf{g}\| + \|\mathbf{d}\|). \tag{C.163}$$

This estimate follows from (C.159) together with an estimate

$$\|a\| \leq C(\|\mathbf{g}\| + \|\mathbf{d}\|)$$

for an appropriate constant C, which we get from (C.162).

The original boundary value problem (C.153) for the functions $v_i^{\mp}$, $i \in \mathbb{Z}$, with boundary conditions (C.154)–(C.156) is equivalent to a fixed point equation

$$\mathbf{v} = \mathcal{F}_\omega(\mathbf{v}, \lambda) \tag{C.164}$$

in $\mathcal{V}_\omega$, where

$$\mathcal{F}_\omega(\mathbf{v}, \lambda) = \hat{\mathbf{v}}(\omega, \lambda, \mathcal{H}(\mathbf{v}, \lambda), \mathbf{d}(\omega, \lambda)),$$

and

$$\mathcal{H}(\mathbf{v}, \lambda) = (H_i^+(\mathbf{v}, \lambda), H_i^-(\mathbf{v}, \lambda))_{i\in\mathbb{Z}} \tag{C.165}$$

with

$$H_i^{\mp}(\mathbf{v}, \lambda)(t) = h^{\pm}(t, v_i^{\mp}(t), \lambda). \tag{C.166}$$

To finish the proof of Theorem C.1 it remains to show that equation (C.164) has a unique solution $\mathbf{v}(\omega, \lambda)$. The justification of this runs parallel to the proof of Lemma C.24. The bound (C.163) gives

$$\begin{aligned} \|\mathcal{F}_\omega(\mathbf{v}, \lambda)\| &= \|\hat{\mathbf{v}}(\omega, \lambda, \mathcal{H}(\mathbf{v}, \lambda), \mathbf{d}(\omega, \lambda))\| \\ &\leq \hat{C}(\|\mathcal{H}\| + \|\mathbf{d}\|). \end{aligned} \tag{C.167}$$

For the rest of the argument we can follow the proof of Lemma C.24 almost verbatim—using the estimate (C.167) instead of (C.103) to show that $\mathcal{F}_\omega(\cdot, \lambda)$ is a contraction on a closed ball $B[0, \epsilon] \subset \mathcal{V}_\omega$. We conclude with the remark that the resulting map $\mathbf{v}(\omega, \cdot)$ is continuously differentiable.

C.4.2. Estimates of the jumps. In this section and the next, estimates and expansions for the jumps in Lin orbits are derived. The discussion of estimates of the derivatives of the jumps is postponed to the next section. We repeat the statement of Theorem C.3 on estimates of the jumps.

Assume the saddle quantity $\mu^s + \mu^u > 0$. There is a smooth reparametrization of the parameter λ, so that the bifurcation equations $\Xi_i = 0$ are equivalent to

$$\langle \psi, \Xi_i(\omega, \lambda) \rangle = \lambda - e^{2\mu^s(\lambda)\omega_i} \mathcal{E}^s(\lambda) + R_i(\omega, \lambda) = 0,$$

$i \in \mathbb{Z}$, where the quantity $\mathcal{E}^s(0) \neq 0$. There is a $\delta > 1$ such that

$$\begin{aligned} R_i(\omega, \lambda) = {}& \mathcal{O}(e^{2\mu^s(\lambda)\omega_i\delta}) + \mathcal{O}(e^{2\mu^s(\lambda)\omega_{i+1}\delta}) \\ &+ \mathcal{O}(e^{2\alpha^s(\omega_{i-1}+\omega_i)}) + \mathcal{O}(e^{2\alpha^s(\omega_i+\omega_{i+1})}) + \mathcal{O}(e^{2\alpha^s(\omega_{i+1}+\omega_{i+2})}), \end{aligned}$$

where $\alpha^s > \mu^s$ can be chosen arbitrarily close to μ^s.

C.4.2.1. *Estimate of the residual term.* We start with an outline of the proof of Theorem C.3. Parts of the derivations are postponed to lemmas that are formulated and proved afterwards.

Outline of the proof of Theorem C.3. We proceed along the lines of Appendix C.3.2.1, replacing ω by the sequence $\omega = (\omega_i)_{i\in\mathbb{Z}}$. With $\xi_i(\omega,\lambda)$ as in (C.8) defined by

$$\Xi_i(\omega,\lambda) = \xi^\infty(\lambda) + \xi_i(\omega,\lambda),$$

with

$$\xi^\infty(\lambda) = h^s_\lambda(0) - h^u_\lambda(0),$$

we will prove that

$$\langle\psi, \xi_i(\omega,\lambda)\rangle = -e^{2\mu^s(\lambda)\omega_i}\mathcal{E}^s(\lambda) + R_i(\omega,\lambda).$$

As a consequence of (C.45), we have that for sufficiently large t, $h^s_\lambda(t)$ and $h^u_\lambda(-t)$ belong to the stable and unstable eigenspaces of p.

As counterparts to (C.105)–(C.108) we obtain corresponding indexed quantities: with (C.152) we have

$$\xi_i(\omega,\lambda) = v_i^+(\omega,\lambda)(0) - v_i^-(\omega,\lambda)(0), \tag{C.168}$$

where $v_i^\pm$ are given by the unique solution of the fixed point equation (C.164). Write

$$\langle\psi, \xi_i(\omega,\lambda)\rangle = T_i^1(\omega,\lambda) - T_i^2(\omega,\lambda), \tag{C.169}$$

with

$$\begin{aligned} T_i^1(\omega,\lambda) &= \langle\psi, P^+(\lambda,0)v_i^+(\omega,\lambda)(0)\rangle,\\ T_i^2(\omega,\lambda) &= \langle\psi, P^-(\lambda,0)v_i^-(\omega,\lambda)(0)\rangle. \end{aligned}$$

Proceeding along the lines of Appendix C.3.2 we end up with

$$\begin{aligned} T_i^1(\omega,\lambda) = \Big\langle &\Phi^+(\lambda,0,\omega_{i+1})^T P^+(\lambda,0)^T\psi, \\ &\tilde{P}(\lambda,\omega_{i+1})\Big[h^u_\lambda(-\omega_{i+1}) - h^s_\lambda(\omega_{i+1}) + (\mathrm{id} - P^-(\lambda,-\omega_{i+1}))v_{i+1}^-(\omega,\lambda)(-\omega_{i+1}) \\ &\qquad - (\mathrm{id} - P^+(\lambda,\omega_{i+1}))v_i^+(\omega,\lambda)(\omega_{i+1})\Big]\Big\rangle \\ &- \Big\langle\psi, \int_0^{\omega_{i+1}} \Phi^+(\lambda,0,s)P^+(\lambda,s)h^+(s,v_i^+(\omega,\lambda)(s),\lambda)\,ds\Big\rangle \end{aligned} \tag{C.170}$$

and

$$\text{(C.171)}\quad T_i^2(\omega,\lambda) = \Big\langle \Phi^-(\lambda,0,-\omega_i)^T P^-(\lambda,0)^T \psi,$$
$$(\mathrm{id} - \tilde{P}(\lambda,\omega_i))\Big[h_\lambda^s(\omega_i) - h_\lambda^u(-\omega_i) + (\mathrm{id} - P^+(\lambda,\omega_i))v_{i-1}^+(\omega,\lambda)(\omega_i)$$
$$- (\mathrm{id} - P^-(\lambda,-\omega_i))v_i^-(\omega,\lambda)(-\omega_i)\Big]\Big\rangle$$
$$- \Big\langle \psi, \int_{-\omega_i}^0 \Phi^-(\lambda,0,s)P^-(\lambda,s)h^-(s,v_i^-(\omega,\lambda)(s),\lambda)\,ds\Big\rangle.$$

With the same type of arguments which led to (C.110) and (C.111), we find

$$\begin{aligned} T_i^{11} &= \langle \Psi^+(\lambda,\omega_{i+1},0)P^+(\lambda,0)^T\psi, \tilde{P}(\lambda,\omega_{i+1})h_\lambda^u(-\omega_{i+1})\rangle \\ &= e^{-2\mu^u\omega_{i+1}}\langle \eta^+(\lambda),\eta^u(\lambda)\rangle + \mathcal{O}\left(e^{-2\mu^u\omega_{i+1}\delta}\right) \end{aligned}$$

and

$$\begin{aligned} T_i^{21} &= \langle \Psi^-(\lambda,-\omega_i,0)P^-(\lambda,0)^T\psi, (\mathrm{id} - \tilde{P}(\lambda,\omega_i))h_\lambda^s(\omega_i)\rangle \\ &= e^{2\mu^s\omega_i}\langle \eta^-(\lambda),\eta^s(\lambda)\rangle + \mathcal{O}\left(e^{2\mu^s\omega_i\delta}\right). \end{aligned}$$

Summarizing, we have

$$\begin{aligned} &\langle \psi, \Xi_i(\omega,\lambda)\rangle \\ &\quad = \lambda + e^{-2\mu^u(\lambda)\omega_{i+1}}\langle \eta^+(\lambda),\eta^u(\lambda)\rangle - e^{2\mu^s(\lambda)\omega_i}\langle \eta^-(\lambda),\eta^s(\lambda)\rangle + \tilde{R}_i(\omega,\lambda). \end{aligned}$$

It remains to derive bounds for the terms $\tilde{R}_i$. The indexed equivalent of (C.112) reads

$$\begin{aligned} T_i^{12} &= \langle \Phi^+(\lambda,0,\omega_{i+1})^T P^+(\lambda,0)^T\psi, -\tilde{P}(\lambda,\omega_{i+1})h_\lambda^s(\omega_{i+1})\rangle \\ &= \mathcal{O}\left(e^{(-\mu^u+\mu^s)\omega_{i+1}\delta}\right), \\ T_i^{22} &= \langle \Phi^-(\lambda,0,-\omega_i)^T P^-(\lambda,0)^T\psi, -(\mathrm{id} - \tilde{P}(\lambda,\omega_i))h_\lambda^u(-\omega_i)\rangle \\ &= \mathcal{O}\left(e^{(-\mu^u+\mu^s)\omega_i\delta}\right). \end{aligned}$$

We proceed as in Appendix C.3.2 to estimate the following indexed terms T_i^{j3}, $j = 1,2$,

$$T_i^{13} = \Big\langle \Phi^+(\lambda,0,\omega_{i+1})^T P^+(\lambda,0)^T\psi,$$
$$\tilde{P}(\lambda,\omega_{i+1})\big[(\mathrm{id} - P^-(\lambda,-\omega_{i+1}))v_{i+1}^-(\omega,\lambda)(-\omega_{i+1})$$
$$- (\mathrm{id} - P^+(\lambda,\omega_{i+1}))v_i^+(\omega,\lambda)(\omega_{i+1})\big]\Big\rangle$$

and

$$T_i^{23} = \Big\langle \Phi^-(\lambda,0,-\omega_i)^T P^-(\lambda,0)^T\psi,\\ (\mathrm{id}-\tilde{P}(\lambda,\omega_i))\big[(\mathrm{id}-P^+(\lambda,\omega_i))v_{i-1}^+(\omega,\lambda)(\omega_i)\\ -(\mathrm{id}-P^-(\lambda,-\omega_i))v_i^-(\omega,\lambda)(-\omega_i)\big]\Big\rangle.$$

In our argument we replace Lemma C.26 by Lemma C.31 to arrive at the following: there is an appropriate constant C such that

$$|T_i^{13}| \le Ce^{(-\mu^u+\alpha^s)\omega_{i+1}}\\ \left(e^{2\alpha^s\omega_i}+e^{2\alpha^s\omega_{i+1}}+e^{2\alpha^s\omega_{i+2}}+e^{\alpha^s(\omega_i+\omega_{i+1})}+e^{\alpha^s(\omega_{i+1}+\omega_{i+2})}\right)$$

and

$$|T_i^{23}| \le Ce^{(\mu^s+\alpha^s)\omega_i}\\ \left(e^{2\alpha^s\omega_{i-1}}+e^{2\alpha^s\omega_i}+e^{2\alpha^s\omega_{i+1}}+e^{\alpha^s(\omega_{i-1}+\omega_i)}+e^{\alpha^s(\omega_i+\omega_{i+1})}\right).$$

The remaining terms are

$$T_i^{14} = -\left\langle \psi, \int_0^{\omega_{i+1}} \Phi^+(\lambda,0,s)P^+(\lambda,s)h^+(s,v_i^+(\omega,\lambda)(s),\lambda)\,ds\right\rangle,$$

$$T_i^{24} = -\left\langle \psi, \int_{-\omega_i}^{0} \Phi^-(\lambda,0,s)P^-(\lambda,s)h^-(s,v_i^-(\omega,\lambda)(s),\lambda)\,ds\right\rangle. \tag{C.172}$$

These are treated in Lemma C.33 below, which replaces Lemma C.30, and which gives

$$|T_i^{14}| = \mathcal{O}\left(e^{4\alpha^s\omega_i}+e^{2\alpha^s(\omega_i+\omega_{i+1})}+e^{3\alpha^s\omega_{i+1}}\right),$$
$$|T_i^{24}| = \mathcal{O}\left(e^{4\alpha^s\omega_{i+1}}+e^{2\alpha^s(\omega_i+\omega_{i+1})}+e^{3\alpha^s\omega_i}\right).$$

The theorem follows by combining the obtained bounds for the terms T_i^{kl}, $k = 1,2$, $l = 1,\dots,4$. As in (C.116) we have

$$\mathcal{E}^s(\lambda) = \langle \eta^-(\lambda), \eta^s(\lambda)\rangle. \qquad \square$$

C.4.2.2. *Auxiliary lemmas.* To prepare for the proofs of Lemmas C.31 and C.33 we define

$$v_i^{\pm,s}(t) = (\mathrm{id}-P^{\pm}(t))v_i^{\pm}(t), \qquad v_i^{\pm,u}(t) = P^{\pm}(t)v_i^{\pm}(t) \tag{C.173}$$

and

$$\|v_i^+\| = \sup_{t\in[0,\omega_{i+1}]} |v_i^+(t)|, \qquad \|v_i^-\| = \sup_{t\in[-\omega_i,0]} |v_i^-(t)|.$$

Recall that $|\cdot|$ denotes the Euclidean norm in $\mathbb{R}^n$ and $\|\cdot\|$ denotes the supremum norm.

Similar to the verification of (C.118) we infer

$$\|\mathbf{v}\| \le C\|\mathbf{d}\|.$$

By the definition of $\mathbf{d} = (d_i)_{i\in\mathbb{Z}}$ in (C.160), this proves that $\|\mathbf{v}\|$ becomes exponentially small as $\Omega \to \infty$.

Lemma C.31. *There is a constant C such that*

$$\|v_i^{+,s}\| \le C(e^{2\alpha^s\omega_{i+1}} + e^{2\alpha^s\omega_i}), \qquad \|v_i^{+,u}\| \le C(e^{\alpha^s\omega_{i+1}} + e^{4\alpha^s\omega_i}),$$
$$\|v_i^{-,s}\| \le C(e^{2\alpha^s\omega_{i+1}} + e^{2\alpha^s\omega_i}), \qquad \|v_i^{-,u}\| \le C(e^{4\alpha^s\omega_{i+1}} + e^{\alpha^s\omega_i}).$$

Proof. We can follow the proof of Lemma C.26. In the equations (C.123)–(C.127) we just need to replace solutions by indexed versions, for instance $v^{+,s}$ by $v_i^{+,s}$. We arrive at estimates

$$\|v_i^{\pm,s}\| \le C(|v_i^{\mp,u}(0)| + \|v_i^{\pm,u}\|^2). \tag{C.174}$$

Now consider $v_i^{\pm,u}$. As in (C.89) and (C.90) (and with the definition of $a_i^{\pm}$ from (C.158)), we write down expressions

$$\begin{aligned}
&P^+(\lambda,t)v_i^+(t)\\
&\quad = \Phi^+(\lambda)(t,\omega_{i+1})P^+(\lambda,\omega_{i+1})v_i^+(\omega_{i+1})\\
&\qquad\qquad - \int_t^{\omega_{i+1}} \Phi^+(\lambda)(t,s)P^+(\lambda,s)h^+(s,v_i^+(s),\lambda)\,ds\\
&\quad = \Phi^+(\lambda)(t,\omega_{i+1})a_{i+1}^+ - \int_t^{\omega_{i+1}} \Phi^+(\lambda)(t,s)P^+(\lambda,s)h^+(s,v_i^+(s),\lambda)\,ds,\\
&P^-(\lambda,t)v_i^-(t)\\
&\quad = \Phi^-(\lambda)(t,-\omega_i)P^-(\lambda,-\omega_i)v_i^-(-\omega_i)\\
&\qquad\qquad + \int_{-\omega_i}^{t} \Phi^-(\lambda)(t,s)P^-(\lambda,s)h^-(s,v_i^-(s),\lambda)\,ds\\
&\quad = \Phi^-(\lambda)(t,-\omega_i)a_i^- + \int_{-\omega_i}^{t} \Phi^-(\lambda)(t,s)P^-(\lambda,s)h^-(s,v_i^-(s),\lambda)\,ds.
\end{aligned}$$

The first of these gives

$$|v_i^{+,u}(t)| \le Ce^{\alpha^s(\omega_{i+1}-t)}|a_{i+1}^+| + C\int_t^{\omega_{i+1}} e^{-\alpha^s(t-s)}|h^{+,u}(s,v_i^+(s),\lambda)|\,ds.$$

With Lemma C.27 applied to a_{i+1}^+, this yields, exploiting $h^{+,u}(v) = \mathcal{O}(|v|^2)$,

$$|v_i^{+,u}(t)| \le Ce^{\alpha^s(\omega_{i+1}-t)}e^{\alpha^s\omega_{i+1}} + C(\|v_i^{+,s}\| + \|v_i^{+,u}\|)^2. \tag{C.175}$$

In the same way we proceed with $v_i^{-,u}$ and end up with

$$|v_i^{-,u}(t)| \le Ce^{\alpha^s(\omega_i+t)}e^{\alpha^s\omega_{i+1}} + C(\|v_i^{-,s}\| + \|v_i^{-,u}\|)^2. \tag{C.176}$$

As $\|v_i^{\pm,u}\|$ is small, we conclude from these estimates that

$$\begin{aligned} \|v_i^{+,u}\| &\le C(e^{\alpha^s\omega_{i+1}} + \|v_i^{+,s}\|^2),\\ \|v_i^{-,u}\| &\le C(e^{\alpha^s\omega_i} + \|v_i^{-,s}\|^2). \end{aligned} \tag{C.177}$$

Equations (C.177) in combination with (C.174) yield

$$\begin{aligned} \|v_i^{+,s}\| &\le C\left(e^{2\alpha^s\omega_i} + (\|v_i^{-,s}\| + \|v_i^{-,u}\|)^2 + (e^{\alpha^s\omega_{i+1}} + \|v_i^{+,s}\|^2)^2\right)\\ &\le C\left(e^{2\alpha^s\omega_i} + (\|v_i^{-,s}\| + \|v_i^{-,u}\|)^2 + e^{2\alpha^s\omega_{i+1}} + \epsilon^+(\Omega)\|v_i^{+,s}\|\right), \end{aligned}$$

where $\epsilon^+(\Omega)$ tends to zero as $\Omega \to \infty$. Similarly we find, with a corresponding $\epsilon^-(\Omega)$ that tends to zero as $\Omega \to \infty$,

$$\|v_i^{-,s}\| \le C\left(e^{2\alpha^s\omega_{i+1}} + (\|v_i^{+,s}\| + \|v_i^{+,u}\|)^2 + e^{2\alpha^s\omega_i} + \epsilon^-(\Omega)\|v_i^{-,s}\|\right).$$

Hence

$$\begin{aligned} \|v_i^{+,s}\| &\le C\left(e^{2\alpha^s\omega_{i+1}} + e^{2\alpha^s\omega_i} + (\|v_i^{-,s}\| + \|v_i^{-,u}\|)^2\right),\\ \|v_i^{-,s}\| &\le C\left(e^{2\alpha^s\omega_{i+1}} + e^{2\alpha^s\omega_i} + (\|v_i^{+,s}\| + \|v_i^{+,u}\|)^2\right). \end{aligned} \tag{C.178}$$

Successively plugging estimates (C.177) and (C.178) into each other yields

$$\begin{aligned} \|v_i^{+,s}\| &\le C\left(e^{2\alpha^s\omega_{i+1}} + e^{2\alpha^s\omega_i} + \hat\epsilon^-(\Omega)\|v_i^{-,s}\|\right),\\ \|v_i^{-,s}\| &\le C\left(e^{2\alpha^s\omega_{i+1}} + e^{2\alpha^s\omega_i} + \hat\epsilon^+(\Omega)\|v_i^{+,s}\|\right), \end{aligned} \tag{C.179}$$

where $\hat\epsilon^\pm(\Omega)$ tends to zero as $\Omega \to \infty$. The lemma is proved by plugging the estimates (C.179) into each other and the resulting formulas into (C.177). □

Consider the integral terms appearing in the expressions for T_i^{14} and T_i^{24} defined in (C.172). Decompose $v_i^{\pm,s}(t)$ into

$$v_i^{\pm,s}(t) = v_i^{\pm,ss}(t) + v_i^{\pm,su}(t),$$

where

$$\begin{aligned} &v_i^{\pm,ss}(t) \in \Phi^\pm(\lambda,t,0)W^\pm,\\ &v_i^{\pm,su}(t) \in \Phi^\pm(\lambda,t,0)\text{span}\{f(\gamma^\pm(\lambda)(0),\lambda)\}. \end{aligned}$$

The following lemma provides bounds for $v_i^{\pm,su}$.

Lemma C.32. *There exists a constant C such that*

$$\begin{aligned} |v_i^{+,su}(t)| &\le Ce^{\alpha^s t}\left(e^{\alpha^s(2\omega_{i+1}-t)} + e^{2\alpha^s\omega_i}\right)^2,\\ |v_i^{-,su}(t)| &\le Ce^{-\alpha^s t}\left(e^{\alpha^s(2\omega_i+t)} + e^{2\alpha^s\omega_{i+1}}\right)^2. \end{aligned}$$

Proof. We follow the line of arguments in the proof of Lemma C.29. As in that proof we combine the estimates of Lemma C.31 with (C.124), (C.125) applied to $v_i^{+,s}$ or $v_i^{+,s}$, and (C.175), (C.176), and end up with

$$|v_i^{+,u}(t)| \leq C\left(e^{\alpha^s(2\omega_{i+1}-t)} + e^{\alpha^s\omega_{i+1}}e^{2\alpha^s\omega_i} + e^{4\alpha^s\omega_i}\right),$$
$$|v_i^{-,u}(t)| \leq C\left(e^{\alpha^s(2\omega_i+t)} + e^{\alpha^s\omega_i}e^{2\alpha^s\omega_{i+1}} + e^{4\alpha^s\omega_{i+1}}\right)$$

and

$$|v_i^{+,s}(t)| \leq Ce^{\alpha^s t}\left(e^{2\alpha^s\omega_{i+1}} + e^{2\alpha^s\omega_i}\right),$$
$$|v_i^{-,s}(t)| \leq Ce^{-\alpha^s t}\left(e^{2\alpha^s\omega_{i+1}} + e^{2\alpha^s\omega_i}\right).$$

Using these terms, we repeat the estimate of the integral term in (C.123) in the proof of Lemma C.29. We find

$$\begin{aligned}&\int_0^t |\Phi^+(t,s)(\mathrm{id}-P^+(\lambda,s))h^{+,s}(s,v_i^+(s),\lambda)|\,ds\\&\leq \int_0^t e^{(\alpha^s-\delta)(t-s)}\left(e^{\alpha^s s}|v_i^{+,u}(s)| + |v_i^{+,s}(s)|\right)\left(|v_i^{+,u}(s)| + |v_i^{+,s}(s)|\right)ds\\&\leq Ce^{\alpha^s t}\left(e^{\alpha^s(2\omega_{i+1}-t)} + e^{2\alpha^s\omega_i}\right)^2.\end{aligned}$$

Similarly we find

$$\begin{aligned}&\int_t^0 |\Phi^-(t,s)(\mathrm{id}-P^-(\lambda,s))h^{-,s}(s,v_i^-(s),\lambda)|\,ds\\&\qquad\qquad\leq Ce^{-\alpha^s t}\left(e^{\alpha^s(2\omega_i+t)} + e^{2\alpha^s\omega_{i+1}}\right)^2.\end{aligned}$$

Since $v_i^{\pm,su}(0) = 0$ we have, using the variation of constants formula,

$$|v_i^{+,su}(t)| \leq \int_0^t |\Phi^+(t,s)(\mathrm{id}-P^+(\lambda,s))h^{+,s}(s,v_i^+(s),\lambda)|\,ds,$$
$$|v_i^{-,su}(t)| \leq \int_t^0 |\Phi^-(t,s)(\mathrm{id}-P^-(\lambda,s))h^{-,s}(s,v_i^-(s),\lambda)|\,ds.$$

Together this proves the lemma. □

Lemma C.33. *There exist constants Ω and c such that for all $|\lambda| < c$ and $\min_{i\in\mathbb{Z}} \omega_i > \Omega$ the following estimates hold:*

$$\left|\int_0^{\omega_{i+1}} \Phi^+(\lambda,0,s)P^+(\lambda,s)h^+(s,v_i^+(s),\lambda)\,ds\right| = \mathcal{O}\left(e^{4\alpha^s\omega_i} + e^{2\alpha^s(\omega_i+\omega_{i+1})} + e^{3\alpha^s\omega_{i+1}}\right),$$

$$\left|\int_{-\omega_i}^{0} \Phi^-(\lambda,0,s)P^-(\lambda,s)h^-(s,v_i^-(s),\lambda)\,ds\right| = \mathcal{O}\left(e^{4\alpha^s\omega_{i+1}} + e^{2\alpha^s(\omega_i+\omega_{i+1})} + e^{3\alpha^s\omega_i}\right).$$

Proof. We give the proof for the "+" sign. We adopt the notation defined in (C.173) for h^+ and write $h^{+,u} = P^+h^+$. The constant C appearing in the estimates may vary from line to line.

With Lemma C.28 we find, again using the exponential dichotomy of Φ^+,

$$\begin{aligned}
&\left|\int_0^{\omega_{i+1}} \Phi^+(\lambda,0,s)h^{+,u}(s,v_i^+(s),\lambda)\,ds\right| \\
&\leq C\int_0^{\omega_{i+1}} \|\Phi^+(\lambda,0,s)P^+(\lambda,s)\|\left(|v_i^{+,u}(s)| + |v_i^{+,su}(s)|\right)|v_i^+(s)|\,ds \\
&\leq C\int_0^{\omega_{i+1}} e^{(\alpha^s-\delta)s}\left(|v_i^{+,u}(s)| + |v_i^{+,su}(s)|\right)|v_i^+(s)|\,ds. \qquad \text{(C.180)}
\end{aligned}$$

Here $\delta > 0$ can be chosen such that $-\alpha^s + \delta < \mu^u$ for all λ sufficiently small.

With the estimate of $|v_i^{+,su}(t)|$ given in Lemma C.32, and the estimates of $|v_i^{+,s}(t)|$ and $|v_i^{+,u}(t)|$ given in the beginning of the proof of Lemma C.32, we find

$$\begin{aligned}
&\left(|v_i^{+,u}(s)| + |v_i^{+,su}(s)|\right)|v_i^+(s)| \\
&\leq C\left(e^{\alpha^s(4\omega_{i+1}-2s)} + e^{\alpha^s(2\omega_{i+1}-s)}e^{2\alpha^s\omega_i} + e^{\alpha^s\omega_{i+1}}e^{4\alpha^s\omega_i} + e^{6\alpha^s\omega_i}\right).
\end{aligned}$$

Using this estimate in (C.180) gives the lemma. □

C.4.3. Derivatives of the jumps. It remains to discuss smoothness properties of the jumps, and in particular to provide estimates of the derivatives of the jumps. We consider the jumps $\xi = (\xi_i)_{i\in\mathbb{Z}}$ as mappings

$$\xi(\cdot,\lambda) : l^\infty(\mathbb{Z},\mathbb{R}) \to l^\infty(\mathbb{Z},\mathbb{R})$$

and correspondingly

$$\langle\psi,\xi_i(\cdot,\lambda)\rangle : l^\infty \to \mathbb{R}.$$

After some basic observations in Appendix C.4.3.1 we prove the differentiability of the jump ξ in Appendix C.4.3.2. In Appendix C.4.3.3 we verify the estimates of the partial derivatives of $\langle\psi,\xi_i(\cdot,\lambda)\rangle$ stated in Proposition C.4. In

Appendix C.4.3.4 we prove Proposition C.5. In our approach we follow and combine material from [**205, 324, 406**].

C.4.3.1. *Calculus on sequence spaces.* We make some remarks on calculus with sequences in $l^\infty(\mathbb{Z},\mathbb{R})$, that are useful for the following sections. For two sequences $\beta = (\beta_i)$ and $\omega = (\omega_i)$ we use notation $\beta\omega = (\beta_i\omega_i)_{i\in\mathbb{Z}}$. If there is a positive lower bound $\Omega > 0$ of ω, so that $\omega_i \geq \Omega$ for all i, then we let $\omega^{-1} \in l^\infty(\mathbb{Z},\mathbb{R})$ be given by $\omega^{-1} = (\omega_i^{-1})_{i\in\mathbb{Z}}$.

Let $\omega \in l^\infty(\mathbb{Z},\mathbb{R})$ be fixed. The mapping $L_\omega : l^\infty(\mathbb{Z},\mathbb{R}) \to l^\infty(\mathbb{Z},\mathbb{R})$ defined by

$$L_\omega(\beta) = \beta\omega$$

is linear. Moreover, if there is a positive lower bound for ω, then L_ω is invertible with $L_\omega^{-1} = L_{\omega^{-1}}$, and both L_ω and L_ω^{-1} are bounded.

Consider a map $g : l^\infty(\mathbb{Z},\mathbb{R}) \to X$ for a Banach space X. Let $h : l^\infty(\mathbb{Z},\mathbb{R})\times l^\infty(\mathbb{Z},\mathbb{R}) \to X$ be given by

$$h(\beta,\omega) = g((\mathbf{1}+\beta)\omega).$$

Here $\mathbf{1}$ is the constant sequence, so $(\mathbf{1}+\beta)\omega = ((1+\beta_i)\omega_i)_{i\in\mathbb{Z}}$.

Lemma C.34. *Let $\omega = (\omega_i)$ be a fixed $l^\infty(\mathbb{Z},\mathbb{R})$-sequence with a lower bound $\Omega > 0$. If $D_\beta h(0,\omega)$ exists, then g is differentiable at ω, and*

$$Dg(\omega) = D_\beta h(0,\omega)L_\omega^{-1}.$$

Proof. This follows from

$$\begin{aligned} g(\omega+\beta\omega) - g(\omega) &= g((\mathbf{1}+\beta)\omega) - g(\omega) \\ &= h(\beta,\omega) - h(0,\omega) \\ &= D_\beta h(0,\omega)\beta + o(\beta) \\ &= D_\beta h(0,\omega)L_\omega^{-1}\beta\omega + o(\beta\omega). \end{aligned}$$

□

Consider Banach spaces X_i, $i \in \mathbb{Z}$, and let X be the space of bounded sequences (x_i), $x_i \in X_i$. Endowed with the supremum norm X is a Banach space.

Lemma C.35. *Let $g : l^\infty(\mathbb{Z},\mathbb{R}) \to X$, $\omega \mapsto (g_i(\omega))_{i\in\mathbb{Z}}$, be a differentiable map. Then the maps $g_i : l^\infty(\mathbb{Z},\mathbb{R}) \to X_i$, $i \in \mathbb{Z}$, are differentiable and $Dg(\omega) = (Dg_i(\omega))_{i\in\mathbb{Z}}$.*

Proof. The projection $P^i : X \to X_i$, $(x_i)_{i\in\mathbb{Z}} \mapsto x_i$ is bounded. Hence $P^i \circ Dg(\omega) = D(P^i g)(\omega)$. □

Lemma C.36. *Let $g_i : l^\infty(\mathbb{Z},\mathbb{R}) \to X_i$ be a differentiable map. Then there exist partial derivatives $D_{\omega_j} g_i$.*

Proof. This follows as in the finite-dimensional case. □

C.4.3.2. *Differentiability of the jumps.* Consider $\xi = (\xi_i)_{i\in\mathbb{Z}}$ with ξ_i given in (C.168), as a mapping $l^\infty(\mathbb{Z},\mathbb{R}) \times \mathbb{R} \to l^\infty(\mathbb{Z},\mathbb{R})$, and also $\langle\xi_i(\cdot,\cdot),\psi\rangle$ as a mapping $l^\infty(\mathbb{Z},\mathbb{R}) \times \mathbb{R} \to \mathbb{R}$. We start with a differentiability statement, asymptotic expansions will be discussed afterwards. Basically we extend the results of Appendix C.3.3.1 to sequences $(\xi_i)_{i\in\mathbb{Z}}$.

Proposition C.37. *The mapping* $\xi : l^\infty(\mathbb{Z},\mathbb{R}) \times \mathbb{R} \to l^\infty(\mathbb{Z},\mathbb{R})$, $(\omega,\lambda) \mapsto (\langle\xi_i,\psi\rangle)_{i\in\mathbb{Z}}$ *is continuously differentiable.*

Proof. Recall from (C.168) that

$$\xi_i(\omega,\lambda) = v_i^+(\omega,\lambda)(0) - v_i^-(\omega,\lambda)(0).$$

So it suffices to show that the function $(v_i^\pm(\cdot,\lambda)(0))_{i\in\mathbb{Z}}$ is continuously differentiable; see at the end of Appendix C.4.1. We will rewrite the problem of finding Lin orbits by replacing the variation of ω_i with time rescalings. This is done by replacing the differential equation $\dot{x} = f(x,\lambda)$ with differential equations $\dot{x} = (1+\beta_i)f(x,\lambda)$ that the different partial orbits in the Lin orbit must satisfy. Note that $\dot{x} = f(x,\lambda)$ and $\dot{x} = (1+\beta)f(x,\lambda)$ have the same orbits, only with a different time parametrization.

Fix a sequence $\omega = (\omega_i)_{i\in\mathbb{Z}}$. Let $0 < \delta < 1$ and let $\beta = (\beta_i)_{i\in\mathbb{Z}} \in l^\infty(\mathbb{Z},\mathbb{R})$ with $|\beta_i| < \delta$. Define

$$\check{h}^s(\beta_{i+1},\lambda)(t) = h^s(\lambda)((1+\beta_{i+1})t),$$
$$\check{h}^u(\beta_i,\lambda)(t) = h^u(\lambda)((1+\beta_i)t).$$

We search solutions

$$\check{x}_i^+(\beta,\omega,\lambda)(\cdot) = \check{h}^s(\beta_{i+1},\lambda)(\cdot) + \check{v}_i^+(\beta,\omega,\lambda)(\cdot)$$

of the differential equation $\dot{x} = (1+\beta_{i+1})f(x,\lambda)$, and

$$\check{x}_i^-(\beta,\omega,\lambda)(\cdot) = \check{h}^u(\beta_i,\lambda)(\cdot) + \check{v}_i^-(\beta,\omega,\lambda)(\cdot)$$

of $\dot{x} = (1+\beta_i)f(x,\lambda)$, with boundary conditions

$$\check{x}_i^+(\beta,\omega,\lambda)(\omega_{i+1}) = \check{x}_{i+1}^-(\beta,\omega,\lambda)(-\omega_{i+1}),$$
$$\check{x}_i^+(\beta,\omega,\lambda)(0) - \check{x}_i^-(\beta,\omega,\lambda)(0) \in Z,$$
$$\check{x}_i^+(\beta,\omega,\lambda)(0) - \check{h}^s(\beta_{i+1},\lambda)(0) \in W^+ \oplus W^- \oplus Z,$$
$$\check{x}_i^-(\beta,\omega,\lambda)(0) - \check{h}^u(\beta_i,\lambda)(0) \in W^+ \oplus W^- \oplus Z.$$

We can obtain $\check{v}_i^\pm$ from a boundary value problem similar to (C.153)–(C.156), namely differential equations,

$$\dot{u}_i^+(t) = (1+\beta_{i+1})\big(D_x f(\check{h}^s(\beta_{i+1},\lambda)(t),\lambda)u_i^+(t) + h^+(t,u_i^+(t),\lambda)\big),$$
$$\dot{u}_i^-(t) = (1+\beta_i)\big(D_x f(\check{h}^u(\beta_i,\lambda)(t),\lambda)u_i^-(t) + h^-(t,u_i^-(t),\lambda)\big),$$

with boundary value conditions

$$u_i^+(\omega_{i+1}) - u_{i+1}^-(-\omega_{i+1}) = \check{h}^u(\beta_{i+1},\lambda)(-\omega_{i+1}) - \check{h}^s(\beta_{i+1},\lambda)(\omega_{i+1})$$

and

$$\begin{aligned} &u_i^+(0), u_i^-(0) \in W^+ \oplus W^- \oplus Z,\\ &u_i^+(0) - u_i^-(0) \in Z, \end{aligned}$$

with $u_i^+(0), u_i^-(0)$ close to 0.

The procedure to solve the boundary value problem is the same as for Lemma C.19. We list the steps in order to comment on the dependence on β. For the first step we consider equations

$$\begin{aligned} \dot{v}_i^+ &= (1+\beta_{i+1})D_x f(h^s(\beta_{i+1},\lambda)(t),\lambda)v_i^+ + \check{g}_i^+(t),\\ \dot{v}_i^- &= (1+\beta_i)D_x f(h^u(\beta_i,\lambda)(t),\lambda)v_i^- + \check{g}_i^-(t) \end{aligned}$$

and boundary conditions

$$\begin{aligned} &(\mathrm{id} - P^+(u_{i-1},\lambda,(1+\beta_i)\omega_i))(v_{i-1}^+(\omega_i) - a_i) = 0,\\ &(\mathrm{id} - P^-(u_i,\lambda,-(1-\beta_i)\omega_i))(v_i^-(-\omega_i) - a_i) = 0,\\ &v_i^+(0), v_i^-(0) \in W^+ \oplus W^- \oplus Z,\\ &v_i^+(0) - v_i^-(0) \in Z. \end{aligned}$$

Here $\check{\mathbf{g}} = (\check{g}_i^-, \check{g}_i^+)_{i\in\mathbb{Z}} \in \mathcal{V}_\omega$ with $\check{g}_i^+(t) = g_i^+((1+\beta_{i+1})t)$, $\check{g}_i^-(t) = g_i^-((1+\beta_i)t)$ and $\mathbf{v} \in \mathcal{V}_\omega$. As in Lemma C.19, a unique solution

$$\begin{aligned} &\check{\mathbf{v}}_\omega : l^\infty(\mathbb{Z},\mathbb{R}) \times \mathbb{R}^n \times \mathcal{V}_\omega \times l^\infty(\mathbb{Z},\mathbb{R}^n) \to \mathcal{V}_\omega,\\ &(\beta,\lambda,\mathbf{g},\mathbf{a}) \mapsto \check{\mathbf{v}}_\omega(\beta,\lambda,\mathbf{g},\mathbf{a}) \end{aligned}$$

is obtained. We find that $\check{v}_i^\pm$ depends only on β_i and β_{i+1} and not on other elements of the sequence β. It is therefore clear that we have differentiability of $\check{\mathbf{v}}_\omega$ with respect to $\beta \in l^\infty(\mathbb{Z},\mathbb{R})$.

Also the next step runs parallel to the corresponding step in Appendix C.4.1. As in (C.162) we get $\mathbf{z} = (a_i)_{i\in\mathbb{Z}}$ from a fixed point equation of the form

$$\mathbf{a} = L_1(\lambda,\omega)\mathbf{a} + L_2(\lambda,\omega)\mathbf{g} + L_3(\lambda,\omega)\mathbf{d} + L_4(\lambda,\omega)w_0^+$$

for linear bounded operators $L_j(\lambda,\omega)(\cdot)$, $j = 1,2,3,4$. The equation for a_i depends only on finitely many β_j. We find that the resulting mapping

$$\begin{aligned} &\check{\mathbf{v}}_\omega : l^\infty(\mathbb{Z},\mathbb{R}) \times \mathbb{R}^n \times \mathcal{V}_\omega \times l^\infty(\mathbb{Z},\mathbb{R}^n) \to \mathcal{V}_\omega,\\ &(\beta,\lambda,\mathbf{g},\mathbf{d}) \mapsto \check{\mathbf{v}}_\omega(\beta,\lambda,\mathbf{g},\mathbf{d}), \end{aligned}$$

depends smoothly on β. Finally we define

$$\check{\mathcal{F}}_\omega(\beta,\mathbf{v},\lambda) = \check{\mathbf{v}}_\omega(\beta,\lambda,\check{\mathcal{H}}(\beta,\mathbf{v},\lambda),\check{\mathbf{d}}(\beta,\lambda)).$$

Here $\check{\mathcal{H}}(\beta, \mathbf{v}, \lambda) = (H_i^+(\beta, \mathbf{v}, \lambda), H_i^-(\beta, \mathbf{v}, \lambda))_{i\in\mathbb{Z}}$, with

$$H_i^{\pm}(\mathbf{v}, \lambda)(t) = (1 + \beta_i)h^{\pm}(t, v_i^{\pm}(t), \lambda)),$$

and $\check{\mathbf{d}} = (\check{d})_{i\in\mathbb{Z}}$, where

$$\check{d}(\beta_{i+1}, \omega_{i+1}, \lambda) = \check{h}^u(\beta_{i+1}, \lambda)(-\omega_{i+1}) - \check{h}^s(\beta_{i+1}, \lambda)(\omega_{i+1}).$$

We conclude that $\check{\mathcal{F}}_\omega$ is continuously differentiable with respect to β.

Consider the fixed point equation

$$\mathbf{v} = \check{\mathcal{F}}_\omega(\beta, \mathbf{v}, \lambda). \tag{C.181}$$

By applying the uniform contraction theorem, we can find a solution $\check{\mathbf{V}}_\omega = ((\check{V}_i^+, \check{V}_i^-))_{i\in\mathbb{Z}}$ of (C.181) depending smoothly on β. So $(\check{V}_i^{\pm}(\beta, \omega, \lambda)(0))_{i\in\mathbb{Z}}$ is continuously differentiable in β. Define, with solution (v_i^+, v_i^-) of (C.164),

$$\check{\mathbf{v}}_\omega(\beta, \lambda) = \check{\mathbf{v}}(\beta, \omega, \lambda) = (\check{v}_i^+, \check{v}_i^-)_{i\in\mathbb{Z}}$$

by

$$\check{v}_i^+(\beta, \omega, \lambda)(t) = v_i^+((1+\beta)\omega, \lambda)((1 + \beta_{i+1})t),$$
$$\check{v}_i^-(\beta, \omega, \lambda)(t) = v_i^-((1+\beta)\omega, \lambda)((1 + \beta_i)t).$$

Since the orbits of $\dot{x} = f(x, \lambda)$ and $\dot{x} = (1 + \beta)f(x, \lambda)$ differ only in time parametrization, we find that $\check{\mathbf{v}}_\omega = \check{\mathbf{V}}_\omega$. By arguments in Appendix C.3.3.1, Lemma C.34, and Lemma C.36, $(v_i^{\pm}(\cdot, \lambda)(0))_{i\in\mathbb{Z}}$ is continuously differentiable. □

C.4.3.3. *Estimates of the derivatives of the jumps.* This section is devoted to the proof of Proposition C.4. In what follows we drop the dependence on λ from the notation. First we consider the partial derivatives of $v_i(\omega)(\cdot)$. By Proposition C.37, $\mathbf{v}(\omega)$ is differentiable with respect to ω. By Lemma C.36, also $v_i(\omega)(\cdot)$ is differentiable with respect to ω. Therefore the partial derivatives $D_{\omega_j} v_i(\omega)(\cdot)$ with respect to ω_j exist. Moreover, the absolute values of these partial derivatives can be bounded by $\|D\mathbf{v}(\omega)\|$.

Lemma C.38. *There is an* $\alpha^s < 0$ *such that*

$$D_{\omega_j} v_i(\omega)(\cdot) = \mathcal{O}(e^{\alpha^s \Omega}).$$

Proof. We consider just $v_i^+(\omega)(\cdot)$. Starting from (C.157), which reads

$$\dot{v}_i^+(t) = D_x f(h_\lambda^s(t), \lambda)v_i^+(t) + g_i^+(t, \lambda),$$

and differentiating with respect to ω_j, yields

$$\left(D_{\omega_j} v_i^+(\omega)\right)^{\cdot}(t) = Df(h^s(t))D_{\omega_j} v_i^+(\omega)(t) + D_{\omega_j} g_i^+(t).$$

Next *replace* the g_i^+-term by $h^+(t, v_i^+(\omega)(t))$, and follow the procedure in the proof of Lemma C.31. Doing so, one sees that each $\alpha^s \in (\mu^s, 0)$ is eligible. □

We can now turn to the proof of the proposition.

Proof of Proposition C.4. The statement follows from differentiating the expression (C.9) in Theorem C.3. So it remains to estimate the derivative of the residual term $R_i(\omega)$. Start from (C.169), which reads

$$\langle \psi, \xi_i(\omega,\lambda)\rangle = T_i^1(\omega,\lambda) - T_i^2(\omega,\lambda),$$

with

$$T_i^1(\omega,\lambda) = \langle \psi, P^+(\lambda,0)v_i^+(\omega,\lambda)(0)\rangle,$$
$$T_i^2(\omega,\lambda) = \langle \psi, P^-(\lambda,0)v_i^-(\omega,\lambda)(0)\rangle.$$

Expressions for T_i^1, T_i^2 are given in (C.170), (C.171). Both T_i^1 and T_i^2 are given as a sum of several terms. By example we study the derivatives of $T_i^1 = T_i^{11} + T_i^{12} + T_i^{13} + T_i^{14}$. Copying the formulas given in Appendix C.4.2, these terms are given by expressions

$$\begin{aligned}
T_i^{11} &= \left\langle \Phi^+(\lambda,0,\omega_{i+1})^T P^+(\lambda,0)^T\psi, \tilde{P}(\lambda,\omega_{i+1})h_\lambda^u(-\omega_{i+1})\right\rangle,\\
T_i^{12} &= \left\langle \Phi^+(\lambda,0,\omega_{i+1})^T P^+(\lambda,0)^T\psi, -\tilde{P}(\lambda,\omega_{i+1})h_\lambda^s(\omega_{i+1})\right\rangle,\\
T_i^{13} &= \Big\langle \Phi^+(\lambda,0,\omega_{i+1})^T P^+(\lambda,0)^T\psi,\\
&\qquad \tilde{P}(\lambda,\omega_{i+1})\big[(\mathrm{id} - P^-(\lambda,-\omega_{i+1}))v_{i+1}^-(\omega,\lambda)(-\omega_{i+1})\\
&\qquad\qquad - (\mathrm{id} - P^+(\lambda,\omega_{i+1}))v_i^+(\omega,\lambda)(\omega_{i+1})\big]\Big\rangle,\\
T_i^{14} &= -\left\langle \psi, \int_0^{\omega_{i+1}} \Phi^+(\lambda,0,s)P^+(\lambda,s)h^+(s,v_i^+(\omega,\lambda)(s),\lambda)\,ds\right\rangle.
\end{aligned}$$

In what follows we suppress the dependence on λ from the notation. First we consider the scalar product $T_i^{11}+T_i^{12}+T_i^{13}$, which we differentiate by means of the product rule. The first factor in this scalar product is

$$F_i^1(\omega) := \Phi^+(0,\omega_{i+1})^T P^+(0)^T\psi$$

and was estimated in (C.68). This yields, for some appropriate constant C,

$$F_i^1(\omega) = e^{-\mu^u\omega_{i+1}}\eta^+ + \mathcal{O}(e^{-\mu^u\omega_{i+1}\delta}) \le Ce^{-\mu^u\Omega}. \tag{C.182}$$

Since $F_i^1(\omega)$ only depends on ω_{i+1}, we have

$$D_{\omega_j}F_i^1(\omega) = 0$$

for $j \neq i+1$. To study the derivative

$$D_{\omega_{i+1}}F_i^1(\omega) = \dot{\Phi}^+(0,\omega_{i+1})^T P^+(0)^T\psi,$$

we recall that $\Phi^+(0,\cdot)^T$ is the transition matrix of $\dot{v} = -\left(Df(h^s_\lambda(t))\right)^T v$. Hence

$$D_{\omega_{i+1}} F_i^1(\omega) = -\left(Df(h^s_\lambda(\omega_{i+1}))\right)^T \Phi^+(0,\omega_{i+1})^T P^+(0)^T \psi$$
$$= -\left(Df(h^s_\lambda(\omega_{i+1}))\right)^T F_i^1(\omega).$$

Incorporating (C.182), we find a constant C (which may be different from the one above) such that

$$D_{\omega_{i+1}} F_i^1(\omega) \leq Ce^{-\mu^u\Omega}.$$

Next consider the second factor in the scalar product $T_i^{11} + T_i^{12} + T_i^{13}$,

$$\text{(C.183)} \quad F_i^2(\omega) := \tilde{P}(\omega_{i+1})\Big[h^u(-\omega_{i+1}) - h^s(\omega_{i+1}) + (\mathrm{id} - P^-(-\omega_{i+1}))v^-_{i+1}(\omega)(-\omega_{i+1}) - (\mathrm{id} - P^+(\omega_{i+1}))v^+_i(\omega)(\omega_{i+1})\Big].$$

The single terms in here have been estimated in Appendix C.4.2, so that we get

$$F_i^2(\omega) = \mathcal{O}(e^{2\alpha^s\Omega}).$$

For the derivatives of $F_i^2(\omega)$, we start with the derivatives of the projections $P^\pm(t)$. From (C.52) we infer

$$P^\pm(t) = \Phi^\pm(t,0)P^\pm(0)\Phi^\pm(0,t).$$

For the "+" term, differentiating with respect to t yields

$$\text{(C.184)} \quad D_{\omega_{i+1}} P^+(\omega_{i+1}) = \dot{P}^+(\omega_{i+1})$$
$$= Df(h^s(\omega_{i+1}))P^+(\omega_{i+1}) - P^+(\omega_{i+1})Df(h^s(\omega_{i+1})).$$

We find that $D_{\omega_{i+1}} P^+(\omega_{i+1}) = \mathcal{O}(1)$, and similarly $D_{\omega_{i+1}} P^-(-\omega_{i+1}) = \mathcal{O}(1)$. Further, with (C.63) and (C.61) we get that also $D_{\omega_{i+1}} \tilde{P}(\omega_{i+1}) = \mathcal{O}(1)$. Note that the term within the square brackets in (C.183) is of order $\mathcal{O}(e^{\mu^s\Omega})$. The estimates of the derivatives of $h^{s/u}$ follow from (C.65), (C.66) and the fact that $h^{s/u}$ solves the differential equation $\dot{x} = f(x)$. So, the derivatives of $h^{s/u}$ are of order $\mathcal{O}(e^{\mu^s\Omega})$ and $\mathcal{O}(e^{-\mu^u\Omega})$, respectively. To estimate the remaining terms we examine (C.184) more closely. To this end we make use of (C.53)–(C.59), and exploit that P commutes with $Df(p)$. This yields that the derivatives of $\mathrm{id} - P^\pm(\pm\omega_{i+1})$ are of order $\mathcal{O}(e^{\alpha^s\Omega})$. Finally $v^\pm_{i+1}(\omega)(\pm\omega_{i+1})$ and its derivatives can be estimated by Lemma C.31 and Lemma C.38, and the fact that $v^\mp_{i+1}(\omega)(\cdot)$ solves

$$\left(D_{\omega_j} v_i^\mp(\omega)\right)^{\cdot}(t) = Df(h^{s/u}(t))D_{\omega_j} v_i^\mp(\omega)(t) + D_{\omega_j} g_i^\mp(t),$$

which we get from (C.157). This yields that the derivatives of

$$(\mathrm{id} - P^\pm(\pm\omega_{i+1}))v_i^\mp(\omega)(\pm\omega_{i+1})$$

are of order $\mathcal{O}(e^{2\alpha^s\Omega})$. Recall that $\alpha^s \in (\mu^s, 0)$ can be chosen arbitrarily close to μ^s.

Now we look at the integral term T_i^{14}. Write

$$I_i(\omega) = \int_0^{\omega_{i+1}} \Phi^+(0,s)P^+(s)h^+(s, v_i^+(\omega)(s))\, ds.$$

For $j \neq i+1$ we have

$$|D_{\omega_j} I_i(\omega)| \leq \int_0^{\omega_{i+1}} |\Phi^+(0,s)P^+(s)D_v h^+(s, v_i^+(\omega)(s))||D_{\omega_j} v_i^+(\omega)(s)|\, ds.$$

Now repeat the estimates performed in the proof of Lemma C.33, replacing $|v_i^+(\omega)(s)|$ by $|D_{\omega_j} v_i^+(\omega)(s)|$. For the latter term we use estimates analogous to those for $v_i^{+,s/u}(s)$ in the proof of Lemma C.32. Together this yields

$$|D_{\omega_j} I_i(\omega)| = \mathcal{O}(e^{3\alpha^s \Omega})$$

for $j \neq i+1$. The term $D_{\omega_{i+1}} I_i(\omega)$ comprises

$$\Phi^+(0, \omega_{i+1})P^+(\omega_{i+1})h^+(\omega_{i+1}, v_i^+(\omega)(\omega_{i+1})).$$

But also this term is of order $\mathcal{O}(e^{3\alpha^s \Omega})$. □

C.4.3.4. *Calculation of the derivative.* We turn to the proof of Proposition C.5, starting with some preliminary considerations.

Lemma C.39. *Let ω^1, ω^2 be two sequences with a common lower bound Ω for which $\omega_i^1 = \omega_i^2$ for all $i \in [-N, N] \cap \mathbb{Z}$. If Ω is sufficiently large, then there exists a constant C such that*

$$|v_0(\omega^1)(0) - v_0(\omega^2)(0)| \leq Ce^{3\alpha^s \Omega} \left(\frac{1}{2}\right)^N.$$

Proof. Define $\tilde{\omega} = (\tilde{\omega}_i)$ by $\tilde{\omega}_i = \min\{\omega_i^1, \omega_i^2\}$. By the triangle inequality,

$$|v_0(\omega^1)(0) - v_0(\omega^2)(0)| \leq |v_0(\omega^1)(0) - v_0(\tilde{\omega})(0)| + |v_0(\tilde{\omega})(0) - v_0(\omega^2)(0)|.$$

For the proof of the lemma we show that both summands on the right-hand side satisfy an inequality as stated in the lemma. We prove this merely for the first summand, noting that the proof for the second one runs parallel.

In order to study $|v_0(\omega^1)(0) - v_0(\tilde{\omega})(0)|$, we define $\mathbf{v}^{\mathbf{R}} = \mathbf{v}(\omega^1)|_{\tilde{\omega}}$ by

$$v_i^{R,+}(\cdot) = v_i^+(\omega^1)(\cdot)|_{[0,\tilde{\omega}_i]} \quad \text{and} \quad v_{i+1}^{R,-}(\cdot) = v_{i+1}^-(\omega^1)(\cdot)|_{[-\tilde{\omega}_{i+1},0]}.$$

So we have in particular $v_i^{R,\pm}(0) = v_i^\pm(\omega^1)(0)$ and, due to this,

$$v_0(\omega^1)(0) - v_0(\tilde{\omega})(0) = v_0^R(\omega^1)(0) - v_0(\tilde{\omega})(0).$$

Now consider $\Delta\mathbf{v} = \mathbf{v}^{\mathbf{R}} - \mathbf{v}(\tilde{\omega})$. Hence $\Delta\mathbf{v} = (\Delta v_i)_{i\in\mathbb{Z}}$ and

$$\Delta v_i^\pm(t) = v_i^{R,\pm}(t) - v_i^\pm(\tilde{\omega})(t).$$

We derive an equation for $\Delta\mathbf{v}$ similar to (C.164): For that purpose define $\mathbf{d}^{\mathbf{R}} = (d_i^R)_{i\in\mathbb{Z}}$ by

$$d_i^R = v_{i-1}^+(\omega^1)(\hat{\omega}_i) - v_i^-(\omega^1)(-\hat{\omega}_i).$$

Further, note that $\mathbf{v}^{\mathbf{R}}$ is the unique solution of the fixed point equation $\mathbf{v} = \hat{\mathbf{v}}(\tilde{\omega}, \mathcal{H}(\mathbf{v}), \mathbf{d}^R)$. Then, since $\hat{\mathbf{v}}(\tilde{\omega}, \cdot, \cdot)$ is linear, $\Delta\mathbf{v}$ solves the equation

$$\begin{aligned}\Delta\mathbf{v} &= \hat{\mathbf{v}}(\tilde{\omega}, \underbrace{\mathcal{H}(\mathbf{v}^{\mathbf{R}}) - \mathcal{H}(\mathbf{v}(\tilde{\omega}))}_{\Delta\mathcal{H}}, \underbrace{\mathbf{d}^{\mathbf{R}} - \mathbf{d}(\tilde{\omega})}_{\Delta\mathbf{d}}) \\ &= \bar{\mathbf{v}}(\tilde{\omega}, \Delta\mathcal{H}, \underbrace{\mathbf{a}(\tilde{\omega}, \Delta\mathcal{H}, \Delta\mathbf{d})}_{\Delta\mathbf{a}}),\end{aligned}$$

where we refer to (C.161) for the latter equality. So we find for the term to be estimated,

$$|v_0(\omega^1)(0) - v_0(\tilde{\omega})(0)| = |\Delta v_0(0)| = |\bar{v}_0((\tilde{\omega}, \Delta\mathcal{H}, \Delta\mathbf{a})(0)|.$$

Following arguments given in the proofs of the Lemmas C.20 and C.21 (combine (C.94) and (C.97) and exploit that the g-terms arising there are $\mathcal{O}(|\Delta v|^2)$), there exist constants $C > 0$ and $\alpha^s < 0$ such that

$$|\Delta v_0(0)| \le Ce^{\alpha^s\Omega}\left(|\Delta a_1^+| + |\Delta a_0^-|\right). \tag{C.185}$$

Using the fixed point equation (C.162), we find a constant $C > 0$ such that

$$\begin{aligned}&|\Delta a_i^+| + |\Delta a_i^-| \\ &\qquad \le C(|\Delta d_i| + |(\mathrm{id} - P^+(\tilde{\omega}_i))\Delta v_{i-1}^+(\tilde{\omega}_i)| + |(\mathrm{id} - P^-(-\tilde{\omega}_i))\Delta v_i^-(-\tilde{\omega}_i)|).\end{aligned}$$

The terms containing Δv can be expressed as in the proof of Lemma C.20. Once more exploiting exponential dichotomies and taking into account that the g-terms arising there are $\mathcal{O}(|\Delta v|^2)$, we end up with

$$\begin{aligned}&|\Delta a_i^+| + |\Delta a_i^-| \\ &\qquad \le C(|\Delta d_i| + Ce^{\alpha^s\tilde{\omega}}(|\Delta v_{i-1}^+(0)| + |\Delta v_i^-(0)|) + \epsilon(\|\Delta v_{i-1}^+\| + \|\Delta v_i^-\|)).\end{aligned}$$

Note that ϵ can be chosen arbitrarily small if Ω is sufficiently large. Similar to Lemma C.21 we can show that

$$\|\Delta v_i^{\mp}\| \le C((|\Delta a_{i+1}^+| + |\Delta a_i^-|) + (\|\Delta h_i^+\| + \|\Delta h_i^-\|)),$$

where we have written $\Delta h_i^{\pm}(t) = h^{\pm}(t, v_i^{R,\pm}(t)) - h^{\pm}(t, v_i^{\mp}(\tilde{\omega})(t)))$. The mean value theorem in combination with $h^{\pm}(t,0) \equiv 0$ and $D_v h^{\pm}(t,0) \equiv 0$ yields $|\Delta h_i^{\pm}(t)| \le \epsilon|\Delta v_i^{\mp}(t)|$. Choosing ϵ sufficiently small we arrive at

$$\|\Delta v_i^{\mp}\| \le C(|\Delta a_{i+1}^+| + |\Delta a_i^-|). \tag{C.186}$$

Combining the last inequalities yields

$$|\Delta a_i^+| + |\Delta a_i^-| \le C|\Delta d_i| + \frac{1}{4}(|\Delta a_{i+1}^+| + |\Delta a_{i-1}^-|). \tag{C.187}$$

Note that for $i \in [-N, N]$ we have $\omega_i^1 = \tilde{\omega}_i$. Hence, compare (C.155) and the definition of d_i in (C.160),

$$\begin{aligned} d_i^R &= v_{i-1}^+(\omega^1)(\hat{\omega}_i) - v_i^-(\omega^1)(-\hat{\omega}_i) \\ &= v_{i-1}^+(\omega^1)(\omega_i^1) - v_i^-(\omega^1)(-\omega_i^1) \\ &= h^-(-\omega_i^1) - h^+(\omega_i^1) \\ &= h^-(-\tilde{\omega}_i) - h^+(\tilde{\omega}_i) \\ &= d_i(\tilde{\omega}), \end{aligned}$$

for $i \in [-N, N]$. So, $|\Delta d_i| = 0$ for $i \in [-N, N]$, and therefore

$$|\Delta a_i^+| + |\Delta a_i^-| \leq \frac{1}{4}(|\Delta a_{i+1}^+| + |\Delta a_{i-1}^-|), \qquad i \in [-N, N].$$

Lemma 4.28 provides

$$|\Delta a_0^-| \leq |\Delta a_0^-| + |\Delta a_0^+| \leq \frac{1}{2^N}\left(|\Delta a_{-N}^-| + |\Delta a_N^+|\right). \tag{C.188}$$

An analogous estimate holds for $|\Delta a_1^+|$. To estimate $|\Delta a_{-N}^-| + |\Delta a_N^+|$, we use the idea of the proof of Lemma C.27. When adapting to the current context, we again take advantage of the fact that $|\Delta d_i| = 0$ for $i \in [-N, N]$. Now, Lemma C.26 or Lemma C.31, respectively, gives

$$|\Delta a_{-N}^-| + |\Delta a_N^+| \leq Ce^{2\alpha^s\Omega}. \tag{C.189}$$

Now, inserting in (C.185) yields the lemma. □

The statement of Lemma C.39 is also true for v_i, with sequences which coincide on a block $[i-N, i+N]$ centered at i.

Lemma C.40. $\left(D_{\omega_j}\xi_i(\omega,\lambda)\right)_{j\in\mathbb{Z}} \in l^1(\mathbb{Z},\mathbb{R})$.

Proof. The λ-dependence is dropped from the notation. We will prove that there is a constant C (uniform in i and j) such that

$$|D_{\omega_j}\xi_i(\omega)| \leq Ce^{3\alpha^s\Omega}\left(\frac{1}{2}\right)^{|j|}. \tag{C.190}$$

We prove the statement only for ξ_0 and $j \neq 0$. Note that the corresponding estimate of $D_{\omega_0}\xi_0(\omega)$ is already done with Proposition C.4 (the same holds true for all $D_{\omega_i}\xi_i(\omega)$, $i \in \mathbb{Z}$). For that we use Lemma C.39. Since Lemma C.39 also holds for v_i, with sequences which coincide on a block centered at i, we can transfer the statement to ξ_i, $i \neq 0$.

We verify the statement for $j = N > 0$. Let $h_N \in \mathbb{R}$. Define $\mathbf{h_N} = (h_{N,k})_{k\in\mathbb{Z}}$ with

$$h_{N,k} = \begin{cases} h_N, & k = N, \\ 0, & \text{otherwise.} \end{cases}$$

Write

$$\begin{aligned} D_{\omega_N}\xi_0(\omega)h_N + \hat{r}_N(h_N) &= \xi_0(\omega + \mathbf{h_N}) - \xi_0(\omega) \\ &= v_0^+(\omega + \mathbf{h_N})(0) - v_0^-(\omega + \mathbf{h_N})(0) - \left(v_0^+(\omega)(0) - v_0^-(\omega)(0)\right). \end{aligned}$$

Note that $\hat{r}_N(h) = o(h)$, as $h \to 0$. Further, the proof of Lemma C.39 reveals that for $N \neq 0$

$$|D_{\omega_N}\xi_0(\omega)h_N + \hat{r}_N(h_N)| \leq Ce^{\alpha^s\Omega}\left(\frac{1}{2}\right)^N (|\Delta a_{-N}^-| + \Delta a_N^+|).$$

Applying the mean value theorem to the Δa-terms gives a (different) constant C such that

$$\begin{aligned} |D_{\omega_N}\xi_0(\omega)h_N + \hat{r}_N(h_N)| &= \left|D_{\omega_N}\xi_0(\omega) + \frac{\hat{r}_N(h_N)}{|h_N|}\right| |h_N| \\ &\leq Ce^{3\alpha^s\Omega}\left(\frac{1}{2}\right)^N |h_N|. \end{aligned}$$

For the latter estimate we exploited that the (partial) derivative of the a-terms also allow an estimate like (C.189). See for this the very end of Appendix C.3.3.2. In the representation of the Δa-terms again take advantage of the fact that the difference of corresponding d_i-terms vanish. So the derivatives of the a-terms are governed by (C.148).

Finally the limit $h_N \to 0$ gives

$$|D_{\omega_N}\xi_0(\omega)| \leq Ce^{3\alpha^s\Omega}\left(\frac{1}{2}\right)^N.$$

The derivation of the constant C shows its independence on i and j. This proves the lemma. □

Remark C.41. The last two inequalities in the proof of Lemma C.40 imply that there is a constant C such that

$$\left|\frac{\hat{r}_N(h_N)}{|h_N|}\right| \leq C\left(\frac{1}{2}\right)^N.$$

■

Now we turn towards the actual proof of Proposition C.5.

Proof of Proposition C.5. First we justify the representation

$$D\xi_i(\omega)\mathbf{h} = \sum_{j\in\mathbb{Z}} D_{\omega_j}\xi_i(\omega)h_j.$$

We prove this statement for ξ_0. The statement for $i \neq 0$ then follows in the same way.

For $\mathbf{h} = (h_j)_{j\in\mathbb{Z}} \in l^\infty(\mathbb{Z},\mathbb{R})$, define $\mathbf{h^N} = (h_j^N)_{j\in\mathbb{Z}}$ by

$$h_j^N = \begin{cases} h_j, & j \in [-N,N], \\ 0, & \text{otherwise.} \end{cases}$$

Write

(C.191)
$$\xi_0(\omega+\mathbf{h}) - \xi_0(\omega) = \big(\xi_0(\omega+\mathbf{h^N}) - \xi_0(\omega)\big) + \big(\xi_0(\omega+\mathbf{h}) - \xi_0(\omega+\mathbf{h^N})\big).$$

The sequences $\omega+\mathbf{h^N}$ and $\omega+\mathbf{h}$ satisfy the assumptions of Lemma C.39. Via (C.168) the results of Lemma C.39 are transferred to ξ_0. So,

$$\xi_0(\omega+\mathbf{h}) - \xi_0(\omega+\mathbf{h^N}) = \mathcal{O}\left(\frac{1}{2^N}\right).$$

The limit $N\to\infty$ in (C.191) yields

$$\xi_0(\omega+\mathbf{h}) - \xi_0(\omega) = \lim_{N\to\infty}\big(\xi_0(\omega+\mathbf{h^N}) - \xi_0(\omega)\big). \tag{C.192}$$

As in the finite-dimensional case the first summand on the right-hand side can be written as

(C.193)
$$\xi_0(\omega+\mathbf{h^N}) - \xi_0(\omega) = D\xi_0(\omega)\mathbf{h^N} + r_N(\mathbf{h^N}) = \sum_{j=-N}^{N} D_{\omega_j}\xi_0(\omega)h_j + r_N(\mathbf{h^N}).$$

Note that $r_N(\mathbf{h^N}) = o(\|\mathbf{h^N}\|)$ and hence also $r_N(\mathbf{h^N}) = o(\|\mathbf{h}\|)$. The limit

$$\lim_{N\to\infty}\sum_{j=-N}^{N} D_{\omega_j}\xi_0(\omega)h_j$$

exists by Lemma C.40. The limit $\lim_{N\to\infty} r_N(\mathbf{h^N})$ exists because of (C.192)–(C.193). Write $r(\mathbf{h})$ for its value. Together this yields

$$\xi_0(\omega+\mathbf{h}) - \xi_0(\omega) = \sum_{j=\mathbb{Z}} D_{\omega_j}\xi_0(\omega)h_j + r(\mathbf{h}).$$

It remains to prove that $r(\mathbf{h}) = o(\|\mathbf{h}\|)$. Write $\xi_0(\omega+\mathbf{h^N}) - \xi_0(\omega)$ as follows:

$$\begin{aligned}
&\xi_0(\omega+\mathbf{h^N}) - \xi_0(\omega) \\
&\quad = \underbrace{\xi_0(\omega+\mathbf{h^N}) - \xi_0(\omega+\mathbf{h^N}-\mathbf{h^0})}_{=D_{\omega_0}\xi_0(\omega+\mathbf{h^N}-\mathbf{h^0})h_0 + r_0(h_0)} + \xi_0(\omega+\mathbf{h^N}-\mathbf{h^0}) - \xi_0(\omega) \\
&\quad\ \vdots \\
&\quad = D_{\omega_0}\xi_0(\omega+\mathbf{h^N}-\mathbf{h^0})h_0 + \hat{r}_0(h_0) \\
&\qquad\quad + D_{\omega_1}\xi_0(\omega+\mathbf{h^N}-(\ldots 0,h_0,h_1,0,\ldots))h_1 + \hat{r}_1(h_1) \\
&\qquad\quad + D_{\omega_{-1}}\xi_0(\omega+\mathbf{h^N}-(\ldots 0,h_{-1},h_0,h_1,0,\ldots))h_{-1} + \hat{r}_{-1}(h_{-1}) \\
&\qquad\quad + \ldots + D_{\omega_N}\xi_0(\omega)h_N + \hat{r}_N(h_N),
\end{aligned}$$

where $r_i(h_i) = o(h_i)$. Further, write the terms in the last equation as

$$D_{\omega_i}\xi_0(\dots) = D_{\omega_i}\xi_0(\omega)\underbrace{D_{\omega_i}\xi_0(\dots) - D_{\omega_i}\xi_0(\omega)}_{=:R_i(\mathbf{h})}.$$

Due to the continuity of the partial derivatives, we have $R_i(\mathbf{h}) \to 0$ as $h \to 0$. This shows

$$r_N(\mathbf{h^N}) = \sum_{j=-N}^{N-1} R_j(\mathbf{h})h_j + \sum_{j=-N}^{N} \hat{r}_j(h_j).$$

By Lemma C.40 and Remark C.41 both $\sum_{j=-N}^{N-1} |R_j(\mathbf{h})|$ and $\sum_{j=-N}^{N} \frac{|\hat{r}_j(h_j)|}{|h_j|}$ converge uniformly. So

$$\begin{aligned}\lim_{\|\mathbf{h}\|\to 0} \frac{r(\mathbf{h})}{\|\mathbf{h}\|} &\le \lim_{\|\mathbf{h}\|\to 0} \lim_{N\to\infty} \left(\sum_{j=-N}^{N-1} |R_j(\mathbf{h})| + \sum_{j=-N}^{N} \frac{|\hat{r}_j(h_j)|}{|h_j|} \right) \\ &= \lim_{N\to\infty} \lim_{\|\mathbf{h}\|\to 0} \left(\sum_{j=-N}^{N-1} |R_j(\mathbf{h})| + \sum_{j=-N}^{N} \frac{|\hat{r}_j(h_j)|}{|h_j|} \right) \\ &= 0.\end{aligned}$$

Next we turn to the estimate of the norm of the derivative $D_\omega\big(R_i(\omega)\big)_{i\in\mathbb{Z}}$. Of course

(C.194) $$\|D_\omega R_i(\omega)\| = \sum_{j\in\mathbb{Z}} |D_{\omega_j} R_i(\omega)| \le Ce^{3\alpha^s\Omega}.$$

The latter estimate results from (C.190) since $D_{\omega_j}R_i(\omega) = D_{\omega_j}\xi_i(\omega)$ for $j \neq i$. Since $\big(R_i(\omega)\big)_{i\in\mathbb{Z}}$ is considered as belonging to l^∞, we have

$$\|D_\omega\big(R_i(\omega)\big)_{i\in\mathbb{Z}}\| = \sup_{i\in\mathbb{Z}} \|D_\omega R_i(\omega)\| \le Ce^{3\alpha^s\Omega}.$$

The latter estimate results from (C.194) exploiting that C does not depend on i. Since $\alpha^s > \mu^s$ can be chosen arbitrarily close to μ^s the term $3\alpha^s$ can be rewritten in the form used in the proposition. □

C.5. Forward and backward Lin orbits

A study of orbits that stay near the homoclinic orbit for positive or negative time, and not necessarily for all time, proceeds through the notions of forward and backward Lin orbits. A forward Lin orbit $x^f = (x_i^f)_{i\in\mathbb{Z}^+}$ is indexed by $i \in \mathbb{Z}^+ = \mathbb{N}$ (the positive integers) whereas a backward Lin orbit $x^b = (x_i^b)_{i\in\mathbb{Z}_0^-}$ is indexed by $i \in \mathbb{Z}_0^- = -\mathbb{N}_0$ (the negative integers including zero). Such orbits are used in Appendix C.6.2 to determine the stable and unstable manifolds of periodic orbits ζ appearing in a neighborhood of a homoclinic orbit. There the forward orbit starts in a neighborhood of $\zeta(0) = \zeta \cap \Sigma$ and the backward orbit ends in a neighborhood of $\zeta(0) = \zeta \cap \Sigma$.

The existence of forward and backward Lin orbits is treated in the following two results.

Write P_{W^+} for the projection related to the direct sum decomposition (C.7) with $\operatorname{im} P_{W^+} = W^+$. The following proposition treats forward Lin orbits.

Proposition C.42. *There is an $\Omega > 0$, so that for each sequence $\omega = (\omega_i)_{i\in\mathbb{Z}^+}$ with $\inf_{i\in\mathbb{Z}^+} \omega_i > \Omega$, each $w_0^+ \in W^+$ and each λ with $|\lambda|$ sufficiently small, there is a unique sequence $(x_i^f)_{i\in\mathbb{Z}^+}$ of partial orbits x_i^f such that*

$$x_i^f(0), x_i^f(2\omega_i) \in \Sigma,$$
$$\Xi_i^f(\omega, \lambda, w_0^+) = x_{i+1}^f(0) - x_i^f(2\omega_i) \in Z,$$
$$P_{W^+}(x_1^f(0) - h_\lambda^s(0)) = w_0^+,$$

where $\Xi^f(\omega, \cdot, w_0^+)$ is differentiable.

Comparison reveals that the first two boundary conditions (here for $i \in \mathbb{Z}^+$) coincide with conditions describing Lin orbits; see Theorem C.1. In addition there is a boundary condition determining the forward Lin orbit at its starting point.

Reversing time brings the second proposition treating backward Lin orbits. Here P_{W^-} is the projection related to the direct sum decomposition (C.7) with $\operatorname{im} P_{W^-} = W^-$.

Proposition C.43. *There is an $\Omega > 0$, so that for each sequence $\omega = (\omega_i)_{i\in\mathbb{Z}_0^-}$ with $\inf_{i\in\mathbb{Z}_0^-} \omega_i > \Omega$, each $w_0^- \in W^-$, and each λ with $|\lambda|$ sufficiently small, there is a unique sequence $(x_i^b)_{i\in\mathbb{Z}_0^-}$ of partial orbits x_i^b such that*

$$x_i^b(0), x_i^b(2\omega_i) \in \Sigma,$$
$$\Xi_{i-1}^b(\omega, \lambda, w_0^-) = x_i^b(0) - x_{i-1}^b(2\omega_{i-1}) \in Z,$$
$$P_{W^-}(x_0^b(2\omega_0) - h_\lambda^u(0)) = w_0^-,$$

where $\Xi^b(\omega, \cdot, w_0^+)$ is differentiable.

These propositions are proved by adapting the construction of Lin orbits in Appendix C.4. Below we discuss the adaptations to prove Proposition C.42. By reversing time, the reasoning also proves Proposition C.43.

Proof of Proposition C.42. The proof runs parallel to that of the existence of Lin orbits, stated in Theorem C.1; see Appendix C.4.1. Here we confine to discuss the necessary adaptions. We follow again the outline presented at the beginning of Appendix C.3.1.2.

For a given sequence of transition times $\omega = (\omega_i)_{i\in\mathbb{N}}$, we define the space of sequences

$$\mathcal{V}^f_\omega = \Big\{\mathbf{v} = (v_0^+, ((v_i^+, v_i^-))_{i\in\mathbb{N}})\ ;$$
$$(v_i^+, v_i^-) \in C[0,\omega_{i+1}] \times C[-\omega_i, 0], \sup_{i\in\mathbb{N}_0} \|v_i^+\|, \sup_{i\in\mathbb{N}} \|v_i^-\| < \infty\Big\}.$$

Endowed with the norm

$$\|\mathbf{v}\| = \max\{\sup_{i\in\mathbb{N}_0} \|v_i^+\|, \sup_{i\in\mathbb{N}} \|v_i^-\|\},$$

where $\mathcal{V}^f_\omega$ is a Banach space.

For convenience we write x_i for x_i^f. With this we can copy most of the notation from Appendix C.4.1. Note that we consider the boundary conditions (C.150) and (C.151) only for $i \in \mathbb{N}$. Additionally we have an initial condition

$$P_{W^+}(x_1(0) - h^s_\lambda(0)) = P_{W^+}(x_0^+(0) - h^s_\lambda(0)) = w_0^+. \tag{C.195}$$

Write x_0^+ and $x_i^\pm$, $i \in \mathbb{N}$, in the form (C.152). For $x_i^\pm$ close to the homoclinic orbit and λ small, the $v_i^\pm$ will be close to zero. We prove that there are unique functions $v_i^\pm(\omega,\lambda)(\cdot)$ such that $x_i^\pm$ satisfy conditions (C.150), (C.151), for $i \in \mathbb{N}$ and (C.195). The functions $v_i^\pm$ solve the (nonlinear) variational equation (C.153) along $h^{s/u}_\lambda$, The conditions (C.150), (C.151), for $i \in \mathbb{N}$ and (C.195) translate to conditions that v_0^+ and $v_i^\pm$, $i \in \mathbb{N}$ must satisfy: (C.154)–(C.156) and

$$P_{W^+} v_0^+(0) = w_0^+. \tag{C.196}$$

To solve (C.153) with conditions (C.154)–(C.156) and (C.196), we proceed as in Appendix C.4.1. First we find a unique solution

$$\bar{\mathbf{v}}^f(\omega,\lambda,\mathbf{g},\mathbf{a},w_0^+) = \big(\bar v_0^+, (\bar v_i^+, \bar v_i^-)_{i\in\mathbb{N}}\big)$$

for the variational equation (C.157) with the boundary conditions (C.154), (C.156), (C.196), for $i \in \mathbb{N}_0$ or $i \in \mathbb{N}$, respectively. The involved sequences $\mathbf{g}$ and $\mathbf{a}$, are defined by $\mathbf{g} = \big(g_0^+, (g_i^+, g_i^-)_{i\in\mathbb{N}}\big)$ and $\mathbf{a} = (a_i^+, a_i^-)_{i\in\mathbb{N}}$. The (additional) dependence on w_0^+ (compared to $\bar{\mathbf{v}}$ obtained in Appendix C.4.1) is due to the initial condition (C.196). Note that only $v_0^+(0)$ depends on w_0^+. Together $\bar{\mathbf{v}}^f(\omega,\cdot,\cdot,\cdot,\cdot)$ maps $\mathbb{R} \times \mathcal{V}^f_\omega \times l^\infty(\mathbb{N},\mathbb{R}^n) \times W^+ \to \mathcal{V}^f_\omega$. The functions $\bar v_i^\pm$ that make up this map do not depend on the entire sequences $\mathbf{g}$ and $\mathbf{a}$. Moreover, $\bar v_i^\pm$ for $i \in \mathbb{N}$ does not depend on w_0^+. Indicating only relevant variables, we may write

$$\bar v_0^+(\cdot) = \bar v_0^+(\omega,\lambda,g_0^+,a_1^+,w_0^+)(\cdot),$$
$$\bar v_i^\pm(\cdot) = \bar v_i^\pm(\omega,\lambda,(g_i^+,g_i^-),(a_{i+1}^+,a_i^-))(\cdot).$$

As counterpart of (C.159) we find that the function $\bar{\mathbf{v}}^f(\omega, \lambda, \cdot, \cdot, \cdot)$ is linear and there exists a constant $\bar{C}$ such that

$$\|\bar{\mathbf{v}}^f(\omega, \lambda, \mathbf{g}, \mathbf{a}, w_0^+)\| \le \bar{C}(\|\mathbf{g}\| + \|\mathbf{a}\| + |w_0^+|).$$

The additional summand $|w_0^+|$ here is due to an estimate

$$|\operatorname{id} + P^+(\lambda, t)\bar{v}_0^+(t)| \le C(\|g_0^+\| + |w_0^+|).$$

Consider d_{i+1} as defined in (C.160) and write $\mathbf{d}(\omega, \lambda) = (d_i(\omega, \lambda))_{i\in\mathbb{N}}$. As for the derivation of (C.161) one shows that there exists $\mathbf{a}(\omega, \lambda, \mathbf{g}, \mathbf{d}, w_0^+)$ so that $\hat{\mathbf{v}}^f(\omega, \lambda, \mathbf{g}, \mathbf{d}, w_0^+)$ defined by

$$\hat{\mathbf{v}}^f(\omega, \lambda, \mathbf{g}, \mathbf{d}, w_0^+) = \bar{\mathbf{v}}^f(\omega, \lambda, \mathbf{g}, \mathbf{a}(\omega, \lambda, \mathbf{g}, \mathbf{d}, w_0^+), w_0^+) \tag{C.197}$$

solves (C.157) with boundary conditions (C.154)–(C.156) and (C.196), for $i \in \mathbb{N}_0$ or $i \in \mathbb{N}$, respectively. Differing from the considerations in Appendix C.4.1, **a** appears in an expression

$$\mathbf{a} = L_1(\lambda, \omega)\mathbf{a} + L_2(\lambda, \omega)\mathbf{g} + L_3(\lambda, \omega)\mathbf{d} + L_4(\lambda, \omega)w_0^+$$

for linear bounded operators $L_j(\lambda, \omega)(\cdot)$, $j = 1, 2, 3, 4$. Solving this fixed point equation provides a map $\hat{\mathbf{v}}^f(\omega, \cdot, \cdot, \cdot, \cdot) : \mathbb{R} \times V_\omega^f \times l^\infty(\mathbb{N}, \mathbb{R}^n) \times W^+ \to V_\omega^f$. It follows from the derivation that $\hat{\mathbf{v}}^f(\omega, \lambda, \cdot, \cdot, \cdot)$ is linear and that there exists a constant $\hat{C}$ such that

$$\|\hat{\mathbf{v}}^f(\omega, \lambda, \mathbf{g}, \mathbf{d}, w_0^+)\| \le \hat{C}(\|\mathbf{g}\| + \|\mathbf{d}\| + |w_0^+|).$$

The original boundary value problem (C.153) for functions $v_i^\pm$, $i \in \mathbb{N}_0$ or $i \in \mathbb{N}$, respectively, with boundary conditions (C.154)–(C.156) and (C.196), is now equivalent to a fixed point equation

$$\mathbf{v} = \mathcal{F}_\omega^f(\mathbf{v}, \lambda, w_0^+) \tag{C.198}$$

in V_ω^f, where

$$\mathcal{F}_\omega^f(\mathbf{v}, \lambda, w_0^+) = \hat{\mathbf{v}}^f(\omega, \lambda, \mathcal{H}(\mathbf{v}, \lambda), \mathbf{d}(\omega, \lambda), w_0^+),$$

with $\mathcal{H}(\mathbf{v}, \lambda) = (H_0^+(\mathbf{v}, \lambda), (H_i^+(\mathbf{v}, \lambda), H_i^-(\mathbf{v}, \lambda))_{i\in\mathbb{N}}$ and where $H_i^\pm$ is defined as in (C.166). Note that $\mathcal{H}$ is a mapping from $V_\omega^f \times \mathbb{R}$ to V_ω^f.

Parallel to the procedure in Appendix C.4.1 we find a unique solution $\mathbf{v}^f(\omega, \lambda, w_0^+)$ to equation (C.198) by applying the uniform contraction theorem. The estimate (C.167) is replaced by

$$\begin{aligned}\|\mathcal{F}_\omega(\mathbf{v}, \lambda, w_0^+)\| &= \|\hat{\mathbf{v}}(\omega, \lambda, \mathcal{H}(\mathbf{v}, \lambda), \mathbf{d}(\omega, \lambda), w_0^+)\| \\ &\le \hat{C}(\|\mathcal{H}\| + \|\mathbf{d}\| + |w_0^+|).\end{aligned}$$

The rest follows as in the proof of Lemma C.24. This also shows that the solution $\mathbf{v}^f(\omega, \cdot, \cdot)$ of (C.198) is continuously differentiable. □

Remark C.44. One can prove Theorem C.1 by showing that for each sequence $(\omega_i)_{i\in\mathbb{Z}}$ there are unique w_0^+ and w_0^- such that the forward and backward Lin orbits $(x_i^f)_{i\in\mathbb{Z}^+}$ and $(x_i^b)_{i\in\mathbb{Z}_0^-}$ satisfy $x_0^b(2\omega_0) - x_1^f(0) \in Z$. Then $(x_i)_{i\in\mathbb{Z}}$ with

$$x_i = \begin{cases} x_i^b, & i \in \mathbb{Z}_0^-, \\ x_i^f, & i \in \mathbb{Z}^+, \end{cases}$$

is the Lin orbit related to $(\omega_i)_{i\in\mathbb{Z}}$. That is, as an alternative to the direct construction in Appendix C.4.1, one could construct forward and backward Lin orbits and couple them to obtain Lin orbits.

Theorem C.1 is then proved by showing that for given $\omega = (\omega_i)_{i\in\mathbb{Z}}$ there are uniquely defined forward and backward Lin orbits $\hat{\mathbf{v}}^f(\omega^f, \lambda, w_0^+)$ and $\hat{\mathbf{v}}^b(\omega^b, \lambda, w_0^-)$ such that

$$v_0^{f,+}(\omega^f, \lambda, w_0^+)(0) - v_0^{b,-}(\omega^b, \lambda, w_0^-)(0) \in Z. \tag{C.199}$$

Here we used shorthand notation ω^f for $(\omega_i)_{i\in\mathbb{Z}^+}$ and ω^b for $(\omega_i)_{i\in\mathbb{Z}_0^-}$. Since

$$P_{W^+} v_0^{f,+}(\omega^f, \lambda, w_0^+)(0) = w_0^+,$$
$$P_{W^-} v_0^{b,-}(\omega^b, \lambda, w_0^-)(0) = w_0^-,$$

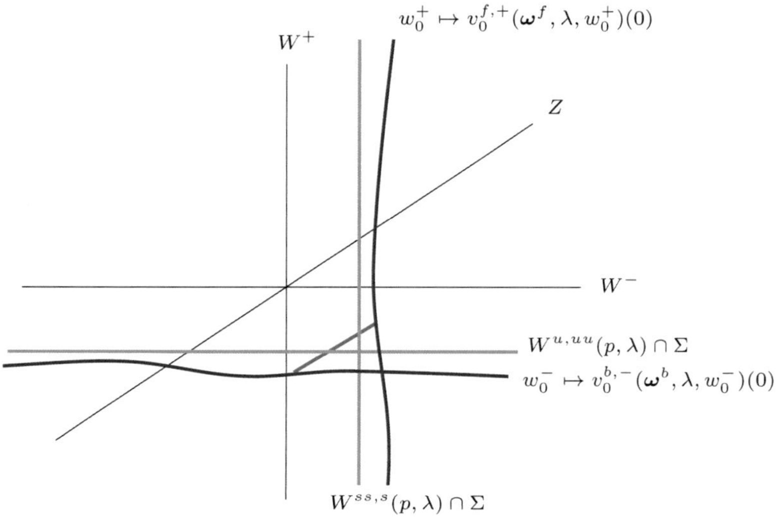

Figure C.5. For Ω large, the traces of $w_0^+ \mapsto v_0^{f,+}(\omega^f, \lambda, w_0^+)(0)$ and $w_0^- \mapsto v_0^{b,-}(\omega^b, \lambda, w_0^-)(0)$ are close to $W^{ss,s}(p,\lambda)\cap\Sigma$ and $W^{u,uu}(p,\lambda)\cap\Sigma$, respectively. Their projections to $W^+ \oplus W^-$ along Z therefore intersect transversely, which implies the coupling needed to prove Theorem C.1.

showing (C.199) is equivalent to showing that there are w_0^+, w_0^- with

$$w_0^- = P_{W^-} v_0^{f,+}(\omega^f, \lambda, w_0^+)(0),$$
$$w_0^+ = P_{W^+} v_0^{b,-}(\omega^b, \lambda, w_0^-)(0).$$

The latter system of equations can form a fixed point equation for (w_0^-, w_0^+) and can be solved by means of the uniform contraction theorem. A geometrical explanation is illustrated in Figure C.5. ■

C.6. Bifurcation analysis with Lin's method

C.6.1. Existence of 1-periodic orbits. Here we study the codimension-1 homoclinic bifurcation with simple real leading eigenvalues, using Lin's method. This bifurcation was treated in Section 4.1.2 using an analysis with cross coordinates.

So we take the context of Section 4.1.2 and of Appendix C.1: a nondegenerate homoclinic orbit with no-orbit-flip and no-inclination-flip conditions and a nonvanishing saddle quantity. We will show how to obtain the bifurcation theorem (see Theorem 4.14) using Lin's method. We copy the statement here. For the saddle quantity we assume $\mu^s + \mu^u > 0$, which is opposite of the condition in Theorem 4.14, but the same as assumed in Appendix C.1. Recall that a change of the direction of time brings one case to the other.

From the bifurcation equations derived in Lin's method, it is straightforward to prove the creation of a periodic orbit from the homoclinic bifurcation.

Theorem C.45. *Let*

$$\dot{x} = f_\lambda(x) = f(x, \lambda) \tag{C.200}$$

be a smooth family of vector fields on $\mathbb{R}^n$*, depending on a real parameter* $\lambda \in \mathbb{R}$*. Assume that for* $\lambda = 0$ *there is a hyperbolic saddle equilibrium* p *and* $Df_0(p)$ *has simple real leading eigenvalues* μ^s, μ^u *with* $\mu^s < 0 < \mu^u$ *and a homoclinic orbit* $h(t)$ *with*

$$\lim_{t\to\infty} h(t) = \lim_{t\to-\infty} h(t) = p.$$

Assume assumptions (i), …, (v) *from page* 393*: a positive saddle quantity* $\mu^s + \mu^u > 0$*, a nondegenerate homoclinic orbit with no-orbit-flip and no-inclination-flip condition, and a generic unfolding condition.*

Then there exists $\delta > 0, \varepsilon > 0$ *so that for* $\lambda \in (0, \delta)$ *(or* $\lambda \in (-\delta, 0)$*, depending on the sign of* $\mathcal{E}^s(0)$*) there is a periodic orbit* $\zeta_\lambda(t)$ *of* (C.200) *of period* $T(\lambda)$ *such that* $T(\lambda)$ *goes to infinity as* $\lambda \to 0$ *and* ζ_λ *approaches* h *as* $\lambda \to 0$*. Furthermore, if* $\mathcal{U}$ *denotes the* ε *neighborhood of* h*, then* ζ_λ *is the unique periodic orbit in* $\mathcal{U}$ *for* $\lambda \in (0, \delta)$ *(or* $\lambda \in (-\delta, 0)$*, respectively). There is no periodic orbit in* $\mathcal{U}$ *for* $\lambda \in (-\delta, 0)$ *(or* $\lambda \in [0, \delta)$*, respectively).*

Proof using Lin's method. As discussed, Lin's method provides bifurcation equations for orbits, where orbits near h are determined by a sequence $\omega = (\omega_i)_{i\in\mathbb{Z}}$ of times that are related to the transition times from a cross section Σ back to itself. The bifurcation equation

$$\Xi(\omega, \lambda) = 0$$

with $\Xi(\omega, \lambda) = (\Xi_i(\omega, \lambda))_{i\in\mathbb{Z}}$, is provided by Theorem C.3.

We will now focus on the creation of 1-periodic orbits in the homoclinic bifurcation, where 1-periodic orbits are periodic orbits following the homoclinic loop just once before closing, thus intersecting a cross section transverse to the homoclinic orbit once. These result as special 1-periodic Lin orbits, namely those for which the jump $\Xi(\omega, \lambda)$ is equal to zero. For 1-periodic orbits, by Corollary C.2, the bifurcation equation $\Xi(\omega, \lambda) = 0$ becomes a single equation depending on a one-dimensional real variable ω, also written as

$$\Xi(\omega, \lambda) = 0.$$

This is regardless of the dimension of the state space. By Corollary C.16 this single equation has an expression

$$\Xi(\omega, \lambda) = \lambda - e^{2\mu^s(\lambda)\omega}\mathcal{E}^s(\lambda) + \mathcal{O}\left(e^{2\mu^s(\lambda)\delta\omega}\right) = 0, \tag{C.201}$$

where $\delta > 1$, and where 2ω is the period of the periodic orbit.

A transformation $(\omega, \lambda) \mapsto (r, \lambda)$ given by

$$r(\omega, \lambda) = e^{2\mu^s(\lambda)\omega}, \qquad \omega(r, \lambda) = \frac{1}{2\mu^s(\lambda)} \ln r,$$

brings (C.201) to an equation

$$\chi(r, \lambda) = \Xi(\omega(r, \lambda), \lambda) = \lambda - r\mathcal{E}^s(\lambda) + \mathcal{O}\left(r^\delta\right) = 0. \tag{C.202}$$

For $r > 0$ the function χ is differentiable with respect to r and

$$D_r\chi(r, \lambda) = D_\omega\Xi(\omega(r, \lambda), \lambda)D_r\omega(r, \lambda) = D_\omega\Xi(\omega(r, \lambda), \lambda)\frac{1}{2\mu^s(\lambda)r}.$$

The higher order term $\mathcal{O}\left(r^\delta\right)$ can be differentiated, and Corollary C.16 shows that the derivative with respect to r gives a term $\mathcal{O}\left(r^{\delta-1}\right)$. As $\delta - 1 > 0$, $\chi(r, \lambda)$ and $D_r\chi(r, \lambda)$ can both be continued continuously to $r = 0$.

The bifurcation equation (C.202) can be treated just as the corresponding equation $y = \Pi(y, \lambda)$ in the proof of Theorem 4.3; see page 192. Depending on the sign of $\mathcal{E}^s(\lambda)$, this equation has a unique solution $r = r^*(\lambda)$ for either $\lambda > 0$ or $\lambda < 0$. The graph of $\frac{1}{\mathcal{E}^s(\lambda)}\left(\lambda + \mathcal{O}\left(r^\delta\right)\right)$ and its fixed points are depicted in Figure C.6. Compare Figure 4.7 illustrating the proof of Theorem 4.3. Since the analysis whose graphical interpretation is depicted in Figure C.6 is based on the contraction principle, the resulting periodic orbit is unique.

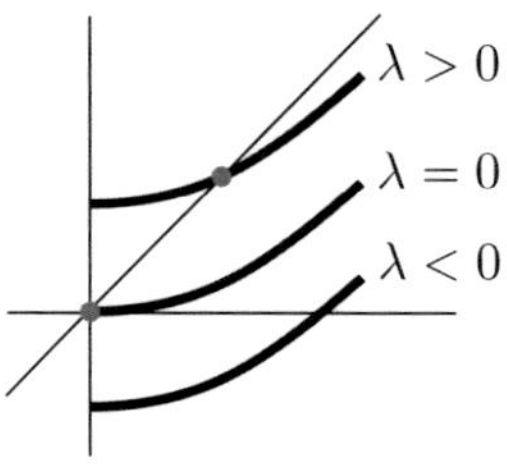

Figure C.6. Drawn are the graphs of $\frac{1}{\mathcal{E}^s(\lambda)}(\lambda + \mathcal{O}(r^\delta))$ and its fixed points in case $\mathcal{E}^s(\lambda) > 0$. The green point corresponds to a periodic orbit while the blue one corresponds to the original homoclinic orbit.

Of course, if the signs of λ and $\mathcal{E}^s(\lambda)$ differ, then (C.202) cannot have any solution (for sufficiently small $r > 0$). Therefore there are no periodic orbits for those λ. □

We emphasize that the bifurcation equation (C.202) is not related to a corresponding Poincaré return map. So we cannot infer the stability of the periodic orbit from the slope of $\frac{1}{\mathcal{E}^s(\lambda)}(\lambda + \mathcal{O}(r^\delta))$ (in its fixed point). Stability and hyperbolicity of the periodic orbit is studied separately in Appendix C.6.2.

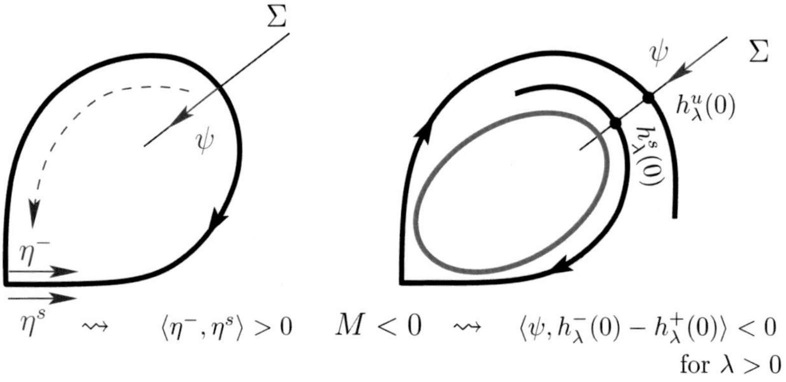

Figure C.7. The statement of Theorem C.45 in the case $M < 0$.

Remark C.46. Suppose the differential equation is in $\mathbb{R}^2$, choose ψ as the quantity $\eta(0)$ in Figure 4.5 ($\eta(0)$ used in Theorem 4.3 and ψ, which spans Z, are basically the same quantity). Assume $M < 0$.

The choice of ψ results in $\mathcal{E}^s > 0$; see the left panel of Figure C.7. The proof of Theorem C.45 shows that there exist periodic orbits for $\lambda > 0$. Because of $M < 0$, the stable and unstable manifolds (of the equilibrium) have a mutual position as depicted in the right panel of Figure C.7. The periodic orbits are unstable, a proof of this based on Lin's method will be given in Appendix C.6.2. ■

C.6.2. Stability analysis. Theorem C.45 provides a periodic orbit ζ_λ bifurcating from a codimension-1 homoclinic orbit with real leading eigenvalues. In this section we continue our study from Appendix C.6.1 by constructing the local stable and unstable manifolds of the periodic orbit ζ_λ. The concept of forward and backward Lin orbits allows us to construct these local stable and unstable manifolds. To some extent we reprove the results of Section 4.1.2.5 by means of Lin's method.

C.6.2.1. *Forward and backward orbits near a periodic orbit.* By Proposition C.43 the determination equation for backward orbits reads

$$\Xi^b(\omega,\lambda,w_0^-) = \left(\Xi_{i-1}^b(\omega,\lambda,w_0^-)\right)_{i\in\mathbb{Z}_0^-} = 0, \tag{C.203}$$

As in Theorem C.3, it has expressions of the form

$$\begin{aligned}\langle\psi,\Xi_{i-1}^b&(\omega,\lambda,w_0^-)\rangle\\ &= \lambda - e^{2\mu^s(\lambda)\omega_{i-1}}\mathcal{E}^s(\lambda) + e^{-2\mu^u(\lambda)\omega_i}\mathcal{E}^u(\lambda) + R_{i-1}(\omega,\lambda,w_0^-).\end{aligned}$$

This follows in the same way as the representations of the jump in Theorem C.3. Let a sufficiently small $\lambda > 0$ be fixed. According to Theorem C.45 there exits a unique periodic orbit ζ_λ. Write $w_p^-(\lambda) = P_{W^-}(\zeta_\lambda(0) - h_\lambda^u(0))$, compare Proposition C.43. Since ζ_λ can be considered a backward Lin orbit with jumps equal to zero, (C.203) has a solution (ω_p^-, w_p^-), where ω_p^- denotes the constant sequence $(\omega_p)_{i\in\mathbb{Z}_0^-}$, and $2\omega_p$ is the minimal period of ζ_λ. We show that near $(\omega, w_0^-) = (\omega_p^-, w_p^-)$ the above determination equation (C.203) can be solved for $(\omega_i)_{i\in\mathbb{Z}^-}$ depending on (ω_0, w_0^-). For the verification we assume $\mathcal{E}^s(\lambda) > 0$ (compare Remark C.46). It is convenient to work with transformed variables. Define the parameter dependent transformation $\omega(\hat{\mathbf{r}},\lambda)$ with $\omega = (\omega_i)_{i\in\mathbb{Z}_0^-}$ and $\hat{\mathbf{r}} = (\hat{r}_i)_{i\in\mathbb{Z}_0^-}$ by

$$\hat{r}_i = e^{2\mu^s(\lambda)\omega_i}. \tag{C.204}$$

For an appropriate $\delta > 1$ we find

$$\langle\psi,\Xi_{i-1}^b(\omega(\hat{\mathbf{r}},\lambda),\lambda,w_0^-)\rangle = \lambda - \hat{r}_{i-1}\mathcal{E}^s(\lambda) + \mathcal{O}(\hat{r}_i^\delta).$$

We continue with a singular rescaling. Write $\hat{r}_i = \lambda r_i$ and $\mathbf{r} = (r_i)_{i\in\mathbb{Z}_0^-}$. So $\hat{\mathbf{r}} = \lambda\mathbf{r}$ and

$$\langle\psi,\Xi_{i-1}^b(\omega(\lambda\mathbf{r},\lambda),\lambda,w_0^-)\rangle = \lambda - \lambda r_{i-1}\mathcal{E}^s(\lambda) + \mathcal{O}(\lambda^\delta)$$

as $\lambda\to 0$. For $\lambda > 0$ we divide by λ and find that the equation $\Xi^b(\mathbf{r},\lambda,w_0^-) = 0$ is equivalent to $\chi(\mathbf{r},\lambda,w_0^-) = 0$ with $\chi(\mathbf{r},\lambda,w_0^-) = (\chi_{i-1}(\mathbf{r},\lambda,w_0^-))_{i\in\mathbb{Z}_0^-}$ and

$$\chi_{i-1}(\mathbf{r},\lambda,w_0^-) = 1 - r_{i-1}\mathcal{E}^s(\lambda) + \mathcal{O}(\lambda^{\delta-1}). \tag{C.205}$$

This way ω_p translates into r_p, $r_p(0) = 1/\mathcal{E}^s(0)$. Let $\mathbf{r}_p(\lambda)$ be the constant sequence $(r_p(\lambda))_{i\in\mathbb{Z}_0^-}$. For fixed small λ the equation $\chi(\mathbf{r},\lambda,w_0^-) = 0$ can be solved, near $(\mathbf{r}_p(\lambda), \lambda, w_p^-)$, for $(r_i)_{i\in\mathbb{Z}^-}$ depending on r_0 and w_0^-. For this we consider χ as an operator

$$\chi : l^\infty \times \mathbb{R} \times \mathbb{R} \to l^\infty.$$

Clearly, $\chi(\mathbf{r}_p(\lambda), \lambda, w_p^-) = 0$, and by construction χ is smooth for $r_i > 0, i \in \mathbb{Z}_0^-$ and $\lambda > 0$. The differentiability of the map χ follows as in Appendix C.4.3. Furthermore, there is a differentiable extension to $\lambda \leq 0$ as long as the r_i stay away from zero—recall that $r_p(0) = 1/\mathcal{E}^s(0) \neq 0$. From (C.205) we infer that

$$D_{(r_i)_{i\in\mathbb{Z}^-}}\chi(\mathbf{r}_p(0), 0, 0) = -\mathcal{E}^s(0)\,\mathrm{id}$$

is invertible. By Proposition C.5 the linear operator

$$D_{(r_i)_{i\in\mathbb{Z}^-}}\chi(\mathbf{r}_p(\lambda), \lambda, w_p^-(\lambda))$$

is still invertible for sufficiently small positive λ. So $\chi(\mathbf{r}, \lambda, w_0^-) = 0$ can be solved using the implicit function theorem.

We summarize the results so far in the following lemma.

Lemma C.47. *Fix $\lambda > 0$ sufficiently small. For each (r_0, w_0^-) taken from a sufficiently small neighborhood of $(r_p(\lambda), w_p^-(\lambda))$ there is a unique backward orbit $x^b(\lambda)$ with $P_{W^-}(x_0^b(\lambda)(2\omega_0(\lambda)) - h_\lambda^u(0)) = w_0^-$, where $e^{2\mu^s(\lambda)\omega_0(\lambda)} = \lambda r_0$.*

Of course $x_0^b(\cdot) = x_0^b(\omega_0, w_0^-)(\cdot)$. We find that $x_0^b(\omega_0, w_0^-)(2\omega_0)$ parametrizes a submanifold M^u of Σ in a neighborhood of $\zeta_\lambda(0)$,

$$M^u = \left\{x_0^b(\omega_0, w_0^-)(2\omega_0)\ ;\ \omega_0 \text{ sufficiently large, } w_0^- \in W^-\right\}, \tag{C.206}$$

of dimension

$$\dim M^u = 1 + \dim W^-.$$

The existence of forward Lin orbits is studied similarly based on Proposition C.42. This leads to an equation $\Xi^f(\omega, \lambda, w_0^+) = 0$ for forward orbits, with $\Xi^f(\omega, \lambda, w_0^+) = \left(\Xi_i^f(\omega, \lambda, w_0^+)\right)_{i\in\mathbb{N}}$ and

$$\Xi_i^f(\omega, \lambda, w_0^+) = \lambda - e^{2\mu^s(\lambda)\omega_i}\mathcal{E}^s(\lambda) + e^{-2\mu^u(\lambda)\omega_{i+1}}\mathcal{E}^u(\lambda) + R_i(\omega, \lambda, w_0^+);$$

see again Theorem C.3. This equation can be treated in the same way as the equation for backward orbits. Near $(\omega, w_0^+) = (\omega_p^+, 0)$, the equation $\Xi^f(\omega, \lambda, w_0^+) = 0$ can be solved for $\omega = (\omega_i)_{i\in\mathbb{N}}$ depending on λ and w_0^+. We may therefore write $x_1^f(\cdot) = x_1^f(w_0^+)(\cdot)$. Here we find that $x_1^f(w_0^+)(0)$ parametrizes a submanifold M^s of Σ in a neighborhood of $\zeta_\lambda(0)$,

$$M^s = \left\{x_1^f(w_0^+)(0)\ ;\ \omega_0 \text{ sufficiently large, } w_0^+ \in W^+\right\}. \tag{C.207}$$

We have

$$\dim M^s = \dim W^+.$$

Note that both manifolds M^u and M^s depend on λ, which we have not included in the notation.

C.6.2.2. *Local stable and unstable manifolds.* The next proposition makes clear that the manifolds M^u and M^s from (C.206), (C.207) are the intersections with Σ of the local stable and unstable manifolds of the periodic orbit ζ_λ.

Proposition C.48. *Fix $\lambda > 0$ sufficiently small. Let $x \in M^s$. Then (with a slight abuse of notation, we use the symbol ω_p both for the sequence and the value that makes up the sequence) the ω-limit set $\omega(x) = \zeta_\lambda$. And similarly, for $x \in M^u$ the α-limit set $\alpha(x) = \zeta_\lambda$. Note that $\zeta_\lambda \dots$ is the minimal period of ζ_λ.*

The remainder of this section contains the proof of the above proposition. We only prove the statement regarding M^s. The proof of the remaining part follows the same pattern.

In what follows we prove that M^s is the local stable manifold of ζ_λ, that is, that points on it converge to ζ_λ when iterating. Fix some small $\lambda > 0$. We have an equation for forward orbits of the form

$$\chi(\mathbf{r}, \lambda, w_0^+) = 0, \tag{C.208}$$

where $\chi(\mathbf{r}, \lambda, w_0^+) = (\chi_{i-1}(\mathbf{r}, \lambda, w_0^+))_{i\in\mathbb{N}}$ and

$$\chi_i(\mathbf{r}, \lambda, w_0^+) = 1 - r_i\mathcal{E}^s(\lambda) + \mathcal{O}(\lambda^{\delta-1}),$$

$i \in \mathbb{N}$, for a $\delta > 1$.

A solution $\omega = \omega(\lambda, w_0^+)$ to $\Xi^f(\omega, \lambda, w_0^+) = 0$ yields a forward orbit $x(\lambda, w_0^+)(\cdot)$ with $x(\lambda, w_0^+)(0)$ in M^s. Note that ζ_λ corresponds to a solution ω_p that is a constant sequence (ω_p), where $2\omega_p$ is the minimal period of ζ_λ (with a slight abuse of notation, we use the symbol ω_p both for the sequence and the value that makes up the sequence). This provides a constant forward orbit $x(\lambda, w_p^+)(\cdot)$. For the proof we show that

$$\lim_{N\to\infty} x(\lambda, w_0^+)\left(\sum_{i=1}^{N} 2\omega_i\right) = x(\lambda, w_p^+)(0).$$

If we regard the forward orbit $x(\lambda, w_0^+)(\cdot)$ as a forward Lin orbit (where the jumps are zero), then the latter limit can be written as $\lim_{i\to\infty} x_i(\lambda, w_0^+)(0) = x(\lambda, w_p^+)(0)$, and if we regard $x(\lambda, w_p^+)(\cdot)$ accordingly, the above limit reads

$$\lim_{i\to\infty} |x_i(\lambda, w_0^+)(0) - x_i(\lambda, w_p^+)(0)| = 0.$$

In accordance with (C.152) the addressed limit is equivalent to

$$\lim_{i\to\infty} |v_i^+(\omega, \lambda, w_0^+)(0) - v_i^+(\omega_p, \lambda, w_p^+)(0)| = 0. \tag{C.209}$$

Here $\omega = \omega(\lambda, w_0^+)$, and ω_p denotes the constant sequence (ω_p), where $2\omega_p$ is the minimal period of ζ_λ. Note that the verification of (C.209) proves Proposition C.48 for the stable manifold.

In what follows we drop the dependence on λ. To study the limit (C.209), we write

$$\text{(C.210)}\quad \begin{aligned}&|v_i^+(\omega, w_0^+)(0) - v_i^+(\omega_p, w_p^+)(0)|\\ &\quad\le |v_i^+(\omega, w_0^+)(0) - v_i^+(\omega, w_p^+)(0)| + |v_i^+(\omega, w_p^+)(0) - v_i^+(\omega_p, w_p^+)(0)|.\end{aligned}$$

We show that both summands on the right-hand side tend to zero as $i \to \infty$. The first summand will be considered in the subsequent Lemma C.49. Further we use this lemma also to prove that $\omega_i \to \omega_p$ as i tends to infinity; see Corollary C.50. Afterward we use this result to study the remaining summand; see proof of Lemma C.52.

The following lemma bounds the first term on the right-hand side of (C.210).

Lemma C.49.

$$\lim_{i\to\infty} |v_i(\omega, w_0^+)(0) - v_i(\omega, w_p)(0)| = 0.$$

Proof. The proof is based on the same idea as for the proof of Lemma C.39. Here however we will work strictly in the context of forward orbits. The sequences of transition times coincide in the v-sequences to be compared, but the v-sequences depend on different w-values. In our notation we drop the upper index f and the dependence on λ.

Let, for given $w \in W^+$, $\mathbf{v}(\omega, w)$ be the unique solution of the fixed point equation (C.198). That is,

$$\mathbf{v}(\omega, w) = \hat{\mathbf{v}}(\omega, \mathcal{H}(\mathbf{v}(\omega, w)), \mathbf{d}(\omega), w) =: \mathcal{F}_\omega(\mathbf{v}(\omega, w), w).$$

Since $\hat{\mathbf{v}}(\omega, \cdot, \cdot, \cdot)$ is linear, we find that $\Delta\mathbf{v} = \mathbf{v}(\omega, w_0^+) - \mathbf{v}(\omega, w_p)$ satisfies

$$\begin{aligned}\Delta\mathbf{v} &= \hat{\mathbf{v}}(\omega, \Delta\mathcal{H}, 0, \Delta w)\\ &= \bar{\mathbf{v}}(\omega, \Delta\mathcal{H}, \mathbf{a}(\omega, \Delta\mathcal{H}, 0, \Delta w), \Delta w);\end{aligned}$$

see (C.197) for the latter equality. Here $\Delta\mathcal{H} = \mathcal{H}(\mathbf{v}(\omega, w_0^+)) - \mathcal{H}(\mathbf{v}(\omega, w_p))$ and $\Delta w = w_0^+ - w_p$. Recall from (C.155) that $\mathbf{d}$ depends only on ω. Denote $\Delta\mathbf{a} = \mathbf{a}(\omega, \Delta\mathcal{H}, 0, \Delta w)$.

In the same way as in the proof of Lemma C.39 we find for $i \ge 2$,

$$|\Delta v_i^\pm| \le C(|\Delta a_{i+1}^+| + |\Delta a_i^-|).$$

Again, by the same arguments as in the proof of Lemma C.39 this leads to

$$|\Delta a_i^+| + |\Delta a_i^-| \le \frac{1}{4}(|\Delta a_{i+1}^+| + |\Delta a_{i-1}^-|),$$

for $i \ge 2$. Lemma 4.28 provides the counterpart of (C.188),

$$|\Delta a_i^-| \le \frac{1}{2^{i-1}}\left(|\Delta a_1^-| + |\Delta a_{2i}^+|\right).$$

An analogous estimate can be obtained for $|\Delta a^+_{i+1}|$. Estimating $|\Delta a^-_1| + |\Delta a^+_{2i}|$ by $||\Delta \mathbf{a}||$ yields the lemma. □

Recall that $\omega = \omega(\lambda, w^+_0)$ is a solution to $\Xi^f(\omega, \lambda, w^+_0) = 0$.

Corollary C.50. *Let $\omega(\lambda, w^+_0) = (\omega_i)_{i\in\mathbb{N}}$, and let $2\omega_p$ be the period of the periodic orbit ζ_λ. Then $\lim_{i\to\infty} \omega_i = \omega_p$.*

Proof. We give the proof in terms of the transformed quantities $\mathbf{r}$. Recall that ω and $\mathbf{r}$ are related by the transformation (C.204) and $\hat{r}_i = \lambda r_i$. The corresponding $\mathbf{r}$ sequences are the result of equation (C.208). Write $\chi_i(\mathbf{r}, w) = 0$ as the fixed point equation

$$r_i = F_i(\mathbf{r}, w).$$

Note that the terms $\chi_i(\mathbf{r}, w^+_0)$ appearing in (C.208) are nothing else but the jumps Ξ_i written in the new coordinates. Together with (C.151) and (C.152) we obtain from Lemma C.49 that

$$\lim_{i\to\infty} |F_i(\mathbf{r}, w) - F_i(\mathbf{r}, w_p)| = 0, \tag{C.211}$$

and that moreover this limit is uniform in w.

Consider the fixed points $\mathbf{r}(w)$ and $\mathbf{r}_p$ of $\mathbf{F}(\cdot, w)$ and $\mathbf{F}(\cdot, w_p)$. These are related to the transition times r_i of the forward orbit defined by w and the periodic orbit under consideration. We define further $\mathbf{F}^N = (F_i)_{i\geq N}$ and correspondingly $\mathbf{r}^N$. By construction, for each N there a $w^N \in W^+$ such that

$$\mathbf{r}^N = \mathbf{F}^N(\mathbf{r}^N, w^N).$$

Since $\mathbf{r}_p$ is a constant sequence, $\mathbf{r}^N_p = \mathbf{F}^N(\mathbf{r}^N_p, w_p)$ is vacuously true.

Now there is $q \in (0, 1)$, independent on w^N, such that

$$\begin{aligned} ||\mathbf{r}^N - \mathbf{r}^N_p|| &= ||\mathbf{F}^N(\mathbf{r}^N, w^N) - \mathbf{F}^N(\mathbf{r}^N_p, w_p)|| \\ &\leq ||\mathbf{F}^N(\mathbf{r}^N, w^N) - \mathbf{F}^N(\mathbf{r}^N_p, w^N)|| + ||\mathbf{F}^N(\mathbf{r}^N_p, w^N) - \mathbf{F}^N(\mathbf{r}^N_p, w_p)|| \\ &\leq q||\mathbf{r}^N - \mathbf{r}^N_p|| + ||\mathbf{F}^N(\mathbf{r}^N_p, w^N) - \mathbf{F}^N(\mathbf{r}^N_p, w_p)||. \end{aligned}$$

Hence there is a $C > 0$ such that

$$|r_N - r_p| = |r^N_N - r_p| \leq ||\mathbf{r}^N - \mathbf{r}^N_p|| \leq C||\mathbf{F}^N(\mathbf{r}^N_p, w^N) - \mathbf{F}^N(\mathbf{r}^N_p, w_p)|| \to 0,$$

as $N \to \infty$. The latter limit is due to (C.211). □

Before bounding the second term on the right-hand side of (C.210) in Lemma C.52 below, we present a generalization of Lemma 4.28.

Lemma C.51. *Let $(a^\pm_i)_{i\in\mathbb{Z}}$ be a sequence of positive numbers such that for all $j \in \mathbb{Z}$*

$$a^-_j + a^+_j \leq \frac{1}{2q}(a^-_{j-1} + a^+_{j+1}) + d,$$

for some $q > 1$ and some d. Then there is a constant $C > 0$ such that for any i

$$a_j^- + a_j^+ \leq \frac{1}{q^i}(a_{j-i}^- + a_{j+i}^+) + Cd.$$

Proof. We follow the pattern as in the proof of Lemma 4.28. First we prove by induction on i that

$$(a_{j-i}^- + a_{j+i}^+) + (a_{j-i}^+ + a_{j+i}^-) \leq \frac{1}{q}(a_{j-i-1}^- + a_{j+i+1}^+) + \frac{4q}{q-1}d. \tag{C.212}$$

Let $i = 0$. By the assumption of the lemma we have

$$2(a_j^- + a_j^+) \leq \frac{1}{q}(a_{j-1}^- + a_{j+1}^+) + 2d.$$

Note that $2 < 4q/(q-1)$. Now assume that (C.212) holds true for some i. Again applying the assumption of the lemma, we obtain

$$\begin{aligned}
&(a_{j-i-1}^- + a_{j+i+1}^+) + (a_{j-i-1}^+ a_{j+i+1}^-)\\
&\leq \frac{1}{2q}(a_{j-i-2}^- + a_{j-i}^+) + \frac{1}{2q}(a_{j+i}^- + a_{j+i+2}^+) + 2d\\
&= \frac{1}{2q}(a_{j-i-2}^- + a_{j+i+2}^+) + \frac{1}{2q}(a_{j+i}^- + a_{j-i}^+) + 2d\\
&\leq \frac{1}{2q}(a_{j-i-2}^- + a_{j+i+2}^+) + \frac{1}{2q}\left((a_{j+i}^- + a_{j-i}^+) + (a_{j+i}^+ + a_{j-i}^-)\right) + 2d\\
&\leq \frac{1}{2q}(a_{j-i-2}^- + a_{j+i+2}^+) + \frac{1}{2q^2}(a_{j-i-1}^- + a_{j+i+1}^+) + \left(2 + \frac{1}{2q}\frac{4q}{q-1}\right)d.
\end{aligned}$$

Therefore

$$(1 - \frac{1}{2q^2})(a_{j-i-1}^- + a_{j+i+1}^+) + (a_{j-i-1}^+ + a_{j+i+1}^-) \leq \frac{1}{2q}(a_{j-i-2}^- + a_{j+i+2}^+) + \frac{2q}{q-1}d$$

and hence

$$(a_{j-i-1}^- + a_{j+i+1}^+) + (a_{j-i-1}^+ + a_{j+i+1}^-) \leq \frac{1}{q}(a_{j-i-2}^- + a_{j+i+2}^+) + \frac{4q}{q-1}d.$$

This finally proves (C.212). So, in particular

$$(a_{j-i}^- + a_{j+i}^+) \leq \frac{1}{q}(a_{j-i-1}^- + a_{j+i+1}^+) + \frac{4q}{q-1}d.$$

Repeatedly invoking the latter estimate yields

$$(a_j^- + a_j^+) \leq \frac{1}{q}(a_{j-1}^- + a_{j+1}^+) + \frac{4q}{q-1}d \leq \cdots \leq \frac{1}{q^i}(a_{j-i}^- + a_{j+i}^+) + \sum_{k=0}^{i-1}\frac{1}{q^k}\frac{4q}{q-1}d. \qquad \square$$

The following lemma bounds the second term on the right-hand side of (C.210).

Lemma C.52. *Let $\omega(\lambda, w_0^+) = (\omega_i)_{i\in\mathbb{N}}$, and let $2\omega_p$ be the period of the periodic orbit ζ_λ. Then $\lim_{i\to\infty} |v_i(\omega, w_p^+)(0) - v_i(\omega_p, w_p^+)(0)| = 0$.*

Proof. As for Lemma C.49 this proof is based on the idea of the proof of Lemma C.39. Still we will work in the context of forward orbits. In difference to Lemma C.49 the sequences of transition times differ while the w-values coincide. For that reason we have to start from (C.187) since the Δd_i do no longer vanish. In our notation we drop again the upper index f and the dependence on λ. Additionally we drop w_p^+ from the notation.

By Corollary C.50 we have $\omega_p = \lim_{i\to\infty} \omega_i$. That is, for for each $N \in \mathbb{N}$ there is an i_N such that

$$|\omega_i - \omega_p| \leq \frac{1}{N}, \tag{C.213}$$

for all $i \geq i_N - N$. Note that this estimate is true in particular for $i \in [i_N - N, i_N + N]$.

We may now proceed as in the proof of Lemma C.39, replacing v_0 by v_{i_N} up to (C.186),

$$|\Delta v_i^{\pm}| \leq C(|\Delta a_{i+1}^{+}| + |\Delta a_i^{-}|),$$

and further up to the counterpart of (C.187),

$$|\Delta a_i^{+}| + |\Delta a_i^{-}| \leq C|\Delta d_i| + \frac{1}{4}(|\Delta a_{i+1}^{+}| + |\Delta a_{i-1}^{-}|).$$

In greater detail, let $\tilde{\omega} = (\tilde{\omega}_i)$ with $\tilde{\omega}_i = \min\{\omega_i, \omega_p\}$, and $\mathbf{v}^{\mathbf{R}} = \mathbf{v}(\omega)|_{\tilde{\omega}}$ with

$$\begin{aligned} v_i^{R,+}(\cdot) &= v_i^{+}(\omega)(\cdot)|_{[0,\tilde{\omega}_i]}, \\ v_{i+1}^{R,-}(\cdot) &= v_{i+1}^{-}(\omega)(\cdot)|_{[-\tilde{\omega}_{i+1},0]}. \end{aligned}$$

Now consider $\Delta\mathbf{v} = \mathbf{v}^{\mathbf{R}} - \mathbf{v}(\tilde{\omega})$. Then $\Delta\mathbf{v} = (\Delta v_i)_{i\in\mathbb{Z}}$ and

$$\Delta v_i^{\pm}(t) = v_i^{R,\pm}(t) - v_i^{\pm}(\tilde{\omega})(t).$$

Define $\mathbf{d}^{\mathbf{R}} = (d_i^R)_{i\in\mathbb{N}}$ by $d_i^R = v_{i-1}^{+}(\omega)(\hat{\omega}_i) - v_i^{-}(\omega)(-\hat{\omega}_i)$ and write

$$\Delta\mathbf{d} = \mathbf{d}^{\mathbf{R}} - \mathbf{d}(\tilde{\omega}).$$

To make use of Lemma C.51 we analyze Δd_i. We find

$$\begin{aligned} d_{i+1}^R &= v_i^{+}(\omega)(\tilde{\omega}_{i+1}) - v_{i+1}^{-}(\omega)(-\tilde{\omega}_{i+1}) \\ &= v_i^{+}(\omega)(\omega_{i+1}) - v_{i+1}^{-}(\omega)(-\omega_{i+1}) \\ &\quad + (v_i^{+}(\omega)(\tilde{\omega}_{i+1}) - v_i^{+}(\omega)(\omega_{i+1})) \\ &\quad + (v_{i+1}^{-}(\omega)(-\omega_{i+1}) - v_{i+1}^{-}(\omega)(-\tilde{\omega}_{i+1})) \\ &= h^u(-\omega_{i+1}) - h^s(\omega_{i+1}) \\ &\quad + (v_i^{+}(\omega)(\tilde{\omega}_{i+1}) - v_i^{+}(\omega)(\omega_{i+1})) \\ &\quad + (v_{i+1}^{-}(\omega)(-\omega_{i+1}) - v_{i+1}^{-}(\omega)(-\tilde{\omega}_{i+1})). \end{aligned}$$

So

$$\begin{aligned}\Delta d_{i+1} &= d^R_{i+1} - d_{i+1}(\tilde{\omega}) \\ &= (h^u(-\omega_{i+1}) - h^u(-\tilde{\omega}_{i+1})) + (h^s(\tilde{\omega}_{i+1}) - h^s(\omega_{i+1})) \\ &\quad + \left(v_i^+(\omega)(\tilde{\omega}_{i+1}) - v_i^+(\omega)(\omega_{i+1})\right) \\ &\quad + \left(v_{i+1}^-(\omega)(-\omega_{i+1}) - v_{i+1}^-(\omega)(-\tilde{\omega}_{i+1})\right).\end{aligned}$$

The single summands on the right-hand side can be estimated by the mean value theorem. For this we exploit that $\dot{h}^{s/u}(t) = f(h^{s/u}(t))$ and

$$\dot{v}_i^{\pm}(t) = Df(h^{s/u}(t))v_i^{\pm}(t) + h^{\pm}(t, v_i^{\pm}(t)).$$

Together with (C.213) we get that there is a constant $C > 0$ such that

$$\Delta d_i \leq C\frac{1}{N},$$

where $i \in [i_N - N, i_N + N]$. Write $d = d(N) = C\frac{1}{N}$. Applying Lemma C.51 yields

$$|\Delta v_{i_N}| = \mathcal{O}\left(\frac{1}{N}\right).$$

This proves the lemma. □

C.6.3. Saddle-focus homoclinic orbits. Lin's method has also been developed for other cases than those with real leading eigenvalues, including complex conjugate leading eigenvalues [**206**] and semisimple leading eigenvalues [**169**]. Here we look at bifurcations from a saddle-focus homoclinic orbit, as considered earlier in Section 4.1.3. As usual we take a parameter-dependent differential equation

$$\dot{x} = f(x, \lambda), \quad x \in \mathbb{R}^n, \lambda \in \mathbb{R}.$$

We list further conditions on the system.

(i) For $\lambda = 0$ there is a hyperbolic saddle equilibrium p and $Df_0(p)$ has a simple nonreal leading stable eigenvalue

$$\mu^s + \phi^s\, i,$$

with $\mu^s < 0$ and $\phi^s \neq 0$, and a simple real leading unstable eigenvalue μ^u. It has a homoclinic orbit $h(t)$ with

$$\lim_{t\to\infty} h(t) = \lim_{t\to-\infty} h(t) = p.$$

For the saddle quantity we assume

$$\mu^s + \mu^u > 0.$$

Differing from Section 4.1.3, we do not restrict to three-dimensional state space. Instead we must assume a number of geometrical conditions which we list here.

(ii) The homoclinic orbit h is nondegenerate:

$$T_{h(0)}W^{ss,s}(p) \cap T_{h(0)}W^{u,uu}(p) = T_{h(0)}\mathrm{span}\,\{f(h(0))\}.$$

(iii) There is no inclination-flip:

$$W^{ss,s,u}(p) \pitchfork_h W^{u,uu}(p),$$
$$W^{s,u,uu}(p) \pitchfork_h W^{ss,s}(p).$$

(iv) The homoclinic orbit h approaches p along leading directions (no orbit-flip): there are η^s and η^u in the generalized real eigenspace X^s of $\mu^s + \phi^s i$ and in the eigenspace X^u of μ^u, respectively, such that

$$h(t) = e^{D_x f(p,0)t}\eta^s + \mathcal{O}(e^{\mu^s t\delta}), \quad \text{as} \quad t \to \infty,$$
$$h(t) = e^{D_x f(p,0)t}\eta^u + \mathcal{O}(e^{\mu^u t\delta}), \quad \text{as} \quad t \to -\infty.$$

Note that the latter condition is equivalent to $\lim_{t\to-\infty} \dot{h}(t)/\|\dot{h}(t)\| \in E^u$. We keep also the generic unfolding condition,

(v)

$$M = \int_{-\infty}^{\infty} \langle \eta(t), D_\lambda f(h(t), 0)\rangle\, dt \neq 0,$$

where η is a bounded solution of the adjoint variational equation $\dot{x} = -Df_0(h(t))^T x$ along h.

We use the notation for Lin's method introduced in Appendix C.1. First we formulate a theorem comprising the equivalents to Theorem C.3, Proposition C.4, and Proposition C.5.

Theorem C.53. *Under the assumptions of this section there is a smooth reparametrization of the parameter λ, so that the bifurcation equations*

$$\langle \psi, \Xi_i(\omega, \lambda)\rangle = 0$$

are given by

(C.214) $$\lambda + \mathcal{E}^{s,c}(\lambda)e^{2\mu^s\omega_i}\sin(2\phi^s\omega_i + \varphi^s) + R_i(\omega, \lambda) = 0,$$

for $i \in \mathbb{Z}$, where μ^s, ϕ^s, and φ^s depend on λ, and $\mathcal{E}^{s,c}(0) \neq 0$.

There is a $\delta > 1$ such that

$$R_i(\omega, \lambda) = \mathcal{O}(e^{2\mu^s\omega_i\delta}) + \mathcal{O}(e^{2\mu^s\omega_{i+1}\delta}) + \mathcal{O}(e^{2\alpha^s(\omega_{i-1}+\omega_i)}) + \mathcal{O}(e^{2\alpha^s(\omega_i+\omega_{i+1})}) + \mathcal{O}(e^{2\alpha^s(\omega_{i+1}+\omega_{i+2})}),$$

where $\alpha^s > \mu^s$ can be chosen arbitrarily close to μ^s.

The mapping $l^\infty \to l^\infty$, $\omega \mapsto (\langle \psi, \Xi_i(\omega, \lambda)\rangle)_{i\in\mathbb{Z}}$ is differentiable and for each $i \in \mathbb{Z}$ holds

$$D\xi_i(\omega)\mathbf{h} = \sum_{j\in\mathbb{Z}} D_{\omega_j}\xi_i(\omega)h_j.$$

Further, with Ω being a lower bound of $\omega \in l^\infty(\mathbb{Z}, \mathbb{R})$ the following estimates of the partial derivatives hold: there is a $\hat{\delta} < 0$ such that

$$D_{\omega_j}\langle \xi_i(\omega,\lambda),\psi\rangle = -D_{\omega_j} e^{2\mu^s(\lambda)\omega_i}\mathcal{E}^s(\lambda) + \mathcal{O}(e^{(2\mu^s(\lambda)+\hat{\delta})\Omega}).$$

Sketch of proof. We adopt the arguments in the proof of Theorem C.3. It remains to verify the specified leading order term

$$\mathcal{E}^{s,c}(\lambda)e^{2\mu^s(\lambda)\omega_i}\sin(2\phi^s\omega_i + \varphi^s).$$

The estimates of the higher order term can be copied word for word.

Recall that the leading order term is contained in

$$T_i^{21} = \langle \Psi^-(\lambda, -\omega_i, 0)(P^-(\lambda,0))^T\psi, (\mathrm{id} - \tilde{P}(\lambda,\omega_i))h_\lambda^s(\omega_i)\rangle.$$

We have to discuss the asymptotic behavior of $\Psi^-(\lambda,-\omega_i,0)(P^-(\lambda,0))^T\psi$ and of h^s; see (C.65) and (C.67). These in turn fall back on Lemma C.13 and Lemma C.14, which are formulated for real leading eigenvalues. However their statement and proofs can be adapted to complex leading eigenvalues. So we find $\eta^s \in E^s$ such that

$$h_\lambda^s(t) = e^{D_xf(p,\lambda)t}\eta^s(\lambda) + \mathcal{O}(e^{\mu^s t\delta})$$

for $t \geq 0$, and an $\eta^- \in (E^u)^\perp$ such that for $t \leq 0$

$$\Phi^-(\lambda,0,t)^T P^-(\lambda,0)^T\psi = e^{-D_xf(p,\lambda)^T t}\eta^-(\lambda) + \mathcal{O}(e^{-\mu^s t\delta}).$$

Since the generalized real eigenspace X^s of $\mu^s + \phi^s\, i$ has dimension 2, the vector η^s has a coordinate representation $(\eta_1^s, \eta_2^s, 0, \dots, 0)$ where $(\eta_1^s,\eta_2^s) \neq (0,0)$, and $e^{D_xf(p,\lambda)t}\eta^s$ acts like

$$e^{\mu^s t}\begin{pmatrix} \begin{pmatrix} \cos(\phi^s t) & \sin(\phi^s t) \\ -\sin(\phi^s t) & \cos(\phi^s t)\end{pmatrix}\begin{pmatrix}\eta_1^s \\ \eta_2^s\end{pmatrix} \\ 0 \\ \vdots \\ 0 \end{pmatrix}.$$

Let $(\eta_1^-, \dots, \eta_n^-)$ be the coordinate representation of η^- with respect to the chosen basis. Since $\eta^- \in (\mathbb{R}^n \ominus X^s)^\perp$ we have $(\eta_1^-, \eta_2^-) \neq (0,0)$. Therefore the leading order term of T_i^{21} has a representation

$$e^{2\mu^s\omega_i}(\eta_1 \sin(2\phi^s\omega_i) + \eta_2\cos(2\phi^s\omega_i)),$$

where

$$(\eta_1,\eta_2) := (\eta_2^s\eta_1^- - \eta_1^s\eta_2^-,\ \eta_1^s\eta_1^- + \eta_2^s\eta_2^-) \neq (0,0).$$

The latter inequality is due to the fact that both (η_1^s,η_2^s) and (η_1^-,η_2^-) are different from $(0,0)$. So there is an angle φ^s such that

$$\sin\varphi^s = \eta_1\left(\eta_1^2+\eta_2^2\right)^{-1/2}, \quad \cos\varphi^s = \eta_2\left(\eta_1^2+\eta_2^2\right)^{-1/2}.$$

Hence

$$e^{2\mu^s\omega_i}(\eta_1 \sin(2\phi^s\omega_i) + \eta_2 \cos(2\phi^s\omega_i)) = \mathcal{E}^{s,c}(\lambda)e^{2\mu^s\omega_i} \sin(2\phi^s\omega_i + \varphi^s),$$

where $\mathcal{E}^{s,c} = \left(\eta_1^2 + \eta_2^2\right)^{1/2}$. By construction $\mathcal{E}^{s,c}(\cdot)$ is smooth and $\mathcal{E}^{s,c}(0) \neq 0$.

The statements that replace Proposition C.4 and Proposition C.5 follow in the same way as the original statements. □

Using this theorem, we find the following bifurcation result.

Theorem C.54. *Under the assumptions of this section the following holds. For $\lambda = 0$ there exist, in any neighborhood of h, infinitely many 1-periodic orbits. Finitely many of them survive for small values $\lambda \neq 0$.*

Proof. Similar to Appendices C.3 and C.6.1 we derive the equation for 1-periodic orbits with minimal period 2ω from (C.214). This leads to an equation

$$\lambda - \mathcal{E}^{s,c}(\lambda)e^{2\mu^s(\lambda)\omega} \sin(2\phi^s\omega + \varphi^s) + R(\omega, \lambda) = 0, \tag{C.215}$$

where $R(\omega, \lambda) = \mathcal{O}(e^{2\mu^s(\lambda)\omega\delta})$ and $D_\omega R(\omega, \lambda) = \mathcal{O}(e^{2\mu^s(\lambda)\omega\delta})$. Equation (C.215) can be solved for $\lambda = \lambda(\omega)$. The shape of the graph of $\lambda(\omega)$ is depicted in Figure C.8. The result now follows easily. □

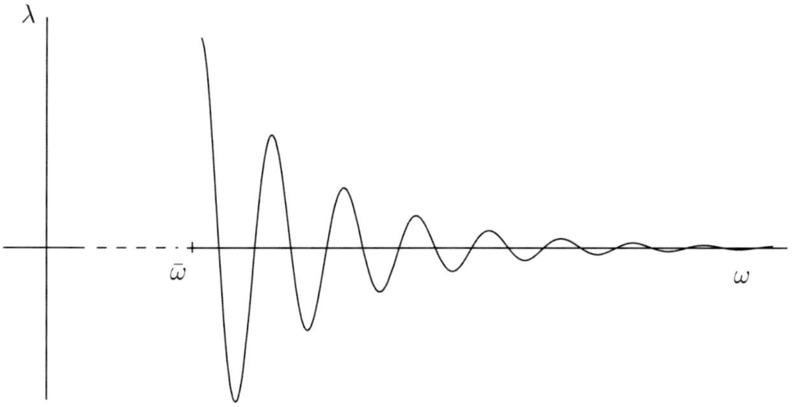

Figure C.8. The curve $\lambda = \lambda(\omega)$ solving (C.215).

Theorem 4.29 shows how shift dynamics, such as in the horseshoe map of Theorem 2.58, occurs near a saddle-focus homoclinic orbit in $\mathbb{R}^3$. The following theorem deals with shift dynamics resulting from Lin's method, valid also in more than three dimensions.

Theorem C.55. *Under the assumptions of this section the following holds. For $\lambda = 0$ there is a closed set $\mathcal{D}$ in the cross section Σ and a first return map Π which leaves $\mathcal{D}$ invariant and which, restricted to $\mathcal{D}$, is topologically conjugate to the shift on two symbols.*

Sketch of proof. We start by explaining the idea and introducing the involved objects, after which we address some details. Theorem C.54 provides two different 1-periodic orbits ζ_i, $i = 1, 2$. Let $2\hat{\omega}^1, 2\hat{\omega}^2$ be the minimal periods of these orbits. Consider now the space of sequences on two symbols $2\hat{\omega}^1$ and $2\hat{\omega}^2$,

$$\Sigma^2 = \{\hat{\omega} = (\hat{\omega}_i)_{i\in\mathbb{Z}}\ ;\ \hat{\omega}_i \in \{\hat{\omega}^1, \hat{\omega}^2\}\},$$

endowed with the product topology. Given any $\hat{\omega}$, we find solutions $\omega_{\hat{\omega}}$ to the determination equation (C.214) for orbits. Let $\omega_{\hat{\omega}} = (\omega_{\hat{\omega},i})_{i\in\mathbb{Z}}$ be this solution, and let $\gamma_{\hat{\omega}}$ be the corresponding orbit with $\gamma_{\hat{\omega}}(0) \in \Sigma$. Define

$$\mathcal{D} = \{\gamma_{\hat{\omega}}(0)\ ;\ \hat{\omega} \in \Sigma^2\}.$$

The first return map Π is defined by

$$\Pi(\gamma_{\hat{\omega}}(0)) = \gamma_{\hat{\omega}}(2\omega_{\hat{\omega},1}),$$

and the topological conjugation $\mathfrak{h} : \Sigma^2 \to \mathcal{D}$ will be defined by

$$\mathfrak{h}(\hat{\omega}) = \gamma_{\hat{\omega}}(0).$$

To provide some of the details, we discuss the solutions of (C.214). Removing $\lambda = 0$ from the notation, this becomes

$$\mathcal{E}^{s,c} e^{2\mu^s \omega_i} \sin(2\phi^s \omega_i + \varphi^s) + R_i(\omega) = 0, \tag{C.216}$$

where $i \in \mathbb{Z}$. For our analysis we choose sufficiently large minimal periods and keep them fixed throughout. Take $\delta = \frac{1}{3}|\hat{\omega}^1 - \hat{\omega}^2|$ and let $\mathcal{B}_{\hat{\omega}}$ be the Cartesian product

$$\mathcal{B}_{\hat{\omega}} = \bigtimes_{i\in\mathbb{Z}} B[\hat{\omega}_i, \delta]$$

contained in $\left(B[\hat{\omega}^1, \delta] \cup B[\hat{\omega}^2, \delta]\right)^{\mathbb{Z}}$. It can be shown (using the contraction mapping principle) that for each given sequence $\hat{\omega}$, (C.216) can be solved in $\mathcal{B}_{\hat{\omega}}$. Rewrite for this (C.216) as a fixed point equation

$$\omega = \omega - \left[D\mathbf{L}(\hat{\omega})\right]^{-1} \Xi(\omega) =: \mathcal{A}_{\hat{\omega}}(\omega),$$

where

$$\mathbf{L}(\omega) = \left(\mathcal{E}^{s,c} e^{2\mu^s \omega_i} \sin(2\phi^s \omega_i + \varphi^s)\right)_{i\in\mathbb{Z}}$$

and

$$\Xi(\omega) = \left(\mathcal{E}^{s,c} e^{2\mu^s \omega_i} \sin(2\phi^s \omega_i + \varphi^s) + R_i(\omega)\right)_{i\in\mathbb{Z}}.$$

Note that $D\mathbf{L}(\hat{\omega})$ is invertible, and that the fixed points of $\mathcal{A}_{\hat{\omega}}$ coincide with the zeros of (C.216). Further, $D\mathcal{A}_{\hat{\omega}}(\hat{\omega}) = D\left(R_i(\hat{\omega})\right)_{i\in\mathbb{Z}}$ tends to zero as $\hat{\omega}^1, \hat{\omega}^2$ tend to infinity (compare Proposition C.5).

Now we explain how it can be seen that $\mathfrak{h}$ is a homeomorphism. Using our standard notation, as in (C.152) and with h denoting the homoclinic orbit, we may write

$$\mathfrak{h}(\hat{\omega}) = \gamma_{\hat{\omega}}(0) = h_0^s(0) + v_1^+(\omega_{\hat{\omega}}, 0, 0) = h(0) + v_1^+(\omega_{\hat{\omega}}, 0, 0).$$

The continuity of $\mathfrak{h}$ can be shown in two steps. Write $\mathfrak{O} = \{\omega_{\hat{\omega}} \; ; \; \hat{\omega} \in \Sigma^2\}$, which is contained in (l^∞, ρ). Here $\rho : l^\infty \times l^\infty \to \mathbb{R}_0^+$ is a metric inducing the product topology, for instance

$$\rho(\omega^1, \omega^2) = \sum_{i \in \mathbb{Z}} \frac{1}{2^{|i|}} |\omega_i^1 - \omega_i^2|.$$

First we verify the continuity of the map $H : \Sigma^2 \to \mathfrak{O}$ defined by

$$H(\hat{\omega}) = \omega_{\hat{\omega}}.$$

Clearly, H is a one-to-one mapping. So, it is enough to show that $\mathfrak{O}$ is compact and that H^{-1} is continuous [**102**, Thm. XI.2.1]. Since the continuity of H^{-1} is obvious, it remains to verify the compactness of $\mathfrak{O}$. By construction $\mathfrak{O}$ is a subset of $\left(B[\hat{\omega}^1, \delta] \cup B[\hat{\omega}^2, \delta]\right)^{\mathbb{Z}}$ which is compact by Tychonoff's theorem [**102**, Thm. XI.1.4]. Further $\mathfrak{O}$ is the set of zeros of $\Xi(\cdot)$ inside $\mathcal{B}_{\hat{\omega}}$. Arguments as in the proof of Lemma C.39 show that this map is continuous. (Consider two sequences ω^1, ω^2 for which $|\omega_i^1 - \omega_i^2| = \mathcal{O}(\frac{1}{N})$ for all $i \in [-N, N] \cap \mathbb{Z}$. Then by similar estimates as in the proof of Lemma C.39 one gets that also $|v_0(\omega^1)(0) - v_0(\omega^2)(0)| = \mathcal{O}(\frac{1}{N})$.) From this the compactness of $\mathfrak{O}$ follows.

To show continuity of $\mathfrak{h}$ it remains to show that the map $\mathfrak{O} \to \mathcal{D}$, $\omega_{\hat{\omega}} \mapsto h(0) + v_1^+(\omega_{\hat{\omega}}, 0, 0)$ is continuous. This again follows as the continuity of $\Xi(\cdot)$. We conclude that $\mathfrak{h} : \Sigma^2 \to \mathcal{D}$ is continuous. Since Σ^2 is compact, $\mathfrak{h}$ is a homeomorphism.

Let σ be the left shift operator on Σ^2. From the uniqueness part of Theorem C.1 it follows that

$$\mathfrak{h}(\sigma\hat{\omega}) = \gamma_{\sigma\hat{\omega}}(0) = \gamma_{\hat{\omega}}(\omega_{\hat{\omega},1}) = \Pi(\gamma_{\hat{\omega}}(0)) = \Pi(\mathfrak{h}(\hat{\omega})),$$

or in other words,

$$\mathfrak{h} \circ \sigma = \Pi \circ \mathfrak{h}.$$

As $\mathfrak{h}$ is a homeomorphism, this establishes that $\mathfrak{h}$ provides a topological conjugacy between the left shift operator σ on Σ^2 and the first return map Π on $\mathcal{D}$. $\square$

Bibliography

[1] *American Mathematical Society Translations. Series 2, Vol. 46: Eleven papers on number theory, algebra and functions of a complex variable*, American Mathematical Society, Providence, R.I., 1965.

[2] *American Mathematical Society Translations, Ser. 2, Vol. 118*, American Mathematical Society Translations, Series 2, vol. 118, American Mathematical Society, Providence, R.I., 1982.

[3] R. Abraham, J. E. Marsden, and T. S. Raţiu, *Manifolds, tensor analysis, and applications*, Global Analysis Pure and Applied: Series B, vol. 2, Addison-Wesley Publishing Co., Reading, MA, 1983. MR697563

[4] R. Abraham and J. Robbin, *Transversal mappings and flows*, W. A. Benjamin, Inc., New York-Amsterdam, 1967. An appendix by Al Kelley. MR240836

[5] R. Abraham and S. Smale, *Nongenericity of Ω-stability*, Global Analysis (Proc. Sympos. Pure Math., Vols. XIV, XV, XVI, Berkeley, Calif., 1968), Proc. Sympos. Pure Math., XIV-XVI, Amer. Math. Soc., Providence, RI, 1970, pp. 5–8. MR271986

[6] D. Aeyels, *Generic observability of differentiable systems*, SIAM J. Control Optim. **19** (1981), no. 5, 595–603, DOI 10.1137/0319037. MR626654

[7] V. S. Afraimovic, V. V. Bykov, and L. P. Shilnikov, *The origin and structure of the Lorenz attractor* (Russian), Dokl. Akad. Nauk SSSR **234** (1977), no. 2, 336–339. MR462175

[8] V. Afraimovich and S.-B. Hsu, *Lectures on chaotic dynamical systems*, AMS/IP Studies in Advanced Mathematics, vol. 28, American Mathematical Society, Providence, RI; International Press, Somerville, MA, 2003, DOI 10.1090/amsip/028. MR1956214

[9] V. Afraimovich and T. Young, *Relative density of irrational rotation numbers in families of circle diffeomorphisms*, Ergodic Theory Dynam. Systems **18** (1998), no. 1, 1–16, DOI 10.1017/S0143385798097648. MR1609511

[10] J. C. Alexander, *Spontaneous oscillations in two 2-component cells coupled by diffusion*, J. Math. Biol. **23** (1986), no. 2, 205–219, DOI 10.1007/BF00276957. MR829133

[11] J. C. Alexander and J. A. Yorke, *Global bifurcations of periodic orbits*, Amer. J. Math. **100** (1978), no. 2, 263–292, DOI 10.2307/2373851. MR474406

[12] A. Algaba, E. Freire, E. Gamero, and A. J. Rodriguez-Luis, *An exact homoclinic orbit and its connection with the Rössler system*, Phys. Lett. A **379** (2015), no. 16-17, 1114–1121, DOI 10.1016/j.physleta.2015.02.017. MR3318223

[13] K. T. Alligood and J. A. Yorke, *Families of periodic orbits: virtual periods and global continuability*, J. Differential Equations **55** (1984), no. 1, 59–71, DOI 10.1016/0022-0396(84)90088-3. MR759827

[14] V. Anagnostopoulou, C. Pötzsche, and M. Rasmussen, *Nonautonomous bifurcation theory—concepts and tools*, Frontiers in Applied Dynamical Systems: Reviews and Tutorials, vol. 10, Springer, Cham, 2023, DOI 10.1007/978-3-031-29842-4. MR4633309

[15] A. A. Andronov and E. A. Leontovich, *Some cases of the dependence of the limit cycles upon parameters*, Echenye zapiski Gorkovskogo Universiteta **6** (1937), 3–24.

[16] A. A. Andronov, E. A. Leontovich, I. I. Gordon, and A. G. Maĭer, *Qualitative theory of second-order dynamic systems*, Halsted Press [John Wiley & Sons], New York-Toronto; Israel Program for Scientific Translations, Jerusalem-London, 1973. Translated from the Russian by D. Louvish. MR350126

[17] A. A. Andronov, E. A. Leontovich, I. I. Gordon, and A. G. Maĭer, *Theory of bifurcations of dynamic systems on a plane*, Halsted Press [John Wiley & Sons], New York-Toronto; Israel Program for Scientific Translations, Jerusalem-London, 1973.

[18] A. A. Andronov, and L. Pontrjagin, *Systèmes grossiers*, C. R. (Dokl.) Acad. Sci. URSS, n. Ser. **14** (1937), 247–250.

[19] V. Araújo and I. Melbourne, *Existence and smoothness of the stable foliation for sectional hyperbolic attractors*, Bull. Lond. Math. Soc. **49** (2017), no. 2, 351–367, DOI 10.1112/blms.12037. MR3656303

[20] V. I. Arnold, *Small denominators. I. Mapping the circle onto itself* (Russian), Izv. Akad. Nauk SSSR Ser. Mat. **25** (1961), 21–86. MR140699

[21] V. I. Arnold, *Geometrical methods in the theory of ordinary differential equations*, 2nd ed., Grundlehren der mathematischen Wissenschaften [Fundamental Principles of Mathematical Sciences], vol. 250, Springer-Verlag, New York, 1988. Translated from the Russian by Joseph Szücs [József M. Szűcs], DOI 10.1007/978-1-4612-1037-5. MR947141

[22] V. I. Arnold, *Ordinary differential equations*, Springer Textbook, Springer-Verlag, Berlin, 1992.

[23] V. I. Arnold, V. S. Afrajmovich, Yu. S. Ilyashenko, and L. P. Shilnikov, *Bifurcation theory and catastrophe theory*, Springer-Verlag, Berlin, 1999. Translated from the 1986 Russian original by N. D. Kazarinoff; Reprint of the 1994 English edition from the series Encyclopaedia of Mathematical Sciences [*Dynamical systems. V*, Encyclopaedia Math. Sci., 5, Springer, Berlin, 1994; MR1287421 (95c:58058)]. MR1733750

[24] V. I. Arnold and A. Avez, *Ergodic problems of classical mechanics*, W. A. Benjamin, Inc., New York-Amsterdam, 1968. Translated from the French by A. Avez. MR232910

[25] D. K. Arrowsmith and C. M. Place, *An introduction to dynamical systems*, Cambridge University Press, Cambridge, 1990. MR1069752

[26] B. Aulbach and B. Kieninger, *An elementary proof for hyperbolicity and chaos of the logistic maps*, J. Difference Equ. Appl. **10** (2004), no. 13-15, 1243–1250, DOI 10.1080/10236190410001652810. MR2100725

[27] J. Auslander and J. A. Yorke, *Interval maps, factors of maps, and chaos*, Tohoku Math. J. (2) **32** (1980), no. 2, 177–188, DOI 10.2748/tmj/1178229634. MR580273

[28] C. Baesens, J. Guckenheimer, S. Kim, and R. S. MacKay, *Three coupled oscillators: mode-locking, global bifurcations and toroidal chaos*, Phys. D **49** (1991), no. 3, 387–475, DOI 10.1016/0167-2789(91)90155-3. MR1115870

[29] J. Banks, J. Brooks, G. Cairns, G. Davis, and P. Stacey, *On Devaney's definition of chaos*, Amer. Math. Monthly **99** (1992), no. 4, 332–334, DOI 10.2307/2324899. MR1157223

[30] J. Barkmeijer, *Periodic attractors as a result of diffusion*, Ergodic Theory Dynam. Systems **7** (1987), no. 3, 319–335, DOI 10.1017/S0143385700004089. MR912372

[31] G. R. Belitskii, *Functional equations, and conjugacy of local diffeomorphisms of finite smoothness class* (Russian), Funkcional. Anal. i Priložen. **7** (1973), no. 4, 17–28. MR331437

[32] J. A. Beloqui, *Modulus of stability for vector fields on* 3*-manifolds*, J. Differential Equations **65** (1986), no. 3, 374–395, DOI 10.1016/0022-0396(86)90025-2. MR865068
[33] M. Benedicks and L. Carleson, *On iterations of* $1 - ax^2$ *on* $(-1, 1)$, Ann. of Math. (2) **122** (1985), no. 1, 1–25, DOI 10.2307/1971367. MR799250
[34] M. Benedicks and L. Carleson, *The dynamics of the Hénon map*, Ann. of Math. (2) **133** (1991), no. 1, 73–169, DOI 10.2307/2944326. MR1087346
[35] P. Bergé, Y. Pomeau, and C. Vidal, *Order within chaos: Towards a deterministic approach to turbulence*, A Wiley-Interscience Publication, John Wiley & Sons, Inc., New York; Hermann, Paris, 1986. With a preface by David Ruelle; Translated from the French by Laurette Tuckerman. MR882723
[36] M. S. Berger, *Nonlinearity and functional analysis: Lectures on nonlinear problems in mathematical analysis*, Pure and Applied Mathematics, Academic Press [Harcourt Brace Jovanovich, Publishers], New York-London, 1977. MR488101
[37] P. Berger, *Generic family with robustly infinitely many sinks*, Invent. Math. **205** (2016), no. 1, 121–172, DOI 10.1007/s00222-015-0632-6. MR3514960
[38] G. D. Birkhoff, *On the periodic motions of dynamical systems*, Acta Math. **50** (1927), no. 1, 359–379, DOI 10.1007/BF02421325. MR1555257
[39] G. D. Birkhoff, *Nouvelles recherches sur les systèmes dynamiques*, Mem. Pontif. Acad. Sci. Novi Lyncaei, III. Ser. **1** (1934), 85–216.
[40] L. S. Block and W. A. Coppel, *Dynamics in one dimension*, Lecture Notes in Mathematics, vol. 1513, Springer-Verlag, Berlin, 1992, DOI 10.1007/BFb0084762. MR1176513
[41] R. I. Bogdanov, *Bifurcations of a limit cycle of a certain family of vector fields on the plane* (Russian), Trudy Sem. Petrovsk. **2** (1976), 23–35. MR442988
[42] R. I. Bogdanov, *The versal deformation of a singular point of a vector field on the plane in the case of zero eigenvalues*, Trudy Sem. Petrovsk. (1976), no. Vyp. 2, 37–65.
[43] C. Bonatti and L. J. Díaz, *Persistent nonhyperbolic transitive diffeomorphisms*, Ann. of Math. (2) **143** (1996), no. 2, 357–396, DOI 10.2307/2118647. MR1381990
[44] C. Bonatti, L. J. Díaz, and M. Viana, *Dynamics beyond uniform hyperbolicity: A global geometric and probabilistic perspective; Mathematical Physics, III*, Encyclopaedia of Mathematical Sciences, vol. 102, Springer-Verlag, Berlin, 2005. MR2105774
[45] W. M. Boothby, *An introduction to differentiable manifolds and Riemannian geometry*, 2nd ed., Pure and Applied Mathematics, vol. 120, Academic Press, Inc., Orlando, FL, 1986. MR861409
[46] A. Bowers and N. J. Kalton, *An introductory course in functional analysis*, Universitext, Springer, New York, 2014. With a foreword by Gilles Godefroy, DOI 10.1007/978-1-4939-1945-1. MR3289046
[47] A. Bressan, *Tutorial on the center manifold theorem*, Hyperbolic systems of balance laws, Lecture Notes in Math., vol. 1911, Springer, Berlin, 2007, pp. 327–344. MR2348938
[48] M. Brin and G. Stuck, *Introduction to dynamical systems*, Cambridge University Press, Cambridge, 2002, DOI 10.1017/CBO9780511755316. MR1963683
[49] H. W. Broer, F. Dumortier, S. J. van Strien, and F. Takens, *Structures in dynamics: Finite-dimensional deterministic studies*, Studies in Mathematical Physics, vol. 2, North-Holland Publishing Co., Amsterdam, 1991. MR1134128
[50] H. W. Broer, G. B. Huitema, F. Takens, and B. L. J. Braaksma, *Unfoldings and bifurcations of quasi-periodic tori*, Mem. Amer. Math. Soc. **83** (1990), no. 421, viii+175, DOI 10.1090/memo/0421. MR1041003
[51] H. W. Broer and F. Takens, *Dynamical systems and chaos*, Applied Mathematical Sciences, vol. 172, Springer, New York, 2011, DOI 10.1007/978-1-4419-6870-8. MR2721948
[52] P. Brunovsky, *On one-parameter families of diffeomorphisms*, Comment. Math. Univ. Carolinae **11** (1970), 559–582. MR279827

[53] P. Brunovsky, *On one-parameter families of diffeomorphisms. II. Generic branching in higher dimensions*, Comment. Math. Univ. Carolinae **12** (1971), 765–784. MR309130

[54] A. Burchard, B. Deng, and K. Lu, *Smooth conjugacy of centre manifolds*, Proc. Roy. Soc. Edinburgh Sect. A **120** (1992), no. 1-2, 61–77, DOI 10.1017/S0308210500014980. MR1149984

[55] K. Burns and H. Weiss, *A geometric criterion for positive topological entropy*, Comm. Math. Phys. **172** (1995), no. 1, 95–118. MR1346373

[56] X. Cabré, E. Fontich, and R. de la Llave, *The parameterization method for invariant manifolds. III. Overview and applications*, J. Differential Equations **218** (2005), no. 2, 444–515, DOI 10.1016/j.jde.2004.12.003. MR2177465

[57] R. Camassa, G. Kovačič, and S.-K. Tin, *A Melnikov method for homoclinic orbits with many pulses*, Arch. Rational Mech. Anal. **143** (1998), no. 2, 105–193, DOI 10.1007/s002050050102. MR1650010

[58] Y. Cao and S. Kiriki, *The basin of the strange attractors of some Hénon maps*, Chaos Solitons Fractals **11** (2000), no. 5, 729–734, DOI 10.1016/S0960-0779(98)00181-7. MR1739465

[59] Y. Cao, S. Luzzatto, and I. Rios, *The boundary of hyperbolicity for Hénon-like families*, Ergodic Theory Dynam. Systems **28** (2008), no. 4, 1049–1080, DOI 10.1017/S0143385707000776. MR2437219

[60] L. Carleson and T. W. Gamelin, *Complex dynamics*, Universitext: Tracts in Mathematics, Springer-Verlag, New York, 1993, DOI 10.1007/978-1-4612-4364-9. MR1230383

[61] M. L. Cartwright and J. E. Littlewood, *On non-linear differential equations of the second order. I. The equation $\ddot{y} - k(1 - y^2)y + y = b\lambda k\ \cos(\lambda t + a)$, k large*, J. London Math. Soc. **20** (1945), 180–189, DOI 10.1112/jlms/s1-20.3.180. MR16789

[62] A. De Carvalho, M. Lyubich, and M. Martens, *Renormalization in the Hénon family. I. Universality but non-rigidity*, J. Stat. Phys. **121** (2005), no. 5-6, 611–669, DOI 10.1007/s10955-005-8668-4. MR2192529

[63] E. Catsigeras and H. Enrich, *Homoclinic tangencies near cascades of period doubling bifurcations* (English, with English and French summaries), Ann. Inst. H. Poincaré C Anal. Non Linéaire **15** (1998), no. 3, 255–299, DOI 10.1016/S0294-1449(98)80119-4. MR1629345

[64] E. Catsigeras and H. Enrich, *Persistence of the Feigenbaum attractor in one-parameter families*, Comm. Math. Phys. **207** (1999), no. 3, 621–640, DOI 10.1007/s002200050739. MR1727238

[65] A. Chenciner, *Bifurcations de points fixes elliptiques. I. Courbes invariantes* (French), Inst. Hautes Études Sci. Publ. Math. **61** (1985), 67–127. MR783349

[66] A. Chenciner, *Bifurcations de points fixes elliptiques. II. Orbites periodiques et ensembles de Cantor invariants* (French), Invent. Math. **80** (1985), no. 1, 81–106, DOI 10.1007/BF01388549. MR784530

[67] A. Chenciner, *Bifurcations de points fixes elliptiques. III. Orbites périodiques de "petites" périodes et élimination résonnante des couples de courbes invariantes*, Inst. Hautes Études Sci. Publ. Math. (1988), no. 66, 5–91.

[68] S.-N. Chow, B. Deng, and B. Fiedler, *Homoclinic bifurcation at resonant eigenvalues*, J. Dynam. Differential Equations **2** (1990), no. 2, 177–244, DOI 10.1007/BF01057418. MR1050642

[69] S.-N. Chow and J. K. Hale, *Methods of bifurcation theory*, Grundlehren der Mathematischen Wissenschaften, vol. 251, Springer-Verlag, New York-Berlin, 1982. MR660633

[70] P. Collet and J.-P. Eckmann, *Iterated maps on the interval as dynamical systems*, Progress in Physics, vol. 1, Birkhäuser, Boston, MA, 1980. MR613981

[71] P. Collet and J.-P. Eckmann, *On the abundance of aperiodic behaviour for maps on the interval*, Comm. Math. Phys. **73** (1980), no. 2, 115–160. MR573469

[72] P. Collet, J.-P. Eckmann, and H. Koch, *Period doubling bifurcations for families of maps on* $\mathbf{R}^n$, J. Statist. Phys. **25** (1981), no. 1, 1–14, DOI 10.1007/BF01008475. MR610688

[73] E. Colli, *Infinitely many coexisting strange attractors* (English, with English and French summaries), Ann. Inst. H. Poincaré C Anal. Non Linéaire **15** (1998), no. 5, 539–579, DOI 10.1016/S0294-1449(98)80001-2. MR1643393

[74] C. Conley, *Isolated invariant sets and the Morse index*, CBMS Regional Conference Series in Mathematics, vol. 38, American Mathematical Society, Providence, RI, 1978. MR511133

[75] C. Conley, *The gradient structure of a flow. I*, Ergodic Theory Dynam. Systems **8*** (1988), no. Charles Conley Memorial Issue, 11–26, 9, DOI 10.1017/S0143385700009305. With a comment by R. Moeckel. MR967626

[76] W. A. Coppel, *Dichotomies in stability theory*, Lecture Notes in Mathematics, Vol. 629, Springer-Verlag, Berlin-New York, 1978. MR481196

[77] M. J. Costa, *Saddle-node horseshoes giving rise to global Hénon-like attractors*, An. Acad. Brasil. Ciênc. **70** (1998), no. 3, 393–400. MR1753031

[78] E. Cotton, *Sur les solutions asymptotiques des équations différentielles* (French), Ann. Sci. École Norm. Sup. (3) **28** (1911), 473–521. MR1509144

[79] M. G. Crandall and P. H. Rabinowitz, *Bifurcation from simple eigenvalues*, J. Functional Analysis **8** (1971), 321–340, DOI 10.1016/0022-1236(71)90015-2. MR288640

[80] S. Crovisier, *Saddle-node bifurcations for hyperbolic sets*, Ergodic Theory Dynam. Systems **22** (2002), no. 4, 1079–1115, DOI 10.1017/S0143385702000664. MR1926277

[81] S. Crovisier and E. Pujals, *Strongly dissipative surface diffeomorphisms*, Comment. Math. Helv. **93** (2018), no. 2, 377–400, DOI 10.4171/CMH/438. MR3811756

[82] J. H. Curry and J. A. Yorke, *A transition from Hopf bifurcation to chaos: computer experiments with maps on* $\mathbf{R}^2$, The structure of attractors in dynamical systems (Proc. Conf., North Dakota State Univ., Fargo, N.D., 1977), Lecture Notes in Math., vol. 668, Springer, Berlin-New York, 1978, pp. 48–66. MR518547

[83] P. De Maesschalck, F. Dumortier, and R. Roussarie, *Canard cycles—from birth to transition*, Ergebnisse der Mathematik und ihrer Grenzgebiete. 3. Folge. A Series of Modern Surveys in Mathematics [Results in Mathematics and Related Areas. 3rd Series. A Series of Modern Surveys in Mathematics], vol. 73, Springer, Cham, 2021, DOI 10.1007/978-3-030-79233-6. MR4304039

[84] W. de Melo, *Structural stability of diffeomorphisms on two-manifolds*, Invent. Math. **21** (1973), 233–246, DOI 10.1007/BF01390199. MR339277

[85] W. de Melo, *Moduli of stability of two-dimensional diffeomorphisms*, Topology **19** (1980), no. 1, 9–21, DOI 10.1016/0040-9383(80)90028-2. MR559473

[86] W. de Melo and S. J. van Strien, *Diffeomorphisms on surfaces with a finite number of moduli*, Ergodic Theory Dynam. Systems **7** (1987), no. 3, 415–462, DOI 10.1017/S0143385700004120. MR912376

[87] W. de Melo and S. J. van Strien, *One-dimensional dynamics*, Ergebnisse der Mathematik und ihrer Grenzgebiete (3) [Results in Mathematics and Related Areas (3)], vol. 25, Springer-Verlag, Berlin, 1993.

[88] A. de Roos, *Modeling Population Dynamics*, Syllabus, University of Amsterdam, 2019.

[89] H. F. DeBaggis, *Dynamical systems with stable structures*, Contributions to the Theory of Nonlinear Oscillations, vol. II, Princeton Univ. Press, Princeton, NJ, 1952, pp. 37–59. MR51991

[90] B. Deng, *The Šil′nikov problem, exponential expansion, strong* λ*-lemma,* C^1*-linearization, and homoclinic bifurcation*, J. Differential Equations **79** (1989), no. 2, 189–231, DOI 10.1016/0022-0396(89)90100-9. MR1000687

[91] B. Deng, *Homoclinic twisting bifurcations and cusp horseshoe maps*, J. Dynam. Differential Equations **5** (1993), no. 3, 417–467, DOI 10.1007/BF01053531. MR1235038

[92] B. Deng, *Exponential expansion with principal eigenvalues: Nonlinear dynamics, bifurcations and chaotic behavior*, Internat. J. Bifur. Chaos Appl. Sci. Engrg. **6** (1996), no. 6, 1161–1167, DOI 10.1142/S0218127496000655. MR1409417

[93] R. L. Devaney, *An introduction to chaotic dynamical systems*, The Benjamin/Cummings Publishing Co., Inc., Menlo Park, CA, 1986. MR811850

[94] R. Devaney and Z. Nitecki, *Shift automorphisms in the Hénon mapping*, Comm. Math. Phys. **67** (1979), no. 2, 137–146. MR539548

[95] L. J. Díaz, V. Horita, I. Rios, and M. Sambarino, *Destroying horseshoes via heterodimensional cycles: generating bifurcations inside homoclinic classes*, Ergodic Theory Dynam. Systems **29** (2009), no. 2, 433–474, DOI 10.1017/S0143385708080346. MR2486778

[96] L. J. Díaz, I. L. Rios, and M. Viana, *The intermittency route to chaotic dynamics*, Global analysis of dynamical systems, Inst. Phys., Bristol, 2001, pp. 309–327. MR1858480

[97] J. Dieudonné, *Foundations of modern analysis*, Pure and Applied Mathematics, Vol. 10-I, Academic Press, New York-London, 1969. Enlarged and corrected printing. MR349288

[98] E. J. Doedel, B. Krauskopf, and H. M. Osinga, *Global organization of phase space in the transition to chaos in the Lorenz system*, Nonlinearity **28** (2015), no. 11, R113–R139, DOI 10.1088/0951-7715/28/11/R113. MR3424889

[99] A. Douady and J. H. Hubbard, *Itération des polynômes quadratiques complexes* (French, with English summary), C. R. Acad. Sci. Paris Sér. I Math. **294** (1982), no. 3, 123–126. MR651802

[100] A. Douady and J. H. Hubbard, *Étude dynamique des polynômes complexes. Partie II* (French), Publications Mathématiques d'Orsay [Mathematical Publications of Orsay], vol. 85, Université de Paris-Sud, Département de Mathématiques, Orsay, 1985. With the collaboration of P. Lavaurs, Tan Lei and P. Sentenac. MR812271

[101] G. F. D. Duff, *Limit-cycles and rotated vector fields*, Ann. of Math. (2) **57** (1953), 15–31, DOI 10.2307/1969724. MR53301

[102] J. Dugundji, *Topology*, Allyn and Bacon Series in Advanced Mathematics, Allyn and Bacon, Inc., Boston, Mass.-London-Sydney, 1978. Reprinting of the 1966 original. MR478089

[103] F. Dumortier, *Nonstabilisable jets of diffeomorphisms in* $\mathbf{R}^2$ *and of vector fields in* $\mathbf{R}^3$, Ann. of Math. (2) **124** (1986), no. 3, 405–440, DOI 10.2307/2007090. MR866706

[104] F. Dumortier, J. Llibre, and J. C. Artés, *Qualitative theory of planar differential systems*, Universitext, Springer-Verlag, Berlin, 2006. MR2256001

[105] F. Dumortier, R. Roussarie, and J. Sotomayor, *Generic* 3*-parameter families of vector fields on the plane, unfolding a singularity with nilpotent linear part. The cusp case of codimension* 3, Ergodic Theory Dynam. Systems **7** (1987), no. 3, 375–413, DOI 10.1017/S0143385700004119. MR912375

[106] F. Dumortier, R. Roussarie, J. Sotomayor, and H. Zoladek, *Bifurcations of planar vector fields: Nilpotent singularities and Abelian integrals*, Lecture Notes in Mathematics, vol. 1480, Springer-Verlag, Berlin, 1991, DOI 10.1007/BFb0098353. MR1166189

[107] J.-P. Eckmann and P. Wittwer, *A complete proof of the Feigenbaum conjectures*, J. Statist. Phys. **46** (1987), no. 3-4, 455–475, DOI 10.1007/BF01013368. MR883539

[108] C. Elphick, E. Tirapegui, M. E. Brachet, P. Coullet, and G. Iooss, *A simple global characterization for normal forms of singular vector fields*, Phys. D **29** (1987), no. 1-2, 95–127, DOI 10.1016/0167-2789(87)90049-2. MR923885

[109] M. Engel, C. Kuehn, and B. de Rijk, *A traveling wave bifurcation analysis of turbulent pipe flow*, Nonlinearity **35** (2022), no. 11, 5903–5937, DOI 10.1088/1361-6544/ac9504. MR4500885

[110] M. J. Feigenbaum, *Quantitative universality for a class of nonlinear transformations*, J. Statist. Phys. **19** (1978), no. 1, 25–52, DOI 10.1007/BF01020332. MR501179

[111] N. Fenichel, *Persistence and smoothness of invariant manifolds for flows*, Indiana Univ. Math. J. **21** (1971/72), 193–226, DOI 10.1512/iumj.1971.21.21017. MR287106

[112] N. Fenichel, *Asymptotic stability with rate conditions*, Indiana Univ. Math. J. **23** (1973/74), 1109–1137, DOI 10.1512/iumj.1974.23.23090. MR339276

[113] N. Fenichel, *The orbit structure of the Hopf bifurcation problem*, J. Differential Equations **17** (1975), 308–328, DOI 10.1016/0022-0396(75)90046-7. MR410800

[114] N. Fenichel, *Asymptotic stability with rate conditions. II*, Indiana Univ. Math. J. **26** (1977), no. 1, 81–93, DOI 10.1512/iumj.1977.26.26006. MR426056

[115] B. Fiedler and S. Liebscher, *Bifurcations without parameters: some ODE and PDE examples*, Proceedings of the International Congress of Mathematicians, Vol. III (Beijing, 2002), Higher Ed. Press, Beijing, 2002, pp. 305–316. MR1957541

[116] A. Fowler and M. McGuinness, *Chaos—an introduction for applied mathematicians*, Springer, Cham, 2019, DOI 10.1007/978-3-030-32538-1. MR4297799

[117] J. E. Franke and J. F. Selgrade, *Hyperbolicity and chain recurrence*, J. Differential Equations **26** (1977), no. 1, 27–36, DOI 10.1016/0022-0396(77)90096-1. MR467834

[118] T. W. Gamelin, *Complex analysis*, Undergraduate Texts in Mathematics, Springer-Verlag, New York, 2001, DOI 10.1007/978-0-387-21607-2. MR1830078

[119] N. K. Gavrilov and A. L. Shilnikov, *Example of a blue sky catastrophe*, Methods of qualitative theory of differential equations and related topics, Amer. Math. Soc. Transl. Ser. 2, vol. 200, Amer. Math. Soc., Providence, RI, 2000, pp. 99–105, DOI 10.1090/trans2/200/09. MR1769566

[120] N. K. Gavrilov and L. P. Shilnikov, *Three-dimensional dynamical systems that are close to systems with a structurally unstable homoclinic curve. I* (Russian), Mat. Sb. (N.S.) **88(130)** (1972), 475–492. MR310355

[121] N. K. Gavrilov and L. P. Shilnikov, *Three-dimensional dynamical systems that are close to systems with a structurally unstable homoclinic curve. II* (Russian), Mat. Sb. (N.S.) **90(132)** (1973), 139–156, 167. MR334280

[122] M. Georgi, *Bifurcations from homoclinic orbits to non-hyperbolic equilibria in reversible lattice differential equations*, Nonlinearity **21** (2008), no. 4, 735–763, DOI 10.1088/0951-7715/21/4/005. MR2399823

[123] M. Golubitsky and V. Guillemin, *Stable mappings and their singularities*, Graduate Texts in Mathematics, Vol. 14, Springer-Verlag, New York-Heidelberg, 1973. MR341518

[124] M. Golubitsky and D. G. Schaeffer, *Singularities and groups in bifurcation theory. Vol. I*, Applied Mathematical Sciences, vol. 51, Springer-Verlag, New York, 1985, DOI 10.1007/978-1-4612-5034-0. MR771477

[125] N. Goncharuk, Y. G. Kudryashov, and N. Solodovnikov, *New structurally unstable families of planar vector fields*, Nonlinearity **34** (2021), no. 1, 438–454, DOI 10.1088/1361-6544/abb86e. MR4208446

[126] S. V. Gonchenko, V. S. Gonchenko, and L. P. Shilnikov, *On a homoclinic origin of Hénon-like maps*, Regul. Chaotic Dyn. **15** (2010), no. 4-5, 462–481, DOI 10.1134/S1560354710040052. MR2679759

[127] S. V. Gonchenko and L. P. Shilnikov, *Invariants of Ω-conjugacy of diffeomorphisms with a structurally unstable homoclinic trajectory* (Russian, with Ukrainian summary), Ukrain. Mat. Zh. **42** (1990), no. 2, 153–159, DOI 10.1007/BF01071004; English transl., Ukrainian Math. J. **42** (1990), no. 2, 134–140. MR1053413

[128] S. V. Gonchenko, L. P. Shilnikov, and D. V. Turaev, *On models with nonrough Poincaré homoclinic curves*, Phys. D **62** (1993), no. 1-4, 1–14, DOI 10.1016/0167-2789(93)90268-6. Homoclinic chaos (Brussels, 1991). MR1207413

[129] S. V. Gonchenko, L. P. Shilnikov, and D. V. Turaev, *Dynamical phenomena in systems with structurally unstable Poincaré homoclinic orbits*, Chaos **6** (1996), no. 1, 15–31, DOI 10.1063/1.166154. MR1376892

[130] S. V. Gonchenko, D. V. Turaev, P. Gaspard, and G. Nicolis, *Complexity in the bifurcation structure of homoclinic loops to a saddle-focus*, Nonlinearity **10** (1997), no. 2, 409–423, DOI 10.1088/0951-7715/10/2/006. MR1438259

[131] S. Gonchenko, D. Turaev, and L. P. Shilnikov, *Homoclinic tangencies of arbitrarily high orders in conservative and dissipative two-dimensional maps*, Nonlinearity **20** (2007), no. 2, 241–275, DOI 10.1088/0951-7715/20/2/002. MR2290462

[132] V. S. Gonchenko, Yu. A. Kuznetsov, and H. G. E. Meijer, *Generalized Hénon map and bifurcations of homoclinic tangencies*, SIAM J. Appl. Dyn. Syst. **4** (2005), no. 2, 407–436, DOI 10.1137/04060487X. MR2173535

[133] G. R. Goodson, *Chaotic dynamics: Fractals, tilings, and substitutions*, Cambridge Mathematical Textbooks, Cambridge University Press, Cambridge, 2017. MR3617651

[134] A. Gorodetski and V. Kaloshin, *How often surface diffeomorphisms have infinitely many sinks and hyperbolicity of periodic points near a homoclinic tangency*, Adv. Math. **208** (2007), no. 2, 710–797, DOI 10.1016/j.aim.2006.03.012. MR2304335

[135] J. Graczyk and G. Świątek, *Generic hyperbolicity in the logistic family*, Ann. of Math. (2) **146** (1997), no. 1, 1–52, DOI 10.2307/2951831. MR1469316

[136] C. Grebogi, E. Ott, and J. A. Yorke, *Crises, sudden changes in chaotic attractors, and transient chaos*, Phys. D **7** (1983), no. 1-3, 181–200, DOI 10.1016/0167-2789(83)90126-4. Order in chaos (Los Alamos, N.M., 1982). MR719052

[137] V. Grines, Yu. Levchenko, V. Medvedev, and O. Pochinka, *The topological classification of structurally stable 3-diffeomorphisms with two-dimensional basic sets*, Nonlinearity **28** (2015), no. 11, 4081–4102, DOI 10.1088/0951-7715/28/11/4081. MR3424904

[138] D. M. Grobman, *Homeomorphism of systems of differential equations* (Russian), Dokl. Akad. Nauk SSSR **128** (1959), 880–881. MR121545

[139] D. M. Grobman, *Topological classification of neighborhoods of a singularity in n-space* (Russian), Mat. Sb. (N.S.) **56(98)** (1962), 77–94. MR138829

[140] J. Gruendler, *The existence of homoclinic orbits and the method of Melnikov for systems in* $\mathbf{R}^n$, SIAM J. Math. Anal. **16** (1985), no. 5, 907–931, DOI 10.1137/0516069. MR800787

[141] J. Guckenheimer, *Bifurcation and catastrophe*, Dynamical systems (Proc. Sympos., Univ. Bahia, Salvador, 1971), Academic Press, New York-London, 1973, pp. 95–109. MR345139

[142] J. Guckenheimer, *On the bifurcation of maps of the interval*, Invent. Math. **39** (1977), no. 2, 165–178, DOI 10.1007/BF01390107. MR438399

[143] J. Guckenheimer and P. Holmes, *Nonlinear oscillations, dynamical systems, and bifurcations of vector fields*, Applied Mathematical Sciences, vol. 42, Springer-Verlag, New York, 1983, DOI 10.1007/978-1-4612-1140-2. MR709768

[144] J. Guckenheimer and R. F. Williams, *Structural stability of Lorenz attractors*, Inst. Hautes Études Sci. Publ. Math. **50** (1979), 59–72. MR556582

[145] J. Hadamard, *Sur l'itération et les solutions asymptotiques des équations différentielles*, Bull. Soc. Math. Fr. **29** (1901), 224–228.

[146] W. Hahn, *Stability of motion*, Die Grundlehren der mathematischen Wissenschaften, Band 138, Springer-Verlag New York, Inc., New York, 1967. Translated from the German manuscript by Arne P. Baartz. MR223668

[147] J. K. Hale, *Ordinary differential equations*, 2nd ed., Robert E. Krieger Publishing Co., Inc., Huntington, NY, 1980. MR587488

[148] J. K. Hale and H. Koçak, *Dynamics and bifurcations*, Texts in Applied Mathematics, vol. 3, Springer-Verlag, New York, 1991, DOI 10.1007/978-1-4612-4426-4. MR1138981

[149] J. K. Hale, L. A. Peletier, and W. C. Troy, *Exact homoclinic and heteroclinic solutions of the Gray-Scott model for autocatalysis*, SIAM J. Appl. Math. **61** (2000), no. 1, 102–130, DOI 10.1137/S0036139998334913. MR1776389

[150] M. Haragus and G. Iooss, *Local bifurcations, center manifolds, and normal forms in infinite-dimensional dynamical systems*, Universitext, Springer-Verlag London, Ltd., London; EDP Sciences, Les Ulis, 2011, DOI 10.1007/978-0-85729-112-7. MR2759609

[151] P. Hartman, *On local homeomorphisms of Euclidean spaces*, Bol. Soc. Mat. Mexicana (2) **5** (1960), 220–241. MR141856

[152] P. Hartman, *On the local linearization of differential equations*, Proc. Amer. Math. Soc. **14** (1963), 568–573, DOI 10.2307/2034276. MR152718

[153] B. D. Hassard, N. D. Kazarinoff, and Y. H. Wan, *Theory and applications of Hopf bifurcation*, London Mathematical Society Lecture Note Series, vol. 41, Cambridge University Press, Cambridge-New York, 1981. MR603442

[154] S. Hayashi, *Connecting invariant manifolds and the solution of the C^1 stability and Ω-stability conjectures for flows*, Ann. of Math. (2) **145** (1997), no. 1, 81–137, DOI 10.2307/2951824. MR1432037

[155] P. Hazard, M. Martens, and C. Tresser, *Infinitely many moduli of stability at the dissipative boundary of chaos*, Trans. Amer. Math. Soc. **370** (2018), no. 1, 27–51, DOI 10.1090/tran/6940. MR3717973

[156] G. Hek, A. Doelman, and P. Holmes, *Homoclinic saddle-node bifurcations and subshifts in a three-dimensional flow*, Arch. Ration. Mech. Anal. **145** (1998), no. 4, 291–329, DOI 10.1007/s002050050131. MR1664538

[157] M. Hénon, *A two-dimensional mapping with a strange attractor*, Comm. Math. Phys. **50** (1976), no. 1, 69–77. MR422932

[158] D. Henry, *Geometric theory of semilinear parabolic equations*, Lecture Notes in Mathematics, vol. 840, Springer-Verlag, Berlin-New York, 1981. MR610244

[159] T. H. Hildebrandt and L. M. Graves, *Implicit functions and their differentials in general analysis*, Trans. Amer. Math. Soc. **29** (1927), no. 1, 127–153, DOI 10.2307/1989282. MR1501380

[160] M. W. Hirsch, *Differential topology*, Graduate Texts in Mathematics, No. 33, Springer-Verlag, New York-Heidelberg, 1976. MR448362

[161] M. W. Hirsch and C. C. Pugh, *Stable manifolds and hyperbolic sets*, Global Analysis (Proc. Sympos. Pure Math., Vols. XIV, XV, XVI, Berkeley, Calif., 1968), Proc. Sympos. Pure Math., XIV-XVI, Amer. Math. Soc., Providence, RI, 1970, pp. 133–163. MR271991

[162] M. W. Hirsch, C. C. Pugh, and M. Shub, *Invariant manifolds*, Lecture Notes in Mathematics, Vol. 583, Springer-Verlag, Berlin-New York, 1977. MR501173

[163] M. W. Hirsch, S. Smale, and R. L. Devaney, *Differential equations, dynamical systems, and an introduction to chaos*, 3rd ed., Elsevier/Academic Press, Amsterdam, 2013, DOI 10.1016/B978-0-12-382010-5.00001-4. MR3293130

[164] P. J. Holmes, *Averaging and chaotic motions in forced oscillations*, SIAM J. Appl. Math. **38** (1980), no. 1, 65–80, DOI 10.1137/0138005. MR559081

[165] A. J. Homburg, *Global aspects of homoclinic bifurcations of vector fields*, Mem. Amer. Math. Soc. **121** (1996), no. 578, viii+128, DOI 10.1090/memo/0578. MR1327210

[166] A. J. Homburg, *Periodic attractors, strange attractors and hyperbolic dynamics near homoclinic orbits to saddle-focus equilibria*, Nonlinearity **15** (2002), no. 4, 1029–1050, DOI 10.1088/0951-7715/15/4/304. MR1912285

[167] A. J. Homburg, *Invariant manifolds near hyperbolic fixed points*, J. Difference Equ. Appl. **12** (2006), no. 10, 1057–1068, DOI 10.1080/10236190600986628. MR2267488

[168] A. J. Homburg, R. de Vilder, and D. Sands, *Computing invariant sets*, Internat. J. Bifur. Chaos Appl. Sci. Engrg. **13** (2003), no. 2, 497–504, DOI 10.1142/S0218127403006674. MR1972164

[169] A. J. Homburg, A. C. Jukes, J. Knobloch, and J. S. W. Lamb, *Bifurcation from codimension one relative homoclinic cycles*, Trans. Amer. Math. Soc. **363** (2011), no. 11, 5663–5701, DOI 10.1090/S0002-9947-2011-05193-7. MR2817404

[170] A. J. Homburg and J. Knobloch, *Multiple homoclinic orbits in conservative and reversible systems*, Trans. Amer. Math. Soc. **358** (2006), no. 4, 1715–1740, DOI 10.1090/S0002-9947-05-03793-1. MR2186994

[171] A. J. Homburg, H. Kokubu, and V. Naudot, *Homoclinic-doubling cascades*, Arch. Ration. Mech. Anal. **160** (2001), no. 3, 195–243, DOI 10.1007/s002050100159. MR1869442

[172] A. J. Homburg and B. Sandstede, *Homoclinic and heteroclinic bifurcations in vector fields*, Handbook of dynamical systems. Volume 3, Amsterdam: Elsevier, 2010, pp. 379–524.

[173] A. J. Homburg and H. Weiss, *A geometric criterion for positive topological entropy. II. Homoclinic tangencies*, Comm. Math. Phys. **208** (1999), no. 2, 267–273, DOI 10.1007/s002200050757. MR1729086

[174] A. J. Homburg and T. Young, *Universal scalings in homoclinic doubling cascades*, Comm. Math. Phys. **222** (2001), no. 2, 269–292, DOI 10.1007/PL00005578. MR1859599

[175] A. J. Homburg and T. Young, *Intermittency in families of unimodal maps*, Ergodic Theory Dynam. Systems **22** (2002), no. 1, 203–225, DOI 10.1017/S0143385702000093. MR1889571

[176] A. J. Homburg, and T. Young, *Intermittency and Jakobson's theorem near saddle-node bifurcations*, Discrete Contin. Dyn. Syst. **17** (2007), no. 1, 21–58.

[177] E. Hopf, *Abzweigung einer periodischen Lösung von einer stationären eines Differentialsystems* (German), Ber. Verh. Sächs. Akad. Wiss. Leipzig Math.-Nat. Kl. **95** (1943), no. 1, 3–22. MR39141

[178] F. C. Hoppensteadt and E. M. Izhikevich, *Weakly connected neural networks*, Applied Mathematical Sciences, vol. 126, Springer-Verlag, New York, 1997, DOI 10.1007/978-1-4612-1828-9. MR1458890

[179] L. Hörmander, *The analysis of linear partial differential operators. III: Pseudodifferential operators*, Grundlehren der mathematischen Wissenschaften [Fundamental Principles of Mathematical Sciences], vol. 274, Springer-Verlag, Berlin, 1985. MR781536

[180] R. B. Hoyle, *Pattern formation: An introduction to methods*, Cambridge University Press, Cambridge, 2006, DOI 10.1017/CBO9780511616051. MR2229391

[181] S. Hu, *A proof of C^1 stability conjecture for three-dimensional flows*, Trans. Amer. Math. Soc. **342** (1994), no. 2, 753–772, DOI 10.2307/2154651. MR1172297

[182] H. J. Hupkes and S. M. Verduyn Lunel, *Lin's method and homoclinic bifurcations for functional differential equations of mixed type*, Indiana Univ. Math. J. **58** (2009), no. 6, 2433–2487, DOI 10.1512/iumj.2009.58.3661. MR2603755

[183] Yu. Ilyashenko, Yu. Kudryashov, and I. Schurov, *Global bifurcations in the two-sphere: a new perspective*, Invent. Math. **213** (2018), no. 2, 461–506, DOI 10.1007/s00222-018-0793-1. MR3827206

[184] Yu. Ilyashenko and W. Li, *Nonlocal bifurcations*, Mathematical Surveys and Monographs, vol. 66, American Mathematical Society, Providence, RI, 1999, DOI 10.1090/surv/066. MR1650842

[185] Yu. S. Ilyashenko and S. Yu. Yakovenko, *Nonlinear Stokes phenomena in smooth classification problems*, Nonlinear Stokes phenomena, Adv. Soviet Math., vol. 14, Amer. Math. Soc., Providence, RI, 1993, pp. 235–287. MR1206045

[186] G. Iooss, *Bifurcation of maps and applications*, North-Holland Mathematics Studies, vol. 36, North-Holland Publishing Co., Amsterdam-New York, 1979. MR531030

[187] G. Iooss and D. D. Joseph, *Elementary stability and bifurcation theory*, 2nd ed., Undergraduate Texts in Mathematics, Springer-Verlag, New York, 1990, DOI 10.1007/978-1-4612-0997-3. MR1026101

[188] M. C. Irwin, *A new proof of the pseudostable manifold theorem*, J. London Math. Soc. (2) **21** (1980), no. 3, 557–566, DOI 10.1112/jlms/s2-21.3.557. MR577730

[189] M. C. Irwin, *Smooth dynamical systems*, Pure and Applied Mathematics, vol. 94, Academic Press, Inc. [Harcourt Brace Jovanovich, Publishers], New York-London, 1980. MR586942

[190] C. G. J. Jacobi, *Über die figur des gleichgewichts*, Ann. Phys. Chem. **33** (1834), 229–233.

[191] M. V. Jakobson, *Absolutely continuous invariant measures for one-parameter families of one-dimensional maps*, Comm. Math. Phys. **81** (1981), no. 1, 39–88. MR630331

[192] A. Joets, *Apollonios, premier géomètre des singularités*, Quadrature **66** (2007), 37–41.

[193] L. Jonker and D. Rand, *Bifurcations in one dimension. I. The nonwandering set*, Invent. Math. **62** (1981), no. 3, 347–365, DOI 10.1007/BF01394248. MR604832

[194] L. Jonker and D. Rand, *Bifurcations in one dimension. II. A versal model for bifurcations*, Invent. Math. **63** (1981), no. 1, 1–15, DOI 10.1007/BF01389190. MR608525

[195] I. Kan, H. Koçak, and J. A. Yorke, *Antimonotonicity: concurrent creation and annihilation of periodic orbits*, Ann. of Math. (2) **136** (1992), no. 2, 219–252, DOI 10.2307/2946605. MR1185119

[196] J. L. Kaplan and J. A. Yorke, *Preturbulence: a regime observed in a fluid flow model of Lorenz*, Comm. Math. Phys. **67** (1979), no. 2, 93–108. MR539545

[197] A. Katok, *Lyapunov exponents, entropy and periodic orbits for diffeomorphisms*, Inst. Hautes Études Sci. Publ. Math. **51** (1980), 137–173. MR573822

[198] A. Katok and B. Hasselblatt, *Introduction to the modern theory of dynamical systems*, Encyclopedia of Mathematics and its Applications, vol. 54, Cambridge University Press, Cambridge, 1995. With a supplementary chapter by Katok and Leonardo Mendoza, DOI 10.1017/CBO9780511809187. MR1326374

[199] A. Kelley, *The stable, center-stable, center, center-unstable, unstable manifolds*, J. Differential Equations **3** (1967), 546–570, DOI 10.1016/0022-0396(67)90016-2. MR221044

[200] M. Kellner, *Bifurcations from codimension-one D_{4m}-equivariant homoclinic cycles*, Dissertation Technische Universität Ilmenau, 2022.

[201] J. Kennedy and J. A. Yorke, *Topological horseshoes*, Trans. Amer. Math. Soc. **353** (2001), no. 6, 2513–2530, DOI 10.1090/S0002-9947-01-02586-7. MR1707195

[202] H. Kielhöfer, *Bifurcation theory: An introduction with applications to partial differential equations*, 2nd ed., Applied Mathematical Sciences, vol. 156, Springer, New York, 2012, DOI 10.1007/978-1-4614-0502-3. MR2859263

[203] P. E. Kloeden and M. Rasmussen, *Nonautonomous dynamical systems*, Mathematical Surveys and Monographs, vol. 176, American Mathematical Society, Providence, RI, 2011, DOI 10.1090/surv/176. MR2808288

[204] J. Knobloch, *Lin's method for discrete dynamical systems*, J. Differ. Equations Appl. **6** (2000), no. 5, 577–623, DOI 10.1080/10236190008808247. MR1802448

[205] J. Knobloch, *Lin's method for discrete and continuous dynamical systems and applications*, Technische Universität Ilmenau, 2004.

[206] J. Knobloch, J. S. W. Lamb, and K. N. Webster, *Using Lin's method to solve Bykov's problems*, J. Differential Equations **257** (2014), no. 8, 2984–3047, DOI 10.1016/j.jde.2014.06.006. MR3249278

[207] J. Knobloch and T. Rieß, *Lin's method for heteroclinic chains involving periodic orbits*, Nonlinearity **23** (2010), no. 1, 23–54, DOI 10.1088/0951-7715/23/1/002. MR2576372

[208] M. Kot, *Elements of mathematical ecology*, Cambridge University Press, Cambridge, 2001, DOI 10.1017/CBO9780511608520. MR2006645

[209] R. L. Kraft, *Chaos, Cantor sets, and hyperbolicity for the logistic maps*, Amer. Math. Monthly **106** (1999), no. 5, 400–408, DOI 10.2307/2589144. MR1699258

[210] S. G. Krantz and H. R. Parks, *The implicit function theorem*, Birkhäuser Boston, Inc., Boston, MA, 2002. History, theory, and applications, DOI 10.1007/978-1-4612-0059-8. MR1894435

[211] B. Krauskopf and T. Rieß, *A Lin's method approach to finding and continuing heteroclinic connections involving periodic orbits*, Nonlinearity **21** (2008), no. 8, 1655–1690, DOI 10.1088/0951-7715/21/8/001. MR2425933

[212] A. Kriegl and P. W. Michor, *The convenient setting of global analysis*, Mathematical Surveys and Monographs, vol. 53, American Mathematical Society, Providence, RI, 1997, DOI 10.1090/surv/053. MR1471480

[213] M. Krupa, B. Sandstede, and P. Szmolyan, *Fast and slow waves in the FitzHugh-Nagumo equation*, J. Differential Equations **133** (1997), no. 1, 49–97, DOI 10.1006/jdeq.1996.3198. MR1426757

[214] I. Kupka, *Contribution à la théorie des champs génériques* (French), Contributions to Differential Equations **2** (1963), 457–484. MR165536

[215] Y. A. Kuznetsov, *Elements of applied bifurcation theory*, 3rd ed., Applied Mathematical Sciences, vol. 112, Springer-Verlag, New York, 2004, DOI 10.1007/978-1-4757-3978-7. MR2071006

[216] R. Labarca and S. Plaza, *Global stability of families of vector fields*, Ergodic Theory Dynam. Systems **13** (1993), no. 4, 737–766, DOI 10.1017/S0143385700007641. MR1257032

[217] O. E. Lanford III, *A computer-assisted proof of the Feigenbaum conjectures*, Bull. Amer. Math. Soc. (N.S.) **6** (1982), no. 3, 427–434, DOI 10.1090/S0273-0979-1982-15008-X. MR648529

[218] S. Lang, *Real and functional analysis*, 3rd ed., Graduate Texts in Mathematics, vol. 142, Springer-Verlag, New York, 1993, DOI 10.1007/978-1-4612-0897-6. MR1216137

[219] J. A. Langa, J. C. Robinson, and A. Suárez, *Stability, instability, and bifurcation phenomena in non-autonomous differential equations*, Nonlinearity **15** (2002), no. 3, 887–903, DOI 10.1088/0951-7715/15/3/322. MR1901112

[220] W. F. Langford, *Numerical studies of torus bifurcations*, Numerical methods for bifurcation problems (Dortmund, 1983), Internat. Schriftenreihe Numer. Math., vol. 70, Birkhäuser, Basel, 1984, pp. 285–295. MR821035

[221] J. M. Lee, *Introduction to smooth manifolds*, 2nd ed., Graduate Texts in Mathematics, vol. 218, Springer, New York, 2013. MR2954043

[222] E. Leontovich, *On the generation of limit cycles from separatrices* (Russian), Doklady Akad. Nauk SSSR (N.S.) **78** (1951), 641–644. MR42576

[223] M. Levi, *Qualitative analysis of the periodically forced relaxation oscillations*, Mem. Amer. Math. Soc. **32** (1981), no. 244, vi+147, DOI 10.1090/memo/0244. MR617687

[224] M. Levi, F. C. Hoppensteadt, and W. L. Miranker, *Dynamics of the Josephson junction*, Quart. Appl. Math. **36** (1978/79), no. 2, 167–198, DOI 10.1090/qam/484023. MR484023

[225] G. Levin, W. Shen, and S. van Strien, *Transversality for critical relations of families of rational maps: an elementary proof*, New trends in one-dimensional dynamics, Springer Proc. Math. Stat., vol. 285, Springer, Cham, 2019, pp. 201–220, DOI 10.1007/978-3-030-16833-9_11. MR4043216

[226] G. Levin, W. Shen, and S. van Strien, *Transversality in the setting of hyperbolic and parabolic maps*, J. Anal. Math. **141** (2020), no. 1, 247–284, DOI 10.1007/s11854-020-0130-7. MR4174043

[227] N. Levinson, *A second order differential equation with singular solutions*, Ann. of Math. (2) **50** (1949), 127–153, DOI 10.2307/1969357. MR30079

[228] T. Y. Li and J. A. Yorke, *Period three implies chaos*, Amer. Math. Monthly **82** (1975), no. 10, 985–992, DOI 10.2307/2318254. MR385028

[229] X.-B. Lin, *Using Mel′nikov's method to solve Šilnikov's problems*, Proc. Roy. Soc. Edinburgh Sect. A **116** (1990), no. 3-4, 295–325, DOI 10.1017/S0308210500031528. MR1084736

[230] P. Liu, J. Shi, and Y. Wang, *Imperfect transcritical and pitchfork bifurcations*, J. Funct. Anal. **251** (2007), no. 2, 573–600, DOI 10.1016/j.jfa.2007.06.015. MR2356424

[231] E. N. Lorenz, *Deterministic nonperiodic flow*, J. Atmospheric Sci. **20** (1963), no. 2, 130–141, DOI 10.1175/1520-0469(1963)020⟨0130:DNF⟩2.0.CO;2. MR4021434

[232] D. Ludwig, D. D. Jones, and C. S. Holling, *Qualitative Analysis of Insect Outbreak Systems: The Spruce Budworm and Forest*, Journal of Animal Ecology **47** (1978), no. 1, 315–332.

[233] A. M. Lyapunov, *The general problem of the stability of motion*, Internat. J. Control **55** (1992), no. 3, 521–790, DOI 10.1080/00207179208934253. Translated by A. T. Fuller from Édouard Davaux's French translation (1907) of the 1892 Russian original; With an editorial (historical introduction) by Fuller, a biography of Lyapunov by V. I. Smirnov, and the bibliography of Lyapunov's works collected by J. F. Barrett; Lyapunov centenary issue. MR1154209

[234] M. Lyubich, *Dynamics of quadratic polynomials. I, II*, Acta Math. **178** (1997), no. 2, 185–247, 247–297, DOI 10.1007/BF02392694. MR1459261

[235] M. Lyubich, *Feigenbaum-Coullet-Tresser universality and Milnor's hairiness conjecture*, Ann. of Math. (2) **149** (1999), no. 2, 319–420, DOI 10.2307/120968. MR1689333

[236] M. Lyubich and M. Martens, *Renormalization in the Hénon family, II: the heteroclinic web*, Invent. Math. **186** (2011), no. 1, 115–189, DOI 10.1007/s00222-011-0316-9. MR2836053

[237] I. P. Malta and J. Palis, *Families of vector fields with finite modulus of stability*, Dynamical systems and turbulence, Warwick 1980 (Coventry, 1979/1980), Lecture Notes in Math., vol. 898, Springer, Berlin-New York, 1981, pp. 212–229. MR654891

[238] R. Mañé, *A proof of the C^1 stability conjecture*, Inst. Hautes Études Sci. Publ. Math. **66** (1988), 161–210. MR932138

[239] L. Markus and H. Yamabe, *Global stability criteria for differential systems*, Osaka Math. J. **12** (1960), 305–317. MR126019

[240] J. E. Marsden and M. McCracken, *The Hopf bifurcation and its applications*, Applied Mathematical Sciences, Vol. 19, Springer-Verlag, New York, 1976. With contributions by P. Chernoff, G. Childs, S. Chow, J. R. Dorroh, J. Guckenheimer, L. Howard, N. Kopell, O. Lanford, J. Mallet-Paret, G. Oster, O. Ruiz, S. Schecter, D. Schmidt, and S. Smale. MR494309

[241] M. Martcheva, *An introduction to mathematical epidemiology*, Texts in Applied Mathematics, vol. 61, Springer, New York, 2015, DOI 10.1007/978-1-4899-7612-3. MR3409181

[242] J. Martinet, *Singularities of smooth functions and maps*, London Mathematical Society Lecture Note Series, vol. 58, Cambridge University Press, Cambridge-New York, 1982. Translated from the French by Carl P. Simon. MR671585

[243] B. Marx and W. Vogt, *Dynamische Systeme. Theorie und Numerik*, Heidelberg: Spektrum Akademischer Verlag, 2011.

[244] L. E. Matson, *The Malkus-Lorenz water wheel revisited*, American Journal of Physics **75** (2007), 1114–1122.

[245] J. P. May, *A concise course in algebraic topology*, Chicago Lectures in Mathematics, University of Chicago Press, Chicago, IL, 1999. MR1702278

[246] R. M. May, *Simple mathematical models with very complicated dynamics*, Nature, London **261** (1976), no. 5560, 459–467.

[247] V. S. Medvedev, *A new type of bifurcations on manifolds* (Russian), Mat. Sb. (N.S.) **113(155)** (1980), no. 3(11), 487–492, 496. MR601891

[248] V. S. Medvedev, *The bifurcation of the "blue sky catastrophe" on two-dimensional manifolds*, Math. Notes **51** (1992), no. 1, 76–81.

[249] J. D. Meiss, *Differential dynamical systems*, Revised edition, Mathematical Modeling and Computation, vol. 22, Society for Industrial and Applied Mathematics (SIAM), Philadelphia, PA, 2017, DOI 10.1137/1.9781611974645. MR3614477

[250] V. K. Melnikov, *On the stability of a center for time-periodic perturbations* (Russian), Trudy Moskov. Mat. Obšč. **12** (1963), 3–52. MR156048

[251] K. R. Meyer, *The implicit function theorem and analytic differential equations*, Dynamical systems—Warwick 1974 (Proc. Sympos. Appl. Topology and Dynamical Systems, Univ. Warwick, Coventry, 1973/1974; presented to E. C. Zeeman on his fiftieth birthday), Lecture Notes in Math., Vol. 468, Springer, Berlin-New York, 1975, pp. 191–208. MR650636

[252] J. Milnor, *On the concept of attractor*, Comm. Math. Phys. **99** (1985), no. 2, 177–195. MR790735

[253] J. Milnor, *Dynamics in one complex variable*, 3rd ed., Annals of Mathematics Studies, vol. 160, Princeton University Press, Princeton, NJ, 2006. MR2193309

[254] J. Milnor and W. Thurston, *On iterated maps of the interval*, Dynamical systems (College Park, MD, 1986), Lecture Notes in Math., vol. 1342, Springer, Berlin, 1988, pp. 465–563, DOI 10.1007/BFb0082847. MR970571

[255] J. Montaldi, *Singularities, bifurcations and catastrophes*, Cambridge University Press, Cambridge, 2021, DOI 10.1017/9781316585085. MR4273545

[256] L. Mora and M. Viana, *Abundance of strange attractors*, Acta Math. **171** (1993), no. 1, 1–71, DOI 10.1007/BF02392766. MR1237897

[257] C. A. Morales and M. J. Pacifico, *Inclination-flip homoclinic orbits arising from orbit-flip*, Nonlinearity **14** (2001), no. 2, 379–393, DOI 10.1088/0951-7715/14/2/311. MR1819803

[258] M. Morse, *Relations between the critical points of a real function of n independent variables*, Trans. Amer. Math. Soc. **27** (1925), no. 3, 345–396, DOI 10.2307/1989110. MR1501318

[259] J. Moser, *Stable and random motions in dynamical systems: With special emphasis on celestial mechanics*, Annals of Mathematics Studies, No. 77, Princeton University Press, Princeton, NJ; University of Tokyo Press, Tokyo, 1973. Hermann Weyl Lectures, the Institute for Advanced Study, Princeton, N. J. MR442980

[260] J. R. Munkres, *Topology*, Prentice Hall, Inc., Upper Saddle River, NJ, 2000. Second edition of [MR0464128]. MR3728284

[261] J. Murdock, *Normal forms and unfoldings for local dynamical systems*, Springer Monographs in Mathematics, Springer-Verlag, New York, 2003, DOI 10.1007/b97515. MR1941477

[262] J. D. Murray, *Mathematical biology. I: An introduction*, 3rd ed., Interdisciplinary Applied Mathematics, vol. 17, Springer-Verlag, New York, 2002. MR1908418

[263] J. D. Murray, *Mathematical biology. II: Spatial models and biomedical applications*, 3rd ed., Interdisciplinary Applied Mathematics, vol. 18, Springer-Verlag, New York, 2003. MR1952568

[264] Ju. I. Neimark, *Some cases of the dependence of periodic motions on parameters* (Russian), Dokl. Akad. Nauk SSSR **129** (1959), 736–739. MR132256

[265] S. E. Newhouse, *Nondensity of axiom* A(a) *on* S^2, Global Analysis (Proc. Sympos. Pure Math., Vols. XIV, XV, XVI, Berkeley, Calif., 1968), Proc. Sympos. Pure Math., XIV-XVI, Amer. Math. Soc., Providence, RI, 1970, pp. 191–202. MR277005

[266] S. E. Newhouse, *Diffeomorphisms with infinitely many sinks*, Topology **13** (1974), 9–18, DOI 10.1016/0040-9383(74)90034-2. MR339291

[267] S. E. Newhouse, *The abundance of wild hyperbolic sets and nonsmooth stable sets for diffeomorphisms*, Inst. Hautes Études Sci. Publ. Math. (1979), no. 50, 101–151.

[268] S. E. Newhouse, J. Palis, and F. Takens, *Bifurcations and stability of families of diffeomorphisms*, Inst. Hautes Études Sci. Publ. Math. **57** (1983), 5–71. MR699057

[269] S. E. Newhouse, D. Ruelle, and F. Takens, *Occurrence of strange Axiom A attractors near quasiperiodic flows on* T^m, $m \geq 3$, Comm. Math. Phys. **64** (1978/79), no. 1, 35–40. MR516994

[270] E. Nijholt, T. Pereira, F. C. Queiroz, and D. Turaev, *Chaotic behavior in diffusively coupled systems*, Comm. Math. Phys. **401** (2023), no. 3, 2715–2756, DOI 10.1007/s00220-023-04699-5. MR4616652

[271] I. Nikolaev and E. Zhuzhoma, *Flows on 2-dimensional manifolds: An overview*, Lecture Notes in Mathematics, vol. 1705, Springer-Verlag, Berlin, 1999, DOI 10.1007/BFb0093599. MR1707298

[272] V. P. Nozdracheva, *Bifurcations of a structurally unstable separatrix loop* (Russian), Differentsial′nye Uravneniya **18** (1982), no. 9, 1551–1558, 1654. MR672159

[273] B. E. Oldeman, B. Krauskopf, and A. R. Champneys, *Death of period-doublings: locating the homoclinic-doubling cascade*, Phys. D **146** (2000), no. 1-4, 100–120, DOI 10.1016/S0167-2789(00)00133-0. MR1787407

[274] I. M. Ovsyannikov and L. P. Shilnikov, *Systems with a saddle-focus homoclinic curve* (Russian), Mat. Sb. (N.S.) **130(172)** (1986), no. 4, 552–570, DOI 10.1070/SM1987v058n02ABEH003120; English transl., Math. USSR-Sb. **58** (1987), no. 2, 557–574. MR867343

[275] N. H. Packard, J. P., Crutchfield, J. D., Farmer, and R. S. Shaw, *Geometry from a time teries*, Phys. Rev. Lett. **45** (1980), 712–716.

[276] J. Palis, *A differentiable invariant of topological conjugacies and moduli of stability*, Dynamical systems, Vol. III—Warsaw, Astérisque, No. 51, Soc. Math. France, Paris, 1978, pp. 335–346. MR494283

[277] J. Palis, *On the C^1 Ω-stability conjecture*, Inst. Hautes Études Sci. Publ. Math. (1988), no. 66, 211–215.

[278] J. Palis and W. de Melo, *Geometric theory of dynamical systems: An introduction*, Springer-Verlag, New York-Berlin, 1982. Translated from the Portuguese by A. K. Manning. MR669541

[279] J. Palis and C. C. Pugh, *Fifty problems in dynamical systems*, Dyn. Syst., Proc. Symp. Univ. Warwick 1973/74, Lect. Notes Math. 468, 345-353, 1975.

[280] J. Palis and S. Smale, *Structural stability theorems*, Global Analysis (Proc. Sympos. Pure Math., Vols. XIV, XV, XVI, Berkeley, Calif., 1968), Proc. Sympos. Pure Math., XIV-XVI, Amer. Math. Soc., Providence, RI, 1970, pp. 223–231. MR267603

[281] J. Palis and F. Takens, *Stability of parametrized families of gradient vector fields*, Ann. of Math. (2) **118** (1983), no. 3, 383–421, DOI 10.2307/2006976. MR727698

[282] J. Palis and F. Takens, *Hyperbolicity and sensitive chaotic dynamics at homoclinic bifurcations*, Cambridge Studies in Advanced Mathematics, vol. 35, Cambridge University Press, Cambridge, 1993. Fractal dimensions and infinitely many attractors. MR1237641

[283] K. J. Palmer, *Exponential dichotomies and transversal homoclinic points*, J. Differential Equations **55** (1984), no. 2, 225–256, DOI 10.1016/0022-0396(84)90082-2. MR764125

[284] H.-O. Peitgen, H. Jürgens, and D. Saupe, *Chaos and fractals: New frontiers of science*, 2nd ed., Springer-Verlag, New York, 2004. With a foreword by Mitchell J. Feigenbaum, DOI 10.1007/b97624. MR2031217

[285] M. M. Peixoto, *On structural stability*, Ann. of Math. (2) **69** (1959), 199–222, DOI 10.2307/1970100. MR101951

[286] M. M. Peixoto, *Structural stability on two-dimensional manifolds*, Topology **1** (1962), 101–120, DOI 10.1016/0040-9383(65)90018-2. MR142859

[287] L. M. Perko, *A global analysis of the Bogdanov-Takens system*, SIAM J. Appl. Math. **52** (1992), no. 4, 1172–1192, DOI 10.1137/0152069. MR1174053

[288] L. M. Perko, *Rotated vector fields*, J. Differential Equations **103** (1993), no. 1, 127–145, DOI 10.1006/jdeq.1993.1044. MR1218741

[289] L. Perko, *Differential equations and dynamical systems*, 3rd ed., Texts in Applied Mathematics, vol. 7, Springer-Verlag, New York, 2001, DOI 10.1007/978-1-4613-0003-8. MR1801796

[290] O. Perron, *Über Stabilität und asymptotisches Verhalten der Integrale von Differentialgleichungssystemen* (German), Math. Z. **29** (1929), no. 1, 129–160, DOI 10.1007/BF01180524. MR1544998

[291] O. Perron, *Über Stabilität und asymptotisches Verhalten der Lösungen eines Systems endlicher Differenzengleichungen* (German), J. Reine Angew. Math. **161** (1929), 41–64, DOI 10.1515/crll.1929.161.41. MR1581191

[292] S. Plaza and J. Vera, *Bifurcation and stability of families of hyperbolic vector fields in dimension three* (English, with English and French summaries), Ann. Inst. H. Poincaré C Anal. Non Linéaire **14** (1997), no. 1, 119–142, DOI 10.1016/S0294-1449(97)80151-5. MR1437191

[293] V. A. Pliss, *A reduction principle in the theory of stability of motion* (Russian), Izv. Akad. Nauk SSSR Ser. Mat. **28** (1964), 1297–1324. MR190449

[294] A. Pogromsky, T. Glad, and H. Nijmeijer, *On diffusion driven oscillations in coupled dynamical systems*, Internat. J. Bifur. Chaos Appl. Sci. Engrg. **9** (1999), no. 4, 629–644, DOI 10.1142/S0218127499000444. MR1700932

[295] H. Poincaré, *Sur l'équilibre d'une masse fluide animée d'un mouvement de rotation* (French), Acta Math. **7** (1885), no. 1, 259–380, DOI 10.1007/BF02402204. MR1554685

[296] H. Poincaré, *Les méthodes nouvelles de la mécanique céleste. Tome III*, Paris: Gauthier-Villars et Fils, 1899.

[297] Y. Pomeau and P. Manneville, *Intermittent transition to turbulence in dissipative dynamical systems*, Comm. Math. Phys. **74** (1980), no. 2, 189–197. MR576270

[298] T. Poston and I. Stewart, *Catastrophe theory and its applications*, Surveys and Reference Works in Mathematics, No. 2, Pitman, London-San Francisco, Calif.-Melbourne; distributed by Fearon-Pitman Publishers, Inc., Belmont, CA, 1978. With an appendix by D. R. Olsen, S. R. Carter and A. Rockwood. MR501079

[299] E. Pujals, M. Shub, and Y. Yang, *Stable and non-symmetric pitchfork bifurcations*, Sci. China Math. **63** (2020), no. 9, 1837–1852, DOI 10.1007/s11425-019-1758-5. MR4145921

[300] J. D. M. Rademacher, *Homoclinic orbits near heteroclinic cycles with one equilibrium and one periodic orbit*, J. Differential Equations **218** (2005), no. 2, 390–443, DOI 10.1016/j.jde.2005.03.016. MR2177464

[301] I. L. Rios, *Unfolding homoclinic tangencies inside horseshoes: hyperbolicity, fractal dimensions and persistent tangencies*, Nonlinearity **14** (2001), no. 3, 431–462, DOI 10.1088/0951-7715/14/3/302. MR1830902

[302] J. W. Robbin, *On the existence theorem for differential equations*, Proc. Amer. Math. Soc. **19** (1968), 1005–1006, DOI 10.2307/2035361. MR227583

[303] J. W. Robbin, *A structural stability theorem*, Ann. of Math. (2) **94** (1971), 447–493, DOI 10.2307/1970766. MR287580

[304] R. C. Robinson, *Structural stability of C^1 flows*, Dynamical systems—Warwick 1974 (Proc. Sympos. Appl. Topology and Dynamical Systems, Univ. Warwick, Coventry, 1973/1974; presented to E. C. Zeeman on his fiftieth birthday), Lecture Notes in Math., Vol. 468, Springer, Berlin-New York, 1975, pp. 262–277. MR650640

[305] R Robinson Clark, *Structural stability of C^1 diffeomorphisms*, J. Differential Equations **22** (1976), no. 1, 28–73, DOI 10.1016/0022-0396(76)90004-8. MR474411

[306] R. C. Robinson, *Differentiability of the stable foliation for the model Lorenz equations*, Dynamical systems and turbulence, Warwick 1980 (Coventry, 1979/1980), Lecture Notes in Math., vol. 898, Springer, Berlin-New York, 1981, pp. 302–315. MR654897

[307] R. C. Robinson, *Bifurcation to infinitely many sinks*, Comm. Math. Phys. **90** (1983), no. 3, 433–459. MR719300

[308] Robinson, R. C., *Horseshoes for autonomous Hamiltonian systems using the Mel′nikov integral*, Ergodic Theory Dynam. Systems **8*** (1988), no. Charles Conley Memorial Issue, 395–409.

[309] R. C. Robinson, *Dynamical systems*, second ed., Studies in Advanced Mathematics, CRC Press, Boca Raton, FL, 1999.

[310] R. C. Robinson and R. F. Williams, *Finite stability is not generic*, Dynamical systems (Proc. Sympos., Univ. Bahia, Salvador, 1971), Academic Press, New York-London, 1973, pp. 451–462. MR331430

[311] M. L. Rosenzweig and R. H. MacArthur, *Graphical representation and stability conditions of predator-prey interactions*, The American Naturalist **97** (1963), no. 895, 209–223.

[312] O. E. Rössler, *An equation for continuous chaos*, Phys. Lett., A **57** (1976), no. 5, 397–398.

[313] O. E. Rössler and F. F. Seelig, *A Rashevsky-Turing system as a two-cellular flip-flop*, Zeitschrift für Naturforschung B **27** (1972), no. 12, 1444–1448.

[314] R. Roussarie, *On the number of limit cycles which appear by perturbation of separatrix loop of planar vector fields*, Bol. Soc. Brasil. Mat. **17** (1986), no. 2, 67–101, DOI 10.1007/BF02584827. MR901596

[315] R. Roussarie and C. Rousseau, *Almost planar homoclinic loops in $\mathbf{R}^3$*, J. Differential Equations **126** (1996), no. 1, 1–47, DOI 10.1006/jdeq.1996.0042. MR1382055

[316] R. Roussarie and F. Wagener, *A study of the Bogdanov-Takens bifurcation*, Resenhas **2** (1995), no. 1, 1–25. MR1358328

[317] D. Ruelle, *Small random perturbations of dynamical systems and the definition of attractors*, Comm. Math. Phys. **82** (1981/82), no. 1, 137–151. MR638517

[318] D. Ruelle, *Small random perturbations and the definition of attractors*, Geometric dynamics (Rio de Janeiro, 1981), Lecture Notes in Math., vol. 1007, Springer, Berlin, 1983, pp. 663–676, DOI 10.1007/BFb0061440. MR730293

[319] D. Ruelle and F. Takens, *On the nature of turbulence*, Comm. Math. Phys. **20** (1971), 167–192. MR284067

[320] R. J. Sacker, *On invariant surfaces and bifurcation of periodic solutions of ordinary differential equations*, ProQuest LLC, Ann Arbor, MI, 1964. Thesis (Ph.D.)–New York University. MR2615427

[321] R. J. Sacker, *On invariant surfaces and bifurcation of periodic solutions of ordinary differential equations. Chapter II. Bifurcation-mapping method*, J. Difference Equ. Appl. **15** (2009), no. 8-9, 759–774, DOI 10.1080/10236190802357735. Reprinted from New York Univ. Report IMM-NYU 333, October 1964, Courant Inst., New York. MR2543839

[322] B. Saltzman, *Finite amplitude free convection as an initial value problem-I*, J. Atmospheric Sci. **19** (1962), no. 4, 329–341.

[323] J. A. Sanders, F. Verhulst, and J. Murdock, *Averaging methods in nonlinear dynamical systems*, 2nd ed., Applied Mathematical Sciences, vol. 59, Springer, New York, 2007. MR2316999

[324] B. Sandstede, *Verzweigungstheorie homokliner Verdopplungen*, Stuttgart: Univ. Stuttgart, 1993.

[325] B. Sandstede, *Constructing dynamical systems having homoclinic bifurcation points of codimension two*, J. Dynam. Differential Equations **9** (1997), no. 2, 269–288, DOI 10.1007/BF02219223. MR1451292

[326] B. Sandstede, *Center manifolds for homoclinic solutions*, J. Dynam. Differential Equations **12** (2000), no. 3, 449–510, DOI 10.1023/A:1026412926537. MR1800130

[327] B. Sandstede and T. Theerakarn, *Regularity of center manifolds via the graph transform*, J. Dynam. Differential Equations **27** (2015), no. 3-4, 989–1006, DOI 10.1007/s10884-015-9473-7. MR3435143

[328] A. Sard, *The measure of the critical values of differentiable maps*, Bull. Amer. Math. Soc. **48** (1942), 883–890, DOI 10.1090/S0002-9904-1942-07811-6. MR7523

[329] D. G. Schaeffer and J. W. Cain, *Ordinary differential equations: basics and beyond*, Texts in Applied Mathematics, vol. 65, Springer, New York, 2016, DOI 10.1007/978-1-4939-6389-8. MR3561103

[330] U. Schalk and J. Knobloch, *Homoclinic points near degenerate homoclinics*, Nonlinearity **8** (1995), no. 6, 1133–1141. MR1363403

[331] M. Scheffer, *Critical transitions in nature and society*, Princeton University Press, Princeton, NJ, 2009.

[332] M. V. Shashkov and L. P. Shilnikov, *On the existence of a smooth invariant foliation in Lorenz-type mappings* (Russian, with Russian summary), Differentsial′nye Uravneniya **30** (1994), no. 4, 586–595, 732; English transl., Differential Equations **30** (1994), no. 4, 536–544. MR1299844

[333] M. V. Shashkov and D. V. Turaev, *An existence theorem of smooth nonlocal center manifolds for systems close to a system with a homoclinic loop*, J. Nonlinear Sci. **9** (1999), no. 5, 525–573, DOI 10.1007/s003329900078. MR1707981

[334] A. L. Shilnikov, *On bifurcations of the Lorenz attractor in the Shimizu-Morioka model*, Phys. D **62** (1993), no. 1-4, 338–346, DOI 10.1016/0167-2789(93)90292-9. Homoclinic chaos (Brussels, 1991). MR1207431

[335] L. P. Shilnikov, *A case of the existence of a denumerable set of periodic motions* (Russian), Dokl. Akad. Nauk SSSR **160** (1965), 558–561. MR173047

[336] L. P. Shilnikov, *On a problem of Poincaré-Birkhoff* (Russian), Mat. Sb. (N.S.) **74(116)** (1967), 378–397. MR232999

[337] L. P. Shilnikov, *The generation of a periodic motion from a trajectory which is doubly asymptotic to a saddle type equilibrium state* (Russian), Mat. Sb. (N.S.) **77(119)** (1968), 461–472. MR255922

[338] L. P. Shilnikov, *Mathematical problems of nonlinear dynamics: a tutorial*, J. Franklin Inst. B **334** (1997), no. 5-6, 793–864, DOI 10.1016/S0016-0032(97)00039-2. Visions of nonlinear science in the 21st century (Sevilla, 1996). MR1486282

[339] L. P. Shilnikov, A. L. Shilnikov, D. V. Turaev, and L. O. Chua, *Methods of qualitative theory in nonlinear dynamics. Part I*, World Scientific Series on Nonlinear Science. Series A: Monographs and Treatises, vol. 4, World Scientific Publishing Co., Inc., River Edge, NJ, 1998. With the collaboration of Sergey Gonchenko (Sections 3.7 and 3.8), Oleg Sten′kin (Section 3.9 and Appendix A) and Mikhail Shashkov (Sections 6.1 and 6.2), DOI 10.1142/9789812798596. MR1691840

[340] L. P. Shilnikov, , A. L. Shilnikov, D. V. Turaev, and L. O. Chua, *Methods of qualitative theory in nonlinear dynamics. Part II*, World Scientific Series on Nonlinear Science. Series A: Monographs and Treatises, vol. 5, World Scientific Publishing Co., Inc., River Edge, NJ, 2001.

[341] L. P. Shilnikov and D. V. Turaev, *Simple bifurcations leading to hyperbolic attractors: Computational tools of complex systems, I*, Comput. Math. Appl. **34** (1997), no. 2-4, 173–193, DOI 10.1016/S0898-1221(97)00123-5. MR1478758

[342] L. P. Shilnikov and D. V. Turaev, *A new simple bifurcation of a periodic orbit of "blue sky catastrophe" type*, Methods of qualitative theory of differential equations and related topics, Amer. Math. Soc. Transl. Ser. 2, vol. 200, Amer. Math. Soc., Providence, RI, 2000, pp. 165–188, DOI 10.1090/trans2/200/13. MR1769570

[343] T. Shimizu and N. Morioka, *On the bifurcation of a symmetric limit cycle to an asymmetric one in a simple model*, Phys. Lett. A **76** (1980), no. 3-4, 201–204, DOI 10.1016/0375-9601(80)90466-1. MR595639

[344] M. Shishikura, *The Hausdorff dimension of the boundary of the Mandelbrot set and Julia sets*, Ann. of Math. (2) **147** (1998), no. 2, 225–267, DOI 10.2307/121009. MR1626737

[345] A. N. Shoshitaishvili, *Bifurcations of topological type of singular points of vector fields that depend on parameters* (Russian), Funkcional. Anal. i Priložen. **6** (1972), no. 2, 97–98. MR296977

[346] A. N. Shoshitaishvili, *The bifurcation of the topological type of the singular points of vector fields that depend on parameters*, Trudy Sem. Petrovsk. (1975), no. Vyp. 1, 279–309.

[347] M. Shub, *Global stability of dynamical systems*, Springer-Verlag, New York, 1987. With the collaboration of Albert Fathi and Rémi Langevin; Translated from the French by Joseph Christy, DOI 10.1007/978-1-4757-1947-5. MR869255

[348] J. Sijbrand, *Properties of center manifolds*, Trans. Amer. Math. Soc. **289** (1985), no. 2, 431–469, DOI 10.2307/2000247. MR783998

[349] C. P. Simon, *A 3-dimensional Abraham-Smale example*, Proc. Amer. Math. Soc. **34** (1972), 629–630, DOI 10.2307/2038421. MR295391

[350] D. Singer, *Stable orbits and bifurcation of maps of the interval*, SIAM J. Appl. Math. **35** (1978), no. 2, 260–267, DOI 10.1137/0135020. MR494306

[351] S. Smale, *On gradient dynamical systems*, Ann. of Math. (2) **74** (1961), 199–206, DOI 10.2307/1970311. MR133139

[352] S. Smale, *Stable manifolds for differential equations and diffeomorphisms*, Ann. Scuola Norm. Sup. Pisa Cl. Sci. (3) **17** (1963), 97–116. MR165537

[353] S. Smale, *Diffeomorphisms with many periodic points*, Differential and Combinatorial Topology (A Symposium in Honor of Marston Morse), Princeton University Press, Princeton, NJ, 1965, pp. 63–80.

[354] S. Smale, *Structurally stable systems are not dense*, Amer. J. Math. **88** (1966), 491–496, DOI 10.2307/2373203. MR196725

[355] S. Smale, *Differentiable dynamical systems*, Bull. Amer. Math. Soc. **73** (1967), 747–817, DOI 10.1090/S0002-9904-1967-11798-1. MR228014

[356] J. Sotomayor, *Generic bifurcations of dynamical systems*, Dynamical systems (Proc. Sympos., Univ. Bahia, Salvador, 1971), Academic Press, New York-London, 1973, pp. 561–582. MR339280

[357] J. Sotomayor, *Generic one-parameter families of vector fields on two-dimensional manifolds*, Inst. Hautes Études Sci. Publ. Math. (1974), no. 43, 5–46.

[358] C. Sparrow, *The Lorenz equations: bifurcations, chaos, and strange attractors*, Applied Mathematical Sciences, vol. 41, Springer-Verlag, New York-Berlin, 1982. MR681294

[359] S. Sternberg, *Local C^n transformations of the real line*, Duke Math. J. **24** (1957), 97–102. MR102581

[360] S. Sternberg, *Local contractions and a theorem of Poincaré*, Amer. J. Math. **79** (1957), 809–824, DOI 10.2307/2372437. MR96853

[361] S. Sternberg, *On the structure of local homeomorphisms of euclidean n-space. II*, Amer. J. Math. **80** (1958), 623–631, DOI 10.2307/2372774. MR96854

[362] S. Sternberg, *Lectures on differential geometry*, Prentice-Hall, Inc., Englewood Cliffs, N.J., 1964.

[363] S. Sternberg, *Dynamical systems*, Dover Publications, Inc., Mineola, NY, 2010.

[364] D. Stowe, *Linearization in two dimensions*, J. Differential Equations **63** (1986), no. 2, 183–226, DOI 10.1016/0022-0396(86)90047-1. MR848267

[365] S. H. Strogatz, *Nonlinear dynamics and chaos: With applications to physics, biology, chemistry, and engineering*, 2nd ed., Westview Press, Boulder, CO, 2015. MR3837141

[366] P. Szmolyan, *Transversal heteroclinic and homoclinic orbits in singular perturbation problems*, J. Differential Equations **92** (1991), no. 2, 252–281, DOI 10.1016/0022-0396(91)90049-F. MR1120905

[367] F. Takens, *A nonstabilizable jet of a singularity of a vector field*, Dynamical systems (Proc. Sympos., Univ. Bahia, Salvador, 1971), Academic Press, New York-London, 1973, pp. 583–597. MR339265

[368] F. Takens, *Normal forms for certain singularities of vectorfields* (English, with French summary), Ann. Inst. Fourier (Grenoble) **23** (1973), no. 2, 163–195, DOI 10.5802/aif.467. MR365620

[369] F. Takens, *Unfoldings of certain singularities of vectorfields: generalized Hopf bifurcations*, J. Differential Equations **14** (1973), 476–493, DOI 10.1016/0022-0396(73)90062-4. MR339264

[370] F. Takens, *Forced oscillations and bifurcations*, Applications of global analysis, I (Sympos., Utrecht State Univ., Utrecht, 1973), Commun. Math. Inst. Rijksuniv. Utrecht, No. 3 - 1974, Rijksuniversiteit Utrecht, Mathematisch Instituut, Utrecht, 1974, pp. 1–59. MR478235

[371] F. Takens, *Singularities of vector fields*, Inst. Hautes Études Sci. Publ. Math. (1974), no. 43, 47–100.

[372] F. Takens, *Detecting strange attractors in turbulence*, Dynamical systems and turbulence, Warwick 1980 (Coventry, 1979/1980), Lecture Notes in Math., vol. 898, Springer, Berlin-New York, 1981, pp. 366–381. MR654900

[373] F. Takens, *A note on the differentiability of centre manifolds*, Dynamical systems and partial differential equations (Caracas, 1984), Univ. Simon Bolivar, Caracas, 1986, pp. 101–104.

[374] F. Takens, *Intermittency: global aspects*, Dynamical systems, Valparaiso 1986, Lecture Notes in Math., vol. 1331, Springer, Berlin, 1988, pp. 213–239, DOI 10.1007/BFb0083075. MR961102

[375] F. Takens, *Abundance of generic homoclinic tangencies in real-analytic families of diffeomorphisms*, Bol. Soc. Brasil. Mat. (N.S.) **22** (1992), no. 2, 191–214, DOI 10.1007/BF01232942. MR1179485

[376] F. Takens, *Forced oscillations and bifurcations*, Global analysis of dynamical systems, Inst. Phys., Bristol, 2001, pp. 1–61.

[377] L. Tedeschini-Lalli and J. A. Yorke, *How often do simple dynamical processes have infinitely many coexisting sinks?*, Comm. Math. Phys. **106** (1986), no. 4, 635–657. MR860314

[378] M. A. Teixeira, *Generic bifurcation in manifolds with boundary*, J. Differential Equations **25** (1977), no. 1, 65–89, DOI 10.1016/0022-0396(77)90180-2. MR442994

[379] G. Teschl, *Ordinary differential equations and dynamical systems*, Graduate Studies in Mathematics, vol. 140, American Mathematical Society, Providence, RI, 2012, DOI 10.1090/gsm/140. MR2961944

[380] R. Thom, *Stabilité structurelle et morphogénèse: Essai d'une théorie générale des modèles* (French), Mathematical Physics Monograph Series, W. A. Benjamin, Inc., Reading, MA, 1972. MR488155

[381] J. M. T. Thompson and H. B. Stewart, *Nonlinear dynamics and chaos*, 2nd ed., John Wiley & Sons, Ltd., Chichester, 2002. MR1963884

[382] H. Thunberg, *Periodicity versus chaos in one-dimensional dynamics*, SIAM Rev. **43** (2001), no. 1, 3–30, DOI 10.1137/S0036144500376649. MR1854645

[383] H. Thunberg, *Unfolding of chaotic unimodal maps and the parameter dependence of natural measures*, Nonlinearity **14** (2001), no. 2, 323–337, DOI 10.1088/0951-7715/14/2/308. MR1819800

[384] Y. Togawa, *A modulus of 3-dimensional vector fields*, Ergodic Theory Dynam. Systems **7** (1987), no. 2, 295–301, DOI 10.1017/S0143385700004028. MR896800

[385] È. A. Tomberg and V. A. Yakubovich, *Conditions for self-induced oscillations in nonlinear systems* (Russian), Sibirsk. Mat. Zh. **30** (1989), no. 4, 180–194, 219, DOI 10.1007/BF00971765; English transl., Siberian Math. J. **30** (1989), no. 4, 641–653 (1990). MR1017621

[386] È. A. Tomberg and V. A. Yakubovich, *On a problem of Smale* (Russian, with Russian summary), Sibirsk. Mat. Zh. **41** (2000), no. 4, iv, 926–928, DOI 10.1007/BF02679702; English transl., Siberian Math. J. **41** (2000), no. 4, 771–773. MR1785614

[387] C. Tresser, *About some theorems by L. P. Šil'nikov* (English, with French summary), Ann. Inst. H. Poincaré Phys. Théor. **40** (1984), no. 4, 441–461. MR757766

[388] C. Tresser and P. Coullet, *Itérations d'endomorphismes et groupe de renormalisation* (French, with English summary), C. R. Acad. Sci. Paris Sér. A-B **287** (1978), no. 7, A577–A580. MR512110

[389] M. Tsujii, *A note on Milnor and Thurston's monotonicity theorem*, Geometry and analysis in dynamical systems (Kyoto, 1993), Adv. Ser. Dynam. Systems, vol. 14, World Sci. Publ., River Edge, NJ, 1994, pp. 60–62. MR1314828

[390] M. Tsujii, *A simple proof for monotonicity of entropy in the quadratic family*, Ergodic Theory Dynam. Systems **20** (2000), no. 3, 925–933.

[391] W. Tucker, *The Lorenz attractor exists* (English, with English and French summaries), C. R. Acad. Sci. Paris Sér. I Math. **328** (1999), no. 12, 1197–1202, DOI 10.1016/S0764-4442(99)80439-X. MR1701385

[392] W. Tucker, *A rigorous ODE solver and Smale's 14th problem*, Found. Comput. Math. **2** (2002), no. 1, 53–117, DOI 10.1007/s002080010018. MR1870856

[393] D. V. Turaev, *An example of a resonant homoclinic loop of infinite cyclicity* (English, with English and Russian summaries), Mosc. Math. J. **5** (2005), no. 1, 283–293, DOI 10.17323/1609-4514-2005-5-1-283-293. MR2153477

[394] D. V. Turaev, *Maps close to identity and universal maps in the Newhouse domain*, Comm. Math. Phys. **335** (2015), no. 3, 1235–1277, DOI 10.1007/s00220-015-2338-4. MR3320312

[395] A. M. Turing, *The chemical basis of morphogenesis*, Philos. Trans. Roy. Soc. London Ser. B **237** (1952), no. 641, 37–72. MR3363444

[396] M. M. Vainberg and V. A. Trenogin, *The Ljapunov and Schmidt methods in the theory of non-linear equations and their subsequent development* (Russian), Uspehi Mat. Nauk **17** (1962), no. 2(104), 13–75. MR154113

[397] M. M. Vainberg and V. A. Trenogin, *Theory of branching of solutions of non-linear equations*, Noordhoff International Publishing, Leiden, 1974.

[398] J. B. van den Berg, W. Hetebrij, and B. Rink, *The parameterization method for center manifolds*, J. Differential Equations **269** (2020), no. 3, 2132–2184, DOI 10.1016/j.jde.2020.01.033. MR4093728

[399] B. van der Pol, *On "relaxation-oscillations"*, The London, Edinburgh, and Dublin Philosophical Magazine and Journal of Science **2** (1926), no. 11, 978–992.

[400] S. A. van Gils, M. Krupa, and V. Tchistiakov, *Homoclinic twist bifurcation in a system of two coupled oscillators*, J. Dynam. Differential Equations **12** (2000), no. 4, 733–806, DOI 10.1023/A:1009094505023. MR1826962

[401] S. J. van Strien, *Center manifolds are not C^∞*, Math. Z. **166** (1979), no. 2, 143–145, DOI 10.1007/BF01214040. MR525618

[402] S. J. van Strien, *On the bifurcations creating horseshoes*, Dynamical systems and turbulence, Warwick 1980 (Coventry, 1979/1980), Lecture Notes in Math., vol. 898, Springer, Berlin-New York, 1981, pp. 316–351. MR654898

[403] S. J. van Strien, *One parameter families of vectorfields: bifurcations near saddle-connections*, Utrecht University, 1982.

[404] A. Vanderbauwhede, *Centre manifolds, normal forms and elementary bifurcations*, Dynamics reported, Vol. 2, Dynam. Report. Ser. Dynam. Systems Appl., vol. 2, Wiley, Chichester, 1989, pp. 89–169. MR1000977

[405] A. Vanderbauwhede, *Bifurcation of degenerate homoclinics*, Results Math. **21** (1992), no. 1-2, 211–223, DOI 10.1007/BF03323080. MR1146644

[406] A. Vanderbauwhede and B. Fiedler, *Homoclinic period blow-up in reversible and conservative systems*, Z. Angew. Math. Phys. **43** (1992), no. 2, 292–318, DOI 10.1007/BF00946632. MR1162729

[407] A. Vanderbauwhede and G. Iooss, *Center manifold theory in infinite dimensions*, Dynamics reported: expositions in dynamical systems, Dynam. Report. Expositions Dynam. Systems (N.S.), vol. 1, Springer, Berlin, 1992, pp. 125–163. MR1153030

[408] A. Vanderbauwhede and S. A. van Gils, *Center manifolds and contractions on a scale of Banach spaces*, J. Funct. Anal. **72** (1987), no. 2, 209–224, DOI 10.1016/0022-1236(87)90086-3. MR886811

[409] G. Vegter, *Bifurcations of gradient vectorfields*, Bifurcation, ergodic theory and applications (Dijon, 1981), Astérisque, vol. 98, Soc. Math. France, Paris, 1982, pp. 39–73. MR724443

[410] M. Vellekoop and R. Berglund, *On intervals, transitivity = chaos*, Amer. Math. Monthly **101** (1994), no. 4, 353–355, DOI 10.2307/2975629. MR1270961

[411] F. Verhulst, *Nonlinear differential equations and dynamical systems*, 2nd ed., Universitext, Springer-Verlag, Berlin, 1996. Translated from the 1985 Dutch original, DOI 10.1007/978-3-642-61453-8. MR1422255

[412] F. Verhulst, *Henri Poincaré: Impatient genius*, Springer, New York, 2012, DOI 10.1007/978-1-4614-2407-9. MR2961945

[413] M. Viana, *Global attractors and bifurcations*, Nonlinear dynamical systems and chaos (Groningen, 1995), Progr. Nonlinear Differential Equations Appl., vol. 19, Birkhäuser, Basel, 1996, pp. 299–324, DOI 10.1007/s00030-011-0129-y. MR1391502

[414] Y. H. Wan, *Computation of the stability condition for the Hopf bifurcation of diffeomorphisms on R^2*, SIAM J. Appl. Math. **34** (1978), no. 1, 167–175, DOI 10.1137/0134013. MR467833

[415] J. C. Wells, *Invariant manifolds on non-linear operators*, Pacific J. Math. **62** (1976), no. 1, 285–293. MR418164

[416] H. Whitney, *Differentiable even functions*, Duke Math. J. **10** (1943), 159–160. MR7783

[417] H. Whitney, *The general type of singularity of a set of $2n-1$ smooth functions of n variables*, Duke Math. J. **10** (1943), 161–172. MR7784

[418] H. Whitney, *On singularities of mappings of euclidean spaces. I. Mappings of the plane into the plane*, Ann. of Math. (2) **62** (1955), 374–410, DOI 10.2307/1970070. MR73980

[419] R. F. Williams, *Expanding attractors*, Inst. Hautes Études Sci. Publ. Math. **43** (1974), 169–203. MR348794

[420] R. F. Williams, *The structure of Lorenz attractors*, Inst. Hautes Études Sci. Publ. Math. (1979), no. 50, 73–99.

[421] E. Yanagida, *Branching of double pulse solutions from single pulse solutions in nerve axon equations*, J. Differential Equations **66** (1987), no. 2, 243–262, DOI 10.1016/0022-0396(87)90034-9. MR871997

[422] J. A. Yorke and K. T. Alligood, *Period doubling cascades of attractors: a prerequisite for horseshoes*, Comm. Math. Phys. **101** (1985), no. 3, 305–321. MR815187

[423] E. C. Zeeman, *Bifurcation, catastrophe, and turbulence*, New directions in applied mathematics (Cleveland, Ohio, 1980), Springer, New York-Berlin, 1982, pp. 109–153. MR661287

[424] E. C. Zeeman, *Appendix: A catastrophe machine*, Towards a theoretical biology. Volume 4, Edinburgh: Edinburgh University Press, 2010, pp. 276–282.

[425] E. Zeidler, *Nonlinear functional analysis and its applications. I: Fixed-point theorems*, Springer-Verlag, New York, 1986. Translated from the German by Peter R. Wadsack, DOI 10.1007/978-1-4612-4838-5. MR816732

Index

SELECTED PUBLISHED TITLES IN THIS SERIES

246 **Ale Jan Homburg and Jürgen Knobloch,** Bifurcation Theory, 2024
245 **Bennett Chow and Yutze Chow,** Lectures on Differential Geometry, 2024
244 **John M. Lee,** Introduction to Complex Manifolds, 2024
243 **J. M. Landsberg,** Quantum Computation and Quantum Information, 2024
242 **Jayadev S. Athreya and Howard Masur,** Translation Surfaces, 2024
241 **Thorsten Theobald,** Real Algebraic Geometry and Optimization, 2024
240 **Nam Q. Le,** Analysis of Monge–Ampère Equations, 2024
239 **K. Cieliebak, Y. Eliashberg, and N. Mishachev,** Introduction to the h-Principle, Second Edition, 2024
238 **Julio González-Díaz, Ignacio García-Jurado, and M. Gloria Fiestras-Janeiro,** An Introductory Course on Mathematical Game Theory and Applications, Second Edition, 2023
237 **Michael Levitin, Dan Mangoubi, and Iosif Polterovich,** Topics in Spectral Geometry, 2023
236 **Stephanie Alexander, Vitali Kapovitch, and Anton Petrunin,** Alexandrov Geometry, 2024
235 **Bennett Chow,** Ricci Solitons in Low Dimensions, 2023
234 **Andrea Ferretti,** Homological Methods in Commutative Algebra, 2023
233 **Andrea Ferretti,** Commutative Algebra, 2023
232 **Harry Dym,** Linear Algebra in Action, Third Edition, 2023
231 **Luís Barreira and Yakov Pesin,** Introduction to Smooth Ergodic Theory, Second Edition, 2023
230 **Barbara Kaltenbacher and William Rundell,** Inverse Problems for Fractional Partial Differential Equations, 2023
229 **Giovanni Leoni,** A First Course in Fractional Sobolev Spaces, 2023
228 **Henk Bruin,** Topological and Ergodic Theory of Symbolic Dynamics, 2022
227 **William M. Goldman,** Geometric Structures on Manifolds, 2022
226 **Milivoje Lukić,** A First Course in Spectral Theory, 2022
225 **Jacob Bedrossian and Vlad Vicol,** The Mathematical Analysis of the Incompressible Euler and Navier-Stokes Equations, 2022
224 **Ben Krause,** Discrete Analogues in Harmonic Analysis, 2022
223 **Volodymyr Nekrashevych,** Groups and Topological Dynamics, 2022
222 **Michael Artin,** Algebraic Geometry, 2022
221 **David Damanik and Jake Fillman,** One-Dimensional Ergodic Schrödinger Operators, 2022
220 **Isaac Goldbring,** Ultrafilters Throughout Mathematics, 2022
219 **Michael Joswig,** Essentials of Tropical Combinatorics, 2021
218 **Riccardo Benedetti,** Lectures on Differential Topology, 2021
217 **Marius Crainic, Rui Loja Fernandes, and Ioan Mărcuţ,** Lectures on Poisson Geometry, 2021
216 **Brian Osserman,** A Concise Introduction to Algebraic Varieties, 2021
215 **Tai-Ping Liu,** Shock Waves, 2021
214 **Ioannis Karatzas and Constantinos Kardaras,** Portfolio Theory and Arbitrage, 2021
213 **Hung Vinh Tran,** Hamilton–Jacobi Equations, 2021
212 **Marcelo Viana and José M. Espinar,** Differential Equations, 2021
211 **Mateusz Michałek and Bernd Sturmfels,** Invitation to Nonlinear Algebra, 2021

For a complete list of titles in this series, visit the
AMS Bookstore at **www.ams.org/bookstore/gsmseries/**.